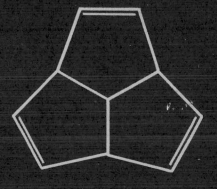

Organic Chemistry

Organic Chemistry

DONALD J. CRAM, *Professor of Chemistry,*

University of California at Los Angeles

GEORGE S. HAMMOND, *Professor of Chemistry,*

California Institute of Technology

McGraw-Hill **BOOK COMPANY, INC.**

New York   Toronto   London   **1959**

The text typeface of this book is Bodoni Book; the chemical symbols and formulas, Futura Demibold Condensed.   The type has been set directly on film by the Intertype Fotosetter. Felix Cooper is the illustrator.

Preface

The remarkable growth of organic chemistry during the last twenty years
has created serious problems for the teacher, particularly with respect to
elementary courses. The introduction of new and valuable theoretical
concepts into conventional schemes of presentation has been particularly
difficult. In most textbooks, theory appears as an appendage to otherwise self-consistent and classical discussions organized around the important classes of organic compounds. As a result, modern texts have
assumed an encyclopedic character. In an attempt to cope with this
problem, the authors of this book have developed a novel approach to
elementary organic chemistry.

In courses that we have taught in our respective universities, we
have tried to find a new basis of organization which would both be economical and reflect recent advances in the field. By thorough integration
of fact and theory, we tried to produce a fundamental course into whose
pattern could be introduced, without disruption or unmanageable growth,
the results of research as they became available. We found that facts
were best taught when collated by theory, and that theory was most
thoroughly understood when illustrated and developed through facts. By
use of such a blend, we were able to minimize the taxonomic aspects of
organic chemistry and to stress principles. This book is the product of
our experimentation.

The first four chapters deal with structure, nomenclature, occurrence,
and uses of the main classes of compounds. A few simple chemical reactions are introduced here to illustrate the interconversion of functional
groups and to show the principles involved in degradative structure determination. Chapter 5 treats the chemical bond in terms of both resonance
and molecular-orbital methods. In Chapter 6 stereochemistry is discussed
in terms of bond angles and distances, free and restricted rotation about
bonds, symmetry properties of molecules, and the configurations of ring
compounds. Chapter 7 presents the relationships between physical prop-

erties and structures of organic compounds.   Chapter 8 introduces the
subject of correlation of structure with chemical reactivity.   Acid-base
reactions, familiar to students from their study of general chemistry, are
used as a vehicle to illustrate resonance, inductive, and steric effects.
Chapter 9 explains our scheme for classification of organic reactions and
introduces reaction mechanisms.   Chapters 8 and 9 provide a transition
between the static and dynamic descriptions of organic chemistry.

In Chapters 10 through 20 reactions are discussed class by class.
Although reactions fall naturally into three main categories—substitution,
addition, and elimination—these classes have been subdivided to reduce
discussions to convenient lengths.   *The classification is operational rather
than mechanistic,* although discussions of reaction mechanisms naturally
fit easily into the scheme.   Preparative methods are stressed, and synthetic sequences are frequently presented as units.

The last nine chapters are concerned with timely and useful special
topics.   Included are a chapter on heterocyclic compounds, three chapters on natural products (grouped according to biogenetic relationships),
a chapter on natural and synthetic polymers, and chapters on petroleum,
spectra, nomenclature, and chemical literature.

In a sense, we have attempted to examine organic chemistry from
three different points of view.   The first group of chapters treats relationships based on structure; the second group emphasizes the relationship
among organic reactions; and the third group illustrates associations based
upon the origin, use, and chemical technology of organic compounds.
Thus students are given a thorough introduction to the descriptive part
of the subject before they are exposed to a comprehensive treatment of
reactions, and they have a good grasp of fundamental concepts of both
structure and reactivity before they encounter the subject of complex
molecules and their reactions.   In this scheme, the important facts and
concepts are repeatedly reviewed in varying contexts.   The problems that
appear at the end of each chapter serve to illustrate and develop the principles introduced in the text.   In each set, there are at least two problems
which are unusually difficult and which will stimulate the better students
to think originally.

We believe that certain further advantages are associated with this
organization.   Chemical reactions and their applications to synthesis are
introduced only after the structures of *both reactant and product* are
familiar to the student.   The early introduction of stereochemistry and
theories of chemical reactivity allows these concepts to be used throughout the discussions of reactions.   The organization of reactions into classes
allows consideration of mechanism, scope, limitations, and side reactions
to be applied to whole groups of transformations.   Many subjects such
as physical properties, acid-base theory, structure elucidation, spectra,
nomenclature, and bibliography, which are ordinarily scattered, are given
integrated treatment.   The relationship between laboratory and lecture
is strengthened by introduction in the first four chapters of enough struc-

tural concepts and reactions to provide a background for laboratory work for at least a term. The discussions of physical properties and acid-base reactions early in the course serve as useful adjuncts to laboratory work.

The book obviously includes more material than can be presented in a single course; however, in every chapter except the first four, sections of material may be omitted without loss of continuity. We have found that this flexibility allows the teacher to stress whichever of the three general sections he chooses. Thus a course designed for both chemistry and nonchemistry majors could emphasize the material in the first and third sections, whereas a course designed only for chemistry majors might stress the second group of chapters.

Our greatest ambition in writing this book has been to bring students in their first course closer to the frontiers of organic chemistry. We hope that our organization eliminates the waste usually involved in reorientation of students' thinking when they pass from an elementary course either to an advanced course or to research. If this book serves these purposes, we have succeeded.

We are indebted to many persons who contributed to this book. Professors Corwin Hansch and G. Ross Robertson served us well as critics during the preparation of the second draft of the manuscript. Our graduate students and postdoctoral fellows provided us with generous helpings of criticism of the manuscript, and they exercised tolerance and good judgment when our preoccupation with writing left them with an unusually large measure of independence in their research efforts. Others who read parts of the manuscript and offered helpful criticism include Professors Lawrence Bartell, Jerome Berson, Charles DePuy, Edward Leete, Harden McConnell, and Peter Yates, and Drs. John Hogg and Jay Kochi. Dr. John Schaefer read the entire page proof.

DONALD J. CRAM

GEORGE S. HAMMOND

Contents

H

He

Li Be   B C N O F Ne

Na Mg   Al Si P S Cl A

K Ca Sc Ti V Cr Mn Fe Co Ni Cu Zn Ga Ge As Se Br Kr

Rb Sr Y Zr Nb Mo Tc Ru Rh Pd Ag Cd In Sn Sb Te I Xe

Cs Ba * Hf Ta W Re Os Ir Pt Au Hg Tl Pb Bi Po At Rn

Fr Ra **

 * La Ce Pr Nd Pm Sm Eu Gd Tb Dy Ho Er Tm Yb Lu

** Ac Th Pa U Np Pu Am Cm Bk Cf E Fm Mv

1

Introduction

Nature of Organic Chemistry

Organic chemistry is concerned with compounds which contain carbon and hydrogen, and which may also contain other elements such as oxygen, nitrogen, halogens, sulfur, phosphorus, and some of the metals. The striking feature of the subject is the vast number of organic compounds known and the almost limitless number capable of existence. Over one million different organic compounds have now been identified. Each year thousands of new substances are being either discovered in nature or prepared in the laboratory. An impressive record of development in the field is found in the numbers of compounds known at various dates. In 1880 the number was approximately 12,000; in 1910 it was 150,000; in 1940, about 500,000. It is not uncommon for a research chemist to prepare *over a thousand new compounds* during his lifetime.

Remarkable variation in physical and chemical properties is found in organic compounds. At one extreme are plastics and rubber, composed of large molecules capable of exhibiting a great variety of desired physical characteristics, such as rigidity, elasticity, tensile strength, and molding properties. At the other is methane gas, one of the smallest organic molecules, which boils at $-162°C$.† This substance is the principal component of natural gas. Some compounds such as a certain phthalocyanine pigment will stand red heat, whereas one rather simple compound, with formula C_4H_4, explodes if allowed to come to room temperature. Fast photographic film represents an extreme case of chemical reactivity of an organic compound, which may be contrasted with the great chemical stability of teflon, a carbon-fluorine plastic so inert that it will resist even corrosive fluorine gas.

† All temperatures given in this book are in degrees centigrade unless designated otherwise.

1

Organic compounds constitute most of the materials associated with living organisms. This fact accounts for the name given the field, for it was thought once that only living organisms could synthesize organic compounds. Although the great bulk of naturally occurring organic materials have been photosynthesized by plants and microorganisms from carbon dioxide, water, and nitrogen, many compounds can now be prepared in the laboratory from carbon, hydrogen, water, nitrogen, and oxygen.

The chief sources of organic materials are coal, petroleum, natural gas, wood, and agricultural products. The property common to all these substances and to almost all organic substances is that they are fuels and burn to produce carbon dioxide and water with the liberation of heat. Our deposits of coal and petroleum are huge energy reservoirs. This point can be illustrated through two highly simplified equations.

$$CO_2 + H_2O + light \xrightarrow{\text{Organisms}} \text{organic compounds} + O_2$$
$$\text{Organic compounds} + O_2 \xrightarrow{\text{Combustion}} CO_2 + H_2O + heat$$

History

Although people have been deliberately carrying out organic reactions since the discovery of fire, the field was not elevated from an art to a science until the nineteenth century. The ensuing development can be roughly divided into three overlapping periods.

The beginning of the first period is lost in the advance of chemistry as a general science, an advance that gathered momentum toward the latter part of the eighteenth century. This was a period of groping, of trial and error, a period when the prejudices of medieval beliefs affected much of the thought concerning natural processes. "Organic compounds" were supposed to contain a characteristic "vital force" out of which life processes were made. This *vitalistic theory* was later dismissed by numerous experiments demonstrating that "organic compounds" could be prepared from inorganic materials. One of the first experiments of this type was carried out by Wöhler (in 1828), who converted ammonium cyanate, an inorganic compound, to urea, which had been known as an organic compound because of its presence in human urine.

$$NH_4OCN \xrightarrow{\text{Heat}} CO(NH_2)_2$$

Ammonium   Urea
cyanate

The main advances of this period were of a general chemical nature, and lay in the recognition of the power of elemental analysis and molecular weight determination, which provided data leading to molecular formulas.

The second period started in 1859 with the birth of the *structural theory* of organic compounds. Seldom in history had an idea borne more fruit than the simple concept advanced by Kekulé and Couper that organic molecules possess structural features, with *atoms of carbon* as the main building blocks and *chemical bonds* as the mortar. The ability of carbon to form strong bonds to carbon, hydrogen, oxygen, nitrogen, sulfur, and halogens provides the foundations for the science. The structural theory supplied a basis for determining the order in which different atoms are bonded to one another in a molecule. The resulting *sequence formulas* gave a rational explanation for the existence of the great variety of organic compounds that were known even at that time. A third dimension was added to organic formulas by the hypothesis advanced by van't Hoff and Le Bel in 1874 that the four bonds of carbon are directed toward the corners of a tetrahedron, at the center of which the carbon atom is situated. This hypothesis for the first time brought molecular architecture into organic chemistry, and provided an explanation for many observations that the structural theory in its early form failed either to explain or to represent.

Elaboration of the rules governing the structure and formation of organic compounds occupied the efforts of organic chemists through the end of the nineteenth century, until World War I. This exciting "classical period" was marked by two major endeavors: the construction of compounds through organic reactions; the elucidation of the structures of organic substances by molecular degradation. During this time, *ball-and-stick models* allowed the chemist to visualize structures of organic compounds, the balls representing atoms, and the sticks representing bonds.

The third, or "modern," period, which began with the end of World War I, has been one of refinement and exploitation. During this phase organic chemistry has derived considerable inspiration from the related fields of physical chemistry and physics. Extensive correlations of physical and chemical properties with molecular structure have been elaborated. Such correlations allow chemists to specify a set of properties desired in a product, to predict what molecular structures will have these properties, and to synthesize by rational means compounds possessing these structures.

The world has been in an "Organic Chemical Age" for almost thirty years, and the era is just reaching maturity. Multimillion-dollar industries based on organic compounds have taken their places alongside the other commercial giants of our civilization. Farm products, wood, coal, petroleum, and natural gas have been chemically tailored to provide organic products that vitally affect our environment. Fabrics, dyes, paints, coatings, and structural materials literally surround us. Rubber takes the violence out of movement, gasoline fuels our travel, gas both warms and cools our houses, plastics fashion our implements, and drugs guard our health and prolong our lives. Unprecedented opportunities to exercise the imagination are available in organic research, and much still remains to be done. The cultural movement of the twentieth century is in the hands of the scientists, and the organic chemist is playing a prominent role in providing direction for this movement.

Characterization of Organic Compounds

One of the goals of organic chemistry is to achieve complete descriptions of individual organic compounds. General procedures have evolved which can be applied to most organic compounds and which provide a step-by-step approach to the final goal, the detailed structural formula. This section of the book is devoted to a description of those steps which permit a compound to be thoroughly enough characterized so that it may be distinguished from all other compounds.

Molecular Homogeneity. Every organic compound possesses a distinct set of physical and chemical properties that differentiates it from every other compound. The physical properties most commonly used for characterizing a compound are melting point, boiling point, adsorption behavior, and interactions (absorption, refraction, diffraction, and rotation) with light and other radiation. Common techniques for separating organic compounds from one another are differential extraction, crystallization, distillation, and adsorption. A compound is usually considered pure if its physical (and sometimes chemical) properties do not change when it is subjected to procedures based on the above techniques.

Qualitative Elemental Analysis. Once pure, a compound is further characterized by identification of its elements. If the compound burns in air, one knows that carbon and hydrogen are probably present, particularly if the flame contains soot. In another procedure, molecular destruction of the substance by fusion with sodium metal converts any nitrogen, sulfur, or halogen into inorganic salts, which can be detected by appropriate qualitative tests.

Quantitative Elemental Analysis and Molecular Formulas. In quantitative combustion analysis, a weighed portion of a compound is burned in oxygen over hot copper oxide at about 700°. Carbon dioxide and water are produced in essentially 100% yields, and are individually captured and weighed in absorption tubes. This is accomplished by first passing the combustion gases through a tube containing magnesium perchlorate (Anhydrone), which absorbs the water vapor and converts it to water of hydration; then by leading them through a tube containing finely divided sodium hydroxide (Ascarite), which absorbs and converts the carbon dioxide to sodium carbonate.

The *per cent composition* of carbon and hydrogen in the unknown compound can be calculated by utilizing the stoichiometric principles of general chemistry. Should the sum of these percentages equal approximately 100%, no other elements are present in the molecule. If the sum is less than 100%, and qualitative tests reveal the absence of elements such as nitrogen, sulfur, and halogens, then oxygen is probably present. Frequently the oxygen content is assumed to be the difference between the sum of the percentages of carbon and hydrogen and 100%. A better procedure involves the direct determination of oxygen content by decomposing the substance in an atmosphere of oxygen-free nitrogen. The products are passed over carbon at $1120°$, and the oxygen is quantitatively converted to carbon monoxide. This gas is passed into iodine pentoxide, and the liberated iodine is titrated with thiosulfate.

The following example illustrates the method of calculating the per cent composition of an unknown compound (I) known to contain only carbon, hydrogen, and oxygen.

Wt. of I	Wt. of CO_2	Wt of H_2O
4.337 mg	10.35 mg	3.42 mg

$$10.35 \text{ mg } (CO_2) \cdot \frac{12.01 \text{ (formula wt. C)}}{44.01 \text{ (formula wt. } CO_2)} = 2.824 \text{ mg C}$$

$$3.42 \text{ mg } (H_2O) \cdot \frac{2.018 \text{ (formula wt. } H_2)}{18.02 \text{ (formula wt. } H_2O)} = 0.383 \text{ mg H}$$

$$\% \text{ C in I} = \frac{\text{mg C}}{\text{mg sample}} \cdot 100\% = \frac{2.824}{4.337} \cdot 100\% = 65.11\% \text{ C}$$

$$\% \text{ H in I} = \frac{\text{mg H}}{\text{mg sample}} \cdot 100\% = \frac{0.383}{4.337} \cdot 100\% = 8.83\% \text{ H}$$

$$100.00\% - 65.11\% - 8.83\% = 26.06\% \text{ O}$$

The *empirical formula* of I can now be determined.

$$\frac{65.11 \text{ (\% C)}}{12.01 \text{ (at. wt. C)}} = 5.421 \qquad \frac{8.83 \text{ (\% H)}}{1.008 \text{ (at. wt. H)}} = 8.76 \qquad \frac{26.06 \text{ (\% O)}}{16.00 \text{ (at. wt. O)}} = 1.628$$

Compound I contains carbon, hydrogen, and oxygen atoms in the same ratios as the numbers of the formula.

$$C_{5.421}H_{8.76}O_{1.628}$$

The lowest of the numbers (that of oxygen in this case) is divided into each of the three numbers appearing as subscripts in the formula, and a new formula results in which oxygen has the value of unity.

$$C_{3.34}H_{5.39}O_1$$

The numbers in the subscript are now converted to the smallest possible set of whole numbers by multiplying each of them by the smallest integer that will accomplish this objective. In the sample calculation, the integer is 3.

$$C_{10.02}H_{16.17}O_3$$

The small deviations from whole numbers of the resulting subscripts represent the experimental error, and the true empirical formula is written as follows:

$$C_{10}H_{16}O_3$$

The *molecular formula,* which denotes the actual number of atoms of each element in the molecule, can now be indicated in a general way, n being some integer. To find the value of n, the approximate molecular weight of I must be determined.

$$[C_{10}H_{16}O_3]_n$$

A number of physical methods can be employed to determine molecular weight. The *vapor-density method* makes use of the appearance of the molecular-weight term in the ideal gas law [Eq. (1)]. It can be applied only to gases and low-boiling liquids.

(1)   Mol. wt. $= \dfrac{gRT}{PV}$ $g =$ grams
$R = 0.08205$ (liter)(atm)/(deg)(mole)
$T =$ absolute temperature
$P =$ pressure, atm
$V =$ volume, liters

The *cryoscopic method* (freezing-point-lowering method), which is most generally used in organic chemistry, makes use of Eq. (2). The high value of K_F (39.7) for camphor makes this substance the most commonly used solvent (Rast method), although the accuracy is frequently only $\pm 10\%$. Such accuracy is usually sufficient to differentiate between possible values of n.

(2)   Mol. wt. $= \dfrac{1000g\,K_F}{\triangle^+ G}$ $g =$ grams of solute
$G =$ grams of solvent or melt
$K_F =$ molal freezing-point-lowering constant
$\triangle^+ =$ freezing point of solvent minus freezing point of solution

According to a third method (that of Signer), separate solutions of two compounds are placed in two chambers, respectively, of an evacuated system. The same solvent is used in each solution. The chambers are now connected with each other, and allowed to come to vapor equilibrium with each other by isothermal distillation of the common solvent. In one solution is dissolved a compound of known molecular weight, and in the other, the substance of unknown molecular weight. At equilibrium, the volumes of each solution are measured, and the molecular weight of the unknown compound is calculated with Eq. (3).

(3) $M_\mu = \dfrac{W_\mu M_s V_s}{W_s V_\mu}$ $M_\mu =$ mol. wt. of unknown compound
$M_s =$ mol. wt. of standard compound
$W_\mu =$ wt. of unknown compound
$W_s =$ wt. of standard compound
$V_\mu =$ volume of solution of unknown compound
$V_s =$ volume of solution of standard compound

This method depends on Raoult's law, which requires that the mole fractions of solute in both solutions at equilibrium be equal. Molecular weights are thus estimated, usually with an accuracy of $\pm 2\%$. Common solvents used are acetone, methylene chloride, chloroform, and ether. Azobenzene (molecular weight = 168.2) is the most commonly employed standard. This method of obtaining molecular weights is limited to nonvolatile compounds.

The Signer and Rast determinations of molecular weight can be applied only when the unknown compound dissolves completely in the solvent or melt and does not decompose, dissociate, or associate in any way during the determination.

Suppose that the Rast method, applied to compound I, gives a molecular weight of 342, which allows the molecular formula of I to be written.

$$[C_{10}H_{16}O_3]_n = 2 \quad \text{or} \quad C_{20}H_{32}O_6$$

Such a compound should give the following carbon, hydrogen, and oxygen analyses: C, 65.19%; H, 8.75%; O, 26.06%. These values compare with those determined experimentally as follows: C, 65.11%; H, 8.83%; O, 26.06%.

Should a compound contain nitrogen, a Dumas analysis is frequently used to determine the per cent of this element in the compound. The unknown substance is mixed with cupric oxide (CuO) and brought to a dull-red heat, which results in complete oxidation of the organic material. The resulting gases are passed over a surface of hot copper to reduce nitrogen oxides to nitrogen. The other, more reactive gases are chemically absorbed, and the residual volume of nitrogen is measured at carefully determined temperatures and pressures. The weight of nitrogen can be calculated (ideal gas law), and is divided by the initial-sample weight to give the fraction of the element in the original compound.

Sulfur and halogens are determined by complete destruction of the organic compound with hot fuming nitric acid (Carius method), or sodium peroxide (Parr method). The sulfate or halide ions in the residue are precipitated and weighed as barium sulfate or silver halide.

A striking feature of these elemental analyses is that they can be carried out on a micro scale, since not more than 3 to 4 mg of material is required for carbon and hydrogen microanalysis, and not more than 3 to 8 mg is needed for a micro Dumas determination of nitrogen. Usually the differences between "calculated" and "found" values in research reports of per cent composition are not more than 0.30%.

Physical Measurements. Of the other methods of characterizing organic molecules, a few require further mention. The X-ray diffraction pattern of powdered crystalline solids provides, in a sense, a "fingerprint" of a substance, since no two different organic molecules give the same detailed pattern. Diffraction patterns obtained with single crystals of organic compounds have enabled crystallographers to arrive at detailed (three-dimensional) structural formulas for compounds whose structures were previously not known. Tremendous labor is involved in carrying

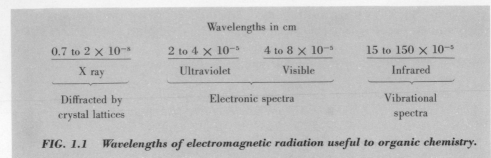

FIG. 1.1 *Wavelengths of electromagnetic radiation useful to organic chemistry.*

out the calculations necessary to determine a structure by this method, and it has been applied only to unusual or important compounds.

Absorption spectra play a prominent role in characterizing organic compounds. The most useful part of the spectrum of electromagnetic radiation is that which runs from 2×10^{-5} cm to 150×10^{-5} cm in wavelength. Certain types of organic compounds absorb light in the ultraviolet and visible region of the spectrum (see Fig. 1.1) at characteristic wavelengths and intensities, which are due to the excitation of the more loosely held electrons in the molecules. Almost all organic substances absorb in the infrared region, and the intensity of absorption of radiation as the wavelength is changed varies to give detailed patterns, commonly used to characterize or identify compounds. Absorption in this part of the spectrum is associated with vibrations of the various parts of the molecule with respect to one another. Perhaps the outstanding feature of these spectra is that they not only provide a means of recognizing the molecule as a whole, but also frequently allow identification of some of its parts. Chapter 27 contains a detailed discussion of the application of these techniques to organic chemistry.

The Electron Pair as a Chemical Bond

A chemical bond is a force which restrains the motions of atoms (or nuclei) in a molecule. This restraint fixes the distances between atoms in molecules within very narrow limits. Thus in a molecule of hydrogen (H_2), the two atoms are kept from flying apart by the force of a chemical bond. In organic chemistry, bonds are usually represented in structural formulas (see next section) by dashes that connect the symbols for the atoms being held together. Thus the hydrogen molecule is represented in the following way: $H—H$.

A detailed discussion of the nature of the chemical bond is reserved for Chap. 5. However, a brief description of the chemical bond is introduced here.

In inorganic chemistry, many molecules and ions are encountered which are composed of groups of atoms held together by bonds strong enough to preserve themselves under a variety of conditions. These bonds are composed of *pairs of electrons* simultaneously attracted by the positive charges in the nuclei of the atoms that are bonded. In many cases, each bonded atom contributes one electron to each bond, and thus neither atom assumes a net charge. In other cases, one atom contributes both of the bonding electrons and the other atom none; as a result, the former atom assumes a formal positive charge, and the latter a formal negative charge. Atoms are often held together by double bonds, and in effect four electrons are shared by two nuclei. Even triple bonds are occasionally found, in which six electrons are involved simultaneously with two nuclei. In the examples of inorganic molecules and ions in Fig. 1.2, electrons are symbolized by dots and crosses to indicate, for counting purposes, which atoms contribute electrons to which bonds. The non-bonding electrons in the outer shell of each element are also included.

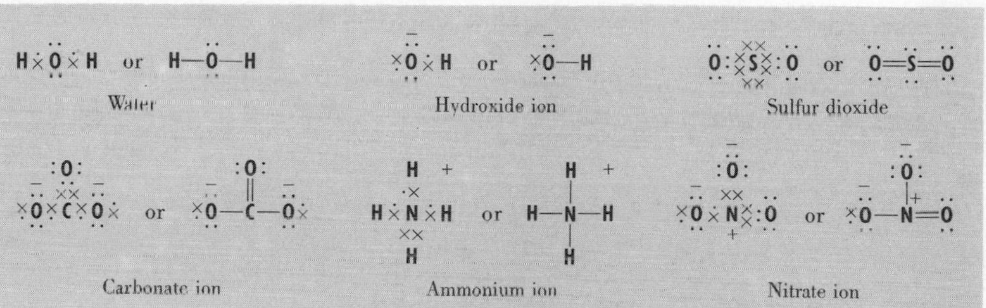

FIG. 1.2   *Electronic formulas for inorganic compounds and ions.*

In these compounds and ions, as a result of the bonds, each nucleus is provided with an electronic atmosphere which resembles that of a noble gas. The hydrogen atoms in water are each involved with two electrons, and are therefore similar in this respect to helium. The oxygen atoms are each surrounded by eight electrons, and therefore resemble neon. The same is true of all the oxygen, nitrogen, sulfur, and carbon atoms in the formulas. These relationships can be understood by comparing the electronic environments of the elements in the abbreviated periodic table of Fig. 1.3 with those of the atoms in the molecules and ions. Only the electrons in the outer shell of each element are shown.

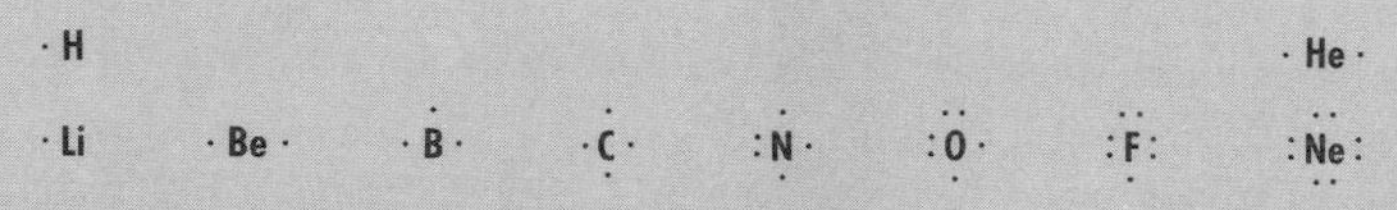

FIG. 1.3   *Abbreviated periodic table.*

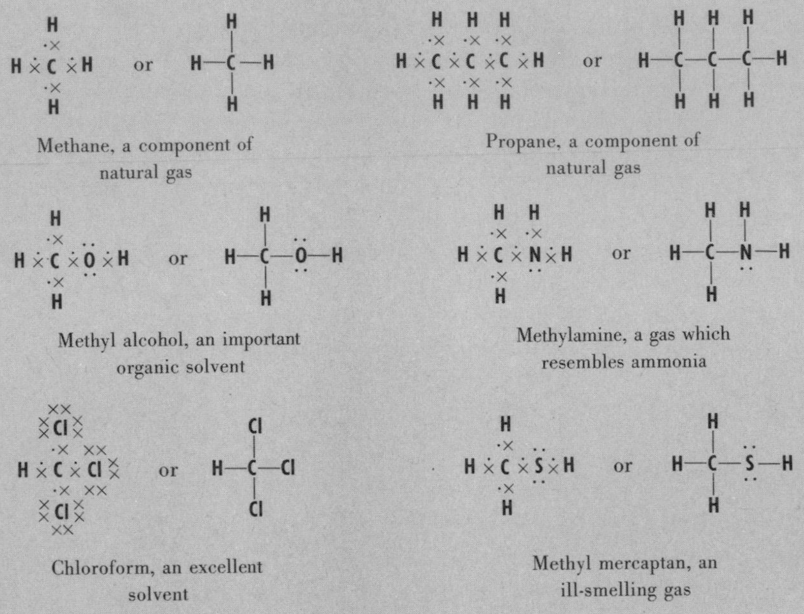

FIG. 1.4   Formulas of a number of simple organic compounds.

Methane, a component of natural gas

Propane, a component of natural gas

Methyl alcohol, an important organic solvent

Methylamine, a gas which resembles ammonia

Chloroform, an excellent solvent

Methyl mercaptan, an ill-smelling gas

Structural Formulas of Organic Compounds

The same principles that govern bond formation in inorganic compounds apply even more cogently to organic compounds. An outstanding feature of organic chemistry is the ability of carbon to bond to carbon to form chains of atoms with arrangements and lengths capable of almost infinite variation. These chains are covered with a skin of hydrogen atoms, broken in places by atomic assemblies involving oxygen, nitrogen, halogens, or sulfur. The structures of these compounds are represented by graphic formulas in which dashes stand for bonds (electron pairs) and atomic symbols for atoms. These formulas are based on the *ball-and-stick model* for organic compounds, and they provide an adequate method of indicating which atoms are bonded to which other atoms.

As a result of the tendency of elements in organic compounds to acquire an electronic environment resembling that of the rare gases, a certain number of bonds are characteristically associated with each element. Thus hydrogen has one bond, carbon four bonds, oxygen two bonds, nitrogen three or four bonds, halogens one bond, and sulfur two or four bonds. With rare exceptions, only carbon will unite with a second atom of its own kind. These principles are illustrated with the formulas for a number of simple organic compounds in Fig. 1.4.

In many molecules, *multiple bonds* between two atoms are encountered, and therefore bonds are frequently referred to as being *single, double,* or *triple,* depending on whether two, four, or six electrons are involved. Thus ethane contains a carbon-carbon single bond; ethylene, a carbon-carbon double bond; and acetylene, a carbon-carbon triple bond.

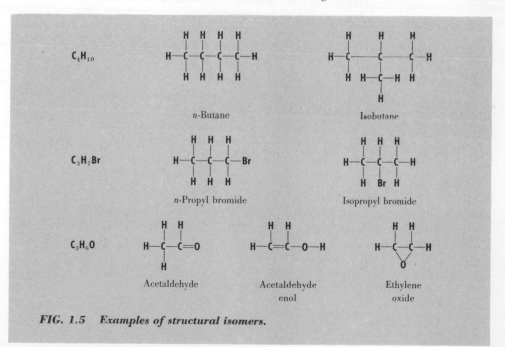

| Ethane, a component of natural gas | Ethylene, a by-product of gasoline production | Acetylene, prepared from coke and limestone |

In any of the three examples given above, only one reasonable structural formula can be drawn once the molecular formula is specified. However, as the number of atoms in a molecule increases, more than one structural formula can be drawn per molecular formula. Compounds which possess the same molecular formula but different structures are referred to as *structural isomers,* and the phenomenon is known as *structural isomerism.* The number of possible structural isomers increases very rapidly as the number of atoms in molecular formulas increases. Thus 2 structural formulas can be drawn for C_4H_{10}, 18 for C_8H_{18}, and calculations have been made which indicate that 62,491,178,805,831 structural formulas can be drawn for $C_{40}H_{82}$. The structural formulas of a number of isomeric compounds are illustrated in Fig. 1.5.

FIG. 1.5   *Examples of structural isomers.*

To differentiate among possible structures for a molecule of known molecular formula, a large number of physical and chemical methods are available. These methods are diverse. They depend on detailed knowledge of chemical reactions, and on correlations between structural units and physical properties. An illustration of the sort of methodology that is applied to this kind of problem is found in the following argument:

Presume that a compound of unknown structure possesses the molecular formula II, for which two structural formulas can be drawn, III and IV.

C_2H_6O

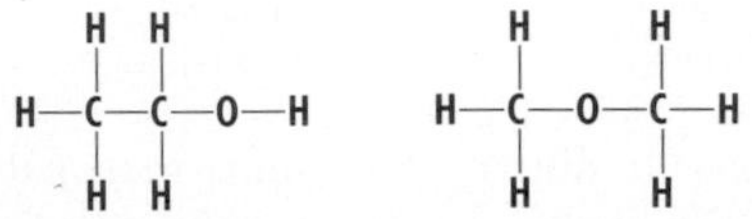

$$H-\underset{\underset{H}{|}}{\overset{\overset{H}{|}}{C}}-\underset{\underset{H}{|}}{\overset{\overset{H}{|}}{C}}-O-H \qquad\qquad H-\underset{\underset{H}{|}}{\overset{\overset{H}{|}}{C}}-O-\underset{\underset{H}{|}}{\overset{\overset{H}{|}}{C}}-H$$

II   III   IV

The compound when treated with sodium metal produces hydrogen gas. When passed over hot aluminum oxide (Al_2O_3), it produces water and a substance C_2H_4. These facts strongly suggest that compound II possesses structure III and not IV, for these reasons:

It is known that water produces hydrogen when treated with sodium.

$$2Na + 2H_2O \longrightarrow H_2 + 2NaOH$$

Formula III contains an **O—H** group, as does the formula of water (**H—O—H**), whereas formula IV in no way resembles that of water. Therefore, structure III for compound II offers an explanation for the behavior of II when treated with sodium, whereas structure IV does not.

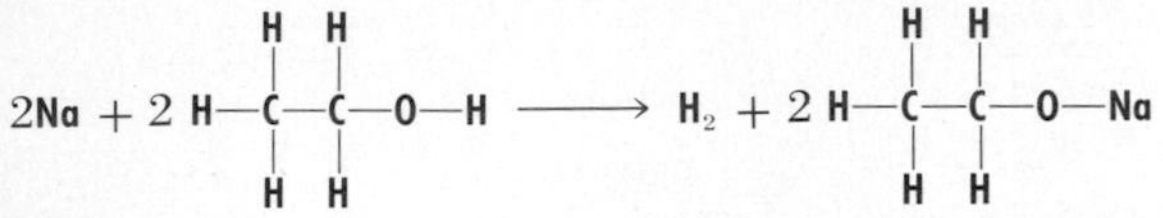

$$2Na + 2\ H-\underset{\underset{H}{|}}{\overset{\overset{H}{|}}{C}}-\underset{\underset{H}{|}}{\overset{\overset{H}{|}}{C}}-O-H \longrightarrow H_2 + 2\ H-\underset{\underset{H}{|}}{\overset{\overset{H}{|}}{C}}-\underset{\underset{H}{|}}{\overset{\overset{H}{|}}{C}}-O-Na$$

Only one structural formula, that of ethylene, can be drawn for the molecule C_2H_4.

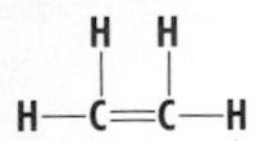

$$H-\underset{\underset{H}{|}}{\overset{\overset{H}{|}}{C}}=\underset{\underset{H}{|}}{\overset{\overset{H}{|}}{C}}-H$$

Ethylene contains carbon bonded to carbon, and of formulas III and IV, only the former contains carbon bonded to carbon. Thus structure III seems more likely to apply to compound II, and the reaction can be formulated in a reasonable way.

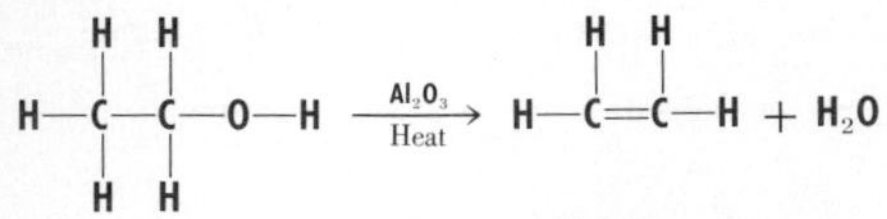

$$H-\underset{\underset{H}{|}}{\overset{\overset{H}{|}}{C}}-\underset{\underset{H}{|}}{\overset{\overset{H}{|}}{C}}-O-H \xrightarrow[\text{Heat}]{Al_2O_3} H-\underset{\underset{H}{|}}{\overset{\overset{H}{|}}{C}}=\underset{\underset{H}{|}}{\overset{\overset{H}{|}}{C}}-H + H_2O$$

Ethylene

Deductions of this kind are frequently confirmed through synthesis by rational means of substances whose structures might conform to that of the compound of unknown constitution. Thus compounds possessing structures III and IV might be synthesized from molecules whose structures are unambiguous because of their simplicity. The substance corresponding to III can be prepared by addition of the elements of water to ethylene in the presence of a sulfuric acid catalyst.

$$H-O-H + H-\overset{\displaystyle H}{\underset{\displaystyle H}{C}}=\overset{\displaystyle H}{\underset{\displaystyle H}{C}}-H \xrightarrow{H_2SO_4} H-\overset{\displaystyle H}{\underset{\displaystyle H}{C}}-\overset{\displaystyle H}{\underset{\displaystyle H}{C}}-O-H$$

III

The compound possessing structure IV could reasonably be anticipated from the reactions formulated.

$$2Na + 2\ H-\overset{\displaystyle H}{\underset{\displaystyle H}{C}}-O-H \longrightarrow H_2 + 2\ H-\overset{\displaystyle H}{\underset{\displaystyle H}{C}}-O-Na$$

$$H-\overset{\displaystyle H}{\underset{\displaystyle H}{C}}-O-Na + H-\overset{\displaystyle H}{\underset{\displaystyle H}{C}}-Cl \longrightarrow H-\overset{\displaystyle H}{\underset{\displaystyle H}{C}}-O-\overset{\displaystyle H}{\underset{\displaystyle H}{C}}-H + NaCl$$

IV

The physical properties of III correspond to those of the original substance whose structure was determined, while the properties of IV are quite different. With methods similar to the one described, the structural formulas of thousands of organic compounds have been established.

Organic Reactions

Most of the million or so organic compounds that have now been described were prepared by synthetic sequences in which one substance was converted to a second, which in turn was changed to a third, etc. Clearly, many million reactions were run to accumulate this large number of compounds. Fortunately, both organic compounds and reactions fall into classes, a knowledge of which allows a chemist to predict, with a high probability of success, what reactions will occur with a given compound under a specified set of conditions. Predictions of this kind are largely based on reasoning by analogy, which in turn rests on extensive correlations between the structure and chemical behavior of compounds.

One of the outstanding characteristics of organic reactions is their variety. Organic compounds react in the gaseous, liquid, and solid phases, as well as on the surface of solid catalysts. Useful reaction conditions include temperatures that range from -70 to $900°$ and pressures that vary from a few millimeters to several hundred atmospheres. Reactions vary in reaction time from minute fractions of a second to several months or years.   The number of types of organic reactions is in the hundreds, and the number of modifications of these is in the thousands.   In some reactions (e.g., combustion), carbon chains are torn completely to pieces.   In others (e.g., the formation of polyethylene plastic from ethylene), very long carbon chains are built from small organic units.   Most transformations are confined to the making and breaking of a relatively small number of bonds as compared to the total number in the molecule.

Organization of Book

This book may be roughly divided into three sections.   The first eight chapters deal largely with the structural concepts of the science. In this section the structures, nomenclature, occurrence, and physical properties of organic compounds are treated.   The character of the chemical bond and stereochemistry of organic compounds are explained; this is followed by a discussion of the correlation of structure and reactivity as related to acid-base theory.   The next block of 12 chapters treats organic reactions, class by class.   The last group of chapters deals with special topics, in which the fundamentals of the first 20 chapters are illustrated and elaborated through treatment of the chemistry of natural products, petroleum, polymers, and other important materials.   A chapter on spectra, a reference chapter on nomenclature, and one on the chemical literature complete the book.

Problems

1. List the materials you can see from where you are sitting that you think might be made of organic compounds.

2. A compound was found to contain 87.8% carbon and 12.2% hydrogen.   What is the empirical formula of this substance?

3. A compound was subjected to combustion analysis.   A weight of 3.898 mg of the substance when burned gave 3.172 mg of water and 12.969 mg of carbon dioxide. What is the probable empirical formula of the compound?

4. Qualitative analysis of a compound demonstrated the absence of halogens, nitrogen, sulfur, and phosphorus.   Combustion analysis of 3.493 mg of the compound gave 2.817 mg of water and 9.394 mg of carbon dioxide.   Determine the probable empirical formula of the substance.

5. A compound was found to contain 69.0% carbon, 14.9% hydrogen, and 16.1% nitrogen.   A Rast molecular weight determination involved 2.50 mg of solute and 28.5 mg of solvent, and gave a melting-point depression of 12.9°. Calculate the molecular formula of this compound.

6. A molecule was known by its mode of synthesis to contain 10 atoms of carbon per molecule, along with unknown numbers of chlorines, hydrogens, and oxygens. Analysis indicated that the substance contained 60.5% carbon, 5.55% hydrogen, 16.1% oxygen, and 17.9% chlorine.   Calculate the molecular formula of the substance.

7. A 1.65 ml sample of a 0.105 molar azobenzene solution in methylene chloride was allowed to come to isothermal equilibrium with 22.5 mg of an unknown compound in 1.38 ml of methylene chloride.   The final volumes were 1.21 ml for the azobenzene solution and 1.82 ml for the unknown solution. What is the molecular weight of the unknown compound, as determined by the Signer method, used here?

8. With 40.6 mg of a compound, 45.1 mg of azobenzene, and methylene chloride as solvent, a Signer molecular weight was determined. After 4 days at 50°, the system came to equilibrium, and the volumes were 1.80 ml and 1.41 ml in the azobenzene and "unknown" chambers, respectively. Calculate the molecular weight of the unknown compound.

9. Write out all possible unique structural formulas that correspond to the following molecular formulas:

a. C_3H_4 *c.* $C_3H_3F_3$ *e.* C_3H_6O *g.* C_3H_7N
b. C_4H_8 *d.* C_3H_8O *f.* C_3H_9N

10. What is wrong with the following molecular formulas?

a. C_2H_5 *c.* CH_3O *e.* C_2H_4Cl
b. C_2H_4N *d.* CH_5S

11. Write out structures for the following compounds and ions, utilizing both the bonding and nonbonding electrons in the outer shell of each element. Use both crosses and dots for the electrons to indicate which atoms contribute electrons to each bond.

a. HCN   *c.* HCO_3^- *e.* ClO_4^- *g.* NO_3^-
b. CO_2 *d.* PO_4^{3-} *f.* NO_2^- *h.* HOCl

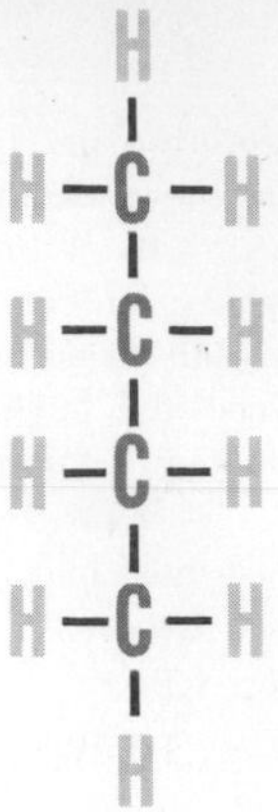

$$H-C-H$$
(structure at top right, a four-carbon chain with hydrogens)

2

Hydrocarbons

Classification

The term *hydrocarbon* refers to those organic compounds which contain only carbon and hydrogen. Hydrocarbons and derived compounds fall into three large classes, which are defined in terms of structural concepts. *Aliphatic hydrocarbons* are composed of chains of carbon atoms not arranged in the form of cycles. Substances belonging to this group are sometimes referred to as *open-chain compounds*. In *alicyclic hydrocarbons*, the carbon chains form cycles. Aside from a few exceptional ring compounds, aliphatic and alicyclic hydrocarbons of like molecular weight are similar in both physical and chemical properties. The third group consists of the *aromatic hydrocarbons*, which contain six-membered rings into which are fitted three carbon-carbon double bonds. Special physical and chemical properties are associated with this arrangement of double bonds in aromatic systems. Figure 2.1 shows examples of the three classes of hydrocarbons.

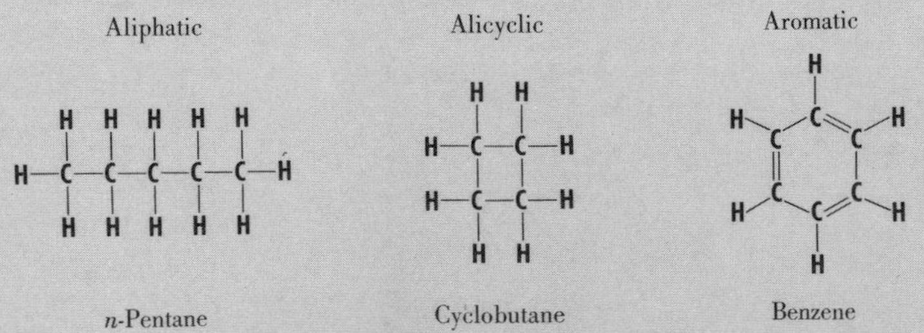

FIG. 2.1   *Examples of classes of hydrocarbons.*

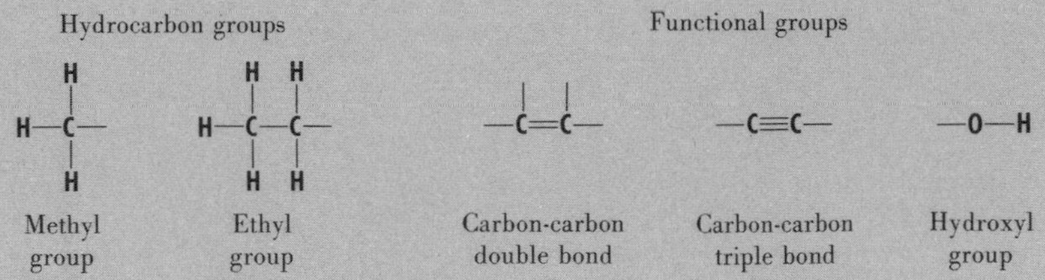

Hydrocarbon groups   Functional groups

| Methyl group | Ethyl group | Carbon-carbon double bond | Carbon-carbon triple bond | Hydroxyl group |

FIG. 2.2   *Examples of hydrocarbon and functional groups.*

In spite of their vast number, organic compounds are composed of a relatively small number of different kinds of parts, which can be assembled in an almost infinite number of different ways. The study of the science can be greatly simplified by classifying these parts into two large categories, the *functional groups* and the *hydrocarbon groups*. These parts are given special names, although they normally have no existence as discrete entities. While some of the functional groups contain only carbon and hydrogen, most of them contain other elements, such as nitrogen or oxygen (see Fig. 2.2). In this chapter, the structures of hydrocarbons and hydrocarbon groups will be developed. In Chaps. 3 and 4, the structures of the functional groups containing elements other than carbon, and the classes of compounds based on these groups, will be discussed.

Structure and Nomenclature

Alkanes. The alkanes (paraffins) are aliphatic hydrocarbons which contain the maximum number of hydrogen atoms compatible with the requirement that carbon always possesses four bonds and hydrogen one. Thus alkanes are said to be saturated, and they are represented by the general formula C_nH_{2n+2}, where n is an integer. All compounds corresponding to the structural formulas that can be written for alkanes with one to nine carbon atoms are known. Some substances with n higher than 50 have been prepared in a pure state. This general formula describes what is known as a *homologous series,* members of which are referred to as *homologues* of one another. Each member of this series differs from its immediate neighbors by a methylene group (CH_2).

The structures of these compounds may be written in a number of different ways, as indicated by the formulas for the eight simplest alkanes (Fig. 2.3). The detailed structural formulas display separately all of the carbon-hydrogen bonds, but such representation is tedious. Simple abbreviations known as condensed structural formulas are commonly written. Individual bonds are omitted in the condensed formulas, and the hydrogen atoms attached to a given carbon are shown at the immediate right of the carbon symbol concerned. In the condensed formulas,

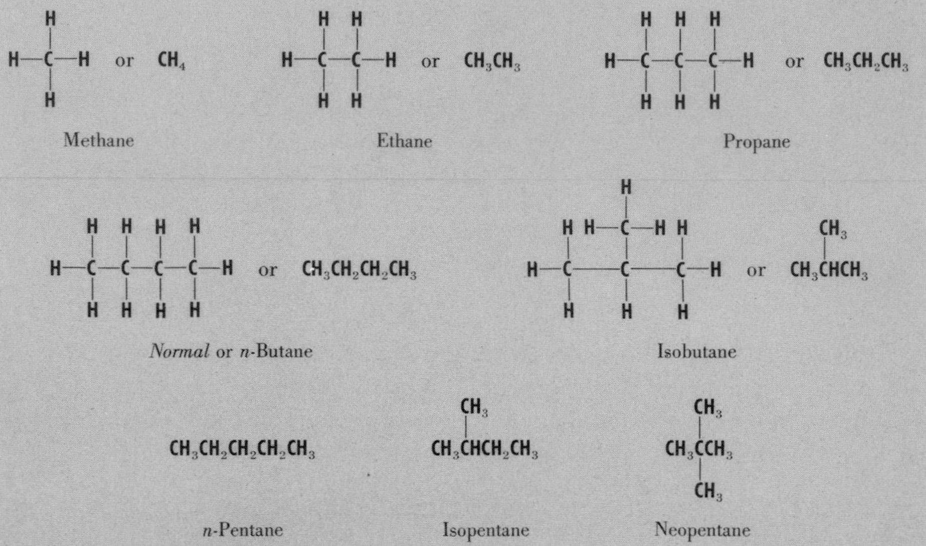

FIG. 2.3   Formulas of the eight simplest alkanes.

the horizontal bonds between carbon atoms are also usually omitted, but the vertical bonds are generally included.   The carbon chains are, as far as possible, written along a line, although the actual molecules occupy three dimensions, and the chains can assume a variety of shapes.   Such simplified representation is largely imposed by the limitations of typewriter and printing press.

The saturated hydrocarbon groups, in a formal sense, are derived from the parent hydrocarbon by simply removing one hydrogen from the molecule.   More than one hydrocarbon group can be derived from each of the alkanes that contain more than two carbon atoms, since removal of different hydrogens from the hydrocarbon leads to different groups. These groups are sometimes called *alkyl groups,* and are symbolized by the letter R.   Figure 2.4 indicates the structures and common names of the simple alkyl groups.   The prefixes *n-, sec-,* and *tert-* in the names are written as shown, but are pronounced *normal, secondary,* and *tertiary.*

The nomenclature of organic chemistry involves both common and systematic names, the former being applied to simple compounds, and the latter usually to more complex substances.   Chapter 28 is devoted to a detailed description of both kinds of nomenclature, and the material of that chapter should be used for reference purposes.   A much shorter description of how the various classes of compounds are named is found in this chapter and in Chaps. 3 and 4.

The names and some of the physical properties of the normal saturated hydrocarbons are listed in Table 2.1.   Much of the nomenclature of organic compounds is based on the first 10 names in this table. The names of the branched hydrocarbons containing five or fewer carbon atoms, which are given in Fig. 2.3, are modifications of the names of the normal compounds. The prefix *iso-*, when added to the name of a simple aliphatic compound, indicates the presence in the molecule of a $(CH_3)_2CH$ group. In general, systematic nomenclature is applied to branched alkanes that contain more than five carbon atoms.

The International Union of Chemistry (IUC) has developed a system of nomenclature for organic compounds which allows a unique name to be given to each possible compound. Familiarity with a relatively small number of names and rules permits formulas and IUC names to be translated one into the other with great ease. The system can best be learned through practice.

As applied to alkanes, the IUC system establishes the following rules. The *longest hydrocarbon chain* in the compound to be named is selected. The basic part of the name is that of this chain. The chain names are listed in Table 2.1.

The chain is numbered from the end closest to branches in the chain. The positions of the *hydrocarbon groups* may now be located by the number of the carbon atom of the parent chain to which they are attached. The names of these hydrocarbon groups are prefixed to the name of the parent chain, and are arranged in alphabetical order. The longest chain in the hydrocarbon group is selected, and numbered from the end closest to its point of attachment to the parent chain. The following examples will help clarify the system:

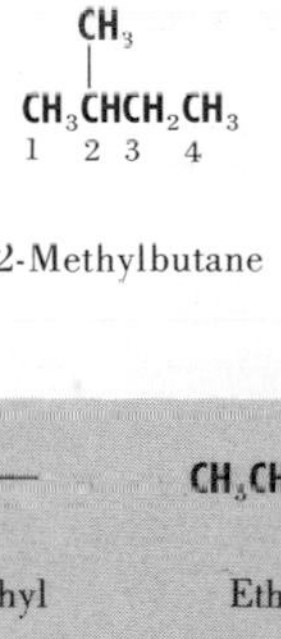

2-Methylbutane 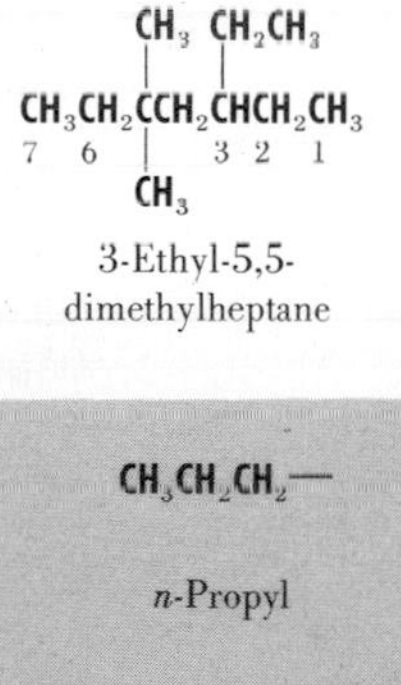   3-Ethyl-5,5-dimethylheptane 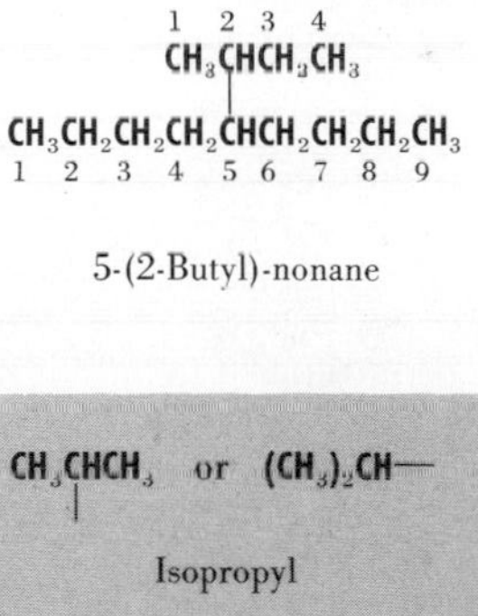   5-(2-Butyl)-nonane

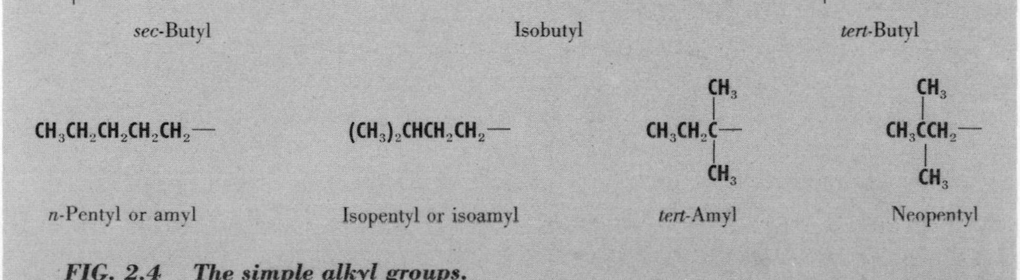

FIG. 2.4   *The simple alkyl groups.*

TABLE 2.1   Normal Saturated Hydrocarbons

Name	Formula	Mp, °C	Bp, °C	Sp. gr. (liquid)	State under atmospheric conditions
Methane	CH_4	−183	−162	0.4240	Gas
Ethane	C_2H_6	−172	−89	0.5462	Gas
Propane	C_3H_8	−187	−42	0.5824	Gas
n-Butane	C_4H_{10}	−135	0	0.5788	Gas
n-Pentane	C_5H_{12}	−130	36	0.6264	Liquid
n-Hexane	C_6H_{14}	−94	69	0.6594	Liquid
n-Heptane	C_7H_{16}	−91	98	0.6837	Liquid
n-Octane	C_8H_{18}	−57	126	0.7028	Liquid
n-Nonane	C_9H_{20}	−54	151	0.7179	Liquid
n-Decane	$C_{10}H_{22}$	−30	174	0.7298	Liquid
n-Undecane	$C_{11}H_{24}$	−26	196	0.7404	Liquid
n-Dodecane	$C_{12}H_{26}$	−10	216	0.7493	Liquid
n-Tridecane	$C_{13}H_{28}$	−6	(230)	0.7568	Liquid
n-Tetradecane	$C_{14}H_{30}$	6	251	0.7636	Liquid
n-Pentadecane	$C_{15}H_{32}$	10	268	0.7688	Liquid
n-Hexadecane	$C_{16}H_{34}$	18	280	0.7749	Liquid
n-Heptadecane	$C_{17}H_{36}$	22	303	0.7767	Liquid
n-Octadecane	$C_{18}H_{38}$	28	308	0.7767	Solid
n-Nonadecane	$C_{19}H_{40}$	32	330	0.7776	Solid
n-Eicosane	$C_{20}H_{42}$	36		0.7777	Solid
n-Heneicosane	$C_{21}H_{44}$	40		0.7782	Solid
n-Docosane	$C_{22}H_{46}$	44		0.7778	Solid
n-Tricosane	$C_{23}H_{48}$	47		0.7797	Solid
n-Tetracosane	$C_{24}H_{50}$	51		0.7786	Solid
n-Pentacosane	$C_{25}H_{52}$	53			Solid
n-Triacontane	$C_{30}H_{62}$	66			Solid
n-Pentatriacontane	$C_{35}H_{72}$	75		0.7814	Solid
n-Tetracontane	$C_{40}H_{82}$	81			Solid
n-Pentacontane	$C_{50}H_{102}$	92		0.7940	Solid
n-Hexacontane	$C_{60}H_{122}$	99			Solid
n-Dohexacontane	$C_{62}H_{126}$	101			Solid
n-Tetrahexacontane	$C_{64}H_{130}$	102			Solid
n-Heptacontane	$C_{70}H_{142}$	105			Solid

Modifications of the IUC system are sometimes employed.   For instance, names of hydrocarbon groups, such as *tert*-butyl (see Fig. 2.4), are sometimes prefixed to the names of parent chains, as in the example.

$$\overset{1}{CH_3}\overset{2}{CH_2}\overset{3}{CH_2}\overset{4}{CH}\overset{5}{CH_2}\overset{6}{CH_2}\overset{7}{CH_2}\overset{8}{CH_3}$$

$$CH_3CCH_3$$

$$CH_3$$

4-*tert*-Butyloctane

Alkenes. The *alkenes* are aliphatic hydrocarbons which contain one or more carbon-carbon double bonds. These compounds are said to be *unsaturated,* since they do not carry the maximum possible number of hydrogen atoms, and are sometimes referred to as *olefins.* The general formula C_nH_{2n} describes the homologous series which contains one double bond per molecule, and C_nH_{2n-2}, the series with two double bonds. Members of the latter class are called *alkadienes,* or simply *dienes.* *Trienes* and higher *polyenes* are also known.

Common and partially systematic names are frequently applied to the simpler alkenes (see Fig. 2.5). As soon as the four-carbon alkenes are reached, the IUC system is best employed. In this system, the *longest chain carrying the carbon-carbon double bond* is considered the parent compound, and the chain is numbered from the end that gives the position of the double bond the lowest number. The ending *-ane* found in the names of the alkanes is changed to *-ene* in the alkenes. The position of the double bond is indicated with a prefixed number. *The double bond must be* between two consecutively numbered atoms, and the lower-numbered carbon is used to locate its position. If the chain carries alkyl or other groups, the names of these groups are placed ahead of the number denoting the position of the double bond, as indicated in the examples.

$CH_3CH_2CH_2CH{=}CH_2$ $CH_3CH_2CH{=}CHCH_3$ $\overset{\displaystyle CH_3}{\underset{\displaystyle }{CH_3CHCH{=}CH_2}}$

1-Pentene   2-Pentene   3-Methyl-1-butene

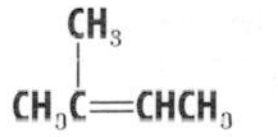

$\overset{\displaystyle CH_3}{CH_3C{=}CHCH_3}$ $\overset{\displaystyle CH_3}{CH_3CH_2C{=}CH_2}$ $\overset{\displaystyle CH_2CH_2CH_3}{CH_3CH_2CH_2CHCH{=}CH_2}$

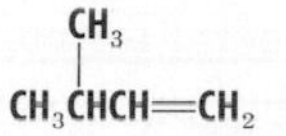

2-Methyl-2-butene 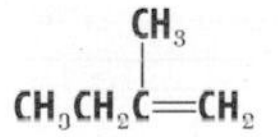   2-Methyl-1-butene 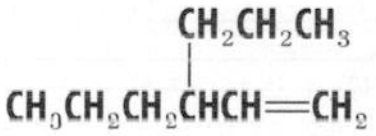   3-Propyl-1-hexene

Alkenes that possess two double bonds (*alkadienes*) can be divided into three classes, members of which are formulated below. Only a few examples of the *allene class* are known. In 1,3-butadiene the double bonds are said to be *conjugated,* since the double-bond systems are joined by a single bond. The *unconjugated dienes* (e.g., 2,5-heptadiene)

$CH_2{=}CH_2$ $CH_3CH{=}CH_2$ $CH_3CH_2CH{=}CH_2$ $CH_3CH{=}CHCH_3$

Ethylene   Propylene or methylethylene   *unsym*-Butene or ethylethylene   *sym*-Butene or *sym*-dimethylethylene

$(CH_3)_2C{=}CH_2$ $(CH_3)_2C{=}C(CH_3)_2$ $\overset{\displaystyle CH_3}{CH_2{=}CCH{=}CH_2}$

Isobutene   Tetramethylethylene   Isoprene

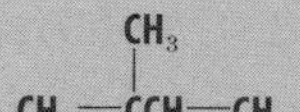

FIG. 2.5   *Common and partially systematic names of the simple alkenes.*

possess at least one saturated carbon atom which intervenes between the two double-bond systems.

$CH_2\!\!=\!\!C\!\!=\!\!CH_2$ $CH_2\!\!=\!\!CH\!\!-\!\!CH\!\!=\!\!CH_2$ $CH_3CH\!\!=\!\!CHCH_2CH\!\!=\!\!CHCH_3$

Allene   1,3-Butadiene   2,5-Heptadiene
                        (conjugated diene)   (unconjugated diene)

$CH(CH_3)_2$
|
$CH_2\!\!=\!\!CHCH_2C\!\!=\!\!CHCH_3$ $(CH_3)_2C\!\!=\!\!CHCH\!\!=\!\!CHCH\!\!=\!\!C(CH_3)_2$

4-(2-propyl)-1,4-hexadiene   2,7-Dimethyl-2,4,6-octatriene
(unconjugated diene)   (conjugated triene)

A number of *alkenyl* groups occur frequently enough in organic chemistry to carry common names, and these are formulated in Fig. 2.6.

$CH_2\!\!=\!\!CH\!\!-$ $CH_2\!\!=\!\!CHCH_2\!\!-$ $CH_3CH\!\!=\!\!CH\!\!-$ $CH_3CH\!\!=\!\!CHCH_2\!\!-$

Vinyl   Allyl   Propenyl   Crotyl

FIG. 2.6   *Common alkenyl groups.*

Alkynes.   The *alkynes* contain a carbon-carbon triple bond.   Acetylene is the simplest member of the class, and the class as a whole is frequently referred to as the *acetylenes*.   The homologous series of monoacetylenes possesses the general formula C_nH_{2n-2}, and for each additional triple bond in the molecule four hydrogens must be removed from the general formula.

The simple alkynes are named as derivatives of acetylene.   The IUC nomenclature as applied to the alkynes is similar to that of the alkenes, except that the ending is changed to *-yne* to indicate the presence of a triple bond.   Examples of each system are formulated.

$CH_3CH_2C\!\!\equiv\!\!CH$ $CH_3C\!\!\equiv\!\!CCH_3$ $CH_3CHC\!\!\equiv\!\!CCH_3$ (with CH_3 substituent)

Ethylacetylene   Dimethylacetylene   Isopropylmethylacetylene

CH_3
|
$CH_3CHCH_2CH_2C\!\!\equiv\!\!CH$ $CH_3C\!\!\equiv\!\!CC\!\!\equiv\!\!CC\!\!\equiv\!\!CCH_3$ $CH_3CH\!\!=\!\!CHCH_2CH_2C\!\!\equiv\!\!CH$

5-Methyl-1-hexyne   2,4,6-Octatriyne   Hepta-5-ene-1-yne
                        (a conjugated   (an unconjugated
                         system)   system)

The only two alkynyl groups encountered frequently enough to be given common names are shown in Fig. 2.7.

$CH\!\!\equiv\!\!C\!\!-$ $CH\!\!\equiv\!\!CCH_2\!\!-$

Ethynyl   Propargyl

FIG. 2.7   *Common alkynyl groups.*

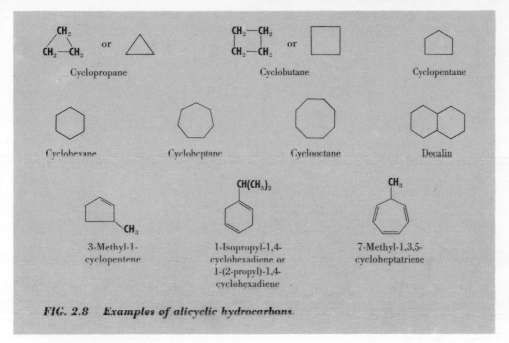

FIG. 2.8 Examples of alicyclic hydrocarbons.

Alicyclic Compounds. Hydrocarbons with chains arranged in rings belong to the *alicyclic* class of compounds. Substances are known which contain rings ranging from 3 to over 30 carbon atoms, and in principle there appears to be no limit to the size of rings that can be formed. Compounds containing carbocyclic rings are named by applying the prefix *cyclo-* to the name of the aliphatic hydrocarbon of carbon content equal to that in the ring system. Double and triple bonds, and alkyl substituents, are located in the molecule by use of numbers in ways suggested by the conventions of nomenclature applied to aliphatic compounds. The methodology becomes evident from the names given the compounds in Fig. 2.8. Frequently formulas consisting only of bonds are drawn for the ring portion of alicyclic compounds, and carbon atoms with their complements of hydrogens are understood to be at the points of intersection of the bonds.

When carbocyclic groups are attached to more complex groups, including aliphatic chains of four or more carbon atoms, the aliphatic chain is considered the parent molecule for nomenclature purposes. The cycle is then treated as a hydrocarbon group in the name, as in the following examples.

Aromatic Hydrocarbons. The aromatic hydrocarbons all possess the common feature of containing one or more six-membered rings, each of which contains three double bonds. The simplest member of the class is benzene. An ambiguity exists as to the exact positions of the double bonds in this ring system, since two equivalent structures can be written for the compound (Fig. 2.9). When two methyl groups are substituted for two adjacent hydrogen atoms on the benzene ring (1,2-dimethylbenzene), the problem becomes acute. A question is immediately raised as to the possibility of two unique structures. In this manner the structure of benzene has become one of the most famous and long-debated problems of organic chemistry.

From infrared spectral measurements and X-ray-diffraction crystal structure determinations, it is clear that benzene is flat and possesses a sixfold axis of symmetry, and that all six of the carbon-carbon bonds of benzene are equivalent. The double bonds in benzene and other aromatics are said to be *delocalized;* each of the six bonds possesses a character intermediate between a single and a double bond. Thus only one kind of 1,2-dimethylbenzene exists, and either structure shown in Fig. 2.9 is an acceptable formula. The two formulas for benzene and 1,2-dimethylbenzene are referred to as *Kekulé formulas,* and are preferred to notations which depict half bonds. Formulas involving half bonds obscure the fact that carbon possesses four bonds, and makes bond counting difficult. A more complete discussion of *aromaticity* will be found in Chap. 5.

The structures of the simplest aromatic hydrocarbons are formulated in Fig. 2.10. The apexes represent carbon atoms, and hydrogen is omitted in these formulas for the sake of simplicity. The positions in the more complex ring systems are numbered in the formulas for nomenclature purposes, since all the carbons that carry hydrogen are subject to substitution by hydrocarbon or functional groups. Azulene, which contains a *fused five- and seven-membered ring system,* is an exception to the more ordinary six-membered cycles found in aromatic chemistry.

Aromatic hydrocarbons are named in a variety of ways. The simple compounds in all cases possess common names, which serve as the

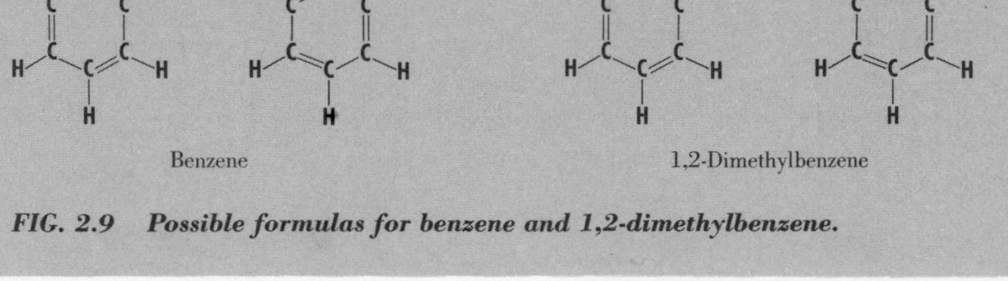

Benzene   1,2-Dimethylbenzene

FIG. 2.9   Possible formulas for benzene and 1,2-dimethylbenzene.

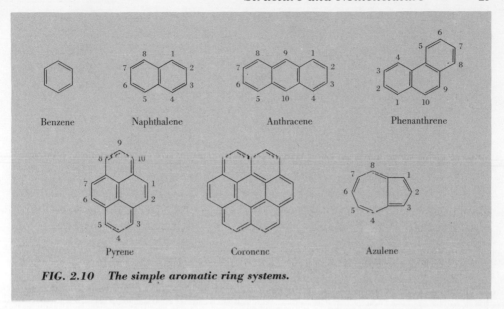

FIG. 2.10 *The simple aromatic ring systems.*

basis of naming derived substances. To indicate the relative positions of two substituents on a benzene ring, the terms *ortho* (*o*-), *meta* (*m*-), and *para* (*p*-) are frequently used, as exemplified in the naming of the three xylenes. In the IUC system, the relative positions of substituents are indicated with numbers.

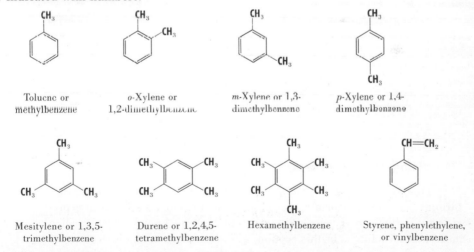

| Toluene or methylbenzene | o-Xylene or 1,2-dimethylbenzene | m-Xylene or 1,3-dimethylbenzene | p-Xylene or 1,4-dimethylbenzene |

| Mesitylene or 1,3,5-trimethylbenzene | Durene or 1,2,4,5-tetramethylbenzene | Hexamethylbenzene | Styrene, phenylethylene, or vinylbenzene |

The naphthalene ring possesses two unique positions designated as α and β, which serve to indicate the point of attachment of substituents in the names of monosubstituted naphthalenes. When benzene or naphthalene rings are attached to aliphatic chains which contain more than four carbon atoms, the aromatic group can be prefixed in the name of the compound. Figure 2.11 lists the common aromatic hydrocarbon groups, which are collectively referred to as *aryl* groups, and which are

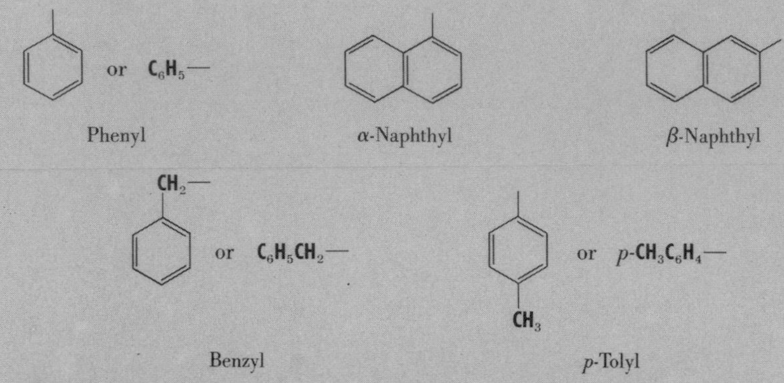

Phenyl   α-Naphthyl   β-Naphthyl

Benzyl   p-Tolyl

FIG. 2.11   Common aromatic hydrocarbon groups.

symbolized by the letters Ar.   The prefix *bi-* is sometimes used to name
symmetrical compounds, such as biphenyl or bibenzyl.   These principles
of nomenclature are illustrated by the names given to the compounds
formulated.

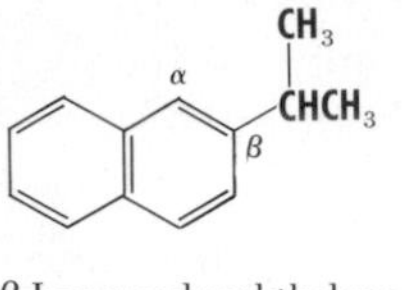

β-Isopropylnaphthalene   2,5-Dimethyl-1-(1-   1,7-Dimethylphenanthrene
or 2-isopropylnaphthalene   naphthyl)-hexane

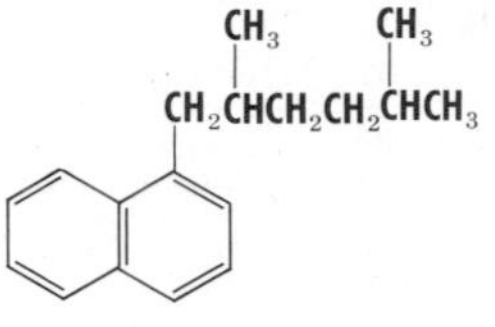

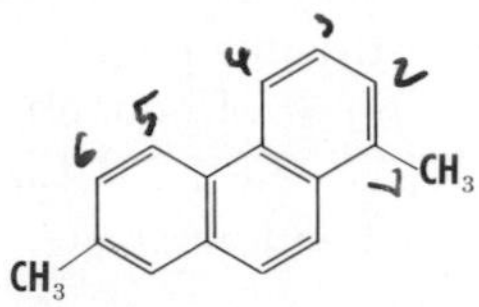

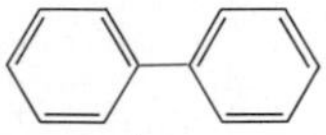

Biphenyl 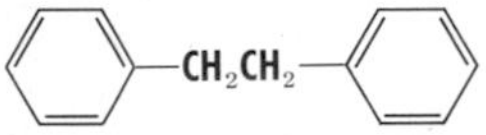   Bibenzyl 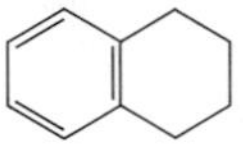   Tetralin or 1,2,3,4-
                                                tetrahydronaphthalene

Elucidation of Structure

Thousands of organic compounds have been related to one another
through reactions to form a vast network of interlocking facts, interpretation of which provides a self-consistent body of knowledge regarding
molecular structure.   In this section, a few reactions of the hydrocarbons
are introduced to show the relationships between saturated and unsaturated compounds, and to illustrate the methods of structure elucidation.

Hydrogenation and Dehydrogenation.   Treatment of acetylenes with
hydrogen gas in the presence of finely divided palladium catalyst results
in the addition of hydrogen to the triple bond, to give first an alkene.   In
a subsequent reaction, the alkene can be converted to a saturated hydrocarbon.   Addition of hydrogen to unsaturated linkages is called

hydrogenation. Both finely divided nickel (Raney nickel) and platinum can be substituted for palladium, but with these catalysts the reaction is more difficult to stop at the alkene stage. When an alkene is the desired product, the palladium is sometimes partially poisoned with lead. In representation of organic reactions, catalysts and reaction conditions are frequently written over or under the arrow.

$$H_2 + CH_3CH_2C\equiv CH \xrightarrow{Pd} CH_3CH_2CH=CH_2$$

1-Butyne   1-Butene

$$H_2 + CH_3CH_2CH=CH_2 \xrightarrow{Pd} CH_3CH_2CH_2CH_3$$

1-Butene   *n*-Butane

Aromatic systems may also be hydrogenated, but the reaction occurs with more difficulty, and requires both acid conditions and a platinum catalyst. Ordinarily, the alicyclic products are not subject to further attack by hydrogen.

$$3H_2 + \underset{\text{Toluene}}{\text{(structure with CH}_3\text{)}} \xrightarrow[\text{H}^+]{\text{Pt}} \underset{\text{Methylcyclohexane}}{\text{(structure with CH}_3\text{)}}$$

A reverse reaction called *dehydrogenation* occurs when hydrocarbons containing six-membered rings are heated with a palladium catalyst. Aromatic ring systems are produced in this manner.

$$\underset{\text{Decalin}}{\text{(structure)}} \xrightarrow[180°]{\text{Pd}} \underset{\text{Naphthalene}}{\text{(structure)}} + 5H_2$$

Oxidation. One of the most useful techniques for elucidating the structure of organic compounds is molecular degradation, in which carbon chains are broken into smaller pieces, and the pieces are then identified. The reaction of unsaturated hydrocarbons with ozone (*ozonization*) represents one of the more useful degradative transformations. In this reaction, the molecule is cleaved at the carbon-carbon double bond, and carbon-oxygen double bonds appear in the fragments. Identification of these fragments frequently allows the structure of the original molecule to be inferred.

$$O_3 + CH_3CH_2CH=CH_2 \longrightarrow \left[CH_3CH_2CH\underset{O-O}{\overset{O}{\diagup\diagdown}}CH_2 \right] \xrightarrow{H_2O + Zn} CH_3CH_2\overset{H}{\underset{}{C}}=O + O=\overset{H}{\underset{}{C}}-H$$

1-Butene   An ozonide, not   Propion-   Formaldehyde
         usually isolated   aldehyde

The method can be illustrated through the use of an example. Ozonization of a certain compound known to be 1-butene yields one molecule each of propionaldehyde and formaldehyde, which are known compounds. A molecule of unknown structure when similarly treated gives the known compounds acetone and acetaldehyde. Clearly the unknown compound must be 2-methyl-2-butene, and the reaction can be formulated.

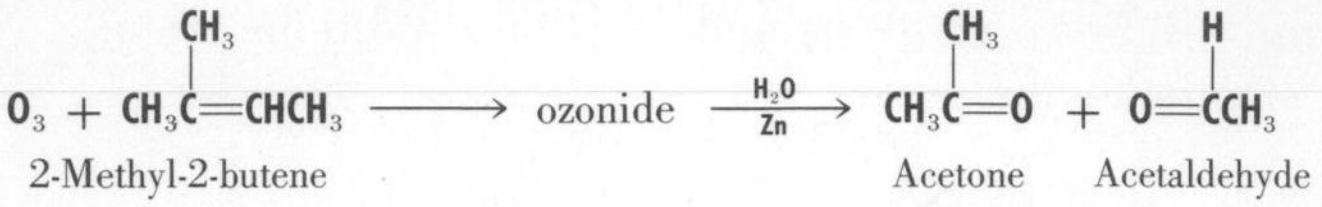

$$O_3 + CH_3\overset{\overset{\displaystyle CH_3}{|}}{C}=CHCH_3 \longrightarrow \text{ozonide} \xrightarrow[\text{Zn}]{H_2O} CH_3\overset{\overset{\displaystyle CH_3}{|}}{C}=O + O=\overset{\overset{\displaystyle H}{|}}{C}CH_3$$

2-Methyl-2-butene   Acetone   Acetaldehyde

A second useful oxidative reaction is termed **C**-*methyl determination.* Most organic compounds when oxidized with hot chromic acid are rapidly converted to carbon dioxide and water. If a molecule contains a grouping CH_3C, acetic acid (CH_3CO_2H) is produced as an intermediate in the reaction. This compound is somewhat more resistant to oxidation than other intermediates, and it can be removed from the reaction mixture by steam distillation and estimated by titration. The yields (per CH_3C group) range from 0 to 100%, but the minimum number of *terminal methyl groups* in a molecule of unknown structure can frequently be found this way. The method has certain limitations. Compounds containing the groups $(CH_3)_2C$ and $(CH_3)_3C$ can give a maximum of one mole of acetic acid per group, and usually much less is obtained. In many compounds in which a methyl group is attached directly to an aromatic system, no acetic acid is produced. The presence of functional groups in molecules usually increases the yield of acetic acid. A number of examples of the reaction are shown below.

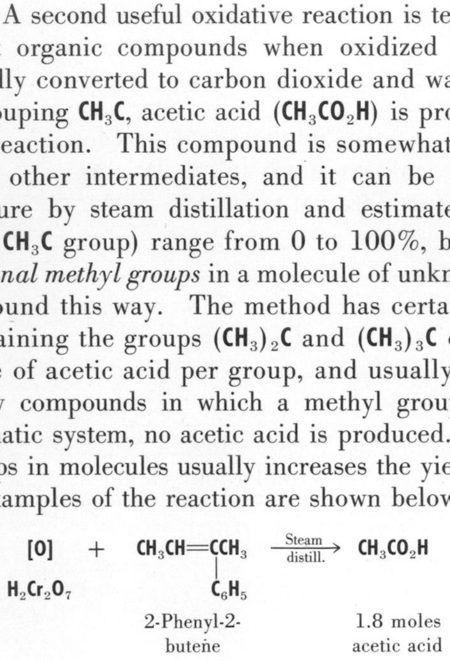

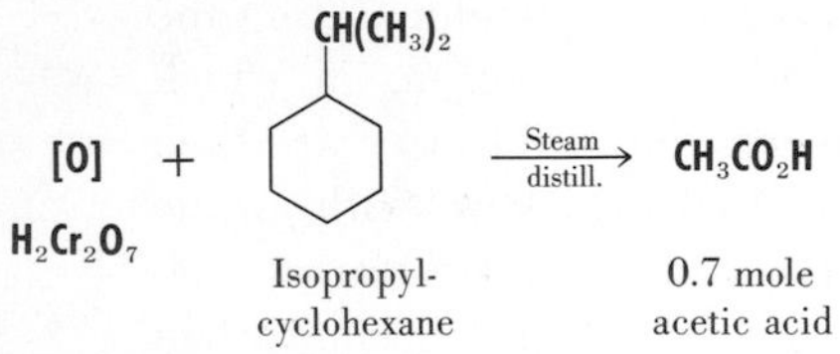

$$\begin{array}{l} [O] \quad + \quad CH_3CH=\overset{\overset{\displaystyle |}{C}CH_3}{\underset{\underset{\displaystyle C_6H_5}{|}}{}} \xrightarrow[\text{distill.}]{\text{Steam}} CH_3CO_2H \\ H_2Cr_2O_7 \end{array}$$

2-Phenyl-2-   1.8 moles
butene   acetic acid

$$\begin{array}{l} [O] \quad + \quad \overset{\displaystyle CH(CH_3)_2}{\bigcirc} \xrightarrow[\text{distill.}]{\text{Steam}} CH_3CO_2H \\ H_2Cr_2O_7 \end{array}$$

Isopropyl-   0.7 mole
cyclohexane   acetic acid

Sites of Unsaturation. Considerable information regarding molecular structure can sometimes be gained from a combination of knowledge of the molecular formula and the number of moles of hydrogen consumed during hydrogenation. This information allows the number of *sites of unsaturation* to be calculated, and permits the number of rings in a molecule to be determined.

Assume that a hydrocarbon of unknown structure possesses the molecular formula $C_{11}H_{14}$, and under acid conditions with a platinum catalyst (exhaustive hydrogenation), three moles of hydrogen are consumed by the compound to give a new substance, $C_{11}H_{20}$, which resists further hydrogenation. The molecular formula of the new compound differs from that of an open-chain saturated hydrocarbon of the same carbon content ($C_{11}H_{24}$) by four hydrogen atoms. Since the $C_{11}H_{20}$ compound is saturated, the absence of these four hydrogen atoms must be due to the presence of two rings in the molecule, each of which decreases the hydrogen count in the molecular formula by two. The original unsaturated hydrocarbon, $C_{11}H_{14}$, must then contain two rings and either three double bonds or one triple and one double bond. In this way, the difference of 10 hydrogen atoms between the original substance ($C_{11}H_{14}$) and the open-chain saturated counterpart ($C_{11}H_{24}$) is accounted for. The original molecule is said to contain five sites of unsaturation, each site being the equivalent of two hydrogen atoms. A double bond or a ring each contains one site, whereas a triple bond contains two, and a benzene nucleus taken as a whole contains four.

Structures of Simple Organic Molecules. With the above reactions and principles as tools, plausible arguments may be presented for the structures of certain of the simpler hydrocarbons. A number of examples of such arguments are given in this section.

An unknown molecule has the molecular formula C_4H_8, which indicates that it must possess one of the structures I through V; all five of these structures contain one site of unsaturation. The compound is readily attacked by hydrogen and palladium to give C_4H_{10}, and is cleaved by ozone to give only *one kind of product*. Only structure V is compatible with these facts. Only compounds possessing structures I, II, and V would react with hydrogen-palladium and with ozone. Of these three alkenes, only V would give only one product on ozonization. In the formulation of the ozonization reaction, the reagents are written over and under the arrow. Through the use of numbers, two separate stages for the reaction are indicated.

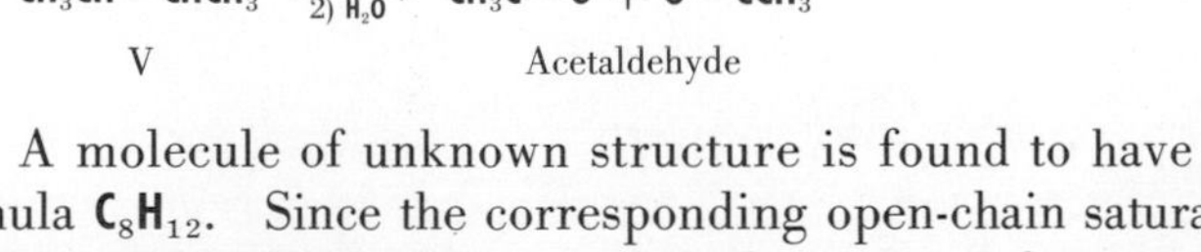

$$CH_3CH_2CH{=}CH_2 \qquad CH_3\overset{\overset{\displaystyle CH_3}{|}}{C}{=}CH_2 \qquad \begin{matrix} CH_2{-}CH_2 \\ | \qquad | \\ CH_2{-}CH_2 \end{matrix} \qquad CH_3CH\overset{\displaystyle CH_2}{\underset{\displaystyle CH_2}{\diagup\diagdown}}$$

I   II   III   IV

$$CH_3CH{=}CHCH_3 \xrightarrow[2)\ H_2O]{1)\ O_3} CH_3\overset{\overset{\displaystyle H}{|}}{C}{=}O \ + \ O{=}\overset{\overset{\displaystyle H}{|}}{C}CH_3$$

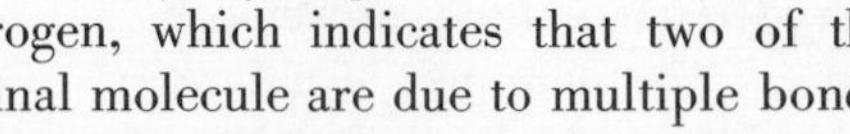

V   Acetaldehyde

A molecule of unknown structure is found to have the molecular formula C_8H_{12}. Since the corresponding open-chain saturated compound is C_8H_{18}, the original substance has three sites of unsaturation. When exhaustively hydrogenated, the substance absorbs only two moles of hydrogen, which indicates that two of the sites of unsaturation in the original molecule are due to multiple bonds. The remaining site is probably a ring, which is resistant to hydrogen and catalyst. If the reaction is carried out with an inactive palladium catalyst, and is stopped after one mole of hydrogen is consumed, a new compound is obtained, C_8H_{14}.

This behavior suggests that two of the sites of unsaturation in the original molecule are due to an acetylenic function, and that the C_8H_{14} compound is the derived alkene.

$$2H_2 + C_8H_{12} \xrightarrow[H^+]{Pt} C_8H_{16}$$

$$H_2 + C_8H_{12} \xrightarrow{Pd} C_8H_{14}$$

Ozonization of C_8H_{14} gives a single compound, $C_8H_{14}O_2$, which when submitted to C-methyl determination gives no acetic acid. Infrared measurements confirm that $C_8H_{14}O_2$ contains no C-methyl groups.

$$O_3 + C_8H_{14} \longrightarrow \text{ozonide} \xrightarrow[Zn]{H_2O} C_8H_{14}O_2$$
No C-methyl
groups

That a single substance containing eight carbon atoms is obtained during ozonization indicates that the reaction opens up a ring. The absence of C-methyl groups in the product demonstrates the compound to be unbranched. Only the cyclooctyne structure meets all the requirements of these data.

Cyclooctyne   Cyclooctene   Octanedial

A plausible argument for the structure of benzene is the following. The substance has the molecular formula C_6H_6 and therefore contains four sites of unsaturation. When the compound is subjected to exhaustive hydrogenation, only three moles of hydrogen are consumed. Therefore, benzene must contain a ring system. When subjected to ozonization, benzene gives only one product, $C_2H_2O_2$, for which only VII is a reasonable structure. These data strongly support a structure for benzene approximated by VI.

VI   VII

Occurrence and Uses

Hydrocarbons occur in abundance in petroleum and natural gas. Methane is the main component of natural gas, with ethane, propane, butane, carbon dioxide, nitrogen, and hydrogen sulfide present in amounts that vary somewhat with the source. The main use of natural gas is as a fuel, and a great system of pipelines laces the North American continent to carry natural gas from the South Central states to other sections of the continent.

Petroleum is a complex mixture of organic compounds in which aliphatic saturated hydrocarbons are the most abundant components. These range from C_1 to C_{30} or C_{40} in carbon content, and vary greatly in composition, depending on the source of the oil. The fraction of petroleum that boils below 200° contains several hundred distinct compounds, among which are alkanes, alkenes, cycloalkanes, and aromatic hydrocarbons.

Natural gas and petroleum are probably of marine origin, being derived from organic compounds elaborated by living organisms. Under the influence of high temperature and pressure, these compounds underwent chemical changes that over long periods of time resulted in the production of petroleum and natural gas, which accumulated in pockets in the upper strata of the earth, entrapped by an overlying rock structure.

Petroleum is the main source of gasoline, which consists of a mixture of hydrocarbons ranging in carbon content from C_3 to C_{10}. Natural gasoline (bp 40–205°) can be obtained directly from petroleum either by distillation or extraction, the amount varying considerably with the source of petroleum. The other principal fractions of petroleum are kerosene (bp 175–325°, C_8 to C_{14}), gas oil (bp above 275°, C_{12} to C_{18}), lubricating oils and greases (above C_{18}), and either asphalt or petroleum coke, depending on the source of the petroleum.

The yield of gasoline from petroleum is more than doubled by controlled pyrolytic decomposition (*cracking*) of the higher-boiling constituents. Cracking processes are usually conducted at 400 to 700° and at pressures that range from atmospheric to 1,200 lb/sq in. Some processes involve catalysts such as silica and alumina. The products include alkanes, alkenes, cycloalkanes, and aromatic hydrocarbons, many of which boil in a range that allows them to be used as gasoline. Similar processes applied to ethane, propane, and the two butanes give ethylene, propylene, and the three butenes, which are useful raw materials for the plastic, rubber, and many other chemical industries. Isobutene (from isobutane) is used to form 2,4,4-trimethyl-1-pentene by an acid-catalyzed reaction with itself. This compound can be converted to isooctane, a high-grade gasoline, by hydrogenation. These alkenes are also used to prepare alcohols, which are put to a variety of uses in the chemical and allied industries. The alkanes themselves are widely used as solvents and as cleaning and dispersing agents. Chapter 26 gives a much more detailed account of the use of petroleum and its products.

$$2(CH_3)_2C\!\!=\!\!CH_2 \xrightarrow{H_2SO_4} (CH_3)_3CCH_2\overset{\overset{\displaystyle CH_3}{|}}{C}\!\!=\!\!CH_2 \xrightarrow{H_2} (CH_3)_3CCH_2CH(CH_3)_2$$

Isobutene   2,4,4-Trimethyl-1-   Isooctane
                       pentene

Hydrocarbons are also found widely distributed in the plant world. A number of the higher-saturated normal hydrocarbons have been isolated from the leaves of waxy plants. Beeswax contains $n\text{-}C_{27}H_{56}$

(heptacosane). Marsh gas produced through the fermentation of cellulose by microorganisms contains methane. Olefinic hydrocarbons occur in nature as plant pigments, essential oils, turpentine, natural rubber, and a multitude of other substances. Acetylenic hydrocarbons are much less common. A few polyacetylenic compounds have been isolated from plants and as products of fungus metabolism. Aromatic ring systems are widely distributed in the plant kingdom, but usually oxygen- or nitrogen-carrying functional groups are present in the molecule.

$$(CH_2C{=}CHCH_2)_n$$
$$\quad\big|$$
$$\quad CH_3$$

Natural rubber

Coal is a second vast natural source of organic compounds. When bituminous coal is heated to temperatures of 1000 to 3000° in the absence of air, the products are coke (carbon), coal tar, coal gas (hydrogen, methane, carbon monoxide), and ammonia. The yield of coal tar is about 3% the weight of coal, and is composed of a complex mixture of organic compounds rich in aromatic hydrocarbons. These are separated from the oxygen-, nitrogen-, and sulfur-containing components by distillation and extraction procedures, to give benzene, toluene, the xylenes, naphthalene, biphenyl, anthracene, phenanthrene, and a variety of other compounds. Some of the less common members of this series are represented below.

α-Methyl-naphthalene   β-Methyl-naphthalene   Acenaphthene   Fluorene

Chrysene   Naphthacene   Fluoranthene

For many years coal was the main source of aromatic compounds, but now petroleum fractions are converted into a wide range of aromatic hydrocarbons. These compounds are of immense industrial importance, since they serve as starting materials in the synthesis of dyes, polymers, plastics, coatings, synthetic rubber, synthetic fabrics, drugs, and many other useful substances. Benzene, toluene, and the xylenes are particularly useful as solvents and as reaction media.

Problems

1. Write all possible names for the following compounds:

a. 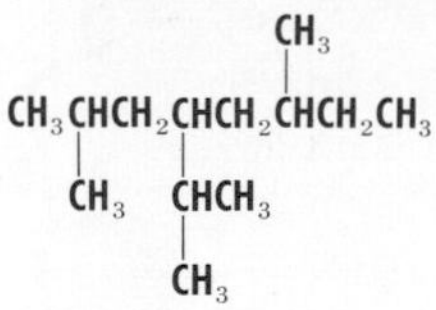 CH₃CHCH₂CHCH₂CHCH₂CH₃ with substituents CH₃ (top), CH₃ CHCH₃ (middle), CH₃ (bottom)

b. 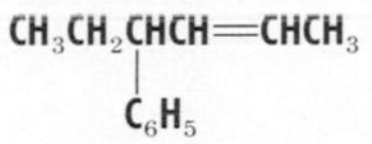 CH₃CH₂CHCH=CHCH₃ with C₆H₅ substituent

c. (CH₃)₃CC≡CC(CH₃)₃

d. 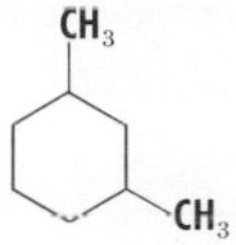 (cyclohexane ring with CH₃ and CH₃ substituents)

e. (CH₃)₃CC₆H₅

f. 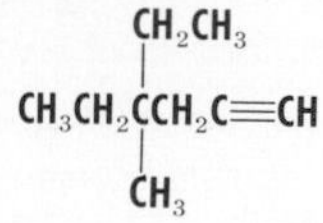 CH₃CH₂CCH₂C≡CH with CH₂CH₃ (top) and CH₃ (bottom) substituents

g. CH₃CH=CHCH=CHCH₃

h. 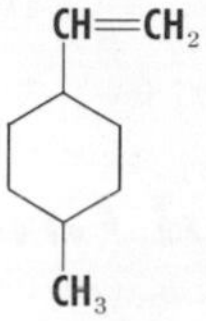 (cyclohexane ring with CH=CH₂ and CH₃ substituents)

i. 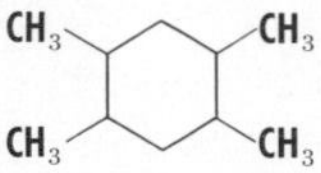 (cyclohexane ring with CH₃ substituents at four positions)

j. 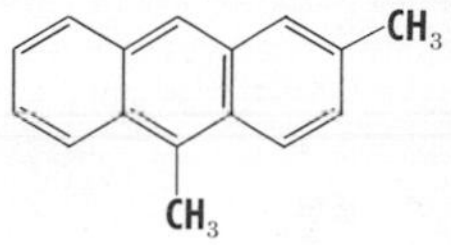 (anthracene ring structure with CH₃, CH₃ substituents)

2. Write structural formulas for the following compounds:

a. *sec*-Butylbenzene
b. 1,2-Dimethyl-1-cyclopentene
c. Vinylacetylene
d. *sym*-Dimethylethylene
    (*sym* = symmetrical)
e. *p*-Methylstyrene
f. Isobutylmethylacetylene
g. Allylbenzene
h. *o*-Diethylbenzene

3. A substance had the molecular formula $C_{10}H_{14}$. Exhaustive catalytic hydrogenation of the substance resulted in the consumption of two moles of hydrogen. When heated with palladium, $C_{10}H_{14}$ gave $C_{10}H_8$ and three moles of hydrogen. Write all possible structural formulas for $C_{10}H_{14}$.

4. A substance possessed a molecular formula C_6H_8 and gave no acetic acid in a C-methyl determination. Exhaustive hydrogenation of the compound resulted in absorption of one mole of hydrogen. Ozonization of the substance gave only one product. With structural formulas, trace the above reactions.

5. Write out all possible structures that fit the following molecular formulas. Name all compounds except those in *a* and *d*.

a. C_4H_9Cl
b. C_4H_6
c. C_6H_6
d. C_4H_7Br
e. C_5H_{10}
f. C_5H_8
g. C_6H_{10}
h. $C_{10}H_8$

6. A compound of unknown structure had the molecular formula C_8H_{12}. When it was subjected to exhaustive hydrogenation, two moles of hydrogen were absorbed. Either the resulting substance (C_8H_{16}) or the original compound when heated with palladium gave *o*-xylene as a product. Ozonization of the original compound gave 1.7 moles of a single substance. With structural formulas, trace these reactions.

7. Compound *A* of unknown structure possessed a molecular formula C_8H_{10}. Catalytic reduction of the substance with hydrogen and an inactive palladium catalyst resulted in the absorption of two moles of hydrogen to give compound *B*. Exhaustive reduction of *A* resulted in the consumption of four moles of hydrogen. Compound *A* gave 1.8 moles of acetic acid in a C-methyl determination. Ozonization of *B* gave two moles of one substance and one mole of a second. Ultraviolet absorption spectral measurements indicated that no conjugated systems of multiple bonds were present in *A*. With structural formulas, trace the above reactions.

8. In all possible cases, write a name different from the one already written for all structural formulas that appear in this chapter.

9. Combine all the hydrocarbon groups of Figs. 2.4, 2.6, 2.7, and 2.11 in pairs to make compounds. Name the compounds.

3

Compounds with Functional Groups
Saturated at Carbon

This chapter is devoted to those classes of compounds which contain functional groups saturated at carbon: their structure, nomenclature, reactions, and the methods of structure elucidation applicable to them. These classes may be regarded as derived from simple inorganic compounds (e.g., halogen acids, water, hydrogen sulfide, or ammonia) by the substitution of hydrocarbon groups for hydrogen. In the resulting substances there appear properties both of inorganic compounds and of the hydrocarbons discussed in the last chapter.

Structure, Nomenclature, and Properties

Organic Halides. Halogen atoms may be substituted for almost any hydrogen atom on a hydrocarbon, and a stable organic halide is obtained. When all the hydrogen is replaced, the resulting compounds are referred to as *halocarbons*. The ability of a single carbon atom to unite with one to four halogen atoms makes possible an enormous number of relatively simple organic halides. The following examples represent important structural types.

CH_3Cl	CH_2Cl_2	$CHCl_3$	CCl_4
Methyl chloride	Methylene chloride	Chloroform	Carbon tetrachloride
Important in organic synthesis	Commercial solvents, widely used for extraction, cleaning, and reaction media		

CCl_2F_2	CFClBrI	$F(CF_2)_nF$
Dichlorodifluoromethane, stable, noncorrosive refrigerant	Bromochlorofluoroiodo-methane, a chemical curiosity	Teflon, a slippery polymer of extreme chemical stability

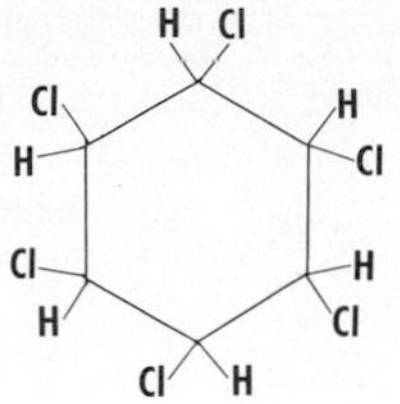

Benzene hexachloride, important insecticide

$H(CH_2CH=CCH_2)_nH$ with Cl below

Chloroprene polymer, a synthetic rubber

$CHCl=CCl_2$

Trichloroethylene, solvent for fats, oils, and resins

Many of the organic halides can be named on the basis of the alkyl groups they contain. A number of alkyl groups with two or three vacant sites on a single carbon atom have been given names, and these are useful in designating those compounds in which two or three halogen atoms are bound to a single carbon atom. Hydrocarbon groups with unbranched chains and a vacant site at each terminal position have also been named, as indicated in Fig. 3.1. When hydrocarbon groups are used to name organic halides, the parts of the name are always separated, as in the examples.

$(CH_3)_2CHBr$	$(CH_3)_3CCl$	$CH_2=CHCH_2F$	$CH_2=CHCl$	C_6H_5I	$C_6H_5CH_2Br$
Isopropyl bromide	*tert*-Butyl chloride	Allyl fluoride	Vinyl chloride	Iodobenzene (Phenyl iodide)	Benzyl bromide

$C_6H_5CHCl_2$	$C_6H_5CCl_3$	CH_3CHCl_2	$I(CH_2)_4I$	$(CH_3)_2CBr_2$	$(CH_3)_3CCH_2F$
Benzal chloride	Benzo chloride	Ethylidene chloride	Tetramethylene iodide	Isopropylidene bromide	Neopentyl fluoride

A number of derived names for the organic halides are in common use, representative examples of which are listed below.

$CH_2=CHCl$	$ClCH=CHCl$	C_6H_5Br	C_6Cl_6
Chloroethylene	*sym*-Dichloroethylene	Bromobenzene	Hexachlorobenzene

In the IUC system, the names of the halogens are prefixed to the name of the parent hydrocarbon, and the position is designated by number. When the chain has several groups, the names of the groups are arranged in alphabetical order. If the parent chain is saturated, it is numbered from that end which gives the lowest numbers to the attached substituents. When unsaturated, the parent skeleton is numbered from that end which gives the lowest numbers to the site(s) of unsaturation.

$-CH_2-$	$-CH_2CH_2-$	$-(CH_2)_3-$	$-(CH_2)_4-$
Methylene	Dimethylene	Trimethylene	Tetramethylene

$CH_3CH=$	$CH_3CH_2CH=$	$(CH_3)_2C=$	$C_6H_5CH=$	$C_6H_5C\equiv$
Ethylidene	Propylidene	Isopropylidene	Benzal	Benzo

FIG. 3.1 *Hydrocarbon groups with two or more vacant sites.*

TABLE 3.1   Physical Properties of Representative Organic Halides

Name	Formula	Mp, °C	Bp, °C	Sp. gr. (liquid)
Methyl chloride	CH_3Cl	−97	−24	0.920
Methyl bromide	CH_3Br	−93	5	1.732
Methyl iodide	CH_3I	−64	42	2.279
Methylene chloride	CH_2Cl_2	−96	41	1.336
Chloroform	$CHCl_3$	−64	61	1.489
Carbon tetrachloride	CCl_4	−23	77	1.575
Ethyl chloride	C_2H_5Cl	−139	13	0.910
Ethyl bromide	C_2H_5Br	−119	38	1.430
Ethyl iodide	C_2H_5I	−111	72	1.933
n-Propyl chloride	$CH_3CH_2CH_2Cl$	−123	46	0.890
Isopropyl chloride	$(CH_3)_2CHCl$	−117	37	0.860
n-Butyl chloride	$CH_3(CH_2)_3Cl$	−123	78	0.884
Isobutyl chloride	$(CH_3)_2CHCH_2Cl$	−131	69	0.866
sec-Butyl chloride	$CH_3CH_2CHClCH_3$		68	0.871
tert-Butyl chloride	$(CH_3)_3CCl$	−29	51	0.851
Vinyl chloride	$CH_2{=}CHCl$	−160	−14	
Allyl chloride	$CH_2{=}CHCH_2Cl$	−136	46	0.938
Fluorobenzene	C_6H_5F	−45	85	
Chlorobenzene	C_6H_5Cl	−45	132	
Bromobenzene	C_6H_5Br	−31	156	
Iodobenzene	C_6H_5I	−29	189	
o-Dichlorobenzene	$o\text{-}C_6H_4Cl_2$		179	
p-Dichlorobenzene	$p\text{-}C_6H_4Cl_2$	53	173	

More detailed discussion of these rules is found in Chap. 29. The system is best learned from actual examples, a number of which are given.

The terms *geminal* (*gem-*) and *vicinal* (*vic-*) are frequently applied to organic halides (and other organic compounds) which carry *two like* substituents on the same or adjacent carbon atoms, respectively. Examples of the use of these terms follow.

CH_3CHBr_2 $BrCH_2CH_2Br$

1,1-Dibromoethane   1,2-Dibromoethane
or *gem*-dibromoethane   or *vic*-dibromoethane

Because of the increase in molecular weight associated with the substitution of halogen for hydrogen atoms in hydrocarbons, it is not surprising to find that the specific gravities (densities) of the organic halides are higher than those of most other organic substances. The boiling and melting points are also higher than those of the hydrocarbons of equal carbon content. As the halogen content of organic compounds increases, flammability decreases. Carbon tetrachloride is used in certain simple fire extinguishers. The lower-molecular-weight organic halides are powerful solvents and are widely used for extractions. The physical properties of a number of typical organic halides are recorded in Table 3.1.

Alcohols, Phenols, and Ethers. These classes of compounds may be considered as derived from water by the substitution of hydrocarbon groups for hydrogen atoms. Substitution of an alkyl group for one hydrogen atom of water gives an *alcohol;* when both hydrogens are replaced by alkyl groups, the result is an *ether.* When aryl groups are involved, either *phenols* or *aryl ethers* are produced. The —**OH** *group* is known as the *hydroxyl,* and the —**O**— as the *ether group.* Figure 3.2 indicates the structural relationships between these classes of compounds.

The simple alcohols are named after the alkyl, cycloalkyl, or alkenyl groups to which the hydroxyl groups are attached. A number of examples are given below.

$$CH_3OH \qquad CH_3CH_2\overset{\overset{\displaystyle OH}{|}}{C}HCH_3 \qquad (CH_3)_3CCH_2OH \qquad CH_2{=}CHCH_2OH$$

Methyl alcohol   *sec*-Butyl alcohol   Neopentyl alcohol   Allyl alcohol

$$C_6H_5CH_2OH \qquad CH_3(CH_2)_4OH \qquad \overset{\overset{\displaystyle CH_2}{\diagup\diagdown}}{CH_2{-}CHOH} \qquad C_6H_5CH{=}CHCH_2OH$$

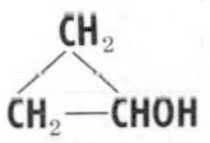

Benzyl alcohol   *n*-Amyl alcohol   Cyclopropyl alcohol   Cinnamyl alcohol

H—Ö—H   R—Ö—H   Ar—Ö—H
  Water   Alcohol   Phenol
                    (R = alkyl)   (Ar = aryl)

R—Ö—R   R—Ö—Ar   Ar—Ö—Ar
 Aliphatic   Aliphatic-aromatic   Aromatic
   ether   ether   ether

FIG. 3.2   *Classes of organic compounds related to water.*

Alcohols are also known as *carbinols*. Methyl alcohol itself could be named simply "carbinol." Many alcohols are conveniently named as derivatives of carbinol, the hydrocarbon groups being considered substitutes for one or more of the hydrogen atoms of carbinol. This nomenclature is particularly useful because the names allow the formulas to be easily visualized. The system emphasizes the classification of alcohols as *primary, secondary,* or *tertiary*, depending on whether one, two, or three of the hydrogens of carbinol are replaced by hydrocarbon groups. Methyl alcohol itself is also classified as a *primary* alcohol. The examples illustrate the system and the classification.

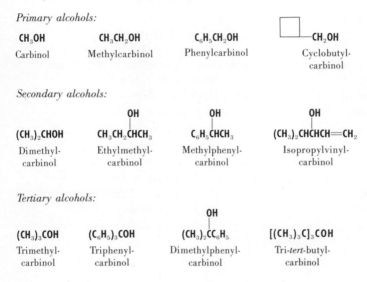

Primary alcohols:

CH₃OH — Carbinol
CH₃CH₂OH — Methylcarbinol
C₆H₅CH₂OH — Phenylcarbinol
☐—CH₂OH — Cyclobutyl-carbinol

Secondary alcohols:

(CH₃)₂CHOH — Dimethyl-carbinol
CH₃CH₂CHCH₃ (OH) — Ethylmethyl-carbinol
C₆H₅CHCH₃ (OH) — Methylphenyl-carbinol
(CH₃)₂CHCHCH=CH₂ (OH) — Isopropylvinyl-carbinol

Tertiary alcohols:

(CH₃)₃COH — Trimethyl-carbinol
(C₆H₅)₃COH — Triphenyl-carbinol
(CH₃)₂CC₆H₅ (OH) — Dimethylphenyl-carbinol
[(CH₃)₃C]₃COH — Tri-*tert*-butyl-carbinol

The carbinol system of nomenclature has been extended to certain hydrocarbon groups and thence to other compounds, such as the organic halides. A few examples make the system clear.

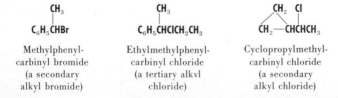

C₆H₅CHBr (CH₃) — Methylphenyl-carbinyl bromide (a secondary alkyl bromide)

C₆H₅CHCICH₂CH₃ (CH₃) — Ethylmethylphenyl-carbinyl chloride (a tertiary alkyl chloride)

CH₂—CHCHCH₃ (CH₂ Cl) — Cyclopropylmethyl-carbinyl chloride (a secondary alkyl chloride)

Aliphatic and alicyclic compounds containing two hydroxyl groups are referred to as *glycols;* three hydroxyl groups, as *trihydric* alcohols; and two or more, as *polyhydric* alcohols. Alternate terms are *diols, triols,* and *polyols*. Although 1,2-glycols (*vic*-glycols) are common, 1,1-glycols (*gem*-glycols) are only occasionally encountered, since they usually lose a molecule of water to form a **C=O** linkage. Vinyl alcohols (*enols*) also tend to be unstable relative to their isomers containing the **C=O** linkage, with which they are usually in equilibrium.

$$CH_3CH(OH)_2 \rightleftharpoons CH_3\overset{\overset{\textstyle H}{|}}{C}=O + H_2O$$

A 1,1-diol
(a *gem*-glycol)

Acetaldehyde

$$CH_2=CHOH \rightleftharpoons CH_3\overset{\overset{\textstyle H}{|}}{C}=O$$

Vinyl alcohol

A few glycols may be named after alkyl groups with two open valences. Many of the polyols have common names.

$HOCH_2CH_2OH$	$HO(CH_2)_3OH$	$\overset{\overset{\textstyle OH}{\textstyle |}}{HOCH_2CHCH_2OH}$	$HOCH_2(CHOH)_4CH_2OH$
Ethylene glycol	Trimethylene glycol	Glycerol	Sorbitol

In IUC nomenclature of an alcohol, the longest carbon chain to which hydroxyl is attached is selected as the parent compound, and the chain is numbered from the end closest to the hydroxyl group. The presence of the hydroxyl group is indicated by replacement of the final -*e* in the name of the hydrocarbon chain by -*ol*. The position of the "-*ol*" group is indicated in the standard manner by number prefix. The names of substituents attached to the chain are indicated as in the hydrocarbons (page 19). The presence of two or more hydroxyl groups is noted by use of the suffixes -*diol*, -*triol*, etc. When the chain also contains a double or triple bond, its presence is indicated in the usual way (page 36), and then the ending -*ol* (with number prefix) is added. The system is illustrated in the following examples.

$\overset{\overset{\textstyle CH_3}{\textstyle |}}{CH_3CHCH_2}\overset{\overset{\textstyle CH_3}{\textstyle |}}{\underset{\underset{\textstyle OH}{\textstyle |}}{C}CH_3}$	$CH_3CH_2\overset{\overset{\textstyle Cl}{\textstyle |}}{C}HCH_2\underset{\underset{\textstyle OH}{\textstyle |}}{C}HCH_2OH$	$\overset{\overset{\textstyle CH_3}{\textstyle |}}{CH_3C}=CHCH_2OH$
2,4-Dimethyl-2-pentanol	4-Chloro-1,2-hexanediol	3-Methyl-2-buten-1-ol

Occasionally Greek letters are used to indicate the location of substituents on saturated hydrocarbon chains, as in the following examples. The α-carbon is always the one carrying the hydroxyl (or halogen) group.

$C_6H_5\underset{\alpha}{\overset{\overset{\textstyle OH}{\textstyle |}}{C}H}\underset{\beta}{C}H_3$	$C_6H_5\underset{\beta}{C}H_2\underset{\alpha}{C}H_2OH$	$CH_3\underset{\gamma}{\overset{\overset{\textstyle CH_3}{\textstyle |}}{C}H}\underset{\beta}{C}H_2\underset{\alpha}{C}H_2OH$
α-Phenylethanol	β-Phenylethanol	γ-Methylbutanol

The simpler phenols possess common names which are widely employed, systematic names being used for more complicated structures. In the latter, the position of the hydroxyl group is indicated by number, Greek letter, or by the terms *ortho*, *meta*, or *para*—whichever is appropriate.

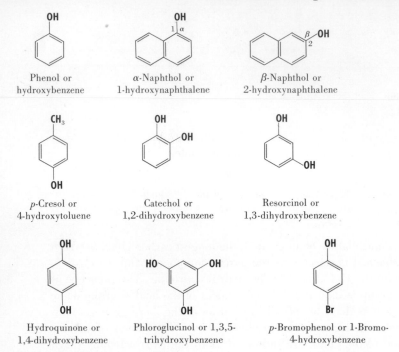

Phenol or
hydroxybenzene

α-Naphthol or
1-hydroxynaphthalene

β-Naphthol or
2-hydroxynaphthalene

p-Cresol or
4-hydroxytoluene

Catechol or
1,2-dihydroxybenzene

Resorcinol or
1,3-dihydroxybenzene

Hydroquinone or
1,4-dihydroxybenzene

Phloroglucinol or 1,3,5-
trihydroxybenzene

p-Bromophenol or 1-Bromo-
4-hydroxybenzene

Ethers are classified as being either *symmetrical* or *unsymmetrical* (*mixed*), depending on likeness or difference in the two hydrocarbon groups attached to oxygen. Both kinds are named according to their hydrocarbon groups, unless the molecule is too complex. In that case, the longest chain is considered the parent compound, and the name of the *alkoxy* or *aryloxy* group is prefixed to the name of the chain, as in the examples.

$CH_3CH_2OCH_2CH_3$

Ether or
diethyl ether

$CH_3OCH_2CH_2CH_2CH_3$

n-Butyl methyl
ether or
1-methoxybutane

$C_6H_5OCH_3$

Anisole, methyl phenyl
ether, or
methoxybenzene

$\overset{\displaystyle OCH_3}{\underset{\displaystyle C_6H_5}{CH_3CHCHCH_3}}$

2-Methoxy-3-
phenylbutane

$HOCH_2CH_2OCH_2CH_2OH$

Diethylene glycol

$CH_3OCH_2CH_2OCH_3$

1,2-Dimethoxyethane

Elements such as oxygen, nitrogen, all of the halogens, sulfur, phosphorus, and silicon are sometimes referred to as *hetero atoms*, and cycles which contain these atoms as part of the ring system are called *heterocycles*. Several important heterocyclic ethers are listed below. The rings are usually numbered starting with the *hetero atom*.

CH₂—CH₂ structures:

Ethylene oxide

Propylene oxide or
1,2-epoxypropane

Trimethylene oxide

Furan   Tetrahydrofuran   Dioxan

Most of the compounds discussed in this section have considerable commercial importance. Methanol, which used to be produced by the distillation of wood (wood alcohol), is now produced in large quantities from carbon monoxide and hydrogen (page 53) for use as a solvent. Ethanol enjoys widespread use as a beverage, and is obtained by the fermentation of many agricultural products. *n*-Butyl alcohol (1-butanol) is also produced by fermentation, and, like ethanol, is a widely used solvent. Ethanol, 2-propanol, and diethyl ether are prepared from ethylene and propylene derived from the cracking of petroleum (Chap. 26). Diethyl ether and ethylene oxide are both excellent general anesthetics. Diethyl ether and tetrahydrofuran are very common reaction and extraction solvents, and are widely used in chemical laboratories. Diethyl ether itself is only slightly soluble in water, is volatile, and can easily be dried. Methanol, ethanol, the propanols, tetrahydrofuran, dioxan, and the polyols are miscible with water in all proportions. This property makes them valuable solvents in certain processes involving polar substances. All the simple alcohols are important raw materials in the synthesis of polymers, fibers, plastics, explosives, and pharmaceutical and research chemicals. In contrast, the aliphatic ethers are relatively inert chemically, and only occasionally are used as reactants in chemical synthesis. Ethylene oxide and trimethylene oxide are also important compounds in synthesis.

Phenols are found in plant products and constitute an important group of flower pigments (Chap. 22), tanning agents, and lignin components of wood. Many of the phenols possess antiseptic properties and are used to cauterize wounds. Phenol itself and the cresols are obtained from coal tar, but most of the phenols are produced commercially from aromatic hydrocarbons. Large quantities of phenol are consumed in the preparation of plastics and dyes. Some of the alkyl-aryl ethers possess pleasant aromatic odors; they give certain plants their fragrance.

The physical properties of the three classes of compounds considered in this section contrast widely with one another. The ethers are relatively volatile, neutral, hydrocarbonlike substances. Alcohols and phenols are highly associated in the liquid state (see Chap. 7), and this fact is probably linked with their relatively high boiling points. Polyols are notably

TABLE 3.2 *Physical Properties of Alcohols, Ethers, and Phenols*

Name	Formula	Mp, °C	Bp, °C	Sp. gr.
Methyl alcohol	CH_3OH	−97	65	0.792
Ethyl alcohol	C_2H_5OH	−114	78	0.789
n-Propyl alcohol	$CH_3CH_2CH_2OH$	−126	97	0.804
Isopropyl alcohol	$(CH_3)_2CHOH$	−89	82	0.786
n-Butyl alcohol	$CH_3(CH_2)_3OH$	−90	118	0.810
Isobutyl alcohol	$(CH_3)_2CHCH_2OH$	−108	108	0.802
sec-Butyl alcohol	$CH_3CHOHCH_2CH_3$		100	0.808
tert-Butyl alcohol	$(CH_3)_3COH$	25	83	0.789
Cyclohexyl alcohol	$C_6H_{11}OH$	−24	162	0.962
n-Octyl alcohol	$CH_3(CH_2)_7OH$	−16	194	0.827
Allyl alcohol	$CH_2{=}CHCH_2OH$	−129	97	0.855
Benzyl alcohol	$C_6H_5CH_2OH$	−15	205	1.046
Ethylene glycol	$HOCH_2CH_2OH$		198	
Glycerol	$HOCH_2CHOHCH_2OH$	18	290	
Dimethyl ether	CH_3OCH_3	−140	−25	0.661
Diethyl ether	$C_2H_5OC_2H_5$	−116	35	0.714
Di-n-butyl ether	$(CH_3CH_2CH_2CH_2)_2O$		141	0.769
Diphenyl ether	$C_6H_5OC_6H_5$	27	259	1.072
Anisole	$C_6H_5OCH_3$	−37	154	0.994
Ethylene oxide	$CH_2{-}CH_2$ $\diagdown O \diagup$		14	
Tetrahydrofuran	(ring structure with O)	−108	65	0.888
Dioxan	$O(CH_2CH_2)_2O$	12	101	
Phenol	C_6H_5OH	43	181	
o-Cresol	$o\text{-}CH_3C_6H_4OH$	30	191	
m-Cresol	$m\text{-}CH_3C_6H_4OH$	11	201	
p-Cresol	$p\text{-}CH_3C_6H_4OH$	36	201	
Catechol	$1,2\text{-}C_6H_4(OH)_2$	105	245	
Resorcinol	$1,3\text{-}C_6H_4(OH)_2$	110	281	
Hydroquinone	$1,4\text{-}C_6H_4(OH)_2$	170		
Phloroglucinol	$1,3,5\text{-}C_6H_3(OH)_3$	219		

high-boiling—a feature that makes glycerine a valuable wetting agent for use in cosmetic preparations, and ethylene glycol an important antifreeze. Like water, alcohols are weakly *amphoteric* substances, whereas phenols are acids, intermediate in strength between the alcohols and the carboxylic acids (Chap. 8). Table 3.2 records the physical properties of some of the important alcohols, ethers, and phenols.

Organic peroxides are related to the alcohols and ethers in the same way that water is related to hydrogen peroxide. The $-O-O-H$ function is known as the *hydroperoxide group*, and the $-O-O-$ function as the *peroxide group.* Only a few organic peroxides are seen in ordinary chemical storage, since the compounds tend to be unstable. A few of the important peroxides and their names are listed. These compounds are used to initiate certain polymerization reactions (Chap. 25).

$(CH_3)_3C—O—O—H$ $(CH_3)_3C—O—O—C(CH_3)_3$

tert-Butyl hydroperoxide   Di-*tert*-butyl peroxide

Mercaptans, Sulfides, and Derived Compounds. The *mercaptans* (*thiols*) and *sulfides* may be considered as derived from hydrogen sulfide, in which hydrogen has been successively replaced by either alkyl or aryl groups. The —S—H, —S—, and —S—S— functions are referred to as the mercapto (thiol), sulfide, and disulfide groups. Trialkyl sulfonium ions, in which sulfur carries a formal positive charge, are also known; they combine with inorganic anions to form salts. General structures for these classes of compounds are indicated in Fig. 3.3.

A number of other classes of compounds containing carbon-sulfur bonds are known which can be regarded as oxygenated derivatives of the mercaptans and sulfides. Figure 3.4 lists the general structures and names of these groups of substances.

Of the organic compounds that contain sulfur, the mercaptans, sulfides, disulfides, and sulfonic acids are the most important, and these classes will be discussed in more detail.

In mercaptan nomenclature, the names of the alkyl or aryl groups attached to sulfur are usually employed. More complex mercaptans are named by adding the term *thiol* to the name of the parent hydrocarbon, in much the same way as alkanols are named. In the nomenclature of the sulfonic acids, the name of the parent hydrocarbon is given first, and the term sulfonic acid is suffixed, with a number to indicate the point of attachment of the function to the hydrocarbon. These rules are illustrated by the names given the following compounds:

		Cl	
$(CH_3)_2CHCH_2SH$	C_6H_5SH	$CH_3CHCH_2CH_2CH_2SH$	$C_6H_5CH_2SCH_2C_6H_5$
Isobutyl mercaptan	Phenyl mercaptan or thiophenol	4-Chloro-1-pentanethiol	Dibenzyl sulfide

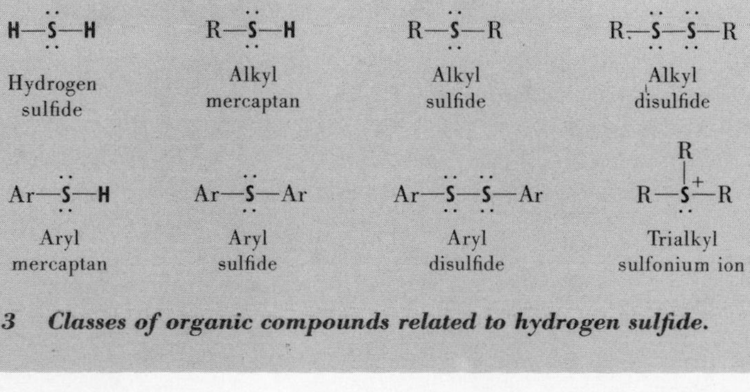

H—S̈—H   R—S̈—H   R—S̈—R   R—S̈—S̈—R

Hydrogen   Alkyl   Alkyl   Alkyl
sulfide   mercaptan   sulfide   disulfide

                                                R
                                                |
Ar—S̈—H   Ar—S̈—Ar   Ar—S̈—S̈—Ar   R—S⁺—R

Aryl   Aryl   Aryl   Trialkyl
mercaptan   sulfide   disulfide   sulfonium ion

FIG. 3.3   *Classes of organic compounds related to hydrogen sulfide.*

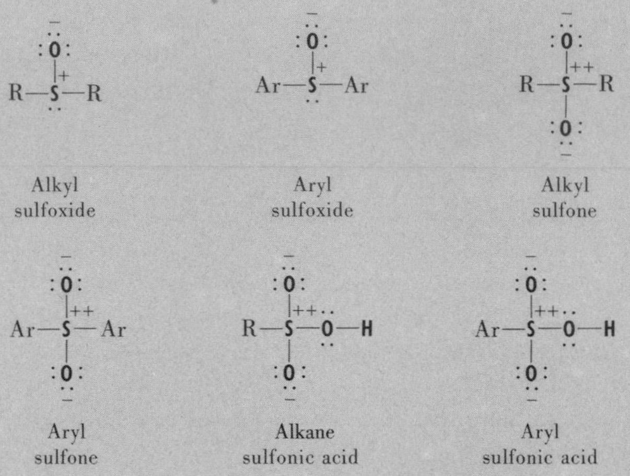

FIG. 3.4   *Classes of oxygenated derivatives of mercaptans and sulfides.*

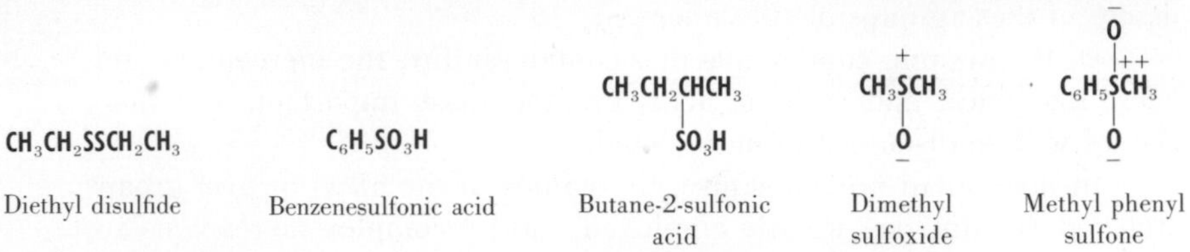

$CH_3CH_2SSCH_2CH_3$ $C_6H_5SO_3H$ $CH_3CH_2CHCH_3$ | SO_3H CH_3SCH_3 | O $C_6H_5SCH_3$

Diethyl disulfide   Benzenesulfonic acid   Butane-2-sulfonic acid   Dimethyl sulfoxide   Methyl phenyl sulfone

A number of naturally occurring organic compounds contain sulfur. Certain proteins contain sulfhydryl (—S—H) and disulfide linkages. Penicillin contains a sulfide linkage. The scent glands of the skunk contain butyl mercaptan. The flavors and odors of onion and garlic are also due to organic sulfides.

Sulfonic acids constitute an important group of industrial chemicals. The acid strength of these compounds approaches that of mineral acids, and this property combined with high solubility in organic solvents makes them an important class of acid catalysts. Arylsulfonic acids are intermediates in the preparation of phenols, detergents, dyes, and many other important chemicals.

Amines and Derived Compounds. The successive substitution of alkyl or aryl groups for hydrogen atoms in ammonia produces the class of compounds known as the amines. The amines are classified as *primary, secondary,* or *tertiary* according to whether one, two, or three of the hydrogen atoms of ammonia have been replaced. Substitution of the four hydrogens of the *ammonium ion* with alkyl groups (one can be aryl) produces *quaternary ammonium* ions. Figure 3.5 illustrates these relationships with general formulas.

The names of simple amines indicate the alkyl or aryl groups attached to nitrogen. Aniline is the common name of the simplest aromatic amine ($C_6H_5NH_2$), and when hydrocarbon or other functional groups are attached to the benzene ring, the substances can be named as derivatives of aniline. When alkyl groups are bonded to the nitrogen atom of aniline, the position of these groups in the compound can be designated in the name by use of the prefix *N*-. Heterocyclic compounds with nitrogen as part of the ring system usually have special names, sometimes suggestive of structure. Heterocyclic rings are numbered, frequently with the hetero atom bearing the lowest number. The following examples serve to illustrate these rules.

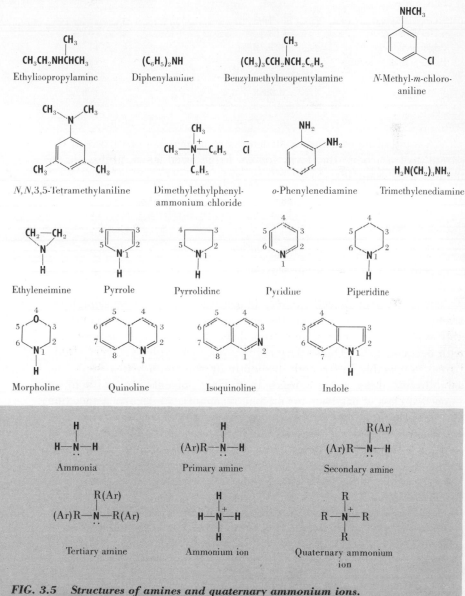

FIG. 3.5   *Structures of amines and quaternary ammonium ions.*

Functional Groups Saturated at Carbon

TABLE 3.3 *Physical Properties of Amines*

Name	Formula	Mp, °C	Bp, °C	Sp. gr.
Methylamine	CH_3NH_2	−93	−7	0.699
Dimethylamine	$(CH_3)_2NH$	−96	7	0.680
Trimethylamine	$(CH_3)_3N$	−124	4	0.662
Ethylamine	$C_2H_5NH_2$	−81	17	0.689
n-Propylamine	$CH_3CH_2CH_2NH_2$	−83	49	0.719
n-Hexylamine	$CH_3(CH_2)_5NH_2$	−19	131	
Ethylenediamine	$H_2NCH_2CH_2NH_2$	9	117	0.892
Pentamethylenediamine	$H_2N(CH_2)_5NH_2$	9	178	0.855
Aniline	$C_6H_5NH_2$	−6	184	1.022
N-Methylaniline	$C_6H_5NHCH_3$		196	

Amines of more complex structure are named as derivatives of the parent hydrocarbon, the term *amino* being used as a prefix, as in the following examples.

| 4-(N-Methylamino)-1-hexene | 1-Amino-3-(2-propyl)-cyclohexane | 1-Amino-3,5-di-hydroxybenzene |

Aliphatic and alicyclic amines in general have about the same basic strength as ammonia, whereas the aromatic amines tend to be considerably weaker. Their odors range from that of ammonia to those associated with decaying fish. Quaternary ammonium hydroxides are very strong bases, comparable in strength to sodium or potassium hydroxide. The solubility of these organic bases in organic solvents makes them an important class of catalysts for organic reactions. Molecular association of amines in the liquid state is not as strong as with the alcohols, which explains their relatively low boiling points as compared with those of alcohols of comparable molecular weight. The lower-molecular-weight amines are soluble in water, and all but a few are soluble in dilute aqueous acid. The physical properties of representative amines are listed in Table 3.3.

The amines are extremely important commercial chemicals; they are used as catalysts, solvents, dyes, medicinals, and as reaction intermediates in chemical synthesis. The substances are widely distributed in nature in the form of *amino acids, proteins,* and *alkaloids,* which are found in most plants. A high proportion of biologically important substances (vitamins, antibiotics, drugs, proteins, etc.) contain amino groups. Many of these compounds are discussed in Chap. 23.

A number of heterocyclic amines, including pyridine, quinoline, and isoquinoline, are obtained from coal tar. Aliphatic amines are prepared either by the reaction of alkyl halides with ammonia or by the reduction of nitroalkanes. Aromatic amines are produced by reduction of nitroaromatic compounds.

Structures which contain two amino groups on the same carbon (*gem*-diamino compounds) are seldom encountered because of the great instability of such an assembly. Organic compounds derived from hydrazine (NH_2—NH_2) are well known, and are similar to amines in their properties. Tertiary amines form oxides, which are *inner salts*. Like the quaternary ammonium compounds, these are very polar. Organic derivatives of hydroxylamine are also known. General structures for these classes of compounds are listed in Fig. 3.6.

Organic nitro compounds bear a formal structural relationship to nitric acid in the sense that both contain the NO_2 group, the former with an alkyl or aryl, the latter with a hydroxyl attached to nitrogen. Organic nitro compounds are *isomeric* with a second class called the organic nitrites, in which alkyl groups are attached to oxygen. Nitrites are related to nitrous acid in the sense that the hydrogen atom in the acid has been replaced by alkyl groups. Figure 3.7 shows the structural relationships between these classes of substances.

Organic nitro compounds are named by prefixing the term *nitro* to the name of the parent hydrocarbon. Alkyl nitrites are named by combining the names of the alkyl groups and the word *nitrite*. The systems are illustrated by the following examples.

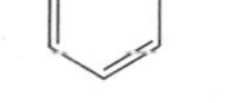

$$CH_3CH_2CHCH_3 \quad\quad CH_3CHCH_2\overset{\underset{\displaystyle CH_3}{|}}{C}{=}CH_2 \quad\quad CH_3CH_2CH_2CH_2CH_2O—N{=}O$$

2-Nitrobutane 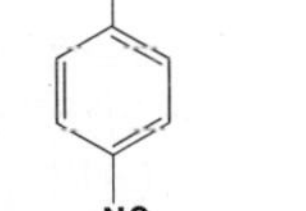   2-Methyl-4-nitro-1-pentene    *n*-Pentyl nitrite

Nitrobenzene   *p*-Nitroaniline 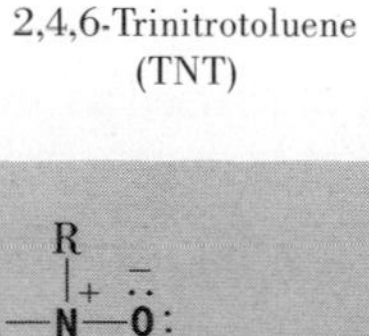   2,4,6-Trinitrotoluene (TNT)

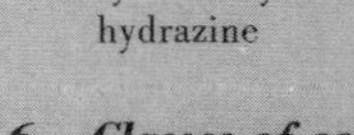

$$(Ar)R—\overset{\overset{\displaystyle H}{|}}{\underset{..}{N}}—\overset{\overset{\displaystyle H}{|}}{\underset{..}{N}}—H \quad\quad R—\overset{\overset{\displaystyle R}{|}}{\underset{\underset{\displaystyle R}{|}}{\overset{+}{N}}}—\overset{..}{\underset{..}{O}}: \quad\quad (Ar)R—\overset{\overset{\displaystyle H}{|}}{\underset{..}{N}}—\overset{..}{\underset{..}{O}}—H$$

Aryl or alkyl hydrazine 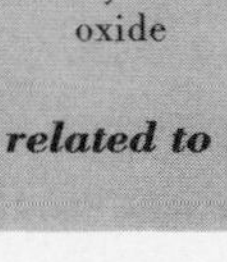   Trialkylamine oxide 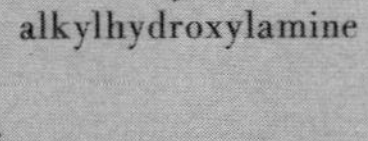   Aryl or alkylhydroxylamine

FIG. 3.6   *Classes of compounds related to the amines.*

Nitric acid | Aryl or alkyl nitro compounds | Nitrous acid | Alkyl nitrite

FIG. 3.7 General structures of organic nitrites and nitro compounds.

Organic nitro compounds are neutral, relatively nonvolatile, organic compounds of a rather polar nature. The lower nitroalkanes are soluble in water. Solubility falls as the molecular weight increases. Nitroaromatic compounds are water-insoluble, high-boiling liquids or are solids. These substances are somewhat toxic, because of their ability to complex with hemoglobin of the blood.

The nitroalkanes are important reaction intermediates in organic synthesis, particularly in the preparation of amines. They also show some promise of becoming useful as rocket fuels. Aromatic nitro compounds are important as solvents, explosives, dyes, perfumes, and as reaction intermediates in the preparation of other classes of compounds. Only a very few naturally occurring substances contain the nitro group.

Reactions

In this section are discussed a few simple organic reactions, which will serve to illustrate the structural relationships among the classes of compounds of this chapter. These transformations are explained with general equations, in which the symbols for alkyl and aryl (R and Ar) are employed, and also with equations involving specific compounds.

Reduction. A number of the compounds treated in previous sections may be converted into hydrocarbons by reduction reactions in which a carbon-hydrogen bond is substituted for a carbon-halogen, carbon-oxygen, or carbon-sulfur bond. One of the simplest reactions involves the conversion of alkyl or aryl halides to unstable organometallic substances. When treated with water these unstable intermediates give the corresponding hydrocarbon. In the equation shown below, and throughout this book, the general symbol X is used to denote the halogens **Cl**, **Br**, or **I**. The reaction may be applied to both alkyl and aryl halides.

$$\mathrm{Mg} + \mathrm{RX} \xrightarrow[\text{ether}]{\text{Diethyl}} \underset{\text{Grignard reagent}}{\mathrm{RMgX}}$$

$$\mathrm{H_2O} + \mathrm{RMgX} \longrightarrow \mathrm{RH} + \mathrm{MgXOH}$$

$$\mathrm{Mg} + \underset{n\text{-Hexyl bromide}}{\mathrm{CH_3(CH_2)_4CH_2Br}} \xrightarrow[\text{ether}]{\text{Diethyl}} \underset{n\text{-Hexylmagnesium bromide}}{\mathrm{CH_3(CH_2)_4CH_2MgBr}}$$

$$\mathrm{H_2O} + \mathrm{CH_3(CH_2)_4CH_2MgBr} \longrightarrow \mathrm{CH_3(CH_2)_4CH_3} + \mathrm{MgBrOH}$$

Alcohols can be readily converted to their corresponding alkyl halides by treatment with such reagents as phosphorus tribromide. If these halides are then converted to hydrocarbons through the Grignard reagent, the over-all reaction sequence provides a means of obtaining hydrocarbons from alcohols.

$$PBr_3 \;+\; 3ROH \longrightarrow 3RBr \;+\; H_3PO_3$$

Phosphorus   Alkyl   Phosphorous
tribromide   bromide acid

$$RBr \xrightarrow[\text{2) }H_2O]{\text{1) Mg, diethyl ether}} RH$$

$$PBr_3 + 3 \; CH_3(CH_2)_5\overset{\overset{\displaystyle CH_3}{|}}{C}HOH \longrightarrow 3 \; CH_3(CH_2)_5\overset{\overset{\displaystyle CH_3}{|}}{C}HBr + H_3PO_3$$

             2-Octanol   2-Bromooctane

$$CH_3(CH_2)_5\overset{\overset{\displaystyle CH_3}{|}}{C}HBr \xrightarrow[\text{2) }H_2O]{\text{1) Mg, diethyl ether}} CH_3(CH_2)_6CH_3$$

                             n-Octane

Mercaptans, sulfides, and disulfides may also be converted to hydrocarbons through the use of *Raney nickel*. This form of nickel is made by treating nickel-aluminum alloy with caustic alkali, thereby dissolving the aluminum and leaving finely divided nickel with hydrogen adsorbed on its surface. The hydrogen is the reducing agent in this reaction. The sulfur is converted to nickel sulfide.

$$Ni[H_2] + RSH \longrightarrow RH + NiS$$

$$Ni[H_2] + RSR \longrightarrow 2 \; RH + NiS$$

$$Ni[H_2] + C_6H_5CH_2CH_2SH \longrightarrow C_6H_5CH_2CH_3 + NiS$$

          β-Phenylethyl   Ethylbenzene
            mercaptan

$$Ni[H_2] + \underset{\text{Tetrahydro-}\atop\text{thiophene}}{\boxed{S}} \longrightarrow \underset{n\text{-Butane}}{CH_3CH_2CH_2CH_3} + NiS$$

When treated with hydrogen in the presence of a finely divided platinum, palladium, or nickel (Raney) catalyst, a nitro compound consumes three moles of hydrogen and gives the corresponding primary amine. In this reaction, nitrogen-oxygen bonds are transformed into nitrogen-hydrogen bonds.

$$3H_2 + RNO_2 \xrightarrow{\;Pt\;} RNH_2 + 2H_2O$$

$$3H_2 + ArNO_2 \xrightarrow{\;Ni\;} ArNH_2 + 2H_2O$$

$$3H_2 + CH_3CH_2CH_2NO_2 \xrightarrow{\;Pt\;} CH_3CH_2CH_2NH_2 + 2H_2O$$

         1-Nitropropane   *n*-Propylamine

$$3H_2 + C_6H_5NO_2 \xrightarrow{\;Pt\;} C_6H_5NH_2 + 2H_2O$$

      Nitrobenzene   Aniline

Addition. This class of reaction involves the addition of the elements of simple molecules such as water, the hydrogen halides, or the halogens themselves to multiple bonds.   The hydrogenation of alkynes and alkenes to give alkanes (page 27) illustrates the addition reaction.   Another example is the addition of halogen to an alkene to give a *vicinal* dihalide.

$$X_2 + a-\overset{a}{\underset{}{C}}=\overset{a}{\underset{}{C}}-a \xrightarrow{CCl_4} a-\overset{a}{\underset{X}{C}}-\overset{a}{\underset{X}{C}}-a \qquad a = H, R, \text{ or } Ar$$

$$Br_2 + CH_3CH{=}CH_2 \xrightarrow{CCl_4} CH_3\overset{Br}{\underset{}{CH}}CH_2Br$$
$$\text{1,2-Dibromopropane}$$

Hydrogen halides also add to alkenes to give the corresponding alkyl halides, a process referred to as *hydrohalogenation*.

$$HX + a-\overset{a}{\underset{}{C}}=\overset{a}{\underset{}{C}}-a \longrightarrow a-\overset{a}{\underset{H}{C}}-\overset{a}{\underset{X}{C}}-a \qquad a = H, R, \text{ or } Ar$$

$$HCl + CH_2{=}CH_2 \longrightarrow CH_3CH_2Cl$$
$$\quad\text{Ethylene}\qquad\qquad\text{Ethyl chloride}$$

In a similar reaction, the elements of water may be added to alkenes to give alcohols.   This *hydration* reaction is used to prepare many of the simpler alcohols from alkenes produced in the cracking of petroleum. Sulfuric acid is used as a catalyst.

$$HOH + a-\overset{a}{\underset{}{C}}=\overset{a}{\underset{}{C}}-a \xrightarrow{H_2SO_4} a-\overset{a}{\underset{H}{C}}-\overset{a}{\underset{OH}{C}}-a$$

$$HOH + CH_2{=}CH_2 \xrightarrow{H_2SO_4} CH_3CH_2OH$$
$$\qquad\text{Ethylene}\qquad\qquad\quad\text{Ethanol}$$

When an unsymmetrical reagent is added to a symmetrical alkene, as in hydration or hydrohalogenation, no question as to point of attachment arises.   With an unsymmetrical alkene, however, two possibilities are obviously offered.   In practice, it has been found that *hydrogen always adds to that carbon which already carries the more hydrogens, and the halide or hydroxyl to the carbon with the lesser number of hydrogens.*   This remarkable specificity is known as *Markownikoff's rule,* and it allows prediction of the structures of the major products in many reactions, of which the following are illustrative.

$$HCl + CH_3\overset{CH_3}{\underset{}{C}}{=}CH_2 \longrightarrow CH_3\overset{CH_3}{\underset{Cl}{C}}CH_3$$
$$\qquad\text{Isobutene}\qquad\qquad\quad\textit{tert-}\text{Butyl chloride}$$

$$\text{HOH} + \text{CH}_3\text{CH}_2\text{CH}{=}\text{CH}_2 \longrightarrow \overset{\displaystyle \overset{\text{OH}}{|}}{\text{CH}_3\text{CH}_2\text{CHCH}_3}$$

$$\text{1-Butene} \qquad\qquad\qquad\qquad \text{2-Butanol}$$

Substitution. Most of the classes of compounds discussed in this chapter are interconvertible through *substitution reactions,* in which one function is substituted for another. An example of this type of transformation, given earlier (page 49), is the conversion of alcohols to alkyl bromides with the aid of phosphorus tribromide. Alkyl chlorides can be prepared by a similar sequence. Since alkyl halides are among the most versatile intermediates in organic synthesis, and alcohols are readily available starting materials, reactions of this sort are of great importance.

Alkanes are susceptible to direct chlorination in the presence of light, which catalyzes the reaction. The reaction is difficult to control, since hydrogens are replaced by chlorine atoms almost at random, and mixtures of halides are produced, as in the following example. The reaction is of considerable industrial importance.

$$\text{Cl}_2 + \text{CH}_4 \xrightarrow[-\text{HCl}]{\text{Light}} \text{CH}_3\text{Cl} + \text{CH}_2\text{Cl}_2 + \text{CHCl}_3 + \text{CCl}_4$$

| Methyl chloride | Methylene chloride | Chloroform | Carbon tetrachloride |

Aromatic hydrocarbons are much easier to substitute with halogen, both brominations and chlorinations being widely used. Ferric salts act as catalysts.

$$\text{Cl}_2 + \text{ArH} \xrightarrow{\text{FeCl}_3} \text{ArCl} + \text{HCl}$$

$$\text{Br}_2 + \text{ArH} \xrightarrow{\text{FeBr}_3} \text{ArBr} + \text{HBr}$$

$$\text{Cl}_2 + \text{C}_6\text{H}_6 \xrightarrow{\text{FeCl}_3} \text{C}_6\text{H}_5\text{Cl}$$

$$\text{Benzene} \qquad\qquad \text{Chlorobenzene}$$

$$\text{Br}_2 + \text{C}_6\text{H}_6 \xrightarrow{\text{FeBr}_3} \text{C}_6\text{H}_5\text{Br}$$

$$\text{Bromobenzene}$$

Alkyl halides may be converted to alcohols in variable yields by treatment with water (hydrolysis). The reaction is of little preparative value, since alkyl halides are usually made from alcohols.

$$\text{HOH} + \text{RX} \longrightarrow \text{ROH} + \text{HX}$$

$$\text{HOH} + \text{C}_6\text{H}_5\text{CH}_2\text{Cl} \longrightarrow \text{C}_6\text{H}_5\text{CH}_2\text{OH} + \text{HCl}$$

$$\text{Benzyl chloride} \qquad\qquad \text{Benzyl alcohol}$$

Phenol can be produced from chlorobenzene by a similar reaction, carried out at high temperatures and pressures in the presence of a basic catalyst.

$$\text{HOH} + \text{C}_6\text{H}_5\text{Cl} \xrightarrow[300°]{\text{NaOH}} \text{C}_6\text{H}_5\text{OH}$$

$$\text{Chloro-} \quad \text{2,500 lb/sq in.} \quad \text{Phenol}$$
$$\text{benzene}$$

Ethers are readily prepared by the reaction of alkyl halides with *sodium alkoxides* or the sodium salts of phenols. Sodium alkoxides result from the action of sodium metal on alcohols, a process similar to the reaction of sodium with water.

$$2Na + 2ROH \longrightarrow 2RONa + H_2$$

$$RONa + RX \longrightarrow ROR + NaX$$

$$2Na + 2CH_3CH_2OH \longrightarrow 2CH_3CH_2ONa + H_2$$
     Ethanol   Sodium ethoxide

$$CH_3CH_2ONa + CH_2{=}CHCH_2Cl \longrightarrow CH_2{=}CHCH_2OCH_2CH_3$$
       Allyl chloride   Allyl ethyl ether

A similar sequence involving the sodium salts of phenols and alkyl halides leads to aryl alkyl ethers.

$$NaOH + ArOH \longrightarrow ArONa + H_2O$$

$$ArONa + RX \longrightarrow ArOR + NaX$$

$$NaOH + C_6H_5OH \longrightarrow C_6H_5ONa + H_2O$$
      Phenol   Sodium
              phenoxide

$$C_6H_5ONa + CH_3Br \longrightarrow C_6H_5OCH_3 + NaBr$$
     Methyl   Anisole
     bromide

Mercaptans are usually prepared by the reaction of sodium bisulfide with alkyl halides. When sodium sulfide is employed, alkyl sulfides are produced.

$$NaSH + RX \longrightarrow RSH + NaX$$

$$NaSH + (CH_3)_2CHCH_2Br \longrightarrow (CH_3)_2CHCH_2SH + NaBr$$
     Isobutyl   Isobutyl
     bromide   mercaptan

$$Na_2S + 2RX \longrightarrow RSR + 2NaX$$

$$Na_2S + 2 CH_3CH_2CH_2Br \longrightarrow (CH_3CH_2CH_2)_2S$$
     n-Propyl   Di-n-propyl sulfide
     bromide

When alkyl halides are heated with ammonia, a series of reactions occurs which leads to four products, in relative amounts determined by the conditions of the reaction, the proportions of the reagents used, and the nature of the alkyl halides. The reaction is illustrated with methyl chloride and ammonia as reactants.

$$2NH_3 + CH_3Cl \longrightarrow CH_3NH_2 + NH_4Cl$$
       Methylamine

$$CH_3NH_2 + CH_3Cl \longrightarrow (CH_3)_2\overset{+}{N}H_2\overset{-}{Cl}$$
      Dimethylammonium
        chloride

$$(CH_3)_2NH + CH_3Cl \longrightarrow (CH_3)_3\overset{+}{N}H\overset{-}{Cl}$$

Trimethylammonium
chloride

$$(CH_3)_3N + CH_3Cl \longrightarrow (CH_3)_4\overset{+}{N}\overset{-}{Cl}$$

Tetramethylammonium
chloride

The reaction can usually be controlled to give as the predominant product the primary or tertiary amine, or the quaternary ammonium salt. In industrial processes, the products are separated by fractional distillation.

Nitroalkanes are produced commercially by treatment of alkanes with nitric acid vapor at temperatures of several hundred degrees. The process yields mixtures of nitroalkanes, which are separated by fractional distillation. In the laboratory, both nitroalkanes and alkyl nitrites are prepared by the reaction of alkyl halides with sodium nitrite. The nitrite ion can react at either oxygen or nitrogen, and usually becomes substituted at both places, to some extent.

$$\overset{+}{Na}O-\overset{-}{N}=O + RX \longrightarrow R-\overset{+}{N}\overset{O}{\underset{O^-}{\diagup}} + R-O-N=O + NaX$$

Sodium   Nitroalkane   Alkyl
nitrite   nitrite

$$NaNO_2 + C_6H_5CH_2Br \longrightarrow C_6H_5CH_2NO_2 + C_6H_5CH_2ONO$$

Benzyl   Phenyl   Benzyl
bromide   nitromethane   nitrite

Aromatic hydrocarbons can be nitrated directly with nitric acid-sulfuric acid mixtures. Under controlled conditions, a single nitro group can readily be introduced into an aromatic ring.

$$HNO_3 + ArH \xrightarrow{H_2SO_4} ArNO_2 + H_2O$$

$$HNO_3 + C_6H_6 \xrightarrow[50°]{H_2SO_4} C_6H_5NO_2 + H_2O$$

Nitrobenzene

Organic from Inorganic Compounds. One of the goals of organic chemistry has been the preparation of useful organic compounds from cheap inorganic starting materials. Two particularly important examples of successful transformations are seen in the industrial manufacture of methanol and acetylene. These compounds are readily converted into other organic compounds through the reactions already given. In such manner, many compounds are ultimately derived from inorganic materials.

$$H_2 + CO \xrightarrow[\substack{400°,\ 3,000 \\ lb/sq\ in.}]{\substack{Metal \\ oxides}} CH_3OH$$

Methanol

$$CaO + 3C \xrightarrow{3000°} CaC_2 + CO$$

Coke   Calcium
carbide

$$H_2O + CaC_2 \longrightarrow HC\equiv CH + Ca(OH)_2$$

Acetylene

Acetylene polymerizes under various conditions to give a number of products, depending on the conditions of the reactions and the catalysts employed.

Newlands - Kal.

$$2HC \equiv CH \xrightarrow[H_2O]{Cu_2Cl_2, \ NH_4Cl} CH_2 = CHC \equiv CH$$

Vinyl acetylene

$$3HC \equiv CH \xrightarrow[\text{tube}]{\text{Hot copper}} C_6H_6$$

Benzene

$$4HC \equiv CH \xrightarrow[\substack{65°, \ 250 \\ lb/sq \ in.}]{Ni(CN)_2}$$

Cyclooctatetraene

Elucidation of Structure

The principles of structure elucidation developed previously (page 29) may be equally well applied to the classes of compounds discussed above. The introduction of elements other than carbon and hydrogen into organic compounds results in some modification of the possible molecular formulas that can be written for these molecules. The fact that halogens and nitrogen usually carry an odd number of bonds means that if a molecule contains an odd number of halogen or nitrogen atoms, the number of hydrogen atoms in the molecule must also be odd. With sulfur- and oxygen-containing compounds, the number of hydrogen atoms is always even. These principles are clarified by examining the molecular formulas of a number of actual compounds.

CH_3CH_2CHCl (with CH_3 branch)

C_4H_9Cl $C_{10}H_6Br_2$ C_9H_7N $H_2N(CH_2)_3NH_2$

                                                                                              $C_3H_{10}N_2$

$CH_2 = CHOCH = CH_2$

C_4H_6O C_6H_6O C_4H_4S $CH_3SO_2CH_3$

                                                                                              $C_2H_6SO_2$

In calculating the number of sites of unsaturation for such compounds, the parent open-chain saturated substances containing halogen, nitrogen, oxygen, or sulfur are employed. *With each halogen atom, one less hydrogen is found in the parent aliphatic compound than in the saturated aliphatic hydrocarbon of equal carbon content. With nitrogen, one more hydrogen atom (per nitrogen) is found. With any of the oxygen or sulfur compounds, the same number of hydrogen atoms are found as in the saturated alkanes of equal carbon content. Carbon-*

oxygen, carbon-nitrogen, and nitrogen-oxygen double bonds each constitute one site of unsaturation, while a carbon-nitrogen triple bond constitutes two. Metal and quaternary ammonium salts cannot be treated in this manner.

These relationships are illustrated by the data of Table 3.4, which lists the structures, names, and molecular formulas of a number of rep-

TABLE 3.4 *Sites of Unsaturation in Representative Compounds*

Structure	Name	Molecular form. comp. parent		No. sites of unsat.	Identification of sites of unsat.
—Br	Bromobenzene	C_6H_5Br	$C_6H_{13}Br$	4	3 C=C's 1 ring
$Cl_2CHCH_2C\equiv CH$	4,4-Dichloro-1-butyne	$C_4H_4Cl_2$	$C_4H_8Cl_2$	2	2 from C≡C
NH₂	3-Amino-cyclohexene	$C_6H_{11}N$	$C_6H_{15}N$	2	1 C=C 1 ring
—NO₂	Nitropropane	$C_3H_5NO_2$	$C_3H_9NO_2$	2	1 N=O 1 ring
$CH_3C\equiv N$	Acetonitrile	C_2H_3N	C_2H_7N	2	2 from C≡N
Quinoline	Quinoline	C_9H_7N	$C_9H_{21}N$	7	4 C=C's 1 C=N 2 rings
Furan	Furan	C_4H_4O	$C_4H_{10}O$	3	2 C=C's 1 ring
—C—CH₃, O	Acetophenone	C_8H_8O	$C_8H_{18}O$	5	3 C=C's 1 C=O 1 ring
OH OH	Catechol	$C_6H_6O_2$	$C_6H_{14}O_2$	4	3 C=C's 1 ring
$CH_2=CHCH_2SH$	Allyl mercaptan	C_3H_6S	C_3H_8S	1	1 C=C
Diphenyl sulfone	Diphenyl sulfone	$C_{12}H_{10}SO_2$	$C_{12}H_{26}SO_2$	8	6 C=C's 2 rings
$CH_3S^{++}OH$	Methane sulfonic acid	$C_1H_4SO_3$	$C_1H_4SO_3$	0	
$(CH_3)_3N^+—O^-$	Trimethyl-amine oxide	C_3H_9NO	C_3H_9NO	0	

resentative compounds. The molecular formulas of the parent saturated aliphatic compounds have been calculated, and the number of sites of unsaturation have been determined and identified.

The interpretation of exhaustive (maximum) hydrogenation data in cases where atoms are lost from a molecular formula is different from the interpretation of such data where hydrogen is simply added. In the reduction of nitro to amino groups, three moles of hydrogen are consumed, only one of which is added. The other two moles are used in breaking nitrogen-oxygen single bonds. Therefore, one can see what has happened during the reaction by comparing the molecular formulas of reactant and product. Thus 1-nitrobutane ($C_4H_9NO_2$) when reduced gives $C_4H_{11}N$, three moles of hydrogen being absorbed. Clearly one mole of hydrogen appeared in the organic product, and the other two went into forming two moles of water.

Problems

1. Write systematic, and where possible, common names for the following compounds:

a. $C_6H_5CHCl_2$

b. $CH_3CHCH=CH_2$
       |
       Br

c. $(CH_3)_3CCH_2OH$

d. $CH_2=CHCH_2OCH_3$

e.

f.

g. $CH_3CHCHCH_2C\equiv CH$
           |
           OH

h.

i. CH_3CHCH_3
         |
         NO_2

j.

k.

l. $CH_3CHNHCCH_3$
         | |
         CH_3   CH_3

m.

n. $C_6H_5CH_2SCH_3$

o. $CH_3CHCHCH_3$
         |
         Br

2. Write structural formulas for the following compounds:

a. Isopropyldimethylamine
b. 3-Methoxycyclopentanol
c. 3,5-Dinitrophenol
d. 6-Bromo-1-naphthol

e. 3-Methylpyridine
f. Tetramethylene fluoride
g. 3-Phenylquinoline

3. With specific compounds and reagents, write equations which illustrate the following conversions:
   a. An acetylene to an alkene to an alcohol to an alkyl halide to a saturated hydrocarbon
   b. An alcohol to an alkyl halide to an unsymmetrical ether
   c. An alkyl halide to a nitro compound to a primary amine to a secondary amine
   d. An alcohol to an alkyl halide to a sulfide to a saturated hydrocarbon
   e. Inorganic materials to acetylene to benzene to bromobenzene to monodeuterobenzene
   f. Inorganic materials to vinylacetylene to butadiene to butane
   g. Inorganic materials to acetylene to benzene to nitrobenzene to aniline
   h. Inorganic materials to acetylene to cyclooctatetraene to cyclooctane
   i. Methane to methyl chloride to methyl mercaptan to methane

4. Write equations for reactions that could be used for the following conversions. Frequently several reactions in sequence are needed. Any inorganic materials may be utilized.

    a. Conversion of any alkenes to ethyl isopropyl ether

    b. Conversion of any acetylene to 2-butanol

    c. Conversion of any alkene to *tert*-butylamine

    d. Conversion of any alkene to isopropyl mercaptan

    e. Conversion of inorganic materials to phenol

    f. Conversion of any hydrocarbon to methylamine

5. Write out synthetic sequences of reactions for the preparation of the following compounds. Inorganic compounds and only the indicated organic compound may be used.

    a. $C_6H_5N^+(CH_3)_3Cl^-$ from inorganic materials only

    b. $CH_3CHCH_2CH_3$ from $CH_3CH_2CH=CH_2$

$$\quad\quad\quad | \atop OH$$

    c. $CH_2ClCHClCHClCH_2Cl$ from inorganic materials only

    d. $C_6H_5CH_2SSCH_2C_6H_5$ from $C_6H_5CH_2OH$

    e. 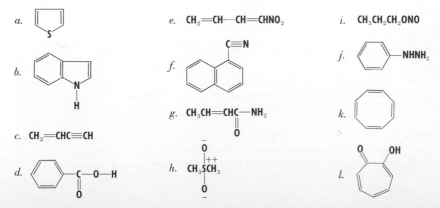 from ⬡—OH

    f. $CH_3CH_2CHBrCH_2Br$ from $CH_3CH_2C\equiv CH$

    g. $(CH_3CH_2)_3N$ from $CH_2=CH_2$

    h. $(CH_3)_2CHOCH(CH_3)_2$ from $CH_3CH=CH_2$

    i. $C_2H_5OCH_3$ from inorganic materials only

6. Compound A possesses a molecular formula C_5H_8O. On exhaustive hydrogenation it absorbs one mole of hydrogen to give B. Both compounds A and B react with sodium metal to give hydrogen. Compound B when treated with phosphorus tribromide gives C, C_5H_9Br. Compound C is treated with magnesium in ether, and the resulting solution is mixed with water to give compound D, C_5H_{10}. This substance is shown by C-methyl determination not to contain any methyl groups. Write equations for the above reactions with use of structural formulas.

7. A compound (A) of unknown structure is found to have the molecular formula $C_6H_{10}S$. When A is subjected to the action of Raney nickel, two moles of a single hydrocarbon are produced from one mole of A. Compound A is found to give 0 moles of acetic acid in a C-methyl determination (page 28). Write equations for the above reactions with use of structural formulas.

8. Calculate the number of sites of unsaturation in the following compounds:

    a. C_4H_7N *d.* $C_7H_{10}SO_3$

    b. $C_6H_{14}N_2$ *e.* C_8H_6NCl

    c. $C_6H_4N_2O_4$ *f.* $C_{10}H_8SCl_2$

9. Identify the sites of unsaturation in the following compounds. Indicate the total number.

    e. $CH_2=CH-CH=CHNO_2$

    g. $CH_3CH=CHC-NH_2$, with $=O$ below

    h. CH_3SCH_3, with O above and O below (sulfone)

    i. $CH_3CH_2CH_2ONO$

4

Compounds with Functional Groups
Unsaturated at Carbon

This chapter deals with those classes of compounds which contain hetero atoms linked to carbon by multiple bonds. Functional groups in these substances contain either carbon-oxygen double bonds ($C{=}O$) or carbon-nitrogen double ($C{=}N$) or triple bonds ($C{\equiv}N$). Figure 4.1 indicates the structures of these functional groups, and the names of the classes characterized by the functions.

Structure, Nomenclature, and Properties

Aldehydes and Ketones. The carbon-oxygen double bond ($C{=}O$) is known as the *carbonyl group*. It is found in most of the classes of compounds listed in Fig. 4.1. The simplest of these are the aldehydes and ketones. A characteristic feature of aldehydes is that they have *at least one hydrogen* bound to the carbonyl group. When the remaining bond is attached to hydrogen, the resulting compound is known as *formaldehyde*. When it is attached to an alkyl group, an aliphatic aldehyde results; when linked to aryl groups, an aromatic aldehyde. These substances may be written in the following different ways:

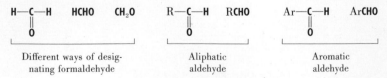

| Different ways of designating formaldehyde | Aliphatic aldehyde | Aromatic aldehyde |

In ketones, the carbonyl group must be bound to two carbon atoms. As a result the simplest ketone (acetone) contains three carbon atoms. Unlike the aldehyde function, which must always occupy a terminal position in a carbon chain, the ketone function must always occupy an internal position, and may be an integral part of an alicyclic molecule. Ketones are classified as being aliphatic, alicyclic, or aromatic, depending on the nature of the hydrocarbon groups attached to the carbonyl function (see below).

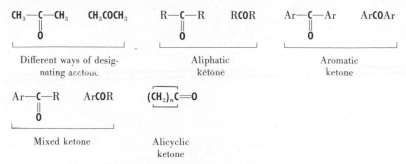

$$CH_3-\overset{\displaystyle \|O}{C}-CH_3 \qquad CH_3COCH_3 \qquad R-\overset{\displaystyle \|O}{C}-R \qquad RCOR \qquad Ar-\overset{\displaystyle \|O}{C}-Ar \qquad ArCOAr$$

Different ways of designating acetone   Aliphatic ketone   Aromatic ketone

$$Ar-\overset{\displaystyle \|O}{C}-R \qquad ArCOR \qquad (CH_2)_nC{=}O$$

Mixed ketone   Alicyclic ketone

The aliphatic aldehydes are named by either of two systems. The first is based on a series of roots derived from the common names of the carboxylic acids (Table 4.3 of next section). The ending *-ic* is changed to the word *aldehyde* in the names of the aliphatic aldehydes. The second (IUC) system makes use of the names of the aliphatic hydrocarbons (Table 2.1), the ending *-e* being changed to *-al* to indicate the presence of the aldehyde function. The structures of the seven simplest aldehydes appear below, along with their names based on the two systems.

CH_2O

Formaldehyde
or methanal

CH_3CHO

Acetaldehyde
or ethanal

CH_3CH_2CHO

Propionaldehyde
or propanal

$CH_3CH_2CH_2CHO$

n-Butyraldehyde
or butanal

$$\underset{3}{CH_3}\underset{2}{\overset{\displaystyle CH_3}{\underset{\displaystyle |}{CH}}}\underset{1}{CHO}$$

Isobutyraldehyde
or 2-methylpropanal

$CH_3(CH_2)_3CHO$

n-Valeraldehyde
or pentanal

$$\underset{\gamma}{CH_3}\underset{\beta}{CH_2}\overset{\displaystyle CH_3}{\underset{\displaystyle |}{\underset{\alpha}{CH}}}CHO$$

α-Methylbutyraldehyde
or 2-methylbutanal

$$-\overset{\displaystyle |}{\underset{\displaystyle \|:O:}{C}}-H$$

Aldehyde

$$-\overset{\displaystyle |}{\underset{\displaystyle |}{C}}-\overset{\displaystyle |}{\underset{\displaystyle \|:O:}{C}}-\overset{\displaystyle |}{\underset{\displaystyle |}{C}}-$$

Ketone

$$-\overset{\displaystyle |}{\underset{\displaystyle \|:O:}{C}}-\overset{..}{\underset{..}{O}}-H$$

Carboxylic acid

$$-\overset{\displaystyle |}{\underset{\displaystyle \|:O:}{C}}-\overset{..}{\underset{..}{O}}-\overset{\displaystyle |}{\underset{\displaystyle |}{C}}-$$

Ester

$$-\overset{\displaystyle |}{\underset{\displaystyle \|:O:}{C}}-\overset{..}{\underset{..}{O}}-\overset{\displaystyle |}{\underset{\displaystyle \|:O:}{C}}-$$

Anhydride

$$-\overset{\displaystyle |}{\underset{\displaystyle \|:O:}{C}}-\overset{..}{\underset{..}{X}}:$$

Acid halide

$$-\overset{\displaystyle |}{\underset{\displaystyle \|:O:}{C}}-N\overset{\diagup}{\diagdown}$$

Amide

$$-\overset{\displaystyle |}{C}{=}\overset{..}{N}-$$

Imine

$$-C{\equiv}\overset{..}{N}$$

Nitrile

FIG. 4.1   *Functional groups unsaturated at carbon.*

TABLE 4.1   *Physical Properties of Aldehydes*

Name	Formula	Mp, °C	Bp, °C	Sp. gr.
Formaldehyde	CH_2O	−92	−21	0.815
Acetaldehyde	CH_3CHO	−123	21	0.781
Propionaldehyde	CH_3CH_2CHO	−81	49	0.807
n-Butyraldehyde	$CH_3(CH_2)_2CHO$	−97	75	0.817
Isobutyraldehyde	$(CH_3)_2CHCHO$	−66	61	0.794
n-Valeraldehyde	$CH_3(CH_2)_3CHO$	−92	104	0.819
Isovaleraldehyde	$(CH_3)_2CHCH_2CHO$	−51	93	0.803
n-Caproaldehyde	$CH_3(CH_2)_4CHO$		129	0.834
Glyoxal	$OHCCHO$	15	50	1.14
Acrolein	$CH_2{=}CHCHO$	−88	53	0.841
Crotonaldehyde	$CH_3CH{=}CHCHO$	−77	104	0.859
Benzaldehyde	C_6H_5CHO	−56	179	1.046
Furfural		−31	162	1.156

The positions of substituents attached to the chains of aldehydes are indicated in the IUC names in the usual way, by number.   In the other system, substituents may be indicated with Greek letters.   The *carbon adjacent to the carbonyl* is α, the next β, etc.   The common names of the simple aldehydes, as well as their physical ♦properties, are listed in Table 4.1.

The simple aliphatic and aromatic ketones are named after the hydrocarbon groups attached to the carbonyl.   These groups are listed in alphabetical order and followed by the word *ketone*.   Many of the ketones also have common names (indicated below).   Additional names are listed in Table 4.2, which records the physical properties of the simple ketones.

CH_3COCH_3	$CH_3COCH_2CH_3$	$CH_3COCH(CH_3)_2$
Dimethyl ketone or acetone	Ethyl methyl ketone	Isopropyl methyl ketone

		$\overset{\displaystyle Cl}{\underset{\alpha\ \ \beta}{\vert}}$
$C_6H_5COCH_3$	$C_6H_5COC_6H_5$	$C_6H_5COCHCH_3$
Methyl phenyl ketone or acetophenone	Diphenyl ketone or benzophenone	α-Chloropropiophenone

In the IUC system, ketones are named by changing the ending *-e* of the name of the parent hydrocarbon to *-one*.   The position of the carbonyl group in the chain is indicated by number, the chain being numbered in the usual way (see following examples).

TABLE 4.2   *Physical Properties of Ketones*

Name	Formula	Mp, °C	Bp, °C	Sp. gr.
Acetone	CH_3COCH_3	−95	56	0.792
Ethyl methyl ketone	$CH_3COCH_2CH_3$	−86	80	0.805
Methyl *n*-propyl ketone	$CH_3COCH_2CH_2CH_3$	−78	102	0.812
Diethyl ketone	$C_2H_5COC_2H_5$	−42	102	0.814
2-Hexanone	$CH_3CO(CH_2)_3CH_3$	−57	127	0.830
3-Hexanone	$CH_3CH_2COCH_2CH_2CH_3$		124	0.818
tert-Butyl methyl ketone	$CH_3COC(CH_3)_3$	−53	106	0.811
Cyclohexanone	⬡=O	−45	157	0.949
Biacetyl	$CH_3COCOCH_3$		89	0.975
Acetylacetone	$CH_3COCH_2COCH_3$	−23	137	0.976
Mesityl oxide	$(CH_3)_2C=CHCOCH_3$	−59	131	0.863
Acetophenone	$CH_3COC_6H_5$	20	202	
Propiophenone	$C_2H_5COC_6H_5$	21	218	
Benzophenone	$C_6H_5COC_6H_5$	48	306	

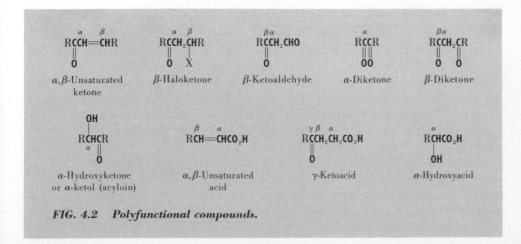

$CH_3CHCH_2COCH_3$
|
C_6H_5
4-Phenyl-2-pentanone

$CH_3CHCHCH_2COCH_3$ (with Cl above and CH$_3$ below)
5-Chloro-4-methyl-2-
hexanone

2-Ethylcyclobutanone

When an aldehyde or ketone contains more than one functional group, the relative position of an additional function is often designated in the name by a Greek letter, as in the examples of Fig. 4.2.

α,β-Unsaturated ketone — $R\overset{\alpha}{C}CH=CHR$

β-Haloketone — $RCCH_2CHR$ (O, X)

β-Ketoaldehyde — $RCCH_2CHO$

α-Diketone — $RCCR$ (OO)

β-Diketone — $RCCH_2CR$ (O O)

α-Hydroxyketone or α-ketol (acyloin) — $R\overset{OH}{C}HCR$

α,β-Unsaturated acid — $RCH=CHCO_2H$

γ-Ketoacid — $RCCH_2CH_2CO_2H$

α-Hydroxyacid — $RCHCO_2H$ (OH)

FIG. 4.2   *Polyfunctional compounds.*

Aldehydes and ketones boil at temperatures (Tables 4.1 and 4.2) somewhat above the boiling points of hydrocarbons and ethers of equal molecular weight, but decidedly lower than those of alcohols. As was evident with the alcohols and ethers (Table 3.2), the specific gravity of compounds containing the carbonyl function increases as the number of functions per molecule increases. The presence in the molecule of an aromatic nucleus also elevates the specific gravity. The monofunctional aldehydes and ketones are neutral substances.

Aldehydes of low molecular weight have obnoxious odors, but higher members of the series are more pleasant-smelling. Some of the aromatic aldehydes are used as flavors. These substances occur in nature, frequently as constituents of essential oils obtained from the kernels of peach, cherry, and other fruits. Many of the ketones, particularly those which contain alicyclic structures, are found in essential oils obtained from plant products. Others are obtained from animal sources and may replace musk in the manufacture of perfumes. Examples of naturally occurring aldehydes and ketones are cited below:

CH₃
$(CH_3)_2C$=$CHCH_2CH_2CHCH_2CHO$

Citronellal, component
of rose oil

CH_3O——⟨ ⟩——CHO

Anisaldehyde
(*p*-Methoxybenzaldehyde),
constituent of anise

CH₃O
HO——⟨ ⟩——CHO

Vanillin, fragrant
principle of the
vanilla bean

CH_3—CH—CH_2—C=O
└$(CH_2)_{12}$┘

Muscone, obtained
from scent glands
of male musk deer

β-Ionone, fragrant
component of the
violet

Aldehydes and ketones are of considerable commercial importance. Formaldehyde is manufactured in tremendous quantities by the catalytic oxidation of methanol with oxygen. It is used in the preparation of artificial fibers, plastics, and biological specimens, and serves as a reducing agent. Certain ketones of low molecular weight are cheap and useful solvents, particularly acetone. A major use for aldehydes and ketones is found in chemical synthesis. The carbonyl group, which can undergo a large number of transformations, is particularly valuable in the construction of carbon chains (Chap. 13).

Carboxylic Acids. Carboxylic acids contain the *carboxyl function*, which consists of a carbonyl and a hydroxyl group attached to the same carbon atom. Since only one bond remains unoccupied on the carboxyl group, this function (like that of the aldehydes) must always occupy a terminal position on a carbon skeleton. The simplest carboxylic acid is formic acid, which has hydrogen attached to the functional group. Alkyl and aryl groups are bound to carboxyl groups in the aliphatic and aromatic acids, respectively.

$$\text{H—C—O—H} \quad \text{HCOOH} \quad \text{HCO}_2\text{H} \qquad \text{R—C—O—H} \quad \text{RCO}_2\text{H} \qquad \text{Ar—C—O—H} \quad \text{ArCO}_2\text{H}$$

| Different ways of designating formic acid | Aliphatic carboxylic acid | Aromatic carboxylic acid |

The common names of the unbranched aliphatic carboxylic acids provide roots for the names of the aldehydes, as well as for a number of classes of compounds derived from the acids (see following sections). These names are listed in Table 4.3; their root portions are in italic type. The same principles apply to the names of the aliphatic dicarboxylic acids, which are also listed.

Positions of substituents on the chains of carboxylic acids are frequently designated by the use of Greek letters, as was done with the aldehydes and ketones. The aromatic acids have common names, and substituents are indicated in the names of substituted compounds in the usual way, as shown in the following examples (see also Fig. 4.2).

$$\text{CH}_3\text{CHCO}_2\text{H}$$

α-Chloropropionic acid

$$\text{CH}_3\text{CCH}_2\text{CO}_2\text{H}$$

β-Ketobutyric acid

$$\text{HO}_2\text{CCH}_2\text{CH}_2\text{CHCO}_2\text{H}$$

α-Hydroxyglutaric acid

m-Nitrobenzoic acid or 3-nitro-benzoic acid

β-Naphthoic acid

Phthalic acid

Isophthalic acid

Terephthalic acid

Cyclohexane-carboxylic acid

The IUC system of nomenclature of the carboxylic acids is based on the names of the aliphatic hydrocarbons, whose final -*e* is changed to -*oic* to indicate the presence of the acid function. The usual rules apply with respect to substituents, as can be seen from the following examples.

$$\text{CH}_3\text{CH}_2\text{CHCHCO}_2\text{H}$$

2-Methyl-3-phenyl-pentanoic acid

$$\text{CH}_3\text{CH}=\text{CHCH}_2\text{CHCO}_2\text{H}$$

2-Amino-4-hexenoic acid

$$\text{HO}_2\text{CCH}_2\text{CHCO}_2\text{H}$$

2-Chlorobutanedioic acid

Some acids are most conveniently named by prefixing the term *carboxy* to the name of the parent compound, while other acids are

TABLE 4.3   Physical Properties of Carboxylic Acids

Name	Formula	Mp, °C	Bp, °C	Sp. gr.	p$K_a^{25°}$
Formic	HCO$_2$H	8.4	101	1.220	3.77
Acetic	CH$_3$CO$_2$H	17	118	1.049	4.76
Propionic	CH$_3$CH$_2$CO$_2$H	−22	141	0.992	4.88
n-Butyric	CH$_3$(CH$_2$)$_2$CO$_2$H	−5	163	0.959	4.82
Isobutyric	(CH$_3$)$_2$CHCO$_2$H	−47	154	0.949	4.85
n-Valeric	CH$_3$(CH$_2$)$_3$CO$_2$H	−35	187	0.939	4.81
Caproic	CH$_3$(CH$_2$)$_4$CO$_2$H	−2	205	0.929	4.85
Enanthic	CH$_3$(CH$_2$)$_5$CO$_2$H	−11	224	0.922	4.89
Caprylic	CH$_3$(CH$_2$)$_6$CO$_2$H	16	237	0.910	4.85
Pelargonic	CH$_3$(CH$_2$)$_7$CO$_2$H	13	254	0.907	4.96
Glycolic	HOCH$_2$CO$_2$H	79			3.83
Lactic	CH$_3$CHOHCO$_2$H	18		1.249	3.87
Acrylic	CH$_2$=CHCO$_2$H	13	141		4.26
Oxalic	HO$_2$CCO$_2$H	187			1.46†
Malonic	HO$_2$CCH$_2$CO$_2$H	135			2.80†
Succinic	HO$_2$CCH$_2$CH$_2$CO$_2$H	185			4.17†
Glutaric	HO$_2$C(CH$_2$)$_3$CO$_2$H	98			4.33†
Adipic	HO$_2$C(CH$_2$)$_4$CO$_2$H	151			4.43†
Pimelic	HO$_2$C(CH$_2$)$_5$CO$_2$H	105			4.47†
Suberic	HO$_2$C(CH$_2$)$_6$CO$_2$H	142			4.52†
Azelaic	HO$_2$C(CH$_2$)$_7$CO$_2$H	106			4.54†
Sebacic	HO$_2$C(CH$_2$)$_8$CO$_2$H	134			4.55†
Tartaric	HO$_2$CCHOHCHOHCO$_2$H (+)	170			
Maleic	HO$_2$CCH=CHCO$_2$H (cis)	130			1.9†
Fumaric	HO$_2$CCH=CHCO$_2$H (trans)	287			3.0†
Malic	HO$_2$CCHOHCH$_2$CO$_2$H	100			
Benzoic	C$_6$H$_5$CO$_2$H	122	249		4.17
Phthalic	o-C$_6$H$_4$(CO$_2$H)$_2$	200			3.00†
Isophthalic	m-C$_6$H$_4$(CO$_2$H)$_2$	348			3.38†
Terephthalic	p-C$_6$H$_4$(CO$_2$H)$_2$	300			3.82†
Salicylic	o-HOC$_6$H$_4$CO$_2$H	159			3.00
Anthranilic	o-H$_2$NC$_6$H$_4$CO$_2$H	145			5.00
Cinnamic	C$_6$H$_5$CH=CHCO$_2$H (trans)	133			4.43
Mandelic	C$_6$H$_5$CHOHCO$_2$H (racemic)	119			3.38

† Based on the dissociation of the first carboxyl group.

named by addition of the term *carboxylic acid* to the name of the hydrocarbon group.

2-Carboxycyclohexanone   Cyclopentanecarboxylic
                                          acid

From the physical properties recorded in Table 4.3, it is clear that carboxylic acids in general possess higher boiling and melting points and specific gravities than compounds of similar molecular weight which belong to the other classes considered thus far. The carboxyl groups of neighboring molecules are closely associated both in the liquid and in the crystalline state (Chap. 7). The acidity of the carboxylic acids is measured by the values of the pK_a's, the lower values correlating with higher strengths (see Chap. 7 for a definition of pK_a). The strongest acids in the table are those with the lowest carbon content, particularly the smaller dicarboxylic acids. Aromatic acids tend to be somewhat stronger than the aliphatic. Aliphatic acids of intermediate molecular weight (particularly those with four to seven carbon atoms) have disagreeable odors, resembling that of rancid butter.

Many of the acids listed in Table 4.3 occur in nature, some in the form of derivatives (amides or esters), some in the free state. Amino acids (Chap. 23) are components of proteins, which make up the muscle and tissue of animals. Many other acids play an important role in the metabolism and synthesis of fats by enzyme systems, and others are inter mediates or end products in microbiological processes. Acetic acid (vinegar) is the end product in the fermentation of most agricultural products, and is the "common denominator" of many synthetic and degradative operations associated with the metabolism of food and building of tissue in mammals.

Most of the simpler carboxylic acids are commercial chemicals. Acetic acid is a powerful solvent, and an important reagent in the preparation of pharmaceuticals, plastics, artificial fibers, and coatings. The phthalic acids and adipic acid are employed in the synthesis of fibers such as Dacron and nylon. Salicylic acid is the active principle liberated by aspirin in the body; oxalic acid is an important reducing agent; and benzoic acid (as a salt) is used as a food preservative.

Acid Halides and Anhydrides. Acid halides are characterized by the attachment of a carbonyl to a halogen, usually chlorine. As the name suggests, anhydrides contain the elements of two carboxyl groups minus a mole of water. The function consists of two carbonyl groups bound by an oxygen.

R—C—X RCOX ∥ O	Ar—C—X ArCOX ∥ O	R—C—O—C—R RCO₂COR ∥ ∥ O O
Different ways of writing aliphatic acid halide	Aromatic acid halide	Aliphatic anhydride

Ar—C—O—C—Ar ArCO₂COAr ∥ ∥ O O	R—C—O—C—Ar RCO₂COAr ∥ ∥ O O
Aromatic anhydride	Aliphatic-aromatic anhydride

TABLE 4.4   **_Physical Properties of Acid Halides and Anhydrides_**

Name	Formula	Mp, °C	Bp, °C	Sp. gr.
Acetyl fluoride	CH_3COF		21	0.993
Acetyl chloride	CH_3COCl		52	1.104
Acetyl bromide	CH_3COBr		77	1.52
Acetyl iodide	CH_3COI		108	1.98
Propionyl chloride	CH_3CH_2COCl		80	1.065
n-Butyryl chloride	$CH_3CH_2CH_2COCl$		102	1.028
Benzoyl chloride	C_6H_5COCl		197	1.212
Acetic anhydride	$(CH_3CO)_2O$	−73	140	1.082
Propionic anhydride	$(CH_3CH_2CO)_2O$	−45	168	1.012
n-Butyric anhydride	$(CH_3CH_2CH_2CO)_2O$	−75	198	0.969
Benzoic anhydride	$(C_6H_5CO)_2O$	42	360	1.199
Succinic anhydride	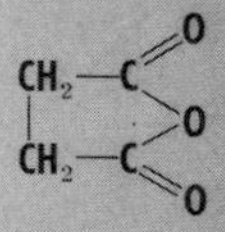	120	261	
Phthalic anhydride	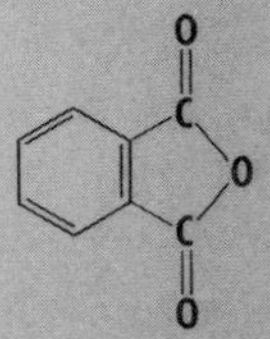	132	285	

Acid halides (or acyl halides) are named by combining the stems of the common names of the carboxylic acids (Table 4.3) with the suffix _-yl_ or _-oyl,_ and adding the name of the halide ion, as in the examples.

CH_3COCl $CH_3CH_2CH_2COF$ C_6H_5COCl $ClOCCH_2CH_2COCl$

Acetyl   Butyryl   Benzoyl   Succinoyl
chloride   fluoride   chloride   chloride

Formyl chloride, which may be presumed to be the acid halide of lowest molecular weight, has never been prepared. All attempts at preparation have resulted in the formation of carbon monoxide and hydrogen halide. However, formyl fluoride is known.

$$[H\!-\!\underset{\underset{O}{\|}}{C}\!-\!X] \longrightarrow CO + HX$$

The anhydrides are named by replacing the word _acid_ with _anhydride_ in the name of the parent acid. Simple formic anhydride is unknown, although _mixed_ anhydrides of formic and other acids have been prepared. Cyclic anhydrides with five or six atoms in the ring are common substances, as seen below.

$CH_3CO_2COCH_3$ or $(CH_3CO)_2O$ $(CH_3CH_2CH_2CO)_2O$ $(C_6H_5CO)_2O$

Acetic anhydride   Butyric anhydride   Benzoic anhydride

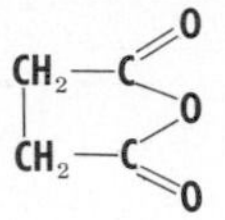

Succinic anhydride 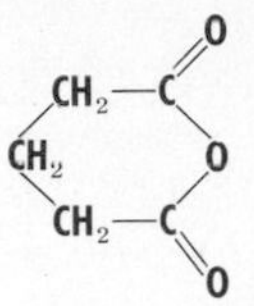   Glutaric anhydride 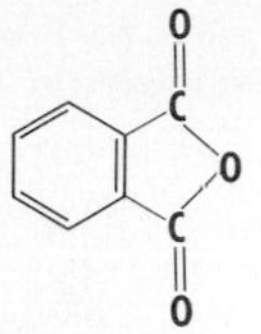   Phthalic anhydride

Table 4.4 lists the physical properties of representative members of the two families of compounds. All the substances, except the last three anhydrides, are liquid at room temperature. Because of the presence of halogen in the acid halides, and three oxygen atoms in the anhydrides, the specific gravities of these liquids are all rather high.

These compounds possess obnoxious odors, are usually lacrimators, and readily react with water to give acids. Acid halides have never been observed in nature.

The acid halides and anhydrides are used as *acylating agents* in the preparation of compounds which contain *acyl groups*. The structures of acyl groups are indicated in Fig. 4.3, along with the structures of a number of other oxygen- and nitrogen-containing groups.

Esters and Lactones. Esters may be considered structural derivatives of carboxylic acids, in which the hydrogen of the carboxyl group has been replaced by an alkyl or aryl group.

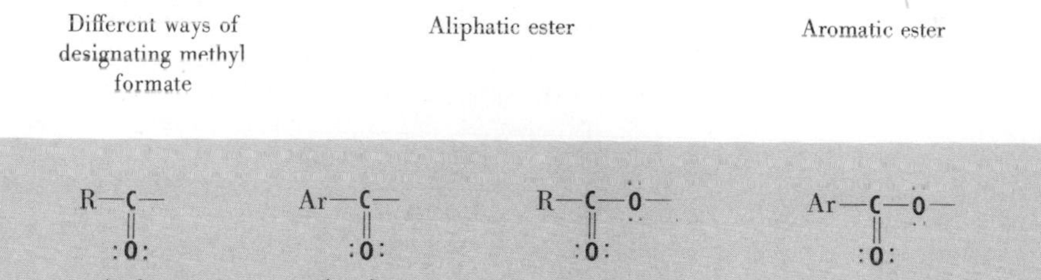

Different ways of designating methyl formate

Aliphatic ester

Aromatic ester

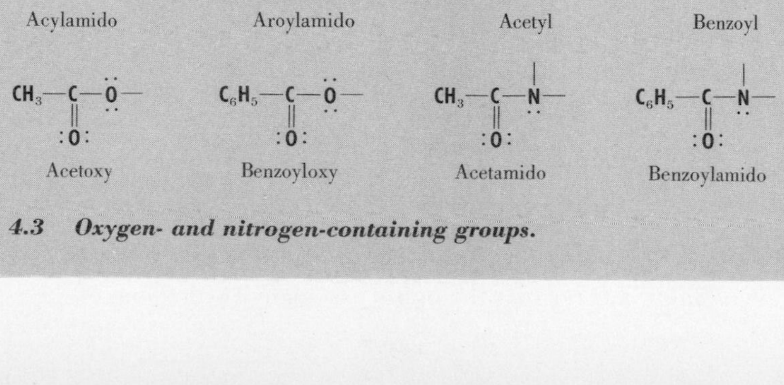

FIG. 4.3   *Oxygen- and nitrogen-containing groups.*

TABLE 4.5   Physical Properties of Esters

Name	Formula	Bp. °C	Sp. gr.
Methyl formate	HCO_2CH_3	32	0.974
Ethyl formate	$HCO_2CH_2CH_3$	54	0.906
Methyl acetate	$CH_3CO_2CH_3$	57	0.924
Ethyl acetate	$CH_3CO_2CH_2CH_3$	77	0.901
n-Propyl acetate	$CH_3CO_2CH_2CH_2CH_3$	102	0.886
n-Butyl acetate	$CH_3CO_2(CH_2)_3CH_3$	127	0.882
n-Amyl acetate	$CH_3CO_2(CH_2)_4CH_3$	148	0.879
Methyl propionate	$CH_3CH_2CO_2CH_3$	80	0.915
Methyl n-butyrate	$CH_3(CH_2)_2CO_2CH_3$	102	0.898
Methyl n-valerate	$CH_3(CH_2)_3CO_2CH_3$	127	0.910
Methyl benzoate	$C_6H_5CO_2CH_3$	199	
Ethyl benzoate	$C_6H_5CO_2CH_2CH_3$	213	
Methyl salicylate (oil of wintergreen)	OH / CO₂CH₃	223	
Acetylsalicylic acid (aspirin)	OCOCH₃ / COOH	Mp 137°	

R—C—O—Ar RCO_2Ar Ar—C—O—R $ArCO_2R$
‖   ‖
O   O

Mixed ester   Mixed ester

Esters are named as derivatives of the corresponding acids, the *-ic* or *-oic* ending of the acid being changed to *-ate*. The name of the alkyl or aryl group substituted for the hydrogen of the acid is placed before the name of the acid. In some names, the ester function is treated as a substituent, and terms such as *carbomethoxy* (CH_3O_2C—) and *carboethoxy* ($CH_3CH_2O_2C$—) are prefixed to the names of the parent skeletons. The following examples illustrate these principles.

$CH_3CO_2C_6H_5$ $C_6H_5CO_2CH_2C_6H_5$ $CH_3CH_2CO_2C(CH_3)_3$

Phenyl acetate   Benzyl benzoate   *tert*-Butyl propionate

CH_3 CH_3
| |
$CH_3CHCH_2CH_2CO_2CHCH_2CH_3$

2-Butyl 4-methylpentanoate   Carbomethoxycyclobutane —CO₂CH₃

Esters tend to be liquids with boiling points much lower than those of carboxylic acids of equal molecular weight (see Table 4.5). The volatile esters have agreeable odors, which resemble those of the more familiar fruits. Table 4.6 records the odors associated with some of the more common esters. This property makes them useful as ingredients in artificial essences and flavors. Esters are powerful solvents, particularly for large molecules, and are extensively used in lacquers and in extraction of antibiotics from fermentation liquors.

Esters are widely distributed throughout the plant and animal kingdoms. Perhaps their most important natural sources are the fats and oils, which are esters derived from long-chain *fatty acids* (16 to 18 carbon atoms) and glycerol (page 39). Tristearin is an example of a fat.

$$CH_2O_2C(CH_2)_{16}CH_3$$
$$CHO_2C(CH_2)_{16}CH_3$$
$$CH_2O_2C(CH_2)_{16}CH_3$$

Tristearin

Lactones are cyclic esters, usually containing four-, five-, or six-membered rings. These ring systems are referred to as β-, γ-, or δ-lactones, depending on the point of linkage to form a ring. These compounds are useful in chemical synthesis, particularly propiolactone, which is a commercial chemical.

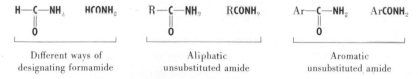

β-Propiolactone γ Butyrolactone δ-Valerolactone

Amides, Imines, and Nitriles. The amide linkage combines a carbonyl and an amine group in the same function. Amides are in a sense derivatives of carboxylic acids, in which the hydroxyl has been replaced with an amino, alkylamino, arylamino, or dialkylamino group.

$H—C—NH_2$ $\,\,$ $HCONH_2$	$R—C—NH_2$ $\,\,$ $RCONH_2$	$Ar—C—NH_2$ $\,\,$ $ArCONH_2$
$\overset{\|}{O}$	$\overset{\|}{O}$	$\overset{\|}{O}$
Different ways of designating formamide	Aliphatic unsubstituted amide	Aromatic unsubstituted amide

TABLE 4.6 *Odors of Common Esters*

Name	Odor characteristic of
n-Butyl acetate	Banana
n-Octyl acetate	Orange
Methyl *n*-butyrate	Pineapple
n-Amyl butyrate	Apricot
Isoamyl butyrate	Pear
Isoamyl isovalerate	Apple

TABLE 4.7   *Physical Properties of Amides*

Name	Formula	Mp, °C	Bp, °C
Formamide	$HCONH_2$	2	193
Dimethylformamide	$HCON(CH_3)_2$		153
Acetamide	CH_3CONH_2	82	222
Propionamide	$CH_3CH_2CONH_2$	80	213
n-Butyramide	$CH_3(CH_2)_2CONH_2$	116	216
n-Valeramide	$CH_3(CH_2)_3CONH_2$	106	
n-Caproamide	$CH_3(CH_2)_4CONH_2$	101	
Benzamide	$C_6H_5CONH_2$	130	
Acetanilide	$CH_3CONHC_6H_5$	114	304

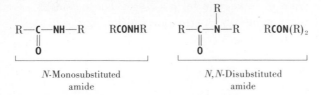

N-Monosubstituted amide   *N,N*-Disubstituted amide

Amides are named as derivatives of the corresponding carboxylic acids, the word *amide* being substituted for *-ic acid* in the name of the parent acid.   The presence of alkyl or aryl substituents attached to nitrogen is marked by prefixing the letter *N* and the name of the substituent to the name of the unsubstituted amide, as in the examples.

CH_3CONH_2 $C_6H_5CONH_2$ $CH_3CONHC_6H_5$ $CH_3CH_2CON(CH_3)_2$

Acetamide   Benzamide   *N*-Phenylacetamide   *N,N*-Dimethyl-
                                       (Acetanilide)   propionamide

With the exception of formamide, the unsubstituted amides are crystalline solids at room temperature, and possess even higher boiling points and specific gravities than do the carboxylic acids of comparable molecular weight.   The relatively high melting points of amides make them useful derivatives for characterizing carboxylic acids, from which they can easily be made.   Apparently amides are highly associated in both the liquid and the solid state.   Dimethylformamide is a useful solvent, particularly good as a reaction medium when both polar and nonpolar compounds need to be brought into contact with one another. The physical properties of some of the simple amides are listed in Table 4.7.

Proteins, which constitute much of the tissue of living organisms, are complex amides of high molecular weight.   These compounds, which are among the most important of natural products, are discussed in detail in Chap. 25.   Some of the synthetic fibers are also polyamides.

$$\text{R}$$
$$|$$
$$-(\text{CONHCH})_n- \qquad -\text{CO}[\text{NH}(\text{CH}_2)_6\text{NHCO}(\text{CH}_2)_4\text{CO}]_n\text{NH}-$$

Simplified formula　　　　　　Simplified formula
for protein　　　　　　　　for nylon

Lactams are the cyclic counterparts of the open-chain amides, and are referred to as β-, γ-, or δ-lactams, depending on the point of attachment of nitrogen to the hydrocarbon chain.

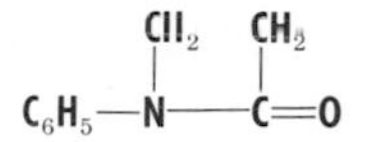

N-Phenyl-β-　　　　　γ-Butyrolactam　　　δ-Valerolactam
propiolactam

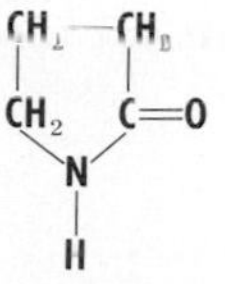

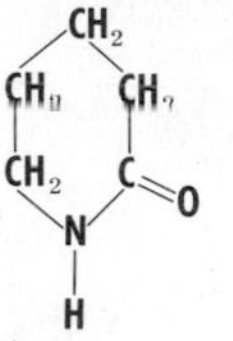

Imides contain two acyl groups attached to the same nitrogen. The most commonly encountered members of the class are cyclic. In these substances, which bear a structural resemblance to the anhydrides, an **NH** replaces the central oxygen of the anhydride function.

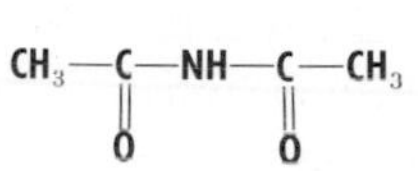

Acetylimide 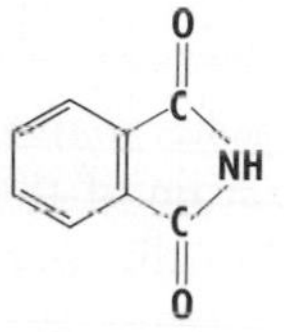　　　　　　Phthalimide 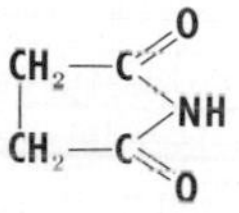　　　　　Succinimide

Another variation of the amide linkage is found in *urea,* in which two amino groups are attached to the same carbonyl group. This substance is a product of metabolism in the animal organism and is the starting material for the synthesis of certain plastics. The urea molecule is frequently incorporated in the ring systems found in such natural products as vitamin B_2 (Chap. 23) and caffeine and in such synthetic drugs as the barbiturates, an important class of sedatives used in sleeping pills.

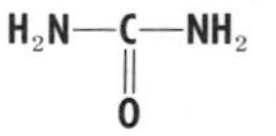

Urea 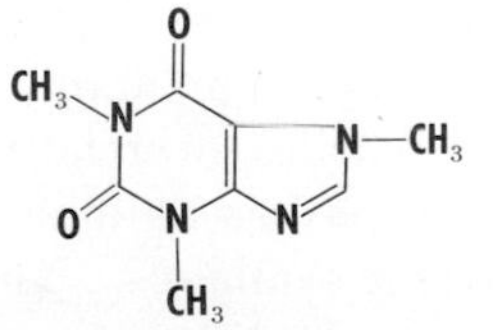　　　　　　　　Caffeine 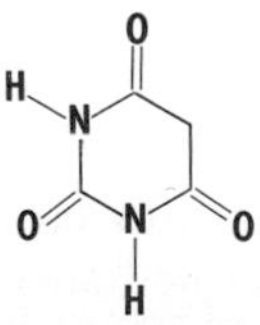　　　　　　Barbituric acid

Imines are compounds which contain carbon-nitrogen double bonds as a characteristic functional group. They are much less stable than aldehydes and ketones, which are their oxygen analogues. Two of the imines stable enough to be isolated possess the following structures:

$$\text{C}_6\text{H}_5\text{CH}=\text{NH} \qquad \text{C}_6\text{H}_5\text{CH}=\text{NC}_6\text{H}_5$$

Benzaldimine　　　　Benzalaniline

Related classes of compounds in which nitrogen carries other groups are somewhat more stable. The *oximes, hydrazones,* and *semicarbazones* all tend to be crystalline compounds. They are readily formed from aldehydes and ketones, and are used as crystalline derivatives to characterize the parent carbonyl compounds.

$$\begin{array}{ccc}
\overset{a}{\underset{b}{\diagup}}C{=}N{-}OH & \overset{a}{\underset{b}{\diagup}}C{=}N{-}NH_2 & \overset{a}{\underset{b}{\diagup}}C{=}N{-}NHC_6H_5 \\
\text{Oxime} & \text{Hydrazone} & \text{Phenylhydrazone}
\end{array}$$

$$\overset{a}{\underset{b}{\diagup}}C{=}N{-}NH{-}\underset{\underset{O}{\|}}{C}{-}NH_2 \qquad a \text{ and } b = \text{H, R, or Ar}$$

Semicarbazone

Nitriles (*cyanides*), which contain a carbon-nitrogen triple bond as a functional group, may be considered derivatives of hydrogen cyanide.

$$\underbrace{H{-}C{\equiv}N \quad HCN}_{} \qquad \underbrace{R{-}C{\equiv}N \quad RCN}_{} \qquad \underbrace{Ar{-}C{\equiv}N \quad ArCN}_{}$$

| Different ways of writing hydrogen cyanide | Aliphatic nitrile | Aromatic nitrile |

Nitriles are named by substituting the suffix *-onitrile* for *-ic acid* in the names of the carboxylic acids. Application of this rule to simple **HCN** would of course yield "formonitrile," but this particular choice of name has not found any support. Such names as acetonitrile and butyronitrile are in common use, however. Occasionally the term *cyano-* is used as a prefix to indicate the presence of a nitrile group in a compound.

$$CH_3C{\equiv}N \qquad C_6H_5C{\equiv}N \qquad N{\equiv}CCH_2CO_2H$$

| Acetonitrile | Benzonitrile | Cyanoacetic acid |

$$\underset{\underset{Cl}{|}}{CH_3CH_2CHC{\equiv}N} \qquad \overset{C_6H_5}{\underset{|}{CH_3CH_2CHCH_2C{\equiv}N}}$$

| α-Chlorobutyronitrile | 3-Phenylpentanonitrile |

Nitriles tend to be liquids with boiling points comparable to those of alcohols of similar molecular weight. Nitriles of relatively low molecular weight (e.g., acetonitrile) enjoy some use as solvents, but nitriles serve mainly as intermediates in organic syntheses. The nitrile functional group is seldom encountered in natural products.

Reactions

Reactions typical of the classes of compounds discussed in the previous sections will now be described. Most of these reactions involve the conversion of one functional group into another. These transformations provide a means of indicating the structural relationships among the classes of compounds. They also are the steps used in the design of rational synthetic sequences for the preparation of desired compounds.

Oxidation and Reduction. The terms *oxidation* and *reduction* as applied in organic chemistry have a somewhat different meaning from that current in the inorganic field. In organic chemistry, oxidation involves the *removal of hydrogen* and (or) the addition of oxygen or some other hetero atom to a compound. Reduction always involves the *addition of hydrogen* to an organic compound and frequently the removal of oxygen or some other hetero atom. In Fig. 4.4, classes of compounds are arranged in series which represent different states of oxidation and reduction.

Many classes of compounds may be interconverted by oxidation and reduction reactions. Thus simple *primary* alcohols are oxidized to give aldehydes, which in turn are oxidized to carboxylic acids. Sometimes the general symbols [O] and [H] are used in chemical equations; the former stands for an oxidizing and the latter for a reducing agent.

$$RCH_2OH \xrightarrow{[O]} RCHO \xrightarrow{[O]} RCO_2H$$

$$CH_3CH_2OH \xrightarrow{H_2Cr_2O_7} CH_3CHO \xrightarrow[Ag_2O]{HNO_3 \atop or} CH_3CO_2H$$

    Ethanol   Acetaldehyde   Acetic acid

Similarly, *secondary* alcohols may be readily oxidized to ketones. *Tertiary* alcohols resist the action of many reagents which oxidize primary and secondary alcohols.

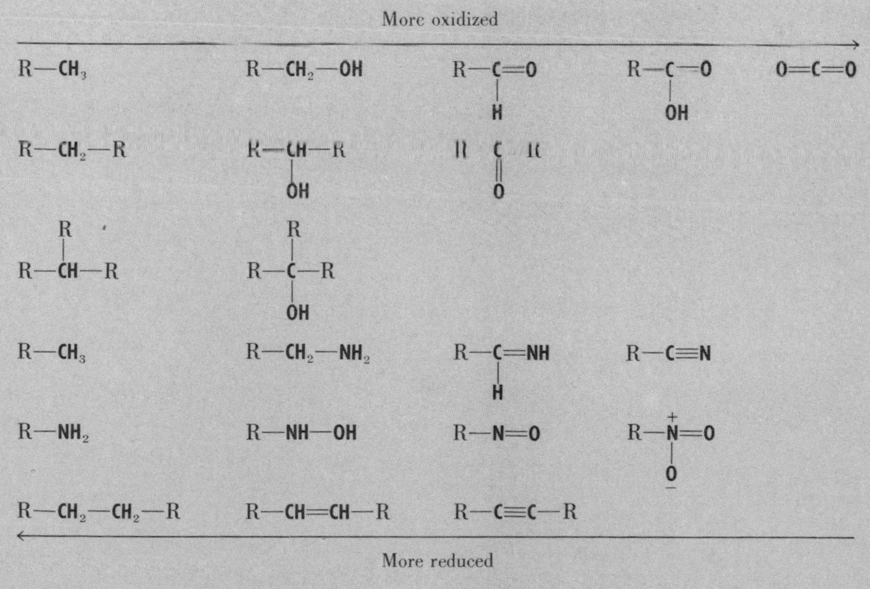

FIG. 4.4   *Relative states of oxidation and reduction.*

$$R-\underset{\underset{OH}{|}}{CH}-R \xrightarrow{[O]} R-\underset{\underset{O}{||}}{C}-R$$

$$C_6H_5\underset{\underset{OH}{|}}{CHCH_3} \xrightarrow[CH_3CO_2H]{CrO_3} C_6H_5\underset{\underset{O}{||}}{CCH_3}$$

α-Phenylethanol   Acetophenone

A number of reducing agents are available which perform tasks opposite to those of oxidizing agents. Hydrogen absorbed on such catalysts as finely divided platinum, palladium, or nickel converts aldehydes and ketones to alcohols.

$$H_2 + RCHO \xrightarrow{Pt} RCH_2OH$$

$$H_2 + CH_3\underset{\underset{CH_3}{|}}{CHCHO} \longrightarrow CH_3\underset{\underset{CH_3}{|}}{CHCH_2OH}$$

Isobutyraldehyde   Isobutyl alcohol

Lithium aluminum hydride (**LiAlH₄**) is perhaps the most versatile of the reducing agents, being capable of converting aldehydes and carboxylic acids to primary alcohols, and ketones to secondary alcohols. No generally successful method has been found of stopping the reduction of carboxylic acids at the aldehyde stage. Mixtures of lithium and aluminum alkoxides are the first reduced products, but these intermediates are not isolated. Instead they are directly converted into alcohols by treatment with dilute aqueous acid. The reductions are usually carried out in diethyl ether as solvent.

$$RCHO \xrightarrow{LiAlH_4} [RCH_2OLi + (RCH_2O)_3Al] \xrightarrow{H_3O^+} RCH_2OH$$

$$C_6H_5CH_2CHO \xrightarrow[2) H_3O^+]{1) LiAlH_4} C_6H_5CH_2CH_2OH$$
Phenylacetaldehyde   β-Phenylethanol

$$RCO_2H \xrightarrow{LiAlH_4} [RCH_2OLi + (RCH_2O)_3Al] \xrightarrow{H_3O^+} RCH_2OH$$

$$CH_3(CH_2)_3CO_2H \xrightarrow[2) H_3O^+]{1) LiAlH_4} CH_3(CH_2)_3CH_2OH$$
Pentanoic acid   1-Pentanol

$$RCOR \xrightarrow{LiAlH_4} [R_2CHOLi + (R_2CHO)_3Al] \xrightarrow{H_3O^+} R_2CHOH$$

$$CH_3\underset{\underset{CH_3}{|}}{CHCOCH_3} \xrightarrow[2) H_3O^+]{1) LiAlH_4} CH_3\underset{\underset{CH_3}{|}}{CHCH}\underset{\underset{OH}{|}}{CHCH_3}$$

3-Methyl-2-butanone   3-Methyl-2-butanol

Amines do not undergo useful oxidation reactions similar to those of alcohols. Amines can be produced from nitriles and amides by reduction of the latter substances with lithium aluminum hydride. The intermediate metal-amine salts are not isolated, but are decomposed with water to give the desired amines. Ether is the usual solvent.

$$RC\equiv N \xrightarrow[\text{2) H}_2\text{O}]{\text{1) LiAlH}_4} RCH_2NH_2$$

$$CH_3CH_2CH_2C\equiv N \xrightarrow[\text{2) H}_2\text{O}]{\text{1) LiAlH}_4} CH_3CH_2CH_2CH_2NH_2$$

$$\left.\begin{array}{l} RCONH_2 \\ RCONHR \\ RCONR_2 \end{array}\right] \xrightarrow[\text{2) H}_2\text{O}]{\text{1) LiAlH}_4} \left[\begin{array}{l} RCH_2NH_2 \\ RCH_2NHR \\ RCH_2NR_2 \end{array}\right.$$

$$CH_3CH_2CON(CH_3)_2 \xrightarrow[\text{2) H}_2\text{O}]{\text{1) LiAlH}_4} CH_3CH_2CH_2N(CH_3)_2$$

N,N-Dimethyl-propionamide · · · · · · · · · · · Dimethyl-*n*-propylamine

Other oxidizing and reducing agents accomplish some of the above reactions and many others, but discussion of them is reserved for Chap. 19.

Acylation. The preparation of esters and amides involves a process termed *acylation*, so called because acyl groups are substituted for hydrogen on substances such as water, alcohols, carboxylic acids, and primary or secondary amines. Acid halides are the most common acylating agents. They are prepared from carboxylic acids as follows:

$$PX_3 + 3\ \overset{\text{O}}{\underset{\|}{RC}}\!\!-\!OH \longrightarrow \overset{\text{O}}{\underset{\|}{RC}}\!\!-\!X + H_3PO_3$$

$$PCl_3 + 3\ \overset{\text{O}}{\underset{\|}{CH_3C}}\!\!-\!OH \longrightarrow 3\ \overset{\text{O}}{\underset{\|}{CH_3C}}\!\!-\!Cl + H_3PO_3$$

Acetic acid · · · · · · · · · Acetyl chloride

The acylation reactions are summarized below in terms of general formulas. Tertiary amines such as pyridine (page 45) catalyze the reactions and neutralize the acid formed (**HX**), but they are not necessary, since in most cases the reaction proceeds readily without catalyst.

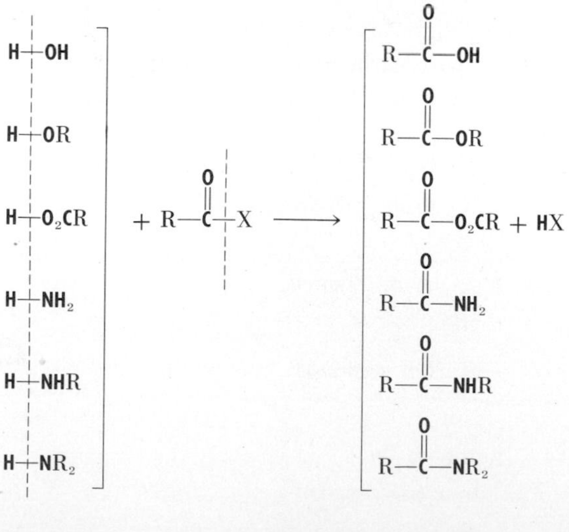

$$\left.\begin{array}{l} H\!-\!OH \\[1ex] H\!-\!OR \\[1ex] H\!-\!O_2CR \\[1ex] H\!-\!NH_2 \\[1ex] H\!-\!NHR \\[1ex] H\!-\!NR_2 \end{array}\right] + R\!-\!\overset{\text{O}}{\underset{\|}{C}}\!-\!X \longrightarrow \left[\begin{array}{l} R\!-\!\overset{\text{O}}{\underset{\|}{C}}\!-\!OH \\[1ex] R\!-\!\overset{\text{O}}{\underset{\|}{C}}\!-\!OR \\[1ex] R\!-\!\overset{\text{O}}{\underset{\|}{C}}\!-\!O_2CR + HX \\[1ex] R\!-\!\overset{\text{O}}{\underset{\|}{C}}\!-\!NH_2 \\[1ex] R\!-\!\overset{\text{O}}{\underset{\|}{C}}\!-\!NHR \\[1ex] R\!-\!\overset{\text{O}}{\underset{\|}{C}}\!-\!NR_2 \end{array}\right.$$

Examples of these important reactions are found in every branch of organic chemistry. Acyl chlorides are the most commonly used acylating agents (see below).

$$\text{H—O—H} + C_6H_5\overset{\overset{\text{O}}{\|}}{C}\text{—Cl} \longrightarrow C_6H_5\overset{\overset{\text{O}}{\|}}{C}\text{—O—H} + HCl$$

Benzoyl   Benzoic
chloride   acid

$$\text{H—O—CH}_2\text{CH}_3 + \text{CH}_3\text{CH}_2\text{CH}_2\overset{\overset{\text{O}}{\|}}{C}\text{—Cl} \longrightarrow \text{CH}_3\text{CH}_2\text{CH}_2\overset{\overset{\text{O}}{\|}}{C}\text{—O—CH}_2\text{CH}_3 + HCl$$

Ethyl   n-Butyryl   Ethyl n-butyrate
alcohol   chloride

$$\text{H—O—}\overset{\overset{\text{O}}{\|}}{C}\text{CH}_3 + \text{CH}_3\overset{\overset{\text{O}}{\|}}{C}\text{—Cl} \longrightarrow \text{CH}_3\overset{\overset{\text{O}}{\|}}{C}\text{—O—}\overset{\overset{\text{O}}{\|}}{C}\text{CH}_3 + HCl$$

Acetic   Acetyl   Acetic
acid   chloride   anhydride

$$2\,\text{H—}\overset{\overset{\text{H}}{|}}{\text{N}}\text{—H} + \text{CH}_3\text{CH}_2\overset{\overset{\text{O}}{\|}}{C}\text{—Cl} \longrightarrow \text{CH}_3\text{CH}_2\overset{\overset{\text{O}}{\|}}{C}\text{—}\overset{\overset{\text{H}}{|}}{\text{N}}\text{—H} + \text{NH}_4\text{Cl}$$

Propionyl   Propionamide
chloride

$$2\,\text{H—}\overset{\overset{\text{H}}{|}}{\text{N}}\text{—CH}_3 + \text{CH}_3\text{CH}_2\underset{\underset{\text{CH}_3}{|}}{\text{CH}}\overset{\overset{\text{O}}{\|}}{C}\text{—Cl} \longrightarrow \text{CH}_3\text{CH}_2\underset{\underset{\text{CH}_3}{|}}{\text{CH}}\overset{\overset{\text{O}}{\|}}{C}\text{—}\overset{\overset{\text{H}}{|}}{\text{N}}\text{—CH}_3 + \text{CH}_3\overset{+}{\text{N}}\text{H}_3\overset{-}{\text{Cl}}$$

Methyl-   α-Methylbutyryl   N-Methyl-α-methyl-
amine   chloride   butyramide

$$2\,\text{H—}\overset{\overset{\text{CH}_3}{|}}{\text{N}}\text{—CH}_3 + \text{CH}_3(\text{CH}_2)_4\overset{\overset{\text{O}}{\|}}{C}\text{—Cl} \longrightarrow \text{CH}_3(\text{CH}_2)_4\overset{\overset{\text{O}}{\|}}{C}\text{—}\overset{\overset{\text{CH}_3}{|}}{\text{N}}\text{—CH}_3 + (\text{CH}_3)_2\overset{+}{\text{N}}\text{H}_2\overset{-}{\text{Cl}}$$

Caproyl chloride   N,N-Dimethyl-
caproamide

Although acid halides are the most vigorous of the acylating agents, anhydrides may also be employed to prepare carboxylic acids, esters, and amides. In general, they perform the same tasks as acid halides, as the following examples indicate.

$$\left.\begin{array}{l}\text{H}\!\!+\!\!\text{OH} \\[1em] \text{H}\!\!+\!\!\text{OR} \\[1em] 2\,\text{H}\!\!+\!\!\text{NH}_2\end{array}\right\} + \text{R}\overset{\overset{\text{O}}{\|}}{C}\!\!+\!\!\text{O}_2\text{CR} \longrightarrow \left[\begin{array}{l}\text{R}\overset{\overset{\text{O}}{\|}}{C}\text{—O—H} + \text{HO}_2\text{CR} \\[1em] \text{R}\overset{\overset{\text{O}}{\|}}{C}\text{—O—R} + \text{HO}_2\text{CR} \\[1em] \text{R}\overset{\overset{\text{O}}{\|}}{C}\text{—NH}_2 + \overset{+}{\text{N}}\text{H}_4\overset{-}{\text{O}}_2\text{CR}\end{array}\right.$$

$$\text{H—O—H} + \text{CH}_3\overset{\overset{\text{O}}{\|}}{C}\text{—O—}\overset{\overset{\text{O}}{\|}}{C}\text{CH}_3 \longrightarrow 2\,\text{CH}_3\overset{\overset{\text{O}}{\|}}{C}\text{—O—H}$$

Acetic anhydride   Acetic acid

$$H-O-CH_3 + C_6H_5\overset{O}{\overset{\|}{C}}-O-\overset{O}{\overset{\|}{C}}C_6H_5 \longrightarrow C_6H_5\overset{O}{\overset{\|}{C}}-O-CH_3 + C_6H_5\overset{O}{\overset{\|}{C}}-O-H$$

Benzoic   Methyl   Benzoic
anhydride   benzoate   acid

$$2\ H-\overset{H}{\underset{|}{N}}-H + CH_3\overset{O}{\overset{\|}{C}}-O-\overset{O}{\overset{\|}{C}}CH_3 \longrightarrow CH_3\overset{O}{\overset{\|}{C}}-NH_2 + \overset{+}{NH_4}\overset{-}{O_2}CCH_3$$

Acetic   Acetamide   Ammonium
anhydride   acetate

Even esters are acylating agents for such materials as water and ammonia, although acidic or basic catalysts are usually needed to make the reaction occur in a reasonable amount of time.

$$\begin{bmatrix} H\!\!+\!\!OH \\ \\ H\!\!+\!\!NH_2 \end{bmatrix} + R\overset{O}{\overset{\|}{C}}\!\!+\!\!OR \longrightarrow \begin{bmatrix} R\overset{O}{\overset{\|}{C}}-O-H + HOR \\ \\ R\overset{O}{\overset{\|}{C}}-NH_2 + HOR \end{bmatrix}$$

The only acylation reactions which amides are capable of performing involve water as the other reagent, and the reaction occurs only in the presence of strong acids or bases.

$$H-O-H + \begin{bmatrix} R\overset{O}{\overset{\|}{C}}-NH_2 \\ R\overset{O}{\overset{\|}{C}}-NHR \\ R\overset{O}{\overset{\|}{C}}-NR_2 \end{bmatrix} \xrightarrow{HCl} R\overset{O}{\overset{\|}{C}}-O-H + \begin{bmatrix} H-NH_2 \\ H-NHR \\ H-NR_2 \end{bmatrix}$$

$$H-O-H + CH_3(CH_2)_3\overset{O}{\overset{\|}{C}}-\overset{H}{\underset{|}{N}}-CH_3 \xrightarrow{HCl} CH_3(CH_2)_3\overset{O}{\overset{\|}{C}}-O-H + H-\overset{H}{\underset{|}{N}}-CH_3$$

N-Methyl-*n*-valeramide   *n*-Valeric acid   Methylamine

An inspection of the above acylation reactions indicates that the various classes of compounds involved can be arranged in decreasing order of their power as acylating agents. Thus any class of compound in the following series can be used directly in the preparation of any class to the right of it.

$$R\overset{O}{\overset{\|}{C}}X > R\overset{O}{\overset{\|}{C}}O\overset{O}{\overset{\|}{C}}R > R\overset{O}{\overset{\|}{C}}OR > R\overset{O}{\overset{\|}{C}}N\overset{a}{\underset{b}{<}} > R\overset{O}{\overset{\|}{C}}OH > R\overset{O}{\overset{\|}{C}}O \qquad a \text{ and } b = \text{H, R, or Ar}$$

These reactions are frequently classified in other ways, attention being focused on the compound undergoing acylation. Thus a reaction involving water as a reactant is called *hydrolysis*, one with an alcohol, *alcoholysis*, one with ammonia, *ammonolysis*. The reaction leading to the formation of esters is called *esterification*. In certain special cases, usually with natural fats, the alkaline hydrolysis of an ester yields a soap. Thus the special term *saponification* indicates hydrolysis of esters under alkaline conditions.

$$3NaOH + \begin{matrix} CH_2O_2C(CH_2)_nCH_3 \\ CHO_2C(CH_2)_nCH_3 \\ CH_2O_2C(CH_2)_nCH_3 \end{matrix} \longrightarrow \begin{matrix} CH_2OH \\ CHOH \\ CH_2OH \end{matrix} + 3NaO_2C(CH_2)_nCH_3$$

A fat ($n = 14$ or 16)   Glycerol   A soap

Addition. Addition of the elements of water to triple bonds provides a means of preparing two of the classes of compounds considered in this chapter. Nitriles react with water (hydrolysis) in the presence of a strong acid or base to give first an amide, which can then be either isolated or converted directly to the carboxylic acid. In the first reaction, the two hydrogen atoms of water become bonded to nitrogen, and the oxygen to carbon.

$$H_2O + RC{\equiv}N \xrightarrow{\text{Acid}} RC\overset{\overset{\displaystyle O}{\|}}{}—NH_2$$

$$H_2O + CH_3CH_2CH_2C{\equiv}N \xrightarrow{\text{Acid}} CH_3CH_2CH_2C\overset{\overset{\displaystyle O}{\|}}{}—NH_2$$

n-Butyronitrile n-Butyramide

Acetylenes add water in very much the same way. Two hydrogen atoms go to one carbon and oxygen to the other to produce a carbonyl group. The reaction is catalyzed by sulfuric acid and mercuric sulfate. When one of the carbon atoms of the acetylene function carries hydrogen and the other does not, the two hydrogen atoms of water add to the carbon already possessing hydrogen. This selectivity provides another example of Markownikoff's rule, which was originally formulated to predict the sites of addition of the elements of water to unsymmetrical alkenes (page 50). Only acetylene itself gives an aldehyde. Substituted acetylenes always become ketones, as may be seen from the following examples.

$$H_2O + RC{\equiv}CH \xrightarrow[\text{HgSO}_4]{\text{H}_2\text{SO}_4} RCCH_3 \ \ (\overset{\displaystyle O}{\|})$$

$$H_2O + HC{\equiv}CH \xrightarrow[\text{HgSO}_4]{\text{H}_2\text{SO}_4} CH_3CH \ \ (\overset{\displaystyle O}{\|})$$

Acetylene   Acetaldehyde

$$H_2O + CH_3C{\equiv}CH \xrightarrow[\text{HgSO}_4]{\text{H}_2\text{SO}_4} CH_3CCH_3 \ \ (\overset{\displaystyle O}{\|})$$

Methyl acetylene   Acetone

Methods of Extending Carbon Chains. The reactions considered thus far have involved the conversion of different classes of compounds into one another without any changes in the carbon chains. An exception was the ozonization reaction in which carbon chains were degraded (page 29). In this section, a few methods of building carbon skeletons are discussed. This kind of operation is of great importance in synthesizing organic compounds, as will be demonstrated in the next section.

One of the simplest methods of extending a carbon chain by one carbon involves the reaction of an alkyl halide with potassium cyanide to give a nitrile.

$$KC\equiv N + R-X \longrightarrow R-C\equiv N + KX$$

$$KCN + CH_3CH_2Br \longrightarrow CH_3CH_2CN$$

      Ethyl   Propionitrile
      bromide

Since nitriles can be converted to amines (reduction) or to amides or carboxylic acids (hydrolysis), the cyanide reaction provides a route for converting alkyl halides to a number of classes of compounds containing one more carbon atom.

Perhaps the most versatile reactions for constructing carbon skeletons involve *Grignard reagents* (page 48), and are thus known as Grignard reactions. Grignard reagents are prepared from alkyl halides and magnesium in dry ether solution, and *they react with all classes of compounds* except hydrocarbons, ethers, and *tertiary* amines. The reagents are not ordinarily isolated or stored, but are used directly to effect the desired transformation. The preparation of a number of typical Grignard reagents is illustrated.

$$Mg + R-X \xrightarrow{\text{Ether}} R-Mg-X$$

$$Mg + Ar-X \xrightarrow{\text{Ether}} Ar-Mg-X$$

$$Mg + CH_3Cl \xrightarrow{\text{Ether}} CH_3MgCl$$

      Methyl   Methylmagnesium
      chloride   chloride

$$Mg + (CH_3)_2CHBr \xrightarrow{\text{Ether}} (CH_3)_2CHMgBr$$

      Isopropyl   Isopropylmagnesium
      bromide   bromide

$$Mg + C_6H_5Br \xrightarrow{\text{Ether}} C_6H_5MgBr$$

   Bromobenzene   Phenylmagnesium
              bromide

A few reactions involve the addition of Grignard reagents to carbonyl groups. These reactions bear a formal resemblance to the reaction of lithium aluminum hydride with carbonyl groups, except that alkyl or aryl groups in the Grignard reagents are the counterpart of hydrogen in the metal hydride.

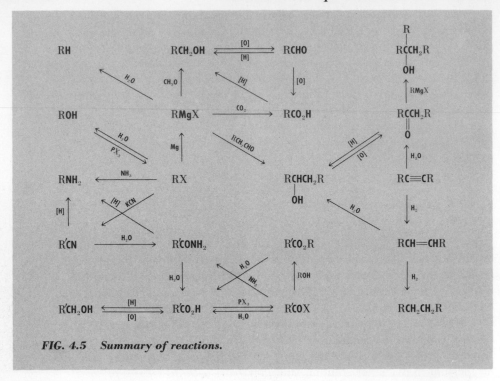

FIG. 4.5   Summary of reactions.

The first product of reaction of a Grignard reagent with a carbonyl-containing compound is a magnesium salt, which is not ordinarily isolated, but is converted directly to the desired organic compound by treatment of the salt with dilute aqueous acid.   The procedure is illustrated by the reaction of phenylmagnesium bromide with the carbonyl group of carbon dioxide.   The final product is benzoic acid.

$$O{=}C{=}O + C_6H_5MgBr \longrightarrow C_6H_5\overset{\displaystyle O}{\overset{\|}{C}}{-}O{-}MgBr$$

Phenylmagnesium
bromide

$$HCl + C_6H_5\overset{\displaystyle O}{\overset{\|}{C}}{-}O{-}MgBr \longrightarrow C_6H_5\overset{\displaystyle O}{\overset{\|}{C}}{-}O{-}H + MgBrCl$$

Benzoic
acid

Perhaps the most important Grignard reactions are those with the carbonyl groups of aldehydes and ketones.   By appropriate choice of aldehyde or ketone, *primary*, *secondary*, or *tertiary* alcohols may be produced.   Thus formaldehyde leads to a *primary*, other aldehydes to *secondary*, and ketones to *tertiary* alcohols.   These reactions are illustrated as follows:

$$CH_2=O + R-MgX \xrightarrow{Ether} R-CH_2-O-MgX \xrightarrow{H_3O^+} R-CH_2-OH$$

Primary alcohol

$$CH_2=O + CH_3CH_2MgCl \xrightarrow{Ether} CH_3CH_2CH_2OMgX \xrightarrow{H_3O^+} CH_3CH_2CH_2OH$$

Ethylmagnesium
chloride

n-Propyl alcohol

$$R-CH=O + R-MgX \xrightarrow{Ether} \overset{R}{\underset{|}{R-CH-O-MgX}} \xrightarrow{H_3O^+} \overset{R}{\underset{|}{R-CH-OH}}$$

Secondary alcohol

$$CH_3CH=O + CH_3CH_2CH_2MgBr \xrightarrow{Ether} \overset{OMgBr}{\underset{|}{CH_3CHCH_2CH_2CH_3}} \xrightarrow{H_3O^+} \overset{OH}{\underset{|}{CH_3CHCH_2CH_2CH_3}}$$

n-Propylmagnesium
bromide

2-Pentanol

$$\overset{}{\underset{O}{R-\overset{||}{C}-R}} + R-MgX \xrightarrow{Ether} \overset{R}{\underset{O-MgX}{R-\overset{|}{\underset{|}{C}}-R}} \xrightarrow{H_3O^+} \overset{R}{\underset{OH}{R-\overset{|}{\underset{|}{C}}-R}}$$

Tertiary alcohol

$$\overset{}{\underset{O}{CH_3\overset{||}{C}CH_3}} + C_6H_5MgX \xrightarrow{Ether} \overset{C_6H_5}{\underset{OMgX}{CH_3\overset{|}{\underset{|}{C}}CH_3}} \xrightarrow{H_3O^+} \overset{C_6H_5}{\underset{OH}{CH_3\overset{|}{\underset{|}{C}}CH_3}}$$

Acetone   Phenyl-
magnesium
bromide

2-Phenyl-2-
propanol

In Fig. 4.5 are summarized the reactions developed thus far which are useful in synthesis.

Synthesis

One of the most important tasks of the organic chemist is the design of synthetic sequences which will lead to desired compounds from available substances as starting materials. These sequences may contain 2 to 30 or more discrete reactions, each of which plays a distinct role in the construction of the final product. Enough reactions have now been introduced to allow simple problems in synthesis to be solved. This section is devoted to the technique of dealing with such problems.

Design of a synthetic scheme usually involves two interlocking problems, the construction of the desired carbon skeleton and the placing of functional groups at the proper positions on the skeleton. Usually carbon skeletons are made by combining two simpler units. Thus far, five such reactions useful in synthesis have been given. They are summarized in the following equations.

(1) $KCN + RX \longrightarrow RCN + KX$

(2) $CO_2 + RMgX \xrightarrow[\text{2) } H_3O^+]{\text{1) Ether}} RCO_2H$

(3) $CH_2O + RMgX \xrightarrow[\text{2) } H_3O^+]{\text{1) Ether}} RCH_2OH$

(4) $RCHO + RMgX \xrightarrow[\text{2) } H_3O^+]{\text{1) Ether}} RCHOHR$

(5) 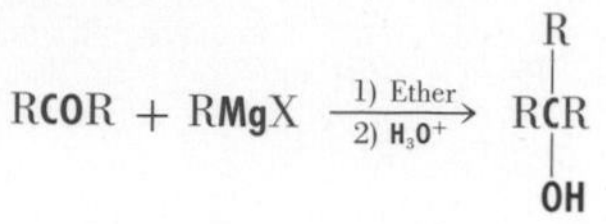 $RCOR + RMgX \xrightarrow[\text{2) } H_3O^+]{\text{1) Ether}} \underset{\underset{OH}{|}}{R}\overset{\overset{R}{|}}{C}R$

Among these reactions, (1), (2), and (3) increase a chain by one carbon, and (4) and (5) by a number depending on the character of R. As written, only (5) would appear to give a branched carbon skeleton, but the other four reactions are also capable of leading from an unbranched to a branched structure by the use of the proper halide as starting material, as is shown in the examples.

$KCN + (CH_3)_2CHBr \longrightarrow (CH_3)_2CHCN + KBr$

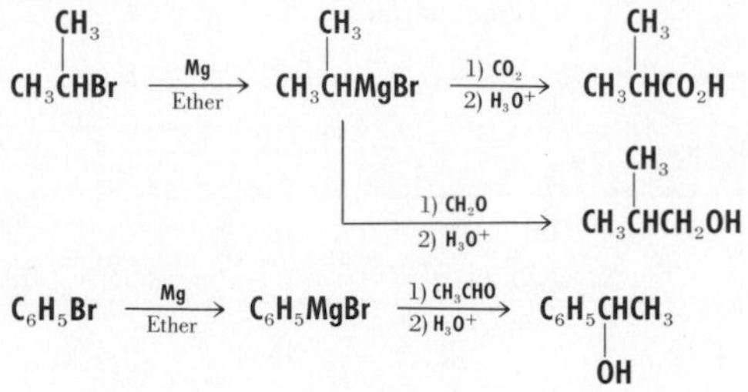

$CH_3\overset{\overset{CH_3}{|}}{C}HBr \xrightarrow[\text{Ether}]{Mg} CH_3\overset{\overset{CH_3}{|}}{C}HMgBr \xrightarrow[\text{2) } H_3O^+]{\text{1) } CO_2} CH_3\overset{\overset{CH_3}{|}}{C}HCO_2H$

$\xrightarrow[\text{2) } H_3O^+]{\text{1) } CH_2O} CH_3\overset{\overset{CH_3}{|}}{C}HCH_2OH$

$C_6H_5Br \xrightarrow[\text{Ether}]{Mg} C_6H_5MgBr \xrightarrow[\text{2) } H_3O^+]{\text{1) } CH_3CHO} C_6H_5\underset{\underset{OH}{|}}{C}HCH_3$

If a chain needs to be extended by two units and yet the desired product must contain a terminal function, two reactions can be used in tandem, for instance (3) and then (2), as in the following example.

$RX \xrightarrow{Mg} RMgX \xrightarrow[\text{2) } H_3O^+]{\text{1) } CH_2O} RCH_2OH \xrightarrow{PX_3} RCH_2X \xrightarrow{Mg} RCH_2MgX \xrightarrow[\text{2) } H_3O^+]{\text{1) } CO_2} RCH_2CO_2H$

In other syntheses, two skeletons have to be constructed separately and then combined. The synthesis of 3-hexanol from any one- or two-carbon starting materials is a problem whose solution requires such an operation. The synthesis might be carried out as follows:

(6) $CH_3CH_2Br \xrightarrow[\text{Ether}]{Mg} CH_3CH_2MgBr \xrightarrow[\text{2) } H_3O^+]{\text{1) } CH_2O} CH_3CH_2CH_2OH$

n-Propyl alcohol

(7) $CH_3CH_2CH_2OH \xrightarrow{PBr_3} CH_3CH_2CH_2Br \xrightarrow[\text{Ether}]{Mg} CH_3CH_2CH_2MgBr$

n-Propyl n-Propyl n-Propylmagnesium
alcohol   bromide   bromide

(8) $CH_3CH_2CH_2OH \xrightarrow{H_2CrO_4} CH_3CH_2CHO$

n-Propyl   Propion-
alcohol   aldehyde

(9) $CH_3CH_2CHO + CH_3CH_2CH_2MgBr \xrightarrow[\text{2) H}_3\text{O}^+]{\text{1) Ether}} CH_3CH_2CHCH_2CH_2CH_3$
$$\underset{\displaystyle OH}{|}$$

Propion-   *n*-Propylmagnesium   3-Hexanol
aldehyde   bromide

In the design of such a synthesis, the following steps are involved. As the product contains six carbon atoms with a function on carbon 3, the final step in the synthesis will probably be the combining of two three-carbon chains. Since 3-hexanol is a secondary alcohol, general reaction (4) would appear to satisfy the essential requirements: that of building the chain and that of putting the right function in the right place in the product. Translated into the needed structures, reaction (4) becomes reaction (9). The problem is now that of preparing propionaldehyde and *n*-propylmagnesium bromide from one- and two-carbon starting materials. Both substances can be prepared from *n*-propyl alcohol, the former by oxidation as shown in reaction (8), the latter by (7). The last step is to prepare *n*-propyl alcohol from simpler units, which can be accomplished by sequence (6). The solution to this problem illustrates the importance of *working from the final step back by stages to the structures of the initial starting materials.*

Frequently the final steps in a synthesis involve the creation of the desired functional group from one which is obtained from the chain-lengthening operation. The solution of the following problem illustrates such a procedure.

Suppose that 2-methylbutane has to be prepared from inorganic starting materials.

$$\text{Inorganic compounds} \longrightarrow CH_3CH_2\underset{\displaystyle CH_3}{\overset{\displaystyle CH_3}{|}}CHCH_3$$

2-Methylbutane

The only organic compounds that have been prepared directly from inorganic starting materials thus far are methanol and acetylene (page 53); these, therefore, are the organic materials available.

$$H_2 + CO \xrightarrow[450°]{\text{Cat.}} CH_3OH$$

$$CaO + 3C \xrightarrow{3000°} CaC_2 + CO$$

$$H_2O + CaC_2 \longrightarrow HC\equiv CH + CaO$$

Only two of the reactions given so far lead to saturated hydrocarbons: reduction of alkenes and treatment of Grignard reagents with water (see Fig. 4.5). The latter seems the more promising reaction because the desired compound contains a branched skeleton such as can be constructed by Grignard reactions, most of which give alcoholic products. Alcohols may readily be converted to halides, and halides to Grignard reagents. Thus any of the following alcohols (I–IV) could be converted to the desired product.

$$
\begin{array}{cccc}
\quad\ CH_3 & \quad\ CH_3 & \quad\ CH_3 & \quad\ CH_3 \\
HOCH_2CH_2CHCH_3 & CH_3CHCHCH_3 & CH_3CH_2CCH_3 & CH_3CH_2CHCH_2OH \\
 & \ \ \ \ OH & \ \ \ \ OH & \\
\ \ \ \ \text{I} & \ \ \ \ \text{II} & \ \ \ \ \text{III} & \ \ \ \ \text{IV}
\end{array}
$$

These alcohols may all be prepared through the use of the proper Grignard reaction [(3), (4), or (5)]. Thus the question becomes one of deciding which starting materials for the Grignard reaction are the easiest to prepare from acetylene and methanol. All the alcohols contain five carbon atoms, and in principle can be constructed from two two-carbon and one one-carbon pieces. In practice, only alcohols II, III, and IV can be so prepared, as can be seen by detailed examination of their structures.

(10) $CH_3CHO \xrightarrow[\text{2) H}_3\text{O}^+]{\text{1) CH}_3\text{CH}_2\text{MgBr}} CH_3CH_2CHCH_3 \xrightarrow{\text{PBr}_3} CH_3CH_2CHCH_3 \xrightarrow[\text{Ether}]{\text{Mg}}$
 with OH below first, Br below second

$CH_3CH_2CHMgBr \xrightarrow[\text{2) H}_3\text{O}^+]{\text{1) CH}_2\text{O}} CH_3CH_2CHCH_2OH$ IV
(with CH₃ groups above)

(11) $CH_3CHO \xrightarrow[\text{2) H}_3\text{O}^+]{\text{1) CH}_3\text{CH}_2\text{MgBr}} CH_3CH_2CHCH_3 \xrightarrow{[O]} CH_3CH_2CCH_3 \xrightarrow[\text{2) H}_3\text{O}^+]{\text{1) CH}_3\text{MgBr}} CH_3CH_2CCH_3$ III
(OH, O, OH below respectively; CH₃ above last)

(12) $CH_3CHO \xrightarrow[\text{2) H}_3\text{O}^+]{\text{1) CH}_3\text{MgBr}} CH_3CHOH \xrightarrow{\text{PBr}_3} CH_3CHBr \xrightarrow{\text{Mg}} CH_3CHMgBr \xrightarrow[\text{2) H}_3\text{O}^+]{\text{1) CH}_3\text{CHO}} CH_3CHCHCH_3$ II
(with CH₃ above each; OH below last)

In these sequences, (10) involves CH_3CHO, CH_2O, and CH_3CH_2Br as starting materials, (11) CH_3CHO, CH_3CH_2Br, and CH_3Br, and (12) only CH_3CHO and CH_3Br. Although any of the sequences are feasible, the last is the simplest, since CH_3CHO can be readily made from acetylene, and CH_3Br from methanol. The total synthesis starting from acetylene and methanol is now summarized as follows:

$CH_3OH \xrightarrow{\text{PBr}_3} CH_3Br \xrightarrow[\text{Ether}]{\text{Mg}} CH_3MgBr$

$HC\equiv CH \xrightarrow[\text{HgSO}_4]{\text{H}_2\text{O}\ \text{H}_2\text{SO}_4} CH_3CHO \xrightarrow[\text{2) H}_3\text{O}^+]{\text{1) CH}_3\text{MgBr}} CH_3CHOH \xrightarrow{\text{PBr}_3} CH_3CHBr \xrightarrow[\text{Ether}]{\text{Mg}} CH_3CHMgBr \xrightarrow[\text{2) H}_3\text{O}^+]{\text{1) CH}_3\text{CHO}}$
(CH₃ above CHOH, CHBr, CHMgBr)

$CH_3CHCHCH_3 \xrightarrow{\text{PBr}_3} CH_3CHCHCH_3 \xrightarrow[\text{Ether}]{\text{Mg}} CH_3CHCHCH_3 \xrightarrow{\text{H}_2\text{O}} CH_3CHCH_2CH_3$
(CH₃ above each; OH, Br, MgBr below respectively)

2-Methylbutane

The above problem illustrates the fact that usually several syntheses are possible, and often two are equally good. In solving the problems in the next section, the summary of reactions found in Fig. 4.5 may be helpful.

Problems

1. Name the following compounds in as many ways as you can:

a. $CH_3CH_2CHCO_2H$
  |
  NH_2

h. $(CH_3)_2C{=}CHCHCH_2CO_2H$
  |
  Cl

o.

b. $CH_3CHCCH_2CH_3$
  | ‖
  CH_3 O

i. $CH_3CH(CH_2)_4CONHC_6H_5$
  |
  CH_3

c. $HO_2C(CH_2)_6CO_2H$

j.

p.

d.

k. $CH_3CHCH_2CO_2CH_3$
  |
  Cl

q. $C_6H_5CCH_2CC_6H_5$
       ‖   ‖
       O O

e. $CH_3CHCHCHO$
  |
  CH_3
  |
  I

l. $C_6H_5CH_2CH_2CO_2CHCH_2CH_3$
                        |
                        CH_3

r $CH_3CH_2NC_6H_5$
  |
  CH_3
  ‖
  O

f. $CH_3CH_2CHOCCH(CH_3)_2$
  | ‖
  CH_3 O

m.
$-CH_2CO_2H$

s.

g. $CH_3CH{=}CHCCH_2CH_3$
              ‖‖
              OO

n. $CH_3CH_2CHCH_2CN$
  |
  CH_3

t. $CH_3C{=}CHCH_2CO_2H$
  |
  CH_3

u. $(CH_3)_3CCC(CH_3)_3$
           ‖
           O

2. Write structures for the following compounds:

a. *p*-Chlorobenzoic acid
b. *tert*-Butyl cyclohexyl ketone
c. Dibenzoylmethane
d. Hexamethylacetone
e. 2-Butyl 4-methylpentanoate

f. 3-Carbethoxycyclobutene
g. α-Methyl-β-aminobutyric acid
h. 4-Methoxy-2-butenoic acid
i. *N*-Methyl-*N*-phenylacetamide
j. 2,4,6-Trichlorononanonitrile

3. Write structures for compounds that belong in the following classes:

a. A β,γ-unsaturated δ-lactone
b. A cyclic unsaturated anhydride
c. An amide of a secondary amine
d. An acyl fluoride
e. An *N*-substituted γ-lactam
f. An α-ketoacid
g. The oxime of an aromatic ketone

h. A γ-diketone
i. A hydrazone
j. An alcohol which resists the action
   of mild oxidizing agents
k. An imide
l. An *N*-substituted urea
m. A semicarbazone

4. Write structural formulas for all compounds possessing the following molecular formulas.

a. $C_4H_8O_2$ b. C_3H_9N c. C_4H_7Cl d. $C_3H_7NO_2$

5. With formulas of specific compounds, write out sequences of reactions for the following conversions:

    a.   An alkene to an aldehyde
    b.   An acetylene to a carboxylic acid
    c.   An aldehyde to an amide
    d.   An alcohol to an *N*-substituted amide
    e.   An alcohol to an ester
    f.   An alkyl halide to a primary amine with one more carbon
    g.   A secondary amine and an acid to a tertiary amine
    h.   An alcohol to an alcohol containing two more carbon atoms
    i.   A ketone to an amine
    j.   A cyclic alkene to a dicarboxylic acid
    k.   A primary alcohol to a ketone
    l.   A primary alcohol to a tertiary alcohol
    m.   A secondary alcohol to a branched carboxylic acid
    n.   An unbranched alcohol to a branched hydrocarbon

6. Write out syntheses of the following compounds from only inorganic starting materials:

a. Ethylamine	*e.* Methyl butyrate	*i.* Propionic anhydride
b. *N*-Ethylacetamide	*f.* α-Methylbutyric acid	*j.* Ethyl methyl ketone
c. *n*-Propyl alcohol	*g.* *n*-Butane	*k.* 3-Methylbutanal
d. *N*-Propylpropionamide	*h.* Diisopropyl ether	*l.* *tert*-Butyl alcohol

7. Write out syntheses of the following compounds from benzene, any other organic compound containing one or two carbon atoms, and any inorganic materials.

a. Benzyl alcohol	*e.* 3-Methyl-3-pentanol	*h.* 3-Phenylpropylamine
b. α-Phenylethanol	*f.* Benzyldimethylamine	*i.* Isopropyl butyrate
c. β-Phenylethanol	*g.* *n*-Butyl isopropyl ketone	*j.* 3-Methylpentanoic acid
d. Triethylcarbinol		

8. Identify the sites of unsaturation in each of the following compounds:

a. 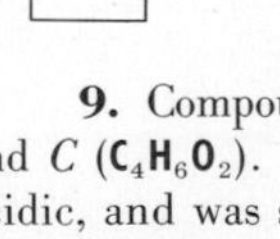   (benzene ring)—CHO

b. $CH_3CH{=}CHCO_2H$

c. 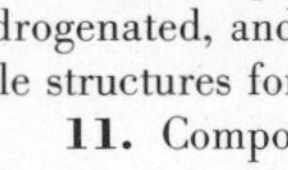   (cyclopentane ring)—$CONH_2$

d. $CH_3C{\equiv}CCN$

e. 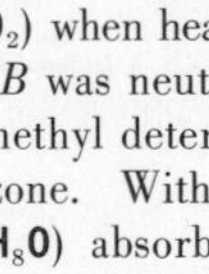 $\begin{array}{c} CH_2{-}C{<}^{O}_{O} \\ | \qquad \\ CH_2{-}C{<}^{O}_{O} \end{array}$

f. $C_6H_5CH{=}NOH$

g. 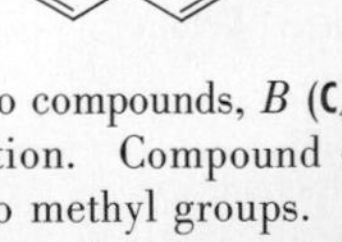 $CH_3{-}CH{-}CH_2$ with $CH_2{-}C{<}^{O}_{O}$ ring forming an anhydride

h. 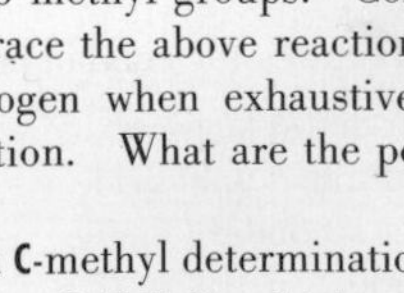   (naphthalene ring)—$\overset{O}{\overset{\|}{C}}$—$CO_2H$

9. Compound *A* ($C_8H_{14}O_2$) when heated with water gave two compounds, *B* ($C_4H_{10}O$) and *C* ($C_4H_6O_2$). Compound *B* was neutral and resisted oxidation. Compound *C* was acidic, and was shown by C-methyl determination to contain no methyl groups. Compound *C* did not react with ozone. With structural formulas, trace the above reactions.

10. Compound *A* (C_5H_8O) absorbed one mole of hydrogen when exhaustively hydrogenated, and gave no acetic acid in a C-methyl determination. What are the possible structures for *A*?

11. Compound *A* (C_4H_6) gave 0.90 mole of acetic acid in a C-methyl determination. When treated with dilute sulfuric acid and mercuric sulfate, *A* gave *B* (C_4H_8O), which gave 1.8 moles of acetic acid in a C-methyl determination. With structural formulas, trace the above reactions.

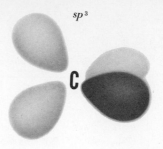

*sp*³

5

Character of the Chemical Bond

In preceding chapters, the ball-and-stick model has been sufficient for specifying which atoms in molecules are bonded to one another. No inquiry was made into the nature of bonding forces or concerning bond lengths, bond angles, bond strengths, rotation about bonds, and subsidiary problems. This and the next chapter are concerned with these problems, and with the more refined concepts of molecular structure required for their solution. Since bonds are composed of electrons, and electrons are subatomic particles, this inquiry must start with atomic structure.

Atomic Structure

The principal tenets of the commonly accepted theory of atomic structure are ordinarily introduced in courses in general chemistry. All atoms consist of positively charged nuclei, which carry nearly all the mass of the atom. Near the nuclei are negative electrons in sufficient number to render the atom neutral as a whole. The number of electrons in a particular element is equal to the atomic number of that element. Hydrogen has a nucleus with a single positive charge (the proton) and a single electron. Helium has a doubly charged nucleus and two external electrons, and so on. Electrons in larger atoms are not all equivalent. A great deal of energy is required to remove an electron from helium, but lithium contains *one* electron that is lost much more easily.

Electrons in atoms may be arranged in groups, or "shells." The first two electrons make up the first shell, which is complete in the very stable helium atom. Eight electrons are needed to fill the second shell, which is complete in the second inert gas, neon. The electrons in incomplete shells are called *valence electrons*, since they are responsible for

TABLE 5.1   *Electronic Structures of Elements*

Element		1st electronic shell	2nd electronic shell			
Element	Representation	$1s$	$2s$	$2p_x$	$2p_y$	$2p_z$
H	+1	↓†				
He	+2	↑ ↓				
Li	+3	↑ ↓	↓			
Be	+4	↑ ↓	↑ ↓			
B	+5	↑ ↓	↑ ↓	↓		

† Arrows indicate sense of the electron spin.

TABLE 5.1   *Electronic Structures of Elements* (Continued)

Element		1st electronic shell	2nd electronic shell			
Element	Representation	1s	2s	$2p_x$	$2p_y$	$2p_z$
C	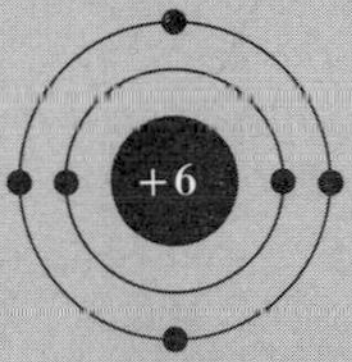 +6	↑ ↓	↑ ↓	↓	↓	
N	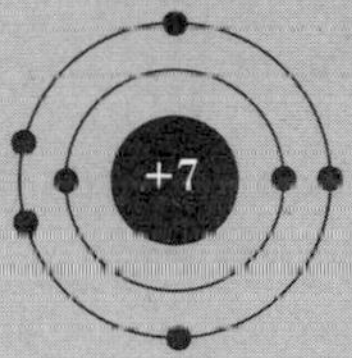 +7	↑ ↓	↑ ↓	↓	↓	↓
O	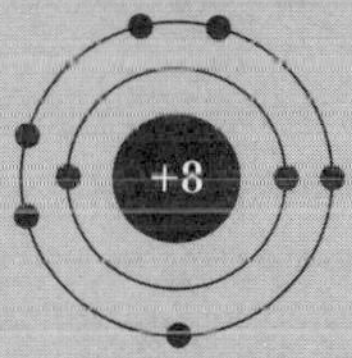 +8	↑ ↓	↑ ↓	↑ ↓	↓	↓
F	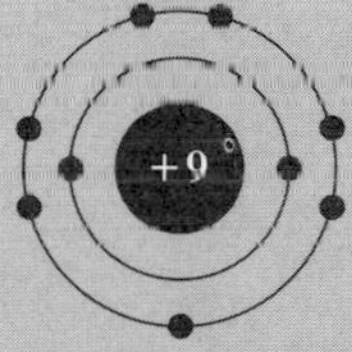 +9	↑ ↓	↑ ↓	↑ ↓	↑ ↓	↓
Ne	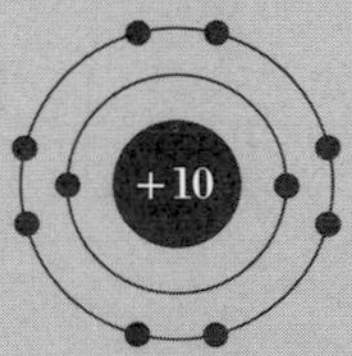 +10	↑ ↓	↑ ↓	↑ ↓	↑ ↓	↑ ↓

chemical properties. The electronic structures of the first 10 elements are summarized in Table 5.1.

Although electrons are strongly attracted to a particular nucleus, they may also interact with other nuclei which are close by. Simultaneous interaction of electrons with *two or more* nuclei gives rise to chemical bonding.

Electrons may in effect be weighed and their energies measured, but their motions cannot be described in detail. This limitation grows out of what is known as the *uncertainty principle,* which states in mathematical language that *one cannot simultaneously know the position of an electron and its energy.* Because of the low mass of an electron, the act of observing it directly disturbs its normal behavior. The principles of classical mechanics cannot be applied to electrons, whose behavior has to be described by the equations of *wave mechanics.* This description takes account of the properties of electrons which resemble those of light rays. Equations of wave mechanics successfully account for many facts concerning electrons, such as their tendency to pair and to have energies dependent on their relative positions in atoms and molecules. Although only the hydrogen atom is completely described mathematically in precise terms, more complex structures may be discussed either with more approximate mathematical methods or with purely qualitative arguments based on analogy to mathematical procedures. This qualitative approach is useful in understanding the structure and reactivity of organic molecules.

Electrons as Bonding Forces. Whenever an electron is close enough to two positive nuclei to be attracted to both at the same time, the electron is bonding the two nuclei. Unless the bonding force is more than offset by repulsion of the electron by other electrons in the vicinity, the net effect will be establishment of a bond. Since electrons can become paired without creation of large repulsive forces, it is reasonable to expect that two electrons produce a stronger bond than one electron. Such is the case in a hydrogen molecule, where a two-electron bond holds two protons at an approximately fixed distance from each other. However, wave mechanics states that this electron pair cannot be localized between the two nuclei. Actually, the electrons spend most of their time in a volume which fits like a capsule around the two nuclei and the intervening space. Electrons may also be described as clouds of negative charge. In the hydrogen molecule, the cloud would be thick near and between the two nuclei, but diffuse at greater distances. Use of a dash to indicate a bond (an electron pair) is a matter of convenience; the dash is in no sense pictorial. Figure 5.1 shows three ways of representing the hydrogen molecule.

FIG. 5.1   *Representations of the hydrogen molecule.*

Just before World War I, Lewis noted that the old rules of valence could be derived from an *electronic theory of valence*. Main ingredients in the theory were recognition of the obviously stable electronic configurations of the rare gases, the principles of electron pairing, and the sharing of pairs of electrons by two nuclei. These notions have been used in the first four chapters in descriptions of structures of organic molecules. A more sophisticated description is needed if the behavior of organic compounds is to be understood, and such a description is now introduced.

Polar Bonds. Many bonds are electrically asymmetric. That is, the electrons are somewhat more associated with one of the two nuclei which they are bonding. Thus hydrogen fluoride molecules become highly oriented when placed in an electric field. Since the fluorine atom has a high affinity for electrons, the bonding electron cloud is concentrated near this element, as indicated in Fig. 5.2.

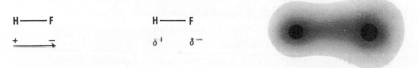

FIG. 5.2   *Representations of the polarity of the hydrogen-fluorine bond.*

Ionization. Intensely polar molecules have a tendency to ionize when dissolved in *polar solvents* (Chap. 7) or when packed in crystals. Salts are prime examples, and the general character of such substances is described as *saltlike*. In lithium fluoride, *complete removal* of an electron from lithium leaves the lithium ion with a stable valence shell of two (helium structure) and gives the fluoride ion a shell of eight electrons (neon structure).

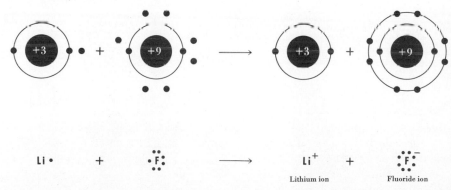

Although lithium and fluorine are bonded in a molecule of lithium fluoride in the gas phase, the bond is so polar as to render the molecule essentially a pair of ions. Very polar bonds are said to possess much *ionic character*. Nonpolar bonds are called *covalent*, a term that implies equal sharing of an electron-pair bond by two nuclei.

Resonance

Many molecules and ions are not completely described by simple electronic structures. The carbonate ion $(CO_3^=)$ may serve as an example.

Trial structure I features the valence electrons of one carbon and three oxygen atoms and the two electrons taken from external nuclei that give the ion its two charges.

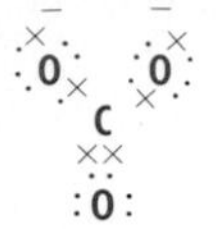

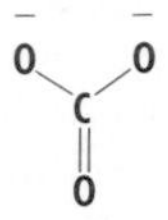

I

Structure I maintains the *octet rule,* since all four atoms are each surrounded by eight electrons. However, physical evidence shows that in the carbonate ion *all three* $C—O$ *bonds are equivalent,* and formula I implies a lack of equivalence. This difficulty is overcome by use of the notation of formula II in Fig. 5.3, where the discontinuous bonds imply some binding between carbon and oxygen over and above that of ordinary carbon-oxygen single bonds. The weakness of this notation is that *the valence electrons cannot be accounted for readily.*

The *resonance method of formulating molecules and ions* accounts for both symmetry properties and all valence electrons. In III (Fig. 5.3), the carbonate ion is described by three different formulas connected by a *double-headed arrow.* This arrow symbolizes the superposition of the three structures on one another. Taken as a group, these structures describe the electronic configuration.

Great care must be exercised always to distinguish the symbol $\longleftrightarrow$ from the symbols $\rightleftharpoons$ and $\rightleftharpoons$. The latter state that a reaction occurs which is reversible. The double-headed arrow never describes

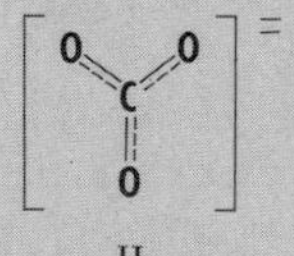

II

Indicates symmetry

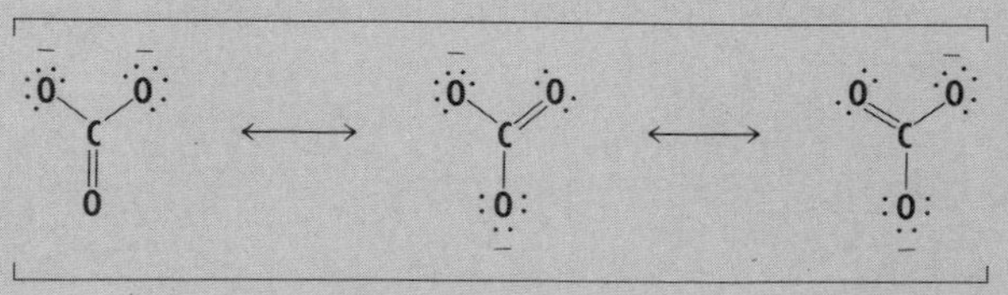

III

Resonance structures

FIG. 5.3   Representations of carbonate ion.

what happens, but indicates an ambiguous state of affairs with respect to the location of certain bonds in molecules.

Each individual part of III (Fig. 5.3) is called a *resonance structure,* even though all three are required to represent the actual structure of the ion. Each resonance structure must individually be a proper Lewis electronic structure. Since all the resonance structures represent the same physical entity, they must all indicate the same positions of atoms within the system.

One must be careful to distinguish resonance structures from mere equilibration of isomers. For example, the substances with formulas IV and V must not be connected with a resonance symbol, since the hydrogen atom cannot be close enough to both carbon and oxygen to be bonded to both simultaneously. The formulas represent two isomeric molecules which can be readily interconverted in a real chemical transformation.

A notable example of an organic compound whose structure requires something like a resonance representation is benzene, C_6H_6. Chemically the substance does not resemble simpler unsaturated molecules very closely, and physical methods have demonstrated the molecule to be planar and highly symmetrical, with all carbon-carbon bond distances equal. Thus the molecule has a sixfold axis of symmetry. The structure is best represented by use of two equivalent resonance formulas, neither of which by itself describes the structure completely.

Benzene

Dipolar Structures. Formate ion is an example of another symmetrical species possessing two "one and a half bonds." The resonance method is

Formate ion

also used to describe formic acid, which can be considered as derived from formate ion by addition of a proton to one of the oxygens. Hydrogen is heavy enough to be located close to one of the two oxygens, and so structure VI can be written for the molecule. However, interaction

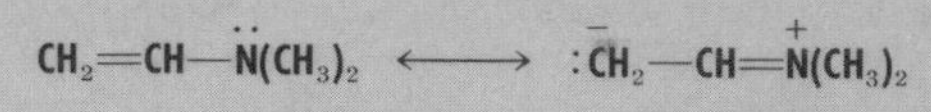

$$CH_2=CH-\overset{..}{N}(CH_3)_2 \longleftrightarrow \ \overset{-}{:}CH_2-CH=\overset{+}{N}(CH_3)_2$$

Dimethylvinylamine

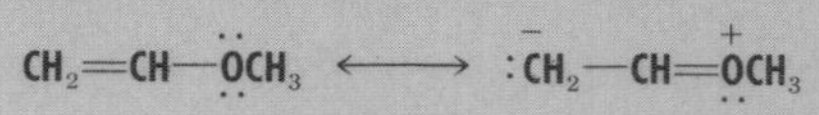

$$CH_2=CH-\overset{..}{\underset{..}{O}}CH_3 \longleftrightarrow \ \overset{-}{:}CH_2-CH=\overset{+}{O}CH_3$$

Methyl vinyl ether

$$CH_2=CH-\overset{..}{\underset{..}{F}}: \longleftrightarrow \ \overset{-}{:}CH_2-CH=\overset{+}{F}:$$

Vinyl fluoride

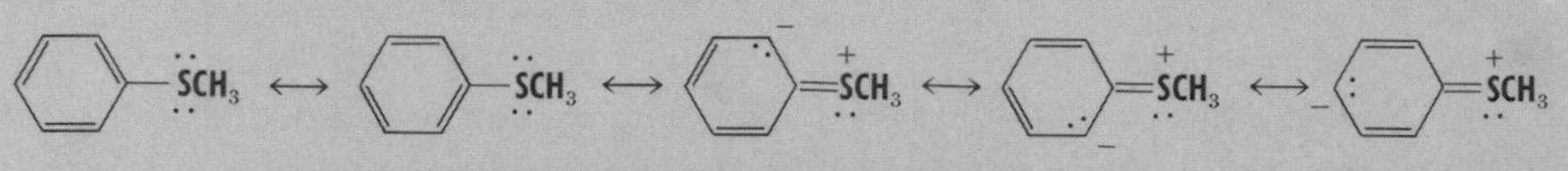

Methyl phenyl sulfide

FIG. 5.4   *Resonance involving nonbonding electrons.*

between electrons bonding the carbon to the two oxygen atoms still exists even in the neutral molecule, and the compound is best represented as a *hybrid* of structures VI and VII.

VI   VII

Formic acid

Resonance structures, such as VII, which carry formally separated charges are called *dipolar contributors to the resonance hybrid.* Although such structures are seldom as important in describing a molecule as non-polar structures, such as VI, inclusion of dipolar species often improves structural representations substantially.   When two or more nonequivalent resonance structures contribute to a hybrid, they seldom make equal contributions, and frequently one resonance formula more truly repre-sents the molecular structure than another.   Thus different resonance formulas must be assigned different weights in accurate descriptions of molecules.

Interaction of *nonbonding electrons* of nitrogen, oxygen, sulfur, and halogen atoms with attached unsaturated carbon skeletons is often of great importance in organic compounds.   The formulas of Fig. 5.4 illus-trate the contribution of such structures to resonance hybrids.

Single, double, and triple bonds which hold together different kinds of nuclei are usually polarized because of different affinities of nuclei for electrons.   This polarization is indicated by inclusion of *ionic structures* in resonance representations.   In dipolar contributors to the hybrid, one nucleus becomes electron deficient and the other electron rich, and charge separation results.   Ionic structures imply in no way that a compound can ionize. Ionic structures are useful for describing the polar character of bonds between carbon and electron-attracting elements, such as oxygen, sulfur, nitrogen, and halogens. Similar structures describe the polarity of certain bonds between carbon and hydrogen, as well as between hydrogen and oxygen, sulfur, nitrogen, and halogens. Examples of such structures are given in Fig. 5.5.

Because of analogy to an approximate mathematical device in wave mechanics, ionic structures are sometimes included even in discussion of symmetrical bonds. Such structures have little meaning when single bonds between identical elements are polarized, as in VIII and IX, but are much more important when double and triple bonds are involved, as in X and XI. In resonance formulas, these dipolar structures must be written in pairs so as to maintain over-all symmetry of the bond.

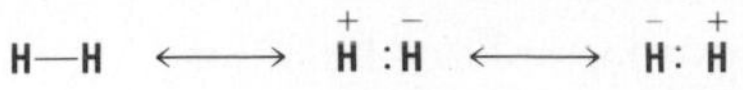

$$H-H \longleftrightarrow \overset{+}{H} \overset{-}{:H} \longleftrightarrow \overset{-}{H:} \overset{+}{H}$$

VIII

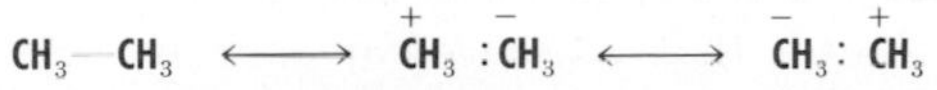

$$CH_3-CH_3 \longleftrightarrow \overset{+}{CH_3} \overset{-}{:CH_3} \longleftrightarrow \overset{-}{CH_3:} \overset{+}{CH_3}$$

IX

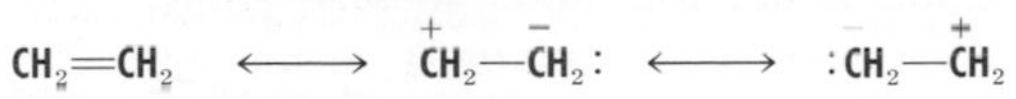

$$CH_2=CH_2 \longleftrightarrow \overset{+}{CH_2}-\overset{-}{CH_2:} \longleftrightarrow :CH_2-\overset{+}{CH_2}$$

X

$$H-C\equiv C-H \longleftrightarrow H-\overset{+}{C}=\overset{-}{C}\ H \longleftrightarrow H-\overset{-}{C}-\overset{+}{C}-H$$

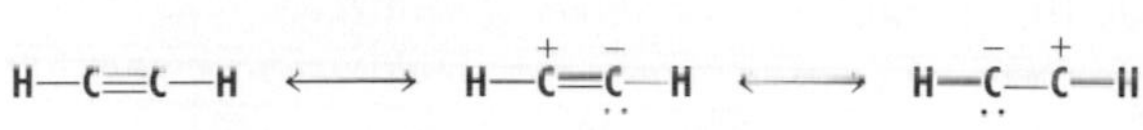

XI

A third type of dipolar structure is absolutely necessary in representations of bonds in which one bonded nucleus donates *both electrons which compose the bond*. This situation is encountered in certain nitrogen-oxygen and sulfur-oxygen bonds. Thus, in nitromethane, nitrogen donates both electrons to the nitrogen-oxygen single bond of each reso-

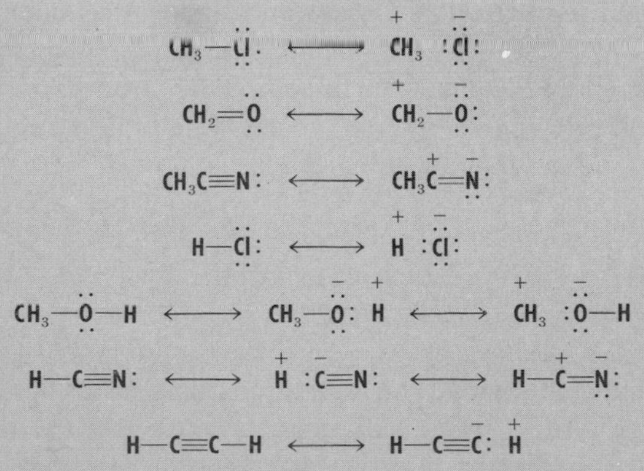

$$CH_3-\overset{..}{Cl}. \longleftrightarrow \overset{+}{CH_3} \ :\overset{..}{\underset{..}{Cl}}:$$

$$CH_2=\overset{..}{O} \longleftrightarrow \overset{+}{CH_2}-\overset{..}{\underset{..}{O}}:$$

$$CH_3C\equiv\overset{..}{N}: \longleftrightarrow \overset{+}{CH_3C}=\overset{-}{\underset{..}{N}}:$$

$$H-\overset{..}{Cl}: \longleftrightarrow \overset{+}{H} \ :\overset{..}{\underset{..}{Cl}}:$$

$$CH_3-\overset{..}{O}-H \longleftrightarrow \overset{-}{CH_3-\overset{..}{O}:} \overset{+}{H} \longleftrightarrow \overset{+}{CH_3} \ :\overset{-}{\underset{..}{O}}-H$$

$$H-C\equiv\overset{..}{N}: \longleftrightarrow \overset{+}{H} \ :C\equiv\overset{-}{\underset{..}{N}}: \longleftrightarrow H-\overset{..}{\underset{..}{C}}=\overset{-}{\underset{..}{N}}:$$

$$H-C\equiv C-H \longleftrightarrow H-C\equiv\overset{-}{C}: \overset{+}{H}$$

FIG. 5.5 *Resonance involving ionic structures.*

nance structure, and nitrogen therefore carries a formal positive charge and oxygen a formal negative charge.

$$CH_3-N\overset{+}{\underset{}{}}\overset{\cdot\overset{..}{O}\cdot}{\underset{\underset{-}{\cdot\overset{..}{O}\cdot}}{}} \longleftrightarrow CH_3-\overset{+}{N}\overset{\cdot\overset{..}{O}\cdot}{\underset{\underset{}{\cdot\overset{..}{O}\cdot}}{}}$$

Nitromethane

Conjugated Systems.   Many different kinds of experiments have demonstrated that some sort of coupling exists between ends of systems of conjugated multiple bonds, such as butadiene.

$$CH_2{=}CH{-}CH{=}CH_2$$
Butadiene

A formal similarity exists between the above formula of butadiene and either of the single resonance structures used to represent benzene (page 93).   A limited physical similarity is found in the fact that the central bond of butadiene is slightly shorter than most carbon-carbon single bonds.   Since carbon-carbon double bonds are shorter than single bonds (Chap. 6), the central bond of butadiene may possess some double-bond character.   Structures XII and XIII provide a means of representing this fact.   These structures must always be *shown together* in order to avoid the implication that butadiene is polarized and possesses positive and negative ends.

XII   XIII

Butadiene as a resonance hybrid

Unlike the dipolar structures written for most of the other molecules in this chapter, structures XII and XIII have no mathematical counterpart in the valence-bond description of the butadiene molecule.   These structures are used to maintain continuity in the presentation of the resonance concept.   More accurate representations of the butadiene structure involve new symbols found in the following representations of the butadiene molecule.

$$CH_2{=}CH{-}CH{=}CH_2 \longleftrightarrow \overset{\ulcorner\text{-------------}\urcorner}{CH_2{-}CH{=}CH{-}CH_2}$$

$$CH_2{=}CH{-}CH{=}CH_2 \longleftrightarrow \uparrow\cdot CH_2{-}CH{=}CH{-}CH_2\cdot\downarrow$$

In simple conjugated systems containing unsymmetrical bonds, one kind of dipolar structure is usually so much more important than its oppositely charged counterpart that the latter may be ignored.   Thus structures XIV and XV in the resonance hybrid of acrolein have little significance, and are not usually written.   These structures represent oxygen as being positive relative to carbon. Oxygen is at the far right of the periodic table whereas carbon is in the center. Thus oxygen has greater electron affinity than carbon, and structures XIV and XV are not important.

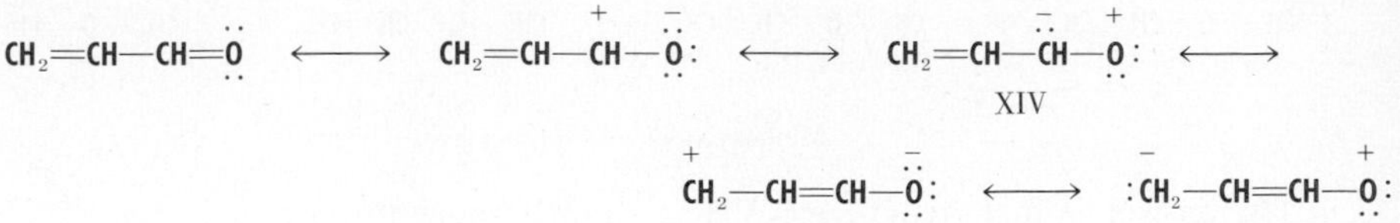

Acrolein

Similarly, double bonds conjugate with triple bonds, as in acrylonitrile, and double or triple bonds conjugate with aromatic nuclei, as in the following resonance hybrids.

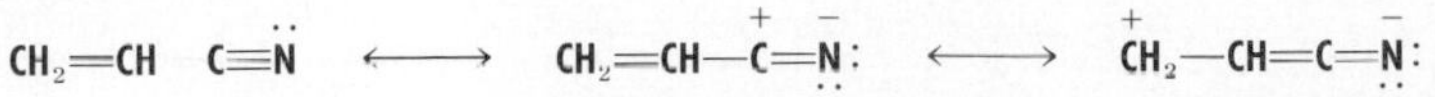

Acrolein resonance hybrid

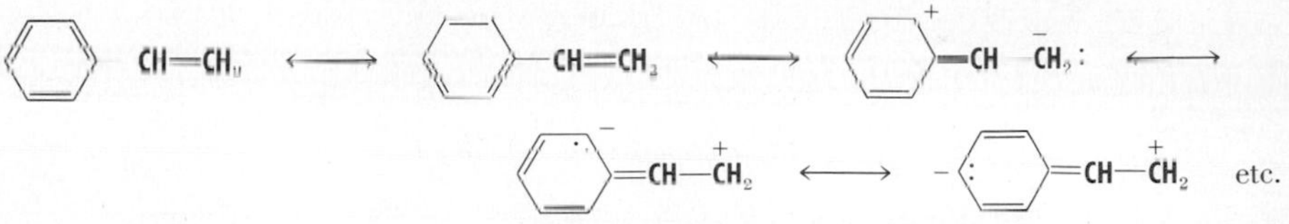

Styrene resonance hybrid

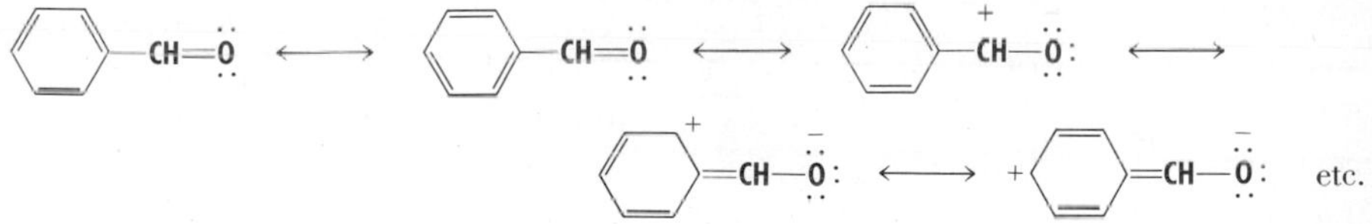

Benzaldehyde resonance hybrid

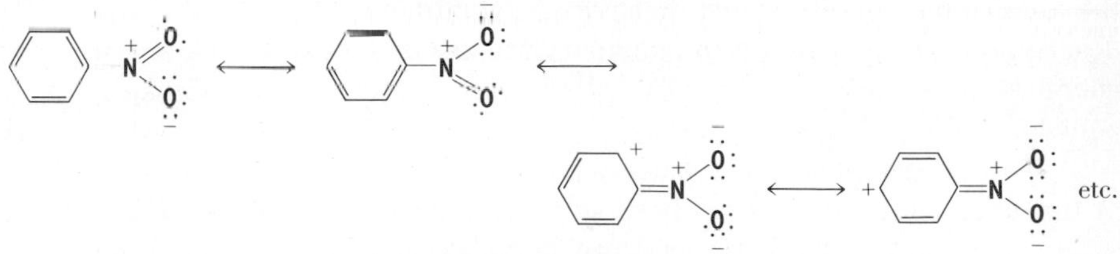

Nitrobenzene resonance hybrid

A superficially anomalous situation is encountered when hetero atoms such as oxygen, sulfur, nitrogen, or halogens are singly bonded directly to systems of double bonds. The problem can be most clearly defined in terms of actual examples. According to the resonance method, three of the four main contributors to the structure of methoxyethylene are dipolar. In structure XVI, oxygen carries a negative charge, while in XVII oxygen possesses a positive charge. In XVI, no bond is shown between oxygen and the vinyl group, while in XVII a double bond is found between these entities. The question arises whether oxygen in the actual molecule is over-all negative or positive, and whether the oxygen-vinyl bond is more or less than one single bond.

$$CH_3\!-\!\overset{..}{\underset{..}{O}}\!-\!CH\!=\!CH_2 \quad\longleftrightarrow\quad CH_3\ \overset{+}{:}\overset{-}{\underset{..}{O}}\!-\!CH\!=\!CH_2 \quad\longleftrightarrow\quad CH_3\!-\!\overset{-}{\underset{..}{O}}\overset{+}{:}\ CH\!=\!CH_2 \quad\longleftrightarrow\quad CH_3\!-\!\overset{+}{O}\!=\!CH\!-\!CH_2\overset{-}{:}$$

XVI   XVII

Methoxyethylene resonance hybrid

The answer is that structure XVII is slightly more important in the hybrid than XVI, although to a large extent the two structures cancel each other. The same problem is illustrated in the structure of chlorobenzene, but in this case structure XVIII is important enough to make halogen the negative end of the molecule.

XVIII

Chlorobenzene resonance hybrid

Electrons as Waves

The uncertainty involved in describing electronic behavior is revealed when a beam of electrons is passed through an extremely narrow slit. Similarly to light, the beam of electrons will spread out somewhat after passing through the slit. In other words, shadows cast by electronic beams do not have sharp edges. This and other similarities between electrons and light led to the successful application of wave mechanics to the description of electronic behavior. Qualitative aspects of these descriptions are very useful in chemistry for discussions of the nature of chemical bonds, and this section will be devoted to a survey of such concepts.

The Hydrogen Atom. The basic wave equation for the simple system of two interacting particles has been solved to give exact answers. Exact solutions to wave equations for more complex systems have not been found. In place of these, approximate mathematical solutions have been developed through use of the proton and electron of the hydrogen atom as a model. It is assumed in these approximate methods that solutions for more complex systems resemble the exact solution of the wave equation for the hydrogen atom. More important for present purposes is the fact that purely qualitative discussions of electronic interactions in atoms and molecules can be carried on in terms of hydrogenlike functions.

Solutions to the wave equation for the hydrogen atom are obtainable only for certain discrete values of the energy of the atom. Thus the energy that binds the electron to the nucleus is quantized. The atom absorbs energy from its environment only in *quanta* which match differences between two energy levels of the atom.

Solutions of the wave equation that correspond to various discrete energy levels are obtained as functions of the positions of the proton and electron with respect to each other. The distance between the two particles is involved, along with angular coordinates which give the concentration of the function in different directions in space. Functions are usually expressed in terms of the position of the electron relative to the proton. The latter is treated as a fixed point. Although the wave functions can be calculated for any place in space, their values are small except for separations on the order of angstrom units ($1 A = 10^{-8}$ cm) or less. The probability that the electron is at a certain point in space is proportional to the square of the value of the function for that point. Since squares are involved, the probability is never negative, even though the function itself may take on negative values at some points. Functions are usually tabulated in order of increasing energy, and that state in which the atom is most stable is referred to as the *lowest energy level*. Higher levels are unstable, and electrons fall back to the lower levels by emitting radiation. In the lowest level, the average distance between the electron and proton is 0.529 A, but there is considerable probability that the electron is farther from the nucleus. In spite of attraction of + for − , the electron is not captured by the nucleus because the potential energy thus consumed would raise the kinetic energy of the system to excessively high levels. A violation of the uncertainty principle would be involved, since if the electron stayed permanently in the nucleus, its position and momentum could be specified more precisely than is permitted by the principle.

The lowest-lying wave function or *orbital* for the hydrogen atom is spherically symmetrical. In other words, the value of the wave function depends only on distance and not at all on direction. For historical reasons, the function is called the *hydrogen 1s orbital*. It is often represented schematically as a sphere with a fuzzy surface (to indicate the absence of sharp boundaries). The next-lowest orbital is also spherically symmetrical, and is known as the *2s orbital*. The next three functions are referred to as *2p* orbitals, and they have the same energy as the *2s* orbitals. The *p* functions are symmetrical about three perpendicular axes. Each orbital has three *quantum numbers*, which describe the parts of the wave function that give the distance from the nucleus and the two angles necessary to locate a point in space. Figure 5.6 provides schematic representations of *s* and *p* orbitals.

A fourth quantum number, called the *spin*, is necessary to complete the description of an electron. A wave function is said to consist of two parts, the space function and the spin function. The electron-pairing phenomenon arises from the fact that the spin function possesses only two possible values.

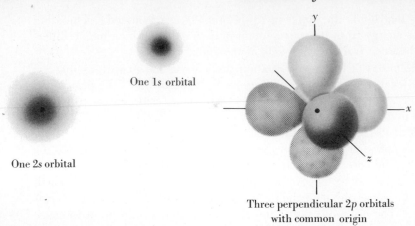

One 1s orbital

One 2s orbital

Three perpendicular 2p orbitals
with common origin

FIG. 5.6   Orbitals.

Polyelectronic Atoms. Since wave equations for polyelectronic atoms have not been solved, one must resort to the hydrogen atom as a model to approximate more complicated solutions for other systems. Each electron is assumed to be described by a wave function similar in form to those applicable to the hydrogen atom. The two electrons of helium are said to occupy the 1s orbital, and each possesses a different spin function.

An important principle of wave mechanics states that no two electrons can have the same quantum numbers. For this reason, the third electron in the lithium atom must be relegated to the higher-energy 2s orbital. Since two electrons of differing spins fit into each orbital, the complete use of the 2s and three 2p orbitals provides for eight electrons in addition to the two in the 1s orbital. Thus in atoms with atomic numbers between 3 (lithium) and 10 (neon), these orbitals are gradually filled with electrons. Because of interactions between electrons, relative energies of orbitals are changed from those in the hydrogen atom. In particular, energies of the 2p orbitals in polyelectronic atoms become somewhat higher than the energy of the 2s orbital in these atoms. In Table 5.1, the orbitals occupied by electrons in the first 10 elements of the periodic table are listed.

Molecular Orbitals. Chemical bonding is due to the fact that a single electron can interact with two nuclei simultaneously. The inability of inert gases with "filled valence shells" to form bonds suggests that a close relationship exists between chemical bonding and the electronic structures of various atoms. Bonding electrons in molecules must have wave functions which resemble atomic orbitals near the bonded nuclei, but which build up in the region between the nuclei. Simply by adding atomic orbitals centered at the two nuclei, wave functions which possess these general properties can be written. The new function is called a *molecular orbital.*

The simplest molecular orbital problem is encountered in the hydrogen molecule ion, H_2^+. The molecular orbital is formed by adding hydrogen $1s$ functions centered at the two nuclei. Calculation of the energy of an electron in such a molecular orbital indicates that considerable binding energy exists. Schematic representations of the hydrogen molecule ion are shown in Fig. 5.7.

The addition of a second electron of opposite spin function to the hydrogen molecule ion increases the binding energy, but does not double it, since some electron-electron repulsion exists. This crude approach gives a value for the energy of formation of a hydrogen molecule from hydrogen atoms, a value close enough to that obtained experimentally to encourage application of the method to more complicated molecules. Thus by use of linear combinations, formed by addition and subtraction of atomic orbitals, first approximations to the distribution of electrons in many molecules can be obtained.

Two kinds of molecular orbitals are used. Localized bond orbitals contain only the coordinates of two nuclei, and describe electrons which as a first approximation bind only two nuclei. Nonlocalized orbitals involve three or more centers, and describe electrons spread more widely over a molecule, holding three or more nuclei together. Electrons in such nonlocalized orbitals may have very long wavelengths, sometimes covering a whole molecule.

Hybrid Orbitals. In bonds to carbon, one $2s$ and three $2p$ orbitals must become involved. The shapes of these orbitals suggest that carbon atoms might form three equivalent bonds at right angles to one another, and a fourth bond with no preferred direction. The physical fact is that all four bonds in compounds like methane (CH_4) are equivalent, and the angle between each pair of bonds is about $109°$. By combination of the four orbitals of carbon with four hydrogen orbitals, a set of four molecular orbitals can be obtained whose shape meets the symmetry requirements of methane. A similar result is obtained by first combining the four bonding orbitals of the carbon atom to give a set of four equivalent *hybrid orbitals.* These new atomic orbitals are called sp^3 hybrids, since they are linear combinations formed from one $2s$ and three $2p$ orbitals.

In Fig. 5.8, the hybridization of atomic orbitals is represented.

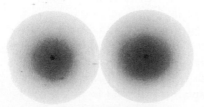

Two hydrogen 1s orbitals

Addition of two hydrogen 1s orbitals to form H_2^+

FIG. 5.7   *Representations of the hydrogen molecule ion, H_2^+.*

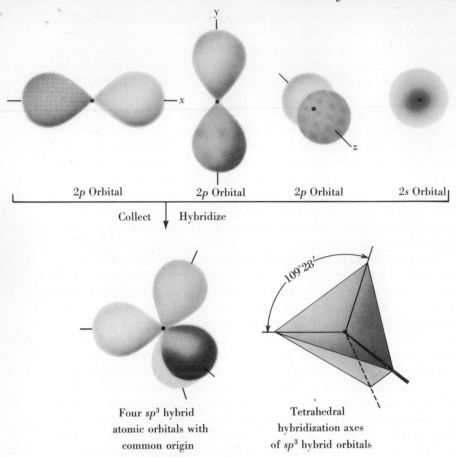

FIG. 5.8   *Hybridization of atomic orbitals.*

Three 2p atomic orbitals are combined with one 2s atomic orbital to form four sp^3 atomic orbitals, all of the same size and shape. Each has a different axis of symmetry, and these axes are 109°28′ from one another. The sp^3 state is called *tetrahedral hybridization* because the four axes of the orbitals radiate from the central carbon atom at the same angle as that made by rays drawn from the corners of a regular tetrahedron to its center. In Fig. 5.8, two of these axes are in the plane, one is behind, and the fourth extends above the plane of the page. *The last two are drawn in perspective. Dark gray indicates extension above the plane of the page and light gray indicates extension behind it.*

With saturated molecules, localized molecular orbitals are formed by combination of one sp^3 orbital with an atomic orbital from a second atom. Thus with methane, the 1s orbital of each hydrogen atom combines with an sp^3 orbital of carbon. In such molecules, the method indicates that the bonding pairs of electrons are essentially localized in each of the four equivalent molecular orbitals. Like the sp^3 atomic orbitals, the new molecular orbitals are tetrahedral in their arrangement about the central carbon atom. This configuration applies to all compounds of the type CZ_4, and with only very small modifications to all saturated carbon atoms in organic molecules. Figure 5.9 provides a graphic representation of the combination of a carbon atom with sp^3 orbitals with four hydrogen atoms with s orbitals.

Two other simple types of hybrids of carbon orbitals are useful in organic chemistry. The equivalent mixing of two p orbitals with an s orbital gives three equivalent sp^2 orbitals, which have symmetry axes in a single plane at 120° from one another. The axis of the third p orbital, which was not used in hybridization, is perpendicular to the plane of the three hybrid orbitals. This *trigonal* state of hybridization has been used in the description of carbon atoms attached to double bonds, since the three groups bound to an unsaturated carbon atom lie in a plane which includes the carbon atom. The description is not unique since a planar model for a molecule such as ethylene is also obtained by placing two tetrahedrons together so that they have a common edge. The two models predict different bond angles. Trigonal hybridization would involve three equal bond angles of 120°, and the tetrahedral model suggests that the H—C—H angle in ethylene should be 109°. In actual fact, the bond angles are usually about 116°.

Two *digonal hybrids* are formed by combination of a $2s$ and a $2p$ atomic orbital of carbon. The resulting sp hybrid orbitals are symmetric about the same axis, and are used in descriptions of molecules, such as acetylene (H—$C{\equiv}C$—H), which are linear. Figure 5.10 contains representations of sp^2 and sp hybridizations of orbitals.

Unsaturated Molecules. Since all six atoms of ethylene lie in the same plane, the carbon atoms must each form three localized bonds with their sp^2 hybrid orbitals. The resulting links are called *sigma bonds* (σ bonds), a term which correctly implies that the localized molecular orbitals involved are symmetrical about the axis of the bond.

The orbitals of the σ bonds account for five electron pairs, leaving only two *valence electrons* of ethylene yet to be assigned to molecular

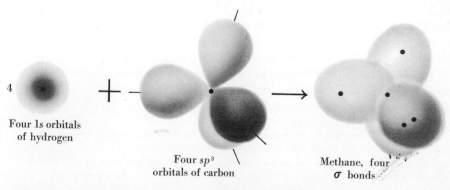

4

Four 1s orbitals
of hydrogen

Four sp^3
orbitals of carbon

Methane, four
σ bonds

FIG. 5.9   Formation of molecular orbitals of methane.

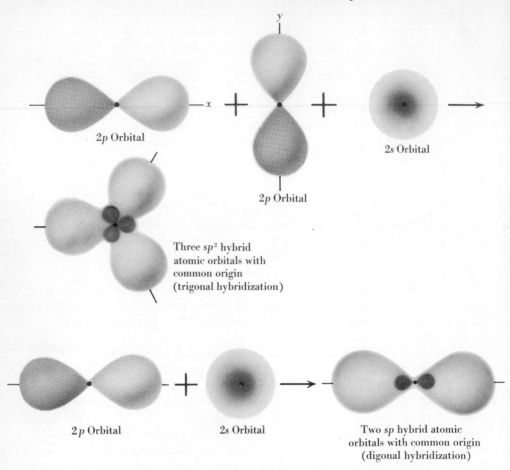

FIG. 5.10 *Hybridization of orbitals of carbon.*

orbitals.   One electron is left in each carbon's p orbital not used in
forming the sp^2 hybrids.   The axes of these p orbitals are parallel, and
the two centers are close enough together to allow the orbitals to overlap.   The molecular orbital produced by adding two atomic p orbitals is
called a *pi* (π) orbital.   Such orbitals do not have axes of symmetry, and
have the property of changing sign when they pass through the plane of
the σ bonds.†   In that plane, the π orbitals have zero values.‡

The four atoms of acetylene lie in a straight line, which indicates
that each carbon forms two σ bonds with its sp hybrid orbitals.   Each
carbon is bonded to one hydrogen and to the other carbon.   Three elec-

---

† The sign of the π orbital has no physical significance.   When the square of the function is
taken to estimate electron density, the value is either positive or zero everywhere.

‡ The arbitrary nature of the formulation of ethylene as having σ and π bonds is revealed by
the fact that a different representation can be made in which the two C—C bonds are equivalent.
Each of these bonds is made by combining a p orbital of one carbon with an sp^2 orbital of
the second carbon.

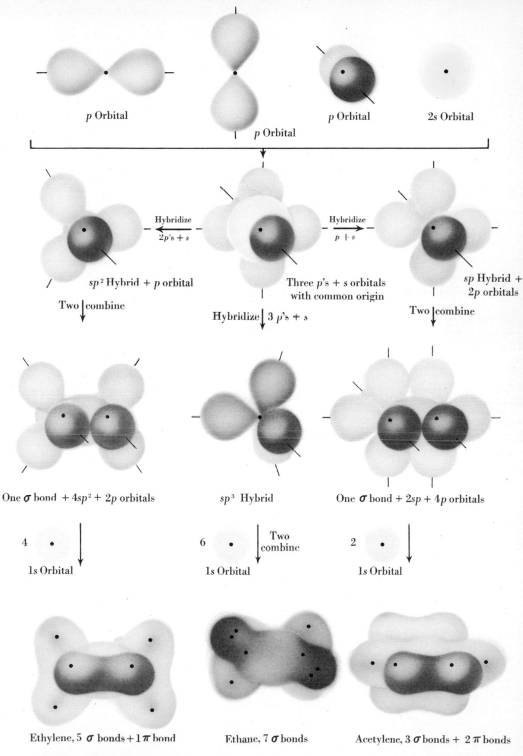

p Orbital

p Orbital

p Orbital

2s Orbital

Hybridize
2p's + s

Hybridize
p + s

sp² Hybrid + p orbital

Three p's + s orbitals
with common origin

sp Hybrid +
2p orbitals

Two | combine

Hybridize | 3 p's + s

Two | combine

One **σ** bond + 4sp² + 2p orbitals

sp³ Hybrid

One **σ** bond + 2sp + 4p orbitals

4

1s Orbital

6

Two
combine

1s Orbital

2

1s Orbital

Ethylene, 5 **σ** bonds + 1 **π** bond

Ethane, 7 **σ** bonds

Acetylene, 3 **σ** bonds + 2 **π** bonds

FIG. 5.11   Hybridization of orbitals.

105

tron pairs are thus accounted for, and four valence electrons remain to
be assigned. One electron is left in each of the four unhybridized *p*
orbitals, two such atomic orbitals being associated with each carbon.
The axes of the two *p* orbitals on *each* carbon are perpendicular to each
other, but the axes of each set of two *p* orbitals on *different* carbons are
parallel, and close enough to overlap. The resulting two π orbitals provide the acetylene molecule with an almost cylindrical π-electron cloud,
whose axis of symmetry is also the axis of symmetry for the three
σ orbitals of acetylene.

In Fig. 5.11, combinations of atomic orbitals of carbon and hydrogen to form the molecular orbitals of ethane, ethylene, and acetylene are
shown in color. The *p* and π orbitals are shown in red, *s* orbitals in
yellow, and the various combinations of *p* and *s* orbitals are shown in
different shades of orange, depending on the number of *p* orbitals and *s*
orbitals used to make the hybrid. Orbitals that extend above the plane
of the page are more deeply colored than orbitals whose axes are in the
plane, which in turn are more deeply colored than those extending behind
the plane.

In conjugated unsaturated molecules, extensive delocalization of
electrons is readily rationalized in terms of π orbitals. In the *planar*
benzene molecule, the *p* orbitals of all carbons are parallel, and each
carbon's *p* orbital overlaps equally with that of each of its two neighbors.
Addition of all six atomic orbitals gives a molecular orbital which is continuous about the whole ring. Other linear combinations of atomic
orbitals give two other molecular orbitals which are less extensive, but
still capable of providing considerable bonding. The six π electrons are
assigned to these three molecular orbitals, and an over-all electron distribution is obtained which is compatible with the requirement that the
molecule possess a sixfold axis of symmetry. These three molecular
orbitals are shown in Fig. 5.12.

Unlike benzene, butadiene is not a rigid molecule, because rotation
about the central carbon-carbon bond can occur (Chap. 6). The two
planar configurations of butadiene provide the best geometry for *p*-orbital
interaction across the middle carbon-carbon bond. Rotation away from
these configurations reduces interaction to zero when the axes of the
p orbitals are perpendicular to each other.

XIX   XX

Two planar configurations of butadiene

In Fig. 5.12, the *p* atomic orbitals of configuration XX of butadiene
are shown. These are combined to form two π molecular orbitals for the
molecule.

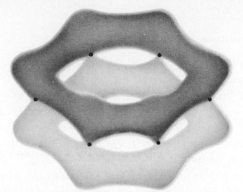

First benzene π orbital

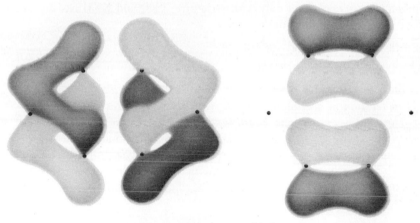

Second and third benzene π orbitals

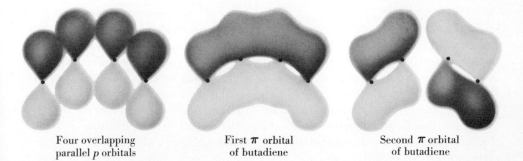

Four overlapping
parallel p orbitals

First π orbital
of butadiene

Second π orbital
of butadiene

FIG. 5.12   *The orbitals of benzene and butadiene.*

Rules for Resonance Structures

Certain rules for writing meaningful resonance structures are suggested by wave mechanics. In a sense, a pair of resonance structures connected by a double-headed arrow implies that a pair of crude molecular wave functions can be written which, when added, provide a new and more representative function. Therefore, the structures must be related in such a way that the two functions will combine. The following rules are based upon these considerations.

1. *All resonance structures in a set must contain the same number of paired electrons.* In organic molecules, the spins of electrons must be paired or unpaired. No intermediate condition exists. Structure XXI indicates that all the electrons of butadiene are paired. Structure XXII indicates that two of the electrons are unpaired. The magnetic properties of the molecule are consistent only with structure XXI, and XXII has no meaning in the description of the molecule.

$$CH_2{=}CH{-}CH{=}CH_2 \qquad \cdot CH_2{-}CH{=}CH{-}CH_2 \cdot$$

    XXI   XXII

2. *The nuclei of molecules must all occupy exactly the same positions in relation to one another in all resonance structures of a set.*

3. *There is maximum π bonding when all atoms attached to unsaturated atoms lie in the same plane.* For example, in allene, the terminal methylene groups are planar, but the two assemblies are perpendicular to each other. As a consequence, this molecule is represented as having two *localized* π bonds.

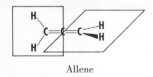

Allene

4. *Structures which represent very high energy configurations are disregarded.* Structure XXIII has little meaning in the description of methane, and the same is true for XXIV as applied to ethane. The energy involved in separating charges in both these structures is too high for them to make significant contributions to the resonance hybrid. Similarly, the electronic configuration of structure XXV is too unstable to make a significant contribution to the structure of nitric acid. In this formula, nitrogen is surrounded by 10 electrons, though the first 10 elements are essentially incapable of expanding their valence shells. Structure XXVI for formaldehyde is poor because oxygen, which has a greater affinity for electrons than carbon, has given up an electron pair to carbon.

$$\bar{H} \quad \overset{\bar{H}}{\underset{\bar{H}}{\overset{4+}{C}}} \quad \bar{H} \qquad \overset{+}{C}H_3 \quad \bar{C}H_3 \qquad H-O-\overset{+}{N}\overset{O}{\underset{O}{\diagdown}} \qquad \overset{+}{C}H_2-\bar{O}$$

     XXIII   XXIV   XXV   XXVI

Resonance Energy

Delocalization of electrons *lowers their energy,* and molecules for which a number of resonance structures may be written turn out to be unexpectedly stable.† For example, 1,3-pentadiene, for which two secondary structures can be written, is more stable than its isomer, 1,4-pentadiene, for which only a single structure can be written.

$$CH_2\!=\!CH\!-\!CH\!=\!CH\!-\!CH_3 \longleftrightarrow \overset{|}{C}H_2\!-\!CH\!=\!CH\!-\!\overset{|}{C}H\!-\!CH_3 \longleftrightarrow \bar{C}H_2\!-\!CH\!=\!CH\!-\!\overset{+}{C}H\!-\!CH_3$$

1,3-Pentadiene resonance hybrid

$$CH_2\!=\!CH\!-\!CH_2\!-\!CH\!=\!CH_2$$

     1,4-Pentadiene

Benzene is the most notable of the "resonance-stabilized" compounds. It is much more stable than would be expected of a substance containing three noninteracting double bonds. *Resonance energies* are measured experimentally through comparisons of the heats of hydrogenation of substances such as benzene and cyclohexene, the latter serving as a standard for the former. If benzene contained three ethylenelike double bonds, the heat evolved in complete hydrogenation of benzene would be three times that liberated in hydrogenation of cyclohexene. The difference between the heats of hydrogenation for a mole of benzene and for three moles of cyclohexene is defined as the *resonance energy of benzene.*

$$\underset{\substack{\text{CH} \\ \parallel \\ \text{CH}}}{} \!+\! 3H_2 \longrightarrow \quad + 49.8 \text{ kcal/mole}$$

$$3 \quad + 3H_2 \longrightarrow \quad 3 \quad + 86.4 \text{ kcal/3 moles}$$

$86.4 - 49.8 = 36.6$ kcal/mole, resonance energy for benzene

---

† An interesting analogy is found in the fact that electrons spread over large molecules have long wavelengths and low energy, just as light of long wavelength has relatively small energy per quantum.

Problems

1. Define the following key terms: atomic orbital, molecular orbital, octet rule, unsaturated, resonance method, resonance energy, sp^3 orbital, sp^2 orbital, sp orbital, σ bond, π bond, p orbital, s orbital.

2. Write sets of resonance structures for the following compounds, and indicate only the more important contributors to the hybrid.

a. CH_3CONH_2	*i.* $CH_2{=}CHBr$	*q.* Naphthalene
b. $CH_3CO_2CH_3$	*j.* $CH_2{=}CHN(CH_3)_2$	*r.* Phenanthrene
c. CH_3CN	*k.* $CH_2{=}CHNO_2$	*s.* α-Naphthol
d. $(CH_3CO)_2O$	*l.* C_6H_5Cl	*t.* $C_6H_5CH{=}CH_2$
e. CH_3COCl	*m.* $C_6H_5OCH_3$	*u.* C_6H_5CN
f. CH_3CO_2H	*n.* $C_6H_5NO_2$	*v.* $C_6H_5CH{=}CHC_6H_5$
g. CH_3NO_2	*o.* $C_6H_5NH_2$	*w.* $p\text{-}CH_3OC_6H_4COCH_3$
h. $CH_2{=}CHCHO$	*p.* $C_6H_5COCH_3$	*x.* Furan

3. Criticize certain of the following structures as significant contributors to the resonance hybrid of the molecule.

a. $CH_3C{\equiv}N \longleftrightarrow CH_3\overset{-}{C}{=}\overset{+}{N} \longleftrightarrow CH_3\overset{++}{C}{-}\overset{=}{N}$

b. $C_6H_5{-}Cl \longleftrightarrow C_6H_5^-\ Cl^+$

c. $CH_2{=}CH{-}CH{=}O \longleftrightarrow \overset{-}{C}H_2{-}CH{=}CH{-}\overset{+}{O}$

d. 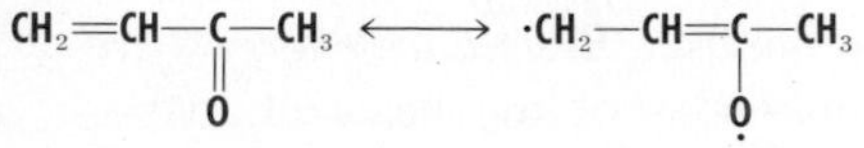 $CH_2{=}CH{-}\underset{\underset{O}{\|}}{C}{-}CH_3 \longleftrightarrow \cdot CH_2{-}CH{=}\underset{\underset{\overset{..}{O}}{}}{C}{-}CH_3$

e.  $CH_3{-}\underset{\underset{O}{\|}}{C}{-}CH{=}\underset{\underset{HO}{}}{C}{-}CH_3 \longleftrightarrow CH_3{-}\underset{\underset{OH}{}}{C}{=}CH{-}\underset{\underset{O}{\|}}{C}{-}CH_3$

f.  $CH_3{-}\overset{+}{N}\underset{\underset{O^-}{}}{\overset{\overset{O}{\diagup\!\|}}{\diagdown}} \longleftrightarrow CH_3{-}N\underset{\underset{O}{}}{\overset{\overset{O}{\diagup\!\|}}{\diagdown}}$

g.

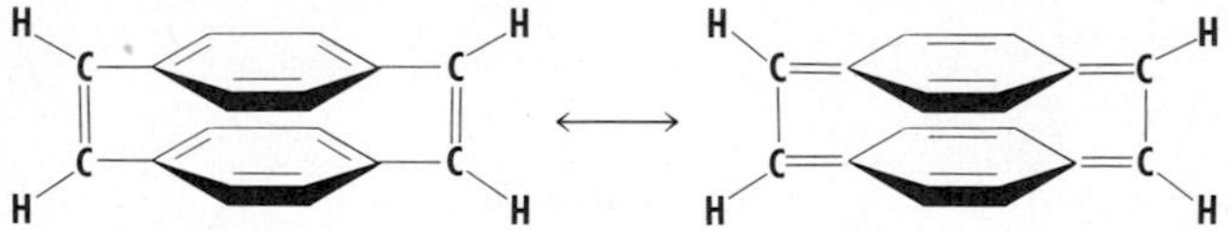

h. $CH_2{=}C{=}O \longleftrightarrow \overset{-}{C}H_2{-}C{\equiv}\overset{+}{O}$

i. $O{=}C{=}C{=}C{=}O \longleftrightarrow \overset{-}{O}{-}C{\equiv}C{-}C{\equiv}\overset{+}{O}$

j. $H{-}N{\equiv}\overset{+}{N}{=}\overset{-}{N} \longleftrightarrow H{-}N{=}N{\equiv}N$

4. The molecule, $CH_2{=}C{=}CH_2$ (allene), possesses the geometry indicated on page 108. What hybrid orbitals of carbon are needed to accommodate this configuration?

5. Devise explanations for the following facts.

a. Anion A is more stable than anion B.

Planar

A

$CH_2{=}CH{-}\overset{-}{C}H{-}CH{=}CH_2$

B

b. Cation *C* is more stable than cation *D*.

$\overset{+}{C}H_2 - CH = CH - CH = CH - CH = CH_2$

Planar

   C   *D*

c. The following species, *E*, *F*, and *G*, are more stable than their counterparts, *H*, *I*, and *J*, respectively.

$CH_2 = CH - \overset{+}{C}H_2$ $CH_2 = CH - \overset{-}{C}H_2$ $CH_2 = CH - \overset{\cdot}{C}H_2$

   E   *F*   *G*

$CH_3CH_2\overset{+}{C}H_2$ $CH_3CH_2\overset{-}{C}H_2$ $CH_3CH_2\overset{\cdot}{C}H_2$

   H   *I*   *J*

d. Acetic acid is a stronger acid than ethanol.

e. Aniline ($C_6H_5NH_2$) is a weaker base than methylamine.

6. Make drawings of the following:

a. A *p* orbital

b. An *s* orbital

c. Orbitals resulting from hybridization of one *p* and one *s*, two *p*'s and one *s*, and three *p*'s and one *s*

d. An orbital resulting from combination of two *sp³* atomic orbitals

e. An orbital resulting from combination of two parallel and overlapping *p* orbitals

f. An orbital resulting from combination of one *sp³* and one *s* atomic orbital

g. The σ orbitals for configuration XX for butadiene

h. The σ orbitals for benzene

6

Stereochemistry

In Chaps. 1 through 5 most formulas are written in ways not intended to show the detailed shapes of molecules. This chapter is devoted to an examination of the architectural features of organic molecules as three-dimensional atomic aggregates.

Bond Angles and Bond Lengths

Fortunately, *bond lengths* and *angles* within functional and hydro-carbon groups vary only slightly from compound to compound. Table 6.1 records the ordinary bond lengths encountered in organic substances, and Table 6.2, the bond angles associated with functional and hydrocarbon groups. Deviations from the values for bond lengths are rare, since energies for stretching or compressing bonds are high. In contrast,

TABLE 6.1   Normal Bond Lengths

Bond	Bond length, A	Bond	Bond length, A
C—H (alkanes)	1.07	C—Br (bromoalkanes)	1.94
N—H (amines)	1.00	C—I (iodoalkanes)	2.14
O—H (alcohols)	0.96	C=C (alkenes)	1.35
S—H (mercaptans)	1.34	C=N (oximes)	1.29
C—C (alkanes)	1.54	C=O (ketones)	1.22
C—N (amines)	1.47	C≡C (alkynes)	1.20
C—O (alcohols)	1.43	C≡N (nitriles)	1.16
C—S (sulfides)	1.81	C=C (benzene)	1.39
C—Cl (chloroalkanes)	1.76		

TABLE 6.2   *Normal Bond Angles*

Bond	Compound	Bond angle	Bond	Compound	Bond angle
C—C—C	$CH_3CH_2CH_3$	112°	H—C=C	$CH_2=CH_2$	122°
H—C—H	CH_2O	120°	O—C=O	HCO_2CH_3	123°
H—C=O	CH_2O	120°	C—O—C	HCO_2CH_3	112°
C—O—H	CH_3OH	105°	C—C=O	CH_3CONH_2	129°
O—N—O	CH_3NO_2	127°	C—N—H	CH_3CONH_2	107°
C—S—H	CH_3SH	100°	N—C=O	CH_3CONH_2	122°
C≡C—H	$HC≡CH$	180°	C—C—N	CH_3CONH_2	109°
O—C=O	HCO_2H	122°	C—O—C	CH_3OCH_3	111°
Cl—C=O	CH_3COCl	123°	C—C—H	△	116°
C—C—Cl	CH_3COCl	105°	H—C—H	△	118°
H—C—H	$CH_2=CH_2$	116°	C—C=O	CH_3COCH_3	120°
C—C—H	C_6H_6	120°			

small deformations ($<10°$) of normal bond angles involve only small amounts of energy, and numerous situations arise in which these bond angles are somewhat expanded or contracted. Extreme bond-angle deformation in a molecule results in abnormal chemical reactivity, but the number of systems exhibiting this characteristic is small. Whenever the geometry of a molecule requires modification of the usual bond angles, the deformation is distributed among as many angles as possible.

The ordinary disposition of bonds about any carbon atom carrying four substituents places all these groups as far from one another as possible, and each of the angles included by the bonds is about 109° (page 102). The three-dimensional character of molecules makes their representation on paper somewhat involved. The formulas of Fig. 6.1 show ways of indicating the arrangement of atoms in methane. In all cases, ordinary lines indicate bonds in the plane of the page, and dashed lines represent bonds extending below the plane of the page. Solid wedges identify bonds standing above the plane of the page. Formulas designed to create an illusion of three dimensions will be used frequently in this book, and the above conventions will be employed.

Rotation about Single Bonds

A discussion of the structure of ethane introduces the problem of rotation of groups about bonds. At temperatures employed by the organic chemist, the two methyl groups can rotate about the carbon-carbon bond. Formula I of Fig. 6.2 represents one of three identical configurations that two methyl groups may assume with respect to each other as one of them is rotated through 360°. Formula II (Fig. 6.2)

Drawings

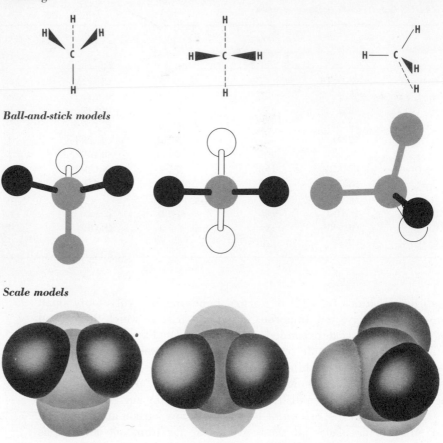

Ball-and-stick models

Scale models

FIG. 6.1   Arrangement of atoms in methane.

portrays one of a second set of three identical rotational arrangements. In III and IV (Fig. 6.3), projection formulas are used in which the reader is "looking down" the carbon-carbon bond, and the plane projections of the other six bonds are arranged like spokes in a wheel. In these drawings, the point of intersection of the three bonds in the center of the circle represents the near carbon atom, and the circle the more distant atom. Three sets of hydrogen atoms *eclipse* one another in II and IV, and the molecule is said to have an *eclipsed configuration.* In I and III, the hydrogen atoms are *staggered* and *noneclipsed.* In open-chain systems, eclipsed arrangements are unstable in comparison to staggered configurations because of the repulsive forces among the hydrogens. Arrangements represented by II and IV are only transitory states in the interconversion of the three resting states represented by I or III. The latter are referred to as *conformers.* At ordinary temperatures, most open-chain molecules possess enough thermal energy for the rapid interconversion of the different possible conformers, which are in equilibrium with one another.

Of the three conformers of *n*-butane obtained by rotation about the central carbon-carbon bond, V and VI are nonsuperimposible mirror images, and VII is different from either of them. Of these, VII is the most stable because the more bulky methyl groups are distributed as far away from one another as possible (see Fig. 6.4). These species rapidly interconvert, and for practical purposes the *substance is homogeneous*.

The same principles govern rotation about other single bonds.

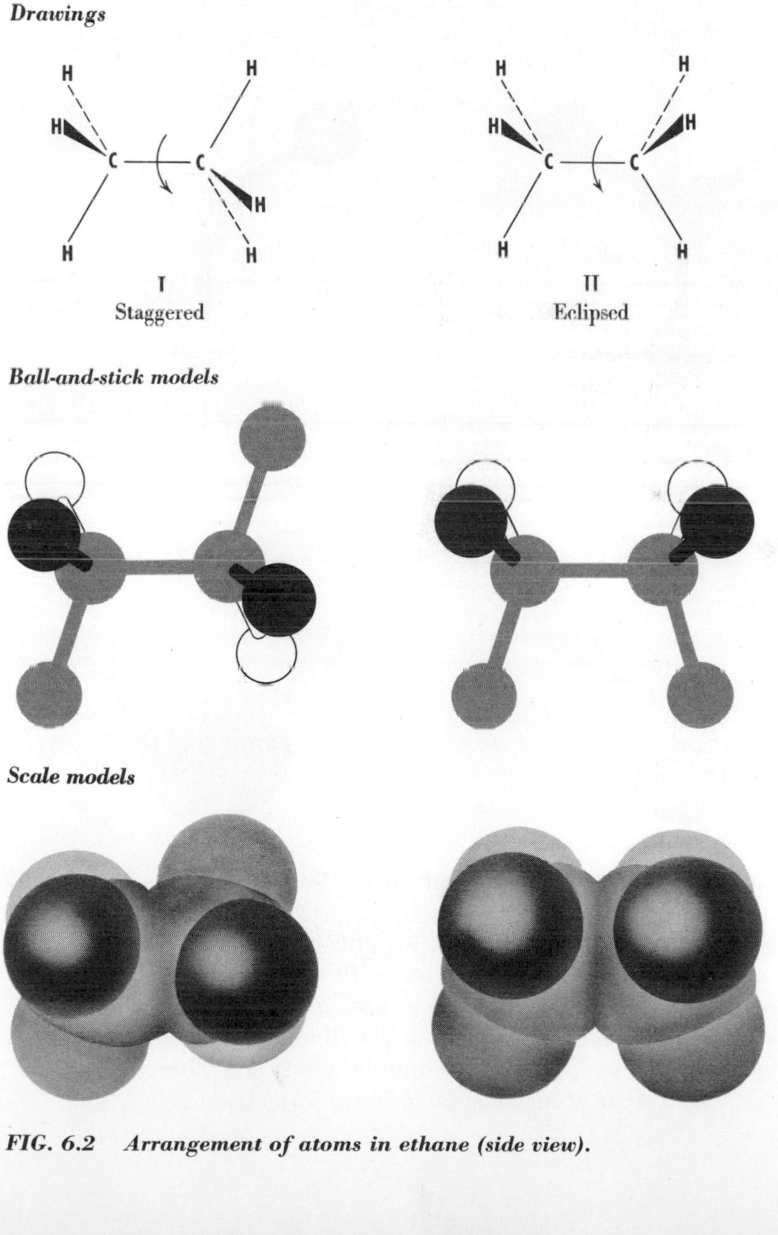

Drawings

I
Staggered

II
Eclipsed

Ball-and-stick models

Scale models

FIG. 6.2   *Arrangement of atoms in ethane (side view).*

Drawings

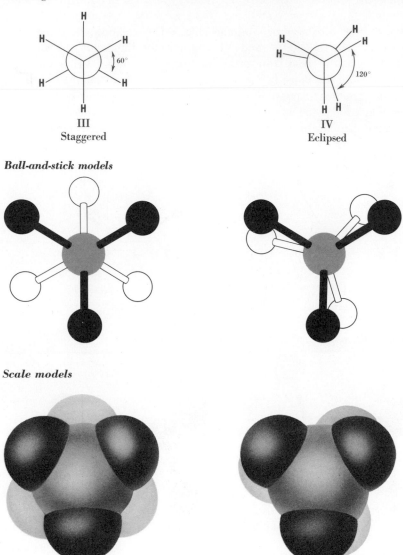

III
Staggered

IV
Eclipsed

Ball-and-stick models

Scale models

FIG. 6.3   *Arrangement of atoms in ethane (end-on view).*

Since bonded hydrogen and halogen in effect possess cylindrical
symmetry, no conformations are associated with these substituents. A
similar generalization applies to acetylenic and nitrile groups. These
substituents and their bonds are linear and cylindrical. Bonds from
carbon to substituents that in turn carry double bonds give rise to three
conformations. A number of such compounds are formulated below, and

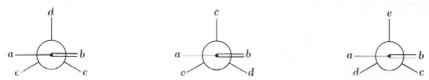

FIG. 6.4   *Three conformers of n-butane.*

Fig. 6.5, with end-on projection formulas, shows the conformations associated with these compounds.

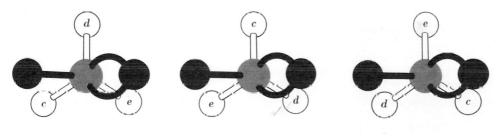

Drawings

Ball-and-stick models

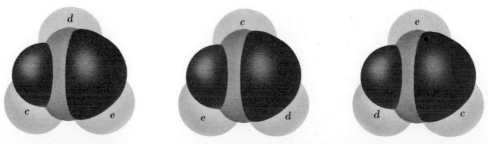

Scale models

FIG. 6.5   *Conformations associated with unsaturated substituents.*

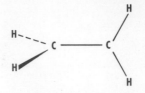

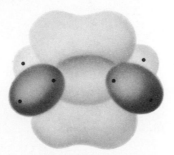

Ethylene

Molecular orbitals of ethylene   π Orbital destroyed by 90°
                                                rotation about double bond

FIG. 6.6   *Rotation about double bonds.*

Restricted Rotation about Double Bonds

The geometry of ethylene is much simpler than that of ethane, since all six atoms of ethylene lie in one plane. The energy barrier to rotation about a carbon-carbon double bond is high enough to hold the four attached substituents in a rigid configuration except at high temperatures.

Ethylene

In molecules where double bonds are conjugated, the thermal energy available at ordinary temperatures approaches the energy needed for rotation about one of the double bonds. For instance in α,β-unsaturated ketones, the barrier to rotation about the carbon-carbon bond is lowered by delocalization of the π electrons of the system. In oximes and similar compounds, rotation about the carbon-nitrogen and nitrogen-nitrogen double bonds is restricted in a way similar to that observed with the carbon-carbon double bond.

Delocalization of electrons in an α,β-unsaturated ketone

| Oxime | Hydrazone | Azo |
| linkage | linkage | linkage |

Examination of the π orbitals of ethylene provides an explanation for the rigidity associated with the carbon-carbon double bond (see Fig. 6.6). If the plane occupied by one CH_2 group is rotated 90° about the axis of the carbon-carbon σ bond, the π molecular orbital is destroyed. The resulting two p orbitals are at right angles to each other, and no orbital overlap can occur. As a consequence, the two electrons occupying these atomic orbitals assume shorter wavelengths and higher-energy configurations.

Geometric Isomerism

A consequence of restricted rotation about double bonds is the phenomenon known as *geometric isomerism*. For example, two different compounds exist which contain the atomic sequence $HO_2CCH—CHCO_2H$; one is known as maleic and the other as fumaric acid. These substances have widely different physical properties. The former melts at 130°, the latter at 270°. When heated to 140° in an open flask, maleic acid gives maleic anhydride and water. In contrast, fumaric acid is recovered unchanged when subjected to the same treatment. However, at 275°, fumaric acid does lose water to form maleic anhydride.

The existence of these two compounds and the difference in their behavior correlate with the concept of restricted rotation about double bonds. In maleic acid, the two carboxyl groups are on the same side of the double bond; in fumaric acid, the carboxyls are on opposite sides. Maleic acid loses water to form a cycle because its two carboxyl groups are close together and can interact with each other. In fumaric acid, the

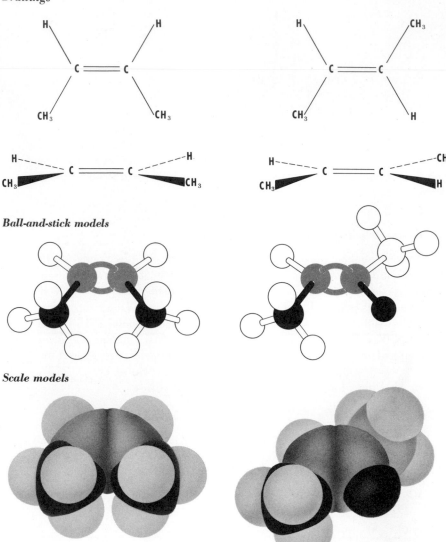

FIG. 6.7   *Representations of the isomeric 2-butenes.*

two carboxyl groups are too far apart to interact, and the molecule is stable until enough thermal energy is available to the system to isomerize the compound to maleic acid, which immediately loses water.

Many other pairs of *geometric isomers* are known, the simplest of which are the two 2-butenes, whose configurations are shown in Fig. 6.7.

Pairs of geometric isomers are normally referred to as *cis* and *trans* isomers.   If two like substituents are attached to different carbons of a carbon-carbon double bond, the cis isomer is the one in which like groups are on the same side, as in *cis*-2-butene (Fig. 6.7). The trans isomer is that in which like groups are on opposite sides. If four different groups are attached to a carbon-carbon double bond, the cis isomer is that in which the two groups with the longest chains are on the same side of the double bond, as in *cis*-3-methyl-3-heptene.

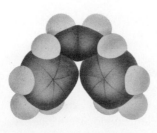

CH₃   H
   \   /
    C === C
   /   \
CH₃CH₂   CH₂CH₂CH₃
cis-3-Methyl-3-heptene

CH₃CH₂   H
      \   /
       C === C
      /   \
   CH₃   CH₂CH₂CH₃
trans 3 Methyl 3 heptene

Frequently, when discussing *parts* of geometric isomers, authors refer to groups as being *cis* or *trans* to each other. For instance, in *cis*-3-methyl-3-heptene, methyl and hydrogen are cis to each other, and ethyl and hydrogen are trans. The distinction between naming the molecule as a whole and referring to the geometric relationship of particular parts must be kept clearly in mind.

The relative stability of geometric isomers can usually be judged by the simple postulate: "Two objects cannot occupy the same space at the same time." For example, *trans*-stilbene is more stable than its cis isomer (see Fig. 6.8). The phenyl groups are far more bulky than hydrogen

Drawings

cis-Stibene

H   H
 \   /
  C   ===   C
 /   \
C₆H₅   C₆H₅
     (mp 1°)

trans-Stilbene

H   C₆H₅
 \   /
  C   ===   C
 /   \
C₆H₅   H
     (mp 124°)

Scale models

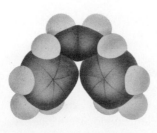

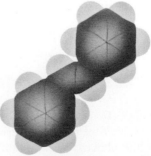

Cannot become planar   Planar

FIG. 6.8   *Geometric isomers of stilbene.*

atoms, and the larger groups *eclipse* and crowd each other when they are on the same side of the molecule. However, in chemical reactions leading to the stilbenes, either or both isomers can be obtained, depending on the characteristics of the starting materials and the reaction. When the isomers are equilibrated with an acid catalyst, the trans isomer predominates in the equilibrium mixture by a factor greater than 100. With smaller groups, such as methyl, the difference in stability of the isomers becomes small. An equilibrium mixture of *cis-* and *trans-*2-butene contains substantial amounts of the cis isomer. Interconversion of cis-trans isomers is difficult if the double bonds carry only saturated hydrocarbon residues. With substituents that can delocalize the π electrons of the double bond, isomerization becomes easier.

When an organic compound possesses more than one suitably substituted carbon-carbon double bond, the number of possible geometric isomers increases. The best way to determine this number is to write down all unique structures and count them. The four structures that can be written for 1-phenyl-1,3-pentadiene are as follows:

cis-cis-1-Phenyl-1,3-pentadiene   *trans-trans*-1-Phenyl-1,3-pentadiene   *cis-trans*-1-Phenyl-1,3-pentadiene   *trans-cis*-1-Phenyl-1,3-pentadiene

Geometric isomerism is frequently encountered in unsymmetric oximes, and occasionally in hydrazones and azo compounds. The energy barrier to interconversion of isomers is smaller in these substances. Nevertheless, both isomers can occasionally be obtained, and they possess distinctly different physical properties. For example, two benzaldoximes are known, which are designated as *syn* and *anti* forms. These prefixes refer to the relative positions of hydrogen and hydroxyl groups, as can be seen from the following formulas.

syn-Benzaldoxime   *anti*-Benzaldoxime
(H and OH cis)   (H and OH trans)

Cyclic Compounds

The tendency for bonds to assume a tetrahedral configuration about saturated carbon has interesting effects on the geometry of carbocyclic compounds. In cyclopropane and cyclobutane the rings are planar. Nonplanar forms of cyclobutane would entail greater angle strain than is found in the planar form. Deformation of angles between bonds from their normal value of 109° makes these substances more reactive than open-chain or larger ring compounds. The extreme example of bond-angle deformation is found in cyclopropene, a known but unstable substance.

$$CH_2$$
$$60°$$
$$CH_2 —— CH_2$$
Cyclopropane

$$CH_2$$
$$CH === CH$$
Cyclopropene

$$CH_2 —— CH_2$$
$$90°$$
$$CH_2 —— CH_2$$
Cyclobutane

Ethylene oxide, ethylene imine, and ethylene sulfide are common compounds, which are unstable as compared to their open-chain counterparts. Their four-membered homologues are also known. As would be expected, they occupy an intermediate position in stability.

$$CH_2 — CH_2$$
$$O$$
Ethylene oxide

$$CH_2 — CH_2$$
$$N$$
$$H$$
Ethylene imine

$$CH_2 — CH_2$$
$$S$$
Ethylene sulfide

If the carbon atoms of cyclopentane were all in one plane, the internal bond angles would each be 108°. However, such an arrangement places all 10 hydrogen atoms in the unfavorable eclipsed configuration. Some of the resulting strain is relieved by the warping of the molecule. The puckered position seems to move like a wave around the ring, allowing the hydrogen atoms to become slightly staggered. Both planar and puckered representations of cyclopentane are found in Fig. 6.9.

The internal bond angles of cyclohexane would be larger than 109° if all carbon atoms were in one plane, and the hydrogen atoms would all be eclipsed. The molecule avoids this potential strain by puckering enough to accommodate the 109° bond angle. At the same time, the hydrogen atoms are placed in completely staggered conformations. The result is the *chair form* of cyclohexane, which rapidly flips back and forth between two equivalent configurations, as shown in Fig. 6.10.

In the chair form of cyclohexane, the 12 bonds to hydrogen can be divided equally into two types. Those which extend straight upward

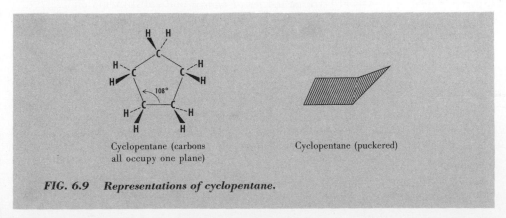

Cyclopentane (carbons all occupy one plane)

Cyclopentane (puckered)

FIG. 6.9   Representations of cyclopentane.

Drawings of chair form

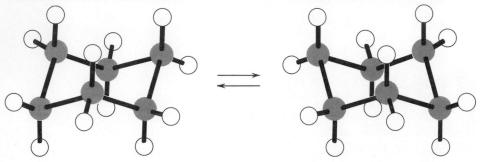

Ball-and-stick models of chair form

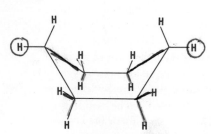

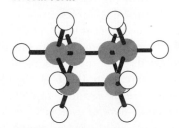

Drawing of boat form

Ball-and-stick model of boat form

FIG. 6.10   Forms of cyclohexane.

(three bonds) or downward are called *axial bonds,* and substituents on these bonds are called *axial substituents.* Those bonds which extend out and away from the center of the ring are called *equatorial bonds,* and they carry *equatorial substituents.* More space is available in equatorial positions, which bulky substituents tend to occupy whenever possible. Figure 6.11 represents the two chair forms of methylcyclohexane in profile. This view allows the eye to look down the plane described by the 1,2,4,5-positions of the molecule. Structure VIII places the space-demanding methyl substituent in the equatorial position, and the rapidly interconverting equilibrium mixture of the two conformers is rich in that component.

Another, less likely, way to obtain 109° bond angles in cyclohexane is to crumple the ring into a structure suggestive of a shallow boat.

Drawings

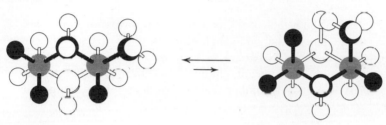

VIII

Methyl group in equatorial (*e*)
position (more stable conformer)

Methyl group in axial (*a*) position
(less stable conformer)

Ball-and-stick models

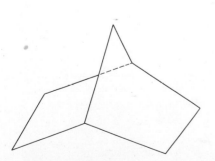

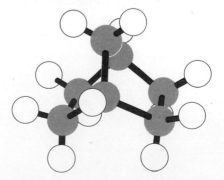

FIG. 6.11   *Profile of methylcyclohexane.*

This form, which places four sets of hydrogen atoms in eclipsed configurations, is energetically unfavorable (see Fig. 6.10). Except in bicyclic
molecules such as [2.2.1]bicycloheptane† (Fig. 6.12), where no other
geometry is possible, the boat form of cyclohexane is not realistic and
not significant.

Five- and six-membered rings containing oxygen and nitrogen in the
ring are found in many known molecules, to which similar conformational
concepts apply in a limited way. The ring systems most abundant both
in nature and in the laboratory are five- and six-membered, undoubtedly

† The nomenclature of bicyclic compounds is discussed in Chap. 28.

Drawing   *Ball-and-stick model*

FIG. 6.12   *Representations of [2.2.1] bicycloheptane.*

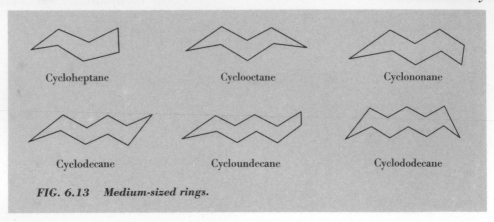

Cycloheptane   Cyclooctane   Cyclononane

Cyclodecane   Cycloundecane   Cyclododecane

FIG. 6.13   Medium-sized rings.

as a consequence of both their stability and ease of formation from open-chain molecules.   The normal bond angles for saturated carbon, nitrogen, and oxygen allow atoms located at 1,5- or 1,6-positions in a chain to wiggle close enough together to permit chemical reactions leading to ring closure.   The structures of a number of saturated heterocyclic compounds are given.

Tetrahydrofuran   Pyrrolidine   Piperidine

Carbocyclic rings containing seven to over thirty carbon atoms have been prepared.   Bond angles in these rings are essentially normal, since the rings pucker as in cyclohexane.   *Medium-sized rings* (eight- through fourteen-membered) are difficult to form because of compression created by bringing large numbers of hydrogen atoms close together.   This compression reaches a maximum in cyclodecane; it largely disappears in the fourteen-membered ring.   Large carbocyclic rings (fifteen-membered

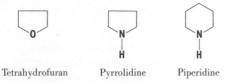

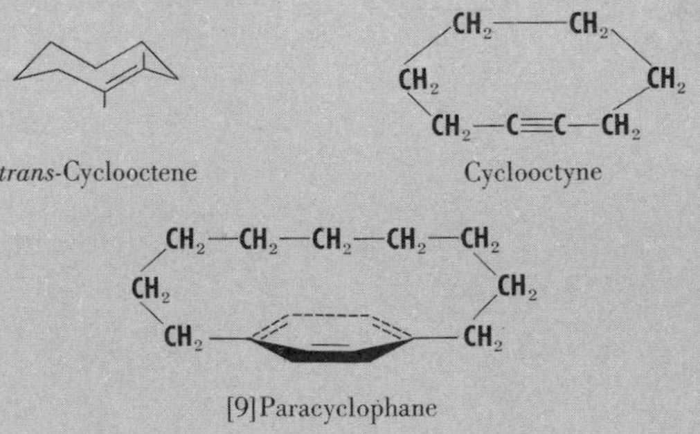

trans-Cyclooctene

$$CH_2—CH_2$$
$$CH_2 \qquad CH_2$$
$$CH_2—C≡C—CH_2$$

Cyclooctyne

$$CH_2—CH_2—CH_2—CH_2—CH_2$$
$$CH_2 \qquad CH_2$$
$$CH_2 \qquad CH_2$$

[9]Paracyclophane

FIG. 6.14   Strained ring systems.

and larger) tend to fold somewhat; their properties resemble those of their open-chain analogues. Conformations of the medium-sized rings appear in Fig. 6.13.

The smallest cycloalkene having the trans configuration about the double bond is *trans*-cyclooctene. The molecule shows considerable evidence of strain. The smallest ring capable of accommodating an acetylenic linkage also contains eight carbon atoms (cyclooctyne), and is also strained. The shortest methylene belt that can be attached to the 1- and 4-positions of a benzene ring is nine-membered. In the resulting molecule, the ordinarily flat benzene ring is bent into the pattern of a very shallow tub. The formulas of these three molecules are indicated in Fig. 6.14.

Molecular Asymmetry

If a plane can be passed through an object in such a way that one side of the plane is the *mirror image* of the other, the object is said to contain a *mirror plane*. An object is said to have a *center of symmetry* if it contains a point such that *any* straight line through that point passes through exactly the same environment in the two directions extending from that point. Objects that possess either a mirror plane or a center of symmetry are said to be *symmetric*, whereas objects that satisfy neither of these conditions are said to be *asymmetric*. Most animals and insects appear to possess mirror planes, while most plants are asymmetric.

Certain organic molecules are asymmetric, and owe this property to either of two structural features. Molecules can be asymmetric because they contain rigid or semirigid structural elements which prevent the substance from assuming symmetrical configurations. The other cause of asymmetry will be discussed in the next section.

Asymmetric molecules are nonsuperimposable on their mirror images, in the same way that our right and left hands are nonsuperimposable. Pairs of molecules that are nonsuperimposable and are the mirror images of each other are called *enantiomers* or *enantiomorphs*.

Figure 6.15 shows the structures of a number of enantiomeric pairs of molecules which owe their asymmetry to some restricted mode of molecular motion. Thus enantiomers IX*a* and IX*b* do not interconvert because of the rigidity imposed on the system by the restriction of rotation about the double bonds. Compound X is symmetric, owing to the presence of a mirror plane in the molecule. Compounds XI*a* and XI*b*, which are also enantiomeric, are incapable of interconversion, because the two five-membered rings share a single carbon atom. Ring systems fused in this way are called *spirans*. Compound XII is a spiran with a plane of symmetry. Enantiomers XIII*a* and XIII*b* maintain their structural integrity only because of restricted rotation of the benzene rings about the bond joining them. The blocking abilities of the groups on the ortho positions of the benzenes prevent these substitu-

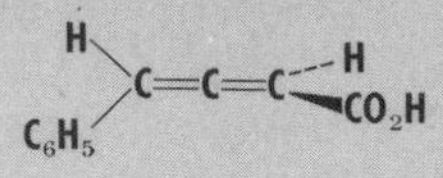

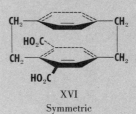
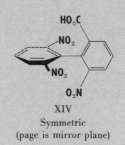

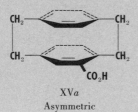

IX*a*
Asymmetric

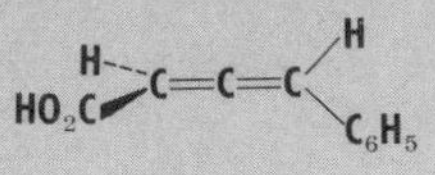

IX*b*
Asymmetric

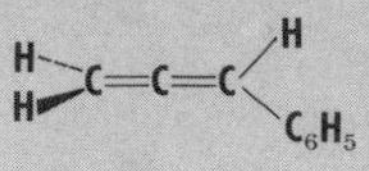

X
Symmetric
(page is mirror plane)

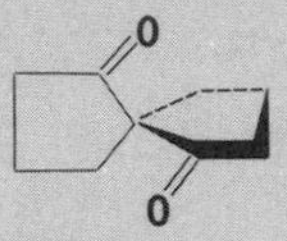

XI*a*
Asymmetric

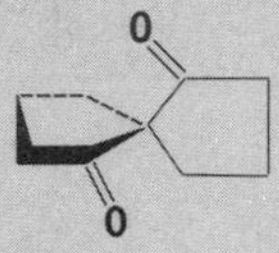

XI*b*
Asymmetric

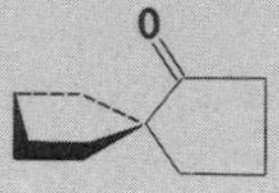

XII
Symmetric
(page is mirror plane)

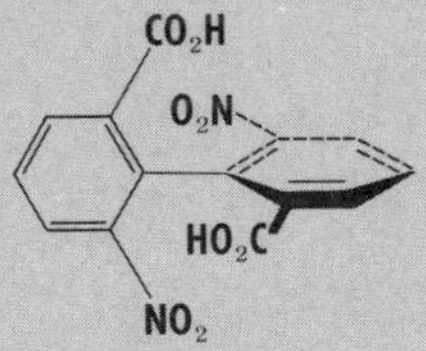

XIII*a*
Asymmetric

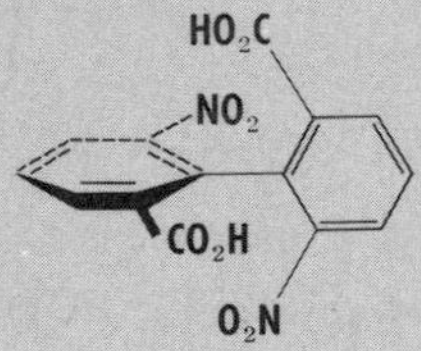

XIII*b*
Asymmetric

XIV
Symmetric
(page is mirror plane)

XV*a*
Asymmetric

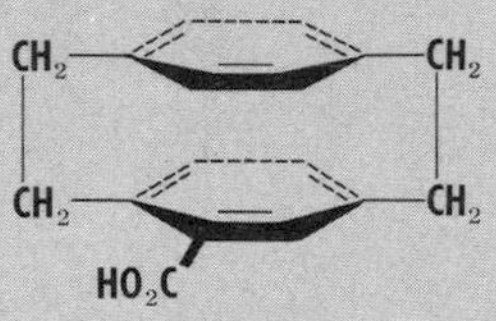

XV*b*
Asymmetric

XVI
Symmetric
(page is mirror plane)

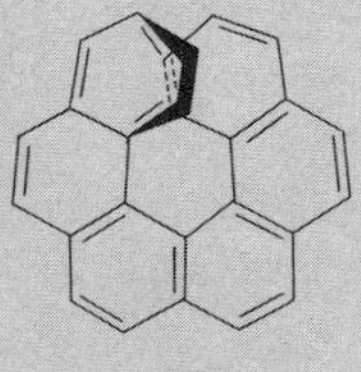

XVII*a*
Asymmetric

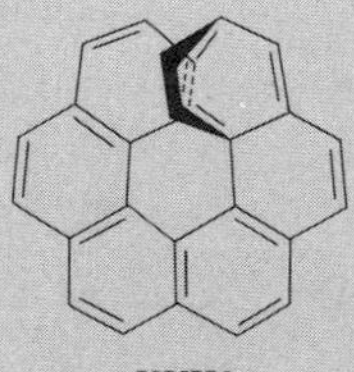

XVII*b*
Asymmetric

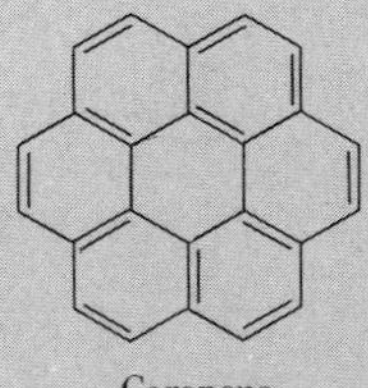

Coronene
Symmetric
(page is one of seven
mirror planes)

FIG. 6.15   Asymmetric and symmetric molecules.

ents from passing each other. Although the same is true in XIV, the molecule possesses a mirror plane. Enantiomers XV*a* and XV*b* have the shape of a molecular sandwich; they do not equilibrate because there is insufficient space to allow the ring carrying the carboxyl group to turn over. Although the same kind of restriction applies to XVI, this molecule has a mirror plane. Enantiomers XVII*a* and XVII*b* are shaped like one turn of a helix, with the outer portions of the terminal benzene rings lying over each other. These rings cannot pass each other, and therefore the enantiomers are stable with respect to each other. By contrast, coronene contains seven mirror planes.

Carbon as an Asymmetric Center

The most common type of molecular asymmetry does not depend upon restriction of internal rotation. The most interesting consequence of the tetrahedral arrangement of bonds about saturated carbon is the multiplicity of ways of assembling four attached substituents *that are different from one another.* When a three-dimensional formula for 2-butanol is drawn, two unique arrangements of the methyl, ethyl, hydrogen, and hydroxyl substituents are possible, XVIII*a* and XVIII*b* of Fig. 6.16. These structures are mirror images (enantiomers) of each other, are nonsuperimposable, and represent two distinctly different compounds.

Drawings

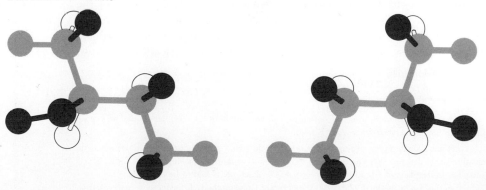

Ball-and-stick models

FIG. 6.16   *Enantiomers of 2-butanol.*

Carbon atoms carrying *four different* substituents are called *asymmetric carbon atoms,* and a star is sometimes placed *near such atoms* in formulas to emphasize this feature.†

Enantiomers appear identical as long as they are in symmetrical environments. Thus the two mandelic acids, XIX*a* and XIX*b*, possess the same melting point, the same solubility in water, and the same acid strength. The usual physical constant which distinguishes enantiomers is their optical rotation. The asymmetric character of *plane-polarized* light‡ is used to make the measurement.

XIX*a*

mp 133°

Solubility, 8.6 g per
100 g water at 20°

XIX*b*

mp 133°

Solubility, 8.6 g per
100 g water at 20°

Enantiomers of mandelic acid

When plane-polarized light is passed through a substance such as XIX*a* (either as a pure liquid or in solution), the planes of polarization of the light entering and leaving the sample are different. The angle between these two planes is a physical characteristic of the asymmetric substance, and varies with the wavelength of light, the temperature, the solvent (if any), and the number of asymmetric molecules in the light path. A substance which can rotate the plane of polarized light is said to be *optically active.*

The physical constant usually reported for optically active compounds is called the *specific rotation,* which is defined by Eqs. (1) and (2). Always recorded along with the specific rotation are the temperature, the wavelength of light, the concentration of the solution and nature of the solvent, or the fact that pure liquid was employed. Frequently, the wavelength is that of the D line of the sodium lamp, in which case D is inserted as a subscript to the specific rotation. When the plane of the light is rotated by the sample in a clockwise§ direction about the axis of the beam, the specific rotation is given a positive sign; if counterclockwise, a negative sign. Immediately after the number of degrees of

(1) $\begin{array}{l}\text{Specific rotation} \\ \text{of a solution}\end{array} = [\alpha]_{\text{wavelength}}^{\text{temp.}} = \dfrac{\text{observed rotation in degrees}}{\text{length of sample (dm)} \times \text{conc (g/ml)}}$

---

† Actually, only molecules and not atoms can be asymmetric, a fact that should be kept in mind when the term *asymmetric carbon* is used.

‡ When a single ray of ordinary light is passed through a properly oriented crystal of calcite (calcium carbonate), two rays emerge. The light of one ray vibrates in a single plane which is perpendicular to the plane of vibration of the second ray. Each ray is said to be *plane-polarized.*

§ In this use of the term *clockwise,* the observer is facing the light beam as it emerges from the sample.

(2) Specific rotation of a neat liquid $= [\alpha]_{wavelength}^{temp.} = \dfrac{\text{observed rotation in degrees}}{\text{length of sample (dm)} \times \text{density (g/ml)}}$

specific rotation, the state of the substance when the rotation was measured is noted in parentheses, as is done below in the formulations of
α-phenylethanol and atrolactic acid. If the density of a liquid is not
known, a rotation is sometimes reported as α observed, in which case the
conditions under which the rotation was determined are listed, as illustrated by the example of 2-phenylbutane. The instrument employed to
measure optical rotations is called a *polarimeter.*

$[\alpha]_D^{27°} = +42.9°$ (neat) $[\alpha]_D^{27°} = -42.9°$ (neat)

Enantiomers of α-phenylethanol

$[\alpha]_D^{15} = +52.0°$ (C 2%, H$_2$O) $[\alpha]_D^{15} - 52.0°$ (C 2%, H$_2$O)

Enantiomers of atrolactic acid

$\alpha_D^{23} = +24.3°$ (neat, $l = 1$ dm) $\alpha_D^{23} = -24.3°$ (neat, $l = 1$ dm)

Enantiomers of 2-phenylbutane

Pure enantiomers possess equal and opposite specific rotations. A
mixture of two enantiomers in equal molar proportions possesses no
optical activity, since the rotations exactly cancel each other. Such a
mixture is called a *racemate*, and is sometimes referred to as a *d,l-*
mixture. The letters *d* and *l*, standing for *dextro* and *levo*, refer to the
sign of rotation. When $(+)$, the rotation is *dextro*; when $(-)$, the
rotation is *levo*; when zero, the material is *d,l*, or $(\pm)$.

Solid racemates occur as *solid solutions, racemic mixtures,* or *racemic
compounds.* In solid solutions, the melting points of the racemates and
enantiomers are identical, and do not change when the substances are
mixed. Racemic mixtures have melting points below those of their components, and addition of either pure component to the mixture raises the
melting point. Racemic compounds have melting points either above or
below those of the pure enantiomers, and addition of small amounts of
an active isomer lowers the melting point of a racemic compound.
These differences in melting-point behavior provide a method of distinguishing these three crystallographic types of solid racemates.

In organic syntheses carried out in the laboratory, ordinarily only symmetrical reagents are used. If asymmetric centers are created in a reaction, the two enantiomers are made in equal amounts, and a racemate is produced. Reduction of pyruvic to lactic acid with hydrogen and platinum provides an example. Hydrogen attacking the carbonyl group comes in from either of two directions with equal probability to give equal amounts of the two enantiomers.

| | 50% | 50% | |

Pyruvic acid   Racemic lactic acid   Pyruvic acid

In nature, catalysts for organic reactions are complex organic molecules (enzyme systems) which are themselves asymmetric. As a result, usually only one enantiomer is produced in the enzymatic creation of an asymmetric center. Almost all naturally occurring compounds that contain asymmetric centers are optically active and are seldom encountered as racemates.

Pyruvic acid   (+)- or (−)-lactic acid, depending on the enzyme system

Many Asymmetric Centers per Molecule

No limit exists to the possible number of asymmetric centers in a single molecule. Many natural products contain from two to ten asymmetric carbon atoms, and molecules of starch (Chap. 25) and proteins (Chap. 25) contain hundreds.

In open-chain molecules without special symmetry properties, the number of *stereomers* (stereoisomers) is equal to 2^n, where n is the number of asymmetric carbon atoms in a compound. The substance 3-phenyl-2-butanol contains two asymmetric carbon atoms; and therefore four stereomers, each with a unique configuration, possess this atomic sequence. These stereomers are all known compounds, possessing the configurations indicated in Fig. 6.17. These structures are nonsuperimposable. Each isomer has a specific rotation different from every other, the enantiomers having equal rotations of opposite sign.[†] Stereomer XX*a* is the enantiomer of XX*b*, and XXI*a* is the enantiomer of XXI*b*. Taken together in equal amounts, XX*a* and XX*b* form one racemate, and

[†] Small deviations from equality of magnitude of rotation represent experimental error or lack of purity.

XXI*a* and XXI*b* form a second. The relationship between any two stereomers must be either enantiomeric or *diastereomeric*. Thus the relationship between XX*a* and XXI*a* is diastereomeric, as is the relationship between XX*b* and XXI*a*. Thus *diastereomers* possess the same configuration at one or more asymmetric centers, and different configurations at one or more asymmetric centers of a molecule. Diastereomers have different physical and chemical properties.

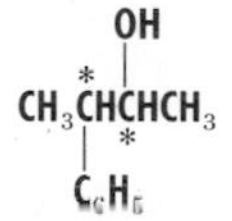

$$\underset{\text{3-Phenyl-2-butanol}}{\overset{\displaystyle \overset{\text{OH}}{\overset{|}{\underset{|}{\underset{\underset{\text{C}_6\text{H}_5}{*}}{\overset{*}{\text{CH}_3\text{CHCHCH}_3}}}}}}{}}$$

Frequently substances have special symmetry properties, and the 2^n formula breaks down. The tartaric acids illustrate this point.

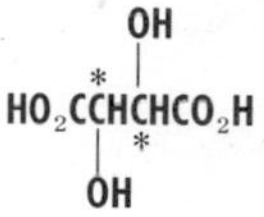

$$\underset{\text{Tartaric acid}}{\overset{\displaystyle \overset{\text{OH}}{\overset{|}{\underset{|}{\underset{\underset{\text{OH}}{*}}{\overset{*}{\text{HO}_2\text{CCHCHCO}_2\text{H}}}}}}}{}}$$

Three stereomers of tartaric acid are known, and three configurations can be written. Two of these represent an enantiomeric pair (XXII*a* and XXII*b*); the third is symmetric. Formulas XXIII*a* and XXIII*b* are simply two ways of indicating the same configuration, and are superimposable simply by rotating one of the formulas in the plane of the paper

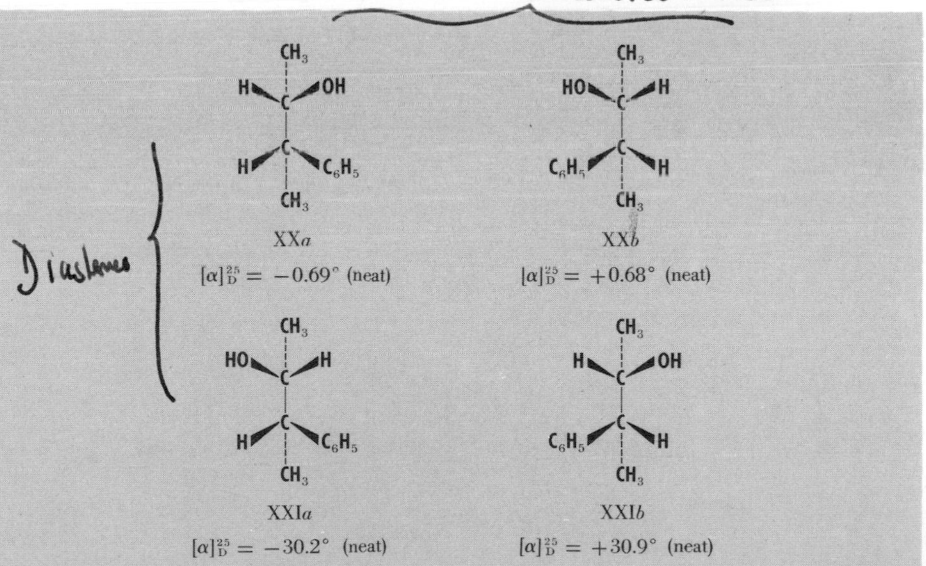

FIG. 6.17   Stereomers of 3-phenyl-2-butanol.

through 180°. This isomer is called *meso*-tartaric acid. Although it contains two asymmetric carbon atoms, the molecule has a mirror plane perpendicular to, and bisecting, the bond between the two central carbon atoms. Compounds which contain asymmetric carbon atoms, but are nonetheless symmetric, are said to be *meso* in configuration, and they are optically inactive. The meso isomer of tartaric acid is a diastereomer of either (+)- or (−)-tartaric acid.

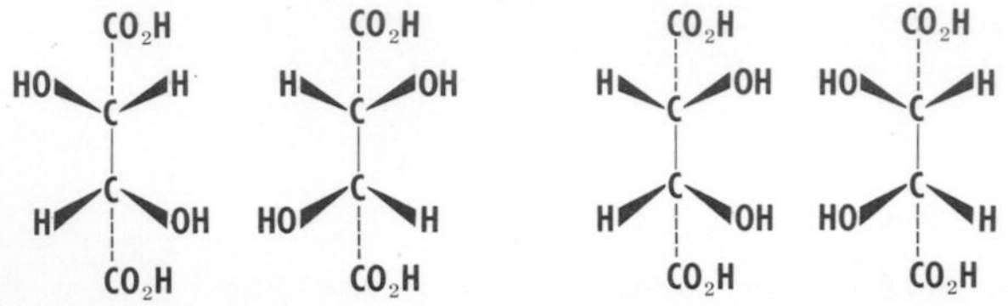

CO₂H	CO₂H	CO₂H	CO₂H

XXIIa XXIIb   XXIIIa XXIIIb

(−)-Tartaric (+)-Tartaric   Two different ways of representing
acid, mp 170° acid, mp 170°   *meso*-tartaric acid, mp 140°.

Racemic or *d,l*- or (±)-   Substance is optically inactive.
tartaric acid, mp 206°

    The difficulty of portraying configurations of molecules increases with the number of asymmetric centers. An adequate substitute for a three-dimensional representation of an open-chain molecule is found in the *Fischer projection formulas* used to show configurations of the isomers of compound XXIV.

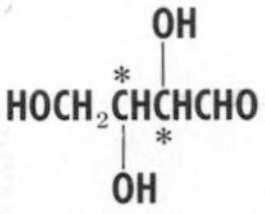

$$\text{HOCH}_2\overset{*}{\text{C}}\text{H}\overset{\text{OH}}{\underset{\text{OH}}{\text{C}}}\text{HCHO}$$

XXIV

    In Fischer formulas, projections of all bonds are written in the plane of the paper. The spine of the molecule is oriented vertically, and the hydrogen atoms and hydroxyl groups are written on the wings (left and right). These flat formulas are understood to represent three-dimensional models in which horizontal bonds are above, and vertical bonds are either in or below, the plane of the paper. The isomers of XXIV are shown below with Fischer formulas.

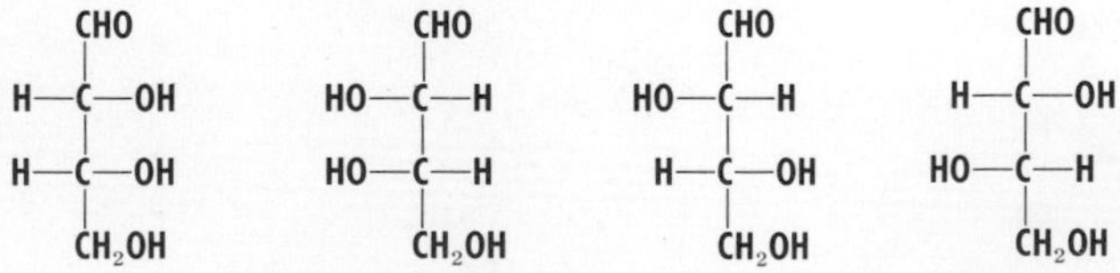

CHO	CHO	CHO	CHO
H—C—OH	HO—C—H	HO—C—H	H—C—OH
H—C—OH	HO—C—H	H—C—OH	HO—C—H
CH₂OH	CH₂OH	CH₂OH	CH₂OH
(−)-Erythrose	(+)-Erythrose	(−)-Threose	(+)-Threose

    Formulas of this type cannot be manipulated with the same freedom as those which take account of all three dimensions. The consequences, with respect to configuration, of various manipulations performed with Fischer formulas are indicated in Fig. 6.18. When the Fischer formula of (−)-threose is rotated 180° in the plane of the paper, no alteration of configuration occurs. Rotation of **C**-2 180° about the (central) bond connecting **C**-2 and **C**-3 converts the Fischer formula for (−)-threose to that for (−)-erythrose. Rotation of the Fischer formula for (−)-threose 180° out of the plane of the paper about either the horizontal or vertical axis gives the Fischer formula for (+)-threose. These changes are followed in Fig. 6.18.

An interesting set of symmetry properties is associated with the system represented by formula XXV, which contains three potentially asymmetric centers. Carbon atoms 2 and 4 are ordinary asymmetric

$$\overset{\text{OH}\ \ \text{OH}}{\underset{\underset{\text{OH}}{*\ \ |\ \ *}}{\text{HOCH}_2\overset{|}{\underset{*}{\text{CH}}}\overset{\overset{*}{|}}{\text{CHCH}}\text{CH}_2\text{OH}}}$$

$$1\ \ 2\ 3\ 4\ 5$$

XXV

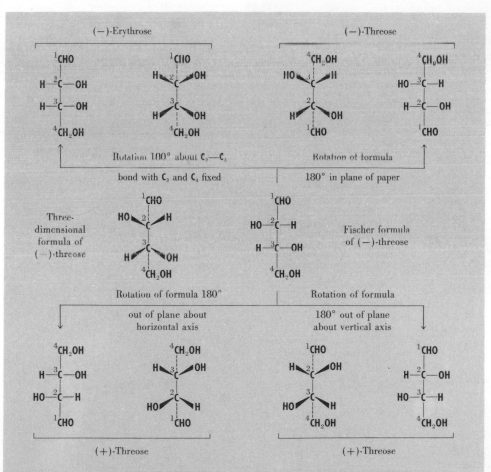

FIG. 6.18   Manipulations of Fischer projection formulas.

centers, but carbon 3 is said to be *pseudoasymmetric,* since its symmetry properties depend on the configurations about carbon atoms 2 and 4. Four stereomeric structures can be written which possess the atomic sequence of XXV. Two of these are symmetric, or meso, forms which contain mirror planes that pass through carbon 3 and its hydrogen and hydroxyl substituents. The two optically active stereomers are enantiomerically related, and taken together represent a racemate. These relationships are shown in Fischer projection formulas as follows:

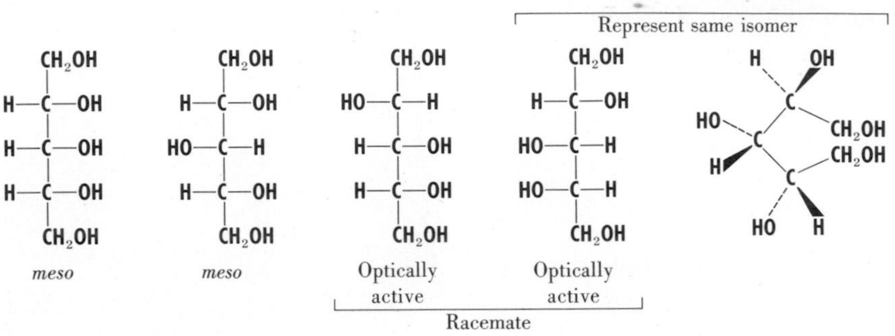

meso   meso   Optically   Optically
                        active   active

Racemate

XXV

In laboratory syntheses of compounds containing two or more asymmetric carbon atoms, mixtures of diastereomers are usually obtained in unequal amounts, the proportions differing with the method of synthesis. In the introduction of a second asymmetric carbon, a *sterically controlled asymmetric induction occurs.* In the examples formulated, the incoming group *does not* come in with equal probability from both sides of the carbon-oxygen double bond. The two sides are not equally exposed to the attacking molecule, because of the asymmetry of the adjacent center.

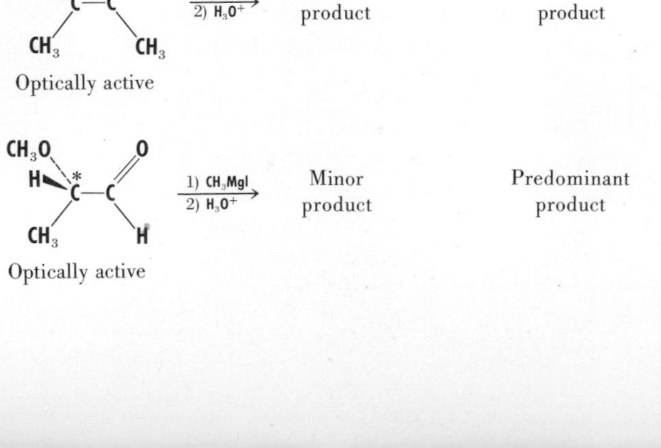

One diastereomer   Other diastereomer

Predominant   Minor
product   product

Minor   Predominant
product   product

Racemization and Epimerization

The term *racemization* describes a process in which an optically active stereoisomer is converted to a racemate. An example of such a reaction is the following. When α-methylbutyric acid is heated, its optical activity is slowly lost, and racemic material is ultimately obtained. This transformation involves the equilibration of each enantiomer with a planar and symmetric intermediate in which hydrogen on the α-carbon has shifted to one of the oxygen atoms of the carboxyl group. In shifting back from oxygen to carbon, hydrogen comes in with equal probability from either above or below the plane of the intermediate to give equal amounts of the two enantiomers.

$(-)$ Isomer   Planar and $(+)$ Isomer
                    symmetric intermediate

If a compound has two or more asymmetric centers, and the configuration *of only one of these* is altered by some reaction, the process is called *epimerization*. For example, when either diastereomer XXVI*a* or XXVI*b* of 1,2-diphenyl-1-propyl formate is dissolved in formic acid, the substance ionizes to give the same cation, which reacts with the solvent to give a mixture of diastereomeric formates. No racemization occurs, since the configuration of the second asymmetric center is never altered.

1,2-Diphenyl-1-propyl   Intermediate cation   1,2-Diphenyl-1-propyl
formate, XXVI*a*   formate, XXVI*b*
                          $+\,HCO_2 \downarrow \uparrow - HCO_2^-$
                               55% XXVI*b*
                               45% XXVI*a*

Reactions in which bonds are broken and made at asymmetric carbon, and which lead largely to a single stereomer, are said to be *stereospecific*. If the configuration is altered in the process, the reaction goes with *inversion of configuration*. If the configuration remains the same, the transformation occurs with *retention of configuration*. These last two terms apply to a single asymmetric center, whereas the terms *racemization* and *epimerization* refer to the symmetry properties of whole molecules. Examples of stereospecific reactions are found in Fig. 6.19.

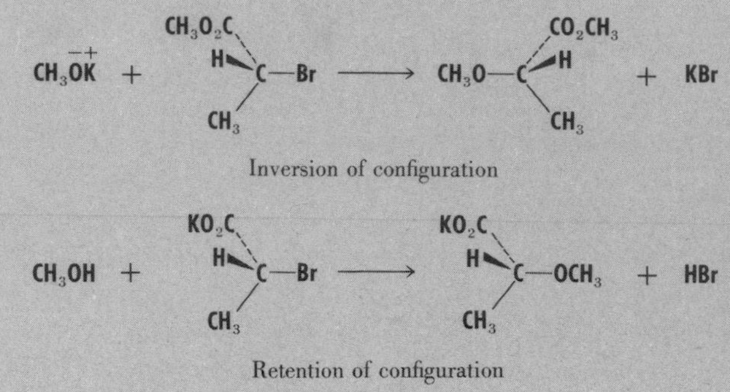

$$CH_3\overset{-+}{O}K \;+\; \underset{CH_3}{\overset{CH_3O_2C}{\underset{\;}{\overset{H}{C}}}}C\!-\!Br \;\longrightarrow\; CH_3O\!-\!\underset{CH_3}{\overset{CO_2CH_3}{\overset{H}{C}}} \;+\; KBr$$

Inversion of configuration

$$CH_3OH \;+\; \underset{CH_3}{\overset{KO_2C}{\overset{H}{C}}}C\!-\!Br \;\longrightarrow\; \underset{CH_3}{\overset{KO_2C}{\overset{H}{C}}}C\!-\!OCH_3 \;+\; HBr$$

Retention of configuration

FIG. 6.19   *Stereospecific reactions.*

Stereoisomerism in Ring Compounds

The same principles apply to both cyclic and open-chain compounds. A single substituent in a saturated carbocyclic ring does not suffice to make a molecule asymmetric, whereas two substituents properly situated can give rise to stereoisomerism.   For instance, three unique stereomeric structures can be written for 1,2-cyclopropanedicarboxylic acid, and these compounds are known.   The terms *cis* and *trans* are applied in naming these isomers, in much the same way as they were applied to the alkenes (page 120).

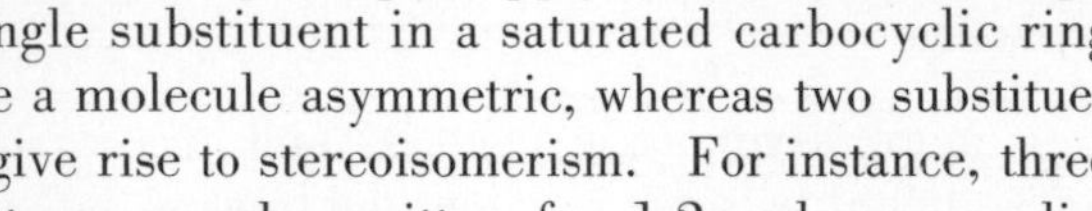

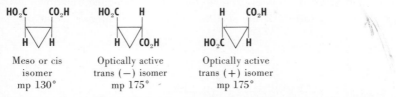

Meso or cis	Optically active	Optically active
isomer	trans (−) isomer	trans (+) isomer
mp 130°	mp 175°	mp 175°

The two stereomers of 4-*tert*-butylcyclohexanol each contain a mirror plane, and are therefore optically inactive.   Both isomers possess the interesting feature of being essentially "frozen" into one conformation (one of two possible chair forms), because the large steric requirements of the *tert*-butyl group cause it to remain in an equatorial position in both compounds.   The terms *cis* and *trans* are also applied to these isomers, in spite of the fact that the ring is puckered.   The nomenclature is based on the disposition of the substituents about a hypothetical planar configuration of the molecule.

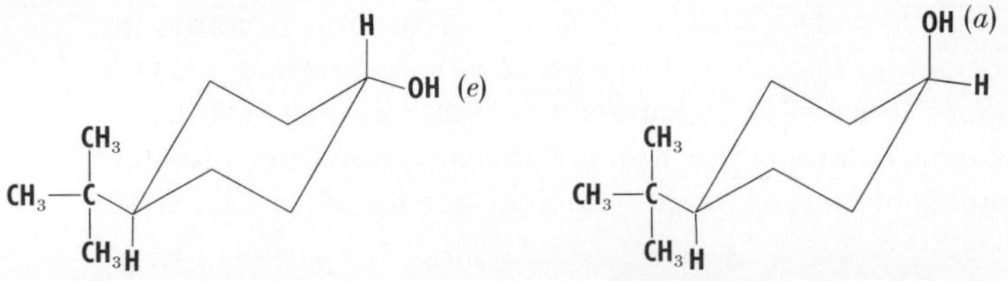

trans-4-*tert*-Butylcyclohexanol (symmetric)   *cis*-4-*tert*-Butylcyclohexanol (symmetric)

The activity of one of the stereoisomers of benzene hexachloride as an insecticide has led to elucidation of the stereochemical structures of many of the isomers. In the interest of simplicity, the rings are written as if planar, and the relative positions of the chlorine atoms are designated by vertical lines. Identification of *the single racemate* among this multitude of compounds was made in an interesting way. The racemate was heated with an optically active amine (brucine), which, being itself asymmetric, could discriminate between the two enantiomers. Although the base reacted with both enantiomers, one was consumed faster than the other. The reaction was stopped before all the racemate had reacted, and the residue was rich in the less reactive isomer. As a result, this material possessed optical activity.

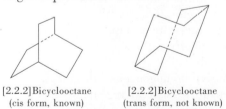

Benzene hexachloride, general formula

Biologically active isomer

Partial reaction catalyzed by brucine → Optically active unreacted isomer recovered

Racemate

In many cases of fused-ring or bicyclic structures, not all theoretically possible stereoisomers are sterically feasible. For instance, in principle, [2.2.2]bicyclooctane (Chap. 28) could exist in both forms drawn below. Clearly, only the cis form can accommodate the bond-length and bond-angle requirements of carbon.

[2.2.2]Bicyclooctane
(cis form, known)

[2.2.2]Bicyclooctane
(trans form, not known)

Resolution of Racemates into Enantiomers

The separation of a racemate into its two enantiomers is called *resolution*. Three methods have been used to resolve racemates. The first of these can occasionally be applied to racemic mixtures which crystallize in such a way that molecules of like configuration gather into

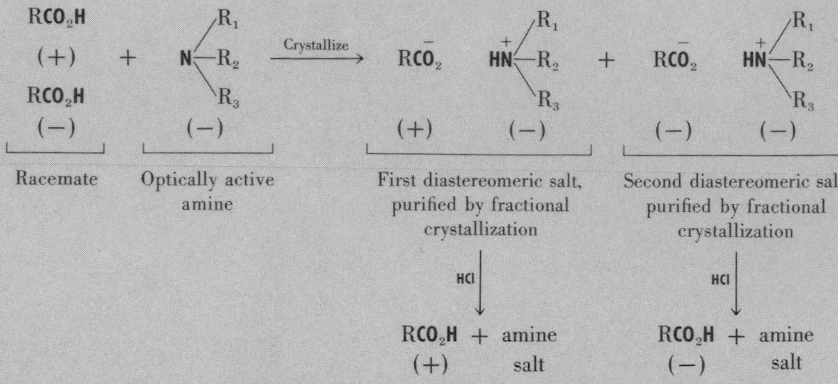

FIG. 6.20   Resolution of a racemic acid.

one kind of asymmetric crystal, and enantiomeric molecules into a second, the first crystal being the mirror image of the second. These crystals may be sorted and collected into two piles of crystals, one rich or pure in one enantiomer, the other in the second enantiomer. Pasteur performed the first resolution of this sort in 1848 in a separation of the $(+)$ and $(-)$ forms of sodium ammonium tartrate.

In a second method of resolution, enzyme systems (either inside or outside an organism) are allowed to consume or chemically modify one enantiomer of a pair. The other is rejected. A case has been recorded in which a racemate was fed to a dog that metabolized one enantiomer and passed the other in its urine. This procedure has not found widespread use.

The third and by far most generally used method involves a chemical procedure. Nature has provided a number of optically active carboxylic acids and amines which contain asymmetric centers. If the racemate is an acid, an optically active amine, such as cinchonine, cinchonidine, quinine, brucine, strychnine, morphine, or thebaine, is used to split the enantiomeric pair. The racemate is mixed with the amine, and *diastereomerically related and optically active salts crystallize.* Since these two salts have different solubility properties, they can be separated by fractional crystallization to give homogeneous substances. Each of the salts is treated with hydrochloric acid to regenerate the original acids, now in optically active forms. If the separation is meticulously carried out, *optically pure* (enantiomerically homogeneous) stereomers may be prepared. If the starting racemate is an amine, an optically active acid is used as resolving agent. Compounds such as $(+)$- and $(-)$-tartaric acid, $(-)$-malic, and $(-)$-mandelic acids are frequently employed. Figure 6.20 traces the steps involved in the resolution of a racemic carboxylic acid.

If a racemate is neither basic nor acidic, a "handle" carrying such a function is temporarily attached to the molecule. After the racemate is resolved, the handle is removed. Thus 2-octanol is converted to its acid phthalate ester, which is resolved, and then the two active alcohols are regenerated by hydrolysis of the ester.

| (±)-2-Octanol | Phthalic anhydride | (±)-Acid phthalate of 2-octanol, resolved through brucine salt |

(−)-Acid phthalate $\xrightarrow{\text{NaOH}}$ (+)-2-octanol + sodium phthalate

(+)-Acid phthalate $\xrightarrow{\text{NaOH}}$ (−)-2-octanol + sodium phthalate

Asymmetric Centers Other than Carbon

Although the arrangement of bonds in amines approaches a tetrahedral configuration (the unshared pair of electrons is equivalent to one bond), no ordinary tertiary amine has been resolved. In molecules of this type, the two forms of the amine are undergoing very rapid inter-conversion, the unshared pair of electrons in a sense passing through nitrogen.

Quaternary ammonium compounds have been resolved, as have amine oxides. Examples of these types of compounds are formulated below.

| Racemate | | An amine oxide |

Unshared pairs of electrons on sulfur (unlike those on nitrogen) are capable of holding configuration at ordinary temperatures, as has been demonstrated by resolution of compounds such as sulfonium salt, XXVII, and sulfoxide, XXVIII.

$$C_2H_5\overset{\overset{\displaystyle \overset{-}{Br}}{\underset{\displaystyle CH_3}{\overset{..}{\underset{}{\overset{+}{S}}}}}{}CH_2CO_2H \qquad C_2H_5\overset{\overset{..}{\underset{\displaystyle O}{\underset{+}{S}}}}{}$$

XXVII   XXVIII

Absolute Configuration and Notation

Ever since the discovery of optical activity, chemists have been beset with two problems. The first is experimental determination of the *absolute configuration* of some optically active molecule, and the second is the invention of some rational system of nomenclature for *specifying the configuration* of stereomers. The first problem has now been solved, and a proposal has been made that might solve the second.

The direction and magnitude of rotation of a compound is simply a physical constant, and *no simple relationship exists between this physical constant and the configuration of a compound.* Assignment of sign of rotation to a three-dimensional formula of a particular enantiomer is a difficult experimental problem, since a method is needed which differentiates the structure of a compound from that of its mirror image. No purely chemical method exists for determining the *absolute configuration* of an optically active molecule. However, optically active compounds may be interconverted by chemical routes without disturbing asymmetric centers, and as a result a series of compounds whose *configurations are known in relation to one another* has been accumulated. Chemical means are also available for determining the relative configurations of two or more asymmetric carbon atoms within the same molecule. If the *absolute configuration* of any single compound within a series whose relative configurations are established is determined, absolute configurations can be assigned to all compounds of the series.

In the absence of means to determine absolute configurations, investigators before 1951 used an *assumed configuration* for the enantiomeric glyceraldehydes as a standard. The (+) isomer was assumed to have structure XXIX, and this spacial arrangement of atoms was named the D configuration. The configuration of the enantiomer of XXIX was designated as L.

$$H\overset{\overset{\displaystyle CHO}{|}}{\underset{\underset{\displaystyle CH_2OH}{|}}{C}}OH \xrightarrow{\text{Several reactions}} H\overset{\overset{\displaystyle CO_2H}{|}}{\underset{\underset{\displaystyle CH_3}{|}}{C}}OH$$

XXIX   XXX

D-(+)-Glyceraldehyde   D-(−)-Lactic acid

The relative configuration of lactic acid has been determined by converting (+)-glyceraldehyde into (−)-lactic acid *without breaking any bonds to the asymmetric carbon atom.* Similarly, relative configurations of many compounds have been established. Figure 6.21 indicates the reactions used to convert D-(+)-glyceraldehyde into a mixture of *meso*- and (−)-tartaric acids. Lack of optical activity in the meso isomer allows the two diastereomers to be readily identified. Furthermore, configurations of both asymmetric carbon atoms of (−)-tartaric acid in relation to D-glyceraldehyde are established by this experiment, as well as configurations of the asymmetric carbon atoms of (+)-tartaric acid.

The nomenclature associated with use of the D-(+)-glyceraldehyde configuration as a standard has been satisfactory only when one asymmetric carbon atom was involved, and when the groups attached to that carbon were not very different from those in glyceraldehyde. In lactic acid, two of the groups (**H** and **OH**) attached to the asymmetric carbon atom are identical with the two in glyceraldehyde. The **CH$_2$OH** and **CH$_3$** groups, and the **CHO** and **CO$_2$H** groups, of the two molecules may be considered similar. Thus (−)-lactic acid, which was demonstrated to possess the configuration of formula XXX, can be designated as D. The system becomes ambiguous in designating configurations of any but the simplest molecules. Different authors, on the basis of different selections of groups as being similar to one another, have designated (+)-tartaric acid as both D and L. When molecules contain two or more asymmetric centers, authors usually resort to trivial names for diastereomers, except where the terms *cis*, *trans*, *meso*, D, and L suffice.

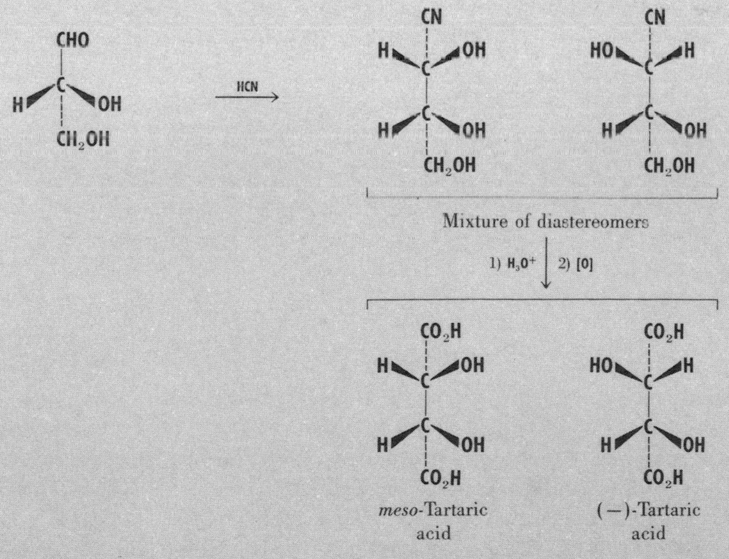

FIG. 6.21   *Relative configuration of (−)-tartaric acid.*

The chances were even that the glyceraldehyde convention would couple a given sign of rotation with the correct configuration. Fortunately, the selection was demonstrated to be correct by experiment in 1951. Normally, X-ray diffraction photographs of crystalline enantiomers are identical. However, by the use of special X rays, the absolute configuration of the sodium rubidium salt of (+)-tartaric acid was determined. Now absolute configurational assignments can be given to compounds whose configurations have been established in relation to (+)-tartaric acid.

Systematic Specification of Configuration

Now that absolute configurations can be assigned to many asymmetric organic compounds, the remaining problem is the unambiguous specification of their configurations through systematic nomenclature. The following notation has been proposed to solve this problem.

If a molecule contains an asymmetric carbon atom, the four *atoms* attached to that carbon are arranged in a sequence of decreasing atomic number. If two or more of these *first atoms* have the same atomic number, a selection is made by comparing the atomic numbers of the *second* group of atoms attached to the first atoms. If ambiguity still persists, the *third, fourth,* etc., sets (working outward from the asymmetric carbon atom) are compared until a selection can be made. In the second group of atoms, those atoms with the highest, next-highest, etc., atomic numbers are always compared. If an atom of the first group carries no substituents, the atomic number of a fictitious second group of atoms is assumed to be zero.

Consider this sequence rule as applied to 2-butanol. Clearly oxygen has the highest and hydrogen the lowest priority. To differentiate between C-1 and C-3, the atoms attached to C-1 (**H, H**, and **H**) must be compared with those of C-3 (**C, H**, and **H**). Obviously C-3 has the higher priority, and the groups can be ordered in the sequence **O**, C-3, C-1, **H**.

2-Butanol

A three-dimensional model of the isomer to be named is now viewed from the side remote from the group of lowest priority, and the sequence (decreasing priority) of the other three groups is noted as being clockwise or counterclockwise. When it is clockwise, the symbol R (for *rectus*) is used to denote the configuration. When it is counterclockwise, the symbol S (for *sinister*) is employed. The three-dimensional formula written for one isomer of 2-butanol in Fig. 6.22 has the R configuration.

With molecules containing more than one asymmetric center, each center is examined, assigned a configuration, and the terms R or S are then

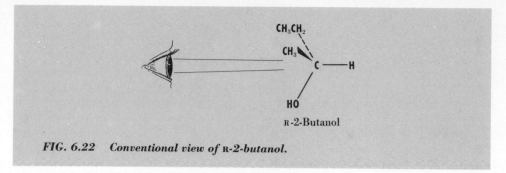

FIG. 6.22 *Conventional view of R-2-butanol.*

incorporated into the systematic name by simply inserting the number of the asymmetric carbon atom in question in front of the letter, as in the following example. The system has been expanded to embrace asymmetric molecules without asymmetric centers, as well as compounds with asymmetric centers other than carbon.

3-s-Chloro-2-s-hydroxypentane

Problems

1. Write out structures for the following substances:

a. The three *conformations* of 2-methylbutane with end-on formulas. Which formulas are superimposable?

b. Three conformations of 2-butanone with three-dimensional formulas

c. The two conformations of *cis*-4-isopropyl-1-methylcyclohexane

d. The two conformations of *trans*-4-isopropyl-1-methylcyclohexane

e. The two conformations of *cis*- and the two conformations of *trans*-1,3-dimethylcyclohexane

2. Using normal bond lengths and bond angles, calculate the following distances:

a. Between C-1 and C-3 of cyclobutane

b. Between C-1 and C-3 of cyclopentane

c. Between C-1 and C-4 of benzene

d. Between C-1 and C-3 of propane

3. Write out structural formulas for the following compounds:

a. *cis*-2,3-Dichloro-2-pentene

b. *trans*-2-Phenyl-2-butene

c. *cis-trans*-1,4-Diphenyl-1,3-butadiene

d. *trans*-4-Methyl-3-octene

e. *anti*-Oxime of α-naphthaldehyde

f. *cis*-1,3-Dichlorocyclobutane

4. State which of the following pairs of compounds you expect to be the more stable, and why.

a. *cis*- or *trans*-2-Butene

b. *cis*- or *trans*-2-Phenyl-2-butene

c. *cis*- or *trans*-1,4-Diphenylcyclohexane

d. *cis*- or *trans*-1,3-Dibromocyclohexane

e. *cis*- or *trans*-1,2-Dimethylcyclopentane

f. *cis*- or *trans*-1-Methyl-4-*tert*-butylcyclohexane

5. Write out three-dimensional formulas for all the isomers of the following compounds. Indicate the enantiomeric and the diastereomeric relationships. Indicate all isomers that are optically active.

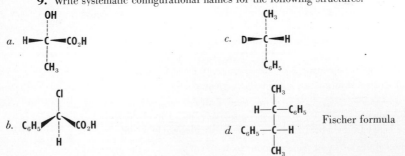

a. CH_3—CH—CH—CH_3
            | |
            Cl   Cl

d. CH_3CH=$CHCH_2CH_2CH$=$CHCH_3$

b. (structure with CH_3, CH_3, CH_3 on ring)

e. CH_3CH=$CHCHCH$=$CHCH_3$
                    |
                    OH

c. (bicyclic structure with OH OH)

f. $CH_3CHCHCHCH_3$
            | |
         C_6H_5 C_6H_5
    (Cl above)

g. (cyclohexane with Cl, Cl, Cl, Cl)

h. (bicyclic structure with —OH, —OH)

6. Write out three-dimensional structures for *all the unique ways* of substituting two carboxyl groups on the two aromatic rings of the compound indicated. State which are optically active. Indicate which structure contains a center but not a plane of symmetry.

CH_2—<═══>—CH_2
CH_2—<═══>—CH_2

7. Define the following terms:

a. Inversion of configuration
b. Retention of configuration
c. Racemization
d. Mirror plane

e. Epimerization
f. Stereospecific
g. Center of symmetry

8. Write out three-dimensional formulas for the following compounds:

a. $C_6H_5CHCH_3$ L configuration
            |
            OH

b. CH_3CHCO_2H D configuration
            |
            NH_2

c. CHClBrI   R configuration

d. $CH_3CH_2CH_2$—C—CH_2CH_3 s configuration
                       |
                      CH_3 (above)
                      OH (below)

e. 3-R-4-s-Dimethylhexane

9. Write systematic configurational names for the following structures:

a. H—C—CO_2H
         (OH above, CH_3 below)

b. C_6H_5—C—CO_2H
         (Cl above, H below)

c. D—C—H
         (CH_3 above, C_6H_5 below)

d. C_6H_5—C—H
         (CH_3 above)
     H—C—C_6H_5
         (CH_3 below)   Fischer formula

10. Differentiate the terms *structure*, *configuration*, and *conformation*. In ordinary molecules, which of these terms apply to states subject to interconversion without making or breaking bonds.

11. Why are *cis*- and *trans*-stilbene more easily interconverted than *cis*- and *trans*-2-butene?

7

Physical Properties

The wide differences in physical properties of organic compounds have long provided means of separating, characterizing, and identifying substances. More recently, extensive correlations of physical properties with structure have revolutionized the art of elucidating the constitution of organic molecules. This chapter deals with such physical properties as transition points (melting and boiling points), solubility, adsorption, and dipole and polarization phenomena, and with the correlation of these properties with structure. Chapter 27 treats the spectral properties of organic compounds. Properties such as hardness, elasticity, viscosity, conductivity, and tensile strength are frequently responsible for the great usefulness of organic materials, but are less fundamental and will not be treated here.

Physical Properties as Means of Identification and Separation

Transition Points. The *melting point* of a solid is that temperature at which the solid becomes a liquid. Pure crystalline solids normally have *sharp* melting points, or undergo the transition over a temperature range of 1° or less. On the other hand, impure crystalline solids usually melt over a much wider range of temperature. Only small volume changes are involved in passing from the solid to the liquid state, and as a consequence, melting points depend very little on pressure. Most crystalline organic compounds have characteristic melting points, which are easily determined and reproduced. These facts make melting points the most widely used physical constants.

The melting range of a crystalline compound is frequently used as an index of its purity. When two different pure crystalline compounds are mixed together, the resulting mixture frequently melts 20 or 30°

below the melting point of the lower-melting component, and over a range of many degrees. In contrast, two different samples of a single compound which come from entirely different sources (e.g., one from the laboratory and the other from nature), when mixed together, exhibit the same melting characteristics as either sample treated separately. This behavior is frequently used to demonstrate the identity of structure of materials from different sources.

Occasionally a single compound can be crystallized to give *two different kinds* of crystals, each with its own melting point and solubility characteristics. This phenomenon is known as *polymorphism*, and the crystalline forms are called *polymorphs*. Fortunately, this potential ambiguity in melting behavior is seldom encountered. However, existence of the phenomenon does show that crystals possess structural units (*unit cells*) which frequently include several individual molecules, and that a given *molecular structure* does not always require the same crystal form.

In a crystal, molecules are usually packed together in orderly and rigid repetitive patterns. Intermolecular forces, referred to as *lattice forces*, hold the crystal together and limit molecular motions. For example, although rotations about carbon-carbon single bonds occur readily in the liquid and vapor phases, these movements are literally frozen in crystals. When brought to its melting point, the crystal disintegrates, since the thermal energy of the molecules within the crystal becomes great enough to overcome the lattice forces, and the molecules break out of their prisons.

The *boiling point* of a liquid is that temperature at which the vapor pressure of the liquid becomes equal to the atmospheric pressure of the system. The boiling point of a liquid depends very markedly on pressure, since volume changes in passing from the liquid to the gaseous state are very large. Thus when boiling points are reported, the pressure must be specified. Whenever possible, boiling points are reported at 760 mm of mercury (one atmosphere of pressure). Boiling points vary widely with structure and provide useful constants for identifying and characterizing liquids. Differences in boiling points allow liquids to be separated by fractional distillation. Pure compounds possess very small boiling ranges, and mixtures usually have considerable ranges, the size of which depends on the boiling points of the individual components. This difference makes boiling range a useful criterion of purity.

In the liquid state, strong intermolecular forces still hold molecules in close proximity to one another, but in a manner which allows rapid molecular movement. Not only do molecules as a whole move about, but their parts flap and rotate in all but the most rigid structures. When their thermal energy becomes great enough, molecules overcome attractive forces and pass into the vapor state, where such forces are usually negligibly small.

Solubility. The dissolution of solid in liquid in some respects resembles the melting of a solid, since the ordered crystal structure is destroyed. Interactions in a dilute solution are for the most part between solute and solvent, although in some instances solute molecules may show a considerable tendency to cluster together. Since the characteristic crystal energies are lost in both melting and dissolution, one can safely generalize that among groups of closely related substances, the higher-melting compounds will usually be the less soluble.

Mixing of two miscible liquids involves the exchange of attractive forces between like molecules for interactions between dissimilar molecules. The familiar generalization "Like dissolves like" is based upon the observation that attractive interactions tend to be greater between similar molecules than between structurally dissimilar pairs. Thus the lower alcohols are soluble in water because the attractive forces between the hydroxyl of water and of an alcohol are similar to those between individual water molecules and individual alcohol molecules. Conversely, water doesn't dissolve in hexane because the combined attractive forces between water molecules and between hexane molecules are greater than those between water and hexane molecules.

Distribution of a material between two immiscible liquids is governed by the relative solubilities of the solute in the two liquids. It is the basis of a well-known procedure for separating mixtures: *liquid-liquid* extraction. Each component of a mixture distributes itself differently between the two liquid phases, and by repeated extractions even rather similar compounds can be separated.

Sometimes high solubility is due to rapid chemical reactions, so that new compounds are formed during the process of solution. For example, a solution of formaldehyde in water contains very little of the carbonyl compound. A reversible reaction occurs between solute and solvent which results in the formation of methylenediol.

$$H_2O + H_2C{=}O \; \rightleftharpoons \; H_2C(OH)_2$$

  Formaldehyde   Methylenediol

Such chemical action can lead to solubilities which appear anomalously high. The most striking and generally useful examples involve acid-base reactions which convert neutral compounds to highly water-soluble ionic species. For example, aniline is very sparingly soluble in water but dissolves readily in aqueous acid by virtue of its conversion to anilinium ion. Neutralization of the solution with strong base regenerates the weakly basic amine, which separates from solution.

$$\overset{+}{H_3}O + C_6H_5NH_2 \; \rightleftharpoons \; C_6H_5\overset{+}{N}H_3 + H_2O$$

  Aniline   Anilinium
                          ion

Adsorption. The ability of organic compounds to become adsorbed on a solid surface varies widely both with the structure of the compound and with the character of the surface. As a result, differences in adsorption tendencies are used both to separate and to characterize compounds. The usual operating technique is known as *chromatography*. In liquid-phase chromatography, a solution of the compounds to be separated is poured through a column of finely divided solid adsorbent, such as alumina (Al_2O_3), silica gel, carbon, or cellulose. The solutes are adsorbed and then *eluted* by passage of a series of solvents through the column. Solvents are chosen in order of increasing affinity for the adsorbing surface, so that the tendency of the *eluant* to displace the adsorbed solutes continually increases. The more weakly adsorbed solutes are eluted first. Under ideal operating conditions, only a small fraction of the free surface area of the adsorbent is covered with solute molecules, so that the latter are repeatedly adsorbed, desorbed, and readsorbed as they pass down the column. The result is a multiple-fractionation process. Such a procedure can be adapted to quantities of material ranging from milligrams to kilograms.

In vapor-phase chromatography, the same principles are applied to adsorption from a gas phase. The mixture of gases is introduced into the column along with a carrier gas which is then used as an eluant. Adsorption of the gases in a suspended liquid phase is also commonly used in vapor-phase chromatography. These techniques are usually limited to small-scale operations.

Selectivity of adsorption and capacity of an adsorbent vary a great deal from one surface to the next. Highly active adsorbents can be rendered impotent if their surfaces are saturated with water, and they must be heated strongly to remove water and other adsorbed materials before use. Control of surfaces can be achieved by standard pretreatment procedures. For example, alumina, which usually has a basic surface, can be given an acidic one by treating it with dilute sulfuric acid. The resulting *acid-washed alumina* is then *activated* with heat.

Paper Chromatography. Paper chromatography is a technique for the separation of closely related mixtures of polar substances. The mixture to be separated is dissolved in a solvent mixture composed of two partially miscible solvents, each saturated with respect to the other. An example of a suitable mixture is phenol saturated with water. The resulting solution is then passed over cellulose either by gravity flow in a column or by capillary action on a paper sheet. Ordinary filter paper, which contains a layer of water adsorbed on its surface, is frequently employed. This water layer forms a stationary phase, and the solute is subjected to innumerable partitions between the water phase and the moving phase as the latter advances. The components of the solute have different solubilities in the two phases, and therefore spend different amounts of time in the stationary and moving phases. As a result, each component moves at a different rate along the paper. Thus the process is a continuous liquid-liquid extraction rather than a multiple adsorption.

Under a given set of conditions, each compound has a particular rate of flow. This characteristic is frequently used to identify such compounds as amino acids (Chap. 23), fatty acids (Chap. 24), steroids (Chap. 24), and carbohydrates (Chap. 22). In some cases, better results are obtained if the paper is pretreated to lay down a layer of the stationary phase before the chromatogram is started. The method is limited to the separation of milligram amounts of material.

Intermolecular Interactions

Correlation of the above physical properties with structure depends upon intermolecular interactions, whose character will be considered briefly in this section. Fundamentally, all molecular interactions depend on the same factors that produce bonding forces within molecules, i.e., the interactions of negative electrons and positive nuclei. However, intermolecular interactions involve distances greater than ordinary bond lengths, and forces between molecules are much weaker than those found in chemical bonds.

Dipole Moment. The dipole moment of a compound measures the tendency of positive and negative charges to become concentrated in two parts of a molecule, respectively. This physical constant is determined by observing the extent to which molecules of a substance orient themselves when placed between the plates of a charged condenser. Molecules with high dipole moments become highly oriented, with their dipoles parallel to the direction of the field. Dipole moments (μ) are reported in terms of Debye units, since values in terms of electrostatic units always include a large negative exponent ($1 D = 10^{-18}$ esu).

Separation of charge in organic molecules is associated with the presence of either formal charges or polarized bonds. The high dipole moment of trimethylamine oxide illustrates the former, and the smaller dipole moment of methyl iodide the latter, as is indicated in Fig. 7.1.

Many molecules with polar bonds do not possess molecular dipoles, because individual *bond moments* are so oriented that they cancel one another. Any molecule that has a center of symmetry (page 127) will not

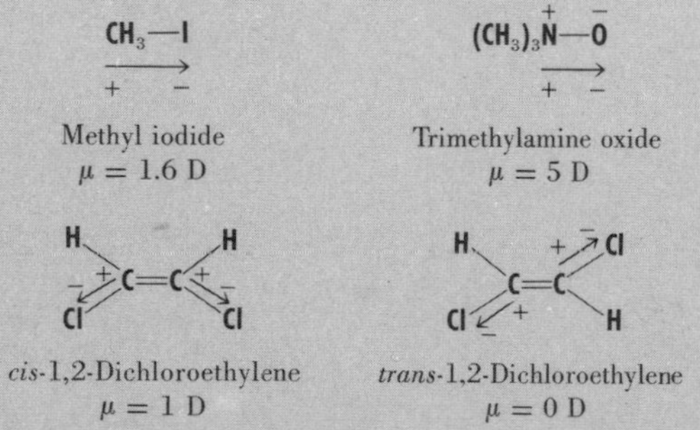

Methyl iodide
$\mu = 1.6$ D

Trimethylamine oxide
$\mu = 5$ D

cis-1,2-Dichloroethylene
$\mu = 1$ D

trans-1,2-Dichloroethylene
$\mu = 0$ D

FIG. 7.1 Dipole moments.

have a dipole moment. The two geometric isomers of 1,2-dichloroethylene illustrate the principle (see Fig. 7.1). Both molecules are planar, and both contain two polar carbon-chlorine bonds. The cis isomer has an appreciable dipole moment, since in this molecule the bond moments are so oriented as to provide over-all electrical dissymmetry. The trans isomer has a zero dipole moment, since the two individual bond moments are aligned so as to cancel each other.

Long-range interactions between groups may produce abnormally large dipole moments as the normal polarity of a bond is extended into an adjacent unsaturated system. Conversely, delocalization of the nonbonding electrons of atoms such as nitrogen, oxygen, or halogen may tend to decrease the normal polarity of molecules. Comparisons of the dipole moments of the following compounds provide illustrations.

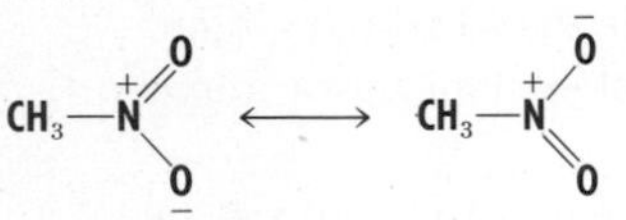

Nitromethane, $\mu = 3.50$ D

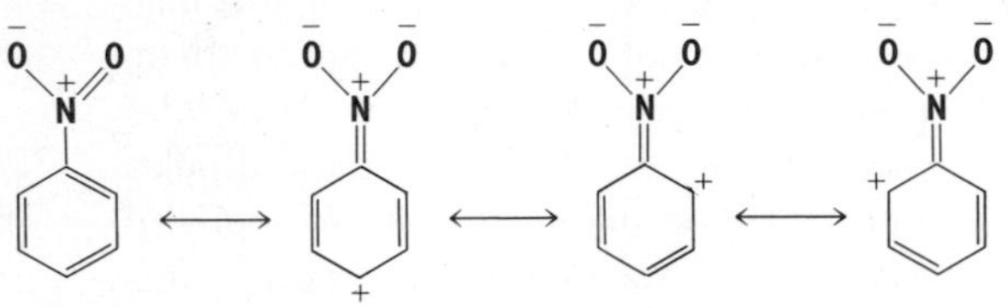

Nitrobenzene, $\mu = 3.95$ D

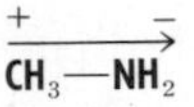

Methylamine, $\mu = 1.33$ D

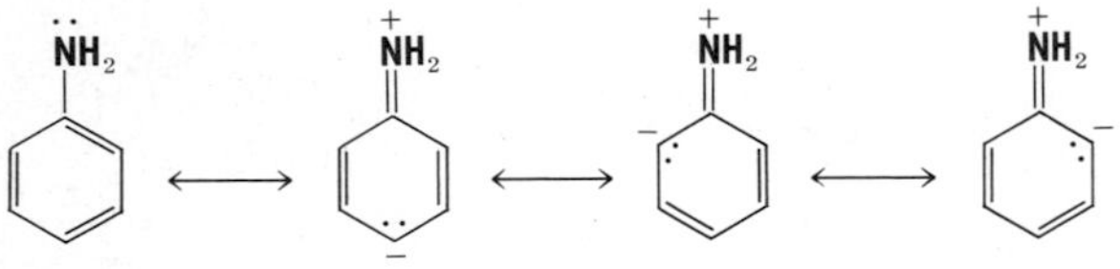

Aniline, $\mu = 1.53$ D

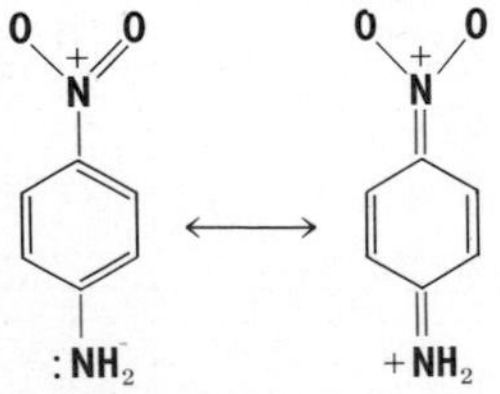

p-Nitroaniline, $\mu = 6.10$ D

Dipole-Dipole Interactions. Strong intermolecular forces arise from interaction of the electric dipoles found in unsymmetrical molecules. In both liquids and solids, there is a strong tendency for dipoles to become aligned and to hold molecules together. As a consequence, compounds which have large dipole moments usually melt and boil at much higher temperatures than nonpolar compounds of comparable molecular weight. The properties of the substances in Table 7.1 illustrate this correlation. Polar resonance structures are included to indicate the character of the dipole.

In the liquid phase, polar molecules tend to orient themselves so that the positive end of the dipole of one molecule is close to the negative pole of another. Arrangements of molecules shown as I, II, and III of Fig. 7.2 outnumber arrangements such as IV and V in liquid acetonitrile. In all cases, the methyl group, which is essentially nonpolar, is represented as an inert sphere.

Strong dipole-dipole interactions may arise between molecules which contain polar bonds but have no dipole moments because of their symmetry properties. These interactions involve only parts of molecules, and the dipoles associated with bonds in two different molecules may align themselves in such a way as to provide some intermolecular compensation for charge separation. A comparison of the physical properties of o- and p-dichlorobenzene indicates that although the ortho isomer possesses a significant dipole moment and the para isomer none, the two isomers have comparable boiling points, and the para isomer is the higher-melting of the two.

o-Dichlorobenzene
mp $-18°$, bp $179°$

p-Dichlorobenzene
mp $53°$, bp $174°$

TABLE 7.1   Influence of Polarity on Transition Points

Polar compound	Mol. wt.	Mp, °C	Bp, °C	Nonpolar compound	Mol. wt.	Mp, °C	Bp, °C
$(CH_3)_2C{=}O \longleftrightarrow (CH_3)_2\overset{+}{C}{-}\overset{-}{O}$	58	-95	57	$n\text{-}C_4H_{10}$	58	-135	-1
$CH_3C{\equiv}N \longleftrightarrow CH_3\overset{+}{C}{=}\overset{-}{N}$	41	-41	82	C_3H_8	44	-187	42
	123	6	211	$C_3H_7\text{-}n$	120	-99	160
$(CH_3)_3\overset{+}{N}{-}\overset{-}{O}$	75	96	<180	$(C_2H_5)_3N$	101	-115	90

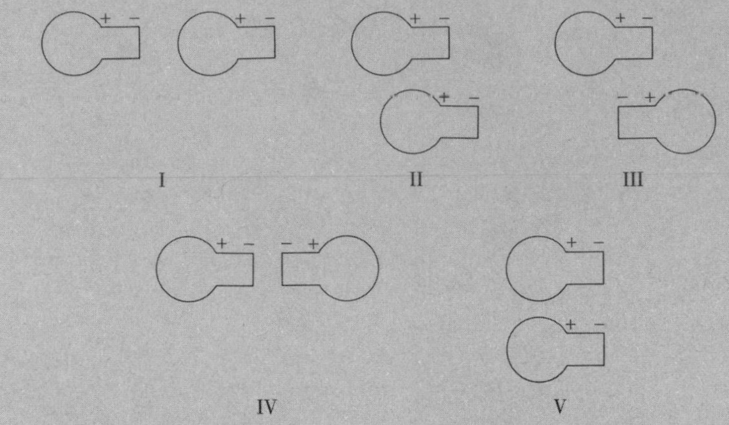

FIG. 7.2   Orientations of acetonitrile in liquid state.

In the liquid state, the molecules of the para isomer can arrange themselves in the manner formulated.

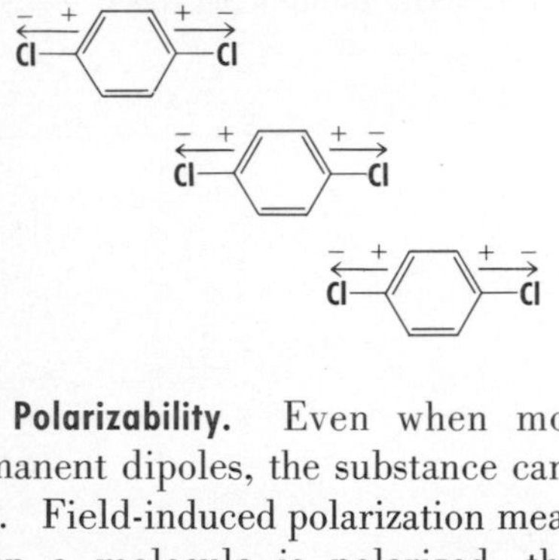

etc.

Polarizability.   Even when molecules of a compound have no permanent dipoles, the substance can be polarized by an applied electric field.   Field-induced polarization measures the *polarizability* of molecules. When a molecule is polarized, the average electron distribution is changed in comparison with that of an identical molecule not subjected to an externally applied field.

Atomic polarizability correlates with predictions based on atomic theory.   Polarization of atoms occurs principally by displacement of the loosely bound valence electrons, and the ease of causing the small displacements parallels the ease of complete loss of electrons by ionization. The alkali metals are highly polarizable, but the cations derived from them have very small polarizabilities.   Halogens are not as easily polarized as metals in the same row of the periodic table, but the corresponding anions are rather highly polarizable.   Within a family of elements, the polarizability always increases as atomic number increases.

In molecules, polarization involves deformation of both bonding and nonbonding electron clouds.   Unsaturated molecules are much more easily deformed than saturated systems, and conjugated unsaturated systems are highly susceptible to polarization. Weak bonds are usually highly polarizable, since the electrons involved are comparatively weakly bound to the molecule.

A physical property directly related to polarizability is the *refractive index*. Light rays travel more slowly through transparent materials than through a vacuum. The ratio of the speed of a beam in air to its speed in a given material is the refractive index. Retardation is due to the interaction of light with electrons, and high refractivity indicates easy polarizability. Refractive indices vary with wavelength of the transmitted light, hence a notation to indicate wavelength must be included in a report of a refractive index. Most refractometers are designed for use with tungsten lamps, but are calibrated to give readings in terms of the sodium D line (5,890 A). Since the refractive index has a strong temperature dependence, temperature is also always included in the notation. Thus refractive indices are usually reported: $n_D^T = \underline{\hspace{2cm}}$. They constitute one of the most easily obtained and most characteristic physical constants that can be found for pure liquids. Table 7.2 lists the refractive indices of typical organic compounds.

Intermolecular Polarization. Interactions of polarizable molecules with one another and with dipolar molecules give rise to intermolecular attractive forces which are normally smaller than those due to dipole-dipole interactions. However, these forces are responsible for the crystal

TABLE 7.2 *Refractive Indices of Pure Liquids*

Compound	T, °C	n_D^T
H_2O	20	1.3330
$CH_3C\equiv N$	17	1.3460
$(CH_3)_2CHCH_2CH_3$	20	1.3549
$CH_3(CH_2)_4F$	20	1.3562
CH_3COCH_3	20	1.3591
$CH_3CH_2CH_2C\equiv CH$	18	1.4079
$CH_3(CH_2)_4Cl$	20	1.4119
$CH_3CH\!=\!CHC\equiv N$	20	1.4156
$HC\equiv CCH_2CH_2C\equiv CH$	20	1.4414
$CH_3(CH_2)_4Br$	20	1.4444
$CH_3(CH_2)_4I$	20	1.4955
C_6H_6	20	1.5017
$C_6H_5NO_2$	20	1.5529
$(C_2H_5)_2Cd$	18	1.5680
![naphthalene with NH₂ NH₂ substituents]	99	1.7083

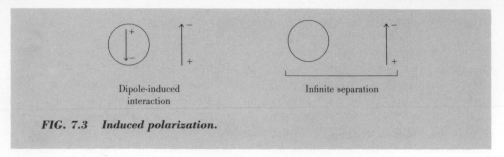

Dipole-induced   Infinite separation
interaction

FIG. 7.3   Induced polarization.

energies of nonpolar solid compounds and for the existence of liquid phases of such materials.

The attraction between a dipole and an easily polarizable molecule having no permanent dipole is readily understood, since the dipole supplies a field to polarize its deformable partner, and a small dipole is induced in the latter. Dipole-induced interactions are pictured in Fig. 7.3.

The explanation for interactions between a pair of polarizable substances, neither of which has a permanent dipole, is less obvious. Such interactions do exist and are mainly responsible for the mutual attraction of molecules such as alkanes. Since the fundamental phenomenon is one of polarization, the forces, known as van der Waals forces, increase with increasing polarizability of the molecules involved. For example, acetylene possesses a lower molecular weight than ethane, yet the unsaturated compound boils 4° higher than the saturated substance.

Hydrogen Bonding. Compounds containing oxygen-hydrogen or nitrogen-hydrogen bonds show evidence of association which exceeds all expectations based upon their molecular weights, dipole moments, and molecular polarizability. For example, water, which contains no highly polarizable atoms, melts at 0° and boils at 100°, whereas dimethyl ether, methyl alcohol, and acetone (compounds of higher molecular weight) boil at −24, 65, and 57° respectively, and melt at very low temperatures. There is no large difference in the dipole moments of these substances. Accordingly, the remarkably high association of water must be due to some short-range interactions which are not reflected in all the gross properties of water molecules. Comparison of physical properties within the series water, methyl alcohol, and dimethyl ether indicates that the hydroxyl group has a pronounced specific effect upon physical properties.

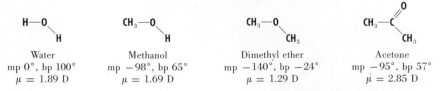

Water	Methanol	Dimethyl ether	Acetone
mp 0°, bp 100°	mp −98°, bp 65°	mp −140°, bp −24°	mp −95°, bp 57°
$\mu = 1.89$ D	$\mu = 1.69$ D	$\mu = 1.29$ D	$\mu = 2.85$ D

A comparison of the structures and physical properties of water and dimethyl ether is particularly instructive. In liquid water, molecules are held together by dipole-dipole interactions between positive hydrogen and negative oxygen atoms. The shape of the water molecule allows many different arrangements in the molecular aggregates, since these partial charges are sterically exposed to those of neighboring molecules. In molecules of dimethyl ether, these partial charges are deeply buried beneath a canopy of relatively nonpolar carbon-hydrogen bonds. As a result, the dipole-dipole interactions must cover longer distances, and their effect is diminished accordingly. Models for aggregates of water and ether molecules are drawn in Fig. 7.4.

Another important factor contributes to the highly associated character of liquids whose molecules contain oxygen-hydrogen or nitrogen-hydrogen bonds. These bonds are highly polar, and the hydrogen atom possesses some of the character of a naked proton. The charge of this nucleus is much less shielded by electrons than the charge of other nuclei. As a result, the intense local field associated with hydrogen bound to oxygen or nitrogen produces strong dipole-dipole interactions. These effects are distinguished by the name *hydrogen bonding*. The strongest hydrogen bonds are those in which the negative pole is a small electronegative atom such as fluorine, oxygen, and nitrogen. The most dramatic illustrations are found in the existence of the HF_2^- ion and the polymeric $(HF)_n$ molecule, which exists in liquid hydrogen fluoride.

$$(F\text{-}\text{-}\text{-}H\text{-}\text{-}\text{-}F)^- \qquad H\text{—}F\text{-}\text{-}\text{-}[H\text{—}F\text{-}\text{-}\text{-}H\text{—}F]_n\text{-}\text{-}\text{-}H\text{—}F$$

Broken lines are usually employed to represent hydrogen bonds in formulas. These bonds place less restriction on the motions of the atoms involved than do ordinary single bonds, since the bonding energies of the former are an order of magnitude smaller. In water, the *hydrogen bond* has been estimated to have an energy of 4.5 kcal/mole, which compares with the average covalent-bond energy of 80 kcal/mole.

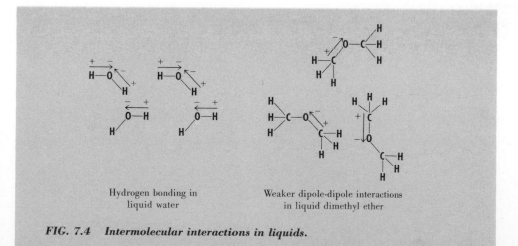

Hydrogen bonding in
liquid water

Weaker dipole-dipole interactions
in liquid dimethyl ether

FIG. 7.4   *Intermolecular interactions in liquids.*

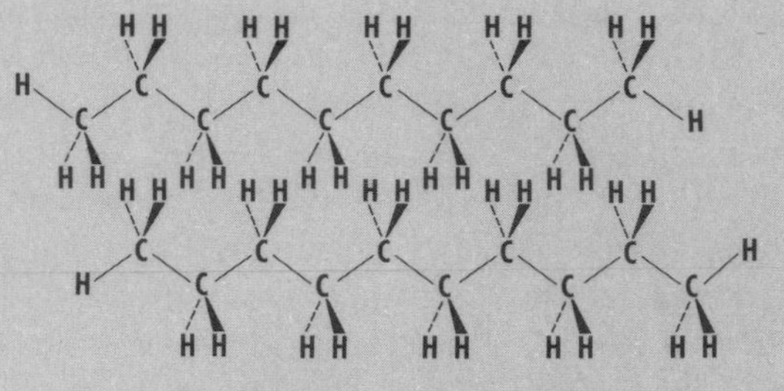

Pair of perfectly aligned molecules

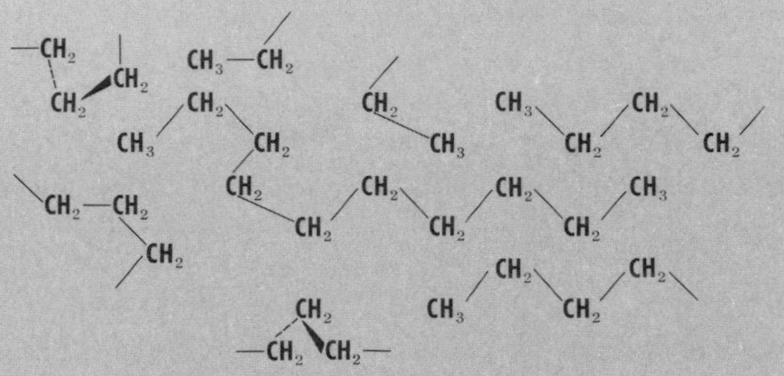

Randomly coiled molecule surrounded
by fragments of others

FIG. 7.5   *Interactions among n-decane molecules.*

Correlations between Physical Properties
and Structure

Nonpolar Compounds.   The physical properties of nonpolar compounds treated in this chapter depend on intermolecular association of molecules in the liquid and solid states.   The attractive forces (van der Waals forces) grow out of the polarizability of these molecules.   The increase in melting and boiling points in a transition from the lower- to the higher-molecular-weight compounds in a homologous series is due to an accumulation of small van der Waals interactions.   Two methane molecules can interact only through two pairs of hydrogens, whereas a pair of perfectly aligned *n*-decane molecules has five points of contact similar to the one in methane. A pair of perfectly aligned molecules of *n*-decane is pictured in Fig. 7.5.

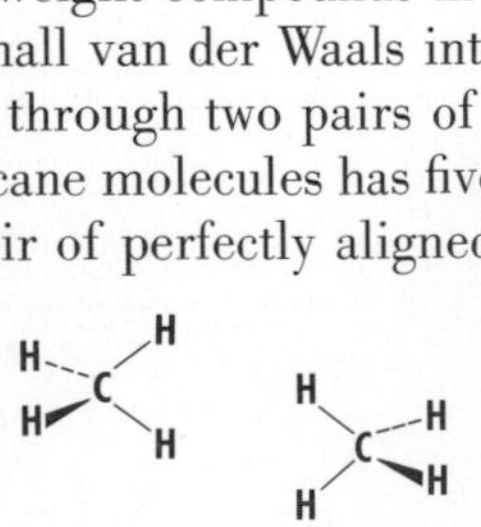

Two molecules of methane

Perfect alignment is probably found only in the highly ordered crystals of solid *n*-decane.   In liquid *n*-decane, the added freedom of motion characteristic of liquids results in extensive disorder. However, with long flexible molecules such as this, the disorder need not reduce the total number of intermolecular interactions by a large amount. If one molecule slips past a particular partner, a piece of a third *n*-decane molecule is likely to be found in position to interact with the first, as is pictured in Fig. 7.5.

TABLE 7.3   *Effect of Symmetry and Rigidity on Transition Points*

Compound	Mp, °C	Bp, °C
$CH_3(CH_2)_3CH_3$	−130	36
$(CH_3)_2CHCH_2CH_3$	−160	28
$(CH_3)_4C$	−20	10
$CH_3(CH_2)_4CH_3$	−94	69
(cyclohexane)	7	81
(benzene)	5.5	80
$CH_3(CH_2)_6CH_3$	−57	126
(1,4-dimethylcyclohexane, CH_3 ... CH_3)	−86	120
(norbornane)	86	Sublimes
(1,4-dimethylbenzene, CH_3 ... CH_3)	13	139
(1,3-dimethylbenzene, CH_3 ... CH_3)	−47	139
$CH_3-⟨\ ⟩-CH_2CH_2-⟨\ ⟩-CH_3$	81	
$CH_2-⟨\ ⟩-CH_2$ / $CH_2-⟨\ ⟩-CH_2$	287	

TABLE 7.4 *Variation in Adsorptivity, Transition Temperatures, and Solubility with Structure*

Order of increasing adsorptivity on alumina	Mp, °C	Bp, °C	Solubility in water
$C_6H_5CH_2CH_2Cl$		200	Insoluble
$C_6H_5COC_6H_5$	49† or 27†	306	Insoluble
$C_6H_5CHCH_3$ $\|$ OH		203	Insoluble
$p\text{-}HOC_6H_4CH_2CH_3$	47	219	Slightly soluble
$C_6H_5CO_2H$	122	249	0.21 g/100 g at 18°

† Different polymorphic forms of the solid.

Two features are worthy of note in the model for liquid *n*-decane. The chains may become coiled rather than extended, and much disorder is found in the orientation of molecules with respect to one another. Both these "randomizing" operations are accomplished with relatively small losses in intermolecular-association energy. If either or both of these operations are impossible with a particular compound, it will have a relatively high melting point and a relatively short liquid-temperature range. This primitive reasoning explains why rigid symmetrical molecules tend to have relatively high melting points, and often sublime directly from the solid to the vapor state. Table 7.3 provides a number of illustrations of the effects of rigidity and symmetry on transition points. Hydrocarbons are chosen to avoid the complications due to orientational phenomena associated with dipolar molecules.

Neopentane affords a good example of a symmetrical molecule lacking opportunity to flex when released from a crystal lattice. If the four methyl groups of any particular molecule are each in contact with a foreign methyl group, the array is automatically a small piece of a crystal. The introduction of any appreciable randomness will sharply decrease the intermolecular interactions.

Neopentane

The condensation of neopentane and *n*-decane from their respective vapor phases may be compared with the problem of crating billiard balls on the one hand and snakes on the other. If the balls are merely poured into a box, a fairly orderly array will result, whereas producing order in a box full of snakes requires considerably more labor.

The consequences of van der Waals interactions in determining solubility of nonpolar substances are quite predictable. The truism "Like dissolves like" applies. Nonpolar substances tend to dissolve in nonpolar solvents, since the randomizing effect of mixing similar but nonidentical molecules produces little change in the total attractive interactions. Once again the analogy to balls and snakes is instructive. Clearly, the mixing of two different kinds of snakes or of two different kinds of balls should result in less disorder than the mixing of balls and snakes.

Most adsorptive surfaces are very polar, and will adsorb nonpolar molecules selectively according to their polarizability. Thus the order of elution from an alumina chromatograph column of a mixture of hexane, hexene, and 1,3-hexadiene is the order of listing. In homologous series, the adsorptivity increases regularly with molecular weight, except in rare cases where high-molecular-weight molecules become too large to fit into the "crevices" in the surface of the adsorbent.

Polar Compounds Polar molecules tend to cling together with great tenacity, as is illustrated by their relatively high boiling and freezing (or melting) points, their affinity for polar surfaces, and their relatively strong propensity for dissolving in polar solvents. Table 7.4 lists a group of compounds of similar molecular weight arranged in the order in which they are eluted from a chromatogram on activated alumina. Melting-point, boiling-point, and solubility data are included for comparison purposes.

The dominant influence of hydrogen bonding on the physical properties of compounds that contain oxygen-hydrogen or nitrogen-hydrogen

TABLE 7.5   *Influence of Hydrogen Bonding on Physical Properties*

Compound	Mp, °C	Bp, °C	Solubility in water
$HOCH_2CH_2OH$	−16	197	Miscible
$CH_3OCH_2CH_2OCH_3$	−58	84	Miscible
$H_2NCH_2CH_2NH_2$	9	117	Miscible
(ring)N—CH$_3$		79	Miscible
$p\text{-}HO_2CC_6H_4CO_2H$	300		0.001 g/100 g (100°)
$p\text{-}CH_3O_2CC_6H_4CO_2CH_3$	140	300	0.3 g/100 g (100°)
$o\text{-}HO_2CC_6H_4CO_2H$	191	(sublimes)	0.54 g/100 g (14°)
(phthalic anhydride structure)	131	285	Slightly soluble

TABLE 7.6   *Hydrogen Bonding and Solubility*

Compound	*Solubility in water*
CH_3OCH_3	7.6 g/100 g (18°)
$C_2H_5OC_2H_5$	7.5 g/100 g (19°)
CH_3COCH_3	Miscible
CH_3CN	Miscible
$(CH_3)_3N$	41 g/100 g (19°)
Compare with	
C_2H_5Br	0.9 g/100 g (30°)
$n\text{-}CH_3(CH_2)_3CH_3$	Insoluble

linkages is illustrated in Table 7.5.   Compounds containing these bonds are listed next to related compounds in which these linkages are absent. The most dramatic effects are associated with molecules which contain two functional groups carrying polar hydrogens, such as ethylene glycol ($HOCH_2CH_2OH$). The boiling point of this substance is over 100° higher than that of 1,2-dimethoxyethane ($CH_3OCH_2CH_2OCH_3$).

The "Like dissolves like" principle requires a special comment in connection with polar solvents. No doubt, an individual water molecule would polarize a hydrocarbon molecule, producing stronger interactions than those between two hydrocarbon molecules. However, water and hydrocarbons are insoluble in each other, because solution can be accomplished only by separating water molecules, thereby sacrificing the very large association energy of liquid water. The principal exceptions to the general insolubility of these compounds in each other occur with molecules which do not have oxygen-hydrogen or nitrogen-hydrogen bonds, but do contain oxygen or nitrogen which can serve as the second partner in a hydrogen-bonded molecular aggregate. Table 7.6 provides examples.

Problems

1. Indicate which of the following compounds should have dipole moments. For compounds without a dipole moment, explain why they can possess polar groups and not have a dipole moment. For compounds that have a dipole moment, draw an arrow in the direction of the dipole, with the head of the arrow as the negative end.

f.

h.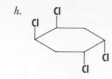

j.

g.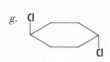

i.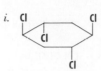

2. Draw all isomers of the following compounds, and arrange them in *decreasing order* of their dipole moments. Indicate which structures have no dipole moments.

a. The dicyanobenzenes

b. The 1,4-dichlorobutadienes

c. meso- and (±)-2,3-diphenylbutane

d. p-Nitro-*N*-methylaniline and *p*-nitrobenzylamine

e. meso-Tartaric and (+)-tartaric acids

3. Which of the compounds in each set would you expect to possess the higher melting point, and which the higher solubility in water? Why?

a. p-$CH_3C_6H_4CO_2H$ and o-$CH_3C_6H_4CO_2H$

b. $(CH_3)_2NCH_2CO_2CH_3$ and $(CH_3)_2NCH_2CO_2$

c. p-$CH_3C_6H_4OH$ and p-$CH_3C_6H_4CH_2OH$

d. HO_2CCO_2H and $CH_3(CH_2)_6CO_2H$

e.

H H	H OH
HO～C—C～OH	HO～C C～H
C_6H_5 C_6H_5	C_6H_5 C_6H_5
meso	Optically active

4. A mixture of naphthalene, ethylene glycol, benzoic acid, and aniline was shaken with equal parts of ether and dilute aqueous sodium hydroxide, and the layers were separated to give ether layer *A* and aqueous layer *B*. Solution *A* was then extracted with an equal volume of dilute hydrochloric acid, and the layers separated to give ether layer *C* and aqueous layer *D*. Solution *B* was made acidic with sulfuric acid, and the resulting solution was extracted with an equal volume of ether. The layers were separated to give ether layer *E* and aqueous layer *F*. This procedure separated the four compounds. Show the distribution of compounds in each of the solutions *A* through *F*.

5. Explain the following facts:

a. o-Hydroxyacetophenone boils about 50° below *m*-hydroxyacetophenone.

b. The boiling points of the isomeric hexanes are as follows:

$CH_3CH_2CH_2CH_2CH_2CH_3$ $(CH_3)_2CHCH_2CH_2CH_3$
         69°   60°

$(CH_3)_2CHCH(CH_3)_2$ $(CH_3)_3CCH_2CH_3$ $CH_3CH_2\overset{\displaystyle CH_3}{\underset{\displaystyle |}{CH}}CH_2CH_3$
        58°   50°   63°

c. Although oxalamide contains a larger number of polar groups than urea, the latter is much more soluble in water.

$\underset{H_2N}{\overset{H_2N}{>}}C{=}O$ $H_2N{-}\overset{O}{\overset{||}{C}}{-}\overset{O}{\underset{||}{C}}{-}NH_2$

Urea, mp 132°   Oxalamide, mp 420°

d. Although water has a lower molecular weight and is a weaker acid than hydrogen sulfide, the latter is a gas and the former a liquid at room temperature.

e. The substance $(CH_3)_3N$ is soluble in water, whereas $(CH_3)_3CH$ is not.

f. On a paper chromatogram with water as the stationary phase and phenol as the moving phase, the following compounds move at rates which *increase* with their order of listing.

HOCH$_2$CHCO$_2$H   CH$_3$CHCO$_2$H   (CH$_3$)$_2$CHCHCO$_2$H

    NH$_2$ NH$_2$ NH$_2$

    Serine   Alanine   Valine

6. Arrange the following compounds in the order in which they would be eluted from a chromatogram on alumina:

p-(CH$_3$)$_2$C$_6$H$_4$ C$_6$H$_5$CH$_2$OCH$_3$ C$_6$H$_5$COCH$_3$ C$_6$H$_5$CH$_2$CH$_2$OH

CH$_3$—⟨ ⟩—CH$_3$ *p*-HOC$_6$H$_4$C$_2$H$_5$ *p*-CH$_3$C$_6$H$_4$CO$_2$H

CH$_3$(CH$_2$)$_3$—⟨ ⟩—(CH$_2$)$_3$CH$_3$

$$\overset{\bar{O}}{\underset{+}{\|}}$$

7. Dimethyl sulfoxide (CH$_3$—S—CH$_3$) is an excellent solvent for **KOC(CH$_3$)$_3$**. Indicate with a crude diagram what you imagine the structure of a solution of potassium *tert*-butoxide in dimethylsulfoxide to be like.

8

Correlation of Structure and Reactivity

Systematic study of organic reactions entails inquiry into the influence of structure on reactivity. The greatest variations are found among compounds that contain different functional groups. However, reactivity also differs widely among members of each class of compounds. Both the electronic properties of a functional group and its environment influence reactivity. Environmental factors include steric and electronic properties of other groups within the molecule and effects due to intermolecular interactions.

Reactions of organic acids and bases, like similar reactions of inorganic compounds, are usually fast and reversible. Consequently, the acidity and basicity of organic compounds are described in terms of equilibrium constants, which are unrelated to problems of reaction rate and path. Acidity and basicity constants provide an excellent source of data for the establishment and examination of theories relating structure with reactivity. The theories are then applied, with appropriate modification, to more complicated reactions.

Proton Acids and Bases

Of organic acids, those containing carboxyl groups are the most important. These ionize when dissolved in water, as illustrated with acetic acid. The ionization constant K_a is defined by Eq. (1).

(1) $\quad CH_3CO_2H \underset{}{\overset{K_a}{\rightleftarrows}} CH_3CO_2^- + H^+ \qquad K_a = \dfrac{[CH_3CO_2^-][H^+]}{[CH_3CO_2H]} = 1.75 \times 10^{-5}$

Amines constitute the most important class of organic bases. When dissolved in water, amines are partially converted to ions. The ionization constant K_b is defined by Eq. (2).

(2) $\quad CH_3NH_2 + H_2O \underset{}{\overset{K_b'}{\rightleftarrows}} CH_3NH_3^+ + OH^- \qquad K_b' = \dfrac{[CH_3NH_3^+][OH^-]}{[CH_3NH_2][H_2O]}, \qquad K_b = K_b'[H_2O]$

TABLE 8.1   Classes of Proton Acids and Bases Arranged in Decreasing Order of Strength

Acids		Bases	
General formula	Name	General formula	Name
$ROSO_2OH$	Alkylsulfuric acid	ArLi	Aryllithium
$ArSO_3H$	Arylsulfonic acid	RNHNa	Alkyl sodamide
RSO_3H	Alkylsulfonic acid	Ar_3CNa	Triarylmethylsodium
RPO_3H_2	Alkylphosphonic acid	ArNHNa	Aryl sodamide
$ArCO_2H$	Arylcarboxylic acid	R_3CONa	Sodium *tert*-alkoxide
RCO_2H	Alkylcarboxylic acid	R_2CHONa	Sodium *sec*-alkoxide
ArOH	Phenol	RCH_2ONa	Sodium *prim*-alkoxide
ArSH	Thiophenol	ArONa	Sodium aryloxide
$RCOCH{=}CHOHR$	Enol	R_2NH	Secondary alkylamine
RSH	Mercaptan	RNH_2	Primary alkylamine
ROH	Alcohol	R_3N	Tertiary alkylamine
$RCOCH_2R$	Ketone (α-hydrogens)	$ArNH_2$	Arylamine
Ar_3CH	Triarylmethane	RCO_2Na	Sodium carboxylate

Proton acids and bases may be defined as being *proton-donors* and *proton-acceptors*, respectively.   The term *conjugate* relates acid-base pairs.   Thus acetate anion ($CH_3CO_2^-$) is the *conjugate base* of acetic acid, and acetic acid (CH_3CO_2H) is the *conjugate acid* of the basic acetate anion. Similarly, the methylammonium ion ($CH_3NH_3^+$) is the conjugate acid of the base, methylamine (CH_3NH_2), and methylamine is the conjugate base of the acid, methylammonium ion.   Application of these definitions to proton acids requires inclusion of solvent molecules in Eq. (1), as is indicated in (3).   The new equilibrium constant K_a' is referred to as the Bronsted acidity constant, and is related to K_a by Eq. (4).

(3) $CH_3CO_2H + H_2O \underset{}{\overset{K_a'}{\rightleftharpoons}} CH_3CO_2^- + H_3O^+$ $K_a' = \dfrac{[CH_3CO_2^-][H_3O^+]}{[CH_3CO_2H][H_2O]}$

(4) $K_a'[H_2O] = K_a$

Dissociation of acids and bases in solvents other than water requires proton transfer either to or from the solvent.

$HA + CH_3C{\equiv}\overset{..}{N} \rightleftharpoons CH_3C{\equiv}\overset{+}{N}H + \overset{-}{A}$

   Acid ionization in acetonitrile

$\overset{..}{B} + C_2H_5OH \rightleftharpoons \overset{+}{B}H + C_2H_5\overset{-}{O}$

   Base ionization of ethanol

It is frequently convenient to express dissociation constants in terms of logarithmic units.   So that positive rather than negative numbers may be compared, the unit is the *negative logarithm* of the acidity or basicity constant, as is indicated in Eqs. (5) and (6). For acetic acid in water, $K_a = 1.75 \times 10^{-5}$, and $pK_a = -\log 1.75 \times 10^{-5} = 4.76$. For methylamine in water, $K_b = 4.3 \times 10^{-4}$, and $pK_b = -\log 4.3 \times 10^{-4} = 3.37$.

(5) $pK_a = -\log K_a$

(6) $pK_b = -\log K_b$ 0.24 $5 - 0.24$ • 4.76

The pK_a's of the conjugate acids of amines and other bases in water are easily calculated from pK_b's through use of the relationships indicated in Eqs. (2), (7), (8), (9), and (10). The equations are developed with protonated methylamine as the conjugate acid, but the final relationship embodied in Eq. (10) is general.

(2) $K_b = \dfrac{[CH_3NH_3^+][OH^-]}{[CH_3NH_2]}$

(7) $K_w = [H^+][OH^-] = 10^{-14}$

(8) $CH_3\overset{+}{N}H_3 \;\rightleftarrows\; CH_3NH_2 + \overset{+}{H}$ $K_a = \dfrac{[CH_3NH_2][H^+]}{[CH_3NH_3^+]}$

(9) $K_a = \dfrac{[CH_3NH_3^+][OH^-][H^+]}{[CH_3NH_3^+]\,K_b} = \dfrac{K_w}{K_b} = \dfrac{10^{-14}}{K_b}$

(10) $pK_a = 14 - pK_b$

Thus the pK_a of methylammonium ion in water is $14 - 3.37 = 10.63$.

Organic acids and bases are very plentiful, and the values of K_a and K_b range over many powers of 10. Table 8.1 lists the more important general classes of organic proton acids and bases arranged roughly in declining order of strength.

Effect of Medium

The degree of dissociation of acids and bases is very solvent-dependent. For example, solutions of hydrogen chloride in benzene will not conduct an electric current, despite the fact that hydrogen chloride is a strong acid in aqueous solution. Although water is superior to other media as an *ionizing solvent,* reactions of many acids and bases can be studied only in nonaqueous solvents, because of the insolubility of un-ionized species in water.

Solvent effects in acid-base equilibria are due to these principal causes:

1. Solvents are ordinarily involved in proton equilibria. Accordingly, ionization constants depend upon the *acidity and (or) basicity of the solvent.*

2. All ions in solution strongly polarize solvent molecules near them. The strength of such interactions is enormous in water solutions

TABLE 8.2 *Effect of Solvent on Dissociation of Acetic Acid at 25°*

Solvent	K_a
Water	1.75×10^{-5}
20% Dioxan—80% water	5.11×10^{-6}
45% Dioxan—55% water	4.93×10^{-7}
70% Dioxan—30% water	4.78×10^{-9}
82% Dioxan—18% water	7.24×10^{-11}
10% Methanol—90% water	1.25×10^{-5}
20% Methanol—80% water	8.34×10^{-6}
100% Benzene	Too small to measure

of ionic compounds, and becomes very small in nonpolar, difficultly polarizable solvents such as hydrocarbons.

3. The electrostatic energy of a charged body decreases as the *dielectric constant* (ε) of the surrounding medium is increased.

The dielectric constant measures the relative effect of the medium on the force with which two oppositely charged plates attract each other. The dielectric constant of a liquid is determined readily by measuring the electrical capacitance of a condenser when empty and when filled with the liquid.

The effect of the dielectric constant makes solvents such as water ($\varepsilon = 80$) and acetonitrile ($\varepsilon = 39$) much better solvents for ions than are low dielectric media such as acetone ($\varepsilon = 21$) and benzene ($\varepsilon = 2.3$). Pure dielectric effects are subordinate in importance to the specific solvation effects listed above.

Table 8.2 illustrates the effect of solvents on the acidity constant of acetic acid.

Structural Effects

Inductive Effects. The data of Table 8.3 demonstrate that ease of removal of protons from a carboxyl group is strongly influenced by the structure of the rest of the molecule. Acidity is a function of the structure of both the carboxylic acid and its conjugate base, and substituent effects involve structural interactions within both species. Chloroacetic acid illustrates the principles involved, as indicated in Fig. 8.1.

Introduction of the polar carbon-chlorine bond should make chloroacetic acid slightly unstable in comparison with acetic acid. The two polar groups $\overset{-\;\;+}{\overleftarrow{\text{Cl}-\text{C}}}$ and $\overset{+\;\;-}{\overrightarrow{\text{CO}_2\text{H}}}$ repel each other, since the positive ends of the two dipoles are held close together in the molecule. If all other factors could be held constant, the dipole-dipole repulsion would make chloroacetic acid stronger (less stable) than acetic. However, the relative

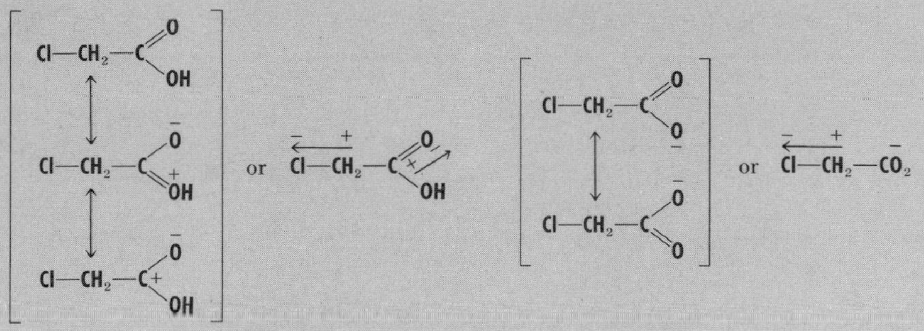

Chloroacetic acid   Chloroacetate anion

FIG. 8.1   *Basis of substituent effects.*

stabilities of chloroacetate and acetate also must be compared before any conclusion is drawn.

The dominant interaction in chloroacetate anion is between the carbon-chlorine dipole and the negative charge of the carboxyl group. Since the positive end of the dipole is pointed toward the negative charge, *the charge is partially neutralized.* Thus *chloroacetate is more stable than acetate anion,* since the latter contains no strong electron-withdrawing group. Introduction of chlorine as a substituent in acetic

TABLE 8.3   *Substituent Effects on Acid Strength*

Acid	*Structure*	K_a *(H$_2$O) at 25°*
Acetic	CH_3CO_2H	1.75×10^{-5}
Propionic	$CH_3CH_2CO_2H$	1.4×10^{-5}
Capric	$CH_3(CH_2)_8CO_2H$	1.5×10^{-5}
Chloroacetic	$ClCH_2CO_2H$	1.55×10^{-3}
Iodoacetic	ICH_2CO_2H	7.5×10^{-4}
Trichloroacetic	Cl_3CCO_2H	3.0×10^{-1}
α-Chlorobutyric	$CH_3CH_2CHClCO_2H$	1.4×10^{-4}
β-Chlorobutyric	$CH_3CHClCH_2CO_2H$	8.9×10^{-5}
γ-Chlorobutyric	$ClCH_2CH_2CH_2CO_2H$	3.0×10^{-5}
Methoxyacetic	$CH_3OCH_2CO_2H$	3.3×10^{-4}
Cyanoacetic	$NCCH_2CO_2H$	4×10^{-3}
Phenylacetic	$C_6H_5CH_2CO_2H$	5×10^{-5}
Benzoic	$C_6H_5CO_2H$	6.35×10^{-4}
p-Chlorobenzoic	$p\text{-}ClC_6H_4CO_2H$	1.04×10^{-4}
p-Nitrobenzoic	$p\text{-}NO_2C_6H_4CO_2H$	3.76×10^{-4}
m-Nitrobenzoic	$m\text{-}NO_2C_6H_4CO_2H$	3.21×10^{-4}
p-Toluic	$p\text{-}CH_3C_6H_4CO_2H$	4.24×10^{-5}
m-Toluic	$m\text{-}CH_3C_6H_4CO_2H$	5.35×10^{-5}

TABLE 8.4   *Ionization Constants of Dibasic Acids*

Name	Formula	K_a (1)	K_a (2)
Oxalic	HO_2CCO_2H	6.5×10^{-2}	6.1×10^{-5}
Malonic	$HO_2CCH_2CO_2H$	1.4×10^{-3}	8.0×10^{-7}
Succinic	$HO_2CCH_2CH_2CO_2H$	6.4×10^{-5}	2.7×10^{-6}

acid makes the acid species less stable and the conjugate base more stable, so the proton becomes easier to remove from the former. This conclusion is in accord with the data, which show that the presence of chlorine increases the ionization constant by a factor of 100.

Substituent effects due to the permanent polarity or polarizability of groups are called *inductive effects,* and are perhaps best understood in terms of dipole-dipole and charge-dipole interactions. The data of Table 8.3 provide examples. For instance, only very small dipoles are associated with methyl-carbon bonds, and K_a's for acetic and propionic acids are very close to each other, as are the K_a's for benzoic and the two toluic acids. In contrast, the cyano group has a strong dipole with positive charge oriented toward the carboxyl group, and as a result K_a's for acids containing this substituent possess decidedly higher values than those which do not. That the effect drops off as the dipole is moved farther from the carboxyl is shown by the decrease in values of K_a in the series α-, β-, and γ-chlorobutyric acid.

$$N{\equiv}CCH_2CO_2H \longleftrightarrow \overset{-}{N}{\equiv}\overset{+}{C}CH_2CO_2H \text{ or } \overset{-}{N}{\overset{+}{\equiv}}CCH_2CO_2H$$

The following groups have strong *electron-withdrawing* inductive effects: NR_3^+, NO_2, ONO_2, CN, CO_2H, CO_2R, $C{=}O$, F, Cl, Br, I, NO, and ONO. *Electron-donating* inductive effects require that substituent groups either carry a negative charge or have a dipole with the negative end directed toward their point of attachment to the carbon chain. The effect of charged groups is illustrated by values of the second ionization constants of dibasic acids (Table 8.4). The large difference (factor of 10^3) between the first and second ionization constants is mainly due to the repulsion between like charges in the second anion. The stepwise ionization of oxalic acid is shown below.

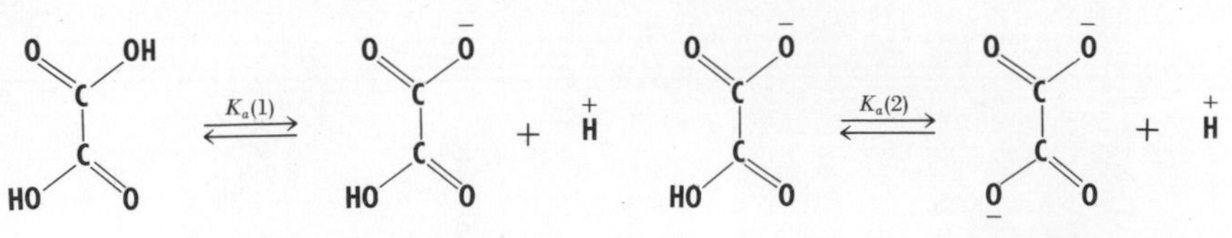

Molecules can have both basic and acidic groups, as is illustrated by the existence of a large number of amino acids in nature (Chap. 23).

An example is glycine, which normally exists as an inner salt, in which

H₂NCH₂CO₂H

Glycine

$H_2NCH_2CO_2H$

Glycine

the proton of the carboxyl group has been transferred to the more basic nitrogen atom. The conjugate acid of glycine loses its first proton from the carboxyl group. The substance is a rather strong acid owing to the electron-withdrawing effect of the formal positive charge on nitrogen. The inner salt can also lose a proton, but is a rather weak acid, because of the formal negative charge on the carboxyl group.

$$\overset{+}{N}H_3CH_2CO_2H \underset{}{\overset{K_a}{\rightleftarrows}} \overset{+}{N}H_3CH_2\overset{-}{C}O_2 + \overset{+}{H} \qquad \overset{+}{N}H_3CH_2\overset{-}{C}O_2 \underset{}{\overset{K_a}{\rightleftarrows}} NH_2CH_2\overset{-}{C}O_2 + \overset{+}{H}$$

| Conjugate acid of glycine $K_a = 4 \times 10^{-3}$ | Glycine inner salt | Glycine inner salt $K_a = 1.6 \times 10^{-9}$ | Glycine anion |

The only groups with strong dipoles in the sense $\overset{+\longrightarrow -}{Y-C}$ are those with Y equal to metal atoms. Since acids decompose compounds that contain carbon-metal bonds, inductive effects associated with such bonds cannot be studied by means of ionization constants. However, the bond between saturated and unsaturated carbon atoms is slightly polar, since of the two, unsaturated carbon has a slightly higher affinity for electrons. For example, toluene has a small dipole moment due in part to the polarity of the methyl-phenyl bond. The electron-donating inductive effect of a methyl group is demonstrated by the fact that the toluic acids are slightly weaker than benzoic acid (Table 8.3).

$$\overset{+\longrightarrow -}{CH_3-C_6H_5}$$

Toluene, $\mu = 0.4$ D

Resonance Effects. Since delocalization of electrons always stabilizes a system, it follows that localization of electrons makes a system less stable. Frequently the attachment of a proton to a base to form the conjugate acid results in restriction of an electron pair which in the free base was able to spread over an unsaturated system. Protonation of the carboxylate anion provides an example. The addition of a proton partially localizes a pair of electrons and destroys the perfect symmetry of the ion. The acid still has some *delocalization energy* because of mixing of the unshared electrons on the oxygen of the hydroxyl with the π orbitals of the carbonyl group. However, this effect in the acid is much smaller than in the carboxylate anion.

$$\left[R-C\overset{O}{\underset{\overset{-}{O}}{\lessgtr}} \longleftrightarrow R-C\overset{\overset{-}{O}}{\underset{O}{\lessgtr}} \right] \underset{-H^+}{\overset{+H^+}{\rightleftarrows}} \left[R-C\overset{O}{\underset{OH}{\lessgtr}} \longleftrightarrow R-C\overset{\overset{-}{O}}{\underset{\overset{+}{OH}}{\lessgtr}} \right]$$

The *resonance effect* is presumed to be the principal reason for the much greater acidity of carboxylic acids as compared with alcohols. The acidity of ethanol is undetectable in water solution, but it is estimated that the ionization constant is about 10^{-16}. The factor of 10^{10} between the acidity constants of ethanol and acetic acid is due largely to delocalization of charge in acetate ion.

$$CH_3CH_2\!-\!O\!-\!H \xrightleftharpoons{K_a} CH_3CH_2\!-\!O^- + H^+ \qquad K_a \cong 10^{-16}$$

The basicity of amines is very sensitive to resonance effects, as is shown by the fact that aniline is a weaker base than the aliphatic amines by 10^6 (see Table 8.5). This dramatic effect is due largely to the delocalization energy of aniline, which is lost when a proton is added to nitrogen.

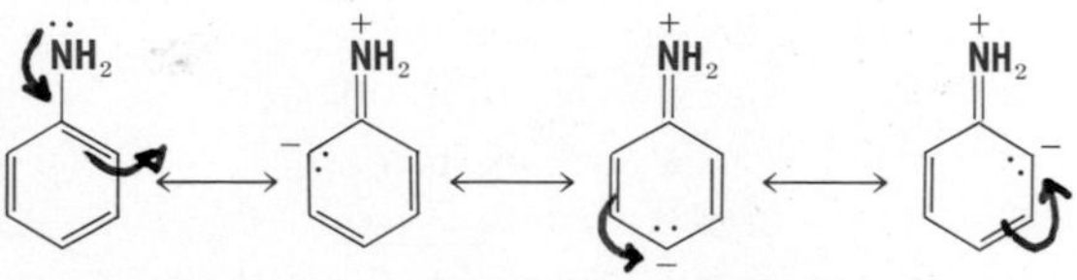

Aniline, electron pair of nitrogen distributed in the benzene ring

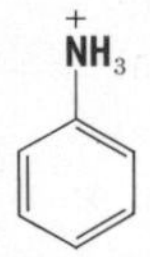

All electrons of nitrogen localized in single bonds

Anilinium ion

The influence of nitro groups in further reducing the basicity of aromatic amines must be due to two factors. The inductive effect of a nitro group is base-weakening because the dipole of the nitrophenyl group repels the positive charge of the anilinium ion. An additional base-weakening effect in *p*-nitroaniline (not present in the meta isomer) results from dispersal of the unshared pair of electrons on nitrogen into the nitro group.

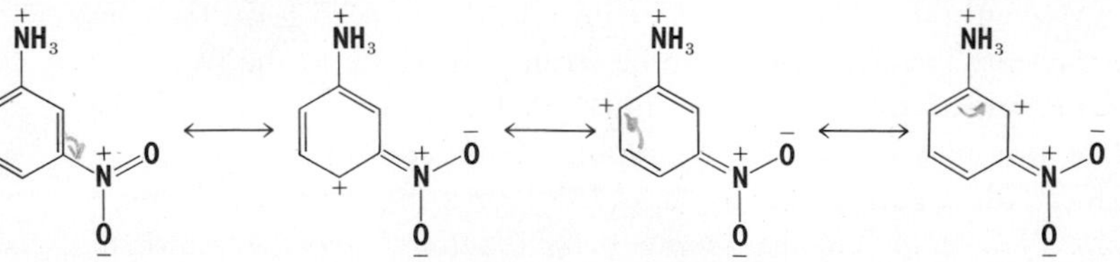

Resonance in *m*-nitroaniline cation

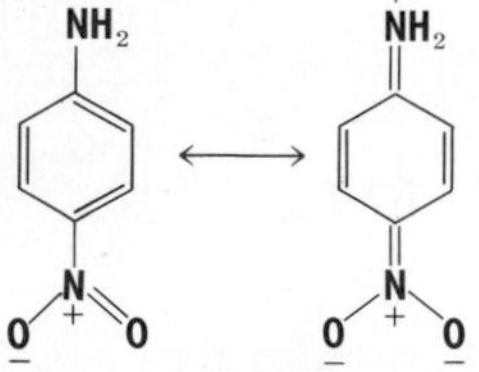

Resonance in *p*-nitroaniline

Amides, in contrast to amines, are not detectably basic in water solution, largely because of delocalization of the electrons of nitrogen.

Resonance in acetamide

When nitrogen is flanked by two carbonyl groups, as in the cyclic imides, the influence of the two groups is strong enough to render compounds weakly acidic even in water solution. Succinimide serves as an example. Both the neutral succinimide molecule and its conjugate base are stabilized, and the same number of significant resonance structures can be formulated for both species. Delocalization is more effective in the anion, since removal of the proton decreases the electron affinity of the nitrogen atom. *Delocalization of electrons is most effective when excess charge is dispersed throughout a system without charge separation.*

Succinimide—delocalization of electrons with charge separation

Succinimide anion—delocalization of charge

Ordinarily oxygen and nitrogen atoms involved in multiple bonding are more weakly basic than those which have only σ bonds. The higher basic strength of methylamine as compared to pyridine illustrates this principle. However, guanidine is the strongest known organic base aside

TABLE 8.5   *Basicity Constants of Amines*

Name	Structure	K_b
Methylamine	CH_3NH_2	5.0×10^{-4}
Dimethylamine	$(CH_3)_2NH$	7.4×10^{-4}
Trimethylamine	$(CH_3)_3N$	7.4×10^{-5}
Aniline	$C_6H_5NH_2$	3.83×10^{-10}
m-Nitroaniline	$m\text{-}NO_2C_6H_4NH_2$	4×10^{-12}
p-Nitroaniline	$p\text{-}NO_2C_6H_4NH_2$	1×10^{-13}

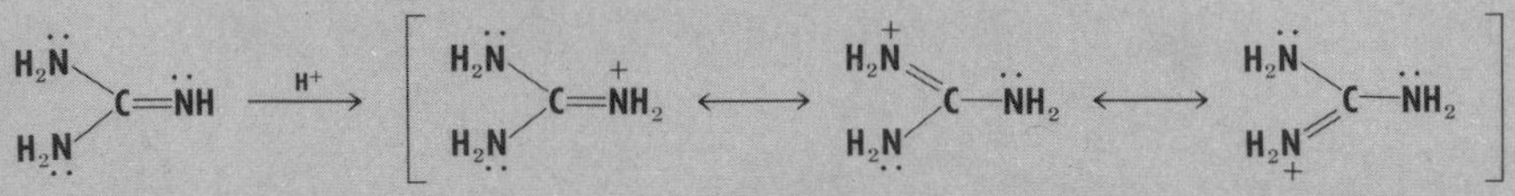

FIG. 8.2   *Resonance in guanidinium ion.*

from the quaternary ammonium bases, a fact attributable to the symmetrical distribution of charge in the guanidinium ion (see Fig. 8.2).

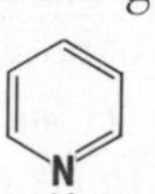

| CH$_3$NH$_2$ | Pyridine | CH$_3$C≡N | C$_6$H$_5$N=NC$_6$H$_5$ |
| Methylamine | Pyridine | Acetonitrile | Azobenzene |

$K_b = 4.38 \times 10^{-4}$ $K_b = 1.4 \times 10^{-9}$ K_b too weak to measure

Another example of resonance effects resulting in increased base strength is found in the greater basicity of 2,6-dimethyl-γ-pyrone as compared to cyclohexanone. The benzenelike resonance of the conjugate acid of the pyrone is undoubtedly responsible for the enhanced basic character of the pyrone. Although ordinary ketones, esters, ethers, and alcohols all show basic properties when treated with strong acids, their base strengths are considerably lower than those of their nitrogen analogues. The conjugate acids of the oxygen compounds are important intermediates in organic reactions in which carbon-oxygen bonds are broken (Chap. 11). The following examples illustrate the basic character of oxygen-containing compounds.

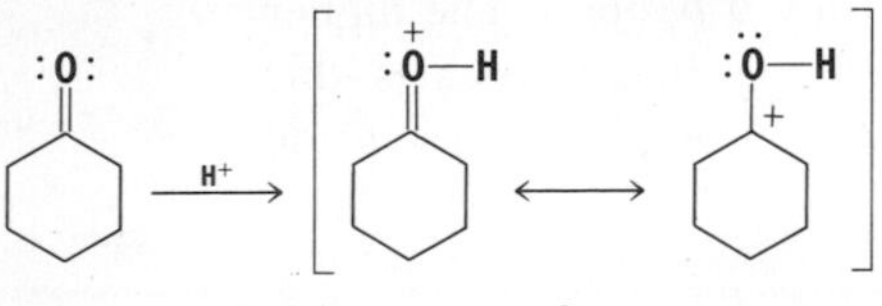

Cyclohexanone as a base

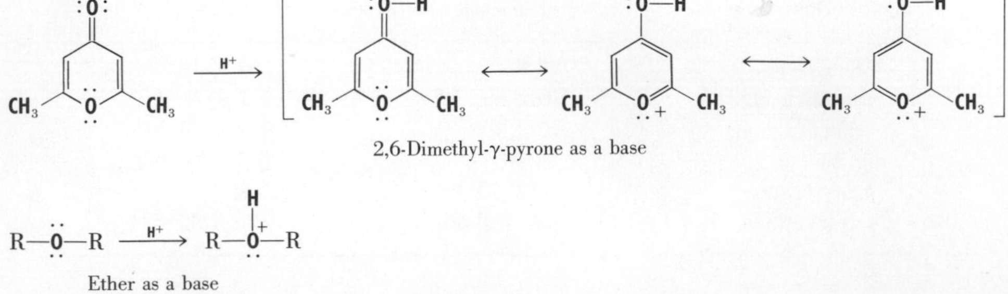

2,6-Dimethyl-γ-pyrone as a base

Ether as a base

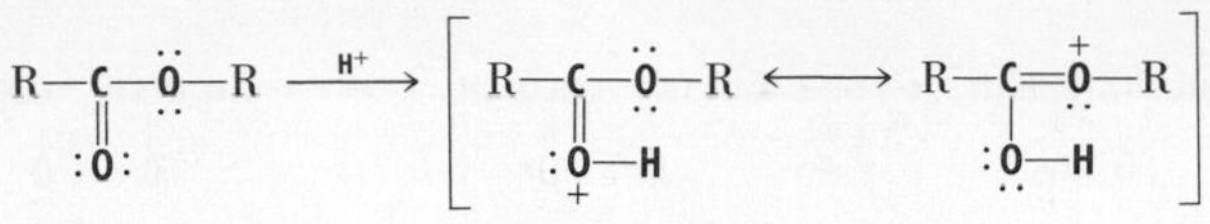

$$R-\overset{\overset{\displaystyle :\!O\!:}{|}}{C}-\overset{..}{O}-R \xrightarrow{\ H^+\ } \left[R-\overset{\overset{\displaystyle \underset{+}{\overset{..}{O}-H}}{|}}{C}-\overset{..}{O}-R \longleftrightarrow R-\overset{\overset{\displaystyle \overset{..}{O}-H}{\|}}{\underset{+}{C}}-R \right]$$

Ester as a base

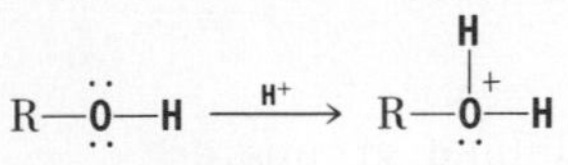

$$R-\overset{..}{\underset{..}{O}}-H \xrightarrow{\ H^+\ } R-\overset{\overset{\displaystyle H}{|}}{\underset{+}{\overset{..}{O}}}-H$$

Alcohol as a base

The resonance effect is responsible for the high acidity of phenols as compared with alcohols. Both phenol and its conjugate base must be somewhat stabilized because of electron delocalization, but the effect is larger in the anion than in the neutral acid.

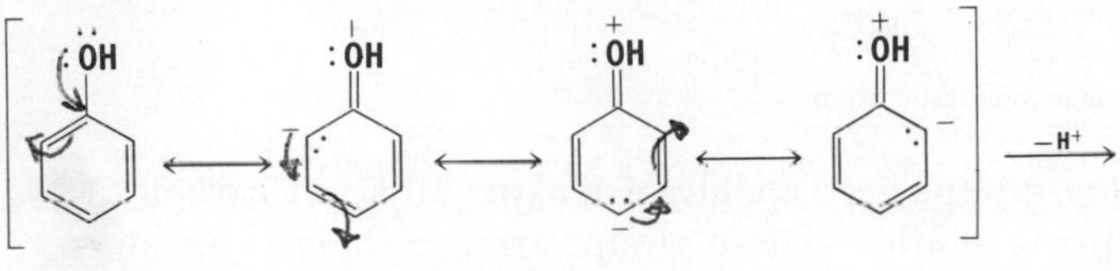

Phenol
$K_a = 1.2 \times 10^{-10}$ (cf. ethanol, $K_a - 10^{-16}$)

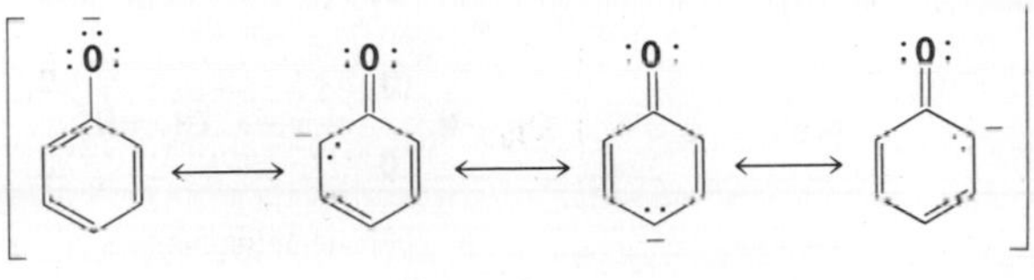

Phenoxide ion

A similar effect makes aliphatic carbonyl compounds enormously more acidic than hydrocarbons. The acidity of simple aldehydes and ketones is not measurable in water, but their conversion to anions in the presence of bases is a critical step in many of their reactions. On the other hand, β-dicarbonyl compounds are measurably acidic in water.

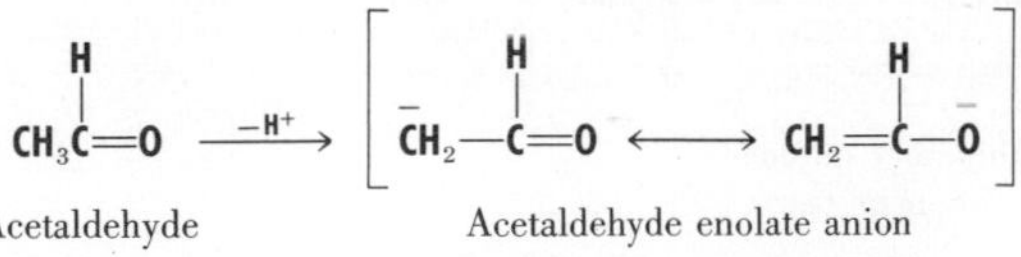

Acetaldehyde   Acetaldehyde enolate anion

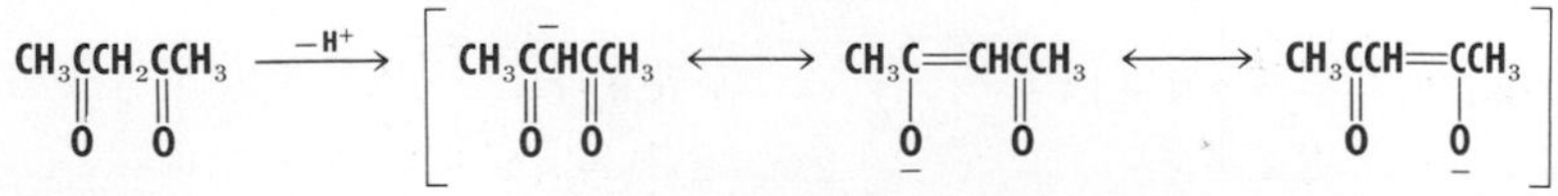

Acetylacetone   Acetylacetonate anion
$K_a = 1.5 \times 10^{-9}$

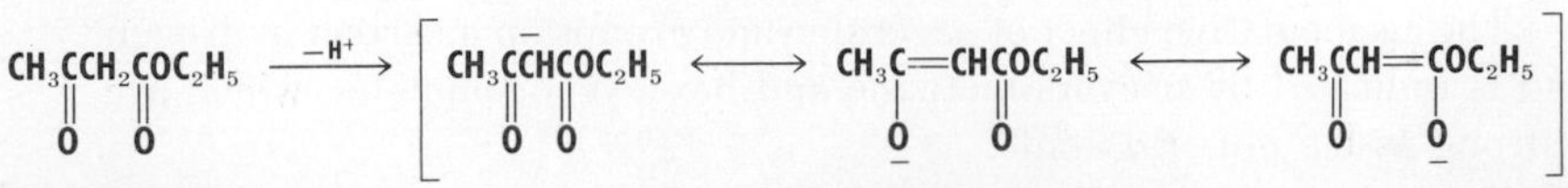

Ethyl acetoacetate   Ethyl acetoacetate anion
$K_a = 7.1 \times 10^{-11}$

$$\underset{\overset{\|}{O}\ \ \overset{\|}{O}}{C_2H_5OCCH_2COC_2H_5} \xrightarrow{-H^+} \left[\underset{\overset{\|}{O}\ \ \overset{\|}{O}}{C_2H_5OC\overset{-}{C}HCOC_2H_5} \longleftrightarrow \underset{\overset{\ \ }{O}\ \ \overset{\|}{O}}{C_2H_5O\overset{-}{C}=CHCOC_2H_5} \longleftrightarrow \underset{\overset{\|}{O}\ \ \overset{\ \ }{\underset{-}{O}}}{C_2H_5OCCH=COC_2H_5} \right]$$

Diethyl malonate
$K_a \sim 10^{-15}$ (probably
not measurable in water)

Diethyl malonate anion

The above examples show that aldehyde and ketone groups are superior to the ester function in their ability to disperse negative charge. Delocalization of electrons within the ester group itself decreases the ability of the carbonyl to accept electrons from external sources.

$$R—C\overset{\diagup O}{\underset{\diagdown OR}{}} \longleftrightarrow R—C\overset{\diagup \overset{-}{O}}{\underset{\diagdown \overset{OR}{+}}{}}$$

Delocalization of electrons in an ester group

Other unsaturated groups are capable of making adjacent carbon-hydrogen bonds relatively acidic. These groups arrange themselves in the order **NO₂ > CN > SO₂CH₃ > (C₆H₅)₃** in their ability to disperse negative charge. Ionization of compounds containing these groups is illustrated.

$$CH_3NO_2 \xrightarrow{-H^+} \left[\overset{-}{C}H_2—\overset{+}{N}\overset{\diagup O}{\underset{\diagdown O}{}} \longleftrightarrow CH_2=\overset{+}{N}\overset{\diagup O}{\underset{\diagdown \overset{O}{-}}{}} \right] \qquad K_a = 6.1 \times 10^{-11}$$

Nitromethane   Nitromethide ion

$$CH_3CN \xrightarrow{-H^+} \left[\overset{-}{C}H_2—C\equiv N \longleftrightarrow CH_2=C=\overset{-}{N} \right] \qquad K_a \sim 10^{-25}$$

Acetonitrile   Acetonitrile conjugate base

$$CH_3SO_2CH_3 \xrightarrow{-H^+} \left[\underset{\overset{\|}{O}}{\overset{\overset{O}{\|}}{\overset{-}{C}H_2—\overset{++}{S}—CH_3}} \longleftrightarrow \underset{\overset{\|}{O}}{\overset{\overset{O}{\|}}{CH_2=\overset{+}{S}—CH_3}} \right] \qquad K_a \sim 10^{-23}$$

Dimethyl sulfone   Dimethyl sulfone
                           conjugate base

$$(C_6H_5)_3CH \xrightarrow{-H^+} \left[(C_6H_5)_2\overset{-}{C}—\bigcirc \longleftrightarrow (C_6H_5)_2C=\bigcirc :^- \quad etc. \right] \qquad K_a \sim 10^{-25}$$

Triphenylmethane   Triphenylmethide ion

The accumulative effect of several cyano groups on a carbon-hydrogen bond is indicated by tricyanomethane and hexacyanoisobutene, which are as strong as the mineral acids.

Tricyanomethane   Hexacyanoisobutene

Study of acidity of some carbon-hydrogen linkages is complicated by the fact that equilibria are sometimes established slowly. In contrast, the rate of equilibration of protons among various oxygen, nitrogen, and sulfur atoms is too fast for measurement by ordinary methods.

Steric Effects. The simplest of a number of stereochemical influences on chemical reactivity is known as *steric compression.* The effect is associated with the confinement of bulky groups within volumes insufficient for the exercise of their normal behavior. Proton acid-base reactions are not particularly sensitive to steric compression, since a proton is so small that its absence or presence in a molecule does not usually affect the volume very much. However, noticeable indirect effects are sometimes associated with the presence or absence of a proton in a system. These are best discussed by reference to actual examples.

The base *N,N*-dimethylaniline is six times weaker than *N,N*-dimethyl-*o*-toluidine. This difference in strength grows out of a configurational difference in the two molecules which is itself an example of steric compression. In both amines, the electron pair on nitrogen is delocalized through resonance, which effect makes both compounds weaker bases than methylamine. However, *N,N*-dimethyl-*o*-toluidine is the stronger base.

N,N-Dimethylaniline
$K_b = 1.15 \times 10^{-9}$

N,N-Dimethyl-*o*-toluidine
$K_b = 7.3 \times 10^{-9}$

These facts are explained with formulas in Fig. 8.3. The configuration needed for maximum interaction of π electrons of the benzene ring with the unshared electrons of nitrogen is that in which all atoms of the molecule are in one plane except the hydrogens of the methyl groups (structure I of Fig. 8.3). This configuration results in no steric compression for *N,N*-dimethylaniline, because there is enough space to accommodate the volumes occupied by the methyl groups of the nitrogen and by the ortho hydrogen atoms. In *N,N*-dimethyl-*o*-toluidine,

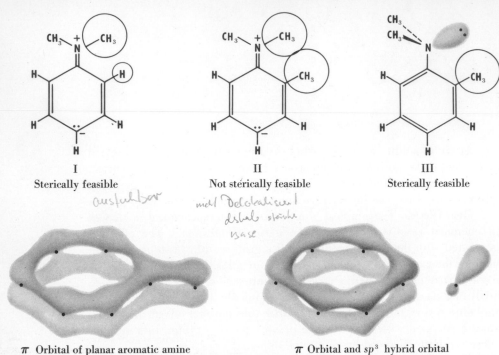

I
Sterically feasible
ausführbar

II
Not sterically feasible
nicht Delokalisiert
deshalb stärke
base

III
Sterically feasible

π Orbital of planar aromatic amine

π Orbital and *sp³* hybrid orbital
of nonplanar aromatic amine

FIG. 8.3   *Steric inhibition of resonance.*

a planar configuration compresses the ortho methyl and one of the methyl groups attached to the nitrogen, as is indicated in structure II. To avoid this strain, the molecule assumes the configuration shown in III.   As a result, resonance structures such as II are less important; the electron pair on nitrogen is more localized; and the substance is a stronger base.   Figure 8.3 also contains a molecular-orbital representation of planar aromatic amines, and an orbital picture of nonplanar aromatic amines.

A second type of steric compression is associated with the decrease in acidity in transition from the simple carboxylic acids to those which possess highly ramified structures.   In ionization of acetic acid, the anion is more stabilized by *solvation effects*† than is the uncharged acid, and this factor tends to increase the acid strength of acetic acid.   With acids such as IV, the charge on the anion (V) is somewhat shielded from solvent molecules by the surrounding methyl groups.   As a result, the anion is less stable, and the acid is weaker.

$$CH_3CO_2H \rightleftharpoons CH_3CO_2^- + H^+$$

Acetic acid   Acetate anion

$K_a = 2.7 \times 10^{-6}$ (50% H_2O, 50% CH_3OH)

† This phrase provides a name for the sum of the various attractive forces between solute and solvent molecules which were discussed in Chap. 7.   These include hydrogen bonding, dipole-dipole interactions, and polarizability phenomena.

$$IV \rightleftharpoons V + H^+$$

$$K_a = 1.1 \times 10^{-7} \ (50\% \ H_2O, \ 50\% \ CH_3OH)$$

The high acidity of formic acid ($K_a = 1.77 \times 10^{-4}$ in water) as compared to acetic acid ($K_a = 1.75 \times 10^{-5}$ in water) may be due in part to the greater availability of space for solvent molecules around the formate anion as compared to the acetate anion. The positive inductive effect of the methyl group in acetic acid must also be slightly acid-weakening.

Lewis Acids and Bases

A general set of definitions of acids and bases has been proposed (by G. N. Lewis) as follows: All substances containing unshared electron pairs are bases; all those containing an element which is two electrons short of having a complete valence shell are acids. Ammonia is a typical base, and boron trifluoride is a typical acid. The reaction of a Lewis acid with a Lewis base produces an addition compound.

Ammonia, a Lewis base   +   Boron trifluoride, a Lewis acid   ⇌   Addition compound

Lewis acids such as aluminum chloride, boron trifluoride, stannic chloride, zinc chloride, and ferric chloride are extremely important catalysts for certain organic reactions. Conversely, even the weakly basic properties of oxygen and halogen compounds can play a critical role in determining the course of reactions.

$AlCl_3$	$SnCl_4$	$ZnCl_2$	$FeCl_3$
Aluminum chloride	Stannic chloride	Zinc chloride	Ferric chloride

Important Lewis acids

Systematic study of Lewis acid-base reactions has been particularly useful in establishing principles of chemical reactivity. Equilibrium constants have been evaluated for the reversible reactions between alkylboron compounds and amines of varying steric requirements. A few examples are listed in Table 8.6.

Comparison of dissociation constants of the trimethylboron adducts shows that replacement of two hydrogen atoms of ammonia by methyl groups is base-strengthening. Such a response is expected. Since the

TABLE 8.6   *Dissociation Constants of Trialkylboron-Amine Compounds at 100°*

Acid	Base	K_d
$(CH_3)_3B$	NH_3	4.6
$(CH_3)_3B$	CH_3NH_2	0.0350
$(CH_3)_3B$	$(CH_3)_2NH$	0.0214
$(CH_3)_3B$	$(CH_3)_3N$	0.472
$(CH_3)_3B$	$(C_2H_5)_3N$	No compound formed
$(CH_3)_3B$	(quinuclidine)	0.0196

electron affinity of carbon is less than that of hydrogen, a methyl group will have a greater electron-donating effect than hydrogen. However, trimethylamine adduct is much more highly dissociated than the adduct from dimethylamine. The methyl groups must be more compressed in trimethylamine-trimethylboron than are the groups in dimethylamine adduct. Figure 8.4 provides a picture of the steric situation in these species.

Triethylamine gives no detectable adduct with trimethylboron, since ethyl require more space than methyl groups. At least one of the three ethyl groups of triethylamine must be folded toward the unshared pair of electrons. In quinuclidine, the carbon atoms are held back by the ring system, and consequently the substance forms a very stable adduct. Configurations of these two compounds are indicated in Fig. 8.5.

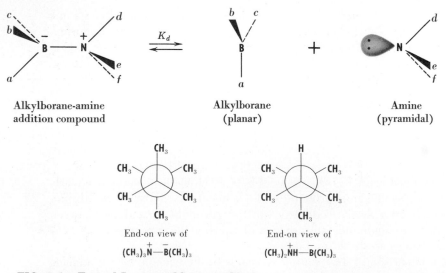

| Alkylborane-amine addition compound | Alkylborane (planar) | Amine (pyramidal) |

End-on view of $(CH_3)_3\overset{+}{N}$—$\overset{-}{B}(CH_3)_3$

End-on view of $(CH_3)_2\overset{+}{N}H$—$\overset{-}{B}(CH_3)_3$

FIG. 8.4   *Typical Lewis acid-base equilibria.*

Aromatic hydrocarbons exhibit some of the properties of Lewis bases, since they react with both protons and Lewis acids to form addition compounds. In some cases, these adducts can be isolated in a crystalline state. In general, the greater the number of aromatic rings per molecule, the more basic the hydrocarbon, and the more readily are addition compounds formed. Anthracene is more basic than naphthalene, which in turn is more basic than benzene.

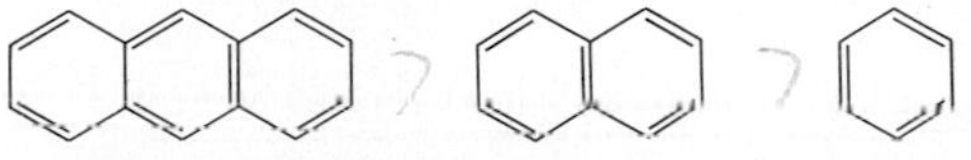

Anthracene   Naphthalene   Benzene

Order of decreasing basicity

Liquid hydrogen fluoride, tetranitromethane, picric acid, and tetracyanoethylene are examples of acids capable of forming adducts with aromatic hydrocarbons.

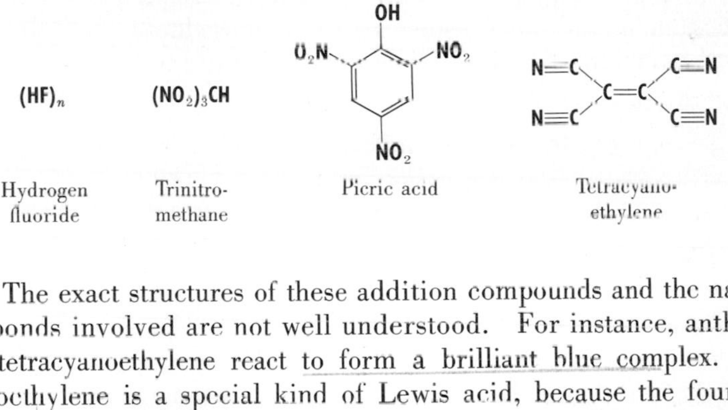

$(HF)_n$ $(NO_2)_3CH$ Picric acid   Tetracyano-
                                                         ethylene

Hydrogen   Trinitro-
fluoride   methane

The exact structures of these addition compounds and the nature of the bonds involved are not well understood. For instance, anthracene and tetracyanoethylene react to form a brilliant blue complex. Tetracyanoethylene is a special kind of Lewis acid, because the four cyano groups all withdraw electrons from the central carbon-carbon double bond, and these two carbons become relatively electron deficient. The π electrons of anthracene make up this deficiency in the complex by partial charge transfer, and the resulting complex is held together by the attraction of unlike charges for each other. In each part of the complex,

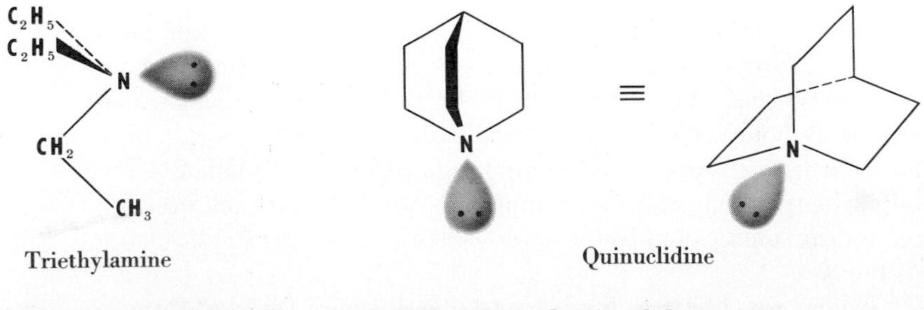

Triethylamine   Quinuclidine

FIG. 8.5   *Configurations of triethylamine and quinuclidine.*

the charge is stabilized by dispersal throughout the system, as is indicated by the use of dashes for partial bonds in the following formulas.

Anthracene   Tetracyanoethylene   Adduct

Tautomerism

The term *tautomerism* designates the structural ambiguity which arises from certain rapid and reversible rearrangements that occur in organic molecules. Most frequently, the term is applied to the migration of a proton between two or more basic and conjugated sites in an organic molecule. In a sense, *tautomeric shifts* of protons are internal acid-base reactions, and the various structural isomers that result from such migrations are known as *tautomers*. When a proton is completely removed from two tautomers, the same resonating anion is produced, as is illustrated in the conversion of both the *carbonyl* and *enol* forms of acetaldehyde into the same enolate anion.

Carbonyl form   Enol form
>99% at equilibrium   <1% at equilibrium

Tautomerism in acetaldehyde

Interconversion of carbonyl and enol forms of aldehydes and ketones is measurably slow, since at some stage a carbon-hydrogen bond must be broken. Many studies of equilibrated systems have been carried out, and tautomerization constants measured. These constants are the ratio of the acidity constants of the carbonyl and enol forms, as indicated in Eq. (11). Constants for a number of carbonyl-containing compounds are recorded in Table 8.7.

$$(11) \quad \text{Tautomerization constant} = K_T = \frac{K_a \text{ of carbonyl form}}{K_a \text{ of enol form}}$$

The enol forms of simple aldehydes and ketones have not been isolated in pure form, because they are so easily converted into the more stable carbonyl forms. Conversions of this type occur very readily, and are catalyzed by both acids and bases, and even by polar surfaces. Both tautomeric forms of β-dicarbonyl compounds have been isolated. The enol and carbonyl forms of these compounds are close to each other in stability, and in some examples of Table 8.7, the enol form is the more stable of the two.

Two factors contribute to the increased stability of the enol form in β-dicarbonyl compounds. The enols are stabilized by a significant resonance energy, similar to that of carboxylic acids. In noncyclic compounds, the enol forms are stabilized by internal hydrogen bonding.

Resonance and hydrogen bonding in enols of β-diketones

Phenol may be regarded as the enol of either 2,4-cyclohexadienone or 2,5-cyclohexadienone. No direct evidence for the existence of either dienone is known. The striking difference in tautomer stabilities between cyclohexanone and phenol (see Table 8.7) illustrates the enormous gain in stability associated with aromatic systems. Movement of hydrogen from carbon to oxygen in transition from either 2,4- or 2,5-cyclohexadienone to phenol allows all six π electrons to become distributed throughout the system.

2,4-Cyclohexadienone   2,5-Cyclohexadienone   Phenol

TABLE 8.7   *Tautomerization Constants of Carbonyl-containing Compounds*

Carbonyl form	Enol form	K_T
		2.5×10^{-6} (in water)
		2.0×10^{-4} (in water)
		6.2×10^{-2} (pure liquid)
		3.6 (pure liquid)
		Too large to measure

Tautomerism is observed in many systems. Esters, acids, and amides are all capable of undergoing tautomeric interconversions, although when only one functional group is involved, the amounts of enol form are not directly measurable. The existence of enols is inferred from a study of the reactions of these compounds.

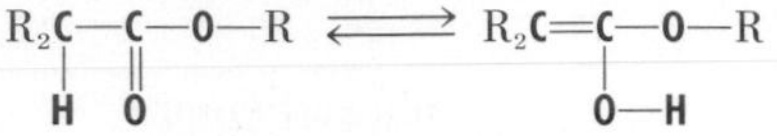

Tautomerism in esters 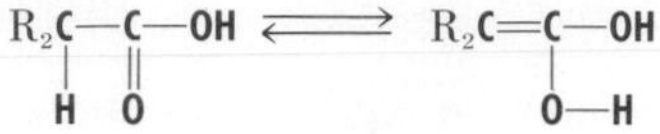   Tautomerism in acids

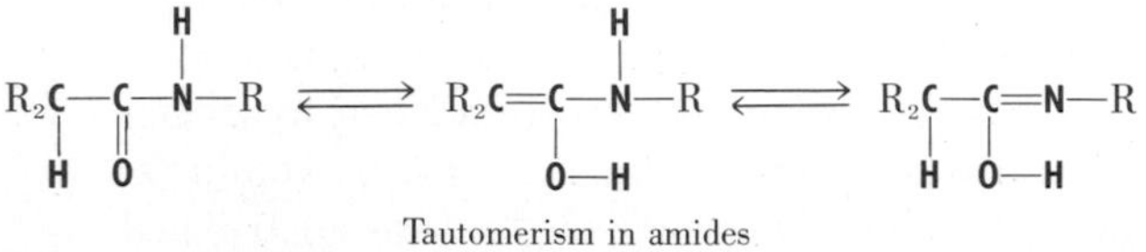

Tautomerism in amides

Nitroalkanes easily equilibrate with their tautomeric *aci*-nitro forms, which are usually present in samples of this class of compound in trace amounts.

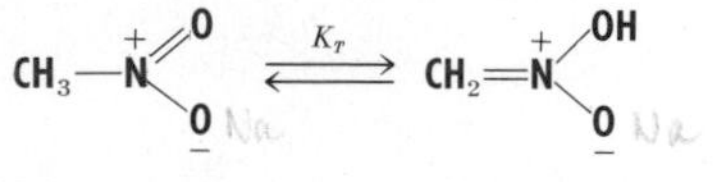

Nitromethane   *aci*-Nitromethane

$$K_T = 1.1 \times 10^{-17} \text{ in water}$$

A large number of semiaromatic ring systems which contain nitrogen are known, and these can usually exist in a number of different tautomeric forms. The imidazole ring system provides an example.

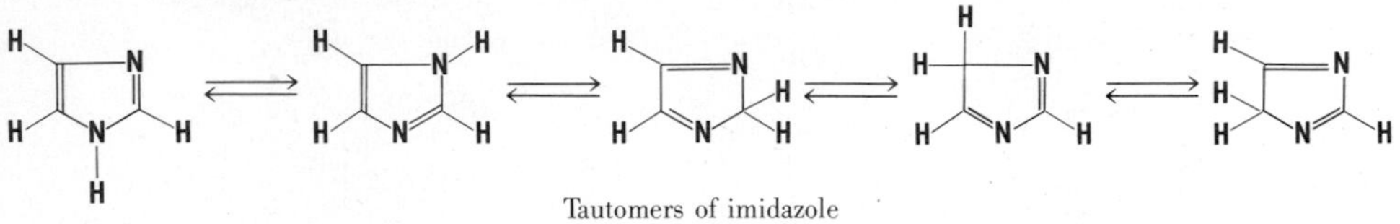

Tautomers of imidazole

Problems

1. Arrange the following compounds in order of decreasing acid strength: CH_3CO_2H, $[(CH_3)_3C]_3CCO_2H$, $CH_3SO_2CH_2CO_2H$, C_6H_5OH, $p\text{-}CH_3C_6H_4OH$, CH_3NO_2, $n\text{-}C_4H_{10}$, $(C_6H_5)_2CH_2$.

2. Classify the following compounds as Lewis acids, Lewis bases, neither, or both: $AlCl_3$, NI_3, $NaOH$, dioxan, pyridine, CH_3NO_2, $FeCl_3$, CH_3Br, CH_3CO_2H, C_6H_6, $(NC)_2C{=}C(CN)_2$.

3. When possible, dipoles within a molecule tend to line up in configurations which allow like charges to be as far as possible from each other. An example is found in glyoxal.

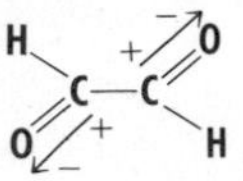

more stable than

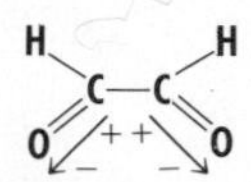

Two configurations for glyoxal

Keeping the above idea in mind, provide an interpretation for the following facts:

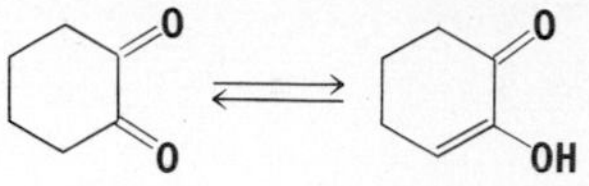

$K_T = 670 \times 10^{-3}$

$CH_3COCOCH_3 \rightleftharpoons CH_3COC\!=\!CH_2$ $K_T = 5.6 \times 10^{-3}$
                                      |
                                      OH

4. In 100% sulfuric acid, acetic acid behaves as a base, taking a proton from sulfuric acid. Write what you think is the structure of the conjugate acid of acetic acid, and justify your choice of this structure over any alternative structures.

5. Quinuclidine is a stronger base than triethylamine toward trimethylboron by an immeasurably large amount, but the basicity of the two compounds toward protons is about the same. Explain this fact.

6. Explain in detail the order of acidity and basicity observed for the following compounds:

  a. CH_3NH_2 is more basic than $C_6H_5NH_2$.

  b. $p\text{-}CH_3COC_6H_4OH$ is more acidic than C_6H_5OH.

  c. 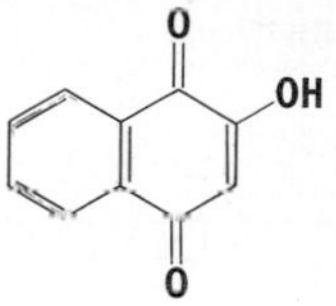 is a much stronger acid than .

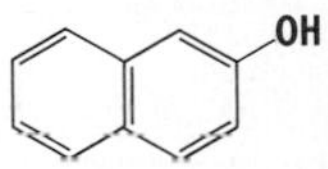

  d. 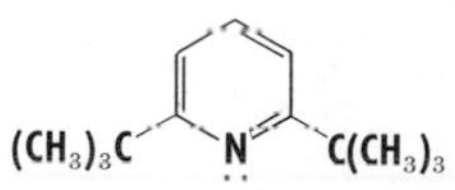 is a much weaker base than .

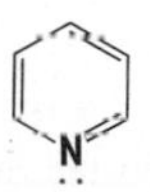

  e. 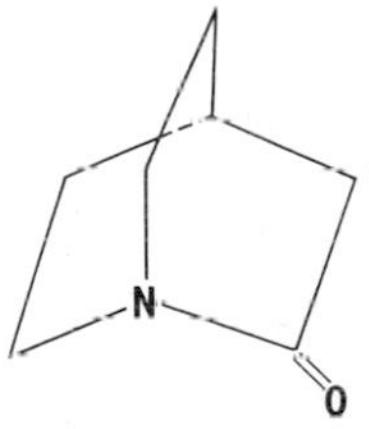 is a much stronger base than $(C_2H_5)_2\overset{..}{N}CC_2H_5$. (*Hint:* Steric and resonance effects are involved!)

  f. $p\,CH_3C_6H_4SO_3H$ dissolved in acetic acid is a stronger acid than when dissolved in water.

  g. is a stronger acid than

  while is a stronger acid than .

  h. $(NO_2)_3CH$ is a stronger acid than $(NO_2)_2CH_2$, which in turn is a stronger acid than NO_2CH_3.

7. Which of the two enols would you expect to be the stronger base, and why?

| Enol of an | Enol of a |
| α-diketone | β-diketone |

8. Arrange the following conjugate acids of amines in decreasing order of acid strength:

$$CH_3\overset{+}{N}H_3 \qquad NH_2-\underset{\underset{\overset{+}{N}H_2}{\|}}{C}-NH_2 \qquad C_6H_5\overset{+}{N}H_3 \qquad p\text{-}NO_2C_6H_4\overset{+}{N}H_3$$

9. Presume that in the formation of the addition compound between tetracyanoethylene and naphthalene (page 182), an electron is completely transferred from hydrocarbon to cyano compound to produce a naphthalene radical-cation and a tetracyanoethylene radical-anion. Draw representative resonance forms for these two species.

10. Write all possible tautomeric structures for the following compounds. Applying the principles of resonance, pick what you think would be the most stable tautomer.

a. $C_6H_5CH(CO_2C_2H_5)_2$

b.

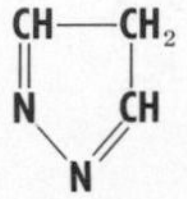

c.

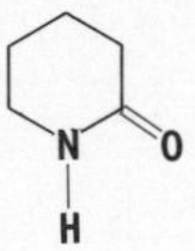

d.

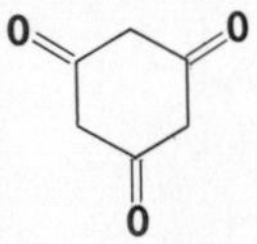

e.

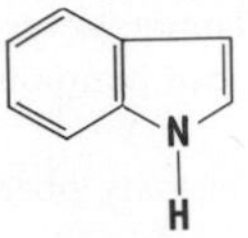

f.

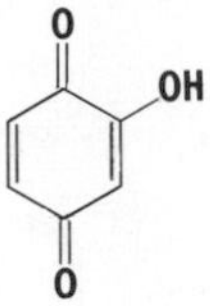

g.

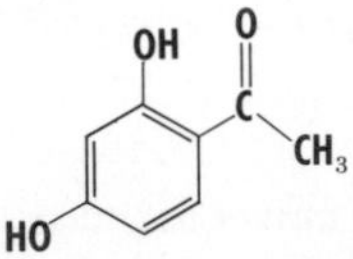

h.

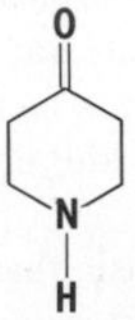

i.

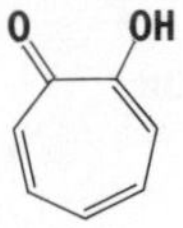

j. $CH_3-\underset{\underset{O}{\|}}{C}-CH_2-NO_2$

11. Interpret the following facts:

a. Although $n\text{-}C_4H_9Na + (C_6H_5)_3CH \longrightarrow (C_6H_5)_3CNa + n\text{-}C_4H_{10}$,

$$n\text{-}C_4H_9Na + \quad \longrightarrow \text{ no reaction.}$$

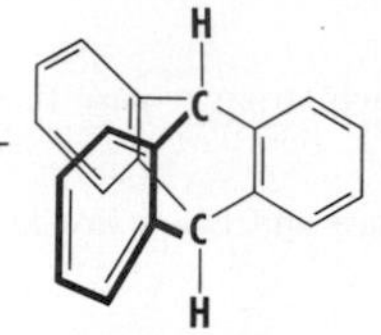

b. In the homologous series of compounds CH_2 $(CH_2)_n$, those with higher values of n are more acidic.

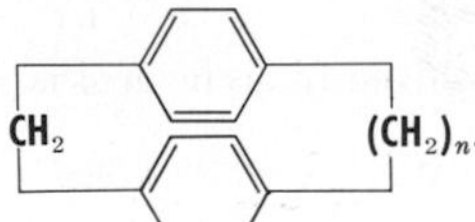

c. In the homologous series of compounds $(CH_2)_n$, those with the smaller values of n are the stronger bases.

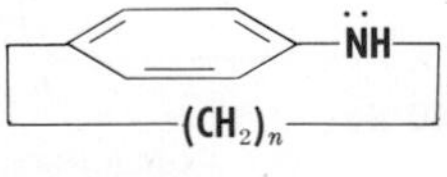

d. In acid strength, $<$

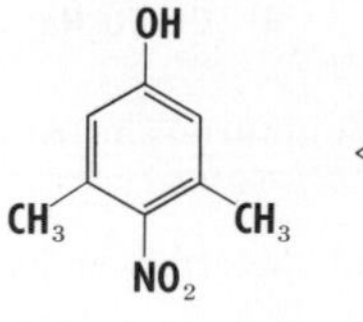

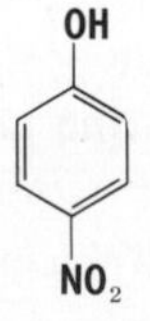

12. With the data in Tables 8.3 and 8.5, make the following calculations:

a. pK_a's of $ClCH_2CO_2H$, $p\text{-}NO_2C_6H_4CO_2H$, and $C_6H_5CO_2H$

b. pK_b's of $C_6H_5NH_2$, $(CH_3)_3N$, and $m\text{-}NO_2C_6H_4NH_2$

c. pK_a's of $C_6H_5NH_3^+$, $(CH_3)_3NH^+$, and $m\text{-}NO_2C_6H_4NH_3^+$

9

Characterization of Organic Reactions

Chapters 10 to 20 deal largely [handelt] with organic reactions, which fall naturally into a number of classes. The distinctive features of these groups arise from differences in the electronic structures of the starting materials, and in the electronic character of the bond-making and bond-breaking processes. In most cases bonds to carbon are involved, but in a few instances only bonds between hetero elements are made and broken. In classifying reactions, attention is focused on what happens at carbon, and the few reactions which do not involve bonds to carbon are introduced in an incidental way at appropriate places. The purpose of this chapter is to indicate the nature of these reaction classes, and to develop terminology and principles needed to discuss the character of organic reactions.

Classes of Bond-making and Bond-breaking Processes

Heterolytic Reactions. *In heterolytic reactions bonds are broken unsymmetrically* and electrons remain coupled. Heterolytic reactions are often catalyzed by acids and bases and are influenced strongly by variations in the polarity of solvents. They usually occur in solution but may also take place on polar surfaces of solid catalysts. Figure 9.1 illustrates the notation commonly used to indicate heterolytic bond cleavages.

Homolytic Reactions. *Bonds are broken symmetrically in homolytic reactions;* electron pairs are divided with one electron going to each nucleus. Intermediates, known as *free radicals*, are usually involved. Homolytic reactions occur in solid, liquid, and gaseous states, as well as on surfaces. They can be initiated thermally, photochemically, or by reagents which contain unpaired electrons. The notation used to indicate homolytic reactions is shown in Fig. 9.1.

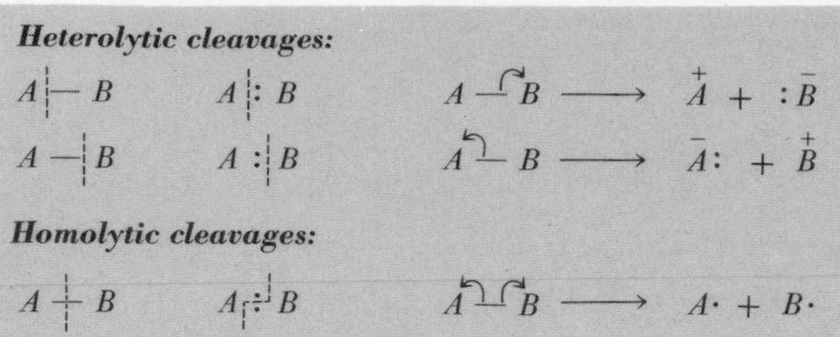

Heterolytic cleavages:

$$A \mid\!\!- B \qquad A \mid\!: B \qquad A \overset{\frown}{-} B \longrightarrow \overset{+}{A} + :\bar{B}$$

$$A -\mid B \qquad A :\mid B \qquad A \overset{\frown}{-} B \longrightarrow \bar{A}: + \overset{+}{B}$$

Homolytic cleavages:

$$A \overset{\mid}{+} B \qquad A \overset{\mid}{\vdots} B \qquad A \overset{\frown\frown}{-} B \longrightarrow A\cdot + B\cdot$$

FIG. 9.1   *Notations for bond-breaking processes.*

Nucleophilic and Electrophilic Reagents.   Polar reagents are classified as *nucleophiles* or *electrophiles*, depending on their role in reactions.   If the reagent *donates* an electron pair to carbon in an organic molecule, the reagent is said to be a nucleophile, and *nucleophilic* (nucleus-loving) in behavior.   Nucleophiles include negatively charged ions, molecules possessing atoms with unshared pairs of electrons, and molecules that contain highly polarized or polarizable bonds.

$$\bar{I} \quad \bar{O}H \quad \bar{O}R \quad \bar{S}R \quad \bar{C}N \quad H_2\ddot{O}: \quad R\ddot{O}H \quad \ddot{N}H_3 \quad R\!-\!M \longleftrightarrow \bar{R}\ \overset{+}{M}$$

Examples of nucleophiles (M = metal)

If a reagent functions by accepting an electron pair from carbon in an organic reaction, the reagent is said to be an *electrophile*, and is *electrophilic* (electron-loving) in behavior.   Electrophiles can be positively charged ions, molecules containing atoms without full octets (Lewis acids), or molecules with highly polarized or polarizable bonds.

$$\overset{+}{H_3}O \quad \overset{+}{N}H_4 \quad R\overset{+}{O}H_2 \quad R_2C\!=\!\overset{+}{O}H \longleftrightarrow R_2\overset{+}{C}\!-\!OH \quad BF_3 \quad AlCl_3 \quad Ar_3B$$

$$I_2 \quad R_2C\!=\!O \longleftrightarrow R_2\overset{+}{C}\!-\!\bar{O}$$

Examples of electrophiles

The terms *acid* and *electrophile*, as well as *base* and *nucleophile*, overlap to some extent.   In this book, the words *electrophilic* and *nucleophilic* refer to the behavior of a species toward carbon rather than other elements, unless otherwise specified.   The term *basic* usually refers to the affinity of a species for protons or Lewis acids, while the term *acidic* applies to the behavior of protons or Lewis acids toward entities that contain unshared pairs of electrons.

A number of examples of electrophilic and nucleophilic reactions discussed in Chaps. 3 and 4 are formulated as follows:

$$\overset{+\ \ -}{KCN} + C_6H_5CH_2Br \longrightarrow C_6H_5CH_2CN + KBr$$

Benzyl bromide   Phenylacetonitrile

$$2\ddot{N}H_3 + CH_3(CH_2)_2\overset{\overset{\displaystyle O}{\parallel}}{C}Cl \longrightarrow CH_3(CH_2)_2\overset{\overset{\displaystyle O}{\parallel}}{C}NH_2 + NH_4Cl$$

Butyryl chloride   Butyramide

Examples of nucleophilic reactions

$$\overset{+}{H_3O} \ \overset{-}{Cl} + CH_3MgCl \longrightarrow CH_4 + MgCl_2 + H_2O$$

      Methylmagnesium
         bromide

$$NO_2^+ \quad + \quad C_6H_6 \longrightarrow C_6H_5NO_2 \quad + \quad H^+$$

(HNO$_3$ + H$_2$SO$_4$)   Benzene   Nitrobenzene

        Examples of electrophilic reactions

Radical Reactions. The number of reagents that initiate homolytic reactions are relatively few. They include biradicals (free radicals containing two unpaired electrons), stable free radicals, short-lived free radicals, ions capable of entering into one-electron transfer processes, and compounds that contain bonds which can be broken homolytically with heat or light. A number of such substances are listed.

Oxygen, a   Sodium nitrosyldisulfonate,   Chlorine atom, a
biradical   a stable radical   short lived radical

Ferric ion, capable   Di-*tert*-butyl peroxide,   *N*-Bromosuccinimide,
of entering into one-   undergoes thermal homolytic   undergoes homolytic
electron transfer process   cleavage of O—O bond to   cleavage of N—Br
          give radicals   bond to give radicals

    Examples of reagents that initiate homolytic reactions

An example of a radical reaction is the conversion of toluene to benzyl bromide with *N*-bromosuccinimide.

N-Bromosuccinimide   Toluene   Succinimide   Benzyl bromide

Classes of Organic Reactions

Organic reactions fall naturally into a number of categories, whose definitions depend primarily on the structural relationships between starting material and product. The three most fundamental reaction classes are *substitution, addition,* and *elimination.*

In substitution reactions, single bonds are made and broken at carbon, and a new (incoming) group is substituted for the old (leaving) group. This process can occur at either saturated carbon (carbon with four σ bonds) or unsaturated carbon (carbon with one or two π bonds), and it

Drawing

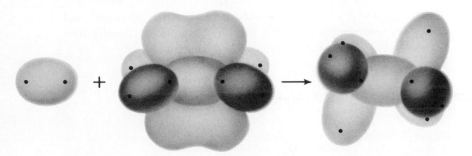

Orbital representation

FIG. 9.2   *Conversion of π bond to two σ bonds.*

is useful to divide substitution reactions into these two groups. A further designation of substitution reactions as nucleophilic, electrophilic, or radical is also helpful. For example, a reaction might be characterized as a nucleophilic substitution at saturated carbon, or as an electrophilic substitution at unsaturated carbon. Representative examples of substitution reactions are formulated below.

$$\overset{+}{\text{Na}}\overset{-}{\text{OCH}}_3 \quad + \quad CH_3CH_2CH_2Br \longrightarrow CH_3CH_2CH_2OCH_3 \quad + \quad \overset{+}{\text{Na}}\overset{-}{\text{Br}}$$

Sodium methoxide   *n*-Propyl bromide   1-Methoxypropane

Nucleophilic substitution at saturated carbon

$$CH_3CH_2OH \quad + \quad C_6H_5\overset{\text{O}}{\overset{\|}{C}}Cl \longrightarrow C_6H_5\overset{\text{O}}{\overset{\|}{C}}OCH_2CH_3 \quad + \quad HCl$$

Ethanol   Benzoyl chloride   Ethyl benzoate

Nucleophilic substitution at unsaturated carbon

$$\overset{-}{\text{FeBr}}_4\overset{+}{\text{Br}} \quad + \quad C_6H_6 \longrightarrow C_6H_5Br \quad + \quad \overset{-}{\text{FeBr}}_4\overset{+}{\text{H}}$$

Bromine–ferric   Bromobenzene
bromide complex

Electrophilic substitution at unsaturated carbon

$$8 \; : \overset{..}{\underset{..}{\text{Cl}}} \cdot \quad + \quad CH_4 \longrightarrow CCl_4 \quad + \quad 4HCl$$

Chlorine atoms   Methane   Carbon
(Cl$_2$ + light)   tetrachloride

Radical substitution reaction

In addition reactions, at least two substituents are added to an unsaturated molecule, and π bonds are converted to σ bonds in the process (see Fig. 9.2). This type of conversion may involve either homolytic or heterolytic processes. Thus either two radicals or a nucleophile and an electrophile may add to a double or triple bond. Carbon-carbon double and triple bonds, carbon-oxygen double bonds, carbon-nitrogen double and triple bonds, and carbon-sulfur double bonds all undergo addition reactions. Examples of typical addition reactions are formulated.

$$H_2 + CH_3CH_2CH_2CH\!-\!CH_2 \xrightarrow{\text{Pd}} CH_3CH_2CH_2CH_2CH_3$$

1-Pentene $\qquad\qquad\qquad$ n-Pentane

Nonpolar (radical) addition reaction

$$\overset{+\,-}{HCN} + \left[C_6H_5\overset{\text{O}}{\overset{\|}{C}}H \longleftrightarrow C_6H_5\overset{\overset{-}{\text{O}}}{\overset{|}{\underset{+}{C}}}H \right] \longrightarrow C_6H_5\overset{\text{OH}}{\overset{|}{C}}HCN$$

Benzaldehyde $\qquad\qquad\qquad$ Mandelonitrile

Nucleophilic (polar) addition reaction

Elimination reactions are essentially the reverse of additions, since two σ bonds are replaced by a π bond. Thus two groups can be lost from two adjacent atoms to produce multiple bonds, such as carbon-carbon double or triple bonds, or carbon-oxygen double bonds, as in the following examples.

$$NaOH + C_6H_5CH_2CH_2Cl \longrightarrow C_6H_5CH\!-\!CH_2 + NaCl + H_2O$$

β-Phenylethyl chloride $\qquad$ Styrene

$\xrightarrow[200°]{\text{Pd}}$ $\qquad$ $+ 5H_2$

Decalin $\qquad\qquad$ Naphthalene

$$[O] + CH_3CHOHCH_3 \longrightarrow CH_3\overset{\text{O}}{\overset{\|}{C}}CH_3 + H_2O$$

$H_2Cr_2O_7$ $\quad$ 2-Propanol $\qquad$ Acetone

Elimination reactions

Organic Reaction Mechanisms

The mechanism of an organic reaction is a description of the path followed by reactants as they are transformed into products. To be complete, the description should cover in detail the changes that occur in the positions of all atoms and bonds, and the changes in energy of the system that accompany these processes. Although few reaction mechanisms are completely understood, the broad outlines of the classes of mechanisms into which most reactions fall can be described. Such descriptions involve a number of principles and terms which will be introduced in this section.

Equilibrium and Kinetic Control of Products. Chapter 8 described a number of reversible acid and base reactions in which equilibrium was established quickly enough to allow the relative amounts of reactants and products to be predicted, after a short time, from equilibrium constants. When these conditions apply, the reaction products are said to be *equilibrium-controlled*. In many cases, two or more products are produced from a given starting material. If the reaction is equilibrium-controlled, the proportion of these two products is a function only of their relative stabilities, and is completely independent of reaction mechanism and rate.

Aside from acid-base reactions, relatively few organic transformations are reversible, and of these even fewer are run under conditions where all possible products become equilibrated. More commonly, at least one step in a reaction is essentially irreversible. In either case, the product distribution is said to be *kinetically controlled*. When two or more products come from the same starting material in a kinetically controlled reaction, their relative yields depend only on the relative rates at which they are produced, and are *independent of their relative stabilities*.

These principles are best illustrated by reference to an actual example in which either kinetic or equilibrium control of products may be realized. When 2-phenyl-2-butyl acetate is heated in acetic acid, a mixture of olefins is produced in which *trans*-2-phenyl-2-butene dominates. Only a trace of *cis*-2-phenyl-2-butene is produced. This reaction involves the loss of acetate ion to give an unstable intermediate, the 2-phenyl-2-butyl cation, which then loses one of the two hydrogen atoms on the adjacent methylene group to give the isomeric 2-phenyl-2-butenes. Under these conditions, the relative amounts of the isomers are a function only of the relative rates of loss of the two protons from the cation. Therefore the product distribution is kinetically controlled.

2-Phenyl-2-butyl acetate   2-Phenyl-2-butyl cation   *trans*-2-Phenyl-2-butene, major product

cis-2-Phenyl-2-butene, trace only

When either 2-phenyl-1-butene or *cis*- or *trans*-2-phenyl-2-butene is heated in acetic acid containing *p*-toluenesulfonic acid, a 4 to 1 ratio of *cis*- to *trans*-2-phenyl-2-butene is produced, irrespective of which alkene is used as starting material. Clearly the three become equilibrated through the 2-phenyl-2-butyl cation as intermediate, and the balance of products is equilibrium-controlled. This experiment demonstrates the cis isomer to be more stable than the trans, while the former experiment indicates that the more unstable isomer is formed from the cation faster than the stable isomer. In the latter experiment, equilibrium is established over a long period of time by way of the slow reversion of the trans isomer to the cation. The cis isomer also adds protons to give the same cation, but more slowly, and as a result this isomer accumulates.

2-Phenyl-2-butyl cation

trans-2-Phenyl-2-butene, minor product

cis-2-Phenyl-2-butene, major product

Transition-state Theory. In most organic reactions, the products are kinetically controlled.† Many reactions involve two or more discrete steps separated by unstable intermediates, which are created in *one reaction stage* and disposed of in a second. Such reactions are said to be *multistage*. Ordinarily one step will be slower than the others; it is referred to as the *rate-controlling step*. Thus in the kinetically controlled conversion of 2-phenyl-1-butene to *trans*-2-phenyl-2-butene (see above), the first and rate-controlling stage was the protonation of the alkene to give 2-phenyl-2-butyl cation, which is an unstable intermediate. The second and fast stage was the ejection of a proton by this intermediate to give *trans*-2-phenyl-2-butene.

Once the rate-controlling step of a reaction has been identified, the effects of variation of structure and of environmental conditions on the rate remain to be described and correlated. The "transition-state theory" provides a useful framework for accomplishing this task.

The slowness of a chemical reaction can usually be attributed to one or both of two factors. First, the acts of breaking and making bonds may require more energy than is possessed by most molecules of a reacting system. The excess energy which must be acquired by reacting molecules is called the *activation energy* of a reaction. The well-known acceleration of reactions as the temperature is raised is due to the increased number of activated molecules in the system.

The second factor which tends to retard a reaction is the frequent requirement that reacting molecules must assume rather improbable configurations. Reacting molecules pass through distorted and constrained configurations which subsequently become relaxed as the molecules pass to products. According to the transition-state theory, the problem of describing reaction rates is merely that of estimating the work required

† Among reactions that can be equilibrium-controlled are found the acid-base reactions, ester formation from alcohol and acid, ester hydrolysis, and certain oxidation-reduction reactions.

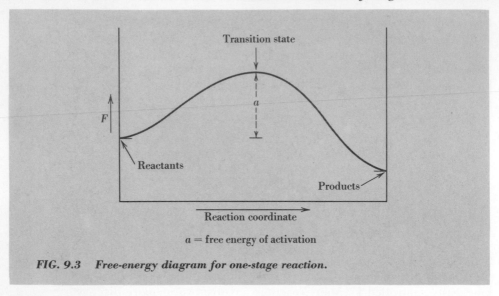

FIG. 9.3   *Free-energy diagram for one-stage reaction.*

to convert molecules of reactants into the *most unstable configuration* through which they must pass on their way to becoming products.   This most unstable state, called the *transition state,* has frequently been compared with the highest point in a mountain pass connecting two valleys. The work required to make transition states is designated by a function called the *free energy* (F), which takes account of both energetic and probability factors.†   The increased *free-energy content* of the transition state is called the *free energy of activation* $(\Delta F^{\ddagger})$.

The course of a reaction can be described in either of two ways. One method is to give an account of the changes in molecular shape during the process in terms of bond lengths, bond angles, and electron distribution.   The second method is to describe the changes in the free-energy content of the molecules.   The two descriptions are not independent, since geometric factors determine the free-energy content.   A common means of representing the relationship is illustrated by Fig. 9.3. Changes in molecular shape are indicated by progress from 0 to 100% reaction along the abscissa, and the rise and fall of free energy is plotted on the ordinate.   Such *free-energy diagrams* are usually schematic in the sense that the reaction-coordinate variable represents a composite change of a number of geometric parameters.   The value of a measures the free energy of activation for the reaction.

Multistage reactions are often represented by similar free-energy diagrams, as illustrated in Fig. 9.4.   The minimum in the curve represents a reaction intermediate in a *two-stage reaction.*   Each of these stages

† Probability factors have to do with the frequency with which a molecule assumes the configuration required for reaction.

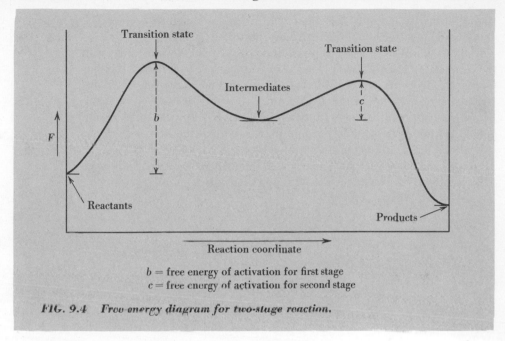

b = free energy of activation for first stage
c = free energy of activation for second stage

FIG. 9.4   Free-energy diagram for two-stage reaction.

is characterized by a specific rate and activation energy, b measuring the activation energy for the slow first stage, and c the activation energy for the fast second stage. The stage with the highest activation energy (b in Fig. 9.4) is called the *rate-determining step*.

Reaction Intermediates.   Transient intermediates in organic reactions vary in stability, their half lives ranging from small fractions of a second to a number of minutes. The most important of these intermediates are substances containing carbon atoms in abnormal valence states. They have been given names and occur frequently in organic reactions. Ions containing positively charged carbon are referred to as *carbonium ions*, and those containing negatively charged carbon are called *carbanions*. Neutral entities containing carbon with one unpaired electron are referred to as *carbon radicals*. Neutral entities containing carbon with two un-

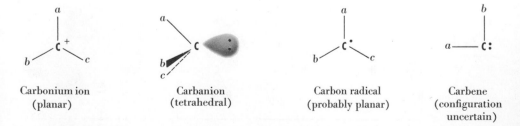

| Carbonium ion (planar) | Carbanion (tetrahedral) | Carbon radical (probably planar) | Carbene (configuration uncertain) |

FIG. 9.5   Configurations of reaction intermediates.

shared electrons and only six valence electrons are called *carbenes*. The configurations of these intermediates are indicated in Fig. 9.5.

The stabilities of these intermediates vary over a wide range with the character of the substituents (*a*, *b*, and *c*) attached to carbon. If either charge or electrons can be distributed in *a*, *b*, and *c*, the intermediates become resonance-stabilized. If electrons are highly delocalized, the configurations can be different from those formulated. In particular, conjugated carbanions flatten and become planar, so that the excess electrons can extend the π orbitals of unsaturated systems, as is shown in Fig. 9.6. Electrons and charge are particularly well delocalized by aryl substituents, which stabilize "trivalent carbon" through resonance.

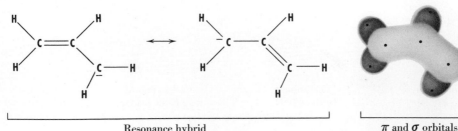

etc.

Triphenyl carbonium ion

etc.

Triphenyl carbanion

etc.

Triphenylmethyl radical

Resonance hybrid π and σ orbitals

FIG. 9.6   *Representation of allyl anion.*

Many organic reactions proceed through intermediates of this type or others which represent electronic modifications of various functional groups. These intermediates will be discussed in connection with the reactions in question.

Problems

1. Compile an extensive list of nucleophiles and electrophiles, and include examples not found in this chapter.

2. Draw a free-energy diagram for reactions that possess the following features. Label the activation energies and transition states for each stage, and intermediates in the reaction.

    a. A one-stage reaction

    b. A two-stage reaction in which the second stage is slower than the first

    c. A three-stage reaction in which the first stage has the highest activation energy and the second intermediate is more stable than the first

    d. $(CH_3)_3CCl \xrightarrow{\text{Slow}} (CH_3)_3\overset{+}{C} + \overset{-}{Cl}$

$$\xrightarrow[\text{Fast}]{H_2O} (CH_3)_3\overset{+}{C}OH_2 \xrightarrow[\substack{\text{Very}\\\text{fast}}]{-H^+} (CH_3)_3COH$$

3. Represent structures that contribute to the resonance hybrid of the following species:

    a. Phenyl carbonium ion (benzyl cation)

    b. $C_6H_5\overset{-}{C}HCN$

    c. $p\text{-}NO_2C_6H_4CH_2^-$

    d. $p\text{-}CH_3OC_6H_4CH_2^+$

    e. $p\text{-}NO_2C_6H_4\overset{..}{C}H_2$

    f. $p\text{-}HOC_6H_4\overset{.}{O}$

    g. $C_6H_5\overset{\cdot}{\underset{\displaystyle O}{C}}C_6H_5$

    h.

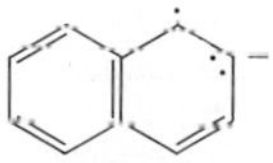

    i. $C_6H_5\overset{..}{C}C_6H_5$ (assume electron spins are paired)

    j. $CH_3CH\!\!=\!\!CH\overset{..}{C}H_2$

    k. $CH_3\overset{.}{C}HCOCH_3$

4. Classify the following reactions as completely as possible:

    a. $C_6H_5SH + C_6H_5CH_2Br \longrightarrow C_6H_5SCH_2C_6H_5 + HBr$

    b. $CH_3\overset{+-}{\underset{\displaystyle O}{C}}AlCl_4 + C_6H_6 \longrightarrow C_6H_5\overset{+-}{\underset{\displaystyle O}{C}}CH_3 + \overset{+-}{HAlCl_4}$

    c. $\cdot\overset{..}{\underset{..}{O}}\!\!-\!\!\overset{..}{\underset{..}{O}}\cdot \;+$

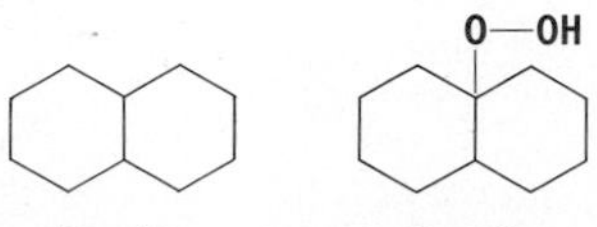

Decalin   Decalin
hydroperoxide

d. $O{=}C{=}O + C_6H_5Li \longrightarrow C_6H_5\overset{\displaystyle O}{\underset{\|}{C}}{-}O{-}Li$

e. $H{-}O{-}H + (CH_3)_2C{=}CH_2 \xrightarrow{\text{H}^+} (CH_3)_3COH$

f. $Zn + C_6H_5{-}\underset{\underset{Cl}{|}}{CH}{-}\underset{\underset{Cl}{|}}{CH}{-}C_6H_5 \longrightarrow C_6H_5CH{=}CHC_6H_5 + ZnCl_2$

g. $H_2 + CH_2{=}CHCH{=}CH_2 \xrightarrow{\text{Pt}} CH_3CH_2CH_2CH_3$

5. In regard to the isomerism of 2-phenyl-1-butene to the two isomeric 2-phenyl-2-butenes described on page 193, interpret the fact that *cis*-2-phenyl-2-butene is more stable than the trans isomer.

6. The following *slowly reversible* reaction was carried out. At the end of 6 hours, a 98% yield of 3-phenyl-2-butanol was produced. Analysis of the diastereomeric mixture gave a predominance of 2 to 1 of diastereomer *A* over *B*. The reaction was continued for 168 hours, and again a high yield of 3-phenyl-2-butanol was obtained, but this time the ratio of diastereomers was 1 to 1. When the reaction was allowed to go on, the same balance of products was observed. Explain these observations.

3-Phenyl-2-butanol
Diastereomer *A*

3-Phenyl-2-butanol
Diastereomer *B*

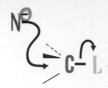

10

Nucleophilic Substitution Reactions
at Saturated Carbon

In a large number of reactions, an anion or a neutral base is released from its attachment to a carbon atom while the latter becomes bonded to another group of the same type. The general reaction and a specific example are shown in Fig. 10.1.

The specific reaction in Fig. 10.1 is described by the statement that the *nucleophilic hydroxide* ion makes a *substitution on the substrate,* methyl chloride, and that the *chloride ion is the leaving group* in the reaction. In the general reaction, the C—L bond undergoes heterolytic cleavage (page 188), since the pair of electrons that formed the bond in the substrate both appear in the product :L. In order to indicate the direction of flow of electrons in equations, curved arrows are frequently added to the formulas. The arrows *do not* imply anything about the detailed mechanism of the reaction, which may be very complex.

This chapter deals only with nucleophilic substitution at saturated

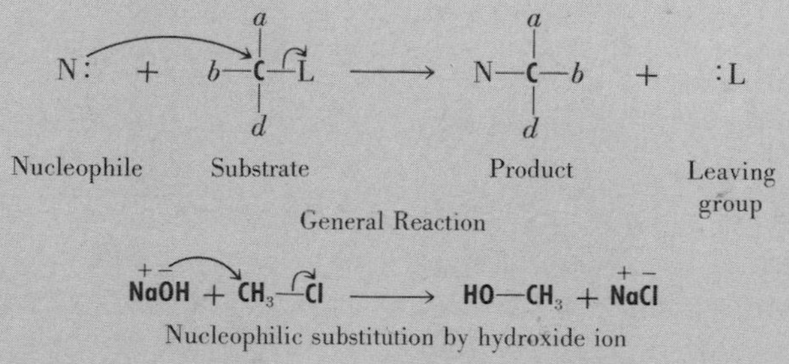

$$N: \quad + \quad b-\underset{\underset{d}{|}}{\overset{\overset{a}{|}}{C}}-L \quad \longrightarrow \quad N-\underset{\underset{d}{|}}{\overset{\overset{a}{|}}{C}}-b \quad + \quad :L$$

Nucleophile   Substrate   Product   Leaving group

General Reaction

$$Na\overset{+}{O}H + CH_3-Cl \longrightarrow HO-CH_3 + Na\overset{+}{C}l^-$$

Nucleophilic substitution by hydroxide ion

FIG. 10.1   *Nucleophilic substitution at a saturated carbon atom.*

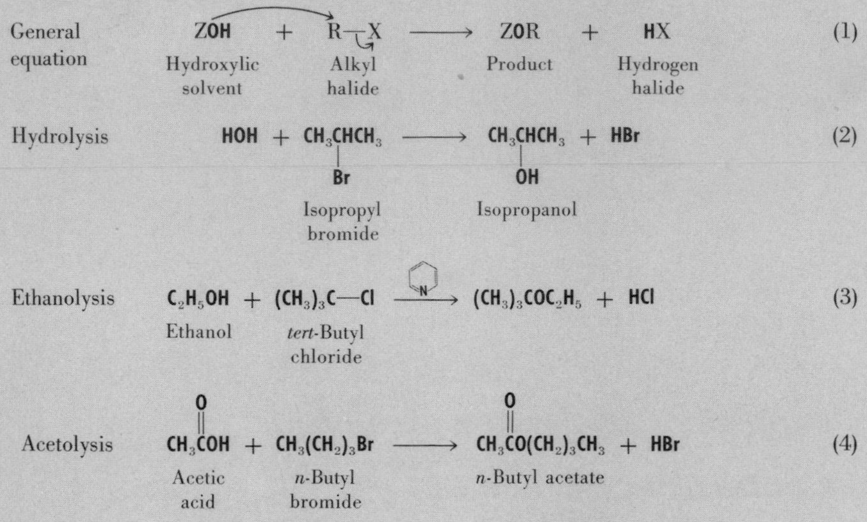

General equation	ZOH	+	R—X $\longrightarrow$	ZOR	+	HX	(1)

General
equation   ZOH   +   R—X $\longrightarrow$ ZOR   +   HX   (1)

     Hydroxylic   Alkyl   Product   Hydrogen
     solvent   halide   halide

Hydrolysis $HOH + CH_3CHCH_3 \longrightarrow CH_3CHCH_3 + HBr$ (2)

                           Br   OH

                        Isopropyl   Isopropanol
                        bromide

Ethanolysis $C_2H_5OH + (CH_3)_3C—Cl \xrightarrow{} (CH_3)_3COC_2H_5 + HCl$ (3)

            Ethanol   *tert*-Butyl
                     chloride

Acetolysis $CH_3\overset{O}{\overset{\|}{C}}OH + CH_3(CH_2)_3Br \longrightarrow CH_3\overset{O}{\overset{\|}{C}}O(CH_2)_3CH_3 + HBr$ (4)

         Acetic   *n*-Butyl   *n*-Butyl acetate
         acid   bromide

FIG. 10.2   Solvolysis of alkyl halides.

carbon atoms. The entire subject of nucleophilic substitution is much too broad for integrated presentation, and many of the generalizations concerning chemical reactivity do not apply equally to substitution at saturated and at unsaturated (Chap. 14) centers.

The attacking nucleophile and the leaving group are of the same general character. They are often anions, but may also be neutral molecules that contain unshared electron pairs. The following examples of nucleophilic substitutions show that the *charge type* of the groups is not of fundamental importance.

$$H—\overset{..}{\underset{..}{O}}: + CH_3—Cl \longrightarrow HO—CH_3 + :\overset{..}{\underset{..}{Cl}}:$$

$$H_3N: + CH_3—Cl \longrightarrow H_3\overset{+}{N}—CH_3 + \overset{-}{Cl}$$
                       Methylammonium
                            ion

$$:\overset{..}{\underset{..}{I}}: + CH_3—\overset{+}{O}H_2 \longrightarrow I—CH_3 + H_2O$$
    Methyloxonium
       ion

The groups *a*, *b*, and *d* in Fig. 10.1, which are attached to the carbon atom undergoing substitution, may vary widely. The nature of these substituents has a profound influence on the reactivity of the substrate and on the relative importance of certain side reactions that compete with substitution.

In the following discussion, attention is focused in turn upon the various bonds that can be made by the general reaction. Such a procedure reflects the use of *reactions as tools to be used in the synthesis of desirable products from available substrates.* In actual practice, syntheses usually involve several steps. The value of individual reactions depends on their being fitted into an over-all plan.

The over-all scope of nucleophilic substitution reactions is summarized in tables at the end of this chapter. Chapter 11 will deal with the mechanisms of nucleophilic substitutions and will thereby establish a rational basis for the correlation of structure with reactivity in such reactions.

Formation of Carbon-Oxygen Bonds

Compounds in which an alkyl group is bound to oxygen are made by *the displacement of various leaving groups by water and other hydroxylic compounds.* The substitutions are carried out by two general methods. First, the reaction may be a *solvolysis,* in which the substrate reacts with a nucleophilic solvent molecule. Figure 10.2 shows a general formulation and several examples of solvolysis reactions of alkyl halides—the most generally available substrates for the preparation of alcohols and ethers by substitution reactions.

As is illustrated by the ethanolysis of *tert*-butyl chloride [Eq. (3)], a tertiary amine may be added to the solvolysis mixture. The amine neutralizes the acid produced, thereby rendering the reaction essentially irreversible.

A second procedure, in which oxyanions serve as nucleophiles, is usually preferable to solvolysis as a method for the preparation of alcohols, ethers, and esters. Metal derivatives of the weakly nucleophilic O—H

General reaction	$\overset{-\ +}{ZOM} + R{-}X \longrightarrow ZO{-}R + \overset{+\ -}{MX}$	(5)
Hydroxide as the nucleophile	$\overset{+\ -}{NaOH} + CH_3CHCH_3 \overset{H_2O-C_2H_5OH}{\underset{solvent}{\longrightarrow}} CH_3CHCH_3 + \overset{+\ -}{NaBr}$ $\qquad\qquad\quad |$ $\qquad\qquad\quad Br \qquad\qquad\qquad\qquad\quad OH$	(6)
Alkoxide as the nucleophile	$\overset{-\ +}{(CH_3)_3COK} + C_2H_5{-}Br \overset{Benzene}{\longrightarrow} (CH_3)_3CO{-}C_2H_5 + \overset{+\ -}{KBr}$ Potassium *tert*-butoxide Substrate	(7)
Carboxylate ion as the nucleophile	$\overset{O}{\overset{||}{CH_3C}}\overset{-\ +}{ONa} + CH_3(CH_2)_3{-}Br \overset{C_2H_5OH}{\longrightarrow} \overset{O}{\overset{||}{CH_3C}}O(CH_2)_3CH_3 + \overset{+\ -}{NaBr}$ Sodium acetate	(8)

FIG. 10.3   *Nucleophilic substitution by oxyanions.*

compounds are prepared by various hydrogen-replacement reactions. The metallic reagents are dissolved, either in the parent hydroxylic compound or in some *inert* solvent, and the substrate is allowed to react with the solution of the negatively charged nucleophile. The specific examples of such reactions shown in Fig. 10.3 are chosen to parallel the examples of solvolysis in Fig. 10.2.

Note that Eq. (7) is not the exact counterpart of Eq. (3). Both reactions give *tert*-butyl ethyl ether as a product, but the primary halide is chosen as a substrate in Eq. (7) and tertiary halide was used in the solvolysis reaction. Reactions (9) and (10), which correspond exactly to (3) and (7), cannot be used to make the ether. The solvolysis of ethyl halides is too slow to be useful, and the reaction of alkoxides with tertiary halides usually gives no detectable amount of the substitution product, because of competition from nucleophilic elimination, a common side reaction in most nucleophilic substitutions.

$$(CH_3)_3COH + CH_3CH_2—Cl \;\;\cancel{\longrightarrow}\;\; (CH_3)_3CO—CH_2CH_3 + HCl \tag{9}$$

Reaction is too slow to be useful.

$$CH_3CH_2\overset{-}{O}\overset{+}{Na} + (CH_3)_3C—Br \;\; \begin{cases} \cancel{\longrightarrow} \; CH_3CH_2O—C(CH_3)_3 + \overset{+}{Na}\overset{-}{Br} \\ \longrightarrow \; CH_3CH_2OH + CH_2{=}C(CH_3)_2 + \overset{+}{Na}\overset{-}{Br} \end{cases} \tag{10}$$

$$100\%$$

Choice of Preparative Procedure. Several alternate routes are usually available for the synthesis of any desired compound. The factors usually considered in choosing the most appropriate of possible procedures are (1) availability and cost of starting materials; (2) rates of the reactions involved; (3) interference from side reactions; and (4) convenience of experimental procedures. The application of these criteria to the reactions listed in Figs. 10.2 and 10.3 is instructive. All the starting materials, except potassium *tert*-butoxide, are available at reasonable prices, and the alkoxide can be prepared easily from *tert*-butanol and potassium metal. Therefore, any of the reactions could be considered for use in a laboratory preparation. Evaluation of the reactions as possible bases for commercial production of the various products would require detailed cost analyses of these reactions and all other routes to the same products. Reaction (8), for example, would certainly be eliminated as a preparative procedure for *n*-butyl acetate, because the same product can be made directly from acetic acid and *n*-butanol (Chap. 14). The rejection of reactions that are too slow or suffer from competition from side reactions was illustrated in the previous paragraph. Experimental convenience would probably lead to the choice of reaction (3), in preference to reaction (7), for the preparation of *tert*-butyl ethyl ether, since (7) would require an extra step, the preparation of the alkoxide. In the following sections, the synthesis of various classes of compounds by nucleophilic substitutions will be considered in detail.

Alcohols. The *hydrolysis* of many substrates according to Eq. (11) gives alcohols as products.

$$H_2O + R{-}L \longrightarrow R{-}OH + H{-}L \tag{11}$$

Halide ions are the most commonly encountered leaving groups, although alkyl sulfate ($ROSO_3^-$), sulfate ($HOSO_3^-$), and sulfonate (RSO_3^- and $ArSO_3^-$) are sometimes employed. The reaction is very generally applicable to substrates possessing a wide variety of substituents. Bases, such as pyridine or sodium acetate, are sometimes added to neutralize the acid produced. When the reactions are carried out under solvolytic conditions (no strong base), the reactivity increases in this order: primary $<$ secondary $\ll$ tertiary. Aryl groups attached to the carbon atom undergoing substitution increase reactivity markedly.

$$H_2O + CH_3{-}Br \longrightarrow CH_3OH + HBr \qquad \text{(very slow)}$$

$$H_2O + (C_6H_5)_3C{-}Cl \longrightarrow (C_6H_5)_3C{-}OH + HCl \qquad \text{(extremely fast)}$$

Trityl chloride   Trityl alcohol
(triphenylcarbinol)

Jamassigl Schnelligkeit

$$H_2O + (CH_3)_2CH{-}I \longrightarrow (CH_3)_2CH{-}OH + HI \qquad \text{(moderate rate)}$$

Isopropyl iodide

The preparation of alcohols of low molecular weight from alkenes, which are readily available by-products in petroleum refining (Chap. 26), involves the hydrolysis of alkyl esters of sulfuric acid. The alkene is treated with aqueous sulfuric acid and first adds the elements of sulfuric acid (Chap. 15). The sulfate ester then undergoes a substitution reaction. The process is often carried out in one stage, so that sulfuric acid functions as a catalyst for the addition of water to the double bond.

$$H_2SO_4 + CH_3CH_2CH{=}CH_2 \longrightarrow CH_3CH_2CHCH_3$$
$$\underset{\textstyle OSO_3H}{|}$$

Markownikow

1-Butene   2-Butyl sulfuric acid

$$H_2O + CH_3CH_2CHCH_3 \longrightarrow CH_3CH_2CHCH_3 + H_2SO_4$$
$$\quad\underset{\textstyle OSO_3H}{|} \qquad\qquad\qquad \underset{\textstyle OH}{|}$$

2-Butanol

Ethanol, which is one of the organic chemicals produced commercially in largest volume, is manufactured by two methods. Ethylene, for the hydration process, is made by the catalytic hydrogenation of acetylene (Chap. 15) and is also produced by the cracking of petroleum. Any chemical that can be made easily from acetylene is abundantly available at low cost, because acetylene can be produced in unlimited amounts from calcium carbide. The second process for the manufacture of ethanol makes use of the fermentation of sugars in grains, potatoes, and fruits.

$$CaO + 3C \xrightarrow{2800°} CaC_2 + CO$$

Calcium
carbide

$$CaC_2 + H_2O \longrightarrow HC{\equiv}CH + CaO$$

$$HC{\equiv}CH + H_2 \longrightarrow H_2C{=}CH_2$$

$$H_2C{=}CH_2 \xrightarrow{H_2SO_4} [CH_3CH_2OSO_3H] \xrightarrow{H_2O} CH_3CH_2OH$$

Fermentation $C_6H_{12}O_6 \xrightarrow{\text{Yeast†}} 2CH_3CH_2OH + 2CO_2$

Sugar

†Yeast contains *enzymes*, which are biological catalysts for this remarkable transformation.

Methanol is manufactured in large amounts by the catalytic hydrogenation of carbon monoxide.

$$CO + 2H_2 \xrightarrow[\substack{350-400° \\ Cr_2O_3 \cdot ZnO}]{3000 \text{ lb/sq in.}} CH_3OH$$

Polyhydric Alcohols. *Vicinal* diols (1,2-diols) are made by the hydrolysis of vicinal dihalides or ethylene oxides. Both types of substrates are in turn produced by addition reactions of alkenes (Chap. 15). Ethylene glycol, the simplest *vicinal* diol, is used widely as a solvent and as a chemical. The compound is best known as the principal constituent of "permanent" antifreeze.

$$CH_2{=}CH_2 \xrightarrow{Cl_2} Cl{-}CH_2{-}CH_2{-}Cl \xrightarrow{H_2O, Na_2CO_3} HOCH_2CH_2OH$$

Ethylene
glycol

$$2CH_2{=}CH_2 + O_2 \xrightarrow[250°]{\text{Ag catalyst}} 2CH_2{-}CH_2 \\ O$$

Ethylene
oxide

$$CH_2{-}CH_2 \underset{O}{\overset{H_2SO_4}{\rightleftharpoons}} CH_2{-}CH_2 + {:}OH_2 \longrightarrow HOCH_2CH_2{-}\overset{+}{O}H_2 \underset{}{\overset{-H^+}{\rightleftharpoons}} HOCH_2CH_2OH$$

A commercial synthesis of the *tryhydric* alcohol glycerol (glycerine) involves no fewer than three nucleophilic substitution reactions. A *homolytic substitution* (Chap. 18) with propylene as a substrate is the key step of the sequence.

$$CH_2{=}CHCH_3 + Cl_2 \xrightarrow{500-600°} CH_2{=}CHCH_2Cl + HCl$$

Allyl
chloride

$$\overset{+}{Na}\overset{-}{OH} + CH_2{=}CHCH_2{-}Cl \longrightarrow CH_2{=}CHCH_2{-}OH + \overset{+}{Na}\overset{-}{Cl}$$

Allyl alcohol

$$\text{HO—Cl} + \text{CH}_2\text{=CHCH}_2\text{OH} \longrightarrow \underset{\underset{\text{Cl}}{|}\ \underset{\text{OH}}{|}}{\text{CH}_2\text{CHCH}_2\text{OH}}$$

Hypochlorous   3-Chloro-1,2-propanediol
acid

$$\underset{\underset{\text{OH}}{|}}{\text{Cl—CH}_2\text{CHCH}_2\text{OH}} \underset{}{\overset{\text{CaO}}{\rightleftharpoons}} \text{Cl—CH}_2\text{CHCH}_2\text{OH} \longrightarrow \text{CH}_2\text{—CHCH}_2\text{OH} + \bar{\text{Cl}}$$

Glycidol
(2,3-Epoxy-1-
propanol)

$$\text{HO} + \text{CH}_2\text{—CHCH}_2\text{OH} \longrightarrow \text{HOCH}_2\text{CHCH}_2\text{OH} \overset{\text{H}_2\text{O}}{\longrightarrow} \text{HOCH}_2\text{CHCH}_2\text{OH} + \text{HO}$$

Glycerol

Side Reactions. Nucleophilic substitutions (e.g., hydrolyses) are usually accompanied by competing reactions. Measurable amounts of alkenes are always formed, by nucleophilic elimination reactions, in the hydrolysis of tertiary substrates. In fact, elimination frequently becomes the principal reaction at high temperatures or with strong bases.

$$\text{H}_2\text{O} + \text{CH}_3\underset{\underset{\text{CH}_3}{|}}{\overset{\overset{\text{CH}_3}{|}}{\text{C}}}\text{Cl} \xrightarrow{25°,\ \text{pure H}_2\text{O}} \text{CH}_3\underset{\underset{\text{CH}_3}{|}}{\overset{\overset{\text{CH}_3}{|}}{\text{C}}}\text{OH} + \text{HCl}$$

$\sim$80%

$$\text{H}_2\text{O} + \text{H}\text{—CH}_2\underset{\underset{\text{CH}_3}{|}}{\overset{\overset{\text{CH}_3}{|}}{\text{C}}}\text{Cl} \xrightarrow{25°,\ \text{pure H}_2\text{O}} \text{CH}_2\text{=C(CH}_3)_2 + \overset{+}{\text{H}_3\text{O}} + \bar{\text{Cl}}$$

Isobutylene   (Aqueous HCl)
$\sim$20%

$$\overset{+}{\text{NaOH}} + \text{H}\text{—CH}_2\underset{\underset{\text{CH}_3}{|}}{\overset{\overset{\text{CH}_3}{|}}{\text{C}}}\text{Cl} \xrightarrow[\text{Reflux}]{\text{C}_2\text{H}_5\text{OH} - \text{H}_2\text{O}} \text{CH}_2\text{=C(CH}_3)_2 + \text{H}_2\text{O} + \overset{+}{\text{Na}}\bar{\text{Cl}}$$

$\sim$100%

The balance between nucleophilic substitution and elimination is often controlled by fine details of substrate structure. The solvolytic reactions of cyclohexyl compounds provide striking illustrations of the effects of subtle changes in structure. All cyclohexyl compounds show a greater tendency to undergo elimination than do acyclic, secondary substrates. Comparison of the behavior of *cis-* and *trans-*4-*tert*-butylcyclohexyl sulfonates shows that even conformational effects exert a strong influence on the course of solvolytic reactions. The configuration of the compounds is determined by the bulky *tert*-butyl group, which insists upon occupying an equatorial position (Chap. 6). The *cis*-toluenesulfonate, in which the leaving group is in an axial position, gives more

olefin than the trans isomer. The distribution of products has been
determined in an acetolysis rather than in a hydrolysis reaction, but
hydrolysis would certainly provide similar results. The yield figures
given with the examples refer only to the distribution between substitution
and elimination. Other products are also formed in significant amounts.

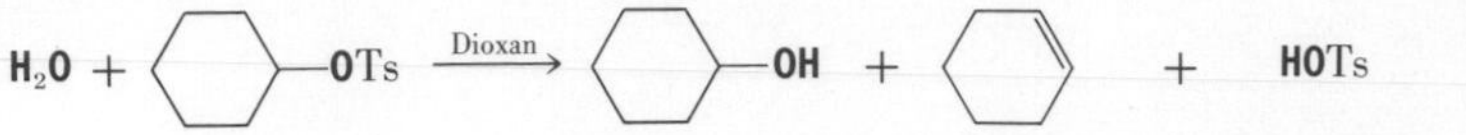

H_2O + Cyclohexyl *p*-toluenesulfonate $\xrightarrow{\text{Dioxan}}$ Cyclohexanol —OH + Cyclohexene + HOTs Toluenesulfonic acid

ax. isl unstabilon !

CH_3COH + $(CH_3)_3C$— ... *cis*-4-*tert*-Butylcyclohexyl *p*-toluenesulfonate $\xrightarrow[-\text{HOTs}]{CH_3CO_2H}$

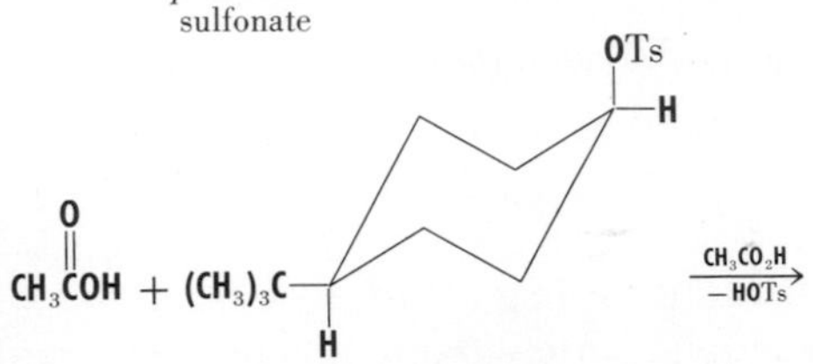

$(CH_3)_3C$— ... 5%   + $(CH_3)_3C$— ... 85% + other products

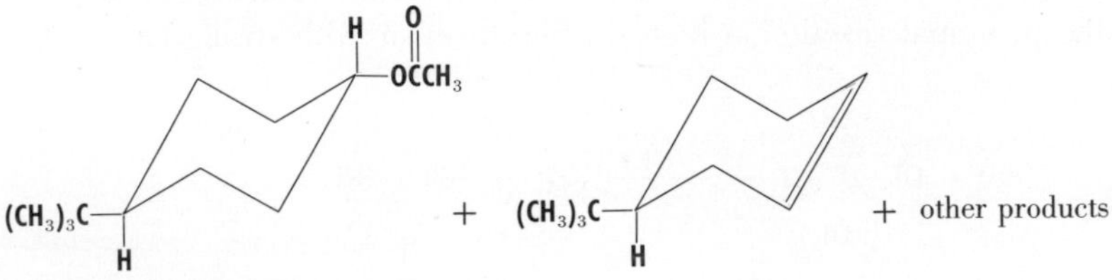

CH_3COH + $(CH_3)_3C$— ... *trans*-4-*tert*-Butylcyclohexyl *p*-toluenesulfonate $\xrightarrow[-\text{HOTs}]{CH_3CO_2H}$

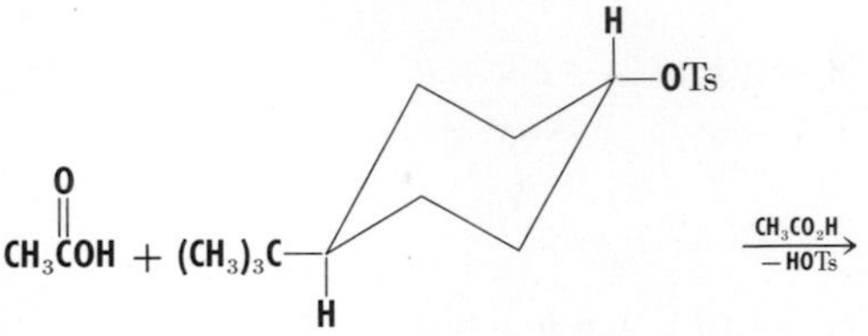

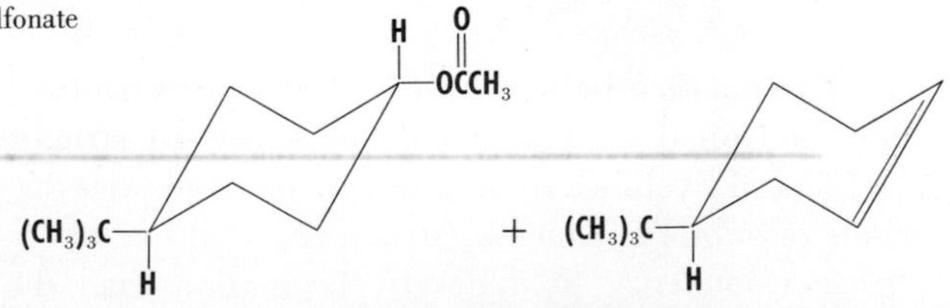

$(CH_3)_3C$— ... 28%   + $(CH_3)_3C$— ... 72%

trugonisch

Another type of side reaction is even more deceptive, since it
often produces products that have the same composition as the materials
expected from simple substitution. However, careful examination reveals
that *molecular rearrangements* have occurred in the reaction. Such
rearrangements may involve a relatively minor change, such as the
migration of a double bond, or they may involve alteration of the carbon

skeleton.   Double-bond migration is often observed during substitutions with allylic substrates.   Skeletal rearrangements are often encountered in highly branched systems.   Examples of molecular rearrangements are shown in Fig. 10.4.   The theoretical basis for understanding such phenomena will be discussed in Chap. 11, and the subject is given comprehensive treatment in Chap. 20.

An interesting, but synthetically useless, type of substitution involves molecular nitrogen as a leaving group.   Primary amines react with nitrous acid to give diazonium salts.   Although aromatic diazonium ions are reasonably stable, aliphatic diazonium salts have never been isolated, probably because the cations decompose almost instantly.   Alcohols and alkenes of both rearranged and unrearranged structures are formed.

$$CH_3CH_2CH_2NH_2 + HNO_2 \xrightarrow{HCl} CH_3CH_2CH_2\overset{+}{-}N\equiv N\ \overset{-}{Cl}$$
n-Propylamine

$$H_2\overset{\frown}{O} + CH_3CH_2\overset{\frown}{CH_2}\overset{+}{-}N\equiv N \xrightarrow{-N_2} CH_3CH_2CH_2OH + CH_3CH=CH_2$$

Ethers.   Alcoholysis of halides, sulfates, and sulfonates to form ethers is about as general as the hydrolysis reaction.   The reactions also show the same side reactions and the same variations in reactivity with the structure of the substrate.   Alkoxides are often used as nucleophiles, the parent alcohol usually serving as a solvent.

Diethyl ether (the "ether" used as an anesthetic) is prepared in large quantities by ethanolysis of ethyl sulfuric acid.   The substrate can be prepared by addition of sulfuric acid to ethylene or by the reaction of ethanol with sulfuric acid.

$$CH_3CH_2OH + H_2SO_4 \xrightarrow{-H_2O} CH_3CH_2\overset{\frown}{O}SO_3H \xrightarrow[-H_2SO_4]{+C_2H_5OH} CH_3CH_2OCH_2CH_3$$

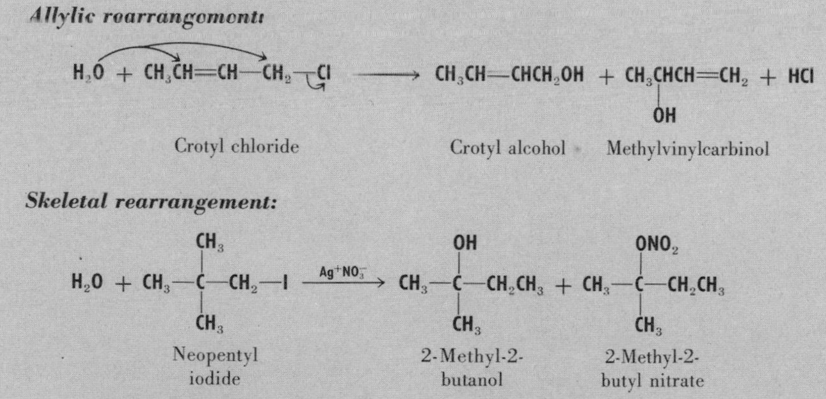

Allylic rearrangements

$$H_2O + CH_3\overset{\frown}{CH}=CH\overset{\frown}{-CH_2}\overset{\frown}{-Cl} \longrightarrow CH_3CH=CHCH_2OH + CH_3CHCH=CH_2 + HCl$$
$$\overset{|}{OH}$$

　　　　　Crotyl chloride　　　　　　Crotyl alcohol　　Methylvinylcarbinol

Skeletal rearrangement:

$$H_2O + CH_3-\overset{\overset{\displaystyle CH_3}{|}}{\underset{\underset{\displaystyle CH_3}{|}}{C}}-CH_2-I \xrightarrow{Ag^+NO_3^-} CH_3-\overset{\overset{\displaystyle OH}{|}}{\underset{\underset{\displaystyle CH_3}{|}}{C}}-CH_2CH_3 + CH_3-\overset{\overset{\displaystyle ONO_2}{|}}{\underset{\underset{\displaystyle CH_3}{|}}{C}}-CH_2CH_3$$

　　　　　Neopentyl　　　　　2-Methyl-2-　　　　2-Methyl-2-
　　　　　iodide　　　　　　　butanol　　　　　butyl nitrate

FIG. 10.4   *Molecular rearrangements in nucleophilic substitution reactions.*

Two general alternatives for the preparation of unsymmetrical ethers must always be considered, since a given alkyl group may be introduced in either the substrate or the nucleophile. For example, benzyl methyl ether may be prepared either by the benzolysis of a methyl halide or by the methanolysis of a benzyl halide. The latter path would ordinarily be the reaction of choice, because solvolytic reactions of methyl substrates are very slow. However, the use of sodium benzoxide with methyl halides leads to a very smooth reaction.

$$CH_3OH + C_6H_5CH_2{-}Cl \xrightarrow{\text{Fast}} CH_3OCH_2C_6H_5 + HCl$$

$$\underset{\substack{\text{Benzyl}\\\text{chloride}}}{} \qquad\qquad \underset{\substack{\text{Benzyl methyl}\\\text{ether}}}{}$$

$$C_6H_5CH_2OH + CH_3{-}I \xrightarrow{\text{Very slow}} C_6H_5CH_2OCH_3 + HI$$

$$\underset{\substack{\text{Benzyl}\\\text{alcohol}}}{}$$

$$C_6H_5CH_2OH \xrightarrow[-H_2]{Na} C_6H_5CH_2\overset{-}{O}\overset{+}{Na} \xrightarrow[\text{Fast}]{CH_3{-}I} C_6H_5CH_2OCH_3 + NaI$$

The preparation of ethers by the reaction of metal alkoxides with alkyl halides, sulfates, or sulfonates is known as the *Williamson synthesis*. Since tertiary substrates undergo elimination virtually exclusively in their reactions with strong bases, tertiary ethers can be made by the Williamson synthesis only by the reactions of tertiary alkoxides with primary or secondary substrates.

$$C_6H_5CH_2\overset{-}{O}\overset{+}{Na} + (CH_3)_3C{-}Br \longrightarrow C_6H_5CH_2OH + CH_2{=}C(CH_3)_2 + NaBr$$

$$(CH_3)_3C\overset{-}{O}\overset{+}{K} + C_6H_5CH_2{-}Br \longrightarrow (CH_3)_3COCH_2C_6H_5$$

Cyclic ethers have become important commercial materials for use both as synthetic intermediates and as solvents. The rings are closed by reactions analogous to the formation of acyclic ether linkages. *Halohydrins* (2-haloalcohols) are readily made from alkenes and cyclize very readily in the presence of a weak base.

$$CH_2{=}CH_2 + HOCl \longrightarrow \underset{\substack{\text{Ethylene}\\\text{chlorohydrin}\\\text{(2-Chloroethanol)}}}{CH_2{-}CH_2} \underset{}{\overset{K_2CO_3}{\rightleftharpoons}} CH_2{-}CH_2 \longrightarrow \underset{\text{Ethylene}\atop\text{oxide}}{CH_2{-}CH_2} + \overset{-}{Cl}$$

$$\overset{+}{Na}\overset{-}{OH} + HOCH_2CH_2CH_2CH_2Cl \longrightarrow \underset{\text{Tetrahydrofuran}}{\begin{array}{c}CH_2{-}CH_2\\ | \qquad | \\ CH_2 \quad CH_2 \\ \backslash O / \end{array}} + H_2O + NaCl$$

Ethers are not ordinarily reactive enough as substrates to be hydrolyzed easily. However, ethylene oxide is unusually reactive because of the strain in the small ring. The compound is hydrolyzed in the presence of either acid or base.

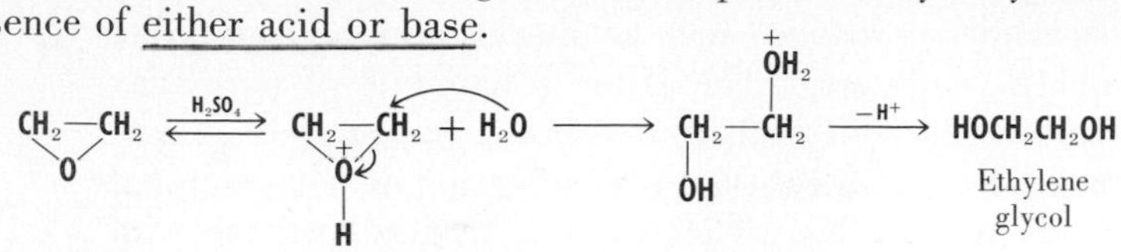

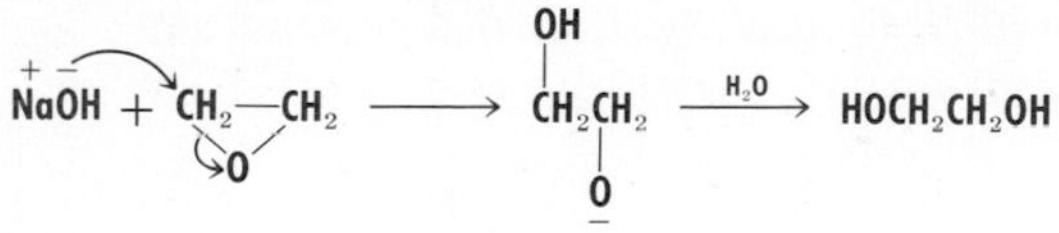

Ethylene oxide also undergoes *polymerization* when treated with acids and bases under pressure. Polymerization is the general term applied to reactions in which small molecules (*monomers*) add to one another to form larger molecules. The *dimers* of ethylene oxide are useful solvents. *High polymers* of ethylene oxide are used in the fabrication of plastics and synthetic *elastomers* (synthetic rubbers). The balance among the various products formed in the reactions of ethylene oxide with water is controlled by varying the concentrations of water and ethylene oxide in the reaction mixtures.

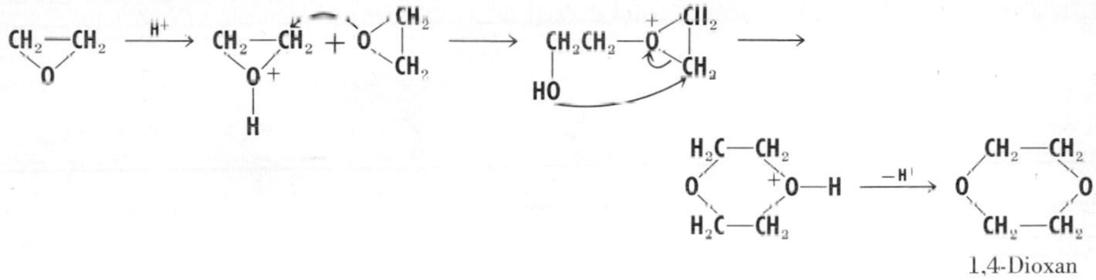

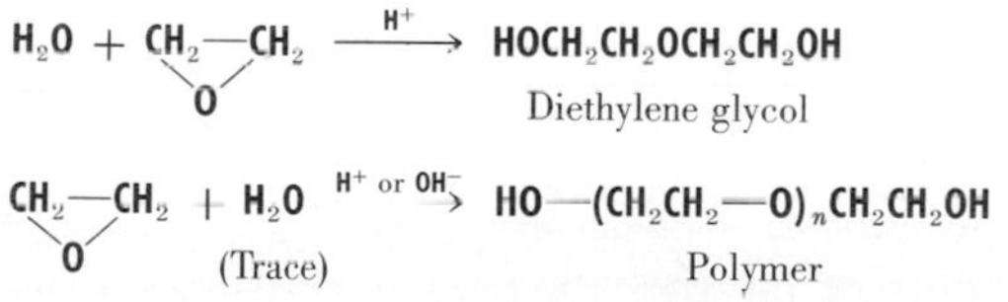

1,4-Dioxan

$$H_2O + CH_2\!-\!CH_2 \xrightarrow{H^+} HOCH_2CH_2OCH_2CH_2OH$$

Diethylene glycol

$$CH_2\!-\!CH_2 + H_2O \xrightarrow{H^+ \text{ or } OH^-} HO\!-\!(CH_2CH_2\!-\!O)_n CH_2CH_2OH$$

(Trace) Polymer

Alkylation of phenols with reagents such as methyl iodide or dimethyl sulfate in the presence of an aqueous or alcoholic base is a minor variant of the Williamson synthesis. Phenols, being more acidic than alcohols, can be converted to anions by aqueous base; hence there is no need to use alkali metals in the preparation of phenoxides. daher

Dimethyl sulfate

Anisole
(Methyl phenyl ether)

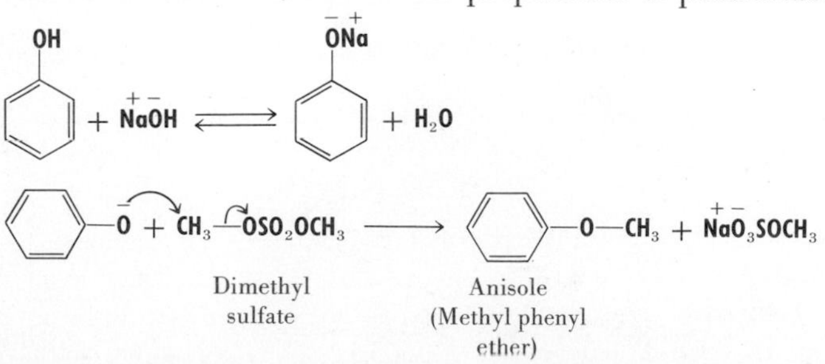

Diazomethane is an interesting alkylating agent that forms methyl ethers with weakly acidic compounds such as phenols and the enol forms of β-diketones and β-ketoesters. The latter reaction is of particular interest because anions derived from β-dicarbonyl compounds tend to be alkylated on carbon, rather than on oxygen, in conventional substitution reactions (page 224). The reaction of diazomethane with acidic compounds may involve the formation of the methyl diazonium ion as an intermediate, but the latter, if formed, would be very short-lived.

$$\underset{\substack{\| \quad \|}}{\overset{\substack{O \quad O}}{CH_3CCH_2CCH_3}} \rightleftharpoons \underset{\substack{\| \quad |}}{\overset{\substack{O \quad OH}}{CH_3CCH=CCH_3}}$$

$$\underset{\substack{\| \quad |}}{\overset{\substack{O \quad OH}}{CH_3CCH=CCH_3}} + CH_2=\overset{+}{N}=\overset{-}{N} \longrightarrow \underset{\substack{\| \quad |}}{\overset{\substack{O \quad O}}{CH_3CCH=CCH_3}} + CH_3-\overset{+}{N}\equiv N \longrightarrow \underset{\substack{\| \quad |}}{\overset{\substack{O \quad OCH_3}}{CH_3CCH=CHCH_3}} + N_2$$

Diazomethane

Diazomethane, which has many uses as a research chemical, is a toxic, explosive gas at room temperature and is usually handled in ether solutions. The compound is made by nucleophilic elimination reactions of *N*-nitrosoamides. The actual elimination probably occurs with diazoesters which are tautomers of the nitrosoamides.

$$\underset{\substack{\| \\ O}}{\overset{\substack{N=O}}{CH_3N-CCH_3}} \overset{Fast}{\rightleftharpoons} \underset{}{\overset{\substack{O \\ \|}}{CH_3N=NOCCH_3}}$$

N-Methyl-*N*-nitrosoacetamide   Methanediazo-
                                              acetate

$$\overset{+}{Na}OH + H-CH_2-N=N-\overset{\substack{O \\ \|}}{OCCH_3} \longrightarrow CH_2=\overset{+}{N}=\overset{-}{N} + H_2O + CH_3CO_2Na$$

Alkyl Peroxides. Alkyl hydroperoxides, **ROOH**, have been studied relatively little, because of their explosive nature. Some are known as the first products of the air oxidation of hydrocarbons (Chap. 18), and others have been synthesized by the acid-catalyzed reaction of alcohols with concentrated hydrogen peroxide. Dialkyl peroxides, which are much more stable than hydroperoxides, may be made by similar nucleophilic substitutions.

$$\underset{\substack{| \\ OH}}{C_6H_5CHCH_3} + H_2SO_4 \rightleftharpoons \underset{\substack{| \\ \overset{OH_2}{+}}}{C_6H_5CHCH_3} + H\overset{-}{S}O_4$$

1-Phenylethanol
(α-Phenylethanol)

$$H-O-O-H + \underset{\substack{| \\ \overset{OH_2}{+}}}{C_6H_5CHCH_3} \longrightarrow \underset{\substack{| \\ OOH}}{C_6H_5CHCH_3} + H_2O + \overset{+}{H}$$

1-Phenylethyl
hydroperoxide

$$\overset{+}{\text{NaO}}\overset{-}{-}\overset{-}{\text{ONa}} + 2(\text{CH}_3)_3\text{CCl} \longrightarrow (\text{CH}_3)_3\text{COOC}(\text{CH}_3)_3 + 2\text{NaCl}$$

Di-tert-butyl
peroxide

Esters. Solvolysis of halides, sulfonates, and sulfates in liquid acids provides esters of the acids. Frequently an amount of the sodium salt of the acid equivalent to the substrate is added. The carboxylate ion of the salt may either react directly as a nucleophile or neutralize the strong acid formed if the primary reaction is with the acid. Note that the acid *may be* the primary reactant, even though it is a weaker nucleophile than the carboxylate ion, since the former will be present in much higher concentration.

$$\underset{O}{\overset{O}{\text{CH}_3\text{COH}}} + (\text{C}_6\text{H}_5)_2\text{CH}{-}\text{Cl} \longrightarrow \text{CH}_3\text{COCH}(\text{C}_6\text{H}_5)_2 + \text{HCl}$$

Benzhydryl   Benzhydryl
chloride   acetate

$$\overset{O}{\text{HCONa}} + \text{CH}_3\text{CH}_2\text{CHCH}_3 \xrightarrow{\text{HCO}_2\text{H}} \underset{\text{OSO}_2\text{CH}_3}{\overset{O\ \ CH_3}{\text{HCOCHCH}_2\text{CH}_3}} + \text{CH}_3\text{SO}_3\text{Na}$$

sec-Butyl   sec-Butyl
methanesulfonate   formate
(sec-Butyl mesylate)

Silver salts of carboxylic acids react very rapidly with alkyl halides. In addition to supplying a nucleophilic anion, the salt provides *electrophilic catalysis by the silver ion*, which coordinates with the halogen and helps pull it away from the substrate. In such reactions, the role of silver ions is analogous to that of hydrogen ions in the catalysis of the substitution reactions of alcohols and ethers.

$$\text{CH}_3\text{CH}_2{-}\overset{..}{\underset{..}{\text{Br}}}: + \overset{+}{\text{Ag}} \longrightarrow \text{CH}_3\text{CH}_2{-}\overset{..+}{\underset{..}{\text{Br}}}{-}\text{Ag}$$

$$\text{CH}_3\text{CO}_2^- + \text{CH}_3\text{CH}_2{-}\overset{+}{\text{Br}}{-}\text{Ag} \longrightarrow \text{CH}_3\text{CO}_2\text{CH}_2\text{CH}_3 + \text{AgBr}$$

Methylation with diazomethane provides an elegant synthesis of methyl esters. The method is very useful, on a small scale, in the synthesis of fine chemicals and in the preparation of esters that are sensitive to acids and bases.

$$\text{C}_6\text{H}_5{-}\text{CO}_2\text{H} + \text{CH}_2\text{N}_2 \longrightarrow \text{C}_6\text{H}_5{-}\text{CO}_2\text{CH}_3$$

Benzoic   Methyl
acid   benzoate

Although the above preparations of esters are rather general and quite useful, they are not as often employed as the preparation discussed in Chap. 14.

Formation of Carbon-Sulfur Bonds

Sulfur compounds show greater nucleophilic reactivity than their oxygen analogues, and substitutions by sulfur-containing nucleophiles often occur under very mild conditions and give high yields. The important reagents that contain nucleophilic sulfur atoms include hydrogen sulfide, bisulfide ion (HS^-), mercaptans (RSH and $ArSH$), mercaptide ions, thiocyanate ions (SCN^-) and disulfide ions $S_2^=$. The common leaving groups include halide, sulfonate and sulfate ions, and water (from conjugate acids of alcohols).

$$CH_3SH + (CH_3)_2CHCH_2{-}Br \longrightarrow CH_3SCH_2CH(CH_3)_2 + HBr$$

Isobutyl methyl
sulfide

$$NaSH + (C_6H_5)_3C{-}Cl \longrightarrow (C_6H_5)_3CSH + NaCl$$

Sodium   Trityl   Trityl mercaptan
bisulfide   chloride   (Tritylthiol)

$$C_6H_5SH + \langle \rangle{-}OSO_2C_6H_4CH_3\text{-}p \longrightarrow \langle \rangle{-}S{-}C_6H_5 + p\text{-}CH_3C_6H_4SO_3H$$

Thiophenol   Cyclohexyl tosylate   Cyclohexyl
phenyl sulfide

$$NaS{-}SNa + CH_3CH_2I \longrightarrow CH_3CH_2SSCH_2CH_3 + 2NaI$$

Diethyl disulfide

$$NaSCN + (CH_3)_2CHBr \longrightarrow (CH_3)_2CHSCN + NaBr$$

Isopropyl
thiocyanate

Ethylene oxide is readily opened by nucleophilic sulfur compounds. The reaction between hydrogen sulfide and the substrate gives 2,2'-dihydroxydiethyl sulfide. The latter compound is converted, by a nucleophilic substitution, to 2,2'-dichlorodiethyl sulfide, a powerful vesicant, which was known as the "mustard gas" used in combat in the late stages of World War I.

$$H_2S + CH_2{-}CH_2 \longrightarrow HSCH_2CH_2OH$$
$$\underset{O}{}$$

2-Mercaptoethanol

$$HOCH_2CH_2SH + CH_2{-}CH_2 \longrightarrow HOCH_2CH_2SCH_2CH_2OH$$
$$\underset{O}{}$$

2,2'-Dihydroxydiethyl sulfide
(β,β'-Dihydroxydiethyl sulfide)

$$2HCl + HOCH_2CH_2SCH_2CH_2OH \longrightarrow ClCH_2CH_2SCH_2CH_2Cl + 2H_2O$$

2,2'-Dichlorodiethyl
sulfide
(Mustard gas)

β-Propiolactone is another compound in which the strain in a small ring makes an oxygen atom an unusually good leaving group.

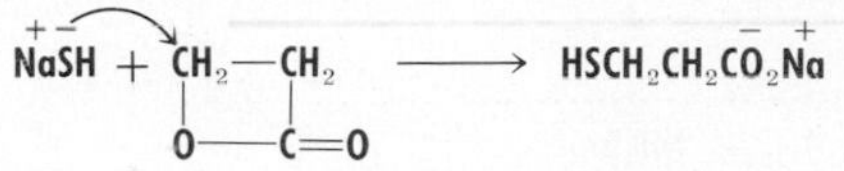

$$NaSH + CH_2{-}CH_2 \longrightarrow HSCH_2CH_2CO_2Na$$
$$O{-}C{=}O$$

Mercaptans have about the vilest odors of any organic compounds. Butyl mercaptan has been isolated from the scent glands of the skunk.

The relative rating of odors is a subjective matter. Mercaptans do not seem equally repulsive to all people; one opinion is that substitution of pyridine or skatole (2-methylindole) for butyl mercaptan would improve an average skunk's prospects of survival—unless the animal succumbed to the vapors himself.

Formation of Carbon-Nitrogen Bonds

Alkylation of ammonia to form amines occurs in stages to form primary, secondary, and tertiary amines and quarternary ammonium salts. If a particular product is desired, it can usually be made to predominate by manipulation of the concentrations of the reactants and other reaction conditions. In each alkylation step, the initial product is an ammonium ion which is equilibrated, by proton transfers, with all other bases in the mixture. Since ammonium ions are not nucleophilic, two equivalents of nucleophile are required for each alkylation step, as shown in Fig. 10.5.

Commercial synthesis of the methylamines is based upon the reaction of ammonia with methyl chloride. The products are separated by large-scale fractional distillation. As a matter of practical convenience, procedures that give mixtures of products or require rigid control of reaction conditions are usually avoided in the research laboratory. However, primary amines can easily be made by using a large excess of ammonia.

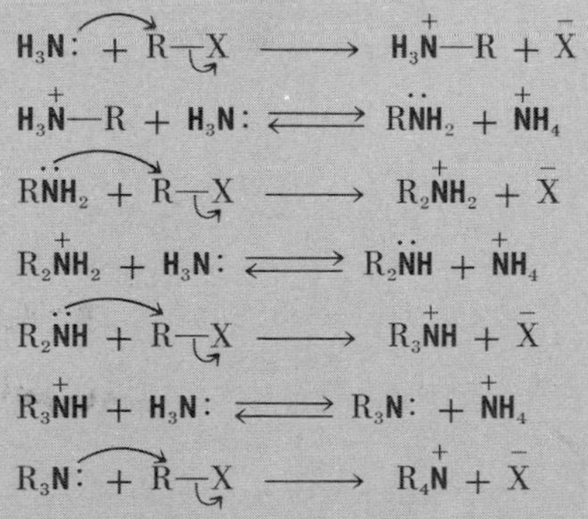

$$H_3N: + R{-}X \longrightarrow H_3\overset{+}{N}{-}R + \overset{-}{X}$$
$$H_3\overset{+}{N}{-}R + H_3N: \rightleftharpoons R\overset{\cdot\cdot}{N}H_2 + \overset{+}{N}H_4$$
$$R\overset{\cdot\cdot}{N}H_2 + R{-}X \longrightarrow R_2\overset{+}{N}H_2 + \overset{-}{X}$$
$$R_2\overset{+}{N}H_2 + H_3N: \rightleftharpoons R_2\overset{\cdot\cdot}{N}H + \overset{+}{N}H_4$$
$$R_2\overset{\cdot\cdot}{N}H + R{-}X \longrightarrow R_3\overset{+}{N}H + \overset{-}{X}$$
$$R_3\overset{+}{N}H + H_3N: \rightleftharpoons R_3N: + \overset{+}{N}H_4$$
$$R_3N: + R{-}X \longrightarrow R_4\overset{+}{N} + \overset{-}{X}$$

FIG. 10.5 *Alkylation of ammonia and amines.*

The alkylation reaction can usually be stopped at the tertiary amine stage in good yield. Secondary amines are ordinarily made by other methods. Quarternary ammonium salts are virtually always made by alkylation of tertiary amines.

$$BrCH_2CH(OC_2H_5)_2 + 2NH_3 \longrightarrow H_2NCH_2CH(OC_2H_5)_2 + NH_4Br$$

1,1-Diethoxy-2-
bromoethane
(Bromodiethylacetal)
            2,2-Diethoxyethylamine

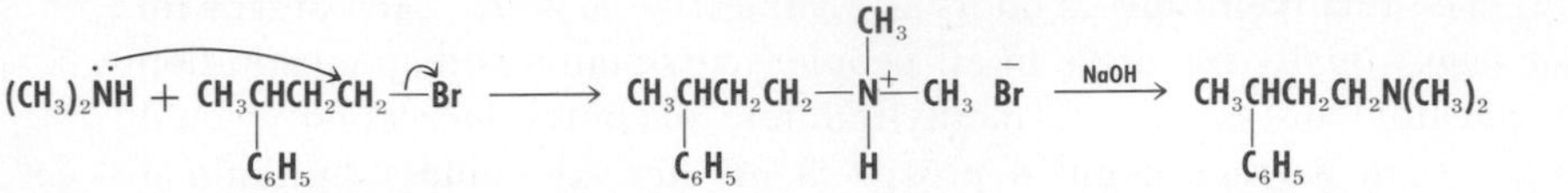

3-Phenyl-1-butyl
bromide
           Dimethyl-[3-phenyl-
1-butyl]-amine

In the *Gabriel synthesis,* a special device is employed to allow primary amines to be prepared uncontaminated by more highly alkylated products. Phthalimide is sufficiently acidic to be converted to a potassium salt by treatment with concentrated potassium hydroxide. The phthalimide ion is a good nucleophile. It is alkylated to give *N*-alkylphthalimides, which can be cleaved with aqueous base to give the primary amine.

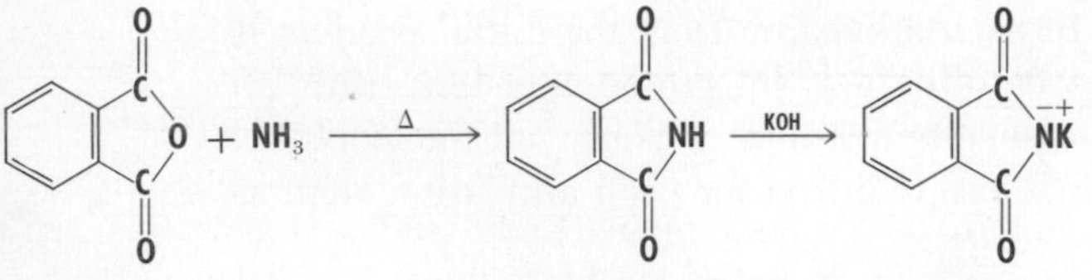

Phthalic
anhydride
           Phthalimide
           Potassium
phthalimide

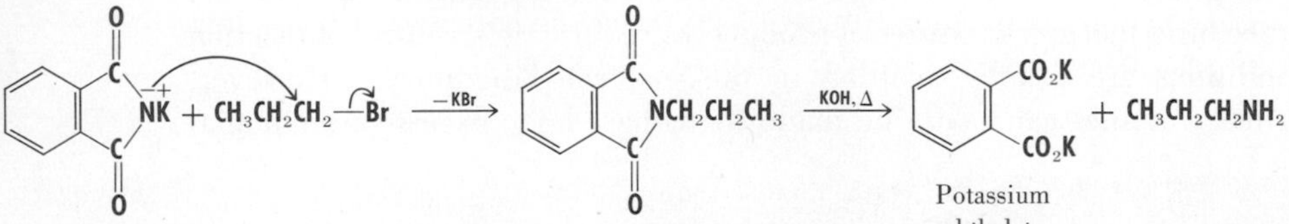

                     Potassium
phthalate

The small ring compounds ethylene oxide and β-propiolactone react readily with ammonia and amines.

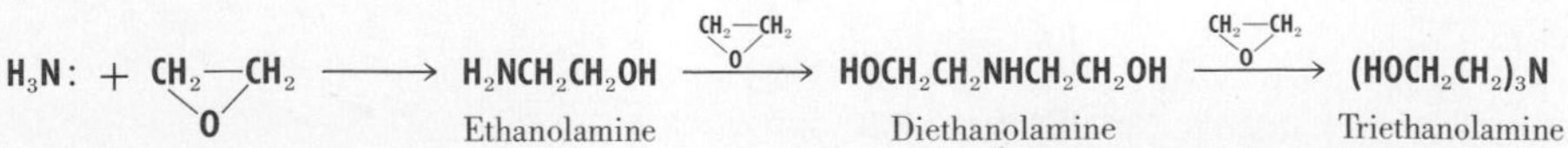

           Ethanolamine
           Diethanolamine
           Triethanolamine

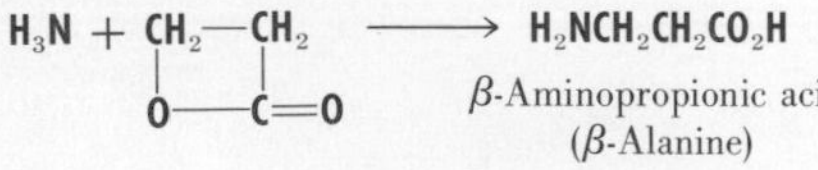

β-Aminopropionic acid
(β-Alanine)

$- H_2O$

Morpholine

Elimination reactions often become predominant in the ammination of secondary substrates, and tertiary substrates generally give only elimination products.

N. Elimination

$$2\overset{\cdot\cdot}{N}H_3 + CH_3\overset{H}{\underset{\underset{\overset{|}{OSO_2C_6H_4CH_3\text{-}p}}{C_6H_5}}{C}}-CHCH_3 \xrightarrow{\text{Dioxan}} CH_3C{=}CHCH_3 + CH_3CH{-}\overset{NH_2}{\underset{C_6H_5}{CH}}CH_3 + p\text{-}CH_3C_6H_4\overset{-}{SO_3}\overset{+}{N}H_4$$

(C₆H₅ under first product)

Major product   Minor product

The azide ion is a powerful nucleophile, giving alkyl azides in nucleophilic substitution reactions. Azides may be reduced to primary amines with hydrogen and a metal catalyst. Hydrazine is a weak nucleophile, but it will react satisfactorily with some primary and secondary halides.

$$K\overset{+}{N}{=}\overset{+}{N}{=}\overset{-}{N} + CH_3\overset{|}{\underset{Br}{CH}}CO_2C_2H_5 \xrightarrow{-KBr} CH_3\overset{\overset{N{=}\overset{+}{N}{=}\overset{-}{N}}{|}}{CH}CO_2C_2H_5 \xrightarrow[-NH_3]{H_2,\ Pt} CH_3\overset{\overset{NH_2}{|}}{CH}CO_2C_2H_5$$

Potassium azide   Ethyl α-bromo-propionate   Ethyl α-azido-propionate   Ethyl α-amino-propionate

$$NH_2NH_2 + CH_3CH_2CH_2I \longrightarrow CH_3CH_2CH_2\overset{+}{N}H_2\overset{-}{N}H_2I \xrightarrow{Na_2CO_3} CH_3CH_2CH_2NHNH_2$$

Hydrazine   n-Propyl hydrazine

When nitrite anion is used as a nucleophile, two products may be formed, since either oxygen or nitrogen may become bonded to the substrate. Anions that can react at two different sites are called *ambident ions*. Nucleophilic attack by silver nitrite on primary halides gives 50% or more nitroalkane and minor amounts of alkyl nitrite. Secondary halides usually give more nitrite ester than nitroalkane, and tertiary substrates give almost exclusively *O*-alkylation and elimination. The problem of ambident reactivity is exceedingly complicated, because silver nitrite gives product distributions considerably different from those obtained from alkali metal nitrites. Striking solvent effects on products have also been reported.

$$\overset{+}{Ag}\overset{-}{O}{-}\overset{\cdot\cdot}{N}{=}O + CH_3(CH_2)_3Br$$

O-alkylation (Dilute soln) → CH₃CH₂CH₂CH₂ON=O + AgBr
n-Butyl nitrite 15%

N-alkylation (Ether soln) → CH₃CH₂CH₂CH₂—$\overset{\overset{O}{\|}}{\underset{O}{N^+}}$ + AgBr
1-Nitrobutane 70%

$$\overset{+}{Ag}\overset{-}{NO_2} + (CH_3)_2CHBr \xrightarrow[-AgBr]{Ether} CH_3\overset{|}{\underset{NO_2}{CH}}CH_3 + CH_3\overset{|}{\underset{ONO}{CH}}CH_3 + CH_2{=}CHCH_3$$

2-Nitro-propane 20%   Isopropyl nitrite 30%

$$\overset{+}{Ag}\overset{-}{NO_2} + (CH_3)_3C{-}Cl \xrightarrow[-AgBr]{Ether} (CH_3)_3CNO_2 + (CH_3)_3CONO + CH_2{=}C(CH_3)_2$$

2-Methyl-2-nitropropane (trace)   *tert*-Butyl nitrite 50%

Formation of Carbon-Halogen Bonds

Alkyl halides are made by three principal methods: (1) nucleophilic substitution reactions with alcohols as substrates; (2) addition of halides and hydrogen halides to carbon-carbon double bonds (Chap. 15); and (3) photochemical chlorination of hydrocarbons (Chap. 18). Since hydroxide ion is a very poor leaving group, *alcohols undergo very few nucleophilic displacements in neutral or alkaline media.* In acid media, alcohols are converted to conjugate acids. Even though the equilibrium concentration of the protonated species may be very small, reactions occur by the release of the neutral water molecule from the positively charged substrate.

$$HBr + (CH_3)_2CHOH \rightleftharpoons (CH_3)_2\overset{+}{C}HOH_2 + \overset{-}{Br}$$

$$\overset{-}{Br} + (CH_3)_2CH\overset{+}{-}OH_2 \longrightarrow (CH_3)_2CH-Br + H_2O$$

Halide ions increase in nucleophilic reactivity as the size of the ions increases. Fluoride is an exceedingly weak nucleophile, and alkyl fluorides cannot usually be made by ordinary nucleophilic substitution. The conversion of primary and secondary alcohols to chlorides is usually carried out in the presence of zinc chloride. The metal halide may help remove the hydroxyl group by reacting as a Lewis acid; it also supplies a high concentration of chloride ions. The *Lucas test,* used to identify alcohols as primary, secondary, or tertiary, depends upon the variation in the rates of reaction of alcohols with a concentrated aqueous hydrochloric acid-zinc chloride solution. The separation of the alkyl chloride as a second phase gives the *visual* evidence of reaction that is desired in characterization tests. Among saturated alcohols, the order of reactivity is tertiary $\gg$ secondary $>$ primary. Allyl and benzyl alcohols react very rapidly with the reagent.

$$ROH + \overset{++}{Zn} \longrightarrow R-\overset{H}{\underset{+}{O}}-\overset{}{\underset{+}{Zn}} \xrightarrow{Cl^-} R-Cl + \overset{+}{Zn}(OH)$$

$$CH_3CH_2OH + HCl \xrightarrow{ZnCl_2} CH_3CH_2Cl + H_2O \qquad \text{very slow}$$

$$(CH_3)_3COH + HCl \xrightarrow{ZnCl_2} (CH_3)_3CCl + H_2O \qquad \text{very fast}$$

$$C_6H_5CH_2OH + HCl \xrightarrow{ZnCl_2} C_6H_5CH_2Cl + H_2O \qquad \text{fast}$$

Concentrated hydrobromic and hydriodic acids react readily with most alcohols. The chief side reaction is molecular rearrangement.

$$HBr + CH_3CH_2CH_2CH_2OH \xrightarrow{\Delta} CH_3CH_2CH_2CH_2Br + H_2O$$

$$C_6H_5CH_2OH + HI \xrightarrow{25°} C_6H_5CH_2I + H_2O$$

$$\underset{\underset{CH_3}{|}}{CH_3CHCH}\underset{\underset{CH_3}{|}}{\overset{\overset{OH}{|}}{CH}}CH_3 + HBr \longrightarrow \underset{\underset{CH_3}{|}}{CH_3CHCH_2}\underset{\underset{CH_3}{|}}{C}Br + H_2O$$

A number of other reagents are frequently used for the preparation of alkyl halides. Alcohols are converted to chlorides by the action of phosphorus pentachloride (**PCl$_5$**), phosphorus trichloride (**PCl$_3$**), phosphorus oxychloride, thionyl chloride (**SOCl$_2$**), or phosgene (**COCl$_2$**). The reagents all convert the hydroxyl groups to inorganic esters with the concomitant formation of hydrogen halides. Then substitution of chloride ions for the new complex leaving group occurs. Phosphorus tribromide is used in the preparation of alkyl bromides.

$$SOCl_2 + CH_3CH_2OH \longrightarrow CH_3CH_2OSCl + HCl$$

Ethyl chlorosulfite

$$\overset{-}{Cl} + CH_3CH_2{-}O{-}S{-}Cl \longrightarrow CH_3CH_2{-}Cl + O{=}S{=}O + \overset{-}{Cl}$$

Net reaction: $SOCl_2 + CH_3CH_2OH \longrightarrow CH_3CH_2Cl + HCl + SO_2$

$$(CH_3)_2CHCH_2OH + PBr_3 \longrightarrow (CH_3)_2CHCH_2OPBr_2 + HBr$$

Isobutyl
dibromophosphite

$$\overset{-}{Br} + (CH_3)_2CHCH_2{-}O{-}PBr_2 \longrightarrow (CH_3)_2CHCH_2Br + \overset{-}{O}{-}PBr_2$$

$$HOPBr_2 + 2(CH_3)_2CHCH_2OH \longrightarrow 2(CH_3)_2CHCH_2Br + P(OH)_3$$

Net reaction: $PBr_3 + 3(CH_3)_2CHCH_2OH \longrightarrow 3(CH_3)_2CHCH_2Br + P(OH)_3$

$$PCl_5 + CH_3(CH_2)_8CH_2OH \longrightarrow CH_3(CH_2)_8CH_2Cl + O{-}PCl_3 + HCl$$

n-Decyl alcohol n-Decyl chloride

Halide salts react with alkyl sulfonates to give the corresponding alkyl halides; but the reaction has limited synthetic value, since only primary and secondary sulfonates can be prepared easily, and even benzyl sulfonates are difficult to handle. The order of nucleophilic reactivity, $I^- > Br^- > Cl^- \gg F^-$, is again observed.

$$p{-}CH_3C_6H_4SO_2Cl + CH_3CH_2CH_2CH_2OH \xrightarrow{\text{Pyridine}} CH_3CH_2CH_2CH_2OSO_2C_6H_4CH_3{-}p$$

p-Toluenesulfonyl n-Butyl p-toluenesulfonate
chloride

$$\overset{+}{K}\overset{-}{I} + CH_3CH_2CH_2CH_2{-}O{-}\overset{O}{\underset{O}{S}}{-}C_6H_4CH_3{-}p \xrightarrow{CH_3CN} CH_3CH_2CH_2CH_2I + p{-}CH_3C_6H_4SO_3K$$

Ether Cleavage. The cleavage of ethers is an important process; but it is not useful primarily for synthetic purposes. Problems of ascertaining the structure of complex molecules by degradative methods are often simplified by breaking the molecule into two simpler units by an ether cleavage. Another use is found in the removal of alkyl groups, usually methyl, that have been introduced to "cover up" or *protect* hydroxyl groups while reactions are carried out on another portion of a poly-functional molecule.

Ether cleavage involves essentially the same problem as displacement of a hydroxyl group from an alcohol. The $C—O$ bonds are ordinarily broken only with the assistance of acids. Hydrogen iodide is the most powerful reagent for this purpose, because *iodide ion is the most powerful nucleophile that can be incorporated in an acidic solution.* The order of reactivity of alkyl groups as substrates is tertiary > secondary > primary. Benzyl and allyl ethers are cleaved with ease, but it is virtually impossible to cleave aryl-oxygen bonds. Consequently, alkyl-aryl ethers are cleaved to give phenols, and diaryl ethers are inert under ordinary reaction conditions.

$$C_6H_5OCH_3 \xrightleftharpoons{H^+} C_6H_5\overset{+}{\underset{H}{O}}CH_3 \xrightarrow{I^-} C_6H_5OH + CH_3I$$
Anisole

$$(CH_3)_3COCH_3 + HI \xrightarrow{25°} (CH_3)_3Cl + CH_3OH$$
tert-Butyl
methyl ether

$$CH_3CH_2OCH_2CH_3 + 2HI \xrightarrow[\text{excess HI}]{\text{Reflux}} 2CH_3CH_2I + H_2O$$

Formation of Carbon-Hydrogen Bonds

Most methods of making $C—H$ bonds are described in other chapters; but one method of limited applicability, involving nucleophilic substitution, will be mentioned here. The development of the metal hydrides in the period since World War II has provided a number of nucleophilic reagents that can donate hydride (H^-) to a wide variety of organic substrates. The most useful member of the group, thus far, has been lithium aluminum hydride.

$$Li^+ \quad H—\overset{\overset{\textstyle H}{|}}{\underset{\underset{\textstyle H}{|}}{\overset{-}{Al}}}—H$$

Lithium aluminum hydride

The reagent is remarkably soluble in ether. It has been widely used in *addition-reduction* reactions (Chap. 13) and has a more limited application in simple nucleophilic substitution. The reagent attacks the more reactive alkyl halides and sulfonates and opens ethylene oxide rings. All four of the hydrogen atoms are available as H^-. Lithium aluminum deuteride, $LiAlD_4$, has been used to introduce deuterium into organic molecules.

$$LiAlH_4 + 4(CH_3)_2CHCH_2—Br \xrightarrow{\text{Ether}} 4(CH_3)_3CH + \overset{+}{Li}\overset{-}{Al}Br_4$$

$$LiAlH_4 + 4CH_3CH\overset{\displaystyle O}{-}CHCH_3 \xrightarrow{\text{Ether}} 4CH_3CH_2CHCH_3 \xrightarrow{H_3O^+} CH_3CH_2CHCH_3$$
$$\underset{OM}{\overset{-\ +}{}} \qquad \underset{OH}{}$$

$$LiAlH_4 + 4C_6H_5\underset{\displaystyle OCH_3}{CHCH_2OTs} \xrightarrow{\text{Ether}} 4C_6H_5\underset{\displaystyle OCH_3}{CHCH_3} + \overset{+\ -}{LiAl}(OTs)_4$$

2-Methoxy-2-
phenylethyl
p-toluenesulfonate

$$LiAlD_4 + C_6H_5\underset{\displaystyle D}{CHCH_3} \xrightarrow{\text{Ether}} C_6H_5\underset{\displaystyle D}{CHCH_3}$$

Ethylbenzene-1-*d*

Carbon as a Nucleophile

In any heterolytic reaction, the designation of the process as nucleophilic or electrophilic is intrinsically ambiguous. The two terms reciprocate in the same way as the related terms, acid and base. Any reaction must involve both an electrophile and a nucleophile. In organic chemistry, reactions are classified with reference to the character of the reagent that attacks carbon. However, the fundamental ambiguity becomes troublesome in the discussion of reactions that form carbon-carbon bonds. In the interest of continuity, the reactions are classified as nucleophilic or electrophilic by designation of carbon compounds that have a very obvious nucleophilic or electrophilic character as reagents. In every case, the reaction can be reclassified by reversing the designation of the reagent and substrate, as is illustrated in Fig. 10.6.

Organometallic compounds contain polar carbon-metal bonds and are considered nucleophilic reagents. Alkyl- and arylmagnesium halides (*Grignard reagents*) and organolithium compounds are decidedly nucleophilic. They are used very widely in synthetic procedures. Although the compounds are not really ionized, much of their chemistry is easily predicted by regarding them as *carbanion donors*.

$$R\!-\!Li \longleftrightarrow \overset{-}{R}\ \overset{+}{Li} \qquad R\!-\!\overset{+\ -}{MgBr} \longleftrightarrow \overset{-}{R}\ \overset{++\ -}{MgBr}$$

Alkyllithium   Grignard reagent

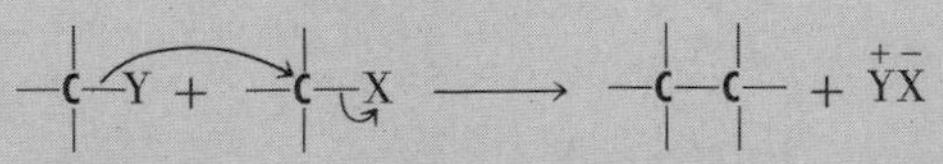

Nucleophilic substitution	Reagent	Substrate
Electrophilic substitution	Substrate	Reagent

FIG. 10.6   *Ambiguity in classification of reactions which form C—C bonds.*

Organometallic Compounds

Although organometallic compounds include stable salts such as cyanides, carbonates, and the metal salts of organic acids, the most important for synthetic purposes are compounds containing carbon-metal bonds. Many methods have been developed for making magnesium and lithium compounds (Chap. 12), but the most general consists of treating an organic halide with a metal. *Ethers are unique as solvents for preparation and use of the reagents.* Diethyl ether is most commonly used, although some compounds, such as aryl and vinyl Grignard reagents, cannot be formed in diethyl ether but are easily made in tetrahydrofuran.

$$CH_3I + Mg \xrightarrow{\ C_2H_5OC_2H_5\ } CH_3MgI$$

Methylmagnesium
bromide

$$CH_3CH_2CH_2CH_2Cl + 2Li \xrightarrow{\ C_2H_5OC_2H_5\ } CH_3CH_2CH_2CH_2Li + LiCl$$

n-Butyllithium

$$C_6H_5Cl + Mg \xrightarrow{\ \ } C_6H_5MgCl$$

Phenylmagnesium
chloride

Lithium and magnesium compounds are very reactive and must be protected carefully from the atmosphere, because they react with oxygen, carbon dioxide, and water vapor. Even very weakly acidic substances, such as alcohols, give an "active hydrogen" reaction with these reagents. Consequently, organometallic compounds cannot be used in hydroxylic solvents. Most other functional groups react with organometallics by addition or substitution; therefore *halides which contain a second functional group cannot usually be converted to stable metallic derivatives.* The only groups compatible with organometallic structures are those of tertiary amines, ethers, alkenes, aromatic rings, and a few inert halides.

Acetylides. Acetylene and monosubstituted acetylenes are sufficiently acidic to be converted to metal acetylides by treatment with powerful bases. Sodamide, which is prepared by dissolving sodium in liquid ammonia in the presence of a trace of ferric chloride, is customarily used in the preparation of acetylides.

$$2Na + 2NH_3 \xrightarrow{\ FeCl_3,\ NH_3\ } 2\overset{+}{N}a\overset{-}{N}H_2 + H_2$$

$$NaNH_2 + RC{\equiv}CH \longrightarrow RC{\equiv}\overset{-}{C}\overset{+}{N}a + NH_3$$

A sodium
acetylide

Occasionally acetylides are made by exchange reactions with more reactive organometallics.

$$\overset{-}{C}H_3\overset{++}{M}g\overset{-}{B}r + H{-}C{\equiv}CR \longrightarrow RC{\equiv}CMgBr + CH_4$$

Copper and silver acetylides are formed when solutions of ammonia complexes of silver or cuprous ions are brought in contact with terminal acetylenes. These acetylides are seldom used in synthesis and are dangerous explosives in the dry state. However, precipitation of acetylides is used as a characteristic test for acetylenic hydrogen atoms.

$$HC\equiv CH + 2Cu(NH_3)_2^+ + 2HO^- \longrightarrow CuC\equiv CCu + 2H_2O + 4NH_3$$

Cuprous
acetylide

$$CH_3C\equiv CH + Ag(NH_3)_2^+ + HO^- \longrightarrow CH_3C\equiv CAg + H_2O + 2NH_3$$

Silver
methyl-
acetylide

Metal Enolates. When a carbon atom is attached to two electron-withdrawing groups, such as $>C=O$, CO_2R, $—C\equiv N$, $—NO_2$, or $>SO_2$, any hydrogen that the carbon also bears becomes weakly acidic. In some instances, the compounds can even be converted to salts by concentrated aqueous base. Other compounds in the group, notably malonic esters, β-ketoesters, and β-diketones, are converted to *sodium enolates* by sodium alkoxides in alcoholic solutions. The dry salts can be isolated, but they are generally used directly in the solutions in which they are prepared. Even though the metal ions may be tightly bound to the anions as metal chelates, the chemistry of the compounds is usually discussed in terms of the reactions of the nucleophilic enolate ions.

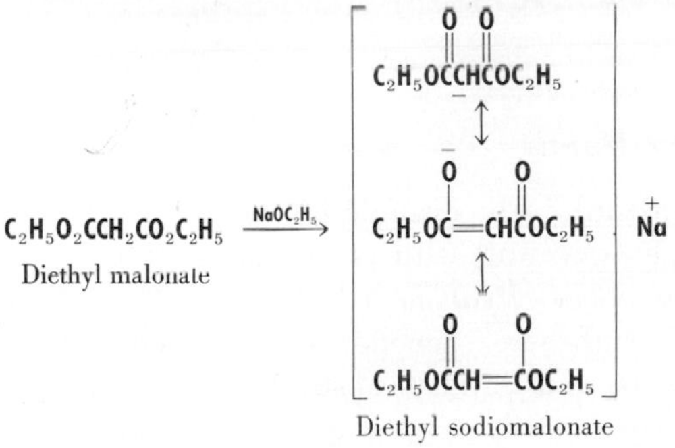

$$C_2H_5O_2CCH_2CO_2C_2H_5 \xrightarrow{NaOC_2H_5}$$

Diethyl malonate

Diethyl sodiomalonate

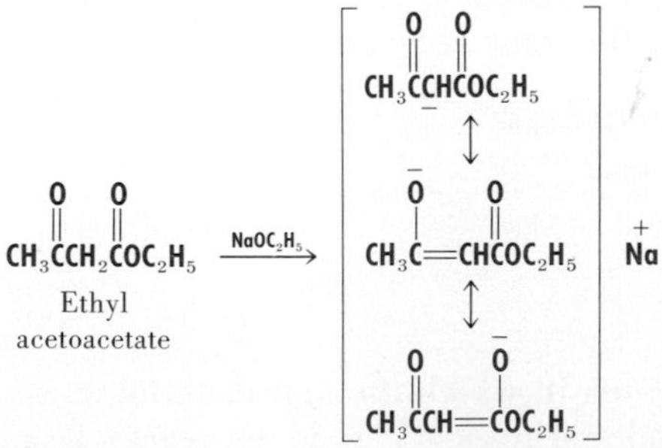

$$CH_3CCH_2COC_2H_5 \xrightarrow{NaOC_2H_5}$$

Ethyl acetoacetate

Ethyl sodioacetoacetate

$$\left[\begin{array}{c} \overset{+}{Na} \\ CH_3-\overset{O}{\underset{\parallel}{C}}-\overset{\uparrow}{\underset{\downarrow}{CH}}-\overset{O}{\underset{\parallel}{C}}-CH_3 \\ \overset{+}{Na} \end{array}\right]$$

$$\overset{O\quad O}{\underset{\parallel\quad\parallel}{CH_3CCH_2CCH_3}} \xrightarrow{\text{NaOC}_2\text{H}_5}$$

Acetylacetone

Sodioacetylacetone
(Sodium acetylacetonate)

Enolates can also be prepared directly from sodium and the dicarbonyl compounds if a trace of alcohol is added as a catalyst. Sodium ethoxide is probably an intermediate in the reaction. Various other strong bases can be used in making metal enolates. A few examples of bases used for the purpose, listed in order of decreasing basicity, are $(C_6H_5)_3CNa > NaH > NaNH_2 > (CH_3)_3COK > CH_3CH_2ONa$.

Formation of Carbon-Carbon Bonds

Cyanide Ion as a Nucleophile. Substitution by cyanide ion provides a method of extending carbon chains by one unit with preservation of a functional group at the end of the sequence. Primary halides and sulfonates are suitable substrates in such syntheses. Secondary compounds give poor yields of substitution products, and tertiary substrates undergo only elimination reactions when treated with metal cyanides. Polar solvents such as ethanol, acetone, dimethylformamide, acetonitrile, and nitromethane are used in order to dissolve the ionic reagents.

$$\overset{+-}{KCN} + CH_3CH_2CH_2CH_2-Br \xrightarrow{\text{Acetone}} CH_3CH_2CH_2CH_2CN + KBr$$

n-Valeronitrile

$$\overset{+-}{KCN} + C_6H_5CH_2-Cl \xrightarrow{\text{Ethanol}} C_6H_5CH_2CN + KCl$$

Phenyl-
acetonitrile

Neopentyl halides, and other substrates in which the approach to the functional carbon atom is sterically hindered (page 177), do not react with cyanide.

$$\overset{+\,-}{KCN} + CH_3\overset{\overset{\displaystyle CH_3}{|}}{\underset{\underset{\displaystyle CH_3}{|}}{C}}CH_2Cl \longrightarrow \text{no reaction}$$

Neopentyl
chloride

The synthesis of nitriles is primarily of importance because of the ease with which the functional group can be converted to other groups of more general importance. Carboxylic acids are formed by the hydrolysis of nitriles, and a number of reducing agents (Chap. 19) convert nitriles to amines.

$$CH_3CH_2CH_2CH_2C\!\!\equiv\!\!N + 2H_2O \xrightarrow{\text{HCl}} CH_3CH_2CH_2CH_2CO_2H + NH_4Cl$$

n-Valeric acid

$$\overset{+\ -}{LiAlH_4} + C_6H_5CH_2C\!\!\equiv\!\!N \xrightarrow{\text{Ether}} \left[(C_6H_5CH_2CH_2N)_2\overset{-+}{AlLi}\right]$$

$$\downarrow H^+,\ H_2O$$

$$C_6H_5CH_2CH_2NH_2$$

β-Phenylethylamine

Acetylides as Nucleophiles. Use of acetylide anions as nucleophiles provides a versatile means of extending carbon chains by two or more carbon atoms. Frequently both ends of the acetylene molecule can be used as nucleophiles. Primary halides and sulfonates are good substrates, whereas secondary alkyl bromides and iodides can be used only if they are relatively free from steric hindrance.

$$HC\!\!\equiv\!\!\overset{-\,+}{CNa} + CH_3CH_2\!\!-\!\!Br \longrightarrow CH_3CH_2C\!\!\equiv\!\!CH + NaBr$$

1-Butyne

$$CH_3CH_2C\!\!\equiv\!\!CH \xrightarrow{\text{NaNH}_2} CH_3CH_2C\!\!\equiv\!\!\overset{-\,+}{CNa} \xrightarrow{(CH_3)_2CHI} CH_3CH_2C\!\!\equiv\!\!C\underset{\underset{\displaystyle CH_3}{|}}{C}HCH_3$$

2-Methyl-3-hexyne

The following sequence illustrates an exploitation of the difference between bromide and chloride as leaving groups. If a symmetrical dihalo compound had been used in the first step, a considerable amount of the diacetylene would have been produced.

$$HC\!\!\equiv\!\!\overset{-\,+}{CNa} + BrCH_2CH_2CH_2Cl \xrightarrow[-30°]{\text{NH}_3} HC\!\!\equiv\!\!CCH_2CH_2CH_2Cl + NaBr$$

5-Chloro-1-pentyne

$$ClCH_2CH_2CH_2C\!\!\equiv\!\!CH \xrightarrow{\text{NaNH}_2,\ \text{NH}_3} ClCH_2CH_2CH_2C\!\!\equiv\!\!\overset{-\,+}{CNa} \xrightarrow[-30°]{\text{Br(CH}_2)_3\text{Cl}} ClCH_2CH_2CH_2C\!\!\equiv\!\!CCH_2CH_2CH_2Cl$$

1,8-Dichloro-4-octyne

$$2KCN + ClCH_2CH_2CH_2C\!\!\equiv\!\!CCH_2CH_2CH_2Cl \xrightarrow[\text{Reflux}]{\text{Acetone}} NCCH_2CH_2CH_2C\!\!\equiv\!\!CCH_2CH_2CH_2CN$$

$$NCCH_2CH_2CH_2C\!\!\equiv\!\!CCH_2CH_2CH_2CN \xrightarrow[\text{Reflux}]{\text{H}_2\text{SO}_4,\ \text{H}_2\text{O}} HO_2CCH_2CH_2CH_2C\!\!\equiv\!\!CCH_2CH_2CH_2CO_2H$$

5-Decynedioic acid

A variety of reactions can be used to convert alkyl acetylenes to a host of other compounds. Two important examples are shown below.

Catalytic hydrogenation:

$$RC{\equiv}CR + H_2 \xrightarrow{Pd} \underset{\underset{\displaystyle H \qquad H}{|\qquad|}}{\overset{\overset{\displaystyle R \qquad R}{|\qquad|}}{C{=}C}} \longrightarrow RCH_2CH_2R$$

cis-Alkene

Hydration to ketones:

$$RC{\equiv}CR' + H_2O \xrightarrow{H_2SO_4,\ HgSO_4} RCH_2\underset{O}{\overset{\|}{C}}R' + RC\underset{O}{\overset{\|}{C}}H_2R'$$

$$RC{\equiv}CH + H_2O \xrightarrow{H_2SO_4,\ HgSO_4} R\underset{O}{\overset{\|}{C}}CH_3 \qquad \text{(No aldehyde produced!)}$$

Alkylation of Enolate Anions. Enolate ions, especially those derived from *diethyl malonate* (malonic ester) and *ethyl acetoacetate* (acetoacetic ester), have been used widely in synthetic sequences. Both compounds can be prepared from acetylene as is shown by the following synthetic schemes. The sequences leading to both compounds are rather long, and involve the use of expensive chemicals, such as bromine and metallic sodium. As a consequence, both esters are too costly for use in large-scale industrial syntheses.

$$CH{\equiv}CH \quad \begin{cases} \xrightarrow{H_2,\ Pd} CH_2{=}CH_2 \xrightarrow{H_2O,\ H_2SO_4} CH_3CH_2OH \\[2em] \xrightarrow{H_2O,\ H^+,\ HgSO_4} CH_3CHO \xrightarrow[\textit{Air oxidation}]{O_2} CH_3\underset{O}{\overset{\|}{C}}OH \end{cases}$$

$$CH_3\underset{O}{\overset{\|}{C}}OH + HOCH_2CH_3 \xrightarrow{H_2SO_4,\ \textit{esterification}} CH_3\underset{O}{\overset{\|}{C}}OCH_2CH_3 + H_2O$$

Ethyl
acetate

$$2CH_3CH_2OH + 2Na \longrightarrow CH_3CH_2ONa + H_2$$

$$CH_3\underset{O}{\overset{\|}{C}}OC_2H_5 + H{-}CH_2\underset{O}{\overset{\|}{C}}OC_2H_5 \xrightarrow[\textit{Ester condensation}]{NaOCH_2CH_3} CH_3\underset{O}{\overset{\|}{C}}CH_2\underset{O}{\overset{\|}{C}}OC_2H_5 + C_2H_5OH$$

Ethyl acetoacetate

$$CH_3\underset{O}{\overset{\|}{C}}OH + Br_2 \xrightarrow{PCl_3} BrCH_2CO_2H \xrightarrow{H_2SO_4,\ C_2H_5OH} BrCH_2CO_2C_2H_5 + H_2O$$

Bromoacetic
acid

Ethyl
bromoacetate

$$KCN + BrCH_2CO_2C_2H_5 \longrightarrow NCCH_2CO_2C_2H_5 + KBr$$

Ethyl cyanoacetate

$$NCCH_2CO_2C_2H_5 + C_2H_5OH \xrightarrow[\substack{\text{(Cf. with} \\ \text{nitrile hydrolysis)}}]{H_2SO_4} \underset{\substack{| \\ CO_2C_2H_5}}{\overset{\substack{CO_2C_2H_5 \\ |}}{CH_2}} + (NH_4)_2SO_4$$

Diethyl
malonate

Sodium enolates of both esters can be alkylated by primary halides unless the halide is badly sterically hindered. Secondary substrates may also be used, but yields are not high, because of competition from elimination reactions and *O*-alkylation of the ambident ions. Tertiary substrates give no *C*-alkylation.

$$CH_2(CO_2C_2H_5)_2 \xrightarrow{NaH} Na\overset{+}{C}\overset{-}{H}(CO_2C_2H_5)_2 \xrightarrow{CH_3I} CH_3CH(CO_2C_2H_5)_2 \xrightarrow{NaOC_2H_5}$$

90%

$$CH_3\overset{-}{C}(CO_2C_2H_5)_2\overset{+}{Na} \xrightarrow{C_2H_5I} \underset{\substack{| \\ CH_3}}{CH_3CH_2C(CO_2C_2H_5)_2}$$

$$CH_3COCH_2CO_2C_2H_5 \xrightarrow{NaOC_2H_5} CH_3COCHCO_2C_2H_5\overset{+}{Na} \xrightarrow{n\text{-}C_4H_9Br} \underset{\substack{| \\ CO_2C_2H_5}}{CH_3COCHCH_2CH_2CH_3}$$

70%

An interesting variation of the malonic ester synthesis has been used in the synthesis of small rings.

$$Na\overset{+}{C}\overset{-}{H}(CO_2C_2H_5)_2 + BrCH_2CH_2CH_2\!-\!Br \xrightarrow{-NaBr} BrCH_2CH_2CH_2CH(CO_2C_2H_5)_2 \xrightarrow{NaOC_2H_5}$$

Trimethylene
bromide

$$Br\!-\!CH_2CH_2CH_2C(CO_2C_2H_5)_2\overset{+}{Na} \longrightarrow \underset{\substack{| \quad | \\ CH_2\!-\!CH_2}}{CH_2\!-\!C(CO_2C_2H_5)_2}$$

Diethyl 1,1-cyclobutane-
dicarboxylate

The most important applications of the acetoacetic ester and malonic ester syntheses depend upon the ease with which a carboxyl group can be removed from the corresponding acids (Chap. 12).

Grignard and Related Reagents. A reaction of *limited synthetic value* is the coupling of the carbon residues of two molecules of alkyl or aryl halide by treatment with sodium. Known as the *Wurtz reaction*, the process undoubtedly involves sodium compounds as intermediates.

$$CH_3CH_2CH_2I \xrightarrow{Na} CH_3CH_2\overset{-}{C}H_2\overset{+}{Na} \xrightarrow{CH_3CH_2CH_2I} CH_3CH_2CH_2\!-\!CH_2CH_2CH_3$$

n-Propylsodium   n-Hexane

The yields in Wurtz reactions are usually poor, and attempts to accomplish the *crossed coupling* of two different halides usually give undesirable mixtures. The *Wurtz-Fittig reaction* employs *aryl and alkyl bromides*. It is much more successful.

$$C_6H_5Br + CH_3CH_2CH_2CH_2Br \xrightarrow{\text{Na}} C_6H_5CH_2CH_2CH_2CH_3 + 2NaBr$$

n-Butylbenzene
70%

Wurtzlike reactions are a serious nuisance in the preparation of Grignard and lithium reagents. The coupling reaction is very important with allyl and benzyl halides (reactive substrates in nucleophilic substitution), and the organometallic reagents can be prepared only by special procedures.

$$2CH_2{=}CHCH_2Br + Mg \xrightarrow{\text{Ether}} CH_2{=}CHCH_2CH_2CH{=}CH_2 + MgBr_2$$

Biallyl

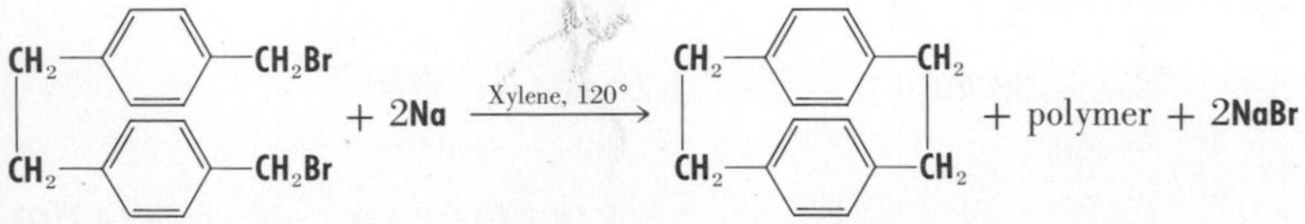

p-Xylylene
3%

Allyl and benzyl Grignard reagents may be prepared by slow passage of a dilute ether solution of the chlorides over a column of specially activated magnesium.

Useful hydrocarbon synthesis sometimes involves the preparation of an organometallic intermediate in a separate step for use in a second, substitution reaction.

$$C_6H_5Br + Mg \longrightarrow C_6H_5MgBr$$

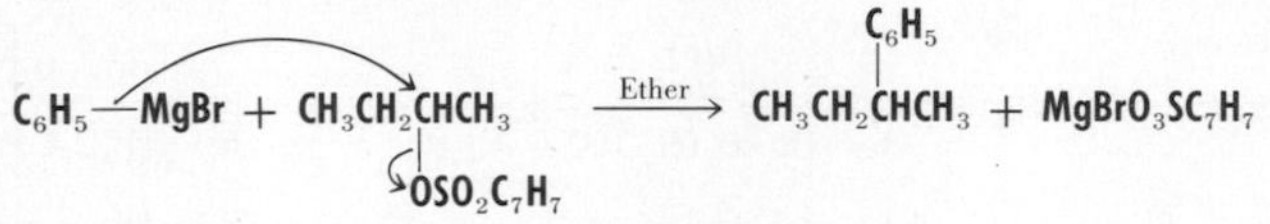

2-Butyl
p-toluenesulfonate

Carbon chains may be extended by two or three carbon atoms by the reactions of organometallic reagents with ethylene oxide and trimethylene oxide. The four-membered ring in trimethylene oxide is somewhat strained, but the compound behaves much more like an ordinary ether than does ethylene oxide. As a consequence, opening the larger ring system by nucleophilic substitution is often a slow and difficult reaction.

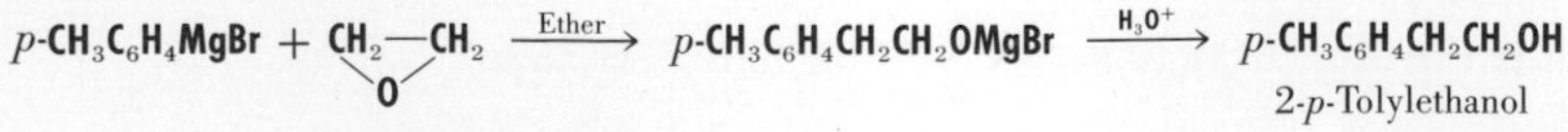

2-p-Tolylethanol

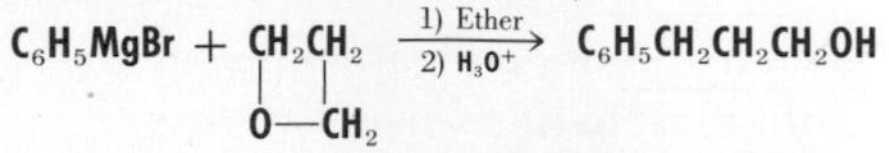

Trimethylene   3-Phenyl-1-propanol
oxide

Nucleophile (N)	Product	Nucleophile (N)	Product
H_2O	Alcohol, R—OH	$R'CNR'$ (O)	N-Alkyl amide, $R'CNR'$ (O, R)
$\overset{-}{H}O\overset{+}{M}$	Alcohol, R—OH		
R'OH	Ether, R—OR'	$R'SO_2N\overset{-}{R'}\overset{+}{M}$	N-Alkyl sulfonamide,
$R'\overset{-}{O}\overset{+}{M}$	Ether, R—OR'		$R'SO_2NR'$ (R)
$R'COH$ (O)	Ester, R'CO—R (O)	Cl^-	Alkyl chloride, R—Cl
$R'C\overset{-}{O}\overset{+}{M}$ (O)	Ester, R'CO—R (O)	Br^-	Alkyl bromide, R—Br
H_2O_2	Hydroperoxide, R OOH	I^-	Alkyl iodide, R—I
$HO\overset{-}{O}\overset{+}{M}$	Hydroperoxide, R—OOH	$SOCl_2$†	Alkyl chloride, R—Cl
		PCl_3†	Alkyl chloride, R—Cl
$R'CH=CR'$ ($\overset{-}{O}\overset{+}{M}$)	Enol ether, $R'CH=CR'$ (O R) or	PCl_5†	Alkyl chloride, R—Cl
		PBr_3	Alkyl bromide, R—Br
$R'CH—CR'$ ($\overset{-}{O}\overset{+}{M}$)	Ketone, R'CHCR' (O, R)	H_2S	Mercaptan, R—SH
		$H\overset{-}{S}\overset{|}{M}$	Mercaptan, R—SH
$R'_2C=N\overset{-}{O}\overset{+}{M}$	Oxime ether, $R'_2C=NO—R$	R'SH	Sulfide, R—SR'
H_2SO_4	Alkyl sulfuric acid,	R'_2S	Sulfonium ion, $R'_2\overset{+}{S}—R$
	R—OSO₃H	$\overset{-}{S_2}\overset{++}{M}$	Disulfide, R—SS—R
$HONO_2$	Alkyl nitrate, R—ONO₂	$\overset{-}{Al}H_4\overset{+}{Li}$	Hydrocarbon, R—H
		$\overset{-}{R'}\overset{+}{M}$	Hydrocarbon, R—R'
NH_3	Primary amine, $\overline{R}—NH_2$	$R'\overset{-}{C}≡C\overset{+}{M}$	Acetylene, R—C≡CR'
		$R'C—\overset{-}{CH}—CR'\overset{+}{M}$ (O O)	
$R'NH_2$	Secondary amine, R—NHR'	$R'\overset{-}{C}=CH—CR'\overset{+}{M}$ (O O)	Diketone,‡ R'CCHCR' (O O, R)
R'_2NH	Tertiary amine, $R'_2N—R$	$R'C—CH=C\overset{-}{R'}\overset{+}{M}$ (O O)	
R'_3N	Quaternary ammonium ion,		
	$R'_3\overset{+}{N}—R$	$\overset{-}{C}N\overset{+}{M}$	Nitrile, R—CN
$O=N—\overset{-}{O}\overset{+}{M}$	Nitro alkane, R—NO₂ or Alkyl nitrite, R—ONO	$R'\overset{-}{CH}CN$	Nitrile, R'CHCN (R)
NH_2NH_2	Alkyl hydrazine, R—NHNH₂		
$\overset{-}{N_3}\overset{+}{M}$	Alkyl azide, R—N₃		

† Substitution by these reagents is complex. The reagents do not themselves possess nucleophilic reactivity, but are converted to other species which are reactive nucleophiles.

‡ Enol ethers are also produced.

Ausdehnung

Scope of the Nucleophilic Substitution Reaction

The scope of nucleophilic substitution reactions is indicated by Tables 10.1 and 10.2, which list the commonly encountered nucleophiles and leaving groups. Many reactions can be written down by combining the two lists, although some of the conceivable combinations do not give experimentally feasible processes. The reactivity of the reagents shown in Table 10.1 varies enormously, and some "weak" nucleophiles will not displace any but the most labile leaving groups. Furthermore, the coexistence of some pairs in the same medium is not possible. For example, the first neutral leaving group in Table 10.2 is H_2O. In order to obtain appreciable amounts of the corresponding substrate species, $R-OH_2^+$, an alcohol must be brought in contact with strong acid, a condition that would destroy many of the nucleophiles listed in Table 10.1.

$$R-\overset{..}{\underset{..}{O}}-H + \overset{+}{H} \rightleftharpoons R\overset{+}{O}H_2$$

$$\underset{\text{Nucleophile}}{N:} + \underset{\substack{\text{Conjugate acid} \\ \text{of nucleophile}}}{\overset{+}{H}} \rightleftharpoons \overset{+}{N}-H$$

Furthermore, no such tabulation can give any indication as to the importance of side reactions such as rearrangement and elimination.

TABLE 10.2   *Leaving Groups in Nucleophilic Substitution*

(R' = alkyl or aryl)

Leaving group	Substrate	Leaving group	Substrate
Cl^-	Alkyl chloride, $R-Cl$	$\overset{-}{O}SO_2R'$	Alkyl sulfonate, $R-OSO_2R'$
Br^-	Alkyl bromide, $R-Br$	$\overset{-}{O}SO_3R'$	Alkyl sulfate, $R-OSO_3R'$
I^-	Alkyl iodide, $R-I$	$\overset{-}{O}SOCl$	Alkyl chlorosulfite, $R-OSOCl$
H_2O	Alcohol, conjugate acid, $R-\overset{+}{O}H_2$	$\overset{-}{O}PCl_2$	Alkyl chlorophosphite, $R-OPCl_2$
ROH	Ether, conjugate acid, $R-\overset{+}{\underset{H}{O}}R$	$\overset{-}{O}PBr_2$	Alkyl bromophosphite, $R-OPBr_2$
		$\overset{-}{O}SO_2R'$	Alkyl sulfite, $R-OSO_2R'$
$\overset{O}{\overset{\|}{O}}-CR'$	Ester, $R-O\overset{O}{\overset{\|}{C}}R'$	$:NH_3$	Ammonium ion, $R-\overset{+}{N}H_3$
$\overset{O}{\overset{\|}{H}O}-CR'$	Ester, conjugate acid, $R-\overset{+}{\underset{H}{O}}-\overset{O}{\overset{\|}{C}}R'$	$:NR'_3$	Ammonium ion, $R-\overset{+}{N}R_3$
		$\overset{+}{N}\equiv N$	Diazonium ion, $R-\overset{+}{N}\equiv N$
$\overset{-}{O}SO_3H$	Alkyl sulfuric acid, $R-OSO_3H$	SR'_2	Sulfonium ion, $R-\overset{+}{S}R'_2$

Repeated allusions to these problems have been made throughout this chapter, and they will be treated again in Chap. 11.   Elimination and rearrangement are given explicit treatment in Chaps. 17 and 20.

Problems

1. Write out syntheses of the following compounds, starting with the appropriate alkyl or aryl halides and other needed reagents.   Indicate the side reactions you would expect, if any.

a. 2-Butanol
b. Ethylbenzene
c. Isopropyl *n*-propyl ether
d. *tert*-Butyl mercaptan
e. 2-Acetoxyhexane (2-hexyl acetate)
f. 1-[1-Naphthyl]-1-dimethylaminoethane

g. Methylacetylene
h. *n*-Hexane
i. 1,2-Propanediol
j. 1,3-Dimethoxybenzene (use a phenol as a starting material)

2. Write out specific examples of the following reactions:
a. One method of extending a carbon chain by one carbon atom
b. Two independent methods of extending a carbon chain by two carbon atoms
c. Two independent methods of extending a carbon chain by three carbon atoms

3. Write out preparative schemes for the following compounds, using only calcium carbide, carbon monoxide, and metal cyanides as the original source of carbon.   Once a particular intermediate has been prepared, it may be used directly in subsequent problems. You will need to use the fact that the addition of sulfuric acid to terminal alkenes always follows the course $H_2SO_4 + RCH=CH_2 \longrightarrow RCH(OSO_3H)CH_3$.

a. Methanol
b. Ethanol
c. Acetic acid
d. Acetaldehyde
e. Methylacetylene
f. Ethyl acetate
g. Ethylene oxide
h. 1-Butanol
i. 2-Butanol
j. Acetone
k. 2-Propanol
l. Ethyl bromide
m. 2-Chloropropane
n. Diethyl malonate
o. Diethyl methylmalonate
   $[CH_2CH(CO_2C_2H_5)_2]$

p. Ethyl 2-methyl-2-carboethoxypentanoate

$$CH_3CH_2CH_2\underset{\underset{CH_3}{|}}{\overset{\overset{CO_2C_2H_5}{|}}{C}}{-}CO_2C_2H_5$$

q. *n*-Hexane
r. 2-Methylhexane
s. Ethyl 2-isopropylacetoacetate
t. Succinic acid ($HO_2CCH_2CH_2CO_2H$)
u. Ethylmethylamine
v. *n*-Butylamine
w. Isopropyl methyl ether
x. 1-Pentanol (try to find the minimum number of steps)
y. $CH_3\overset{*}{C}H_2CH_3$ (C* is carbon-14, which is available as $KC^{14}N$)
z. Diallyl ether

4. In the following synthetic sequences, the structures of the intermediates are omitted.   What are the missing links?

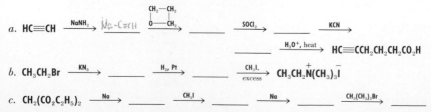

a. $HC{\equiv}CH \xrightarrow{NaNH_2} Na{-}C{\equiv}CH \xrightarrow{\overset{CH_2-CH_2}{\underset{O-CH_2}{\diagup}}} \underline{\qquad} \xrightarrow{SOCl_2} \underline{\qquad} \xrightarrow{KCN}$
$\underline{\qquad} \xrightarrow{H_3O^+,\ heat} HC{\equiv}CCH_2CH_2CH_2CO_2H$

b. $CH_3CH_2Br \xrightarrow{KN_3} \underline{\qquad} \xrightarrow{H_2,\ Pt} \underline{\qquad} \xrightarrow[excess]{CH_3I,} CH_3CH_2\overset{+}{N}(CH_3)_3\overset{-}{I}$

c. $CH_2(CO_2C_2H_5)_2 \xrightarrow{Na} \underline{\qquad} \xrightarrow{CH_3I} \underline{\qquad} \xrightarrow{Na} \underline{\qquad} \xrightarrow{CH_3(CH_2)_3Br} \underline{\qquad}$

d. CH_2=$CHCH_2OH$ $\xrightarrow{\text{Na}}$ _____ $\xrightarrow[\text{O}]{CH_2-CH_2}$ _____ $\xrightarrow{PBr_3}$

_____ $\xrightarrow[\text{2) } H_3O^+]{\text{1) LiAlH}_4, \text{ ether}}$ _____

5. Write equations for the following:

a. Five examples of reactions in which the nucleophile and substrate are in the same molecule. Try to invent some new examples of reactions you would expect to be successful.

b. Two examples which show the alkylation of ambident nucleophiles in two different ways.

c. Five reactions in which the leaving group is neutral (make use of Tables 10.1 and 10.2).

d. Five reactions involving substitution by a neutral nucleophile.

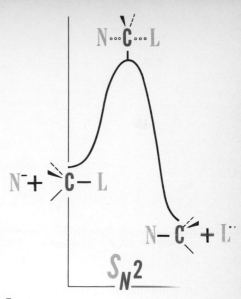

11

Mechanisms and Reactivity in the
Nucleophilic Substitution Reaction

Chapter 10 contained frequent references to variations in the reactivities of nucleophiles, substrates, and leaving groups. Such variations are of paramount importance, since *apparently analogous* compounds often show completely different behavior under a given set of reaction conditions. Such observations show that *reliable generalizations concerning reactivity cannot be made merely by examination of the structures of substrate molecules.* The study of a reaction mechanism is an attempt to take account of the *changes in a molecule that occur in the course of a reaction.*

Nucleophilic Substitution Mechanisms

In a nucleophilic substitution, two changes occur—breaking of the old bond and formation of the new bond. The principal mechanistic variations are associated with changes in the timing of the two processes. Three possibilities can be imagined.

1. Two-step reaction: (*a*) break the old bond and (*b*) make the new bond.

2. Two-step reaction: (*a*) make the new bond and (*b*) break the old bond.

3. One-step reaction in which bond making and bond breaking are simultaneous.

Both mechanisms 1 and 3 are observed in nucleophilic substitutions at saturated carbon atoms. To the best of our knowledge, 2 is not. Kinetics (measurement of reaction rates) and stereochemistry are the tools that have been used most in the study of reaction mechanisms. Kinetic studies often show the time schedule of a reaction. Stereochemical studies show the relationship between the configurations of reactants and products.

Prior ionization (S_N1):

$$R\!-\!X \xrightarrow{\text{Slow}} \overset{+}{R} + \overset{-}{X} \qquad \textit{Carbonium-Ion}$$

$$\overset{-}{N}: + \overset{+}{R} \xrightarrow{\text{Fast}} N\!:\!R$$

One-step substitution (S_N2):

$$\overset{-}{N}: + R\!-\!X \longrightarrow [N\text{---}R\text{---}X]^- \longrightarrow N\!:\!R + \overset{-}{X}$$
$$\text{Transition}$$
$$\text{state}$$

FIG. 11.1   *Mechanisms of nucleophilic substitution reactions.*

A combination of the two types of information may give a very detailed picture of how the reagent and substrate come together during the reaction.

Reactivity of Halides.   In solvolytic reactions in neutral solutions, the order of reactivity of saturated alkyl halides usually varies as follows: tertiary > secondary > primary.   On the other hand, another group of reactions, which usually involve powerful nucleophiles, shows the reverse order: primary > secondary > tertiary.   The contrasting orders are a strong indication that two mechanisms are at work.   The two mechanisms are shown in Fig. 11.1.   Solvolytic reactions often involve prior ionization of the halide to form a carbonium ion, which in turn is captured almost immediately by some nucleophile, usually the solvent.   In the second mechanism, the nucleophile attacks and the leaving group is detached in the same step.

The two mechanisms are presented in their simplest form, but this is sufficient to clarify some of the reactivity relationships.   The speed of

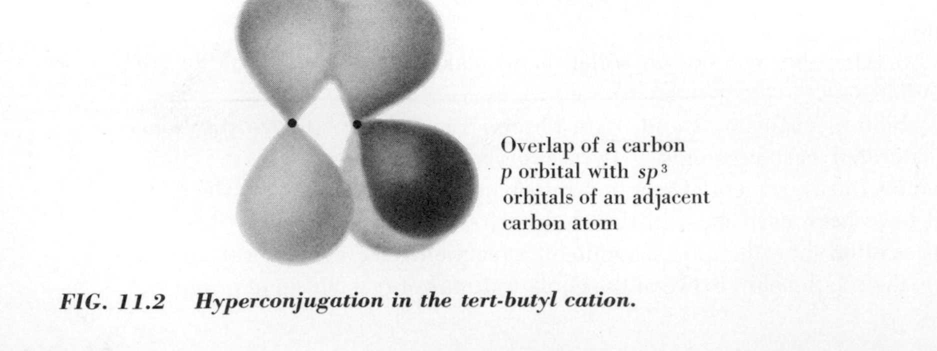

7 more structures

Overlap of a carbon
p orbital with sp^3
orbitals of an adjacent
carbon atom

FIG. 11.2   *Hyperconjugation in the tert-butyl cation.*

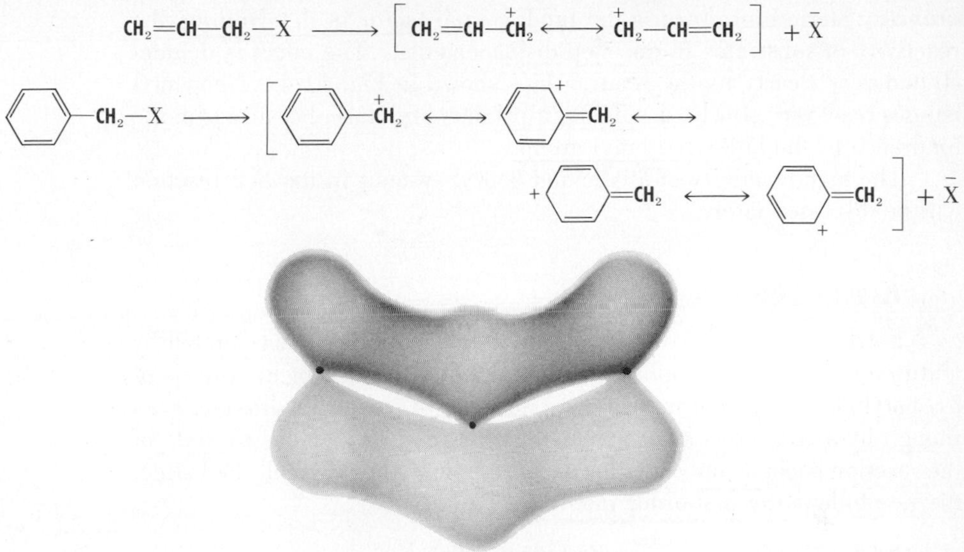

$$CH_2{=}CH{-}CH_2{-}X \longrightarrow \left[CH_2{=}CH{-}\overset{+}{C}H_2 \longleftrightarrow \overset{+}{C}H_2{-}CH{=}CH_2 \right] + \bar{X}$$

Molecular orbital occupied by the
π electrons of the allyl cation

FIG. 11.3   *Ionization of allyl and benzyl halides.*

ionization reactions depends upon the ease of carbonium-ion formation, the reactivity of the leaving group, and the *ionizing power* of the solvent. In reactions that involve carbonium-ion intermediates, *the reaction rate always increases as the stability of the carbonium ion increases.* Carbonium-ion stability increases as the ion becomes more highly branched at the positive center.   The effect is due to *hyperconjugation*, or delocalization of electrons in single bonds attached to the β-carbon, as is shown in Fig. 11.2.

$R = F(\text{carbonium stab})$

zweige, Aste

The high reactivity of allyl and benzyl halides in solvolysis is easily explained, since these systems produce relatively stable cations in which the electron deficiency is spread over the entire conjugated π-electron system.

One-step substitution must involve crowding five groups around the carbon atom.   Even without establishing the direction of approach of the nucleophile, it is obvious that attachment of large groups at the point of substitution will cause the reaction to be difficult because of *steric hin-*

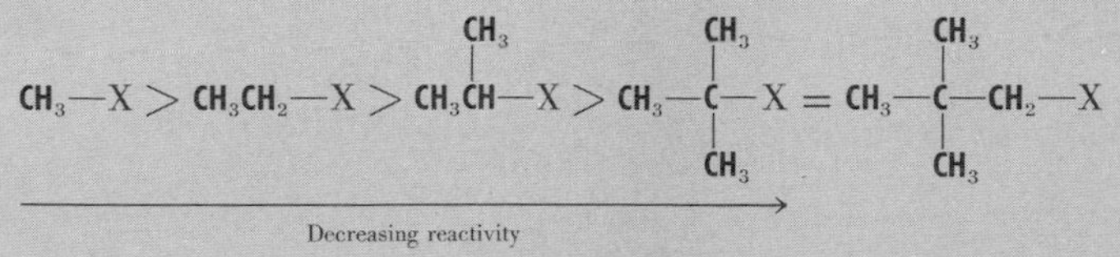

$$CH_3{-}X > CH_3CH_2{-}X > CH_3\overset{CH_3}{\underset{}{C}}H{-}X > CH_3\overset{CH_3}{\underset{CH_3}{C}}{-}X = CH_3\overset{CH_3}{\underset{CH_3}{C}}{-}CH_2{-}X$$

Decreasing reactivity

FIG. 11.4   *Reactivity of halides in one-step substitution reactions.*

drance. Steric hindrance is the fundamental factor in determining the reactivity of substrates in one-step displacements. The effect is demonstrated very clearly by the relationships shown in Fig. 11.4. Neopentyl halides react very slowly, despite their primary structure, because of steric hindrance by the bulky *tert*-butyl group.

The high reactivity of allylic and benzyl systems in the S_N2 reaction will be discussed later.

Kinetic Characteristics

Solvolytic reactions of tertiary halides are usually not accelerated by addition of strong nucleophiles. For example, the rate of hydrolysis of *tert*-butyl chloride is not increased by addition of sodium hydroxide, even though hydroxide ions are consumed in the reaction. Since the rate of the reaction depends only on the concentration of one reactant, the halide, the rate follows the first-order rate law.

$$NaOH + (CH_3)_3CCl \xrightarrow{H_2O - C_2H_5OH} (CH_3)_3COH + NaCl$$

$$Rate = k[(CH_3)_3CCl]$$

To be first order the rate must be proportional to the concentration of one species. If the rate is proportional either to the product of two concentrations or to the square of one concentration, the reaction is second order.

The first-order rate law is consistent with the carbonium-ion mechanism for substitution, since the first, and rate-controlling, step of the reaction does not involve the nucleophilic reagent. The name that has been given to the two-step mechanism is S_N1, meaning *substitution nucleophilic unimolecular.*

The kinetic behavior of primary halides is very different from that of *tert*-butyl chloride and other tertiary halides. Ethyl chloride, for example, does not hydrolyze at an appreciable rate in neutral solution. However, if sodium hydroxide is added, reaction occurs at a rate that is proportional to the concentrations of both the halide and the base. Such a rate law is called *second order.*

$$NaOH + CH_3CH_2Cl \longrightarrow CH_3CH_2OH + NaCl$$

$$Rate = k[CH_3CH_2Cl][NaOH]$$

The one-step mechanism is consistent with the second-order rate law, although other mechanisms could give the same kinetics. The one-step process is called the S_N2 (*substitution nucleophilic bimolecular*) mechanism.

Steric Course of Substitution

Study of the stereochemical course of substitutions at asymmetric carbon atoms has provided a clear picture of the mechanisms of the reactions. In Fig. 11.5, various stereochemical possibilities are illustrated with an optically active *sec*-butyl group.

Substitution with inversion of configuration:

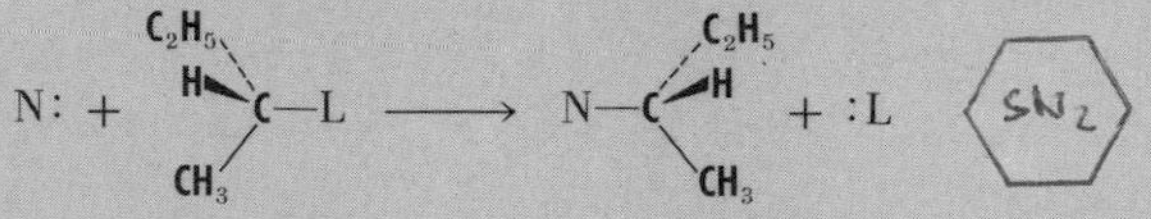

Substitution with retention of configuration:

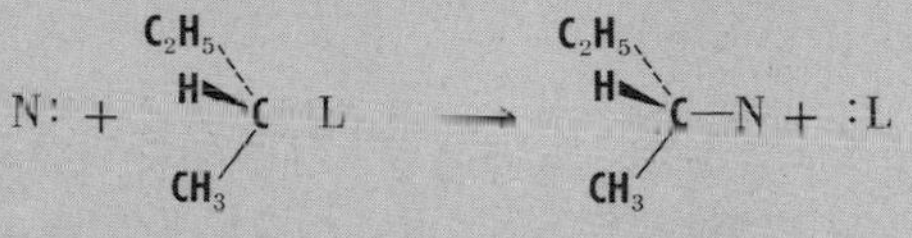

Substitution with racemization:

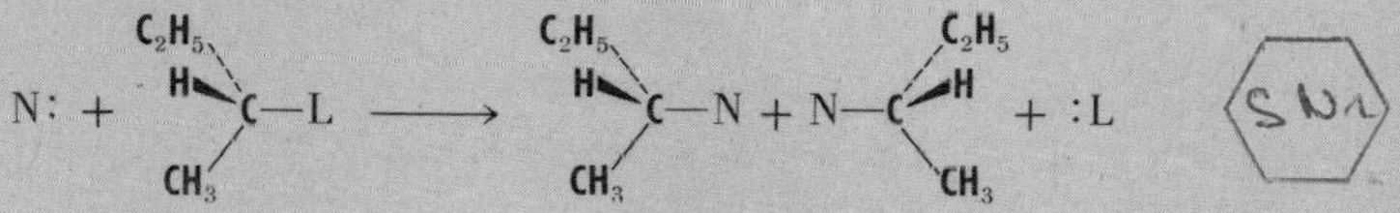

FIG. 11.5   *Possible stereochemical consequences of nucleophilic substitutions.*

In an inversion reaction, the three groups CH_3, C_2H_5, and H attached to the asymmetric center are "pushed through" a plane including the central carbon atom and perpendicular to the C—L bond axis. Substitution with inversion is assumed to involve a transition state such as that shown in Fig. 11.6. Substitution with racemization is not really a special case, since racemization indicates that inversion and retention of configuration have occurred to exactly the same extent. In many reactions, *partial racemization* is observed. In such reactions, both inversion and retention occur, but in unequal amounts. Reactions in which either inversion or retention of configuration predominates completely, or nearly so, are called *stereospecific*.

Stereochemistry of S_N2 Reactions.   *The bimolecular nucleophilic substitution (S_N2) reaction occurs with very clear-cut inversion of configuration.* This fact was established by study of the stereochemistry and kinetics of substitution reactions of sulfonate esters. The equations in Fig. 11.7 indicate a classic set of interlinked reactions that establish the relative configurations of reactants and products in a second-order substitution. The key to the demonstration is the fact that the product of the reaction,

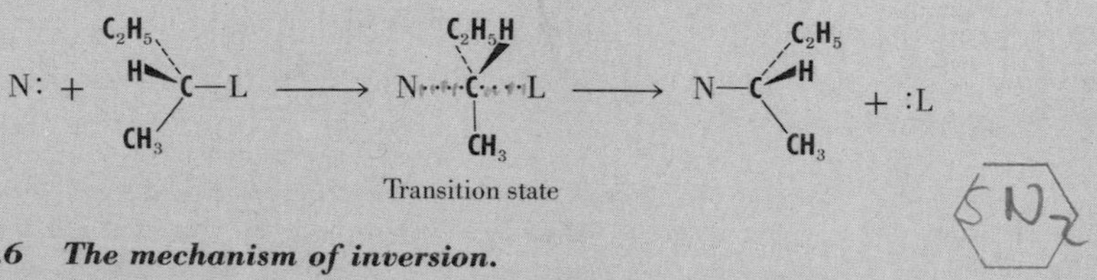

Transition state

FIG. 11.6   *The mechanism of inversion.*

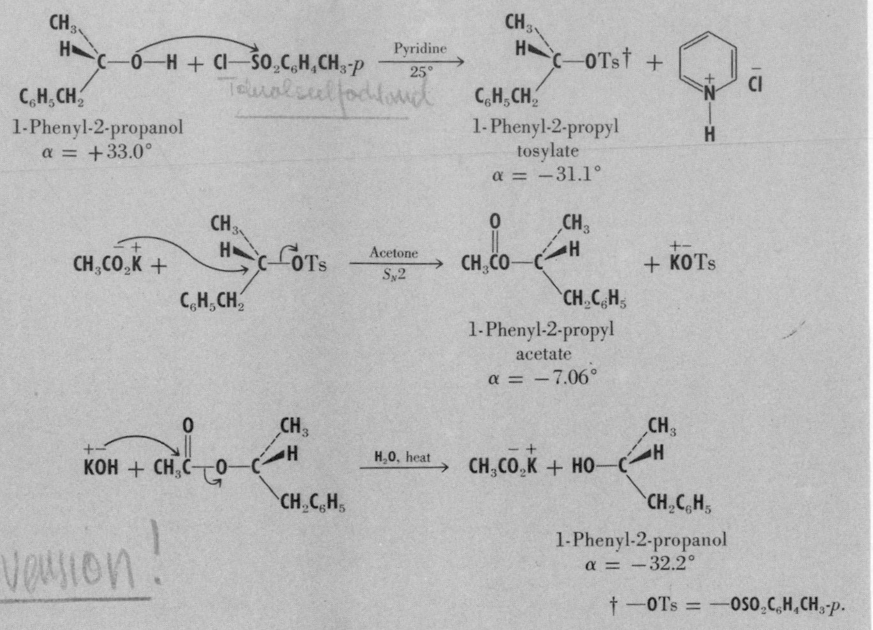

FIG. 11.7 *Demonstration of the steric course of an S_N2 reaction.*

an acetate ester, can be hydrolyzed to the corresponding alcohol in a reaction known to involve cleavage of the acyl-oxygen bond, rather than the alkyl-oxygen bond.[†] The sulfonate ester, which served as a substrate in the substitution step, was made from the alcohol by treatment with toluenesulfonyl chloride, a reaction that almost certainly involves no alteration of configuration at the asymmetric center. The alcohol obtained at the end of the sequence had a rotation opposite in sign, but equal in magnitude, to that of the starting material. Substitution must have involved an inversion, if the stated assumptions are valid.

$$\overset{O}{\overset{\|}{R\text{C}OR'}} + H_2O^{18} \xrightarrow{\text{NaOH}} \overset{O}{\overset{\|}{R\text{C}O^{18}H}} + R'OH$$

The results are interpreted to mean that bimolecular substitution involves a transition state with a spatial arrangement approximately like that shown in Fig. 11.6. Substitution reactions with sulfonate ions as leaving groups are very similar to those in which halide ions are displaced. Therefore, the *assumption* is made that substitutions with *monofunctional halides* as substrates involve inversion of configuration if the products are

[†] Several methods have been used to establish that acyl-oxygen cleavage occurs in the hydrolysis of most carboxylate esters. One of the most direct is study of the hydrolysis reaction in water enriched in the heavy isotope of oxygen, O^{18}. Acid produced in the hydrolysis contains heavy oxygen, but none is introduced into the alcohol.

optically active and if the reaction rate follows the second-order kinetic law. Some such assumption is necessary, since there is no rigorous method for correlation of the configurations of halides with substitution products derived from them.

Stereochemistry of S_N1 Reactions. An S_N1 reaction would be expected to racemize an optically active substrate, since carbonium ions are flat, sp^2 hybrids. Attack of nucleophiles on the planar ions should occur with equal probability from either side of the plane. The hydrolysis of optically active α-phenylethyl chloride, shown in Fig. 11.8, is one of many solvolysis reactions that give virtually complete racemization.

The small net inversion observed in the hydrolysis of α-phenylethyl chloride shows that the carbonium-ion mechanism falls short of accuracy in its predictions by a narrow margin. This result might not be considered a serious matter if it were not for the fact that other first-order solvolyses give much larger amounts of inverted products, and still others give extensive or complete net retention of configuration. Special mechanistic features can usually be found to account for the results, but S_N1 *reactions,* as a group, *do not have a characteristic steric course.*

Inversion by Solvent. The greatest deficiency of the simple carbonium-ion mechanism lies in the omission of the critical role that the solvent must play. All ions in solution interact very strongly with surrounding solvent molecules. The fact that salts will dissolve in water and other solvents shows that solvation energies must be very large. Solvation is, in fact, sufficient to compensate for the huge binding energy that holds an ionic crystal lattice together. Carbonium ions produced in S_N1 reactions must be solvated, and a description of the ions is really incomplete unless the solvent is included. Even though a carbonium ion itself is essentially planar, it may be preferentially attacked on one side by a nucleophilic solvent if the ion is so short-lived that it does not attain a symmetrical solvent atmosphere.

Figure 11.9 summarizes data that illustrate solvolyses with net inversion of configuration. Collapse of the intermediate carbonium ion occurs so rapidly that an appreciable amount of inverted product is formed before the departing bromide ion is replaced by a solvent molecule.

The $S_N i$ Reaction. Reactions of thionyl chloride, and similar reagents,

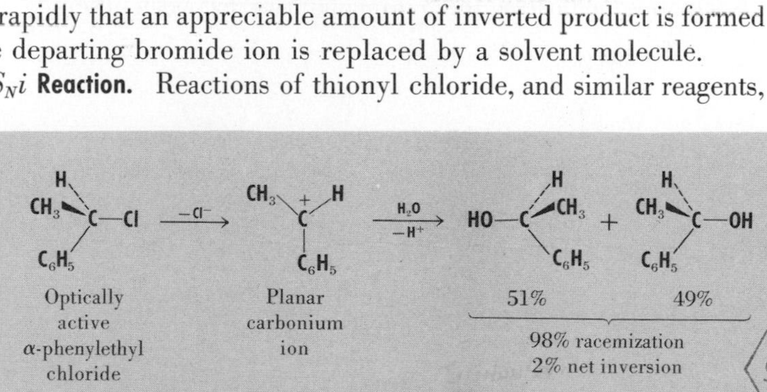

| Optically active α-phenylethyl chloride | Planar carbonium ion | 51% | 49% |

98% racemization
2% net inversion

FIG. 11.8 *Hydrolysis of α-phenylethyl chloride.*

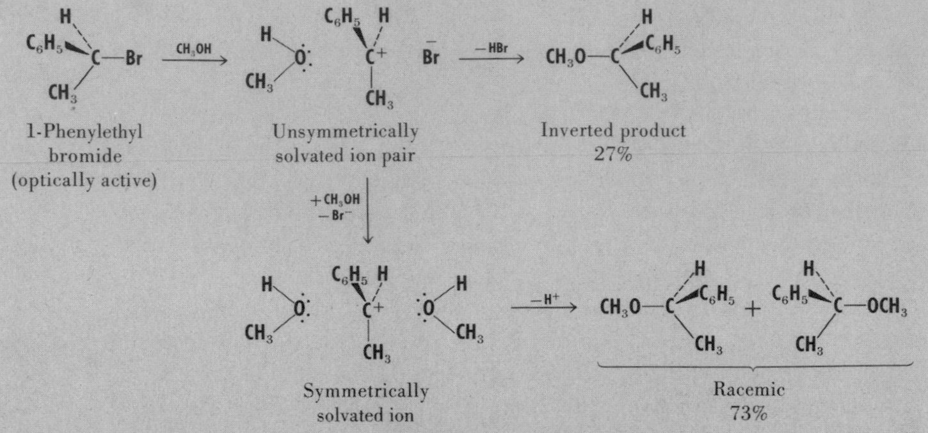

FIG. 11.9   *Methanolysis of 1-phenylethyl bromide.*

with alcohols frequently result in substitution with predominant retention of configuration. Intermediate esters, such as chlorosulfites, are formed. The complex leaving groups decompose during solvolysis to produce nucleophilic anions that capture the carbonium ion before it can become symmetrical. The process is illustrated by the first of the examples in Fig. 11.10. Such mechanisms are designated as $S_N i$, or *substitution nucleophilic internal.* In the presence of bases, such as pyridine, the steric course of the reactions of thionyl chloride with alcohols is changed dramatically. Hydrogen chloride produced in the first step is neutralized to form chloride ions that are sufficiently nucleophilic to decompose the chlorosulfite by an $S_N 2$ mechanism with inversion of configuration.

A number of other substitutions involving complex leaving groups give similar variable stereochemical results that depend upon substrate structure and reaction conditions. The following are examples of reactions in which retention, indicating the $S_N i$ mechanism, has been observed.

$$ROH + PCl_3 \xrightarrow{-HCl} ROPCl_2 \xrightarrow{-POCl} R\text{—}Cl$$

$$ROH + COCl_2 \xrightarrow{HCl} RO\overset{\overset{\displaystyle O}{\|}}{C}Cl \xrightarrow[\Delta]{-CO_2} R\text{—}Cl + CO_2$$

Alkyl
chlorocarbonate
(often isolated)

$$ROH + HBr \xrightarrow[\text{temperature}]{\text{Low}} R\overset{+}{O}H_2\overset{-}{Br} \xrightarrow{-H_2O} R\text{—}Br$$

(Gas)

Neighboring-group Participation. In polyfunctional substrates, a neighboring functional group may often become involved in a substitution reaction. Usually the neighboring group serves as a nucleophile in the first step of an S_N1 reaction.   Frequently the neighboring group attacks the seat of substitution and is then displaced by a second attack, this time by an external nucleophile.   Inversion of configuration occurs in both steps.   Accordingly, the reaction results in *over-all net retention*.   Rearrangement of the neighboring group may also occur if the second nucleophilic attack occurs at the point of the original attachment of the neighboring group.   Examples illustrating some of the possibilities are shown in Fig. 11.11.

Carbonium-ion Rearrangements

Reactions that proceed by the S_N1 mechanism frequently give rearrangements.   The migration of a functional neighboring group is illustrated in Fig. 11.11, and two other types are shown in Fig. 11.12. *If a carbonium ion can be converted to a more stable ion by migration of*

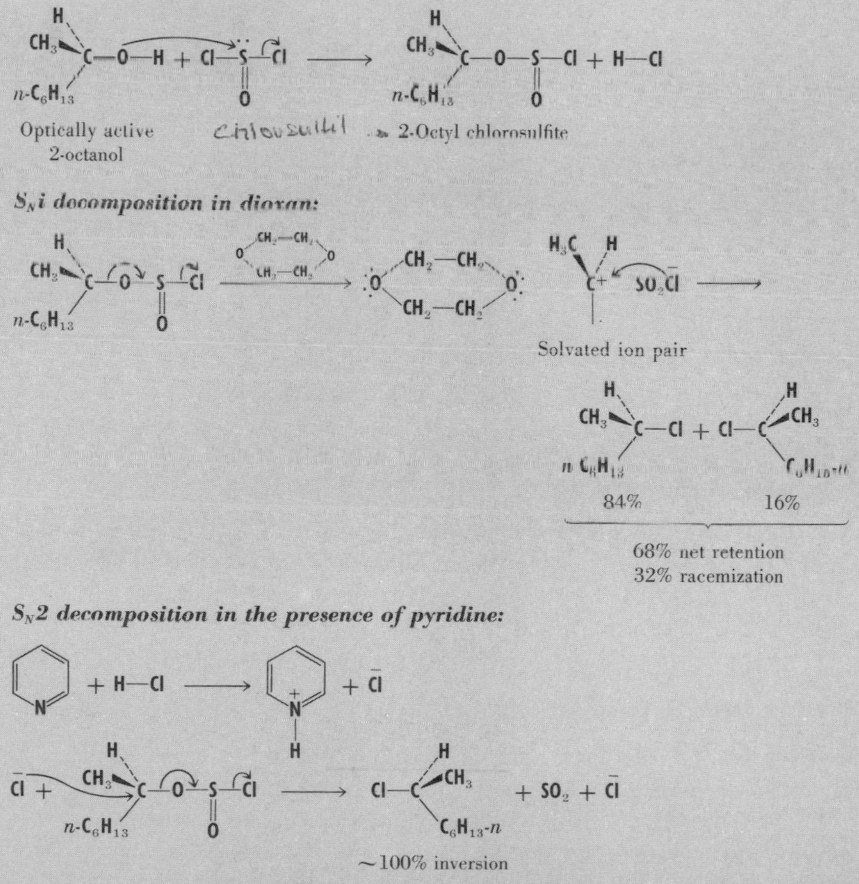

FIG. 11.10   *The reactions of active 2-octanol with thionyl chloride.*

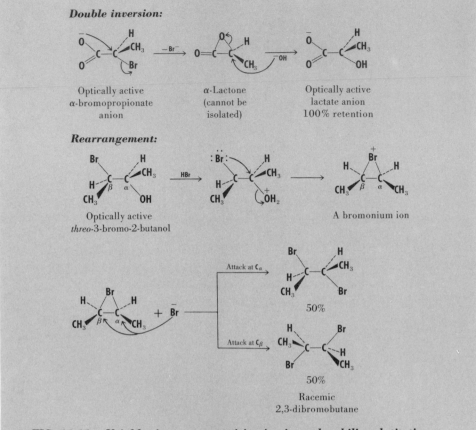

FIG. 11.11   *Neighboring-group participation in nucleophilic substitution.*

an alkyl or aryl group from an adjacent carbon atom, rearrangement will almost inevitably occur.   Allylic cations contain two electron-deficient centers to which nucleophiles can be attached; therefore allylic rearrangements may be expected in the solvolysis of allylic substrates.   The entire subject of molecular rearrangements is treated more extensively in Chap. 20.

Further Reactivity Relationships

Reactivity in S_N2 Reactions.   Steric hindrance in the substrate was mentioned earlier (page 222) as a major factor in determining S_N2 reactivity.   In addition, electronic factors are of importance.   In reactions of negative ions with neutral substrates, strong dipoles in the substrate have a predictable effect.   If the dipole tends to draw electrons away from the seat of substitution, the reaction will be made relatively easy.   An example is found in the high reactivity of α-haloketones and α-haloesters in S_N2

reactions (see the discussion of similar effects on acidity on page 168).

$$HO^- + Cl-CH_2CO_2C_2H_5 \xrightarrow{Fast} HO\cdots\overset{\overset{\displaystyle H \quad H}{\diagdown}}{\underset{\underset{\underset{C_2H_5}{-\downarrow}}{\overset{O_2}{|}}}{\overset{+|}{C}}}\cdots\overset{\delta^-}{Cl} \longrightarrow HOCH_2CO_2C_2H_5 + Cl^-$$

$\langle S_N2 \rangle$

Transition state

Allyl and benzyl compounds are quite reactive in S_N2 reactions unless they are much sterically hindered. The effect shows that the central carbon atom must have some of the character of a carbonium ion in the transition state of an S_N2 reaction. The carbon atom is flattened out to the sp^2 configuration, and electrons can be fed in from attached unsaturated groups, as is shown in Fig. 11.13.

Nucleophilic Reactivity. While all nucleophiles are bases, their reactivity does not always parallel their basic strength. Comparison of nucleophiles *having the same attacking atom* does show that within such a restricted series increased basicity results in increased nucleophilic reactivity. Thus the following series of decreasing reactivities is observed: $C_2H_5O^- > HO^- > C_6H_5O^- > CH_3CO_2^- > H_2O$. However, if one stays within one family in the periodic table, reactivity of nucleophiles in series of analogous ions or molecules increases sharply with increasing atomic

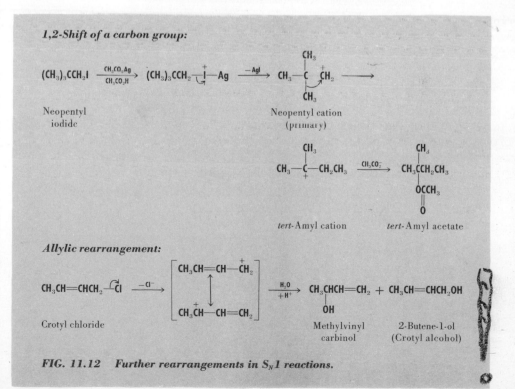

1,2-Shift of a carbon group:

$(CH_3)_3CCH_2I \xrightarrow[CH_3CO_2H]{CH_3CO_2Ag} (CH_3)_3CCH_2 \overset{+}{\underset{}{I}}-Ag \xrightarrow{-AgI} CH_3-\overset{\overset{\displaystyle CH_3}{|}}{\underset{\underset{CH_3}{|}}{C}}\overset{+}{CH_2} \longrightarrow$

Neopentyl   Neopentyl cation
iodide   (primary)

$CH_3-\overset{\overset{\displaystyle CH_3}{|}}{C}-CH_2CH_3 \xrightarrow{CH_3CO_2^-} \overset{\overset{\displaystyle CH_3}{|}}{\underset{\underset{\underset{O}{\overset{||}{OCCH_3}}}{}}{CH_3CCH_2CH_3}}$
       $\overset{+}{}$

tert-Amyl cation   *tert*-Amyl acetate

Allylic rearrangement:

$CH_3CH=CHCH_2-Cl \xrightarrow{-Cl^-} \left[\begin{array}{c} CH_3CH=CH-\overset{+}{CH_2} \\ \updownarrow \\ CH_3\overset{+}{CH}-CH=CH_2 \end{array} \right] \xrightarrow[+H^+]{H_2O} CH_3\underset{\underset{OH}{|}}{CH}CH=CH_2 + CH_3CH=CHCH_2OH$

Crotyl chloride   Methylvinyl   2-Butene-1-ol
                                                 carbinol   (Crotyl alcohol)

FIG. 11.12   *Further rearrangements in S_N1 reactions.*

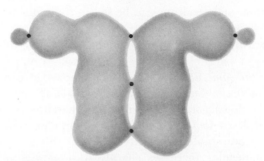

Transition state

π Orbitals of an allylic group overlapping weakly
with sp^3 orbitals of a nucleophilic reagent and a
leaving group

FIG. 11.13   *Stabilization of an S_N2 transition state in an allylic system.*

number.   Thus the following series of decreasing reactivity are observed:
$I^- > Br^- > Cl^- \gg F^-$ and $RS^- > RO^-$.   The effect is probably due to the
ability of the larger, *more polarizable nucleophiles* to give bonding interaction at large internuclear distances.

The reactivity of leaving groups is somewhat surprising.   As would
be expected, *an increase in the basicity of the group decreases its reactivity*
if the polarizability of the group is maintained essentially constant.
However, *increasing the polarizability of the atoms by which leaving groups
are attached to the substrate increases their reactivity*.   Thus the same orders
of reactivity, $I^- > Br^- > Cl^- \gg F^-$ and $RS^- > RO^-$, are observed when
the ions are compared, either as leaving groups or as entering nucleophiles.

Strongly basic leaving groups such as RO^-, HO^-, H_2N^-, and F^-, which
are bound to the substrate by small nonpolarizable atoms, cannot be displaced from saturated centers under ordinary reaction conditions.   This
is the reason for the use of acid catalysts in nucleophilic substitution
reactions of alcohols, ethers, and amines.   Even alkyl fluorides become
susceptible to nucleophilic substitution in concentrated sulfuric acid
solution.

Use is made of the high reactivity of iodide ion, both as a nucleophile and as a leaving group, in the iodide-catalyzed hydrolysis of primary
alkyl chlorides.

$$H_2O + RCH_2Cl \xrightarrow{\text{Very slow}} RCH_2OH + HCl$$

$$I^- + RCH_2Cl \xrightarrow{\text{Fast}} RCH_2I + Cl^-$$

$$H_2O + RCH_2I \xrightarrow{\text{Fast}} RCH_2OH + HCl$$

Variation of the leaving group may have a profound influence on the course of nucleophilic substitution reactions. For example, propylene oxide is opened at the primary (least hindered) position in an S_N2 reaction with potassium iodide. The same compound is always opened at the secondary position in reactions with acidic reagents.

luen wurde sehindeet

The selective nucleophilic attack on the secondary position of the conjugate acid of propylene oxide is most unusual in an S_N2 reaction. Such selectivity is certainly due to the carbonium-ion-like character of the S_N2 transition state (see page 232), and is associated with the high reactivity of the leaving group. Selective attack at the more branched positions of substrates in S_N2 reactions is almost exclusively reserved for substrates that contain positively charged three-membered rings.

In a very general way, effects of variation in leaving groups on reaction rates are similar in S_N1 and S_N2 reactions. The relationships are somewhat dependent on the nature of the solvents in which reactions are carried out.

Some leaving groups are so reactive that substrates containing them are difficult or impossible to prepare. Aliphatic diazonium ions (RN_2^+) have never been isolated, and only one, extraordinary, tertiary sulfonate has ever been prepared (page 246). Benzyl sulfonates tend to be hard to manipulate, and secondary and tertiary iodides deteriorate during storage.

Electrophilic Catalysis. Sluggish leaving groups are often labilized by complexing with electrophilic reagents. Two examples already discussed are catalysis of the reactions of alcohols and ethers by proton donors and catalysis of the reactions of halides by silver ion. Other Lewis acids, such as aluminum chloride and boron trifluoride, are also used in cleavage of ethers and alcohols.

The cleavage of ethers shows the practical application of reactivity

relationships. Acidic conditions are necessary to effect nucleophilic
cleavage of **C—O** bonds. The reagent of choice for cleavage of ethers as
a class is hydrogen iodide, because iodide ion is the most reactive
nucleophile that can be incorporated in strongly acidic solutions. However, sulfuric acid cleaves tertiary ethers very rapidly, since the latter react
by the S_N1 mechanism.

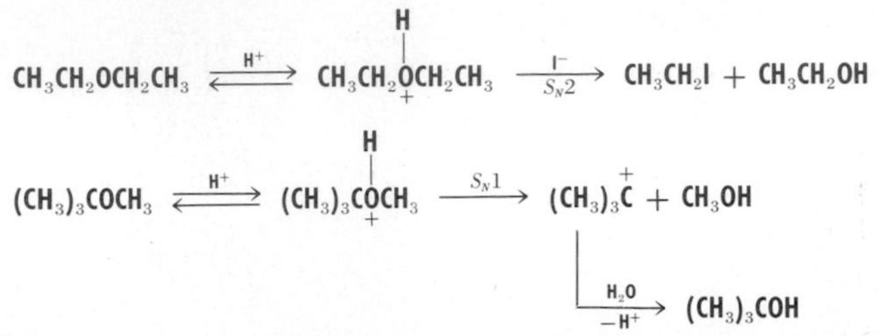

(handwritten in margin: Lösung)

$$CH_3CH_2OCH_2CH_3 \xrightarrow{\ H^+\ } \overset{\overset{H}{|}}{CH_3CH_2\overset{+}{O}CH_2CH_3} \xrightarrow[S_N2]{\ I^-\ } CH_3CH_2I + CH_3CH_2OH$$

$$(CH_3)_3COCH_3 \xrightarrow{\ H^+\ } \overset{\overset{H}{|}}{(CH_3)_3\overset{+}{C}OCH_3} \xrightarrow{\ S_N1\ } (CH_3)_3\overset{+}{C} + CH_3OH$$

$$\xrightarrow[-H^+]{H_2O} (CH_3)_3COH$$

Solvent Effects. The nature of the medium in which a heterolytic
reaction is carried out often has a profound influence on the reaction
rate. The largest medium effects can be anticipated by considering
whether ions are being formed or destroyed, or neither, in the slow step
of the reaction. Good *ionizing solvents* are those in which ions are
stabilized by solvation. Water and formic acid are excellent ionizing
solvents. Other hydroxylic solvents, such as methanol, ethanol, and
acetic acid, are intermediate in their ability to stabilize ions. Polar
solvents such as nitromethane and acetonitrile are also intermediate in
character. Acetone and ether, which will dissolve some ionic materials
(as ion pairs), are not very good ionizing media. Hydrocarbons are
essentially nonionizing solvents.

Reactions of neutral substrates, which go by the S_N1 mechanism, are
accelerated enormously by increasing the ionizing power of the solvent.
On the other hand, an S_N2 reaction between a negative ion and a neutral
substrate is relatively little influenced by medium effects. However, as is
indicated in Fig. 11.14, a reaction between a neutral substrate and a
neutral nucleophile produces ions and is therefore accelerated by
increasing the ionizing power of the medium.

Variation of Mechanism. A number of useful generalizations aid in
predicting the mechanism that may be expected to apply to a given

Mechanism	Reaction	Effect of increasing solvent ionizing power
S_N1	R—Cl $\longrightarrow$ $\overset{+}{R}$ + $\overset{-}{Cl}$	Large acceleration
S_N2	$\overset{-}{HO}$ + R—Cl $\longrightarrow$ ROH + $\overset{-}{Cl}$	Small effects
S_N2	R_3N + R'—Cl $\longrightarrow$ $R_3\overset{+}{N}R'$ + $\overset{-}{Cl}$	Large acceleration

FIG. 11.14   Medium effects on the rates of nucleophilic substitution reactions.

reaction. Although frequent exceptions to the generalizations can be found, mechanistic correlations provide a means of gathering large numbers of individual observations.

The reactions of negative nucleophiles with primary substrates usually involve S_N2 mechanisms. Solvolytic reactions and most reactions of tertiary substrates usually go by the S_N1 mechanism. Electrophilic catalysis is likely to channel reactions into the S_N1 group.

Competitive Reactions. The chief competition in nucleophilic substitution comes from elimination reactions in which the nucleophile attacks a β-hydrogen rather than carbon.

lieber, eher

Elimination:

$$N\colonsep + \underset{\underset{L}{|}}{-\overset{H}{\underset{|}{C}}}-\overset{|}{\underset{|}{C}}- \longrightarrow N\colonsep H + C{=}C + \colonsep L$$

Substitution:

$$N\colonsep + -\overset{H}{\underset{\underset{L}{|}}{C}}-\overset{|}{\underset{|}{C}}- \longrightarrow -\overset{H}{\underset{|}{C}}-\overset{N}{\underset{|}{C}}- + \colonsep L$$

Strong bases, such as HO^-, RO^-, and H_2N^-, are very reactive in hydrogen abstraction and tend to cause elimination. Highly polarizable nucleophiles, such as I^-, RS^-, and $S_2O_3^=$, tend to give nearly exclusive attack on carbon.

benkuvmef l

Elimination also competes with substitution in S_N1 reactions, since the intermediate carbonium ion may lose a proton to a basic solvent molecule.

$$\underset{\underset{CH_3}{|}}{\underset{C}{CH_3\!\diagdown\;+\;\diagup CH_3}} \quad\left[\begin{array}{l} \xrightarrow[\text{Substitution}]{H_2O} (CH_3)_3\overset{+}{C}OH_2 \xrightarrow{H_2O} (CH_3)_3COH + H_3\overset{|}{O} \\[2ex] \xrightarrow[\text{Elimination}]{H_2O} (CH_3)_2C{=}CH_2 + H_3\overset{+}{O} \end{array}\right.$$

Highly branched substrates give a good deal of elimination under S_N1 reaction conditions. The amount of elimination is decreased by lowering of the reaction temperature in both S_N1 and S_N2 reactions.

Problems

1. State concisely the kinetic and stereochemical differences between S_N1 and S_N2 reactions. Why is benzyl chloride more reactive than ethyl chloride in both reactions?

2. Trace the following interconversions with three-dimensional formulas. Show appropriate reagents, catalysts, and solvents.

a. R-2-Butanol $\longrightarrow$ tosylate ester $\xrightarrow[\text{acetone}]{Br^-}$ bromide $\longrightarrow$ alcohol + olefin
(See page 145.)

b. s-1-Phenyl-1-ethanol $\xrightarrow[\text{ether}]{\text{SOCl}_2}$ alkyl chloride $\longrightarrow$ optically active acetate $\longrightarrow$

optically active alcohol $\longrightarrow$ tosylate ester $\longrightarrow$ s-1-phenyl-1-ethyl iodide

3. Arrange the following groups of compounds in order of decreasing reactivity in the reactions indicated.

a. The acetolysis reaction:

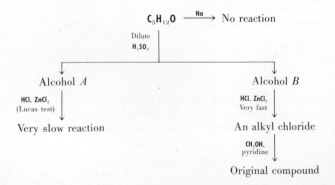

$p\text{-NO}_2\text{C}_6\text{H}_4\text{CH}_2\text{Cl}$ $p\text{-ClC}_6\text{H}_4\text{CH}_2\text{Cl}$ $\text{C}_6\text{H}_5\text{CH}_2\text{Cl}$

b. The S_N2 substitution with potassium iodide in dry acetone:

CH_3OTs $\text{CH}_2{=}\text{CHCH}_2\text{OTs}$ $(\text{CH}_3)_2\text{CHOTs}$

(Only tertiary tosylate known)

c. The methanolysis reaction, with ester anion as the leaving group:

$\text{C}_6\text{H}_5\overset{\overset{\text{CH}_3}{|}}{\underset{\underset{\text{CH}_3}{|}}{\text{C}}}\overset{\overset{\text{O}}{||}}{\text{O}}\text{CC}_6\text{H}_4\text{X-}p$ $\text{X} = \text{H, I, F, NO}_2, \text{OCH}_3, \text{CH}_3$

4. Give examples of the following reactions:

a. Two examples of reactions that would be expected to give retention of configuration.

b. Three examples of reactions that should largely give inversion of configuration.

c. Three examples of reactions that should largely give racemization.

d. Three examples of reactions that are inhibited by steric hindrance.

e. Three examples of reactions that are slow because of adverse electronic effects.

5. Solve the following problem with structural formulas:

$$\text{C}_5\text{H}_{12}\text{O} \xrightarrow{\text{Na}} \text{No reaction}$$

Dilute
H_2SO_4

Alcohol *A*   Alcohol *B*

HCl, ZnCl$_2$
(Lucas test)

HCl, ZnCl$_2$
Very fast

Very slow reaction   An alkyl chloride

CH$_3$OH,
pyridine

Original compound

6. Explain the following observations:

a. Benzyl magnesium bromide can be made in good yield in dilute solutions but not in concentrated solutions.

b. Under conditions that lead to the hydrolysis of *tert*-butyl chloride, $(CH_3)_2CClCO_2C_2H_5$ is stable.

c.

$$CH_3 \overbrace{}^{CH_3}_{CH_3} CH_2Cl$$ reacts slowly with potassium iodide in acetone solution,

whereas benzyl chloride reacts rapidly under the same conditions.

d. The yields of substitution product given in the reactions of *sec*-butyl chloride with $(CH_3)_2N^-$, $(CH_3)_3CO^-$, CH_3O^-, and I^- increase in the order listed.

12

Electrophilic Substitution at Saturated Carbon

Electrophilic, or electron-seeking, reagents can attack suitably substituted carbon atoms in electrophilic substitution reactions. As is shown in Fig. 12.1, the new bond in the product comes from a bond in the substrate, and an electron-deficient leaving group is released.

Metal cations are the best leaving groups in electrophilic substitution reactions, because of the low affinity of metals for electrons. Under special circumstances, a hydrogen ion may be the leaving group. In this case, strong bases are often needed to aid in removal of the proton. Even halogens can be made to leave without their bonding electrons in the presence of suitable catalysts. The role of basic catalysts in electrophilic substitution reactions is analogous to the part played by electrophilic catalysts in nucleophilic substitutions. The catalytic effects are compared in Fig. 12.2.

Like their nucleophilic analogues, electrophilic substitutions may be either synchronous one-step reactions or complex processes involving two or more steps. Relatively little is known about the mechanisms of many electrophilic substitutions, but a few have been studied in great detail. For example, it is known that base-catalyzed displacement of hydrogen often involves the intermediate formation of anions. The analogy to the S_N1 mechanism is shown in Fig. 12.3.

As a matter of convenience, the reactions of both aryl- and alkyl-metallic compounds are discussed in this chapter, although the reactions

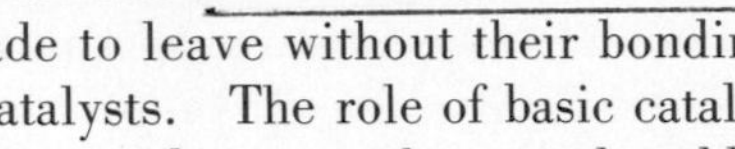

$$E + {-}\!\!\overset{|}{\underset{|}{C}}\!\!{-}L \longrightarrow E{-}\!\!\overset{|}{\underset{|}{C}}\!\!{-} + L$$

FIG. 12.1 *Electrophilic substitution at a saturated carbon atom.*

es wandern immer die Elektronen!

Nucleophilic substitution with acid catalysis:

$$\bar{N} + R\!-\!OH + \overset{+}{H} \longrightarrow N\!-\!R + H_2O$$

Electrophilic substitution with basic catalysis:

$$\overset{+}{E} + R\!-\!H + \bar{OH} \longrightarrow E\!-\!R + H_2O$$

FIG. 12.2 *Comparison of catalytic effects in nucleophilic and electrophilic substitution reactions.*

of aryl-metallics are actually electrophilic substitutions at unsaturated carbon atoms.

Formation of Carbon-Metal Bonds

Formation of magnesium and alkali metal compounds from alkyl halides and the elemental metals was discussed in Chap. 10. The same compounds, and many others, can also be produced by electrophilic substitution reactions.

Metal Exchanges. Exchange of one metal for another by an alkyl or aryl group is often a very rapid reaction and has some value as a preparative method. The usual reactants are an organometallic compound and a metal salt.

$$\overset{-\,+}{XM} + R\!-\!M' \longrightarrow M\!-\!R + \overset{+\,-}{M'X}$$

Exchange reactions of this type contribute to the complexity of ether solutions of Grignard reagents. The reagents are usually represented by the formula R**Mg**X, but significant amounts of dialkyl magnesium are also present.

$$2CH_3CH_2MgBr \underset{\text{}}{\overset{\text{ether}}{\rightleftharpoons}} (CH_3CH_2)_2Mg \ | \ MgBr_2$$

Ethylmagnesium   Diethyl-
bromide   magnesium

$$S_N1: \quad R\!-\!L \longrightarrow \overset{+}{R} + :\bar{L}$$

$$\qquad\qquad\qquad\qquad \bar{N}: \downarrow$$

$$\qquad\qquad\qquad\qquad R\!-\!N$$

Anion formation $R\!-\!H + :\bar{B} \longrightarrow \bar{R} + H\!-\!B$
in S_E reaction

$$\qquad\qquad\qquad\qquad\qquad \overset{+}{E} \downarrow$$

$$\qquad\qquad\qquad\qquad\qquad R\!-\!E$$

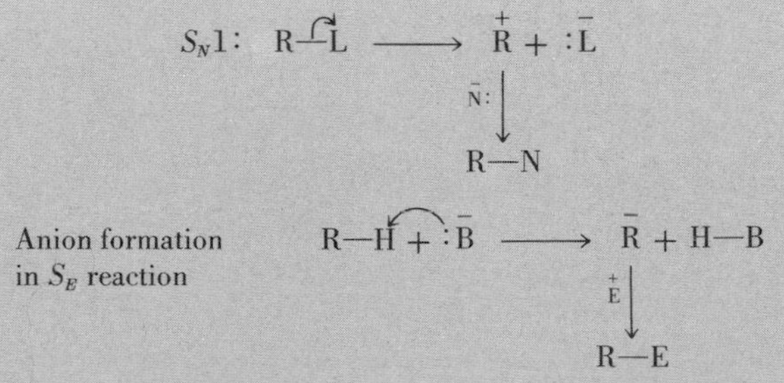

FIG. 12.3 *Comparison of stepwise nucleophilic and electrophilic substitution.*

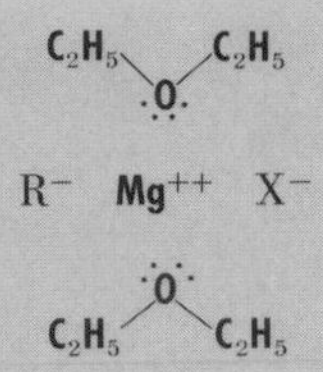

$$C_2H_5 \quad\quad C_2H_5$$
$$\underset{\cdot\,O\,\cdot}{\diagdown\;\diagup}$$

$$R^- \quad Mg^{++} \quad X^-$$

$$\underset{C_2H_5 \quad\quad C_2H_5}{\cdot\,\overset{\cdot\cdot}{O}\,\cdot}$$

FIG. 12.4   Ether-solvated Grignard reagent.

In the above equation, the formulas are written without charge separation.   Actually the magnesium-halide bonds and, to a lesser extent, the magnesium-carbon bonds are very polar, and the compounds might be described as tightly bound ion aggregates.   All magnesium species are also strongly solvated by ether, a fact closely associated with the role of ethers as unique solvents for the reagents, as is shown in Fig. 12.4.

In most metal-exchange reactions, the new carbon-metal bond is less polar than the carbon-metal bond in the substrate.   In other words, the strongest carbon-metal bonds involve metals with a relatively high affinity for electrons. $carbide$

$$\overset{++\;\overset{=}{}}{MgCl_2} + C_6H_5\!-\!Li \xrightarrow{\text{Ether}} C_6H_5MgCl + \overset{+\;-}{LiCl}$$

Phenyl-
lithium

$$\overset{++\;\overset{=}{}}{CdCl_2} + 2CH_3CH_2MgCl \xrightarrow{\text{Ether}} (CH_3CH_2)_2Cd + 2MgCl_2$$

$$HgCl_2 + C_6H_5\overset{\overset{\displaystyle CH_3}{|}}{\underset{\underset{\displaystyle CH_3}{|}}{C}}CH_2MgCl \xrightarrow{\text{Ether}} C_6H_5\overset{\overset{\displaystyle CH_3}{|}}{\underset{\underset{\displaystyle CH_3}{|}}{C}}CH_2HgCl + MgCl_2$$

2-Methyl-2-phenyl-
propylmagnesium chloride
(Neophylmagnesium chloride)

$$C_6H_5\overset{\overset{\displaystyle CH_3}{|}}{\underset{\underset{\displaystyle CH_3}{|}}{C}}CH_2HgCl + C_6H_5\overset{\overset{\displaystyle CH_3}{|}}{\underset{\underset{\displaystyle CH_3}{|}}{C}}CH_2MgCl \xrightarrow{\text{Ether}} C_6H_5\overset{\overset{\displaystyle CH_3}{|}}{\underset{\underset{\displaystyle CH_3}{|}}{C}}CH_2\!-\!Hg\!-\!CH_2\overset{\overset{\displaystyle CH_3}{|}}{\underset{\underset{\displaystyle CH_3}{|}}{C}}C_6H_5 + MgCl_2$$

Dineophylmercury

Metalation Reactions.   The exchange of a hydrogen atom for a metal offers a useful synthetic route to certain organometallics.   Such reactions afford the best measure of the relative acidities of hydrocarbons. Grignard reagents are not sufficiently reactive to function well in most *metalation* reactions.

$$C_6H_6 + C_2H_5Na \xrightarrow{\text{Pentane}} C_6H_5Na + C_2H_6$$

Ethylsodium

$C_6H_5Na + C_6H_5CH_3 \xrightarrow{\text{Pentane}} C_6H_5CH_2Na + C_6H_6$

Phenyl-   Benzylsodium   sodium

$C_6H_5CH_2Na + (C_6H_5)_2CH_2 \longrightarrow (C_6H_5)_2CHNa + C_6H_5CH_3$

Benzylsodium

$(C_6H_5)_2CHNa + (C_6H_5)_3CH \longrightarrow (C_6H_5)_3CNa + (C_6H_5)_2CH_2$

Diphenylmethyl-   Triphenylmethylsodium   sodium

The above reactions show the sequence of hydrocarbon acidities: $Ar_3CH > Ar_2CH_2 > ArCH_3 > ArH > RH$. The acidity of toluene and other arylalkanes is due to resonance stabilization of the highly ionic organometallic compounds (see Fig. 12.5).

Aromatic hydrocarbons are more acidic than alkanes because sp^2 carbon atoms have a higher affinity for electrons than do sp^3 carbon atoms. In general, increasing the s character of hybrid orbitals increases the stability of an unshared electron pair in the orbital. Terminal acetylenes, in which the hydrogen is bound by an sp orbital, are so acidic that the compounds are easily metalated by Grignard reagents (cf. page 220).

$CH_3C{\equiv}CH + CH_3MgBr \longrightarrow CH_3C{\equiv}CMgBr + CH_4$

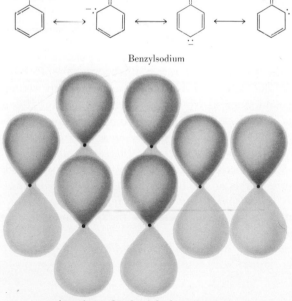

Benzylsodium

Atomic p orbitals of the benzyl system

FIG. 12.5   *Resonance stabilization of benzylsodium.*

Comparisons of the reactivity of metal alkyls indicate the following order of decreasing stability: primary > secondary > tertiary.

Extensive use has been made of *n*-butyllithium as a reagent for preparation of organometallics by metalation. The reaction has been particularly useful for introduction of substituents in the nuclei of aromatic heterocycles, aryl ethers, and arylamines.

$$n\text{-}C_4H_9Br + 2Li \xrightarrow[-10°]{Ether} n\text{-}C_4H_9Li + LiBr$$
$$85\%$$

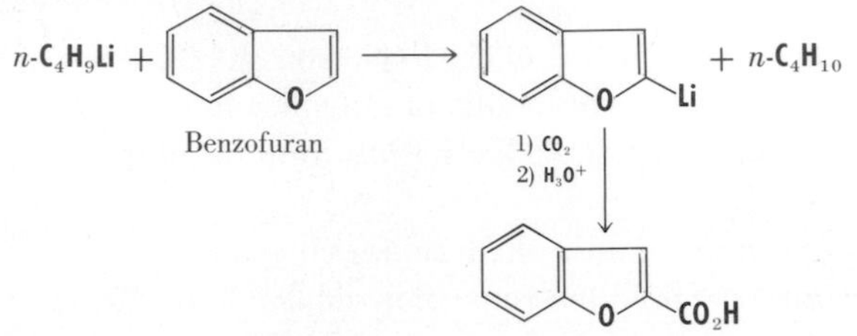

Benzofuran

1) CO$_2$
2) H$_3$O$^+$

Benzofuran-2-carboxylic acid
47%

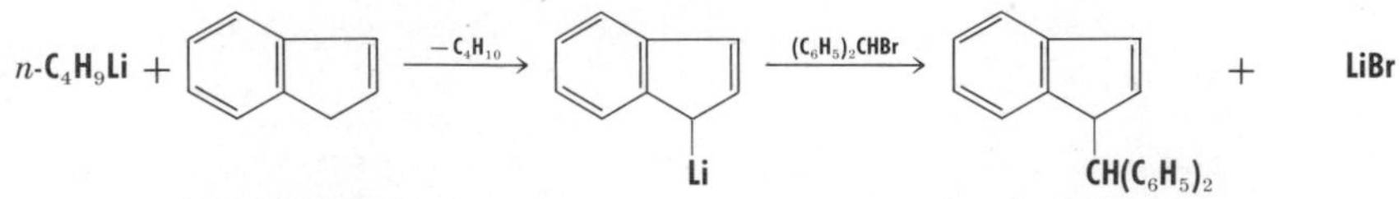

Indene   1-Benzhydrylindene
50%

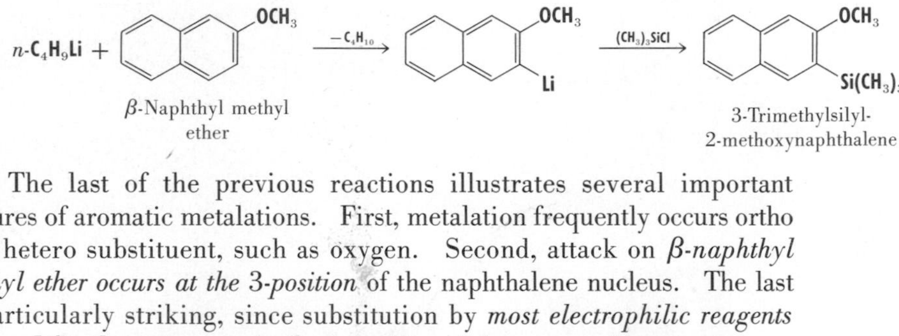

β-Naphthyl methyl
ether   3-Trimethylsilyl-
2-methoxynaphthalene

The last of the previous reactions illustrates several important features of aromatic metalations. First, metalation frequently occurs ortho to a hetero substituent, such as oxygen. Second, attack on *β-naphthyl methyl ether occurs at the 3-position* of the naphthalene nucleus. The last is particularly striking, since substitution by *most electrophilic reagents* (Chap. 16) *always occurs in the 1-position* of the same substrate.

The Halogen-Metal Interconversion. Some aryl halides react with lithium and sodium alkyls to exchange halogen for the metal. The reaction is actually a *nucleophilic attack on halogen* by the anionic alkyl group. The success of the reaction shows the resistance of aromatic carbon atoms to nucleophilic attack.

$$X-X + :\bar{N} \longrightarrow \bar{X}: + X:N$$

FIG. 12.6   *Heterolytic cleavage of molecular halogens.*

α-Bromonaphthalene + $CH_3CH_2CH_2Li$ ⟶ α-Naphthyllithium + $CH_3CH_2CH_2Br$

1) CO_2
2) H_3O^+

α-Naphthoic acid
90%

Organometallics by Metal Reduction. Active metals can be converted to organometallics by reaction with alkyl halides and ethers. Exchange reactions between metals and organometallics derived from less active metals can also be carried out. The reactions are oxidation-reduction reactions rather than simple electrophilic substitutions. They are included in this chapter to round out the discussion of the preparation of organometallic compounds.

$$C_6H_5COCH_3 \ + \ Na\!-\!K \xrightarrow{\text{Ether, }0°} C_6H_5C^-K^+ + CH_3ONa$$
(CH₃ groups)
Sodium-
potassium
alloy (liquid)

$$2Li + CH_3MgBr \xrightarrow{\text{Ether}} CH_3Li + LiBr + Mg$$

$$2Na + CH_3CH_2CH_2CH_2MgBr \xrightarrow{\text{Hexane}} CH_3CH_2CH_2\overset{-}{C}H_2\overset{+}{Na} + NaBr + Mg$$

$$2Na + (C_6H_5)_2Hg \longrightarrow 2C_6H_5Na + Hg$$
Diphenylmercury

Formation of Carbon-Halogen Bonds

The halogens are electrophilic reagents, and behave as weak Lewis acids. As is shown in Fig. 12.6, halogen-halogen bonds are easily cleaved by nucleophilic reagents.

Virtually all organometallics are cleaved smoothly by halogens. However, the reaction has little preparative value, because halides are the commonest starting materials for preparation of organometallics. The reaction has been used to characterize products of metalation and halogen-metal interconversion reactions.

$$+ \ n\text{-}C_4H_9Li \xrightarrow{-C_4H_{10}} + \ Br\!-\!Br \longrightarrow + \ LiBr$$

Occasionally one halogen can be exchanged for another only by way of organometallic intermediates. An example is the conversion of neopentyl chloride to neopentyl iodide. Direct halide exchange is not feasible because of the low reactivity of neopentyl compounds in the S_N2 reaction and the tendency of the system to rearrange during S_N1 reactions (page 241).

$$(CH_3)_3CCH_2Cl + Mg \xrightarrow{\text{Ether}} (CH_3)_3CCH_2MgCl \xrightarrow[-MgCl_2]{HgCl_2} (CH_3)_3CCH_2HgCl \xrightarrow{I_2} (CH_3)_3CCH_2I + HgICl$$

Neopentyl chloride   Neopentyl iodide
                                                                                    50% over-all

α-Halogenation. The α-positions of carbonyl and nitro compounds are susceptible to halogenation in the presence of catalysts. Enols or enolate ions are intermediate in the process. The role of the catalysts is illustrated by the examples in Fig. 12.7.

Base-catalyzed halogenation of methylene and methyl ketones cannot be stopped at the monohaloketone stage. After complete halogenation occurs, the polyhaloketones are cleaved under the basic reaction conditions (page 262).

In the *Hell-Volhard-Zelinsky reaction*, carboxylic acids undergo α-halogenation in the presence of a small amount of phosphorus trichloride. The acid is converted to an acid chloride, which enolizes more readily than the free acid. Since acids and acid chlorides are readily equilibrated under the reaction conditions, only catalytic amounts of phosphorus trichloride are needed.

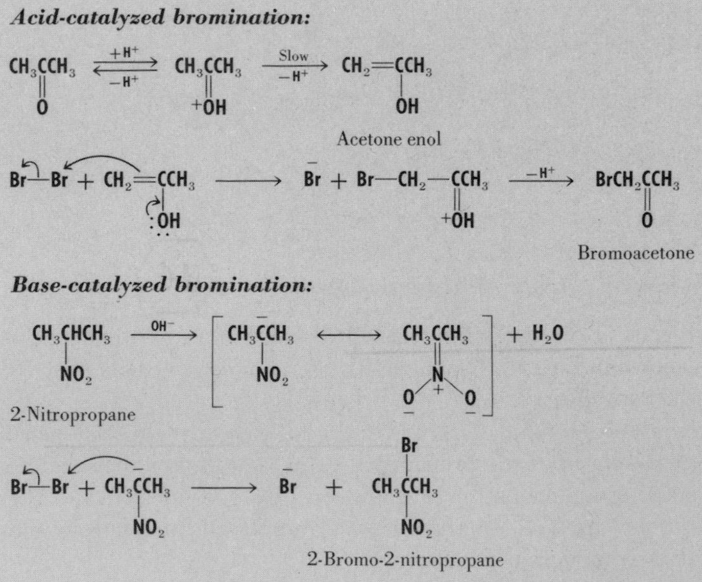

FIG. 12.7 *Catalysis of α-halogenation.*

Hell-Volhard-Zelinsky reaction:

$$CH_3CH_2CH_2CH_2CO_2H + PCl_3 \longrightarrow CH_3CH_2CH_2CH_2COCl$$

$$CH_3CH_2CH_2CH_2COCl \rightleftharpoons CH_3CH_2CH_2CH=CCl \xrightarrow{Br_2} CH_3CH_2CH_2CHBrCOCl$$
$$\underset{OH}{|}$$

$$CH_3CH_2CH_2CHBrCOCl + CH_3CH_2CH_2CH_2CO_2H \rightleftharpoons CH_3CH_2CH_2CHBrCO_2H + CH_3CH_2CH_2CH_2COCl$$

α-Bromovaleric acid

85% yield

Acetic acid is chlorinated in stages by chlorine with a trace of iodine as a catalyst. The iodine forms ICl_3, which is probably the active halogenating agent.

$$I_2 + 3Cl_2 \rightleftharpoons 2ICl_3$$

$$CH_3CO_2H \longrightarrow CH_2=C\underset{OH}{\overset{OH}{<}} \xrightarrow{ICl_3} ClCH_2CO_2H \xrightarrow[Cl_2,\ I_2]{Higher\ temperature}$$

$$Cl_2CHCO_2H \xrightarrow[Cl_2,\ I_2]{Still\ higher\ temperature} Cl_3CCO_2H$$

The method of choice for the synthesis of dichloroacetic acid is the reaction of sodium cyanide with chloral hydrate (hydrate of trichloro-acetaldehyde) in the presence of sodium carbonate. The reaction is obviously complex, and the following mechanism is only speculative.

$$\underset{\text{Chloral hydrate}}{Cl_3CCH(OH)_2} \rightleftharpoons Cl_2\overset{}{C}-CH \xrightarrow{-Cl^-} Cl_2C-CH + \overline{C}N \longrightarrow Cl_2\overset{}{C}-CH \xrightarrow{HCOH}$$

$$\left[Cl_2\overline{C}-C\equiv N \longleftrightarrow Cl_2C=C=\overline{N} \right] \xrightarrow[-HO]{H_2O} Cl_2CHC\equiv N \xrightarrow{H_2O,\ nitrile\ hydrolysis} Cl_2CHCO_2H + NH_3$$

Dichloro-acetic acid

α-Haloacids are converted, by nucleophilic substitution reactions, to useful functional derivatives of carboxylic acids. The most important examples are α-amino- and α-hydroxyacids, which are of biochemical significance.

$$CH_3CH_2CO_2H \xrightarrow{Br_2,\ PCl_3} \underset{Br}{CH_3CHCO_2H}$$

α-Bromo-propionic acid

$\xrightarrow{NH_3}$ $\underset{NH_2}{CH_3CHCO_2H}$

α-Aminopropionic acid
(Alanine)

$\xrightarrow{H_2O,\ HO^-}$ $\underset{OH}{CH_3CHCO_2H}$

α-Hydroxypropionic acid
(Lactic acid)

The Hunsdiecker Reaction. In the Hunsdiecker reaction, the silver salt of a carboxylic acid is treated with bromine. The carboxyl group is lost as carbon dioxide and alkyl or aryl bromides are produced. The reaction is quite general but gives variable yields. It is not certain whether the reaction involves a homolytic or a heterolytic cleavage of the carbon-carbon bond.

$$(CH_3)_3CCH_2CO_2Ag + Br_2 \xrightleftharpoons{CCl_4} (CH_3)_3CCH_2-C-O + Br-Br-Ag \longrightarrow$$

Silver 3,3-dimethyl-
butyrate

$$(CH_3)_3CCH_2Br + CO_2 + AgBr$$
53%

Formation of Carbon-Oxygen and Carbon-Sulfur Bonds

Molecular oxygen and sulfur both react with organometallic compounds. The first product in the reaction with oxygen is the metal salt of a hydroperoxide. Oxidation of Grignard reagents is the only reaction of the class that has been studied carefully. If an excess of the Grignard reagent is used, the peroxide bond is cleaved to give alkoxides. Oxygen molecules contain two unpaired electrons, but these become paired during the first reaction.

$$:O-O: + (CH_3)_3C-MgCl \xrightarrow{Ether} (CH_3)_3C-O-O \; Mg \; Cl \xrightarrow{HCl} (CH_3)_3COOH + MgCl_2$$

tert-Butyl
hydroperoxide
90%

$$O_2 + C_6H_5CH_2CH_2MgCl \xrightarrow{Ether} C_6H_5CH_2CH_2OOMgCl$$

$$\begin{array}{c} C_6H_5CH_2CH_2-O-O-MgCl \\ + \\ C_6H_5CH_2CH_2-MgCl \end{array} \longrightarrow 2C_6H_5CH_2CH_2OMgCl \xrightarrow{HCl} C_6H_5CH_2CH_2OH + MgCl_2$$

β-Phenylethanol
60% over-all

$$S + C_6H_5MgBr \longrightarrow C_6H_5SMgBr \xrightarrow{Acid} C_6H_5SH$$

Thiophenol
80%

Sulfur dioxide is a good electrophile and reacts with Grignard reagents to give high yields of magnesium sulfinates.

$$O=S=O + CH_3(CH_2)_3-MgBr \longrightarrow CH_3(CH_2)_3-S-OMgBr \xrightarrow{H_2O^+} CH_3(CH_2)_3SOH$$

n-Butanesulfinic
acid
69%

Formation of Carbon Bonds to Other Hetero Atoms

Halogens and alkoxyl groups are readily displaced from many nonmetallic halides to form organic derivatives of nitrogen, phosphorus, boron, silicon, etc. The reactions are electrophilic substitutions on carbon, but are perhaps most easily remembered as nucleophilic substitutions by carbon on the hetero atom.

$$C_6H_5\overset{+}{Li} + NH_2\overset{\frown}{\;}OCH_3 \longrightarrow C_6H_5NH_2 + LiOCH_3$$

Methoxyl-
amine

$$3CH_3MgCl + PCl_3 \longrightarrow (CH_3)_3P + 3MgCl_2$$

Trimethyl-
phosphine

$$3C_6H_5MgBr + BCl_3 \longrightarrow (C_6H_5)_3B + 3MgBrCl$$

Triphenyl-
boron

The reaction of silicon tetrachloride with organometallics can be controlled so as to obtain each of the intermediate chlorosilanes as principal products. The fourth substitution is slow even under forcing conditions.

$$C_6H_5MgBr + SiCl_4 \xrightarrow{\text{Ether}} C_6H_5SiCl_3 + MgBrCl$$

(One
equivalent)

Phenyltri-
chlorosilane
65%

$$2C_6H_5MgBr + SiCl_4 \xrightarrow{\text{Ether}} (C_6H_5)_2SiCl_2 + 2MgBrCl$$

Diphenyldi-
chlorosilane
50%

$$3C_6H_5MgBr + SiCl_4 \xrightarrow{\text{Ether}} (C_6H_5)_3SiCl + 3MgBrCl$$

Triphenyl-
chlorosilane
90%

$$4C_6H_5Li + SiCl_4 \xrightarrow{\text{Ether}} (C_6H_5)_4Si + 4LiCl$$

Tetraphenyl-
silane
>95%

Formation of Carbon-Hydrogen Bonds

Formation of carbon-hydrogen bonds by electrophilic substitution covers a wide variety of substrates and reaction conditions. The reactions range from easy cleavage of organometallics by weak acids to cleavage of carbon-carbon bonds by pyrolysis of metallic alkoxides at high temperatures.

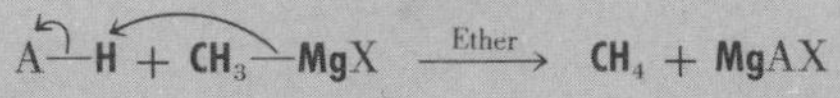

$$A \overset{\frown}{-} H + CH_3 \overset{\frown}{-} MgX \xrightarrow{\text{Ether}} CH_4 + MgAX$$

$$AH = HO—H, RO—H, ArO—H, RCO_2—H, RNH—H, RCONH—H, RC \equiv C—H, RS—H$$

FIG. 12.8   The active hydrogen reaction.

Active-hydrogen Reaction.   Active organometallic compounds, such as Grignard and lithium reagents, react with even very weakly acidic substances.   It is for this reason that solutions of organometallic reagents must be protected from atmospheric moisture during their preparation and use.   Methylmagnesium iodide, which evolves methane gas on acidification, is used in both qualitative characterization and quantitative determination of *active hydrogens* (acidic hydrogen).   Figure 12.8 indicates the scope of the active-hydrogen reaction.

Occasionally the reaction of organometallics with deuterium oxide is used as a way to introduce deuterium into organic molecules.

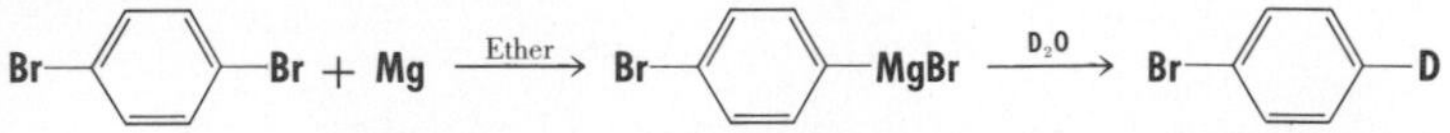

(One	*p*-Bromophenyl-	Bromobenzene-4-*d*
equivalent)	magnesium	
	bromide	

Mercury compounds are stable in neutral, alcoholic, and aqueous solutions but are cleaved by strong acids.

$$\overset{+}{H}\overset{-}{Cl} + CH_3CH_2\underset{\underset{CH_3}{|}}{C}HHgCl \longrightarrow \textit{n-}C_4H_{10} + HgCl_2$$

Dehalogenation.   Replacement of a halogen by hydrogen is a reduction and must be accompanied by production of elemental halogen or some other oxidized product.   Most chlorides and bromides are rather resistant to substitution by protons.   A few compounds contain so-called "positive" halogen and are reduced under mild conditions.   Activation is supplied by one or more electron-withdrawing groups attached to the seat of substitution.   Special mechanisms, such as enol formation, are often involved.   Dehalogenation of an α-haloketone is actually the reverse of the α-halogenation of ketones (page 254).

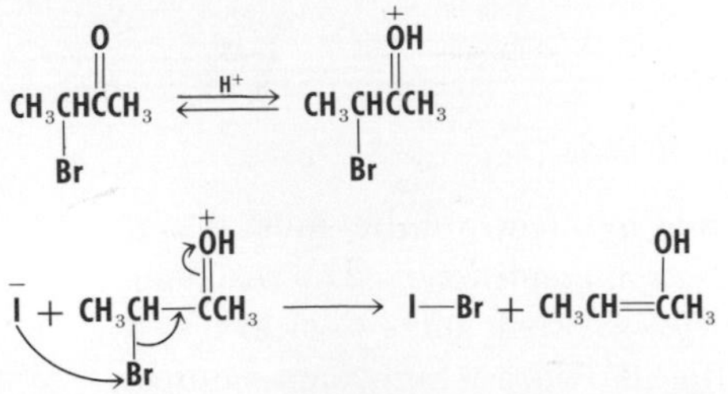

$$\underset{\overset{|}{OH}}{CH_2CH}\!\!=\!\!CCH_3 \;\;\rightleftharpoons\;\; CH_3CH_2\overset{\overset{O}{\parallel}}{C}CH_3$$

Net reaction: $HI + CH_3CHBrCOCH_3 \longrightarrow CH_3CH_2COCH_3 + IBr$

Iodides are readily reduced by hydrogen iodide if phosphorus is added to consume the iodine produced in the primary substitution. Other compounds, such as alcohols, are reduced to hydrocarbons under the reaction conditions if they can first be converted to iodides by nucleophilic substitution.

$$(C_6H_5)_2\underset{\overset{|}{OH}}{C}CO_2H + HI \longrightarrow (C_6H_5)_2\underset{\overset{|}{I}}{C}CO_2H + H_2O$$

Benzilic acid

$$(C_6H_5)_2\underset{\overset{|}{I}}{C}CO_2H + H\!-\!I \longrightarrow (C_6H_5)_2CHCO_2H + I_2 \xrightarrow{P} PI_3$$

Diphenylacetic acid

Cleavage of Carbon-Carbon Bonds. Carbon is not ordinarily a good leaving group in substitution reactions. There is, however, a family of electrophilic substitutions that break carbon-carbon bonds. The substrates are usually anions. The electrophile is often a solvent molecule such as water, alcohols, and even amines. Part of the driving force for breaking the carbon-carbon bond is often supplied by formation of a carbon-oxygen double bond.

$$\bar{B} \; H + -\overset{\overset{+}{O \; M}}{\underset{|}{C}}\!-\!\overset{|}{\underset{|}{C}}\!- \longrightarrow \bar{B}\,\overset{+}{M} + H\!-\!\overset{|}{\underset{|}{C}}\!- + \overset{O}{\underset{\diagdown}{\diagup}}\!\!C$$

The cleavage reactions are the reverse of nucleophilic addition reactions of carbonyl compounds, which will be treated in detail in Chap. 13.

Decarboxylation. Carboxylic acids that have electron-withdrawing substituents on the α-carbon atom eliminate carbon dioxide with unusual ease. Resonance-stabilized anions may often be produced as intermediates.

$$O_2NCH_2CO_2H \xrightarrow{OH^-} O_2NCH_2\!-\!\overset{\overset{O}{\diagup}}{C_{\diagdown O}} \xrightarrow[-CO_2]{\text{Gentle heat}} \underset{O^-}{\overset{O}{\diagdown}}\!\!\overset{+}{N}\!-\!CH_2^- \longleftrightarrow \underset{O^-}{\overset{O}{\diagdown}}\!\!\overset{+}{N}\!=\!CH_2$$

Nitroacetic acid

Enolat

$$\Big\downarrow H_2O$$

$$CH_3NO_2$$

Nitromethane

Malonic acids and β-ketoacids decarboxylate by the above path, giving enolate ions as intermediates. They also decompose, in neutral or acidic solutions, by cyclic mechanisms to give enols, which subsequently revert to more stable tautomeric forms.

$$CH_3C \underset{CH_2}{\overset{O \overset{H}{\diagup} O}{\diagdown C}} C=O \xrightarrow{150°} CH_3C=CH_2 + CO_2$$

Acetoacetic
acid

$$CH_3COCH_3$$

Decarboxylation reactions have found wide application in acetoacetic ester and malonic ester synthetic sequences. Advantage is taken of the ease of alkylation of the enolate ions of the esters. The ester function is hydrolyzed (Chap. 14), giving labile carboxylic acids, which are in turn decarboxylated to give substituted acids and ketones.

Malonic ester synthesis:

$$CH_2(CO_2C_2H_5)_2 \xrightarrow{NaOC_2H_5} \overset{+}{Na}\overset{-}{CH}(CO_2C_2H_5)_2 \xrightarrow{CH_3(CH_2)_2Br} CH_3(CH_2)_2CH(CO_2C_2H_5)_2 \xrightarrow{NaOC_2H_5}$$
$$90\%$$

$$\overset{+}{Na}\ CH_3(CH_2)_2\overset{-}{C}(CO_2C_2H_5) \xrightarrow{CH_3I} CH_3(CH_2)_2\overset{\overset{CH_3}{|}}{C}(CO_2C_2H_5)_2 \xrightarrow[\text{(Ester hydrolysis)}]{NaOH, H_2O, 100°} \xrightarrow{\text{Acidify}}$$
$$70\%$$

$$\underset{CH_3}{\overset{CH_3CH_2CH_2}{\diagdown}}\!\!C\!\!\underset{CO_2H}{\overset{CO_2H}{\diagup}} \xrightarrow[-CO_2]{120°} CH_3CH_2CH_2\underset{\overset{|}{CH_3}}{CH}CO_2H$$

$$\sim100\% \qquad\qquad\qquad\qquad 75\%$$
Methylpropylmalonic   α-Methylvaleric
acid   acid

Acetoacetic ester synthesis:

$$CH_3COCH_2CO_2C_2H_5 \xrightarrow{NaOC_2H_5,\ n\text{-}C_4H_9Br} CH_3COCH(CH_2)_3CH_3 \xrightarrow{NaOH, H_2O} \xrightarrow{H_3O^+}$$
$$\underset{CO_2C_2H_5}{|}$$

$$CH_3COCH(CH_2)_3CH_3 \xrightarrow[-CO_2]{100°,\ \text{trace of acid}} CH_3CO(CH_2)_4CH_3$$
$$\underset{CO_2H}{|} \qquad\qquad\qquad\qquad 55\%\ \text{over-all}$$
n-Amyl methyl
ketone

Di- and triarylacetic acids decarboxylate readily in basic solutions.

$$H_2O + (C_6H_5)_3C\overset{-}{CO_2}\overset{+}{Na} \xrightarrow{100°} (C_6H_5)_3CH + NaHCO_3$$
Sodium triphenyl-
acetate

$$H_2O + (C_6H_5)_2CH\overset{-}{CO_2}\overset{+}{Na} \xrightarrow[-CO_2]{150°,\ HOCH_2CH_2OH} (C_6H_5)_2CH_2 + NaHCO_3$$
Sodium diphenyl-
acetate

Cleavage of Ketones. Ketones that do not have any α-hydrogens (and some that do) can ordinarily be cleaved by sufficiently drastic treatment with bases.   Addition of an anion to the carbonyl group converts the function into a leaving group of reasonable reactivity.   Protons are usually supplied by solvent or by reaction products.

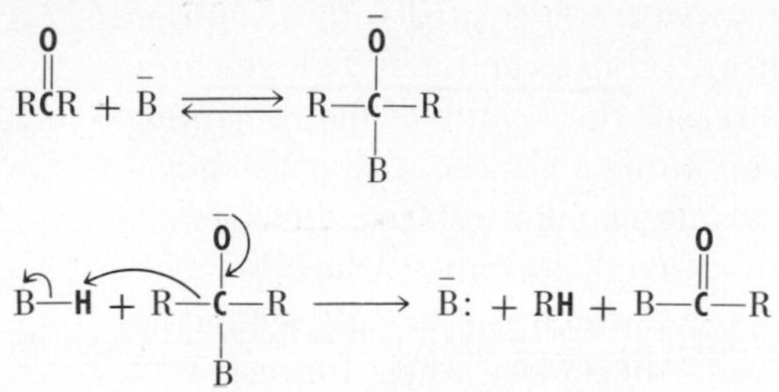

Ketones that are not activated can be split by refluxing with sodamide.

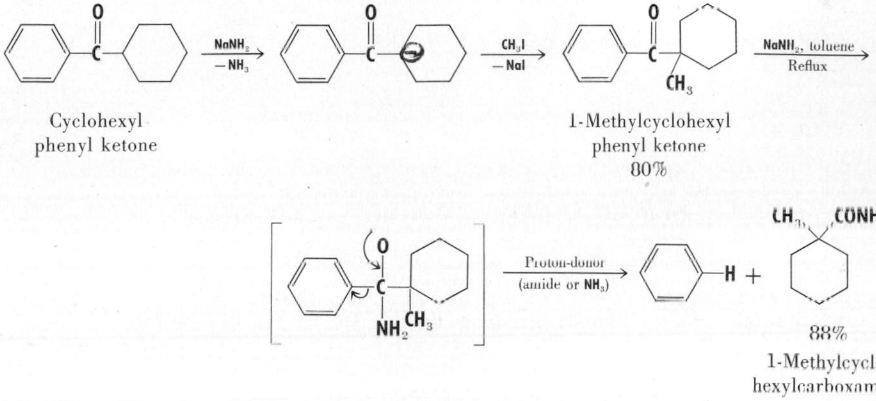

Cyclohexyl
phenyl ketone

1-Methylcyclohexyl
phenyl ketone
80%

88%
1-Methylcyclo-
hexylcarboxamide

β-Diketones and β-ketoesters are easily cleaved by strong bases. Intermediate enolate ions may well be involved in the reactions.

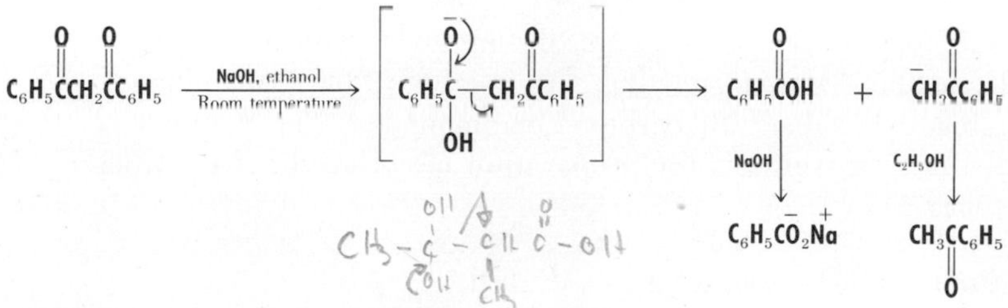

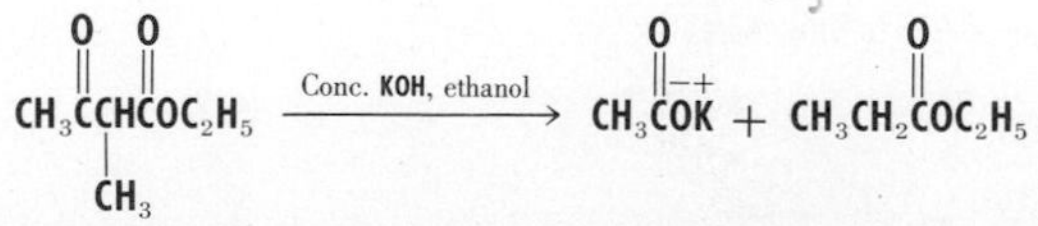

The cleavage reaction of β-ketoesters is favored over the competing reaction of ester hydrolysis (page 77) by the use of concentrated alkali. In synthetic work, the malonic ester synthesis, with decarboxylation, is usually preferred to the acetoacetic ester synthesis. The reason for the preference is the absence of any second cleavage path in the hydrolysis and decarboxylation of malonic esters.

Haloform Cleavage. α,α,α-Trihaloketones are cleaved very readily with dilute base. The reaction is the last step in the *haloform reaction*, which is very commonly used as a characteristic test for methyl ketones. In the test, the material of unknown structure is treated with a solution of halogen in weak base (hypohalite). Base-catalyzed halogenation occurs. Each halogen introduced increases the acidity of the remaining hydrogens attached to the same carbon atom. Consequently, halogenation of methyl groups does not stop at intermediate stages, and trihaloketones are produced. The latter are cleaved, forming carboxylic acids and haloforms. Iodoform is a yellow solid which is sparingly soluble in aqueous solvents; it is easily detected, therefore, when formed in a positive *iodoform reaction*.

$$RCCH_3 + \bar{O}H \longrightarrow RCC\bar{H}_2 + H_2O$$

$$RCC\bar{H}_2 + I_2 \longrightarrow RCCH_2I + \bar{I}$$

$$RCCH_2I \xrightarrow{OH^-} RCCHI \xrightarrow{I_2} RCCHI_2 \xrightarrow{OH^-} RCCI_2 \xrightarrow{I_2} RCCI_3$$

$$RCCI_3 + \bar{O}H \longrightarrow \left[RC\underset{OH}{\overset{O}{\underset{|}{-}}}CI_3 \right] \longrightarrow RCOH + \bar{C}I_3 \longrightarrow R\bar{C}O_2 + HCI_3$$

Iodoform

Net reaction: $RCCH_3 + 3I_2 + 4\bar{O}H \longrightarrow R\bar{C}O_2 + HCI_3 + 3\bar{I} + 3H_2O$

The haloform reaction is given by methyl ketones and other compounds, notably secondary methyl carbinols (CH_3CHOHR) and ethanol, which are readily oxidized to carbonyl compounds. The reaction is occasionally used in synthesis for preparation of carboxylic acids from methyl ketones.

$$(CH_3)_3CCOCH_3 \xrightarrow[\text{2) } H_2O^+]{\text{1) NaOCl}} (CH_3)_3CCO_2H \quad + \quad HCCl_3$$

Pinacalone   Trimethylacetic   Chloroform
                              acid
                          (Pivalic acid)

Cleavage of Alkoxides. Metal alkoxides undergo cleavage when heated to high temperatures. The electrophilic reagents are either proton-donor solvents or decomposition products, such as ketones. The general reaction with a solvent as a proton source is shown in Fig. 12.9.

Ease of cleavage depends a great deal on the nature of the substituents attached to the carbon atom undergoing substitution. Groups such as $\rangle C{=}O$, $-NO_2$, and $-CN$ that are good electron-acceptors render the cleavage very easy, and intermediate anions may often be involved in the reaction.

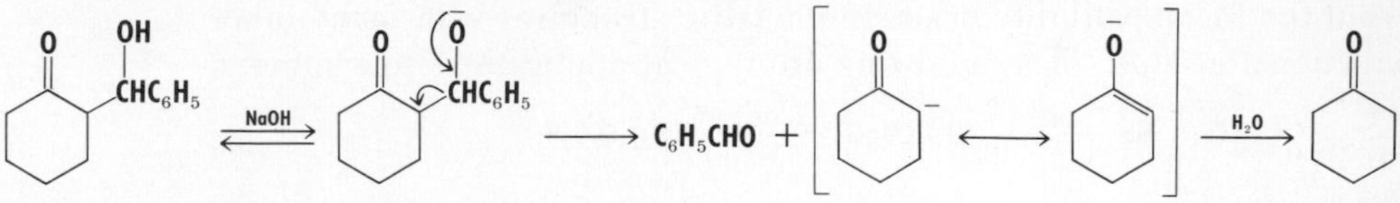

$$\underset{\beta\text{-Nitroethanol}}{HOCH_2CH_2NO_2} \xrightleftharpoons{\text{NaOH aq.}} CH_2O + CH_3NO_2$$

Such activated cleavages are virtually always the reverse of certain well-known addition reactions (Chap. 13).

Very strong base and high temperature are required to effect cleavage of unactivated alkoxide ions.

$$\underset{\text{Benzpinacol}}{(C_6H_5)_2C(OH)\text{—}C(OH)(C_6H_5)_2} \xrightarrow[\text{Dioxan, }90^\circ]{(CH_3)_3CO^-K^+} \underset{\text{Benzhydrol}}{(C_6H_5)_2CHOH} + \underset{\text{Benzophenone}}{(C_6H_5)_2C{=}O}$$

Formation of Carbon-Carbon Bonds

Most electrophilic substitutions in which carbon-carbon bonds are made are classified with other groups of reactions such as nucleophilic additions and substitution reactions. A group of such substitution reactions was discussed in Chap. 10. The association with nucleophilic addition is illustrated by the carbonation of organometallic reagents.

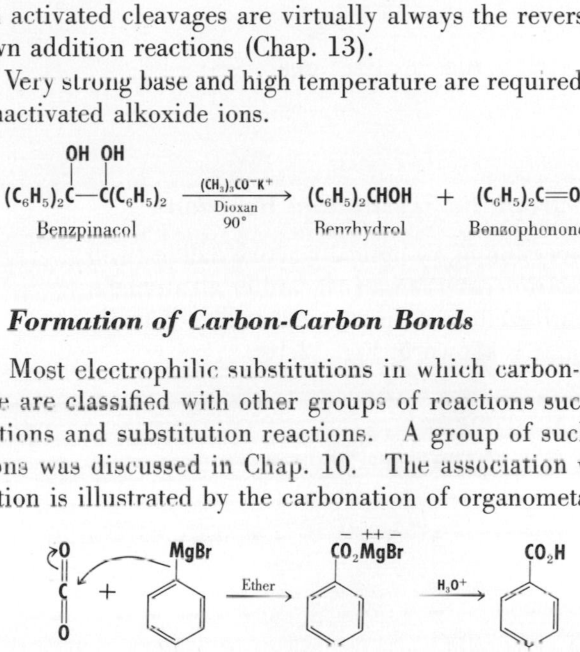

Electrophile Substrate

The carbonation reaction could be considered as either a nucleophilic addition to carbon dioxide or an electrophilic substitution of carbon dioxide for magnesium. Many similar reactions will be discussed in Chap. 13. Carbonation of magnesium and lithium compounds provides one of the most generally useful methods for preparation of carboxylic

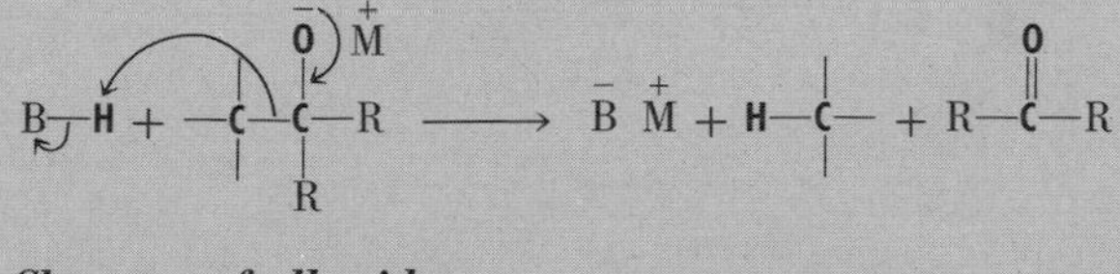

FIG. 12.9 Cleavage of alkoxides.

acids.   Unlike the cyanide synthesis (page 222), the reaction can be used to prepare acids in which the carboxyl group is attached to aromatic or tertiary alkyl groups.   The only serious limitation of the reaction arises from the incompatibility of organometallic structures with many other functional groups.   The following are typical applications to synthesis.

$$(CH_3)_3CCl + Mg \xrightarrow{\text{Ether}} (CH_3)_3CMgCl \xrightarrow[\text{2) } H_3O^+]{\text{1) } CO_2} (CH_3)_3CCO_2H$$

tert-Butyl
chloride

Pivalic acid
62%

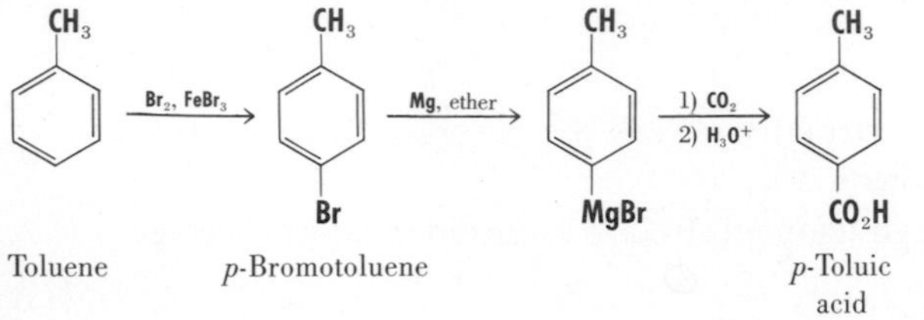

Toluene   *p*-Bromotoluene   *p*-Toluic
acid

Stereochemistry of Electrophilic Substitution Reactions

Organometallics.   The conversion of an optically active halide (with the halogen at the only asymmetric center) to a Grignard or alkali metal reagent, followed by subsequent reaction of the organometallic, virtually always gives racemic products, as is shown in Fig. 12.10.

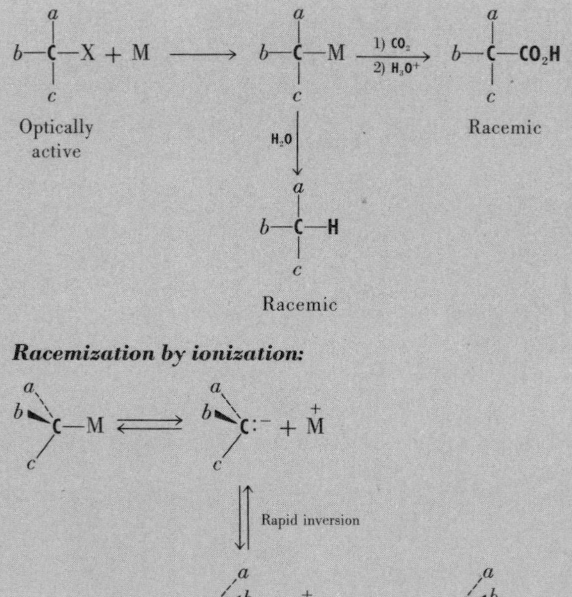

Racemization by ionization:

FIG. 12.10   Racemization of organometallic compounds.

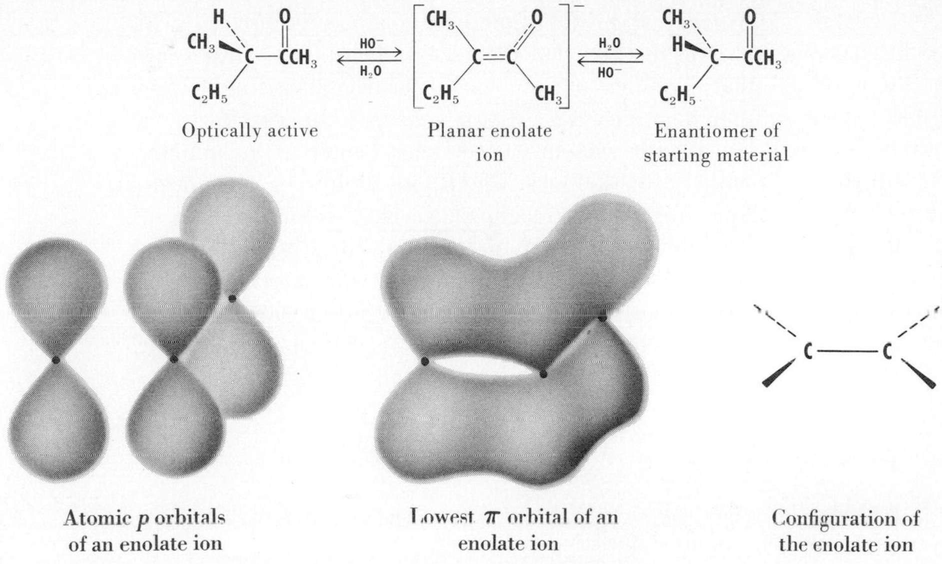

Optically active   Planar enolate   Enantiomer of
              ion   starting material

Atomic p orbitals   Lowest π orbital of an   Configuration of
of an enolate ion   enolate ion   the enolate ion

FIG. 12.11   *Racemization by way of planar enolate ions.*

Probably the great polarity of carbon-metal bonds allows rapid racemization of organometallic compounds by ionization and exchange reactions with the metal halides also present in solution. If free carbanions are formed at any time, they should have a pyramidal configuration; but, like amines and ammonia, they should invert very rapidly (see Fig. 12.10).

Alkenyllithiums can be formed, and brought into reaction, with only limited change of configuration about the adjacent carbon-carbon double bond. Since oximes are stereochemically stable (page 119), the anions related to alkenyllithium reagents might well be stable without the lithium atom.

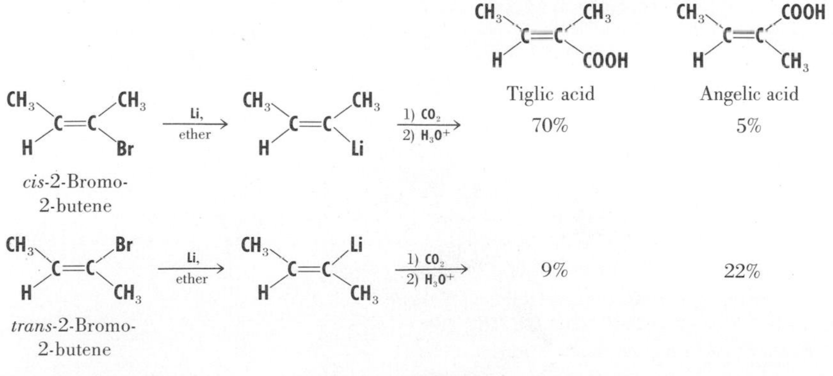

Tiglic acid   Angelic acid

70%   5%

cis-2-Bromo-2-butene   9%   22%

trans-2-Bromo-2-butene

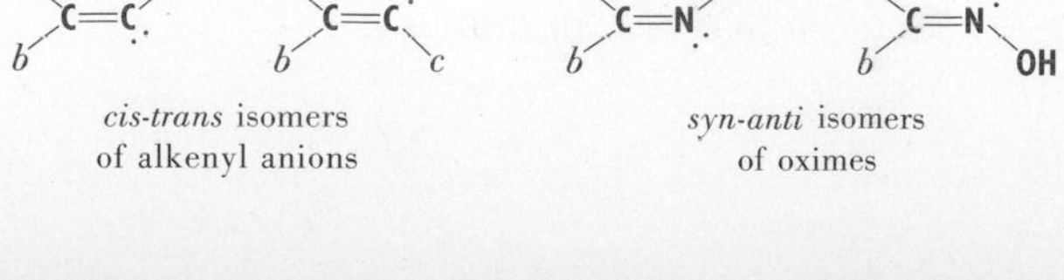

cis-trans isomers   *syn-anti* isomers
of alkenyl anions   of oximes

Enolates. The great stability of enolate ions as compared with alkylcarbanions is due to the fact that the excess electrons go into a low-energy π orbital that includes one or more electron-attracting oxygen atoms. As is indicated in Fig. 12.11, this requires coplanarity of the enolate system. The planar system cannot be a center of asymmetry. Consequently, optically active ketones, which owe their activity to asymmetric α-carbon atoms, are rapidly racemized in basic solutions.

Other Cases. The stereochemistry of electrophilic substitutions that involve neither free anions nor reactive organometallic intermediates is not well defined experimentally. Recent work in the laboratory of one of the authors shows that retention, inversion, or racemization can occur, depending on experimental conditions.

Problems

1. Outline the steps (and the kind of experimental conditions involved) for preparation of the following organometallic compounds:

a. C_6H_5MgBr c. $(CH_3)_3CLi$ e. C_6H_5K

b. $CH_3(CH_2)_3Li$ d. $C_6H_5HgC_6H_5$ f. $(CH_3)_2Cd$

2. Write out reaction sequences, using specific compounds, that illustrate the following:

a. Conversion of a tertiary alkyl halide to an alkane without alteration of the carbon skeleton

b. Conversion of a secondary halide to a carboxylic acid

c. Dehalogenation of a ketone

d. Conversion of a halide to a mercaptan

e. The haloform reaction with a phenyl ketone

f. Preparation of an organometallic compound by a metal exchange reaction

g. Preparation of an organometallic compound by a halogen-metal interconversion reaction

h. Preparation of an organometallic compound by a metalation reaction

i. Preparation of an α-haloacid

3. Using *inorganic materials* and halobenzenes (where needed), devise syntheses of the following compounds. Make intermediates only once in the problem set.

a. $C_6H_5CH_2CH_2HgCl$ d. $CH_3CH_2SO_2H$

b. $(CH_3)_2CHCO_2H$ e. $C_6H_5CH_2CHCO_2H$

c. $CH_3CH_2\underset{\underset{\displaystyle CH_3}{|}}{C}HCO_2H$ $\qquad\qquad\underset{\displaystyle NH_2}{}$

$\qquad\qquad\qquad\qquad\qquad\qquad\qquad$ f. $(CH_3CH_2CH_2)_2Cd$

4. Arrange the following compounds according to the specified order.

a. Decreasing reactivity toward phenylpotassium:

CH_3NH_2, $C_6H_5CH_3$, $(CH_3)_3COH$, CH_3OH, $(C_6H_5)_3CH$, $CH_3(CH_2)_3CH_3$

b. Decreasing reactivity toward triphenylmethane:

CH_3Li, C_6H_5Li, $(CH_3)_2CHLi$, $(CH_3)_3CLi$, $(CH_3)_2CHK$

5. Explain the following observations:

a. $CH_3CH{=}CHCH_2Cl \xrightarrow[\substack{\text{2) } CO_2 \\ \text{3) } H_3O^+}]{\text{1) Mg, ether}} CH_3CH{=}CHCH_2CO_2H + CH_3CHCH{=}CH_2$

$\qquad\qquad\qquad\qquad\qquad\qquad\qquad\qquad\qquad\qquad\qquad\qquad\qquad\quad \underset{\displaystyle CO_2H}{|}$

b. $(C_6H_5)_3CH + CH_3(CH_2)_3Na \xrightarrow{\text{Rapid}} (C_6H_5)_3CNa + CH_3(CH_2)_2CH_3$

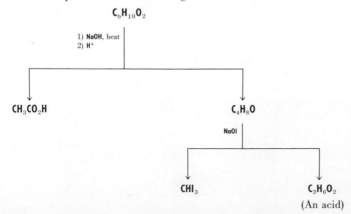

Triptycene

$+ CH_3(CH_2)_3Na \longrightarrow$ no reaction

c. $(C_6H_5)_2CH\!-\!\langle\ \rangle\!-\!Br \xrightarrow[\substack{2)\ CO_2 \\ 3)\ H_3O^+}]{1)\ Li} (C_6H_5)_3CCO_2H$

d. $\xrightarrow{Cl_2,\ NaOH}$ no reaction

$(CH_3)_2CHCC(CH_3)_3 \xrightarrow{Cl_2,\ NaOH} (CH_3)_2\underset{\underset{Cl}{|}}{C}CC(CH_3)_3$

6a. Draw a three-dimensional structure for the predominating product of the following reaction:

$$\underset{C_6H_5}{\overset{CH_3}{}}C\!=\!C\underset{C_6H_5}{\overset{Br}{}} \xrightarrow[\substack{2)\ CO_2 \\ 3)\ H_3O^+}]{1)\ Li}$$

b. How do you account for the fact that optically active 2-phenylbutane is racemized when it is heated at $200°$ with potassium *tert*-butoxide?

7a. Indicate which of the following compounds give iodoform tests:

$CH_3CH_2OH \qquad C_6H_5COCH_3 \qquad C_6H_5COC_2H_5 \qquad CH_3CHOHC_2H_5$

b. Why does $C_6H_5COCH_2COC_6H_5$ give an iodoform test with **NaOI** and strong base?

c. Write out structures of five acids that decarboxylate easily.

8. Write out one example of *each different* kind of reaction that you have studied in which

a. A carbon chain is lengthened.

b. A carbon chain is shortened.

9. Write equations for the following transformations:

$$C_6H_{10}O_2$$

$$\downarrow \substack{1)\ NaOH,\ heat \\ 2)\ H^+}$$

$CH_3CO_2H \qquad\qquad C_4H_8O$

$$\downarrow NaOI$$

$CHI_3 \qquad\qquad\qquad C_3H_6O_2$
(An acid)

$$\underset{/}{\overset{\backslash}{C}} \!=\! \overset{-}{\underset{+}{N}} O$$

$$\downarrow$$

$$-\overset{N}{\underset{|}{\overset{|}{C}}}-\overset{-}{\underset{O}{}}$$

13

Nucleophilic Addition to Unsaturated Carbon

Compounds containing double and triple bonds undergo many *addition reactions*. Frequently multiple bonds are opened by addition of both an electrophile and a nucleophile, as is illustrated in Fig. 13.1. Additions to multiple bonds between carbon and some other element are classified according to the nature of the group added to carbon. Additions to carbon-carbon double and triple bonds are classified by consideration of reaction conditions. If the reaction medium contains strong bases, an addition is usually considered nucleophilic. Most additions to alkenes occur under acidic conditions and are classified as electrophilic additions.

The carbon atoms of polar functional groups, such as $\underset{/}{\overset{\backslash}{C}}\!=\!O$, $\underset{/}{\overset{\backslash}{C}}\!=\!N-$, and $-C\!\equiv\!N$, are all reactive toward nucleophilic reagents. In contrast, unconjugated alkenes, $\underset{/}{\overset{\backslash}{C}}\!=\!\overset{\backslash}{\underset{/}{C}}$, react only with the most powerful nucleophiles. Conjugated dienes, $\underset{/}{\overset{\backslash}{C}}\!=\!\overset{|}{\underset{/}{C}}-\overset{|}{\underset{/}{C}}\!=\!\overset{\backslash}{\underset{/}{C}}$, are more susceptible to nucleophilic attack. Conjugation of carbon-carbon double bonds with electron-withdrawing groups, such as $-CO_2R$, $-COR$, $-NO_2$, $-CN$, and $-SO_2-$, activates the olefinic linkages toward nucleophilic attack.

Nucleophilic additions are most easily thought of as stepwise reactions. When reaction conditions are basic, the first step is the addition

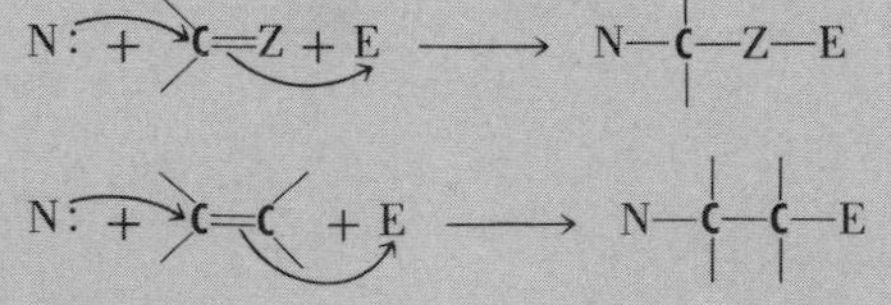

$$N: + \underset{/}{\overset{\backslash}{C}}\!=\!Z + E \longrightarrow N-\overset{|}{\underset{|}{C}}-Z-E$$

$$N: + \underset{/}{\overset{\backslash}{C}}\!=\!\overset{\backslash}{\underset{/}{C}} + E \longrightarrow N-\overset{|}{\underset{|}{C}}-\overset{|}{\underset{|}{C}}-E$$

FIG. 13.1   *Addition reactions.*

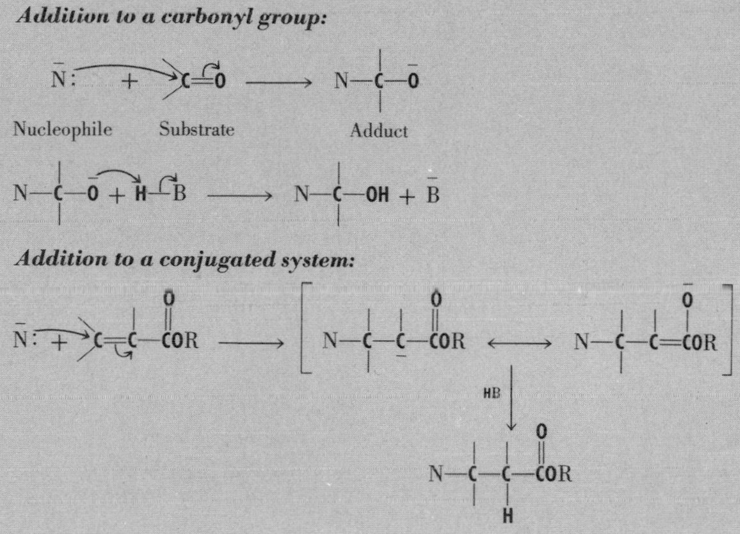

Addition to a carbonyl group:

$$\overset{-}{N}: \;\; + \;\; >C\!\!=\!\!O \longrightarrow N\!-\!\overset{|}{C}\!-\!\overset{-}{O}$$

Nucleophile   Substrate   Adduct

$$N\!-\!\overset{|}{C}\!-\!O + H\!-\!B \longrightarrow N\!-\!\overset{|}{C}\!-\!OH + \overset{-}{B}$$

Addition to a conjugated system:

$$\overset{-}{N}: + \;>C\!\!=\!\!\overset{|}{C}\!-\!\overset{\overset{O}{\|}}{C}OR \longrightarrow \left[N\!-\!\overset{|}{C}\!-\!\overset{|}{C}\!-\!\overset{\overset{O}{\|}}{C}OR \longleftrightarrow N\!-\!\overset{|}{C}\!-\!\overset{|}{C}\!\!=\!\!\overset{\overset{\overset{-}{O}}{}}{C}OR \right]$$

$$\downarrow \text{HB}$$

$$N\!-\!\overset{|}{C}\!-\!\overset{\overset{|}{}}{\underset{H}{C}}\!-\!\overset{\overset{O}{\|}}{C}OR$$

FIG. 13.2   *Nucleophilic addition.*

of the nucleophile to form an intermediate which is usually an anion. Addition is completed by the attachment of a hydrogen ion (or a metal cation) to the negative center. The mechanism is shown in Fig. 13.2.

Coordination of electrophilic catalysts with oxygen or nitrogen increases the reactivity of the substrates toward nucleophiles   Figure 13.3 illustrates acid-catalyzed nucleophilic addition.

Base-catalyzed additions are also common. The catalyst functions by removing weakly acidic protons from reagents to produce a nucleophile which, in turn, adds to the substrate.

Carbon-Halogen Bond Formation

Addition to Carbonyl Groups. Hydrogen halides add reversibly to aldehydes and ketones to give 1,1-halohydrins. These products cannot be isolated in pure form, because equilibrium is established too rapidly in the addition-elimination reaction.

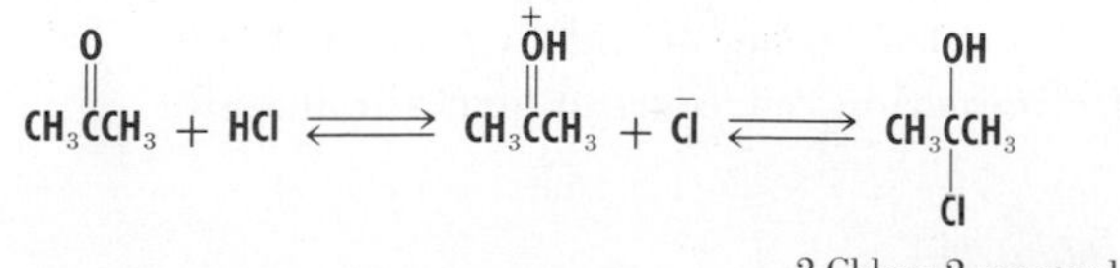

$$CH_3\overset{\overset{O}{\|}}{C}CH_3 + HCl \rightleftharpoons CH_3\overset{\overset{\overset{+}{O}H}{\|}}{C}CH_3 + \overset{-}{Cl} \rightleftharpoons CH_3\underset{\overset{|}{Cl}}{\overset{\overset{OH}{|}}{C}}CH_3$$

2-Chloro-2-propanol

$$>C\!\!=\!\!O + \overset{+}{H} \rightleftharpoons >C\!\!=\!\!\overset{+}{O}H \xrightarrow{\overset{-}{N}:} N\!-\!\overset{|}{C}\!-\!OH$$

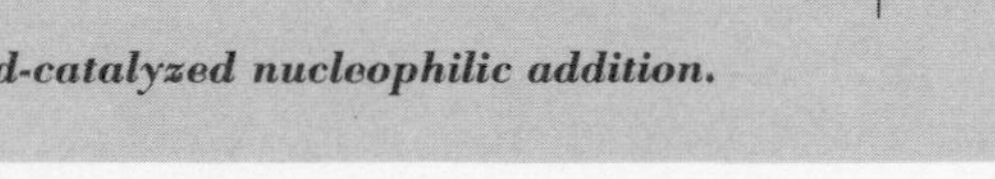

FIG. 13.3   *Acid-catalyzed nucleophilic addition.*

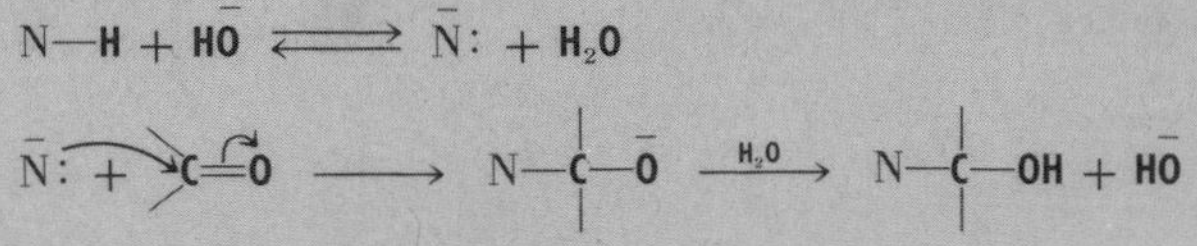

$$N-H + HO^- \rightleftharpoons \bar{N}: + H_2O$$

$$\bar{N}: + {>}C{=}O \longrightarrow N-\underset{|}{\overset{|}{C}}-\bar{O} \xrightarrow{H_2O} N-\underset{|}{\overset{|}{C}}-OH + HO^-$$

FIG. 13.4   *Base-catalyzed nucleophilic addition.*

In alcohol solutions, α-haloethers are formed from 1,1-halohydrins by nucleophilic substitution reactions.   Since equilibrium can be established rapidly only in the presence of acid, α-haloethers may be isolated after the acid catalyst is neutralized.

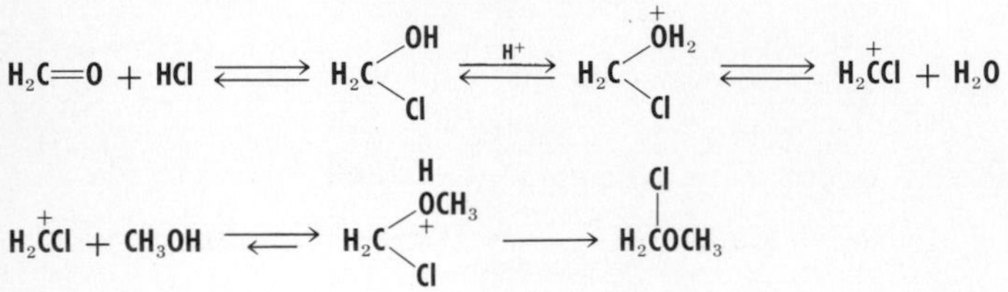

$$H_2C{=}O + HCl \rightleftharpoons H_2C\overset{OH}{\underset{Cl}{\big\langle}} \overset{H^+}{\rightleftharpoons} H_2C\overset{\overset{+}{O}H_2}{\underset{Cl}{\big\langle}} \rightleftharpoons H_2\overset{+}{C}Cl + H_2O$$

$$H_2\overset{+}{C}Cl + CH_3OH \rightleftharpoons H_2C\overset{\overset{H}{\underset{}{\overset{OCH_3}{|}}}}{\underset{Cl}{\overset{+}{\big\langle}}} \longrightarrow H_2\overset{Cl}{\underset{}{C}}OCH_3$$

α-Chloromethyl ether
89%

Aldehydes and ketones can be converted into *gem*-dihalides by treatment with reagents such as phosphorus pentachloride, trichloride, or tribromide.   The reactions probably involve addition of the halogen reagents to the carbonyl group, followed by a nucleophilic substitution reaction by halide ion.

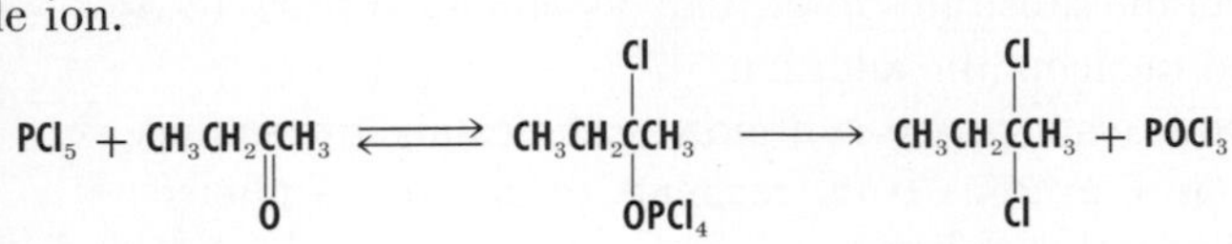

$$PCl_5 + CH_3CH_2\overset{}{\underset{O}{CCH_3}} \rightleftharpoons CH_3CH_2\overset{Cl}{\underset{OPCl_4}{CCH_3}} \longrightarrow CH_3CH_2\overset{Cl}{\underset{Cl}{CCH_3}} + POCl_3$$

Ethyl methyl
ketone

2,2-Dichloro-
butane
50%

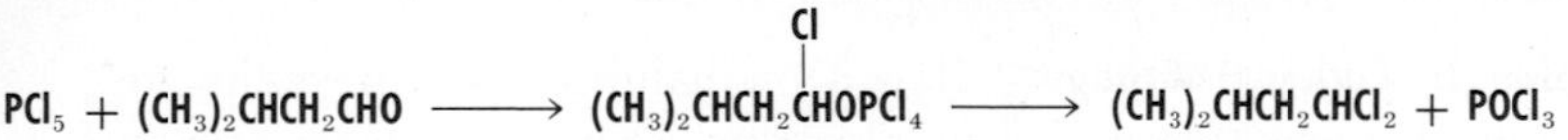

$$PCl_5 + (CH_3)_2CHCH_2CHO \longrightarrow (CH_3)_2CHCH_2\overset{Cl}{CHOPCl_4} \longrightarrow (CH_3)_2CHCH_2CHCl_2 + POCl_3$$

3-Methylbutyr-
aldehyde

1,1-Dichloro-3-
methylbutane
34%

The dihalides can be hydrolyzed to regenerate aldehydes or ketones, or submitted to base-catalyzed elimination reactions to give vinylhalides and acetylenes (Chap. 17).

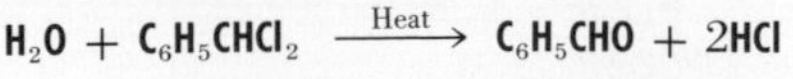

$$H_2O + C_6H_5CHCl_2 \xrightarrow{Heat} C_6H_5CHO + 2HCl$$

Benzal
chloride

Benzaldehyde

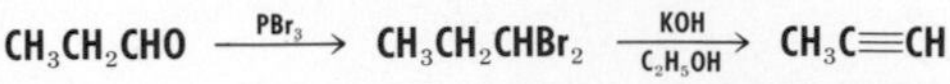

$$CH_3CH_2CHO \xrightarrow{PBr_3} CH_3CH_2CHBr_2 \xrightarrow[C_2H_5OH]{KOH} CH_3C{\equiv}CH$$

Methylacetylene
(1-Propyne)

Addition to α,β-Unsaturated Systems. Hydrogen halides add readily to the carbon-carbon double bonds in α,β-unsaturated aldehydes, ketones, esters, acids, and so forth. In many cases, the first product is a *1,4-addition compound* which tautomerizes to the final product.

$$\overset{+}{H} + CH_2=CHCCH_3 \underset{}{\overset{}{\rightleftharpoons}} \left[CH_2=CHCCH_3 \longleftrightarrow \overset{+}{CH_2}CH=CCH_3 \right]$$
$$\overset{\parallel}{O} \qquad\qquad \overset{\parallel}{OH} \qquad\qquad \overset{\mid}{OH}$$

$$\overline{Cl} + CH_2=CHCCH_3 \longrightarrow ClCH_2CH=CCH_3$$
$$\qquad\quad \overset{\mid}{OH} \qquad\qquad\qquad \overset{\mid}{OH}$$

Enol of β-chloroethyl
methyl ketone

$$ClCH_2CH=CCH_3 \longrightarrow ClCH_2CH_2CCH_3$$
$$\qquad \overset{\mid}{OH} \qquad\qquad\qquad \overset{\parallel}{O}$$

Net reaction: $HCl + CH_2=CHCOCH_3 \longrightarrow ClCH_2CH_2COCH_3$

Methyl vinyl
ketone

β-Chloroethyl
methyl ketone
67%

$$\qquad\qquad \overset{C_2H_5}{\mid}$$
$$HI + CH_3CH=CCO_2H \longrightarrow CH_3CHCHCO_2H$$
$$\qquad\qquad\qquad\qquad\qquad\qquad \overset{\mid}{I}$$

2-Ethyl-2-
butenoic acid

2-Ethyl-3-
iodobutanoic acid

$$\qquad\qquad \overset{CH_3}{\mid} \qquad\qquad\qquad \overset{CH_3}{\mid}$$
$$HBr + CH_2=CCN \longrightarrow BrCH_2CHCN$$

α-Methacrylo-
nitrile

β-Bromoisobutyronitrile
72%

Carbon-Oxygen and Carbon-Sulfur Bond Formation

Carbonyl Hydrates. Aldehydes and ketones add water reversibly, forming *gem*-diols.

$$H_2O + \overset{R}{\underset{R}{>}}C=O \rightleftharpoons \overset{R}{\underset{R}{>}}C\overset{OH}{\underset{OH}{<}}$$

gem-Diol

Only when the carbonyl compound is heavily substituted with electron-withdrawing groups are the *gem*-diols isolable. The stability of such diols is probably due to unfavorable dipole-dipole repulsion in the parent carbonyl compounds.

$$\overset{Cl}{\underset{Cl}{\overset{\mid}{Cl-C-C}}}\overset{+}{\underset{}{\nearrow}}\overset{\overline{O}}{\underset{H}{\diagdown}} + H_2O \longrightarrow Cl_3CCH(OH)_2$$

Chloral hydrate

$$HO_2CCHO + H_2O \longrightarrow HO_2CCH(OH)_2$$

Glyoxylic   Glyoxylic acid
acid   hydrate

Triketoindanone   Ninhydrin

Other carbonyl compounds are extensively converted to *gem*-diols in water solution, but attempts to isolate the diols fail because they are rapidly dehydrated. An example is *formalin,* the solution of 40% formaldehyde in water, which is used to preserve biological specimens. The amount of free formaldehyde in solution is almost undetectably small, but the diol cannot be isolated in an anhydrous condition.

Formaldehyde   Methylenediol

Acetals and Ketals. Addition of alcohols to aldehydes and ketones occurs rapidly in weakly acidic or basic solutions. The first adducts, which are known as *hemiacetals* or *hemiketals*, are unstable in the same way as *gem*-diols.

A hemiacetal

In the presence of acid, a nucleophilic substitution converts hemiacetals and hemiketals to *acetals* and *ketals.*

1,1-Diethoxypropane
(an acetal)

Equilibrium between carbonyl compounds and acetals or ketals is rapidly established under acidic conditions. The substitution step is specifically acid-catalyzed; the diethers can be isolated from neutral or alkaline solutions. Since the ether linkage resists attack by nucleophilic reagents, acetals and ketals are useful as *protective groups.* A polyfunctional aldehyde or ketone is first converted to an acetal or a ketal. Reactions requiring conditions that would destroy carbonyl compounds may then be carried out on another group in the molecule. Finally, the carbonyl group is regenerated by hydrolysis of the acetal group with dilute acid.

$$CH_2=CHCHO + HC(OC_2H_5)_3 \xrightarrow{NH_4^+NO_3^-} CH_2=CHCH(OC_2H_5)_2 + HCO_2C_2H_5$$

Acrolein   Ethyl ortho-
formate   Acrolein diethyl
acetal
73%

$$Br_2 + CH_2=CHCH(OC_2H_5)_2 \xrightarrow[\text{(Chap. 15)}]{\text{Bromine addition}} BrCH_2CHBrCH(OC_2H_5)_2$$

$$2NaOH + BrCH_2CHBrCH(OC_2H_5)_2 \xrightarrow[\text{(Chap. 17)}]{\text{Elimination}} CH\equiv CCH(OC_2H_5)_2 + 2NaBr + 2H_2O$$

$$CH\equiv CCH(OC_2H_5)_2 + H_2O \xrightarrow{H^+} CH\equiv CCHO + 2C_2H_5OH$$

Propargyl
aldehyde

The above equations illustrate the use of ethylorthoformate as a reagent for acetal synthesis under anhydrous conditions. Ammonium nitrate is used as a weakly acidic catalyst in the exchange reaction.

Cyclic hemiacetals and acetals are formed from 1,4- and 1,5-hydroxyaldehydes and hydroxyketones in the presence of anhydrous acids.

4-Hydroxybutanal   2-Hydroxytetra-
hydrofuran
(a cyclic hemiacetal)   2-Methoxytetrahydrofuran

Thiols react even more rapidly than alcohols with aldehydes and ketones to give thioacetals and thioketals. These substances are readily hydrolyzed when warmed with aqueous mercuric chloride.

$$2C_2H_5SH + C_6H_5CH_2COCH_3 \xrightleftharpoons{\text{Dry HCl}} C_6H_5CH_2\underset{\underset{SC_2H_5}{|}}{\overset{\overset{SC_2H_5}{|}}{C}}CH_3$$

Benzyl methyl
ketone   1-Phenyl-2,2-diethylmercaptopropane

$$C_6H_5CH_2\underset{\underset{SC_2H_5}{|}}{\overset{\overset{SC_2H_5}{|}}{C}}CH_3 + H_2O + HgCl_2 \longrightarrow C_6H_5CH_2COCH_3 + Hg(SC_2H_5)_2 + 2HCl$$

Polymers of Aldehydes. Formaldehyde is converted to a crystalline trimer, *trioxan*, by distillation of solutions of the aldehyde in dilute aqueous acid. The slow evaporation of an aqueous solution of formaldehyde leaves a linear polymer (*paraformaldehyde*) as a residue. These high-molecular-weight polymers of formaldehyde can be spun into fibers and are marketed under the trade name of *Delrin*.

$$3CH_2O \longrightarrow$$

Trioxan

$$n\text{-}CH_2O \longrightarrow HOCH_2[OCH_2]_nOCH_2OH$$

Paraformaldehyde

Acetaldehyde undergoes rapid polymerization in the presence of sulfuric acid to give paraldehyde. Acetaldehyde may be recovered if paraldehyde is heated gently in the presence of acid. At $-10°$, acetaldehyde polymerizes to *metaldehyde*, a compound containing an eight-membered ring.

$$3CH_3CHO \xrightarrow[25°]{H_2SO_4} \qquad \xrightarrow[\text{Distill}]{H_2SO_4} 3CH_3CHO$$

Paraldehyde

$$4CH_3CHO \xrightarrow[-10°]{H_2SO_4}$$

Metaldehyde

Isocyanates as Substrates. Isocyanates contain very electrophilic carbon atoms which are joined by double bonds to two electronegative atoms (Fig. 13.5).

$$R\text{—}\ddot{N}\text{=}C\text{=}\ddot{O}: \longleftrightarrow R\text{—}\overset{-}{\underset{..}{\ddot{N}}}\text{—}\overset{+}{C}\text{=}\ddot{O}: \longleftrightarrow R\text{—}\ddot{N}\text{=}\overset{+}{C}\text{—}\overset{-}{\ddot{O}}: \longleftrightarrow$$

$$R\text{—}\overset{-}{\underset{..}{\ddot{N}}}\text{—}\overset{+}{C}\text{≡}O \longleftrightarrow R\text{—}\overset{+}{N}\text{≡}C\text{—}\overset{-}{\ddot{O}}:$$

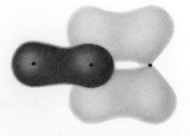

A pair of perpendicular
π orbitals in an isocyanate

FIG. 13.5   Resonance in isocyanates.

Addition of alcohols and thiols to isocyanates produces *urethanes*. Phenylisocyanate is commonly used as a reagent for preparation of characteristic solid derivatives of alcohols and thiols.

$$C_2H_5OH + C_6H_5N{=}C{=}O \longrightarrow \left[C_6H_5\overset{..}{N}{-}\underset{\underset{+}{HOC_2H_5}}{\overset{\overset{O}{\|}}{C}}{=}O \longleftrightarrow C_6H_5N{=}\underset{\underset{+}{HOC_2H_5}}{C}{-}\overset{..}{\overset{..}{O}} \right] \longrightarrow C_6H_5NH\overset{\overset{O}{\|}}{C}OC_2H_5$$

Phenyliso-
cyanate

Ethyl-*N*-phenyl-
carbamate
(a urethane)

$$CH_3SH + C_6H_5N{=}C{=}O \longrightarrow C_6H_5NH\overset{\overset{O}{\|}}{C}SCH_3$$

Methyl-*N*-phenylthiocarbamate

Water adds rapidly to isocyanates to form carbamic acids, which decarboxylate almost immediately.

$$H_2O + CH_3(CH_2)_4N{=}C{=}O \longrightarrow CH_3(CH_2)_4NHCO_2H \longrightarrow CH_3(CH_2)_4NH_2 + CO_2$$

n-Pentylisocyanate

n-Pentylcarbamic
acid

n-Pentylamine

Bisulfite Addition Compounds. Aldehydes and ketones, such as acetone and cyclohexanone, which do not have bulky groups near the functional group add bisulfite ions in aqueous solution. The products are α-hydroxysulfonates, which can be crystallized as sodium salts.

$$HO\overset{..}{\underset{\overset{\|}{O}}{\overset{\|}{S}}}{-}\overset{\overset{O}{\|}}{O} \mid CH_3CH_2CH \longrightarrow CH_3CH_2\overset{\overset{\bar{O}}{\|}}{C}HSO_2OH \rightleftarrows$$

$$CH_3CH_2\overset{\overset{OH}{|}}{C}HS\bar{O}_3 \xrightarrow{Na^+} CH_3CH_2\overset{\overset{OH}{|}}{C}HSO_3^-Na^+$$

Sodium bisulfite adduct of propionaldehyde
(Sodium 1-hydroxypropane-1-sulfonate)

$$Na^+HS\bar{O}_3 + CH_3COCH_2CH_3 \longrightarrow CH_3\overset{\overset{OH}{|}}{\underset{\underset{SO_3^-Na^+}{|}}{C}}CH_2CH_3$$

Carbonyl compounds are easily regenerated from their bisulfite addition compounds by treatment with either acid or base.

$$R\overset{\overset{OH}{|}}{C}HS\bar{O}_3 \rightleftarrows RCHO + HS\bar{O}_3 \overline{}\begin{cases} \xleftarrow{H^+} H_2O + SO_2 \\ \\ \xrightarrow{OH^-} H_2O + S\bar{\bar{O}}_3 \end{cases}$$

Addition to α,β-Unsaturated Systems. The same reagents that add to aldehyde and ketone carbonyl groups will usually add to polarized conjugated systems. Such additions are catalyzed by both acids and bases, although acid conditions are often chosen to avoid base-catalyzed side reactions of the polar functional groups.

$$CH_2{=}CHCOCH_3 \xrightarrow{\ +\ H^+\ } \left[CH_2{=}CHC\overset{\overset{+}{O}H}{\text{COCH}_3} \longleftrightarrow \overset{+}{C}H_2CH{=}\overset{OH}{\text{COCH}_3} \right] \xrightarrow{\ C_2H_5OH\ }$$

Methyl acrylate

$$C_2H_5OCH_2\overset{OH}{\underset{H}{\overset{+}{C}{-}OCH_3}} \xrightarrow{\ -H^+\ } C_2H_5OCH_2CH{=}\overset{OH}{\text{COCH}_3} \longrightarrow C_2H_5OCH_2CH_2\overset{O}{\text{COCH}_3}$$

Methyl β-ethoxypropionate
91%

$$C_6H_5SH \underset{\xrightleftharpoons}{\ NaOCH_3\ (trace)\ } C_6H_5\bar{S} \xrightarrow{\ CH_2{=}CHCOCH_3\ } \left[C_6H_5SCH_2\overset{O}{\underset{}{\bar{C}HCOCH_3}} \longleftrightarrow \right.$$

Thiophenol

$$\left. C_6H_5SCH_2CH{=}\overset{\bar{O}}{\text{COCH}_3} \right] \xrightarrow{\ C_6H_5SH\ } C_6H_5SCH_2CH_2\overset{O}{\text{COCH}_3} + C_6H_5\bar{S}$$

Methyl β-phenyl-
mercaptopropionate
96%

$$C_2H_5OH + CH_2{=}CHCN \xrightarrow{\ H_2SO_4\ } C_2H_5OCH_2CH_2CN$$

Acrylonitrile   β-Ethoxypropionitrile
89%

Additions to Nitriles. Nitriles add water when refluxed with either aqueous acid or base. The addition products are amides, which can, in turn, be hydrolyzed by continued heating. The reaction can ordinarily be stopped at the amide stage.

$$RC{\equiv}N \underset{\xrightleftharpoons}{\ H^+\ } \left[RC{\equiv}\overset{+}{N}H \longleftrightarrow R\overset{+}{C}{=}NH \right] \xrightarrow[-H^+]{\ H_2O\ } RC{=}NH^{OH} \underset{\xrightleftharpoons}{} R\overset{O}{\text{CNH}_2}$$

A nitrile   An amide

$$H\bar{O} + RC{\equiv}N \longrightarrow R\overset{OH}{\underset{}{C}{=}\bar{N}} \xrightarrow{\ H_2O\ } R\overset{OH}{\underset{}{C}{=}NH} \underset{\xrightleftharpoons}{} R\overset{O}{\underset{}{C}{-}NH_2} \xrightarrow[\text{(Chap. 14)}]{\ H_2O\ } RCO_2H + NH_3$$

$$H_2O + CH_3CH_2CH_2CN \xrightarrow{\ H_3O^+\ } CH_3CH_2CH_2CONH_2$$

n-Butyronitrile   *n*-Butyramide

Addition of hydrogen peroxide accelerates the hydration of nitriles in alkaline solutions.

2-Methyl-
benzonitrile
(*o*-Toluonitrile)

2-Methylbenzamide
92%

Nitriles also add alcohols in anhydrous solutions of hydrogen chloride. The products are salts of imino ethers. These salts are readily hydrolyzed to esters by refluxing in aqueous solutions.

$$C_2H_5OH + CH_3(CH_2)_3CN \xrightarrow{HCl} \underset{\underset{H_2NCl}{\overset{\|}{\underset{+\,-}{}}}}{CH_3(CH_2)_3COC_2H_5} \xrightarrow{H_2O,\,\Delta} CH_3(CH_2)_3CO_2C_2H_5 + NH_4Cl$$

Hydrochloride of   Ethyl valerate
ethyl iminovalerate

Carbon-Nitrogen Bond Formation

Additions to Carbonyl Groups. Aldehydes and ketones add primary amines, secondary amines, and ammonia. The adducts, like *gem*-diols, are usually too labile to be isolated. Ammonia addition is typical of reactions involving uncharged nucleophiles. The neutral reactants first combine to give an intermediate that requires a proton shift to complete the addition.

$$H_3N: \overset{+}{} \underset{}{C}\!=\!O \longrightarrow H_3\overset{+}{N}\!-\!\underset{|}{\overset{|}{C}}\!-\!\bar{O} \longrightarrow H_2N\!-\!\underset{|}{\overset{|}{C}}\!-\!OH$$

Chloral, which also forms a stable hydrate, gives a stable ammonia adduct.

$$NH_3 + Cl_3CCHO \longrightarrow \underset{\underset{OH}{|}}{Cl_3CCHNH_2}$$

Chloral ammonia

Formaldehyde reacts with ammonia to give an interesting polycyclic compound, *hexamethylenetetramine*. Each of the four nitrogen atoms in the molecule is at a bridgehead joining two rings. In all, the molecule contains four equivalent rings.

$$NH_3 + CH_2O \longrightarrow [HOCH_2NH_2] \xrightarrow{2CH_2O} \left[\underset{\underset{CH_2OH}{|}}{HOCH_2NCH_2OH}\right] \xrightarrow[CH_2O]{NH_3}$$

Hexamethylenetetramine

Ketenes, which are very reactive toward both electrophilic and nucleophilic reagents, add ammonia and primary and secondary amines to give amides. Similarly, isocyanates add nitrogen compounds to give derivatives of urea.

$$CH_3NH_2 + (CH_3)_2C\!=\!C\!=\!O \longrightarrow \left[\underset{\underset{H_2\overset{+}{N}CH_3}{|}}{(CH_3)_2C\!=\!C\!-\!\bar{O}} \longleftrightarrow \underset{\underset{H_2\overset{+}{N}CH_3}{|}}{(CH_3)_2\bar{C}\!-\!C\!=\!O}\right] \longrightarrow (CH_3)_2CHCONHCH_3$$

Dimethylketene   *N*-Methylisobutyr-
amide

$$(CH_3)_2NH + C_6H_5N\!=\!C\!=\!O \longrightarrow C_6H_5NHCON(CH_3)_2$$

N,N-Dimethyl-*N'*-phenylurea

Ketene itself is a relatively cheap industrial chemical, since it can be made by pyrolysis of acetone. On liquefaction, ketene dimerizes to form *diketene*, which is a useful material in its own right. Addition of acetic acid to ketene vapor provides an economical commercial source of acetic anhydride. Diketene reacts with ethanol to give ethyl acetoacetate.

$$CH_3COCH_3 \xrightarrow{700-750°} CH_4 + CH_2{=}C{=}O \longrightarrow \begin{array}{c} CH_2{=}C{-}O \\ | \quad | \\ H_2C{-}C{=}O \end{array}$$

Diketene

$$CH_3CO_2H + CH_2{=}C{=}O \longrightarrow (CH_3CO)_2O$$

Acetic anhydride

$$\begin{array}{c} CH_2{=}C{-}O \\ | \quad | \\ H_2C{-}C{=}O \end{array} \xrightarrow{C_2H_5OH} \begin{array}{c} CH_2{=}C{-}O \\ | \quad \overset{+}{} \\ H_2C{-}C{-}O{-}C_2H_5 \\ | \\ O \quad H \end{array} \longrightarrow CH_2{=}\overset{\overset{O}{|}}{C}CH_2\overset{\overset{O}{||}}{C}OC_2H_5 \longrightarrow CH_3\overset{\overset{O}{||}}{C}CH_2CO_2C_2H_5$$

Ethyl acetoacetate

Conjugate Addition. Ammonia and its derivatives add smoothly to α,β-unsaturated ketones, aldehydes, esters, and nitriles. The first products from addition of ammonia and primary amines may react again, giving complex mixtures of products.

$$C_2H_5NH_2 + CH_2{=}CHCN \longrightarrow C_2H_5NHCH_2CH_2CN$$

Acrylonitrile   3-Ethylaminopropionitrile

Carbon-Hydrogen Bond Formation

Lithium Aluminum Hydride as a Nucleophile. Lithium aluminum hydride serves as a *hydride-donor* toward polar unsaturated groups. All four hydrogen atoms are available as negative hydrogen. Metallic oxides or amides are first produced and then hydrolyzed to alcohols or amines with dilute aqueous or alcoholic acid. Anhydrous diethyl ether, tetrahydrofuran, and dioxan are commonly used as solvents. Reduction of aldehydes to alcohols illustrates the reaction.

$$\overset{+}{Li}\overset{-}{AlH_4} + 4C_6H_5CHO \longrightarrow (C_6H_5CH_2O)_4\overset{-}{Al}\overset{+}{Li} \xrightarrow{4HCl} 4C_6H_5CH_2OH + AlCl_3 + LiCl$$

Lithium   Benzaldehyde
aluminum
hydride

Lithium ions or various aluminum species complex the carbonyl oxygen atoms and aid in the nucleophilic transfer of hydride from aluminum to carbon. Figure 13.6 gives examples of representative mechanistic possibilities.

The use of lithium aluminum hydride as a reducing agent was first reported in 1947. Since that time, the reagent and related metal hydrides have been widely used in research laboratories. *Lithium aluminum hydride is the only common reagent capable of reducing carboxylic acids.* This reagent also reduces aldehydes, ketones, esters, amides, nitriles, and nitro compounds. In some instances, elimination reactions follow addition, giving intermediates that can add a second hydride.

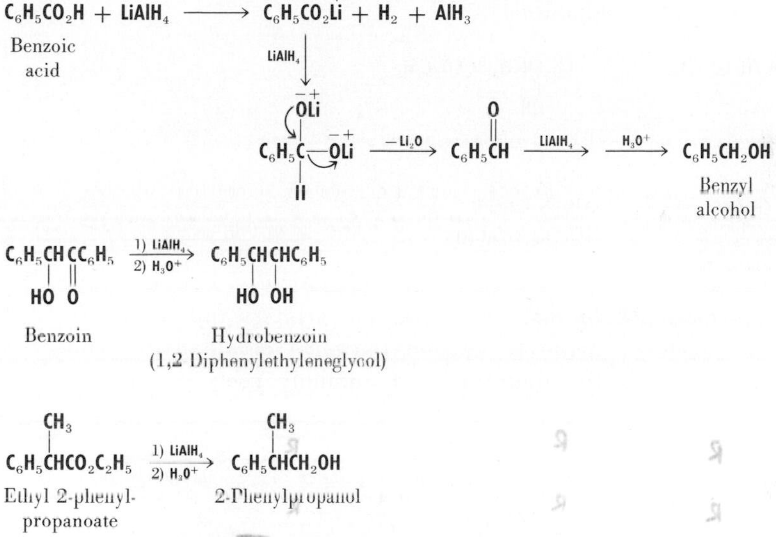

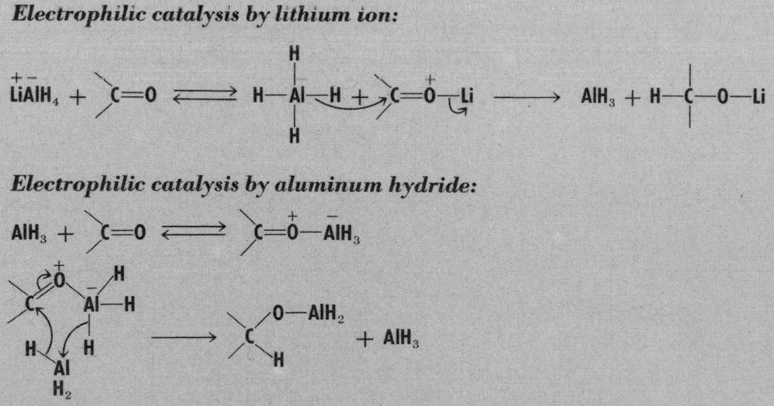

$$C_6H_5CO_2H + LiAlH_4 \longrightarrow C_6H_5CO_2^{-}Li^{+} + H_2 + AlH_3$$

Benzoic
acid

$$C_6H_5CH\underset{HO\ \ O}{\underset{|\ \ ||}{CC_6H_5}} \xrightarrow[2)\ H_3O^+]{1)\ LiAlH_4} C_6H_5\underset{HO\ \ OH}{\underset{|\ \ |}{CHCHC_6H_5}}$$

Benzoin   Hydrobenzoin
(1,2-Diphenylethyleneglycol)

$$\underset{Ethyl\ 2\text{-phenyl-}\atop propanoate}{\overset{CH_3}{\underset{|}{C_6H_5CHCO_2C_2H_5}}} \xrightarrow[2)\ H_3O^+]{1)\ LiAlH_4} \underset{2\text{-Phenylpropanol}}{\overset{CH_3}{\underset{|}{C_6H_5CHCH_2OH}}}$$

Electrophilic catalysis by lithium ion:

Electrophilic catalysis by aluminum hydride:

FIG. 13.6 *Lithium aluminum hydride reduction mechanisms.*

$$2CH_3CH_2CH_2CN \xrightarrow{\text{LiAlH}_4} (CH_3CH_2CH_2CH_2N)_2\overset{-}{Al}\overset{+}{Li} \xrightarrow{\text{H}_2\text{O}^+} 2CH_3CH_2CH_2CH_2NH_2$$

Butyronitrile   *n*-Butylamine

$$(CH_3)_2CHCON(CH_3)_2 \xrightarrow{\text{LiAlH}_4} (CH_3)_2CHC\underset{H}{\overset{\overset{\overset{-}{O}\overset{+}{Li}}{|}}{N}}(CH_3)_2 \xrightarrow[-\text{Li}_2\text{O}]{+\text{LiAlH}_4} (CH_3)_2CHCH_2N(CH_3)_2$$

N,N-Dimethyl-   Dimethylisobutylamine
isobutyramide

Sodium borohydride is a less vigorous, and more selective, reagent than lithium aluminum hydride. The former reduces aldehydes and ketones, but does not react with esters, amides, nitriles, or nitro compounds under ordinary conditions. Water and alcohols may be used as solvents for sodium borohydride reductions.

$$CH_3CCH_2CH_2CO_2C_2H_5 \xrightarrow[\text{2) H}_3\text{O}^+]{\text{1) NaBH}_4} CH_3CHCH_2CH_2CO_2C_2H_5$$
$$\overset{\|}{O} \qquad\qquad\qquad\qquad\qquad \overset{|}{OH}$$

Ethyl 4-ketopentanoate   Ethyl 4-hydroxypentanoate

$$NCCH_2CH_2CHO \xrightarrow[\text{2) H}_3\text{O}^+]{\text{1) NaBH}_4} NCCH_2CH_2CH_2OH$$

3-Cyano-   4-Hydroxybutyronitrile
propionaldehyde

Meerwein-Ponndorf Reduction. Metal salts of primary and secondary alcohols can transfer hydride to carbonyl groups of aldehydes and ketones. Aluminum is the metal most commonly used (Meerwein-Ponndorf reaction).

Since metal alkoxides undergo rapid hydrogen-metal exchange reactions, an alcohol may be used as the source of hydrogen in the presence of a catalytic amount of aluminum alkoxide. Isopropanol and aluminum isopropoxide are frequently used. Reactions can be forced to high conversion by continuous removal of acetone by distillation.

$$\overset{R}{\underset{R}{>}}C{=}O + CH_3CHCH_3 \underset{}{\overset{\text{Al(OC}_3\text{H}_7\text{-}i)_3}{\rightleftarrows}} \overset{R}{\underset{R}{>}}CHOH + CH_3COCH_3$$
$$\overset{|}{OH} \qquad\qquad\qquad\qquad\qquad (\text{Distill})$$

$$(CH_3)_2CHOH + CH_3COCH_2CH_2CH_2Br \xrightarrow{\text{Al(OC}_3\text{H}_7\text{-}i)_3} CH_3CHCH_2CH_2CH_2Br + CH_3COCH_3$$
$$\overset{|}{OH}$$

5-Bromo-2-pentanone   5-Bromo-2-pentanol

$$(CH_3)_2CHOH + CH_3CH{=}CHCHO \xrightarrow{\text{Al(OC}_3\text{H}_7\text{-}i)_3} CH_3CH{=}CHCH_2OH + CH_3COCH_3$$

Crotonaldehyde   Crotyl alcohol

The same reaction becomes a preparative method for oxidation of secondary alcohols to ketones if a large excess of acetone is used as a hydride-acceptor (*Oppenauer oxidation*). Aluminum *tert*-butoxide is usually employed as the catalyst in Oppenauer oxidations. Cyclohexanone and benzoquinone have also been used as hydrogen-acceptors in order to allow reactions to be run at temperatures above the boiling point of acetone.

| 2-Ethylcyclohexanol | Benzoquinone | 2-Ethylcyclo-hexanone 76% | Hydroquinone |

α-Ionol   α-Ionone 80%

Both Ponndorf reductions and Oppenauer oxidations are particularly useful with polyfunctional molecules containing sensitive groups that are destroyed by the conditions of many oxidations and reductions (Chap. 19).

Cannizzaro Reaction. Aldehydes that have *no α-hydrogen* disproportionate in the presence of strong base, giving equal amounts of the corresponding alcohol and carboxylic acid (Cannizzaro reaction). One molecule of aldehyde acts as a hydride-donor and another functions as an acceptor. The first product is an ester which is hydrolyzed under the conditions of the reaction (Chap. 14).

$$RCH_2OCR + HO^- \xrightarrow{\text{Ester hydrolysis}} RCH_2OH + RCO_2^-$$

$$2(CH_3)_3CCHO + NaOH \longrightarrow (CH_3)_3CCH_2OH + (CH_3)_3CCO_2Na$$

Trimethyl-acetaldehyde   2,2-Dimethyl-1-propanol   Sodium pivalate

Formaldehyde is occasionally used as a reducing agent in crossed Cannizzaro reactions.

CH$_2$O +	$\xrightarrow{\text{NaOH}}$	+ HCO$_2$Na
(Excess)		
Veratraldehyde	Veratryl alcohol	
	90%	

Leuckart Reaction.   Ketones and aromatic aldehydes react with ammonium formate at high temperatures to give primary amines.   The first reaction is a condensation of ammonia with the carbonyl compound to produce an imine.   Formate ion then serves as a hydride donor and reduces the imine to an amine.

$$HCO_2^-NH_4^+ \rightleftharpoons HCO_2H + NH_3$$

$$\ce{>C=O} + NH_3 \xrightarrow{-H_2O} \ce{>C=NH} \xrightarrow{NH_4^+} \ce{>C=NH_2^+}$$

$$\ce{C_6H_5CCH_2CH_3} \xrightarrow{HCO_2NH_4} \ce{C_6H_5CHCH_2CH_3}$$

Propiophenone   1-Phenyl-1-propylamine
(Ethyl phenyl
   ketone)

Carbon-Carbon Bond Formation

Most carbon nucleophiles can be added to the carbonyl groups of aldehydes and ketones and to carbon-carbon double bonds activated by conjugation with electron-withdrawing substituents.   The nucleophiles include cyanide ion, enolate ions, and organometallic reagents.

Cyanide Addition.   Hydrogen cyanide addition to aldehydes and many of the more reactive ketones is catalyzed by traces of base.   Need for a basic catalyst indicates that cyanide ion makes the first attack on the substrate (Fig. 13.7).

The α-hydroxynitriles produced in the reaction are commonly known as *cyanohydrins*.   They can be converted to α-hydroxy acids by hydrolysis (page 276) and are *dehydrated* to form α,β-unsaturated nitriles, acids, and acid derivatives.   One of the commercial syntheses of methyl methacrylate, which polymerizes (Chap. 25) to form a transparent plastic known as Plexiglas and Lucite, is based upon the cyanohydrin reaction of acetone.

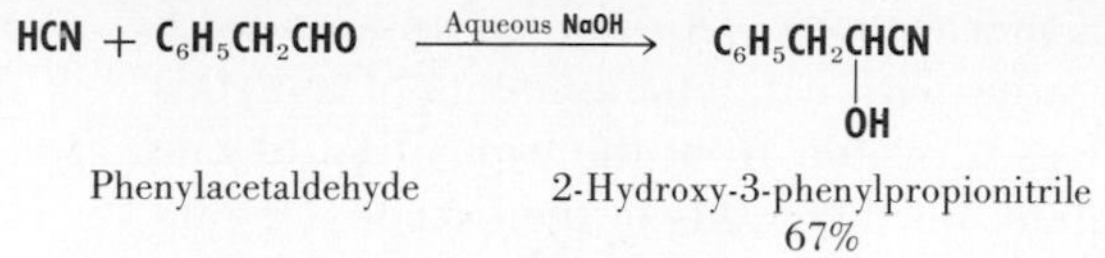

HCN + C₆H₅CH₂CHO $\xrightarrow{\text{Aqueous NaOH}}$ C₆H₅CH₂CHCN
$\qquad\qquad\qquad\qquad\qquad\qquad\qquad\quad$ |
$\qquad\qquad\qquad\qquad\qquad\qquad\qquad\quad$ OH

$\quad$ Phenylacetaldehyde $\qquad$ 2-Hydroxy-3-phenylpropionitrile
$\qquad\qquad\qquad\qquad\qquad\qquad\qquad$ 67%

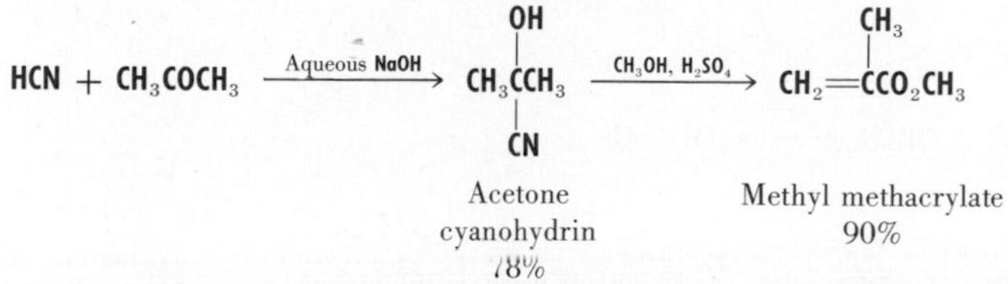

HCN + CH₃COCH₃ $\xrightarrow{\text{Aqueous NaOH}}$ CH₃CCH₃ $\xrightarrow{\text{CH}_3\text{OH, H}_2\text{SO}_4}$ CH₂=CCO₂CH₃

Acetone
cyanohydrin
78%

Methyl methacrylate
90%

These reactions are usually carried out in aqueous solutions prepared by adding slightly less than one equivalent of mineral acid to a solution of sodium cyanide. Water-insoluble aldehydes are sometimes converted to water-soluble bisulfite adducts in order to allow the cyanohydrin reaction to proceed in a homogeneous reaction mixture.

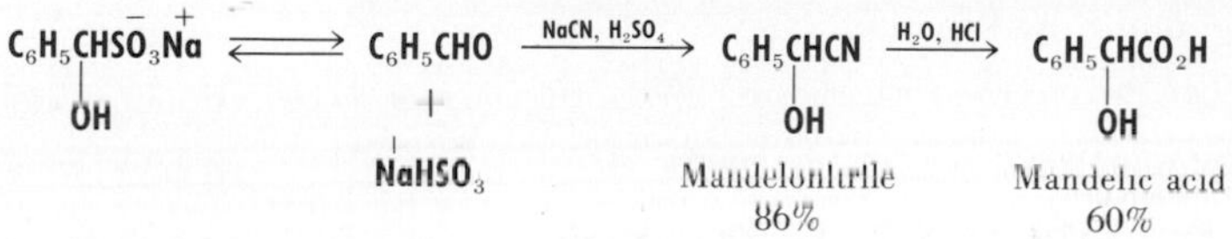

C₆H₅CHSO₃Na $\rightleftharpoons$ C₆H₅CHO $\xrightarrow{\text{NaCN, H}_2\text{SO}_4}$ C₆H₅CHCN $\xrightarrow{\text{H}_2\text{O, HCl}}$ C₆H₅CHCO₂H
| $\qquad\qquad\qquad$ + $\qquad\qquad\qquad\qquad\qquad$ | $\qquad\qquad\qquad\qquad\quad$ |
OH $\qquad\qquad\qquad\qquad\qquad\qquad\qquad\qquad$ OH $\qquad\qquad\qquad\qquad\quad$ OH
$\qquad\qquad$ NaHSO₃ $\qquad\qquad$ Mandelonitrile $\qquad$ Mandelic acid
$\qquad\qquad\qquad\qquad\qquad\qquad\qquad$ 86% $\qquad\qquad\qquad$ 60%

In the *Strecker synthesis* of aminonitriles, an aldehyde or ketone is treated with ammonia and hydrogen cyanide. Cyanide condensation probably occurs with imines as a substrate. Aminonitriles are important primarily because they can be hydrolyzed to amino acids.

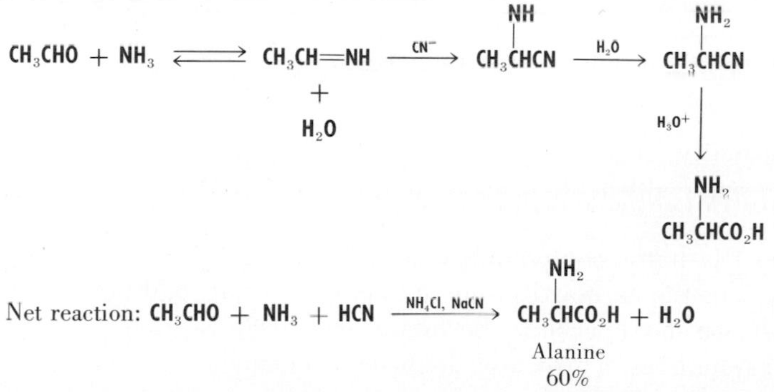

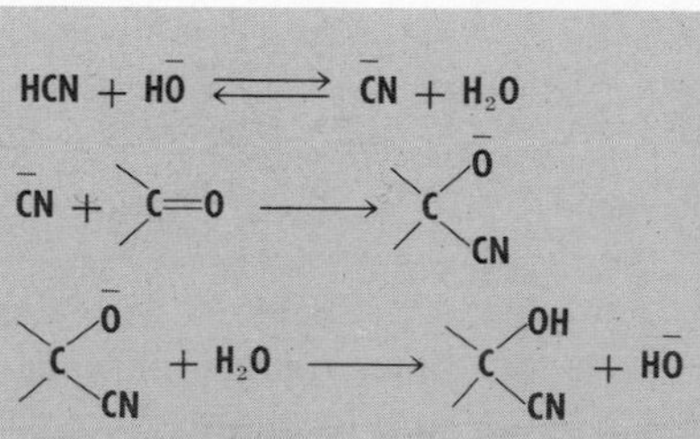

CH₃CHO + NH₃ $\rightleftharpoons$ CH₃CH=NH $\xrightarrow{\text{CN}^-}$ CH₃CHCN $\xrightarrow{\text{H}_2\text{O}}$ CH₃CHCN
$\qquad\qquad\qquad\qquad\qquad\quad$ + $\qquad\qquad\qquad\qquad\quad$ |̄NH $\qquad\qquad\qquad\quad$ NH₂
$\qquad\qquad\qquad\qquad\qquad$ H₂O $\qquad\qquad\qquad\qquad\qquad\qquad\qquad\qquad\quad$ |
$\qquad\qquad\qquad\qquad\qquad\qquad\qquad\qquad\qquad\qquad\qquad\qquad\qquad$ H₃O⁺ |
$\qquad\qquad\qquad\qquad\qquad\qquad\qquad\qquad\qquad\qquad\qquad\qquad\qquad\qquad$ NH₂
$\qquad\qquad\qquad\qquad\qquad\qquad\qquad\qquad\qquad\qquad\qquad\qquad$ CH₃CHCO₂H

Net reaction: CH₃CHO + NH₃ + HCN $\xrightarrow{\text{NH}_4\text{Cl, NaCN}}$ CH₃CHCO₂H + H₂O
$\qquad\qquad\qquad\qquad\qquad\qquad\qquad\qquad\qquad\qquad\qquad\qquad$ |
$\qquad\qquad\qquad\qquad\qquad\qquad\qquad\qquad\qquad\qquad\qquad$ NH₂
$\qquad\qquad\qquad\qquad\qquad\qquad\qquad\qquad\qquad\qquad\qquad$ Alanine
$\qquad\qquad\qquad\qquad\qquad\qquad\qquad\qquad\qquad\qquad\qquad$ 60%

HCN + HŌ $\rightleftharpoons$ ⁻CN + H₂O

⁻CN + >C=O $\longrightarrow$ >C(Ō)(CN)

>C(Ō)(CN) + H₂O $\longrightarrow$ >C(OH)(CN) + HŌ

FIG. 13.7   Cyanohydrin formation.

Aldol and Related Aldehyde Condensations.   Aldehydes undergo *self-condensation* reactions when treated with catalytic amounts of aqueous base.   The basic catalyst removes a proton from the α-position of one molecule, and the resulting enolate ion then adds to the carbonyl group of a second molecule.

$$CH_3CHO + \bar{H}\bar{O} \rightleftharpoons \left[CH_2CH \longleftrightarrow CH_2=CH \right]$$

$$CH_3CH + CH_2CH \longrightarrow CH_3CHCH_2CH \xrightarrow{H_2O} CH_3CHCH_2CH + H\bar{O}$$

Aldol

Aldols (aldehyde-alcohol) may be dehydrated either by heating the basic reaction mixture or by a separate, acid-catalyzed reaction.   The latter is a standard method of eliminating water from alcohols to produce olefins (Chap. 17), but base-catalyzed dehydration is observed only in systems containing acidic hydrogens.

Acid-catalyzed:

$$CH_3CHCH_2CHO \xrightarrow{H^+} CH_3CHCH_2CHO \xrightarrow{-H_2O} CH_3\overset{+}{C}HCH_2CHO$$

$$\downarrow -H^+$$

$$CH_3CH=CHCHO$$

Base-catalyzed:

$$CH_3CHCH_2CHO \xrightarrow{HO^-} CH_3CH-CHCHO \longrightarrow CH_3CH=CHCHO$$

Crotonaldehyde

Dehydration usually occurs under conditions required for the condensation of unreactive aldehydes such as sterically hindered aliphatic or aromatic aldehydes.

The reactivity of carbonyl compounds is regulated by three factors. First, bulky groups near the carbonyl group are compressed by addition of nucleophiles to the carbonyl carbon.   Second, if the carbonyl group is part of a conjugated system, as in aromatic aldehydes, some delocalization energy must be lost in the addition step.

A third factor is the interaction of dipolar substituents with the carbonyl dipole and any charges introduced during the addition step.   An α-halogen, for example, speeds up addition of negative nucleophiles, because dipole-dipole repulsion in the aldehyde is changed to an attractive charge-dipole interaction in the intermediate adduct.

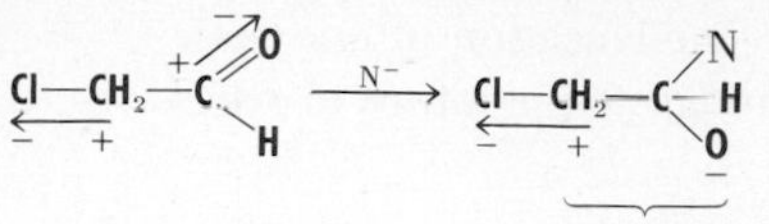

Cl—CH₂—C(=O)H → N⁻ → Cl—CH₂—C(H)(=N)(O⁻)

Dipole-dipole
repulsion

Charge-dipole
attraction

Reactivity of carbonyl compounds in cyanohydrin formation has been studied carefully. Most aldehydes react to give high-equilibrium conversions to products, although benzaldehyde reacts much more slowly than most aliphatic aldehydes. However, *p*-dimethylaminobenzaldehyde does not form a cyanohydrin, because of resonance interaction between the amino and carbonyl groups (Fig. 13.8). Steric hindrance is shown clearly by the comparison of acetophenone and *tert*-butyl phenyl ketone. Under conditions that give 91% conversion of the methyl ketone, the *tert*-butyl ketone gives only 46% of the addition compound.

Crossed condensations between two aldehydes that both have α-hydrogens give complex reaction mixtures and are not used for synthesis. However, an excess of an aldehyde that has no α-hydrogen (such as benzaldehyde or formaldehyde) can serve as a substrate for a second, acidic aldehyde. Pentaerythritol is made by the condensation of three molecules of formaldehyde with acetaldehyde, followed by a crossed Cannizzaro reaction of the trihydroxyaldehyde with formaldehyde. All steps occur in the same reaction mixture.

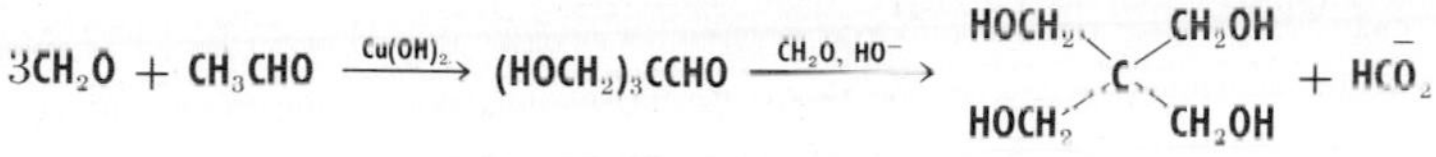

$$3CH_2O + CH_3CHO \xrightarrow{Cu(OH)_2} (HOCH_2)_3CCHO \xrightarrow{CH_2O,\ HO^-} \begin{array}{c} HOCH_2 \quad CH_2OH \\ C \\ HOCH_2 \quad CH_2OH \end{array} + H\bar{C}O_2$$

Pentaerythritol

Pentaerythritol is used in the manufacture of synthetic resins and is converted by reaction with nitric acid to nitrate esters that are highly explosive.

$$(HOCH_2)_4C + 3HNO_3 \xrightarrow{H_2SO_4,\ HNO_3} (O_2NOCH_2)_3CCH_2OH \longrightarrow (O_2NOCH_2)_4C$$

Pentaerythritol
trinitrate
(PETRIN)

Pentaerythritol
tetranitrate
(PETN)

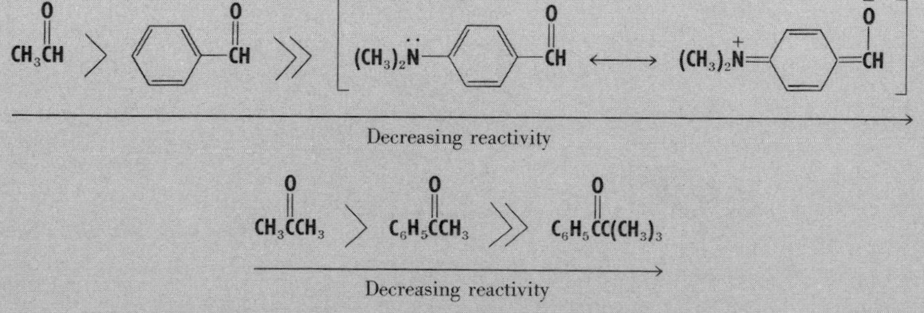

Decreasing reactivity

Decreasing reactivity

FIG. 13.8 *Factors influencing reactivity of carbonyl compounds.*

Acrolein can be made by carrying out the condensation of one mole of formaldehyde with acetaldehyde at a high enough temperature to effect dehydration of the intermediate aldol.

$$CH_2O + CH_3CHO \xrightarrow[300°]{\text{Sodium silicate}} [HOCH_2CH_2CHO] \longrightarrow CH_2\!=\!CHCHO$$
$$\text{Acrolein}$$
$$75\%$$

A number of compounds that have weakly acidic C—H bonds can be added to aldehydes and ketones in the presence of basic catalysts. The reagents include acetylenes, chloroform, malonic ester, acetoacetic ester, and nitroalkanes. Products of such condensations are valuable synthetic intermediates.

$$CHCl_3 \xrightarrow[\text{KOH}]{\text{Powdered}} \bar{C}Cl_3 \xrightarrow{C_6H_5CHO} C_6H_5\overset{\bar{O}}{\underset{}{CH}}CCl_3 \xrightarrow{HCCl_3} C_6H_5\overset{OH}{\underset{}{CH}}CCl_3$$
$$\text{Phenyltrichloro-}$$
$$\text{methylcarbinol}$$
$$41\%$$

$$CH_3COCH_2CO_2C_2H_5 + 2CH_3CHO \xrightarrow[\substack{\text{Excess} \\ \text{aldehyde}}]{K_2CO_3} CH_3CO\overset{HOCHCH_3}{\underset{HOCHCH_3}{C}}CO_2C_2H_5$$

$$CH_3NO_2 \xrightarrow[]{\substack{\text{Aqueous} \\ \text{KOH}}} \left[\bar{C}H_2NO_2 \longleftrightarrow CH_2\!=\!\overset{+}{N}\!\overset{\bar{O}}{\underset{O}{\diagup}} \right] \xrightarrow{CH_3CH_2CH_2CHO}$$

$$CH_3CH_2CH_2\overset{\bar{O}}{\underset{}{CH}}CH_2NO_2 \xrightarrow[-OH^-]{H_2O} CH_3CH_2CH_2\overset{OH}{\underset{}{CH}}CH_2NO_2 \xrightarrow{H_2,\ Pt} CH_3CH_2CH_2\overset{OH}{\underset{}{CH}}CH_2NH_2$$
$$\text{1-Nitro-2-pentanol}$$
$$71\%$$

Condensation of acetylene with aldehydes and ketones is known as *ethynylation.* The reaction produces acetylenic alcohols and was adapted to large-scale commercial operation by a group of German scientists under the leadership of J. W. Reppe.

$$2CH_2O + HC\!\equiv\!CH \xrightarrow[90°]{CuC\equiv CCu} HOCH_2C\!\equiv\!CCH_2OH$$
$$\text{2-Butyne-1,4-diol}$$
$$92\%$$

$$CH_3CHO + HC\!\equiv\!CH \xrightarrow{CuC\equiv CCu} CH_3\overset{OH}{\underset{}{CH}}C\!\equiv\!CH + CH_3\overset{OH}{\underset{}{CH}}C\!\equiv\!C\overset{OH}{\underset{}{CH}}CH_3$$
$$\qquad\qquad 50\% \qquad\qquad\qquad 50\%$$

The synthesis of vitamin A by a group of Swiss chemists included an elegant series of carbonyl condensation reactions. The vitamin is built up from citral, a naturally occurring aldehyde. The first major intermediate, β-ionone, is synthesized as shown in Fig. 13.9, and the conversion of β-ionone to vitamin A is outlined in Fig. 13.10.

Addition of active hydrogen compounds to aldehydes in the presence of ammonia and amines is known as the *Knoevenagel condensation.* Dehydration of the original adducts is often followed by other, secondary reactions.

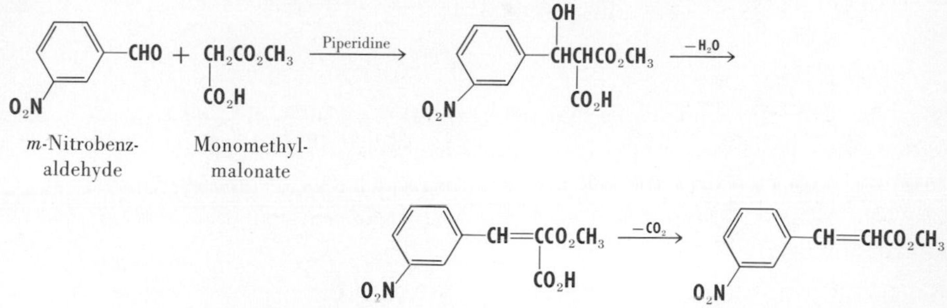

m-Nitrobenzaldehyde Monomethylmalonate

Methyl *m*-nitrocinnamate 86%

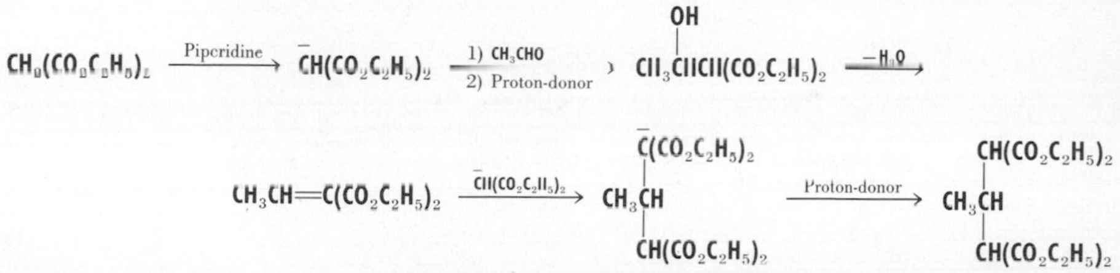

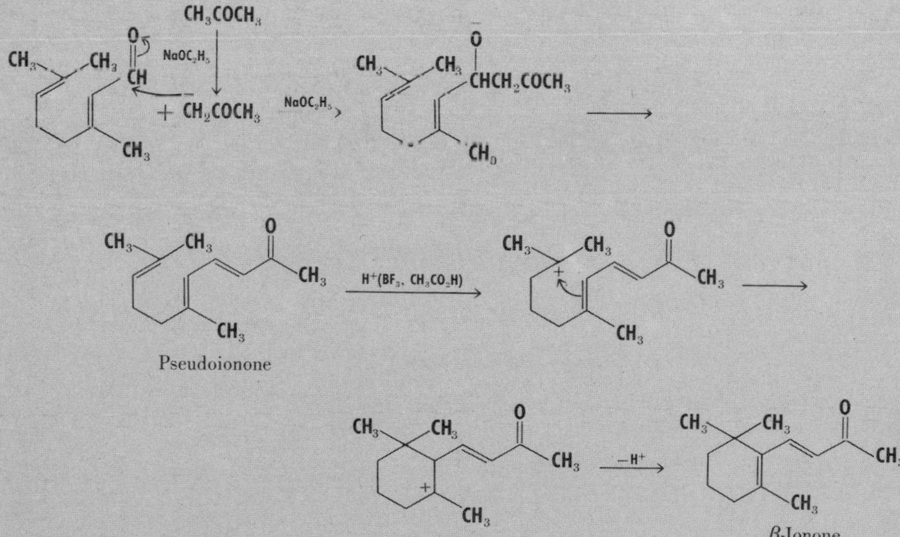

Pseudoionone

β-Ionone

FIG. 13.9 Synthesis of β-ionone.

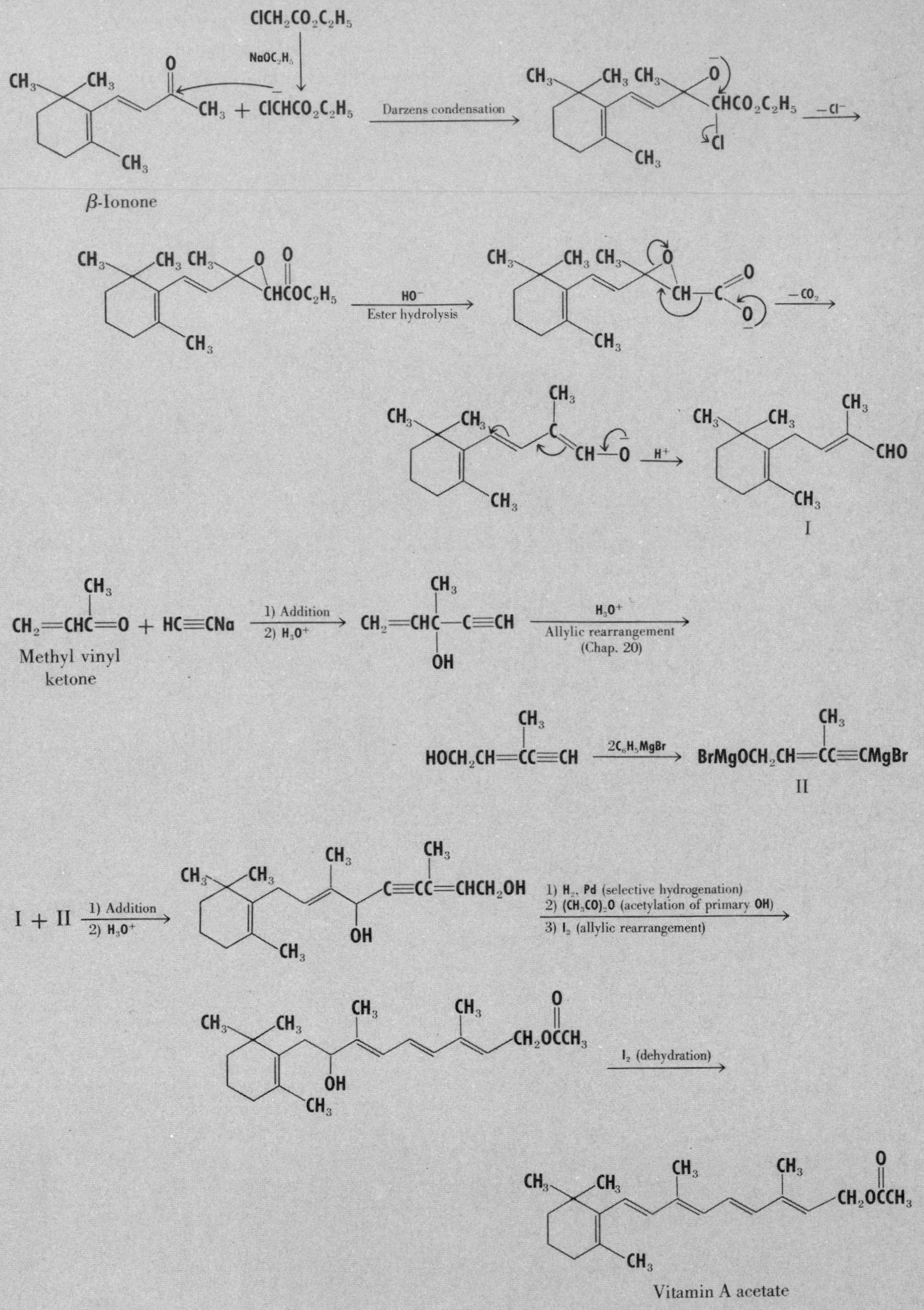

FIG. 13.10   *Synthesis of vitamin A.*

In the *Claisen reaction,* an aldehyde that bears no α-hydrogen is condensed with a ketone or an ester.

$$C_6H_5CHO + CH_3COCH_3 \xrightarrow{10\% \text{ NaOH}} C_6H_5CH=CHCOCH_3$$
Benzalacetone

$$C_6H_5CHO + CH_3CO_2C_2H_5 \xrightarrow{\text{NaOC}_2\text{H}_5,\ 0°} C_6H_5CH=CHCO_2C_2H_5$$
Ethyl cinnamate
70%

In the *Perkin reaction,* an aromatic aldehyde is condensed with an aliphatic anhydride in the presence of the potassium salt of the corresponding carboxylic acid. The reaction has been used frequently for preparation of cinnamic acid and its derivatives. High temperatures are required, since a weak base is used with a weakly acidic reagent.

$$(CH_3CO)_2O + CH_3\overset{-}{C}O_2 \rightleftarrows CH_3CO_2H + \overset{-}{C}H_2\overset{O}{\overset{\|}{C}}\overset{O}{\overset{\|}{C}}CH_3$$
Acetic
anhydride

$$\overset{-}{C}H_2\overset{O}{\overset{\|}{C}}OCCH_3 + C_6H_5CHO \longrightarrow C_6H_5\overset{O^-}{\underset{|}{C}}HCH_2\overset{O}{\overset{\|}{C}}\overset{O}{\overset{\|}{C}}CCH_3$$

$$C_6H_5\overset{O^-}{\underset{|}{C}}HCH_2\overset{O}{\overset{\|}{C}}\overset{O}{\overset{\|}{C}}CCH_3 + CH_3CO_2H \rightleftarrows C_6H_5\overset{OH}{\underset{|}{C}}HCH_2\overset{O}{\overset{\|}{C}}\overset{O}{\overset{\|}{C}}CCH_3 \xrightarrow{-H_2O} C_6H_5CH=CH\overset{O}{\overset{\|}{C}}\overset{O}{\overset{\|}{C}}CCH_3$$

Net reaction: $C_6H_5CHO + (CH_3CO)_2O \xrightarrow[180°]{CH_3CO_2K} C_6H_5CH=CH\overset{O}{\overset{\|}{C}}\overset{O}{\overset{\|}{C}}CCH_3 \xrightarrow[\text{(during isolation)}]{H_2O} C_6H_5CH=CHCO_2H$

Cinnamic acid
60%

Vinylogs† of cinnamic acid are produced if cinnamaldehyde is used as a substrate in the Perkin reaction.

$$C_6H_5CH=CHCHO + (CH_3CO)_2O \xrightarrow[2)\ H_2O]{1)\ CH_3CO_2Na,\ 170°} C_6H_5CH=CHCH=CHCO_2H$$
5-Phenyl-2,4-pentadienoic acid
25%

The *benzoin condensation* is a remarkable self-condensation of aromatic aldehydes. The reaction is *specifically catalyzed by cyanide ions.* Three properties of the catalyst combine to make cyanide a unique catalyst: (1) sufficient nucleophilic reactivity to add to a carbonyl function; (2) a marked acid-strengthening effect on hydrogen atoms attached to carbon atoms adjacent to the —C≡N function; and (3) the

---

† Vinylogs are related by the introduction of —CH=CH— units in a chain. Sometimes compounds are said to contain vinylogous functional groups if two parts of a complex functional group are separated by a —CH=CH— unit. For example, $RCH=CH\overset{O}{\overset{\|}{C}}R'$ might be called a *vinylogous acid.*
$\underset{\underset{OH}{|}}{}$

ability of cyanide to depart from the cyanohydrin structure in the last intermediate.

$$ArCHO + \overset{-}{C}N \;\rightleftharpoons\; ArCHCN \;\; (\overset{\bar{O}}{|})$$

$$ArCHCN \;\longrightarrow\; \left[Ar\overset{OH}{\underset{|}{C}}{-}CN \;\longleftrightarrow\; Ar\overset{OH}{\underset{|}{C}}{=}C{=}\overset{-}{N} \right]$$

$$Ar\overset{OH}{\underset{|}{\underset{-}{C}}}CN + ArCHO \;\longrightarrow\; Ar\overset{OH}{\underset{|}{C}}{-}\overset{}{C}HAr \;\rightleftharpoons\; Ar\overset{O}{\underset{|}{C}}{-}CHAr$$
$$\qquad\qquad\qquad\qquad CN\;\;O \qquad\qquad CN\;\;OH$$

$$Ar\overset{\overset{O}{\|}}{C}{-}CHAr \;\longrightarrow\; Ar\overset{}{C}{-}CHAr + \overset{-}{C}N$$
$$\underset{CN\;\;OH}{} \qquad\qquad \underset{O\;\;OH}{}$$

A benzoin
(or acyloin)

Although the reaction gives good yields with many aromatic aldehydes, it is unsuccessful with aliphatic aldehydes. Probably, competing reactions involving α-hydrogens cause failure with the latter compounds.

$$CH_3O{-}\langle\!\!\bigcirc\!\!\rangle{-}CHO \xrightarrow[\substack{95\%\ C_2H_5OH \\ reflux}]{KCN} CH_3O{-}\langle\!\!\bigcirc\!\!\rangle{-}\overset{O}{\underset{\|}{C}}{-}\overset{OH}{\underset{|}{C}}H{-}\langle\!\!\bigcirc\!\!\rangle{-}OCH_3$$

4,4'-Dimethoxybenzoin
60%

Ketones as Substrates. For both electronic and steric reasons, ketones are less reactive than aldehydes. Since carbon groups have electron-releasing properties slightly greater than that of hydrogen, the carbonyl groups of ketones are less electrophilic than those of aldehydes. Furthermore, hydrogen atoms offer little steric hindrance to addition reactions. Acetone undergoes self-condensation, giving diacetone alcohol, but only a small amount of the product is formed at equilibrium. High yields of diacetone alcohol are obtained by continuously cycling acetone vapor over a basic catalyst, with the small amount of product formed in each pass being retained as a high-boiling residue in a reservoir.

$$2CH_3COCH_3 \underset{Ba(OH)_2}{\rightleftharpoons} CH_3\overset{OH}{\underset{\underset{CH_3}{|}}{C}}CH_2COCH_3$$

Diacetone alcohol
70% by recycling

Acid-catalyzed condensations of aldehydes and ketones are illustrated by the reaction of acetone with anhydrous hydrogen chloride (Fig. 13.11). Mesityl oxide, the first isolable product, reacts with additional acetone, giving phorone and other higher-molecular-weight products. Mixtures of products are usually obtained in acid-catalyzed condensations of carbonyl compounds.

Several valuable synthetic procedures are based upon condensations of ketones with enolates and other similar anions. The reactions are generally similar to reactions of aldehydes, but often require more vigorous reaction conditions.

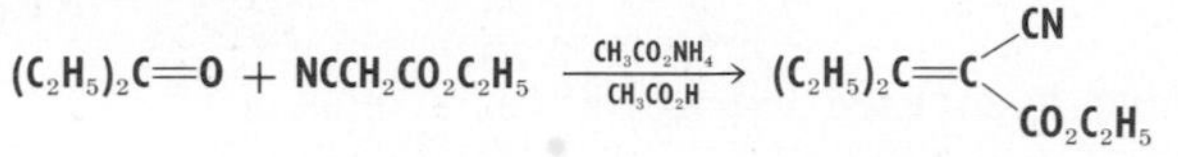

$$(C_2H_5)_2C{=}O + NCCH_2CO_2C_2H_5 \xrightarrow[CH_3CO_2H]{CH_3CO_2NH_4} (C_2H_5)_2C{=}C\underset{CO_2C_2H_5}{\overset{CN}{\big\langle}}$$

Ethyl cyanoacetate   65%

$$+ CH_3NO_2 \xrightarrow{C_2H_5ONa}$$

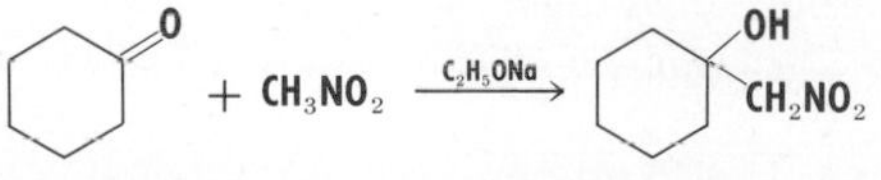

1-Nitromethyl-1-cyclohexanol

In the *Stobbe condensation*, the anion from diethyl succinate adds to a ketone. The first adduct cyclizes by nucleophilic substitution in the more remote ester group. The ring is opened by a base-catalyzed elimination which generates a free carboxyl group.

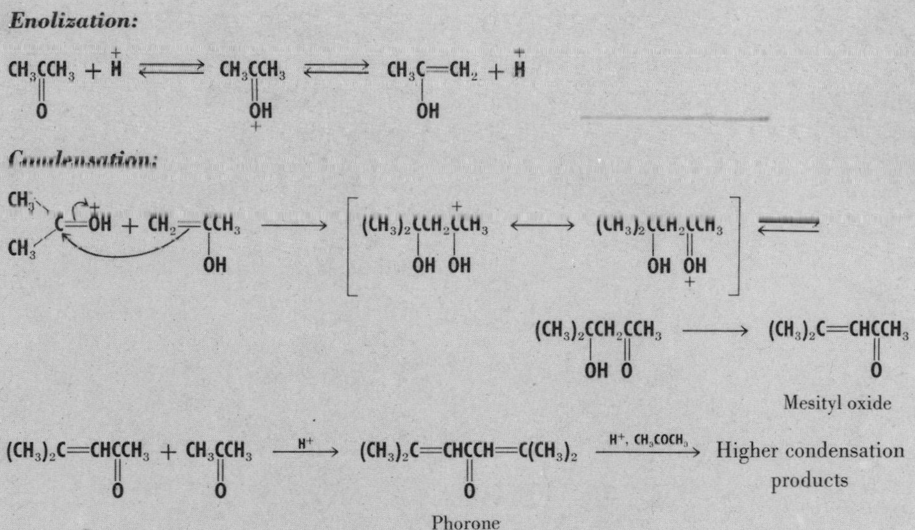

Enolization:

$$CH_3CCH_3 + \overset{+}{H} \rightleftharpoons CH_3CCH_3 \rightleftharpoons CH_3C{=}CH_2 + \overset{+}{H}$$
$$\underset{O}{\,} \qquad \underset{\overset{OH}{+}}{\,} \qquad \underset{OH}{\,}$$

Condensation:

$$(CH_3)_2CCH_2CCH_3 \longrightarrow (CH_3)_2C{=}CHCCH_3$$
$$\underset{OH}{\,}\;\underset{O}{\,} \qquad\qquad \underset{O}{\,}$$

Mesityl oxide

$$(CH_3)_2C{=}CHCCH_3 + CH_3CCH_3 \xrightarrow{H^+} (CH_3)_2C{=}CHCCH{=}C(CH_3)_2 \xrightarrow{H^+,\,CH_3COCH_3} \text{Higher condensation products}$$
$$\underset{O}{\,} \qquad \underset{O}{\,} \qquad\qquad \underset{O}{\,}$$

Phorone

FIG. 13.11   *Acid-catalyzed enolization and condensation of acetone.*

$$CH_2CO_2C_2H_5 \xrightarrow{KOC_4H_9\text{-}t} \bar{C}HCO_2C_2H_5 \xrightarrow{R_2C=O} R_2C-CHCH_2 \xrightarrow{-C_2H_5O^-} \begin{array}{c} O-C=O \\ R_2C \qquad CH_2 \\ CH \\ CO_2C_2H_5 \end{array} \xrightarrow{RO^-}$$

CH₂CO₂C₂H₅   CH₂CO₂C₂H₅   N. Add. CO₂C₂H₅

Diethyl
succinate

$$\begin{array}{c} O-C=O \\ R_2C \quad CH_2 \\ C \\ CO_2C_2H_5 \end{array} \longrightarrow R_2C=CCH_2\bar{C}O_2 \xrightarrow{H_3O^+,\ \text{work-up}} R_2C=CCH_2CO_2H + \begin{array}{c} O-C=O \\ R_2C \quad CH_2 \\ CH \\ CO_2C_2H_5 \end{array}$$

with $CO_2C_2H_5$ substituents

Stobbe condensations have been used extensively in syntheses of polycyclic ring systems. Potassium *tert*-butoxide and sodium hydride are commonly used as basic condensing agents. Aldehydes have only occasionally been used as substrates in Stobbe reactions.

α-Tetralone   Bauschemi   90%

Conjugate Addition. Carbon-carbon double bonds conjugated with *electron sinks* serve as good substrates in nucleophilic additions. The group of reactions is known as *Michael additions*, a name originally applied in a more restricted sense to reactions of acetoacetic ester and malonic ester. Table 13.1 lists reactants commonly used to make carbon-carbon bonds by conjugate addition. Michael reactions are catalyzed by bases such as sodium hydroxide, sodium ethoxide, and amines (usually piperidine).

$$CH_2(CO_2C_2H_5)_2 \xrightarrow{C_2H_5ONa} \bar{C}H(CO_2C_2H_5)_2 \xrightarrow{C_6H_5CH=CHCOC_6H_5} C_6H_5\bar{C}HCHCOC_6H_5 \rightleftharpoons$$

$$CH(CO_2C_2H_5)_2$$

$$C_6H_5CHCH_2COC_6H_5 \xrightarrow{C_2H_5OH} C_6H_5CHCH_2COC_6H_5 + C_2H_5\bar{O}$$

$$\bar{C}(CO_2C_2H_5)_2 \qquad\qquad CH(CO_2C_2H_5)_2$$

$$HCN + (CH_3)_2C=CHNO_2 \xrightarrow[CH_3OCH_2CH_2OCH_3]{KOH} (CH_3)_2CCH_2NO_2$$

$$CN$$

2-Methyl-1-
nitro-1-propene

2,2-Dimethyl-3-
nitropropionitrile
75%

$$CH_3NO_2 + CH_3CH=CHCO_2C_2H_5 \xrightarrow[C_2H_5OH]{C_2H_5ONa} CH_3CHCH_2CO_2C_2H_5$$

$$CH_2NO_2$$

Ethyl crotonate   Ethyl 3-methyl-4-nitrobutyrate
55%

$$CH_2(CO_2C_2H_5)_2 + CH_3CH=CHCH=CHCO_2CH_3 \xrightarrow[CH_3OH]{CH_3ONa} CH_3CHCH_2CH=CHCO_2CH_3 + CH_3CH=CHCHCH_2CO_2CH_3$$

Methyl sorbate $\underset{CH(CO_2C_2H_5)_2}{|}$ $\underset{CH(CO_2C_2H_5)_2}{|}$

       72%   8%

$$CH_3COCH_3 + 3CH_2=CHCN \xrightarrow[t\text{-}C_4H_9OH]{KOH} CH_3COC\overset{\displaystyle CH_2CH_2CN}{\underset{\displaystyle CH_2CH_2CN}{-CH_2CH_2CN}}$$

1,1,1-Tri(2-cyanoethyl)acetone

In the *Mannich reaction*, formaldehyde is used as a substrate in a two-stage condensation reaction. Formaldehyde first reacts with an active methylene compound in an acid-catalyzed addition-elimination reaction. An unsaturated ketone is formed, which then reacts with an amine by conjugate addition.

$$RCOCH_3 \rightleftharpoons R\overset{\displaystyle OH}{C}=CH_2 \xrightarrow{CH_2=OH^+} R\overset{\displaystyle \overset{OH}{||}}{C}CH_2CH_2OH \xrightarrow[2)\ -H_2O]{1)\ -H^+} R\overset{\displaystyle \overset{O}{||}}{C}CH=CH_2 \xrightarrow{R'NH_2} R\overset{\displaystyle \overset{O}{||}}{C}CH_2CH_2NHR'$$

Aldehydes, ketones, and esters serve as active methylene compounds in Mannich reactions.

$$C_6H_5COCH_3 + CH_2O + (CH_3)_2NH \xrightarrow{(CH_3)_2N^+H_2Cl^-} C_6H_5COCH_2CH_2N(CH_3)_2$$

(2-Dimethylamino)ethyl
phenyl ketone

TABLE 13.1   *Reactants in Conjugate Addition*

Substrates	*Nucleophiles*
$\overset{\|}{C}=\overset{\|}{C}$ CHO	$\bar{C}N$
$-\overset{\|}{C}=\overset{\|}{C}-\overset{\overset{O}{\|\|}}{C}-R$	$\overset{\|}{\underset{\|}{\bar{C}}}$ NO_2
$-\overset{\|}{C}=\overset{\|}{C}-\overset{O}{\overset{\|\|}{C}}OR$	$-\overset{\|}{\underset{\|}{C}}-SO_2R$
$-\overset{\|}{C}=\overset{\|}{C}-\overset{\|}{C}=\overset{\|}{C}-\overset{O}{\overset{\|\|}{C}}OR$	$C_6H_5-\overset{\|}{\underset{\|}{\bar{C}}}-CN$
$-\overset{\|}{C}=\overset{\|}{C}-NO_2$	$NC-\overset{\|}{\underset{\|}{\bar{C}}}-CO_2R$
$-\overset{\|}{C}=\overset{\|}{C}-C\equiv N$	$RO_2C-\overset{\|}{\underset{\|}{\bar{C}}}-CO_2R$
$O=\langle\ \rangle=O$	

Organometallic Reagents in Carbonyl Additions

Grignard reagents and organolithium compounds add to carbonyl compounds to produce metal alkoxides which, on hydrolysis, give alcohols. Formaldehyde gives primary alcohols; other aldehydes give secondary alcohols; and ketones give tertiary alcohols. The reaction provides one of the most versatile and reliable methods for building up branched structures.

$$H_2C=O \ + \ (CH_3)_2CHCH_2MgBr \ \xrightarrow{\text{Ether}} \ (CH_3)_2CHCH_2CH_2OMgBr \ \xrightarrow{H_3O^+} \ (CH_3)_2CHCH_2CH_2OH$$
Isoamyl alcohol

$$CH_3CH_2CHO \ + \ C_6H_5MgBr \ \xrightarrow[\text{2) } H_3O^+]{\text{1) Ether}} \ C_6H_5\underset{\underset{OH}{|}}{CH}CH_2CH_3$$

1-Phenyl-1-propanol

$$CH_3\underset{\underset{O}{\|}}{C}CH_3 \ + \ CH_3C{\equiv}CMgBr \ \xrightarrow[\text{2) } NH_4Cl,\ H_2O]{\text{1) Ether}} \ (CH_3)_2\underset{\overset{OH}{|}}{C}C{\equiv}CCH_3$$

4-Methyl-4-hydroxy-2-pentyne

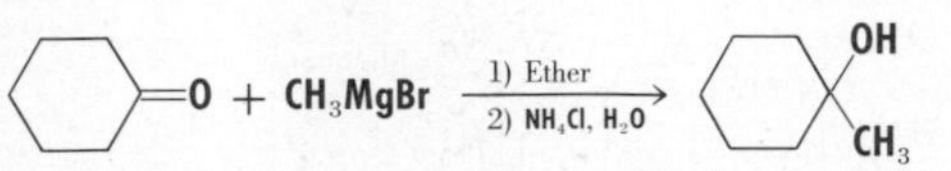

$$\text{(cyclohexanone)}{=}O \ + \ CH_3MgBr \ \xrightarrow[\text{2) } NH_4Cl,\ H_2O]{\text{1) Ether}} \ \text{(cyclohexane ring with OH and } CH_3)$$

1-Methylcyclohexanol

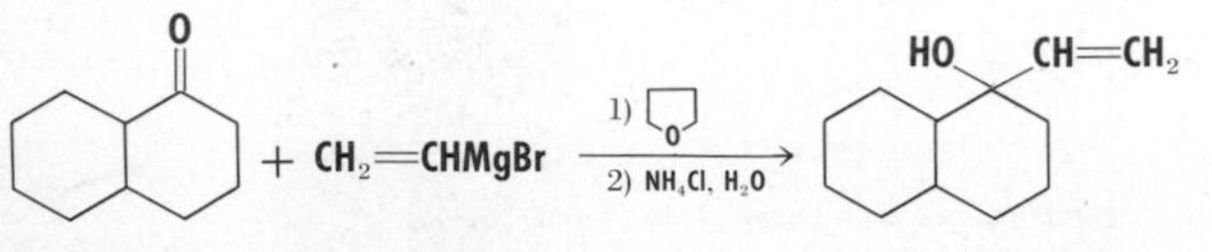

α-Decalone + CH₂=CHMgBr $\xrightarrow[\text{2) } NH_4Cl,\ H_2O]{\text{1) } \square}$ 1-Vinyl-1-decalol

Reaction mixtures formed by addition of organometallics to ketones are hydrolyzed with weak acids such as ammonium chloride in order to avoid the acid-catalyzed dehydration of the tertiary alcohols produced. Side reactions sometimes occur with sterically hindered ketones.

Enolization:

$$RMgX \ + \ CH_3CH_2\underset{\underset{O}{\|}}{C}C(CH_3)_3 \ \longrightarrow \ CH_3CH{=}\underset{\overset{OMgX}{|}}{C}C(CH_3)_3 \ + \ RH$$

Reduction:

$$-\overset{|}{\underset{\underset{H}{|}}{C}}-\overset{|}{C}-MgX \ + \ R\overset{\overset{O}{\|}}{C}R \ \longrightarrow \ \left[\begin{array}{c} \overset{R}{\underset{R}{\rangle}}C{=}\overset{+}{O} \\ H \quad \overset{-}{MgX} \\ \overset{|}{C}-\overset{|}{C} \end{array}\right] \ \longrightarrow \ R_2\overset{|}{\underset{\underset{H}{|}}{C}}-OMgX \ + \ {>}C{=}C{<}$$

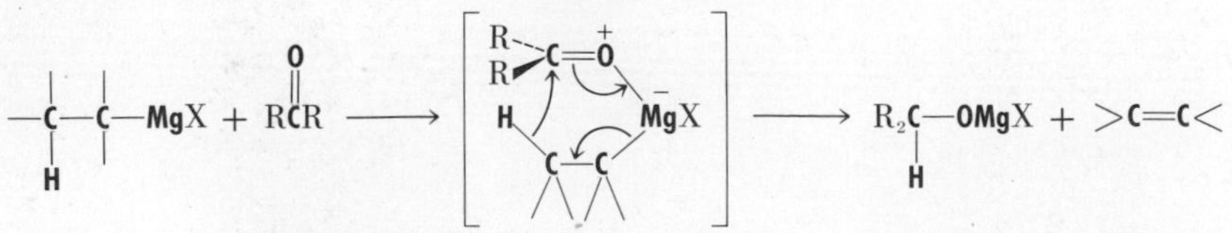

Coordination of a metal atom with a carbonyl oxygen, shown above in the reduction reaction, is undoubtedly also involved in addition and enolization reactions. In general, low reaction temperatures and substitution of lithium compounds for Grignard reagents favor addition in preference to enolization and reduction. Steric hindrance in either the carbonyl compound or the metallic reagent decreases yields of addition product.

$$(CH_3)_3CCOC(CH_3)_3 + (CH_3)_3CLi \xrightarrow[-60°]{Ether} [(CH_3)_3C]_3COLi + [(CH_3)_3C]_2CHOLi + (CH_3)_2C{=}CH_2 \xrightarrow{H_2O}$$

Hexamethylacetone

$$[(CH_3)_3C]_3COH + [(CH_3)_3C]_2CHOH$$

Tri-*tert*-butyl-   Di-*tert*-butylcarbinol
carbinol
81%

Conjugate addition occurs in competition with normal carbonyl addition with α,β-unsaturated ketones. Grignard reagents usually give more conjugate addition than lithium compounds.

$$C_6H_5CH{=}CHCC_6H_5 + C_6H_5MgBr \xrightarrow[2)\ H_3O^+]{1)\ Ether} (C_6H_5)_2CHCH_2CC_6H_5 + C_6H_5CH{=}CHC(C_6H_5)_2$$

Benzalacetophenone   94%   Trace

$$C_6H_5CH{=}CHCC_6H_5 + C_6H_5Li \xrightarrow[2)\ H_3O^+]{1)\ Ether} (C_6H_5)_2CHCH_2CC_6H_5 + C_6H_5CH{=}CHC(C_6H_5)_2$$

13%   69%

Reformatsky Reaction. Grignard and lithium reagents cannot be made from compounds that contain reactive functional groups such as carbonyl, ester, nitro, and many others. However, zinc compounds are less reactive, and zinc reagents can be prepared from α-haloesters and added to aldehydes and ketones.

$$Zn + BrCH_2CO_2C_2H_5 \xrightarrow{Ether} BrZnCH_2CO_2C_2H_5 \xrightarrow{(CH_3)_2CO}$$

$$\underset{OZnBr}{(CH_3)_2CCH_2CO_2C_2H_5} \xrightarrow{H_3O^+} \underset{OH}{(CH_3)_2CCH_2CO_2C_2H_5}$$

Ethyl 3-methyl-3-hydroxybutyrate

Another useful synthesis of tertiary alcohols makes use of reactions of organometallic reagents with esters and acid chlorides. Two molecules of metallic reagent add to the substrate, and alkoxide or chloride ions are eliminated.

$$CH_3MgBr + CH_3CH_2COCH_3 \xrightarrow{Ether} \underset{OCH_3}{\overset{OMgBr}{CH_3CH_2C{-}CH_3}} \xrightarrow{-Mg(OCH_3)Br} CH_3CH_2CCH_3 \xrightarrow{CH_3MgBr}$$

$$\underset{CH_3}{\overset{OMgBr}{CH_3CH_2CCH_3}} \xrightarrow{H_3O^+} \underset{CH_3}{\overset{OH}{CH_3CH_2CCH_3}}$$

2-Methyl-2-butanol
(*tert*-Amyl alcohol)

$$CH_3CH_2CCl + 2C_6H_5MgBr \xrightarrow[2)\ NH_4Cl]{1)\ Ether} \underset{OH}{CH_3CH_2C(C_6H_5)_2}$$

1,1-Diphenyl-1-propanol

Lactones behave as open-chain esters and undergo ring opening to give diols.

$$\text{(γ-Butyrolactone)} + 2CH_3CH_2MgBr \xrightarrow[\text{2) NH}_4\text{Cl}]{\text{1) Ether}} HO(CH_2)_3C(CH_2CH_3)_2 \text{ (OH)}$$

γ-Butyrolactone   4-Ethyl-1,4-hexanediol

Aryl isocyanates add organometallic compounds very easily to form amides.

$$C_6H_5N{=}C{=}O + (CH_3)_2CHMgCl \xrightarrow[\text{2) H}_2\text{O}^+]{\text{1) Ether}} C_6H_5NHCCH(CH_3)_2$$

Isobutyranilide

Nucleophilic Addition to Carbon-Carbon Double Bonds

Alkenes are not attacked by Grignard reagents, but ethylene adds to the very reactive reagents *tert*-butyllithium and isopropyllithium. Double bonds conjugated with aromatic nuclei have also been used as substrates in nucleophilic addition.

$$(CH_3)_3CLi + CH_2{=}CH_2 \xrightarrow{\text{Ether, }-40°} (CH_3)_3CCH_2CH_2Li$$

$$\xrightarrow{\text{H}_2\text{O}} (CH_3)_3CCH_2CH_3 \quad \text{Neohexane}$$

$$\xrightarrow[\text{2) H}_3\text{O}^+]{\text{1) CO}_2} (CH_3)_3CCH_2CH_2CO_2H \quad \text{4,4-Dimethylvaleric acid}$$

$$KNa + C_6H_5COCH_3 \xrightarrow{-\text{NaOCH}_3} C_6H_5C^-K^+ \xrightarrow{(C_6H_5)_2C=CH_2} (C_6H_5)_2CCH_2CC_6H_5 \xrightarrow{\text{H}_2\text{O}} (C_6H_5)_2CHCH_2CC_6H_5$$

Aluminum alkyls add smoothly to terminal alkenes in a reaction that may have considerable synthetic potential. Since aluminum alkyls may be oxidized to alkoxides, the reaction provides a synthetic route to terminal alcohols.

$$3(CH_3)_2C{=}CH_2 + Al + {}^3\!/_2 H_2 \xrightarrow{200°} [(CH_3)_2CHCH_2]_3Al$$

Triisobutylaluminum

$$[(CH_3)_2CHCH_2]_3Al + CH_3CH{=}CH_2 \xrightarrow{\text{Benzene, }100°} \left[(CH_3)_2CHCH_2CHCH_2 \right]_3 Al + \text{Products of repeated addition}$$

$$\xrightarrow[\text{2) H}_3\text{O}^+]{\text{1) O}_2} (CH_3)_2CHCH_2CHCH_2OH$$

If small amounts of certain metal halides such as titanium tetra-chloride are added to trialkyl aluminum compounds, the addition reaction is catalyzed very strongly, and high-molecular-weight polymers are formed from terminal alkenes (Chap. 25).

Synthesis of Alcohols

Many reactions that give alcohols as products have been discussed in this and the three preceding chapters. While still other alcohol-forming reactions will be encountered in later chapters, a sufficient number have been presented to permit evaluation of various procedures as synthetic methods. In devising a synthesis of a particular alcohol, the following possible routes are the most likely to be considered: (1) hydrolysis of halides; (2) reduction of aldehydes, ketones, or carboxylic acids and their derivatives; (3) addition of organometallic reagents to carbonyl compounds; and (4) addition of water to alkenes.

Hydrolysis of primary halides, often a smooth reaction, has limited synthetic value because the required starting materials are not readily available. Halogenation of hydrocarbons (Chap. 18) tends to be nondis-criminating and gives complex halide mixtures difficult to separate. A few hydrocarbons, either because of symmetry or because a single position is activated by an adjacent group, give high yields of pure monochlorides. Cheap and convenient syntheses of alcohols can be based upon such compounds.

$$CH_2{=}CHCH_3 + Cl_2 \xrightarrow[-HCl]{Light} CH_2{=}CHCH_2Cl \xrightarrow{H_2O} CH_2{=}CHCH_2OH$$

But:

$$(CH_3)_4C + Cl_2 \xrightarrow[-HCl]{Light} (CH_3)_3CCH_2Cl \xrightarrow{H_2O}$$

High yield

No reaction or completely rearranged products

Reduction of aldehydes, ketones, acids, esters, and ethylene oxides with lithium aluminum hydride is a highly preferred laboratory procedure for preparing alcohols. Catalytic hydrogenation (Chap. 19) of the same classes of compounds (with the exception of acids) is a more economical method for large-scale industrial operations. The principal methods for synthesis of aldehydes and ketones will be studied in Chaps. 14, 15, and 20, although some methods have already been presented. In general, one can assume that most alkyl aldehydes and ketones containing five carbon atoms or fewer are available commercially at reasonable prices. The same is true of cyclohexanone and many aryl alkyl ketones.

Alcohol syntheses based upon addition of nucleophilic carbon compounds to carbonyl groups have great versatility, as was illustrated by the vitamin A synthesis (page 288). Monofunctional alcohols are often made from Grignard and lithium reagents. Polyfunctional alcohols are very frequently prepared by the addition of enolates (aldol, Knoevenagel, Perkin, Stobbe, etc., condensations).　　Figure 13.12 illustrates some of the possibilities for the synthesis of alcohols from benzaldehyde as a starting material.

Hydration of alkenes is a cheap route to branched alcohols if the corresponding olefins are available.　Petroleum by-products (Chap. 26) include ethylene, propylene, the butenes, and the pentenes.　These alkenes serve as starting materials for preparation of many simple

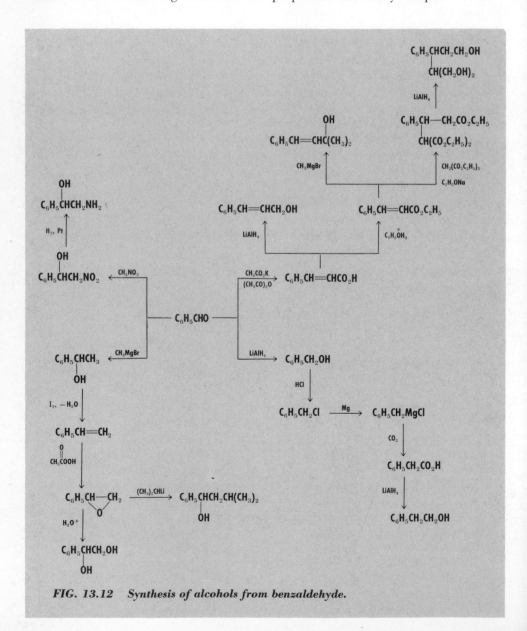

FIG. 13.12　*Synthesis of alcohols from benzaldehyde.*

alcohols and related compounds. The following are randomly chosen examples of syntheses based upon isobutene.

$$(CH_3)_2C{=}CH_2 + H_2O \xrightarrow{H_2SO_4} (CH_3)_3COH \xrightarrow{HCl} (CH_3)_3CCl \xrightarrow{Li}$$

$$(CH_3)_3CLi \xrightarrow[2)\ H_3O^+]{1)\ CO_2} (CH_3)_3CCO_2H \xrightarrow[2)\ H_3O^+]{1)\ LiAlH_4} (CH_3)_3CCH_2OH$$

1) CH₃CHO   CH₂=CH₂
2) H₃O⁺

$$(CH_3)_3CCHCH_3$$
$$\overset{|}{OH}$$

$$(CH_3)_3CCH_2CH_2Li \xrightarrow[2)\ H_3O^+]{1)\ CO_2} (CH_3)_3CCH_2CH_2CO_2H \xrightarrow[2)\ H_3O^+]{1)\ LiAlH_4} (CH_3)_3CCH_2CH_2CH_2OH$$

Problems

1. Make a list of all *classes of substrates* (each having a different functional group or combination of functional groups) and *classes of nucleophiles* (each having different functional groups) found in this chapter.

2. Write out syntheses of the following substances from inorganic materials. Make a particular compound or intermediate only once in the problem set.

a. $(CH_3)_2CHOH$

b. $CH_3CH_2CH_2CH_2OH$

c. $(CH_3)_2CHCH_2NH_2$

d. $CH_3CH(SC_2H_5)_2$

e. $(CH_3)_2CCO_2H$
   $\overset{|}{NH_2}$

f. $CH_3CH_2CONH_2$

g. $CH_3CO_2C_2H_5$

h. $CH_3SCH_2CH_2CN$

i. $CH_3CHCH_2CO_2C_2H_5$
   $\overset{|}{OH}$

j. $CH_3CH{=}CHCH_2OH$

k. $(CH_3)_2CCH_3$
   $\overset{|}{NH_2}$

l. $(CH_3)_2C{=}CHCHCH{=}C(CH_3)_2$
   $\overset{|}{OH}$

m. $CH_3CCH_2CH_3$
   $\overset{O}{\underset{CH_2-CH_2}{\overset{O}{\diagdown\diagup}}}$

n. $CH_3CHClCH_2CO_2H$

o. $NH_2CH_2CO_2H$

p. $(CH_3)_2\overset{+}{N}HCH_2CH_2CN\ Cl^-$

3. Write examples of the following:

a. Meerwein-Ponndorf reaction.

b. An acid-catalyzed condensation reaction.

c. A Michael reaction involving nitromethane.

d. A crossed Cannizzaro reaction.

e. Leuckart reaction.

f. The synthesis of a secondary alcohol by a Grignard reaction.

g. An equilibrium reaction driven to completion by continuous removal of one of the products. Explain.

h. A stable hydrate of an aldehyde. Explain.

i. Three addition reactions to a carbon-nitrogen triple bond.

j. Two different polymers of the same aldehyde.

k. Addition to a vinylogous system. Explain.

l. Use of a γ-carbon as a nucleophile. Explain.

m. Conjugate addition.

n. A reaction that increases the length of the carbon chain by three atoms.

4. Explain the following facts:

a. Ethyl pyruvate $(CH_3\overset{O}{\overset{\|}{C}}C\overset{O}{\overset{\|}{O}}C_2H_5)$ forms a ketal more readily than acetone.

b. If one attempts to carbonate a Grignard reagent by passing a stream of carbon dioxide through an ether solution of the reagent, alcohols, rather than carboxylic acids, are produced.

c. An elimination reaction usually accompanies the Perkin reaction.

d. Cyanide anion catalyzes the benzoin condensation.

e. The substance **OHCCHO** when treated with strong base gives **HOCH₂COOH** rather than a mixture of **CH₂OHCH₂OH** and **HOOCCOOH**.

f. When a 1 to 1 mixture of *p*-nitrobenzaldehyde and *p*-methoxybenzaldehyde is submitted to the benzoin condensation, essentially only two compounds are obtained.

5. Write out syntheses of the following compounds, starting with materials one can buy (such as acetophenone, benzaldehyde, acrylonitrile, nitromethane, acetone, ethyl acetate, etc.).

a. C₆H₅CH=CHCH=CHCH₂OH

b. (C₆H₅)₂C—CHC₆H₅ (*Hint:* Grignard additions can be
      | |
      OH OH
used with hydroxy ketones if an excess of the reagent is used.)

c.   OH
       |
   CH₃CHCHCH₃
       |
      C₆H₅

d.   CH₃
            |
   C₆H₅CHCH₂CH₂CO₂H

e. CH₃OCH₂CH₂COC₂H₅

6. Formulate a mechanism for the *Darzens glycidic ester condensation,* illustrated by the following equation:

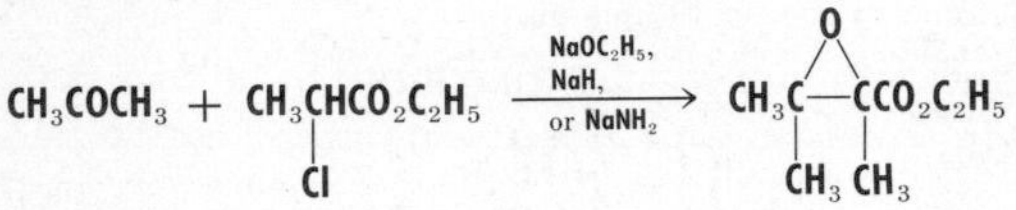

$$CH_3COCH_3 + CH_3CHCO_2C_2H_5 \xrightarrow[\text{or NaNH}_2]{\substack{\text{NaOC}_2\text{H}_5, \\ \text{NaH,}}} CH_3C\text{—}CCO_2C_2H_5$$

with **CH₃CHCO₂C₂H₅** bearing **Cl**, and product **CH₃C—CCO₂C₂H₅** with epoxide O and **CH₃ CH₃**.

Also formulate a mechanism for the acid-catalyzed conversion of a glycidic ester to an aldehyde.

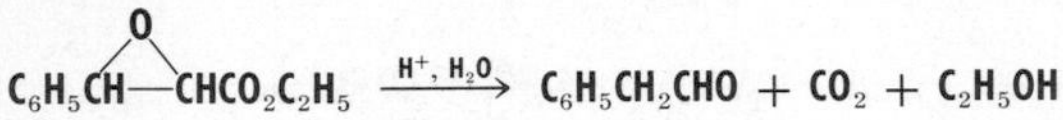

$$C_6H_5CH\text{—}CHCO_2C_2H_5 \xrightarrow{H^+, H_2O} C_6H_5CH_2CHO + CO_2 + C_2H_5OH$$

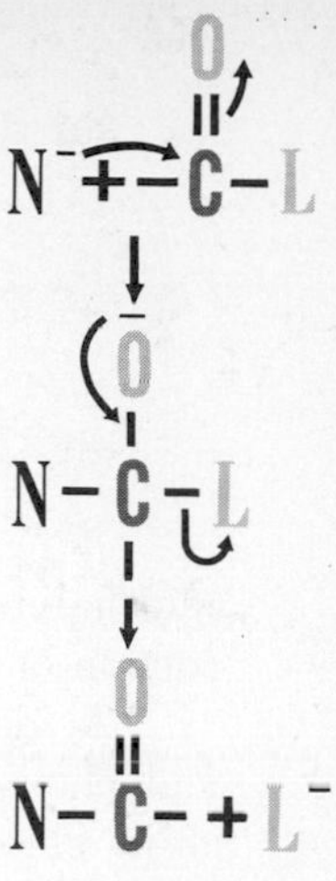

$$N^- \overset{+}{=} \overset{\overset{\displaystyle O}{\|}}{C} - L$$

$$N - \overset{\overset{\displaystyle \bar{O}}{|}}{\underset{|}{C}} - L$$

$$N - \overset{\overset{\displaystyle O}{\|}}{C} - + L^-$$

14

Nucleophilic Substitution at Unsaturated Carbon

Nucleophilic substitution at unsaturated carbon atoms has more in common with nucleophilic additions (Chap. 13) than with nucleophilic substitution at saturated centers (Chaps. 10 and 11). Most substitution reactions of unsaturated groups can be formulated as consisting of two steps: an addition followed by an elimination (Fig. 14.1).

In many cases, addition compounds are formed which have a more or less transient existence. Reactivity relationships in nucleophilic substitutions of unsaturated substrates can usually be explained by the hypothesis that the *rate-controlling transition state in such a substitution closely resembles an adduct.*

In a second type of substitution, a multiple bond is cleaved and replaced by another. Proton shifts are nearly always involved, as indicated in Fig. 14.2.

Carbon-Halogen Bond Formation

Acid chlorides are the only important compounds in which halogen is attached directly to a carbonyl group. Acid bromides and acid iodides may be prepared, but they have no properties that make them superior to acid chlorides for any known chemical purpose. Since all

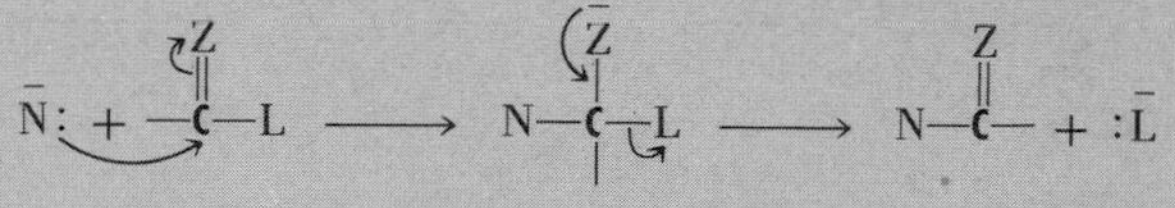

$$\overset{-}{N}: + \overset{\overset{\displaystyle Z}{\|}}{\underset{|}{C}} - L \longrightarrow N - \overset{\overset{\displaystyle \bar{Z}}{|}}{\underset{|}{C}} - L \longrightarrow N - \overset{\overset{\displaystyle Z}{\|}}{C} - + :\bar{L}$$

Z = a hetero atom such as **O, N,** or **S**

FIG. 14.1 *Nucleophilic substitution at an unsaturated carbon atom.*

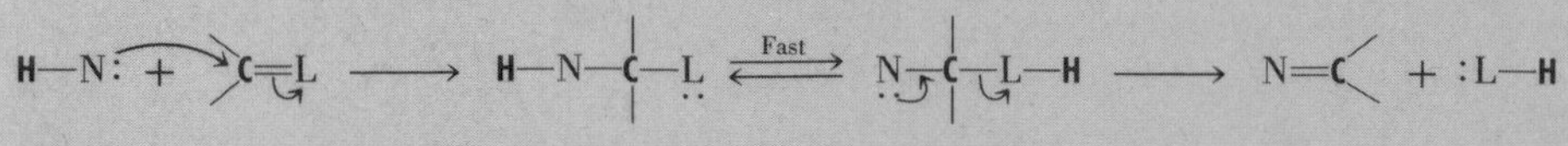

$$H-N: \;\; + \;\; \underset{\text{L}}{\overset{}{C}}=L \longrightarrow H-N-\underset{L}{\overset{|}{C}}-L \underset{\text{Fast}}{\rightleftharpoons} N-\underset{L}{\overset{|}{C}}-L-H \longrightarrow N=C \;\; + \;\; :L-H$$

FIG. 14.2   *Substitution with double-bond formation.*

acid halides are highly reactive, their only use is as reagents for introduction of acyl groups in the course of syntheses.

Acids are the only common starting materials for the synthesis of acid chlorides, and several reagents are utilized as sources of nucleophilic chloride. All the reagents form intermediate mixed anhydrides, so that the leaving group in the substitution is not —OH but a derivative thereof.

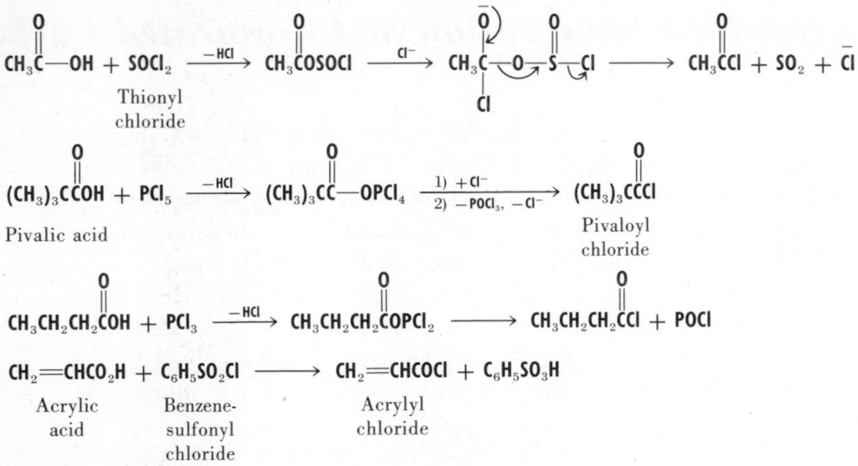

$$CH_3\overset{O}{\overset{||}{C}}-OH + SOCl_2 \xrightarrow{-HCl} CH_3\overset{O}{\overset{||}{C}}OSOCl \xrightarrow{Cl^-} CH_3\overset{O}{\overset{||}{C}}-O-\overset{Cl}{\underset{Cl}{S}}-Cl \longrightarrow CH_3\overset{O}{\overset{||}{C}}Cl + SO_2 + \bar{C}l$$

$$\underset{\text{Thionyl}}{}$$
$$\underset{\text{chloride}}{}$$

$$(CH_3)_3C\overset{O}{\overset{||}{C}}OH + PCl_5 \xrightarrow{-HCl} (CH_3)_3C\overset{O}{\overset{||}{C}}-OPCl_4 \xrightarrow[\text{2) } -POCl_3, -Cl^-]{\text{1) } +Cl^-} (CH_3)_3C\overset{O}{\overset{||}{C}}Cl$$

Pivalic acid Pivaloyl chloride

$$CH_3CH_2CH_2\overset{O}{\overset{||}{C}}OH + PCl_3 \xrightarrow{-HCl} CH_3CH_2CH_2\overset{O}{\overset{||}{C}}OPCl_2 \longrightarrow CH_3CH_2CH_2\overset{O}{\overset{||}{C}}Cl + POCl$$

$$CH_2=CHCO_2H + C_6H_5SO_2Cl \longrightarrow CH_2=CHCOCl + C_6H_5SO_3H$$

Acrylic acid Benzenesulfonyl chloride Acrylyl chloride

Each reagent has its unique characteristics. Thionyl chloride is often the reagent of choice for laboratory preparations, because the only by-products, SO_2 and HCl, are volatile. Interchange with benzenesulfonyl chloride is sometimes a convenient method, because the reaction may be run in hydrocarbon solvents, in which the by-product, benzenesulfonic acid, is insoluble. Exchanges between carboxylic acid chlorides may also be carried out. Benzoyl chloride, which is manufactured by the photochemical chlorination of benzaldehyde (Chap. 18), is a good reagent for preparation of volatile acid chlorides.

$$C_6H_5CHO + Cl_2 \xrightarrow{\text{Light}} C_6H_5COCl + HCl$$

$$C_6H_5COCl + CH_3CO_2H \rightleftharpoons C_6H_5CO_2H + CH_3COCl$$
$$\underset{\substack{\text{(Removed by} \\ \text{distillation)}}}{}$$

Hydrogen chloride *cannot* be used as a reagent in acid chloride preparations because of unfavorable equilibrium relationships.

$$RCO_2H + HCl \rightleftharpoons RCOCl + H_2O$$

The Sandmeyer Reaction.   Aryl halides are generally made by electrophilic substitution reactions (Chap. 16), because S_N reactions are usually very difficult with aromatic substrates.   However, there is one general procedure for introduction of aromatic substituents by nucleophilic substitution.   Aryl diazonium ions react with a variety of cuprous compounds to give substitution products.   The family of reactions is known collectively as *the Sandmeyer reaction.*

$$Cu—N: + Ar—N_2^+ \longrightarrow \overset{+}{Cu} + Ar—N + N_2$$

Cuprous complex
of a nucleophile

The success of the reaction depends upon the stability of aryl diazonium ions.   Unlike their aliphatic analogues, these cations are stable in cold aqueous solutions.   Certain aryl halides, which cannot be made by direct halogenation (Chap. 16), are often synthesized by diazotization of aromatic amines, followed by Sandmeyer reactions.

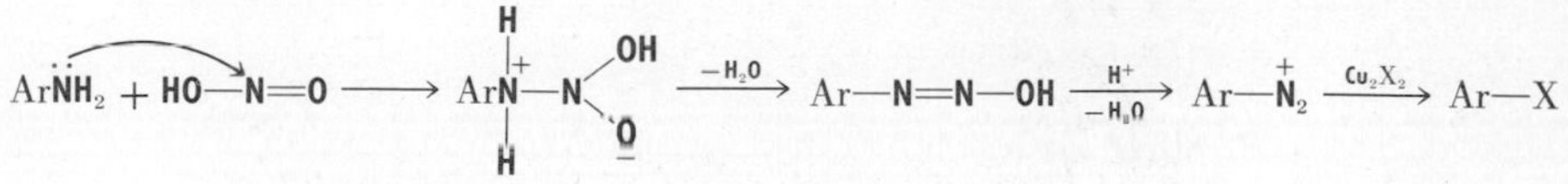

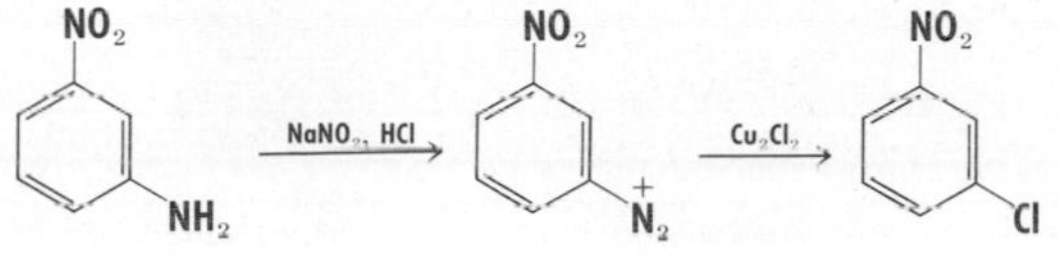

$$ArNH_2 + HO—N=O \longrightarrow ArN—N \overset{OH}{\underset{O}{}} \xrightarrow{-H_2O} Ar—N=N—OH \xrightarrow[-H_2O]{H^+} Ar—N_2^+ \xrightarrow{Cu_2X_2} Ar—X$$

m-Nitroaniline $\xrightarrow{NaNO_2, HCl}$ $\xrightarrow{Cu_2Cl_2}$ *m*-Nitrochlorobenzene

Carbon-Oxygen Bond Formation

A general reaction, shown in Fig. 14.3, occurs with a wide variety of nucleophiles, substrates, and leaving groups.   Important examples are summarized in Table 14.1.

Most but not all combinations of reagents and substrates from those listed in the table can be combined to give effective reactions.   The most important are reactions that interconvert carboxylic acids and their derivatives.   In a second group of reactions, aldehydes and ketones are generated by the hydrolysis of oximes, thioketones, etc.   *Nucleophilic substitution on aryl and vinyl carbon atoms* is ordinarily very difficult, but can be accomplished when the system is activated by electron-withdrawing substituents.

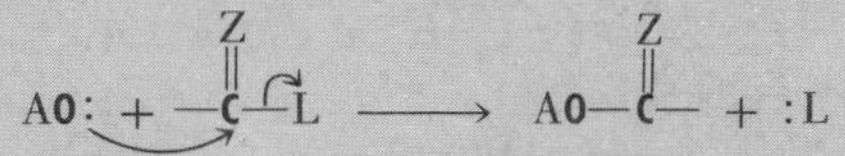

$$AO: + —\overset{Z}{\underset{}{C}}—L \longrightarrow AO—\overset{Z}{\underset{}{C}}— + :L$$

FIG. 14.3   Substitution by an oxygen nucleophile.

TABLE 14.1   Reactants in Nucleophilic Substitutions at Unsaturated Carbon Atoms

AO: (*Nucleophile*)	C=Z (*Substrate*)	Product
H₂O, HO⁻	C=O Ester, amide, acid chloride, anhydride	$\overset{O}{\overset{\|}{-C}}$—OH, acid
ROH, RO⁻	C=O Acid, ester, amide, acid chloride, anhydride	$\overset{O}{\overset{\|}{-C}}$OR, ester
ArOH, ArO⁻	C=O Acid chloride, anhydride	$\overset{O}{\overset{\|}{-C}}$OAr, ester
RCO₂H, RCO₂⁻, ArCO₂H, ArCO₂⁻	C=O Acid chloride	$\overset{O\ \ O}{\overset{\|\ \ \|}{-C}}OCR(Ar)$, anhydride

L (*Leaving group*)	Reactant
:OH	Acid
:OR, :OAr	Ester
:N⟨	Amide
$\overset{O}{\overset{\|}{:OCR(Ar)}}$	Anhydride
:Cl	Acid chloride
:C—	β-Ketoesters, β-diketones, haloketones, etc.

Formation of Acids by Hydrolysis.   All the derivatives of carboxylic acids may be hydrolyzed under widely varying conditions.   Acid chlorides and anhydrides usually react so rapidly with water that they must be protected from atmospheric moisture during storage.

$$C_6H_5\overset{O}{\overset{\|}{C}}Cl + H_2O \xrightarrow[\text{in air}]{\text{Fumes}} C_6H_5CO_2H + HCl$$

$$CH_3\overset{O\ \ O}{\overset{\|\ \ \|}{C}}OCCH_3 + H_2O \xrightarrow[\text{Exothermic}]{\text{Room temperature}} 2CH_3CO_2H$$

The mechanism of acid chloride hydrolysis is typical.   The first step, a *nucleophilic addition* to a polarized carbonyl group, is *followed by elimination* of hydrogen chloride.

$$C_6H_5\overset{O}{\overset{\|}{C}}Cl + H_2\overset{..}{O}: \longrightarrow C_6H_5\overset{\overset{..}{\overset{-}{:O:}}}{\underset{\overset{+}{:OH_2}}{C}}-Cl \rightleftharpoons C_6H_5\overset{:OH}{\underset{\overset{..}{:OH}}{C}}-Cl \xrightarrow{-Cl^-} C_6H_5\overset{:OH}{\underset{\overset{..}{:OH}}{C^+}} \longrightarrow C_6H_5CO_2H + \overset{+}{H}$$

The intermediate adduct, $C_6H_5C(OH)_2Cl$, is an *orthoacid chloride*, a species that has never been isolated. Loss of chloride from the intermediate is rapid because a stable cation, which is actually the conjugate acid of benzoic acid, is formed.

$$C_6H_5\overset{+}{C}{\overset{\displaystyle OH}{\underset{\displaystyle OH}{}}} \longleftrightarrow C_6H_5C{\overset{\displaystyle \overset{+}{O}H}{\underset{\displaystyle OH}{}}} \longleftrightarrow C_6H_5C{\overset{\displaystyle OH}{\underset{\displaystyle \overset{+}{O}H}{}}}$$

Esters are hydrolyzed when they are heated with catalytic amounts of aqueous acid. The reaction is reversible; in many simple cases, equilibrium constants are about unity. If a large excess of water is used, hydrolysis may be made essentially quantitative. On the other hand, if water is removed by slow distillation, the reaction can be used to convert an acid and an alcohol to an ester (*Fischer esterification*).

$$CH_3CH_2CH_2CO_2C_2H_5 + H_2O \underset{50-70°}{\overset{H^+}{\rightleftharpoons}} CH_3CH_2CH_2CO_2H + C_2H_5OH$$

Ethyl butyrate

The acid catalyst increases the electrophilic reactivity of the ester carbonyl group.

$$RC{\overset{\displaystyle O}{\underset{\displaystyle OR'}{}}} + \overset{+}{H} \rightleftharpoons R{-}C{\overset{\displaystyle \overset{+}{O}H}{\underset{\displaystyle OR'}{}}} \longleftrightarrow RC{\overset{\displaystyle OH}{\underset{\displaystyle OR'}{}}} \longleftrightarrow RC{\overset{\displaystyle OH}{\underset{\displaystyle \overset{+}{O}R'}{}}}$$

Alkali also accelerates hydrolysis, but an equivalent amount of base must be used, since the acidic product is converted to carboxylate ions. Alkaline hydrolysis of esters is sometimes termed "saponification" from the special case of soap manufacture from natural fats (page 78).

$$CH_3CO_2C_2H_5 + NaOH \xrightarrow[\text{Reflux}]{20\% \text{ NaOH}} CH_3CO_2Na + C_2H_5OH$$
100%
(by titration)

$$\begin{matrix} \overset{O}{\overset{\|}{CH_2OCR}} \\ \overset{O}{\overset{\|}{CHOCR'}} + 3NaOH \xrightarrow[100°]{15\% \text{ NaOH}} \\ \overset{O}{\overset{\|}{CH_2OCR''}} \end{matrix} \quad \begin{matrix} CH_2OH \\ CHOH \\ CH_2OH \end{matrix} + \begin{matrix} RCO_2^- \\ R'CO_2^- \\ R''CO_2^- \end{matrix} + 3Na^+$$

A fat; R, R', and Glycerol Soaps
R'' are long-
chain saturated 100%
and unsaturated
alkyl groups.

Alkaline ester hydrolysis is representative of a large number of reactions in which a negatively charged nucleophile attacks the carbonyl carbon of a neutral substrate.

$$\overset{O}{\overset{\|}{RC}}{-}OR' + {}^-\bar{O}H \longrightarrow RC{\overset{\displaystyle \bar{O}}{\underset{\displaystyle OH}{}}}OR' \longrightarrow \overset{O}{\overset{\|}{RC}}OH + {}^-\bar{O}R'$$

Normal ionization:

$$CH_3C\underset{O-H}{\overset{O}{\diagup}} + H_2SO_4 \rightleftharpoons \left[CH_3C\underset{OH}{\overset{\overset{+}{O}H}{\diagup}} \longleftrightarrow CH_3C\underset{\overset{+}{O}H}{\overset{OH}{\diagup}} \right] + H\bar{S}O_4$$

Complex ionization of sterically hindered acids:

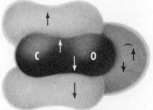

Mesitoic acid

Net reaction: $ArC\overset{O}{\underset{OH}{\diagdown}} + 2H_2SO_4 \rightleftharpoons ArC\equiv\overset{+}{O} + H_3\overset{+}{O} + 2H\bar{S}O_4$

$-C\equiv\overset{+}{O}:$ group, showing two acetylene-like π orbitals and the sp hybrid which possesses an unshared electron pair

FIG. 14.4 *Ionization of carboxylic acids in concentrated sulfuric acid.*

The reactivity of esters in hydrolysis is controlled by the necessity of passing through an intermediate with a tetrahedral carbon atom in the functional group. If a carbonyl group is surrounded by bulky groups, hydrolysis may become very slow. Acid-catalyzed esterification is also subject to steric hindrance, since similar intermediates are involved.

CH_3CO_2H	$\underset{CH_3CH_2}{\overset{CH_3CH_2}{\diagdown}}CHCO_2H$	
1	0.0004	Too slow to measure

Relative rates of acid-catalyzed
esterification with ethanol

Conjugated esters lose a certain amount of resonance energy when converted to addition products and are consequently less reactive than their saturated analogues.

Alkaline hydrolysis, but not acid-catalyzed esterification or hydrolysis, is very sensitive to inductive effects of polar substituents. Trifluoroacetates, which are very easily hydrolyzed, illustrate the effect. In the ester, the dipoles of the carboxyl and trifluoromethyl groups repel each other. In the transition state for hydrolysis, the negative charge is stabilized by charge-dipole interaction.

Sterically hindered aromatic acids and esters may be interconverted by the *Newman procedure.* All acids and esters ionize as bases in concentrated sulfuric acid, but steric hindrance promotes complex ionization and produces acyl cations instead of normal conjugate acids. Figure 14.4 shows the two kinds of ionization.

The —C≡O⁺ group is linear and has essentially the same π orbitals as acetylene. The complex ionization of mesitoic acid relieves steric strain. Esters of hindered acids produce acyl cations by analogous reactions. If a sulfuric acid solution containing acyl cations is diluted with excess water or alcohol, the cations are captured immediately. Since the method is not applicable to unhindered acids and esters, it is an example of *steric acceleration* of a reaction.

The following example of stepwise saponification demonstrates variation in ester reactivity. The aliphatic ester group is hydrolyzed readily. The other two carboxyl functions are both conjugated and sterically hindered, but under forcing conditions the less hindered of the two is selectively attacked. The third could probably be cleaved with sodium hydroxide in a high-boiling solvent such as ethylene glycol.

Amides and nitriles are much harder to hydrolyze than esters. Prolonged heating under reflux with strong acid or base is required to effect cleavage, and even moderately hindered compounds are inert toward hydrolysis for all practical purposes. Amides rather than acids may be produced in high yield from hindered nitriles. The general problem of interconverting amides and nitriles is treated elsewhere (Chap. 17).

$$C_6H_5CH_2CN \xrightarrow[40-50°]{35\% \text{ HCl}} C_6H_5CH_2CONH_2 \xrightarrow[\text{Reflux}]{35\% \text{ HCl}} C_6H_5CH_2CO_2H$$

	84%	80%
Phenylacetonitrile	Phenylacetamide	Phenylacetic acid

Ester Formation. Direct esterification of an acid with an alcohol was discussed above, because of the intimate relationship with ester hydrolysis. Useful ester syntheses by substitution (page 211) and addition (Chap. 15) reactions are treated in other sections. However, the most general laboratory procedures for esterification involve *acylation of alcohols by acid derivatives.* Acid chlorides and anhydrides are often used for the purpose, and the most convenient procedure for converting small samples of acids to esters involves intermediate formation of an acid chloride. Aryl esters constitute a prime example, since they cannot be made by direct esterification of phenols, because of unfavorable equilibrium constants. Even acid chlorides derived from highly hindered acids are converted to esters easily.

A common application of the procedure is conversion of alcohols to characteristic solid derivatives. A sample of the alcohol to be identified is heated with an excess of an acid chloride such as benzoyl chloride, *p*-nitrobenzoyl chloride, or 3,5-dinitrobenzoyl chloride. Excess acid halide is removed by treatment with aqueous base.

Benzyl alcohol   Benzyl 3,5-dinitrobenzoate
mp −15°   mp 112°

Acetic anhydride is often used to esterify alcohols. Tertiary amines catalyze the reactions and probably act by converting the anhydrides to acylammonium ions.

Phenyl acetate

Cyclic anhydrides, such as phthalic anhydride, react easily with alcohols, giving half-esters. An interesting application of the reaction is conversion of optically active alcohols to acidic derivatives which may be resolved into enantiomers by means of optically active bases. After the diastereomeric salts have been purified by recrystallization, the optically active alcohols may be recovered by hydrolysis of the active esters (page 305).

Racemic 2-octanol	Phthalic anhydride	Racemic monooctyl phthalate

Brucine *d*-monooctyl phthalate + Brucine *l*-monooctyl phthalate

Brucine salts, separated by fractional recrystallization

Brucine *d*-monooctyl phthalate $\xrightarrow{\text{HCl}}$ Brucine HCl + *d*-monooctyl phthalate

d-Monooctyl phthalate	Sodium phthalate	*d*-2-Octanol

† Brucine is an optically active, naturally occurring amine (Chap. 23).

Various condensing agents are used to cause rapid esterification of alcohols by acids. Mixed anhydrides are usually formed and serve as substrates in the acylation step. Trifluoroacetic anhydride is particularly effective, but the cost of the reagent discourages its use on a large scale.

Methacrylic acid		Methyl methacrylate

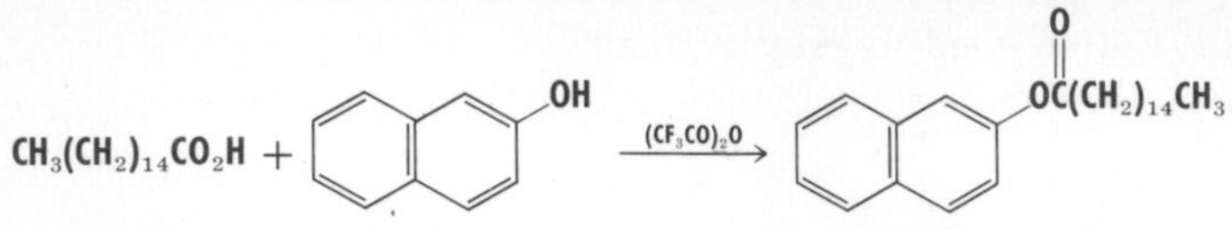

$$CH_3(CH_2)_{14}CO_2H + \overset{OH}{\underset{\text{β-Naphthol}}{\bigcirc\!\bigcirc}} \xrightarrow{(CF_3CO)_2O} \overset{O}{\underset{\text{β-Naphthyl palmitate}}{\overset{\|}{\bigcirc\!\bigcirc}}}{OC(CH_2)_{14}CH_3}$$

Palmitic acid β-Naphthol β-Naphthyl palmitate

Transesterification, or *ester interchange,* occurs when an ester is heated with an alcohol in the presence of acids or bases. The reaction is useful for preparation of esters derived from insoluble acids.

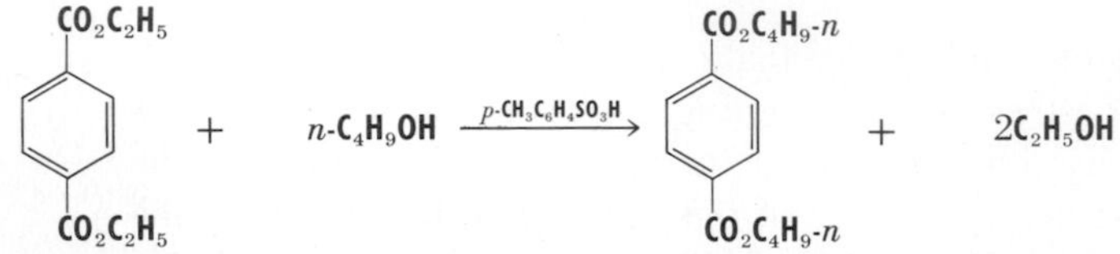

$$\underset{\substack{\text{Diethyl}\\\text{terephthalate}}}{\overset{CO_2C_2H_5}{\underset{CO_2C_2H_5}{\bigcirc}}} + n\text{-}C_4H_9OH \xrightarrow{p\text{-}CH_3C_6H_4SO_3H} \underset{\substack{\text{Di-}n\text{-butyl}\\\text{terephthalate}}}{\overset{CO_2C_4H_9\text{-}n}{\underset{CO_2C_4H_9\text{-}n}{\bigcirc}}} + \underset{\substack{\text{(Removed by}\\\text{distillation)}}}{2C_2H_5OH}$$

Acylating Agents. The relative reactivity of acyl compounds as acylating agents depends on the reactivity of various leaving groups in nucleophilic substitutions at carbonyl carbon atoms. Figure 14.5 shows the usual order of reactivity. Note the inclusion of some groups that have not been discussed explicitly. The sequence of reactivities is quite different from that observed in nucleophilic substitution at saturated carbon atoms (Chap. 10). For example, ester saponification illustrates the reactivity of RO^- as a leaving group. Alkaline cleavage of ethers, the corresponding substitution at saturated centers, is almost never observed.

Anhydride Formation. Anhydrides are made by the displacement of chloride from an acid chloride by a carboxylate ion or by heating an acid with an *acidic dehydrating agent,* such as phosphorus pentoxide or acetic anhydride.

$$\underset{\substack{n\text{-Heptanoic acid}}}{CH_3(CH_2)_5CO_2H} + \underset{\substack{n\text{-Heptanoyl}\\\text{chloride}}}{CH_3(CH_2)_5COCl} \xrightarrow{\text{Pyridine}} \underset{\substack{n\text{-Heptanoic anhydride}}}{(CH_3(CH_2)_5CO)_2O}$$

Leaving groups:

$$:NR_3 > \bar{Cl} > \bar{S}R > \overset{O}{\overset{\|}{\bar{O}\!-\!CR}} > \bar{O}R > \overline{N}HAr > \overline{N}HR \gg \overset{=}{O}$$

Substrates:

$$\overset{O}{\overset{\|+}{RCNR_3}} > \overset{O}{\overset{\|}{RCCl}} > \overset{O}{\overset{\|}{RCSR}} > \overset{O\ O}{\overset{\|\ \|}{RCOCR}} > \overset{O}{\overset{\|}{RCOR}} > \overset{O}{\overset{\|}{RCNHAr}} > \overset{O}{\overset{\|}{RCNHR}} \gg \overset{O}{\overset{\|-}{RCO}}$$

FIG. 14.5   *Reactivity of leaving groups in nucleophilic substitution at unsaturated carbon.*

$$(CH_3CO)_2O + C_6H_5CO_2H \xrightleftharpoons{\text{Excess } (CH_3CO)_2O} (C_6H_5CO)_2O + CH_3CO_2H$$

Benzoic
anhydride
74%

Acetic anhydride is a convenient reagent, since the by-product, acetic acid, can be removed continuously by distillation to force high conversion.

Aromatic Nucleophilic Substitution. Aryl halides are ordinarily very difficult to hydrolyze, although chlorobenzene is converted to phenol commercially under drastic conditions.

Displacement of sulfite ion from aromatic sulfonates effects a fairly standard synthesis of phenols, which also requires drastic treatment.

Nitrogen is the most reactive leaving group in nucleophilic substitution reactions. Oxidation of primary amines with nitrous acid (usually termed "diazotization") produces diazonium ions which lose nitrogen in nucleophilic substitution reactions. If an aqueous solution of a diazonium salt is warmed, substitution by water occurs, and a phenol results.

Naphthols can be made by hydrolysis of naphthylamines in the *Bucherer reaction.* This unusual substitution is catalyzed by sodium bisulfite and probably involves addition to the imino tautomer of the amine. Manipulation of the concentrations of water and ammonia allows the

reaction to be carried out in either direction.   Precursors to α-naphthyl-
amine and β-naphthol can be made by electrophilic substitution reactions
of naphthalene (Chap. 16).   These compounds are converted to α-naphthol
and β-naphthylamine on an industrial scale by Bucherer reactions.

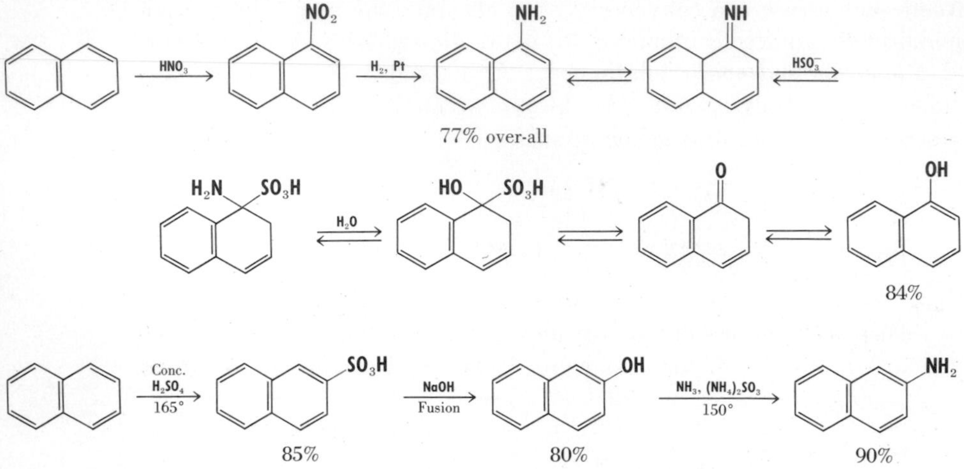

77% over-all

84%

85%   80%   90%

Electron-withdrawing substituents, located ortho and para to the seat
of substitution, greatly facilitate nucleophilic substitution.   Nitro groups
are particularly effective, and picryl chloride is as reactive as a carboxylic
acid chloride.

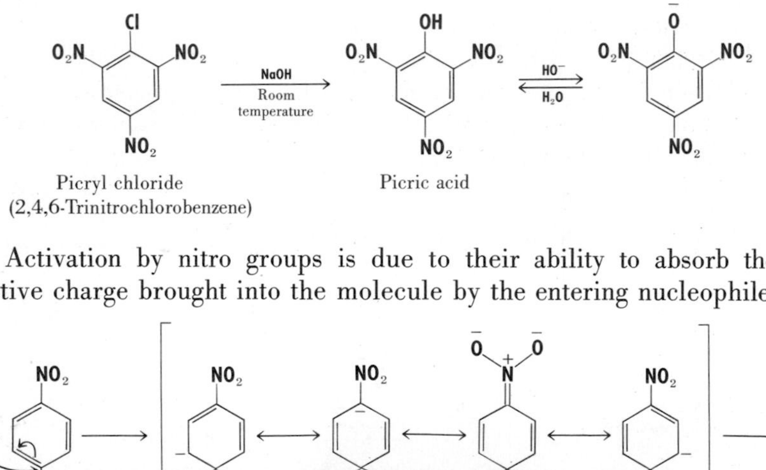

Picryl chloride   Picric acid
(2,4,6-Trinitrochlorobenzene)

Activation by nitro groups is due to their ability to absorb the
negative charge brought into the molecule by the entering nucleophile.

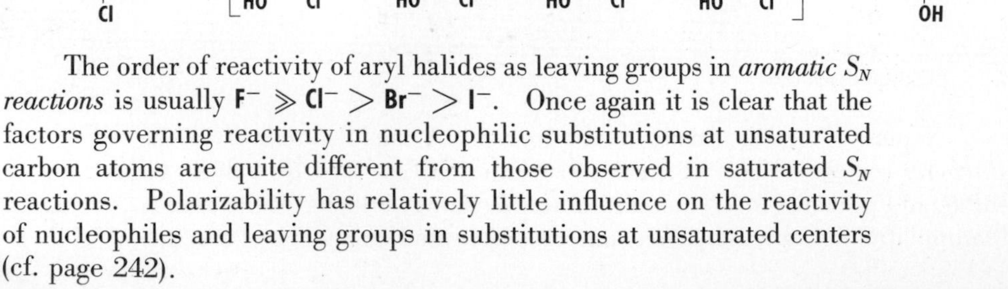

The order of reactivity of aryl halides as leaving groups in *aromatic S_N
reactions* is usually $F^- \gg Cl^- > Br^- > I^-$.   Once again it is clear that the
factors governing reactivity in nucleophilic substitutions at unsaturated
carbon atoms are quite different from those observed in saturated S_N
reactions.   Polarizability has relatively little influence on the reactivity
of nucleophiles and leaving groups in substitutions at unsaturated centers
(cf. page 242).

Carbon-Sulfur Bond Formation

Thiol acids, their esters, thioketones, and thioaldehydes are made by various nucleophilic substitution reactions, as illustrated below.

H_2S + acylating agent $\longrightarrow$ thiol acid

$$H_2S + CH_3\overset{O}{\underset{||}{C}}O\overset{O}{\underset{||}{C}}CH_3 \longrightarrow CH_3\overset{O}{\underset{||}{C}}SH + CH_3CO_2H$$

Thiolacetic
acid

Mercaptan + acylating agent $\longrightarrow$ thiol acid ester

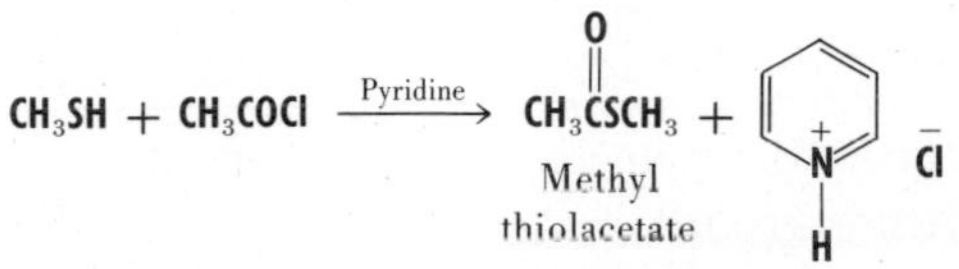

$$CH_3SH + CH_3COCl \xrightarrow{\text{Pyridine}} CH_3\overset{O}{\underset{||}{C}}SCH_3 +$$

Methyl
thiolacetate

H_2S + imino ester $\longrightarrow$ thion ester

$$H_2S + CH_3\overset{NH}{\underset{||}{C}}OCH_3 \longrightarrow CH_3\overset{S}{\underset{||}{C}}OCH_3 + NH_3$$

Methyl   Methyl
iminoacetate   thionacetate

H_2S or P_2S_5 + carbonyl compound $\longrightarrow$ thiocarbonyl compound

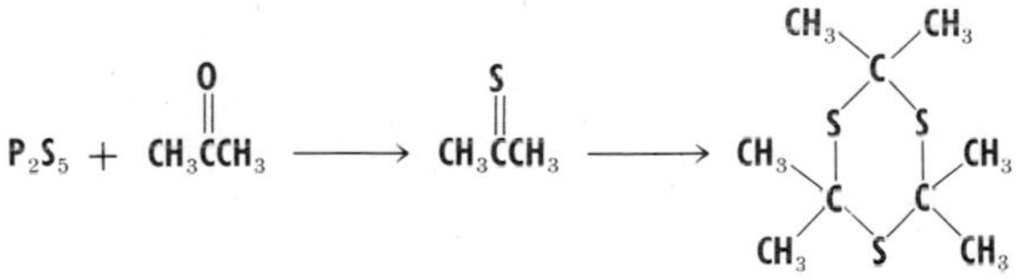

$$P_2S_5 + CH_3\overset{O}{\underset{||}{C}}CH_3 \longrightarrow CH_3\overset{S}{\underset{||}{C}}CH_3 \longrightarrow$$

Thioacetone   Hexamethyl-*sym*-
trithione
(Thioacetone trimer)

$$H_2S + CH_3CHO \xrightarrow{\text{HCl}} CH_3CHS \longrightarrow \text{trimer}$$

Thioacet-
aldehyde

Dithioacids (RCS_2H) are made by reaction of Grignard reagents with carbon disulfide, while thioamides ($RCSNH_2$) are made by addition of hydrogen sulfide to nitriles.

Carbon-Nitrogen Bond Formation

Amide Formation. Amides are prepared by acylation of ammonia or amines with acid chlorides, anhydrides, esters, or acids. The reaction with acids is of limited interest, since pyrolysis of ammonium salts is required. Anhydrides and acid chlorides react violently with ammonia unless the reactions are moderated by cooling, dilution, or slow mixing of the reactants. The following preparations are typical.

$$(CH_3C)_2O + (CH_3)_2NH \longrightarrow CH_3CN(CH_3)_2 + CH_3CO_2H$$

N,N-Dimethyl-
acetamide

$$(C_2H_5)_2CHCOCl + 2NH_3 \xrightarrow{\text{Benzene}} (C_2H_5)_2CHCONH_2 + ((C_2H_5)_2CHCO)_2NH$$

Diethylacetyl chloride	Diethylacetamide 91%	*bis*-Diethyl- acetimide 9%

Ethyl nicotinate	Nicotinamide

The following example demonstrates the selective reaction of an anhydride linkage in preference to an ester group.

Ethyl bicyclo[2,2,2]- octane-1,4-dicarboxylate	Ethyl chloroformate	(Not isolated)	

The reactions are all initiated in the usual way, by attack of the nucleophilic nitrogen on the carbonyl carbon atom. Description of the fast proton transfers in the intermediate is uncertain because of the speed of such reactions.

A large number of special methods have been used successfully for amide preparations. Most of these represent some variant of the direct conversion of an acid and are designed to avoid the pyrolysis required in the direct synthesis from ammonia.

$$C_6H_5CO_2H + NH_3 \longrightarrow C_6H_5CO_2\overset{-}{N}\overset{+}{H_4} \xrightarrow{200°, \text{ sealed tube}} C_6H_5CONH_2 + H_2O$$

Benzamide
50–70%

$$C_6H_5CO_2H + NH_2SO_2NH_2 \xrightarrow{\text{Pyridine, }100°} C_6H_5CONH_2 + NH_2SO_3H$$

	Sulfamide		84%	Sulfamic acid

The ease of formation of amides, as well as the fact that most members of the class are solids, leads to their use as characteristic derivatives in identification of unknown acids and esters.

Cyclic anhydrides are easily converted to cyclic imides, although it is usually necessary to isolate the intermediate, half-amides.

| Phthalic anhydride | Phthalamidic acid | Phthalimide |

Hydroxamic Acids and *N*-Acyl Compounds.   Treatment of reactive acylating agents such as acid chlorides, anhydrides, and esters with hydroxylamine produces hydroxamic acids. The latter are usually not isolated but are converted to derivatives or isolated as salts. Hydroxamic acids are easily detected in solution because they form deeply colored complexes with ferric ions. Active acylating agents are often characterized by conversion to hydroxamic acids.

| Ethyl valerate | A hydroxamic acid | A ferric hydroxamate (purple) |

Hydrazides, acylhydrazines, and azides are formed by the acylation of hydrazine and metal azides. Azides may also be prepared by oxidation of hydrazides with nitrous acid.

Acetyl azide

Carbonyl Condensation with Nitrogen Compounds.   Aldehydes and ketones condense with a number of compounds having the general formula NH_2Z. The products are crystalline sharp-melting solids, useful for characterization of the parent carbonyl compounds.

$$CH_3CCH_3 + NH_2OH \xrightarrow{\text{Weak base}} (CH_3)_2C{=}NOH + H_2O$$

Hydroxyl-amine · · · · Acetoxime

$$C_6H_5COCH_3 \ + \ C_6H_5NHNH_2 \ \xrightarrow{H_3O^+, \ CH_3CO_2H} \ C_6H_5\underset{\underset{CH_3}{|}}{C}{=}NNHC_6H_5 + H_2O$$

Acetophenone   Phenylhydrazine   Acetophenone
phenylhydrazone

$$CH_2{=}CHCHO + O_2N{-}\overset{NO_2}{\underset{}{\bigcirc}}{-}NHNH_2 \ \xrightarrow{HCl, \ C_2H_5OH, \ H_2O} \ CH_2{=}CHCH{=}NNHC_6H_3(NO_2)_2 + H_2O$$

Acrolein   2,4-Dinitrophenyl-   2,4-Dinitrophenylhydrazone
hydrazine   of acrolein

$$\bigcirc{=}O \ + \ NH_2NH\overset{O}{\overset{||}{C}}NH_2 \ \xrightarrow{CH_3CO_2K, \ C_2H_5OH} \ \bigcirc{-}NNHCONH_2$$

Semicarbazide   Cyclohexanone
semicarbazone

Water-soluble compounds may be converted to derivatives in aqueous solution. Acetic acid and ethanol are used as solvents for water-insoluble compounds. It is difficult to prepare hydrazones from hydrazine, because the former tend to react a second time, giving azines.

$$CH_3CHO + NH_2NH_2 \ \longrightarrow \ CH_3CH{=}NNH_2 \ \xrightarrow{CH_3CHO} \ CH_3CH{=}NN{=}CHCH_3$$

Acetaldehyde   Acetaldehyde
hydrazone   azine

All condensations of carbonyl groups with nitrogen compounds are acid-catalyzed. Catalysis by strong acids is not very effective, because of protonation of the nucleophiles to form inactive derivatives of the ammonium ion.

$$R_2C{=}O + \overset{+}{H} \ \rightleftharpoons \ R_2C{=}\overset{+}{O}H$$

$$NH_2OH + \overset{+}{H} \ \rightleftharpoons \ \overset{+}{N}H_3OH \ \rightleftharpoons \ \overset{+}{N}H_3\overset{-}{O}$$

Inactive
hydroxyl-
ammonium ion

These reactions illustrate *general acid catalysis*. In a general acid-catalyzed reaction, the rate is dependent on the concentration of *all acid species in the solution* rather than on just the hydrogen ion concentration. In such a reaction, the active substrate is not the conjugate acid of the carbonyl compound, but a complex between the latter and the acidic catalyst.

$$R_2C{=}O + HB \ \rightleftharpoons \ R_2C{=}O\text{---}H{-}B$$

Hydrogen-bonded complex

$$HO\overset{..}{N}\underset{\overset{|}{H}}{\overset{\overset{|}{H}}{:}} + R_2C{=}O\text{---}H{-}B \ \longrightarrow \ R_2\underset{\underset{\overset{+}{N}H_2OH}{|}}{\overset{\overset{OH}{|}}{C}} \ + \ \overset{-}{B}$$

$$\downarrow$$

$$R_2C{=}NOH$$

General acid-catalyzed reactions can be strongly catalyzed by massive concentrations of weak acids, such as acetic acid, which do not tie up large amounts of the nucleophile. Probably many of the reactions discussed previously in terms of simple proton transfers are actually general acid-catalyzed.

Oxime formation is also base-catalyzed, since hydroxylamine is weakly acidic and can be converted to a more reactive nucleophile by loss of a proton.

$$\text{B:} + \text{NH}_2\text{OH} \rightleftharpoons \overset{+}{\text{BH}} + \text{NH}_2\bar{\text{O}} \rightleftharpoons \bar{\text{N}}\text{HOH}$$

$$\text{R}_2\text{C}=\text{O} + \text{NH}_2\bar{\text{O}} \longrightarrow \text{R}_2\text{C} \underset{\overset{+}{\text{NH}_2\bar{\text{O}}}}{\overset{\bar{\text{O}}}{\diagdown}} \longrightarrow \text{R}_2\text{C}=\text{NOH}$$

or

$$\text{R}_2\text{C}=\text{O} + \bar{\text{N}}\text{HOH} \longrightarrow \text{R}_2\text{C} \underset{\text{NHOH}}{\overset{\bar{\text{O}}}{\diagdown}} \longrightarrow \text{R}_2\text{C}=\text{NOH}$$

Girard's reagent, trimethylaminoacetyl hydrazide hydrochloride, condenses with carbonyl compounds to form water-soluble products. Carbonyl compounds are frequently separated from other materials by extraction with aqueous solutions of the reagent. Aldehydes or ketones are regenerated by acid hydrolysis of Girard derivatives.

$$\text{(CH}_3\text{)}_3\text{N} + \text{ClCH}_2\text{CO}_2\text{C}_2\text{H}_5 + \text{NH}_2\text{NH}_2 \longrightarrow \text{(CH}_3\text{)}_3\overset{+}{\text{N}}\text{CH}_2\text{CONHNH}_2\text{Cl}$$

Girard's reagent

$$\text{(CH}_3\text{)}_3\overset{+}{\text{N}}\text{CH}_2\text{CONHNH}_2 + \text{R}_2\text{C}=\text{O} \underset{\text{HCl, H}_2\text{O}}{\overset{\text{C}_2\text{H}_5\text{OH, CH}_3\text{CO}_2\text{H}}{\rightleftharpoons}} \text{R}_2\text{C}=\text{NNHCOCH}_2\overset{+}{\text{N}}\text{(CH}_3\text{)}_3$$

Primary amines undergo similar condensations, giving *imines* (*Schiff bases*). Imines derived from aliphatic amines are difficult to isolate. Those derived from aromatic amines are easily isolated, although they, too, will undergo further polymerization and condensation.

$$\underset{}{\overset{\overset{\text{O}}{\|}}{\text{CH}_3\text{CC}_2\text{H}_5}} + \text{C}_6\text{H}_5\text{NH}_2 \overset{\text{ZnCl}_2}{\longrightarrow} \text{C}_6\text{H}_5\text{N}=\text{C}\underset{\text{C}_2\text{H}_5}{\overset{\text{CH}_3}{\diagup}}$$

Ethyl methyl ketone anil
(a Schiff base)

Regeneration of an aldehyde or a ketone from an oxime or a hydrazone by direct hydrolysis is difficult, because the equilibrium constants favor the condensation products very strongly.

$$\diagup\!\diagdown\text{C}=\text{O} + \text{NH}_2\text{Z} \overset{K}{\rightleftharpoons} \diagup\!\diagdown\text{C}=\text{NZ} + \text{H}_2\text{O} \qquad K \text{ is large}$$

Recovery of a carbonyl compound can be accomplished by equilibrating the derivative with a reactive carbonyl compound, such as pyruvic acid.

| 3-Methyl-cyclohexanone phenylhydrazone | Pyruvic acid | | |

The last reaction is formally similar to transamination, a process fundamental to the metabolism of amino acids.

$$NH_2CH_2CO_2H + HO_2CCH_2CH_2COCO_2H \rightleftharpoons HO_2CCH_2CH_2CCO_2H \xrightarrow[\text{(Enzyme)}]{\text{H migration}}$$

$$\underset{\text{NCH}_2\text{CO}_2\text{H}}{}$$

Glycine   α-Ketoglutaric acid

$$HO_2CCH_2CH_2CHCO_2H \rightleftharpoons HO_2CCH_2CH_2CHCO_2H + OCHCO_2H$$

$$\underset{\text{N}=\text{CHCO}_2\text{H}}{} \qquad \underset{\text{NH}_2}{}$$

Glutamic acid   Glyoxylic acid

Aromatic Substrates.   Halogen is easily displaced from activated aryl substrates by amines.

4-Piperidinonitrobenzene

The superiority of fluoride over the heavier halides as a leaving group has led to the use of 2,4-dinitrofluorobenzene (Sanger's reagent) as a specific means for characterization of primary and secondary amines.   A particularly valuable application is the marking of terminal units in proteins and polypeptides (Chap. 25).   The peptide is treated with Sanger's reagent, and the product is hydrolyzed to cleave the amide linkages that bind the amino acid units together in the peptide.   Isolation and identification of the amino acid fragment bearing the dinitrophenyl group indicate the terminal unit of the peptide.

$$CH_3CHCO_2H + NH_2CH_2CO_2H + NH_2CH(C_6H_5)CO_2H + NH_3$$

Nonactivated aryl halides undergo substitution to give amines when treated with sodamide in liquid ammonia. Rearrangements are observed regularly in the course of the reaction, and it is evident that the first step is an elimination to form an intermediate, benzyne. The most conclusive evidence for the benzyne intermediate came from experiments using carbon-14 as a tracer.

* Indicates C^{14}.

Randomization of the labeled carbon between two positions was shown by the following degradative scheme.

51.8 ± 1% of total activity   48.1 ± 1% of total activity

Carbon-Hydrogen Bond Formation

Nucleophilic substitution of hydride ions (from donors such as metal hydrides) for the reactive leaving groups of acid chlorides and anhydrides leads to a variety of aldehyde syntheses.

$$\text{LiAlH(OC}_4\text{H}_9\text{-}t)_3 + \text{C}_6\text{H}_5\text{COCl} \xrightarrow{\text{CH}_3\text{OCH}_2\text{CH}_2\text{OCH}_3} \text{C}_6\text{H}_5\text{CHO} + \text{LiCl} + \text{Al(OC}_4\text{H}_9\text{-}t)_3$$

Lithium tri-*tert*-
butoxyaluminum
hydride
                                          Aluminum
tri-*tert*-butoxide

$$\text{LiAlH}_4 + \text{C}_6\text{H}_5\text{CON(CH}_3\text{)C}_6\text{H}_5 \xrightarrow{0°,\,0°} \text{C}_6\text{H}_5\text{CHO} + \text{LiNC}_6\text{H}_5 + \text{AlH}_3$$

N-Methyl-*N*-
phenylbenzamide

$$\text{LiAlH(OC}_2\text{H}_5\text{)}_3 + \text{CH}_3\text{(CH}_2\text{)}_2\text{CON(CH}_3\text{)}_2 \xrightarrow[\text{2) H}_3\text{O}^+]{\text{1) CH}_3\text{O(CH}_2\text{CH}_2\text{O)}_2\text{CH}_3} \text{CH}_3\text{(CH}_2\text{)}_2\text{CHO}$$

Butyraldehyde
85%

A second method involves *desulfurization* of thiol esters with Raney nickel. The latter reagent is prepared by treatment of nickel-aluminum alloy with aqueous sodium hydroxide, which dissolves the aluminum and leaves the nickel in a finely divided state. The metal surface is covered with hydrogen (Ni—H).

$$2\text{Al—Ni} + 2\text{NaOH} + 2\text{H}_2\text{O} \longrightarrow 2\text{NaAlO}_2 + 2\text{Ni—H} + 2\text{H}_2$$

Raney   Raney
alloy   nickel

$$\text{CH}_3\text{CH}_2\text{COCl} \xrightarrow{\text{C}_2\text{H}_5\text{SH}} \text{CH}_3\text{CH}_2\overset{\text{O}}{\overset{\|}{\text{C}}}\text{SC}_2\text{H}_5 \xrightarrow[-\text{NiS}]{+\text{NiH}} \text{CH}_3\text{CH}_2\text{CHO}$$

Ethyl thiol-   Propionaldehyde
propionate   73%

Among other methods for reduction of carboxylic acid derivatives to aldehydes are the *Rosenmund* hydrogenation of acid chlorides, the *McFadyen-Stevens* decomposition of sulfonhydrazides, and the *Sonn-Müller* reduction of imino acid chlorides.

Rosenmund reduction:

$$\text{CH}_3\text{O-}\underset{}{\bigcirc}\text{-}\overset{\text{O}}{\overset{\|}{\text{C}}}\text{—Cl} + \text{H}_2 \xrightarrow{\text{Pd catalyst}} \text{CH}_3\text{O-}\underset{}{\bigcirc}\text{—CHO} + \text{HCl}$$

p-Anisoyl chloride   *p*-Anisaldehyde
                                                  81%

McFadyen-Stevens reaction:

$$\text{C}_6\text{H}_5\text{COCl} + \text{NH}_2\text{NH}_2 \longrightarrow \text{C}_6\text{H}_5\text{CONHNH}_2 \xrightarrow{\text{C}_6\text{H}_5\text{SO}_2\text{Cl}} \text{C}_6\text{H}_5\text{CONHNHSO}_2\text{C}_6\text{H}_5 \xrightarrow[\text{Na}_2\text{CO}_3,\,160°]{\text{HOCH}_2\text{CH}_2\text{OH}}$$

                                    Benzoylhydrazide   1-Benzoyl-2-benzene-
                                      90%   sulfonylhydrazide

$$\left[\text{C}_6\text{H}_5\overset{\text{O}}{\overset{\|}{\text{C}}}\text{N}\text{—NH}\text{—SO}_2\text{C}_6\text{H}_5 \right] \xrightarrow{-\text{C}_6\text{H}_5\text{SO}_2^-} \left[\text{C}_6\text{H}_5\overset{\text{O}}{\overset{\|}{\text{C}}}\text{N}{=}\text{NH} \right] \xrightarrow{-\text{N}_2} \text{C}_6\text{H}_5\text{CHO}$$

                                                                                         70%

Sonn-Müller reduction:

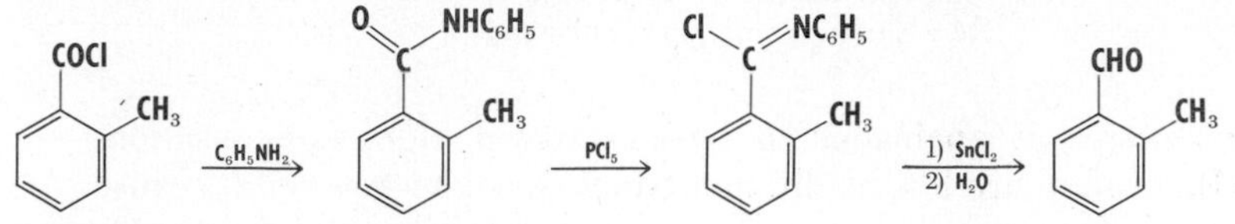

o-Toluyl chloride   N-Phenyl-o-toluamide   o-Tolualdehyde
80%

The obvious difficulties to be overcome in any reductive method for the synthesis of aldehydes arise from self-condensation and further reduction to alcohols.

Carbon-Carbon Bond Formation

Acylation of carbon ranks as one of the most important synthetic procedures in organic chemistry. Two general reaction types are known. In the first group are found reactions of enolate ions and organometallic compounds with acylating agents (Fig. 14.6). In a second family of reactions, weak nucleophiles, such as enols, are acylated by reagents that have been activated by electrophilic catalysts (Fig. 14.7).

The best examples of electrophilic catalysis of unsaturated nucleophilic substitutions are classified as aromatic electrophilic substitutions (Chap. 16). However, some use has been made of Lewis acid-catalyzed condensations of aliphatic compounds.

Ester Condensations. Aliphatic esters that have at least one α-hydrogen undergo self-condensation (*Claisen ester condensation*) to form β-keto-esters. The classical synthesis of ethyl acetoacetate is a prototype for the family of reactions.

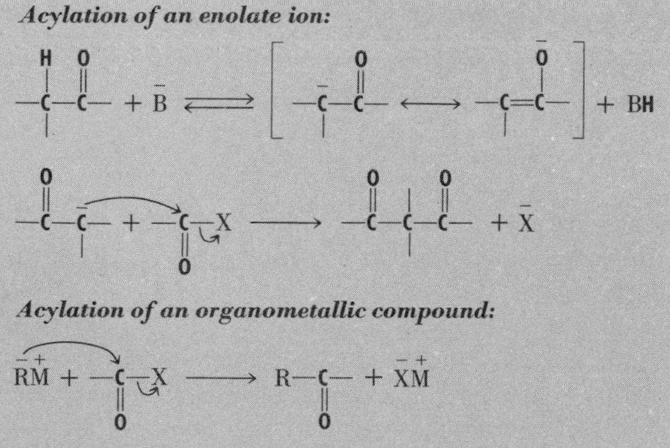

Acylation of an enolate ion:

Acylation of an organometallic compound:

FIG. 14.6   *Carbon-carbon bond formation by an acylation reaction.*

$$2CH_3CO_2C_2H_5 \xrightarrow{C_2H_5ONa} CH_3COCH_2CO_2C_2H_5 \ + \ C_2H_5OH$$

Ethyl acetoacetate   (Continuous

(Acetoacetic ester)   distillation)

75%

The reaction is analogous to base-catalyzed aldol condensations (page 284). Esters are less acidic than aldehydes and ketones (because of interaction between the oxygen atoms in the ester group), but ethoxide ions are sufficiently basic to convert a small amount of ethyl acetate to an enolate ion. Attack of the enolate on ethyl acetate is a typical nucleophilic substitution reaction.

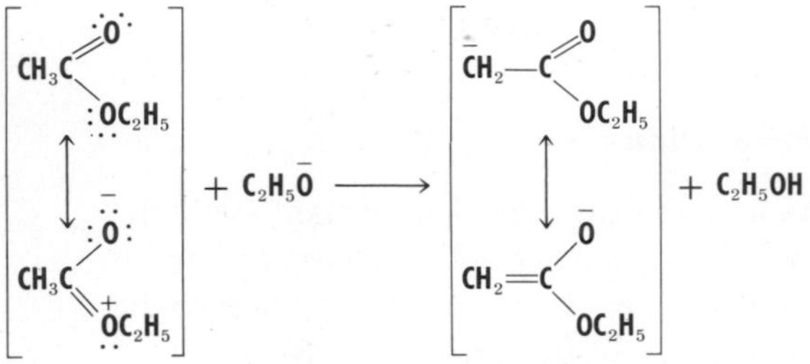

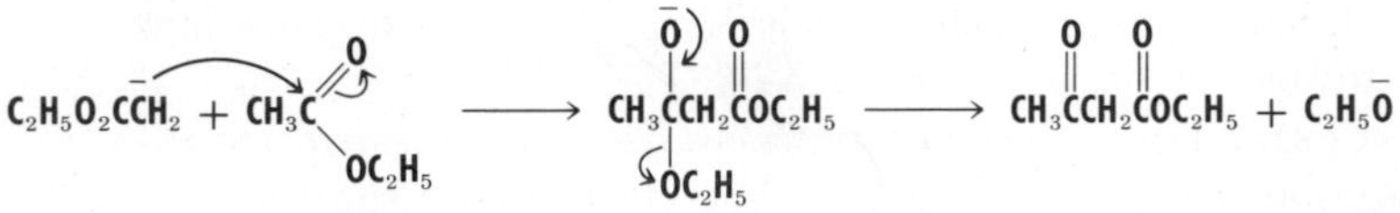

One equivalent of sodium ethoxide is consumed, because the β-ketoester is acidic enough to neutralize ethoxide ion.

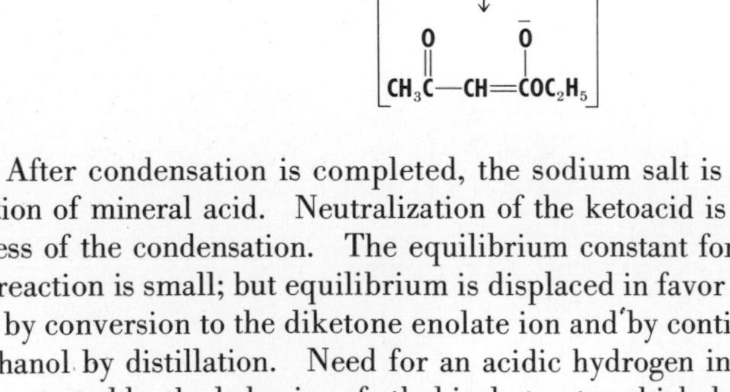

After condensation is completed, the sodium salt is neutralized by addition of mineral acid. Neutralization of the ketoacid is critical for the success of the condensation. The equilibrium constant for the condensation reaction is small; but equilibrium is displaced in favor of the product, both by conversion to the diketone enolate ion and by continuous removal of ethanol by distillation. Need for an acidic hydrogen in the product is demonstrated by the behavior of ethyl isobutyrate, which does not undergo condensation in the presence of sodium ethoxide. However, esters with only a single α-hydrogen will self-condense in the presence of either very

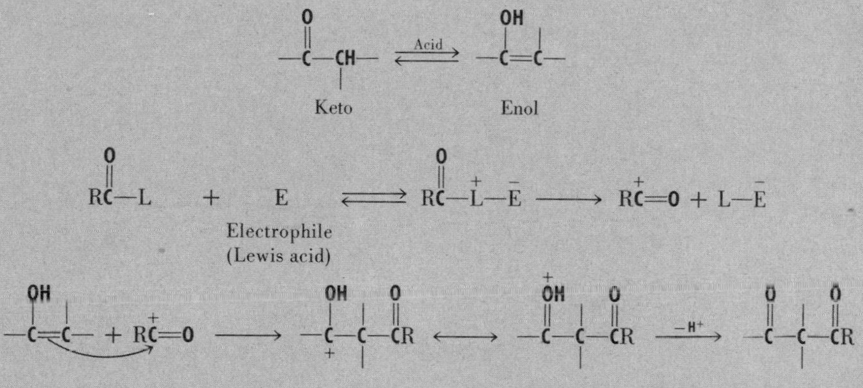

$$\underset{\text{Keto}}{-\overset{\overset{\displaystyle O}{\|}}{C}-\overset{\displaystyle |}{\underset{\displaystyle |}{C}}H-} \quad\underset{\text{Acid}}{\overset{\longrightarrow}{\longleftarrow}}\quad \underset{\text{Enol}}{-\overset{\displaystyle |}{C}=\overset{\overset{\displaystyle OH}{|}}{C}-}$$

$$\underset{\text{Electrophile}}{\overset{\overset{\displaystyle O}{\|}}{R C}-L} \;+\; E \quad\overset{\longrightarrow}{\longleftarrow}\quad R\overset{\overset{\displaystyle O}{\|}}{C}-\overset{+}{L}-E \;\longrightarrow\; R\overset{+}{C}{=}O + L-E$$

Electrophile
(Lewis acid)

$$-\overset{\displaystyle |}{C}=\overset{\overset{\displaystyle OH}{|}}{C}- + R\overset{+}{C}{=}O \;\longrightarrow\; -\overset{\displaystyle |}{\underset{+}{C}}-\overset{\overset{\displaystyle OH}{|}}{\underset{\displaystyle |}{C}}-\overset{\overset{\displaystyle O}{\|}}{C}R \;\longleftrightarrow\; -\overset{\displaystyle |}{C}-\overset{\overset{\displaystyle \overset{+}{O}H}{|}}{\underset{\displaystyle |}{C}}-\overset{\overset{\displaystyle O}{\|}}{C}R \;\overset{-H^+}{\longrightarrow}\; -\overset{\displaystyle |}{C}-\overset{\overset{\displaystyle \overset{..}{O}}{\|}}{\underset{\displaystyle |}{C}}-\overset{\overset{\displaystyle \overset{..}{O}}{\|}}{C}R$$

FIG. 14.7 *Carbon-carbon bond formation in an acid-catalyzed acylation.*

strong bases or bases that react irreversibly because the second product of the acid-base reaction escapes as a gas.

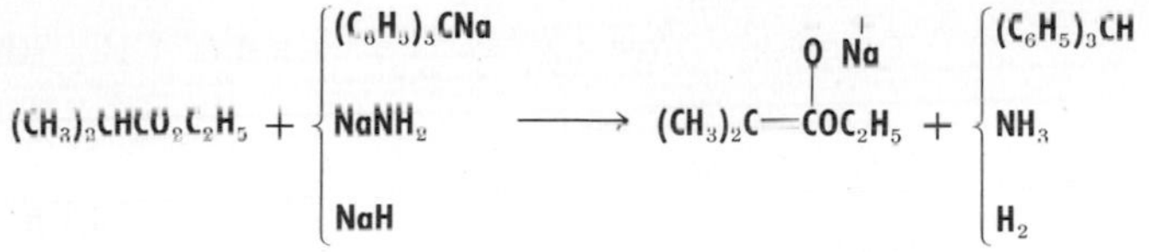

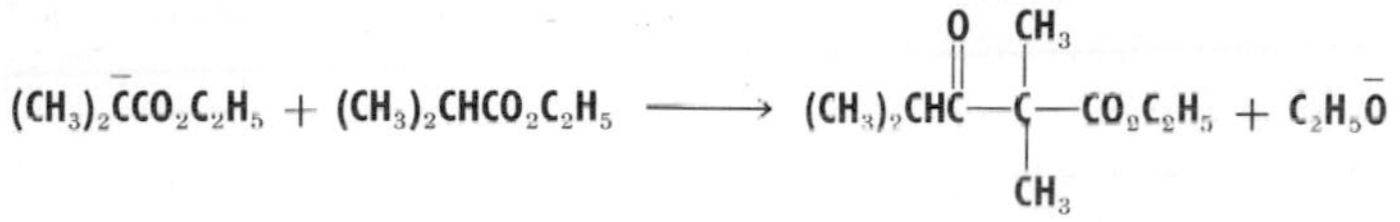

$$(CH_3)_2CHCO_2C_2H_5 \;+\; \begin{cases}(C_6H_5)_3CNa\\[4pt] NaNH_2\\[4pt] NaH\end{cases} \;\longrightarrow\; (CH_3)_2C\overset{\overset{\displaystyle O}{}\;\;\overset{\displaystyle Na}{|}}{=}COC_2H_5 \;+\; \begin{cases}(C_6H_5)_3CH\\[4pt] NH_3\\[4pt] H_2\end{cases}$$

$$(CH_3)_2\overset{-}{C}CO_2C_2H_5 \;+\; (CH_3)_2CHCO_2C_2H_5 \;\longrightarrow\; (CH_3)_2CHC\overset{\overset{\displaystyle O}{\|}}{-}\overset{\overset{\displaystyle CH_3}{|}}{\underset{\underset{\displaystyle CH_3}{|}}{C}}-CO_2C_2H_5 \;+\; C_2H_5\overset{-}{O}$$

Ethyl 2,2,4-trimethyl-
3-ketopentanoate
60%

In the last example, the driving force for condensation is provided by formation of *ethoxide ion, the weakest base in the system.*

Crossed condensations between two different esters are not ordinarily of synthetic value, because a mixture of the four possible ketoesters is produced. However, an ester having no α-hydrogen, but possessing high carbonyl reactivity, can often be condensed with a second ester in good yield. Diethyl oxalate and diethyl carbonate are frequently used in this manner.

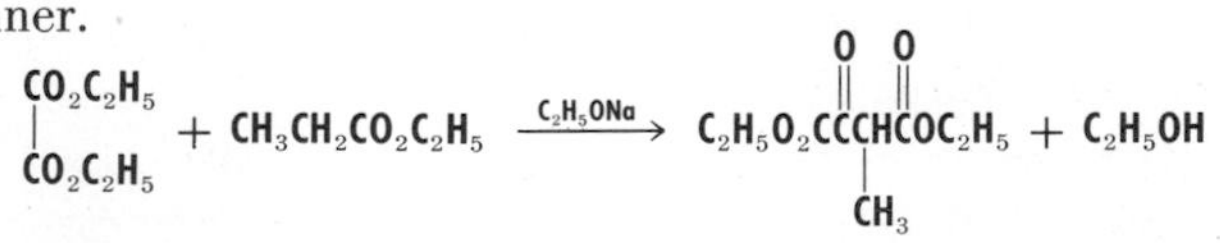

$$\underset{\displaystyle CO_2C_2H_5}{\overset{\displaystyle CO_2C_2H_5}{|}} \;+\; CH_3CH_2CO_2C_2H_5 \;\overset{C_2H_5ONa}{\longrightarrow}\; C_2H_5O_2C\overset{\overset{\displaystyle O\;\;O}{\|\;\;\|}}{C}CHCOC_2H_5 \;+\; C_2H_5OH$$
$$\underset{\displaystyle CH_3}{}$$

Diethyl   Ethyl   Diethyl α-keto-
oxalate   propionate   β-methylsuccinate
70%

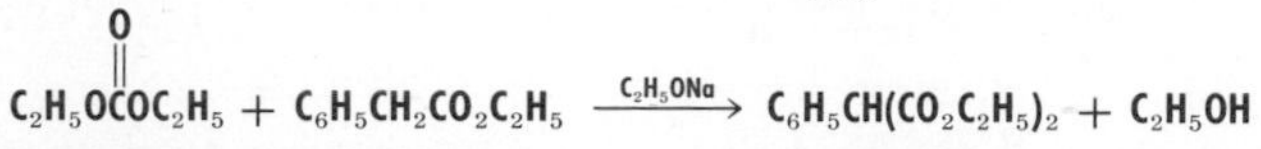

$$C_2H_5O\overset{\overset{\displaystyle O}{\|}}{C}OC_2H_5 \;+\; C_6H_5CH_2CO_2C_2H_5 \;\overset{C_2H_5ONa}{\longrightarrow}\; C_6H_5CH(CO_2C_2H_5)_2 \;+\; C_2H_5OH$$

Diethyl   Ethyl   Diethyl
carbonate   phenylacetate   phenylmalonate

Ethyl formate may be used to introduce formyl groups. For example, formylphenylacetic ester $(C_6H_5CH(CHO)CO_2C_2H_5)$ can be made from ethyl formate and ethyl phenylacetate. The utility of formylation reactions as a synthetic method is limited, because the conditions required to generate enolate ions from esters are also sufficient to cause condensation of the aldehydic products.

$$HCO_2C_2H_5 + CH_3CO_2C_2H_5 \xrightarrow{C_2H_5ONa} HCOCH_2CO_2C_2H_5$$

(Isolated as sodium enolate)
14%

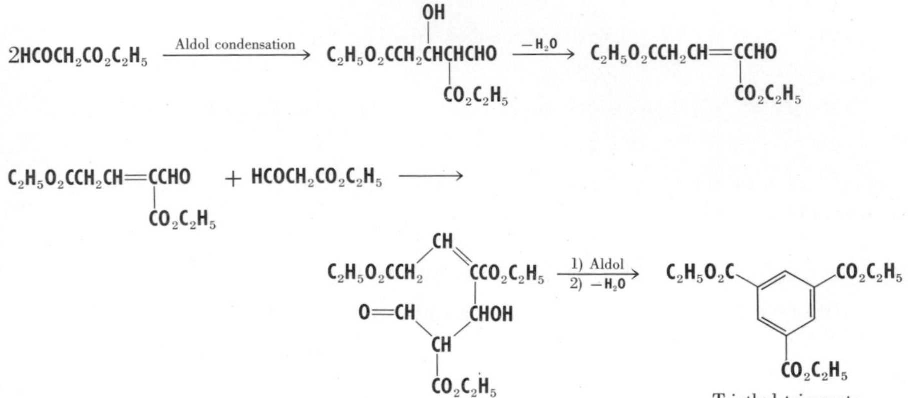

$$C_2H_5O_2CCH_2CH{=}CCHO + HCOCH_2CO_2C_2H_5 \longrightarrow$$

Triethyl trimesate

Even when a mixed ester condensation cannot be carried out, *crossed ketoesters* can often be made by acylation of enolate ions with acid chlorides. Enolates must be preformed by treatment of an ester with a base, such as triphenylmethylsodium, sodium hydride, or sodamide. An acid chloride is then added to the enolate.

Ethyl dimethyl-
benzoyl acetate
79%

Acylation of Other Anions. Enolate ions from ketones and nitriles serve as nucleophiles in useful substitutions on esters and acid chlorides. Because of their high aptitude for self-condensation, aldehydes are not used in this manner. Condensation of an ester with a ketone, a classic method for the preparation of 1,3-diketones, is known as the *Claisen reaction*, in fine distinction from the *Claisen condensation* (of esters).

$$CH_3CN \xrightarrow[Ether]{NaNH_2} \left[\bar{C}H_2CN \longleftrightarrow CH_2{=}C{=}\bar{N} \right] \xrightarrow{CH_3CH_2CO_2C_2H_5} CH_3CH_2COCH_2CN$$

β-Ketovaleronitrile
(Propionylacetonitrile)
40%

$$CH_3COCH_2CO_2C_2H_5 \xrightarrow{Mg(OC_2H_5)_2} CH_3CO\bar{C}HCO_2C_2H_5 \xrightarrow{C_6H_5CH_2COCl} C_6H_5CH_2COCHCOCH_3$$

$$\underset{CO_2C_2H_5}{|}$$

3-Carbethoxy-1-
phenyl-2,4-pentandione

$$\underset{\substack{O \\ \parallel}}{CH_3CCH(CH_3)_2} + (CH_3)_2CHCO_2C_2H_5 \xrightarrow{NaNH_2} (CH_3)_2CHCOCH_2COCH(CH_3)_2$$

Isopropyl methyl   Ethyl isobutyrate   Diisobutyrylmethane
ketone   70%

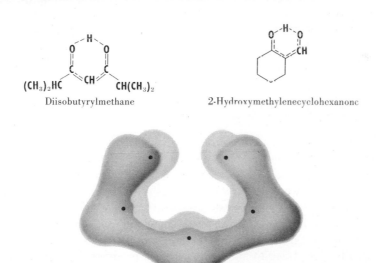

2-Formyl
cyclohexanone
59%

All β-dicarbonyl compounds are somewhat enolic, but their structures are generally represented by diketo formulas. Formyl ketones are usually named by reference to their enol structures. Both of the above compounds are essentially 100% enolic. Figure 14.8 shows structural representations of enolic β-dicarbonyl compounds

Related Condensations. The *acyloin condensation* results from treatment of an ester or a diester with sodium. The reaction is carried out in an aprotic solvent, such as ether or a high-boiling hydrocarbon. Acyloin

Diisobutyrylmethane

2-Hydroxymethylenecyclohexanone

Idealized molecular orbital representation
of an enol of a β-diketone

FIG. 14.8   Enols of β-diketones and β-ketoaldehydes.

condensations have been used with spectacular results in the synthesis of cyclic compounds.

$$Na\cdot + RCOR' \longrightarrow RC{-}OR' + \overset{+}{Na}$$

A radical anion

$$2RC{-}OR' \longrightarrow RC{-}CR \longrightarrow RC{-}CR + 2R'\bar{O}$$

$$RC{-}CR + 2Na\cdot \longrightarrow RC{=}CR + 2\overset{+}{Na} \xrightarrow{H^+} RC{=}CR \rightleftharpoons RC{-}CR$$

An acyloin

Pyrolysis of heavy metal salts of carboxylic acids produces ketones. One carboxyl group is converted to a carbonyl group, and the other is lost as carbon dioxide (carbonate). Although acetone was first discovered as a product of the pyrolysis of calcium salts, the method is now seldom used except for synthesis of cyclic ketones.

$$(CH_3CO_2)_2Ca \xrightarrow{350°} CH_3COCH_3 + CaCO_3$$

$$C_6H_5CH_2CO_2H + CH_3CO_2H \xrightarrow[\text{tube, 450°}]{ThO_2\text{-packed}} C_6H_5CH_2COCH_3$$

60%

$$HO_2C(CH_2)_4CO_2H \xrightarrow{Ba(OH)_2,\ 300°}$$

$$HO_2C(CH_2)_nCO_2H \xrightarrow[\text{Heat}]{Ca(OH)_2} (CH_2)_n \quad C{=}O$$

$n = 8{-}20$ 0–5%

The *Thorpe reaction* involves nucleophilic addition to cyano groups. The reaction is best considered in conjunction with the Claisen ester condensation, since the two reactions accomplish essentially the same synthetic objectives. Highly hindered bases are used to catalyze Thorpe reactions, in order to favor proton abstraction in preference to addition of the base to nitrile groups. The reaction produces imino nitriles, which are usually hydrolyzed to ketonitriles before products are isolated. The only extensive application of the reaction has been in syntheses of cyclic ketones.

$$C_6H_5CH_2CN \xrightarrow{[(CH_3)_2CH]_2N^-Li^+} C_6H_5\bar{C}HCN \xrightarrow{C_6H_5CH_2C{\equiv}N} C_6H_5CH_2\overset{\overset{-}{\overset{+}{NLi}}}{\underset{C_6H_5}{C}}CHCN \xrightarrow{H_2O} C_6H_5CH_2\overset{\overset{NH}{\parallel}}{\underset{C_6H_5}{C}}CHCN$$

80%

$$(CH_2)_n \underset{CN}{\overset{CH_2CN}{<}} \xrightarrow{(C_2H_5)_2N^-Li^+} (CH_2)_n \underset{C=NLi}{\overset{CHCN}{<}} \xrightarrow{H_3O^+} (CH_2)_n \underset{C=O}{\overset{CHCN}{<}}$$

1–70%

There are few useful examples of carbon-carbon bond formation by nucleophilic substitution reactions of aromatic substrates. Coupling of organometallic compounds with aryl halides is of limited use (page 225). Cyanide ion may be used in the Sandmeyer reaction as a method for replacement of aromatic amino groups by a carbon-containing functional group.

| 2,3-Dimethyl-aniline | $\xrightarrow{NaNO_2, HCl}$ | 2,3-Dimethyl-benzenediazonium chloride | $\xrightarrow{Cu_2(CN)_2}$ | 2,3-Dimethylbenzo-nitrile 40% |

Cyclization Reactions

Four reactions that effect cyclization of difunctional aliphatic molecules have been presented in this chapter. Another, the intra-molecular aldol condensation, was discussed in the previous chapter. Much attention has been centered on development of cyclization reactions for both practical and theoretical purposes. Alicyclic ring systems are very common in natural products, and dozens of syntheses of five- and six-membered rings are used in the steroid and terpene fields (Chap. 24). Interest in synthesis of larger rings was stimulated by the discovery by Ruzicka in 1926 that the active principles in two exotic perfume bases, musk and civet, are large-ring ketones. The Himalayan musk deer and the African civet cat produce the compounds, but not in sufficient quantity to satiate the world-wide social demands for perfume ingredients. As a consequence, the Swiss, who have been remarkably successful in the synthesis of fine organic chemicals, turned their attention to the synthesis of large-ring ketones.

Civetone   Muscone

The net conclusions of all studies of cyclization reactions are as follows:

1. Three- and four-membered rings are not produced in high yields in any intramolecular condensation.

2. Five-, six-, and seven-membered rings are very easily made by almost any condensation reaction.

3. The yield of cyclization product drops sharply with the rings in the C_8–C_{14} range, with a minimum at C_{10}.

4. Yields again increase and become more or less constant at about C_{15} or C_{16}.

Development of theories to account for the above observations has been slow but interesting. At the present time, the results are attributed to a combination of internal-angle strains and the interactions beween nonbonded groups attached to the rings (Chap. 6). The conclusions can be summarized as follows:

1. The small rings, C_3 and C_4, are badly strained. Condensation reactions, which are for the most part reversible, do not produce them in appreciable yield, because the equilibrium constants for cyclization are too small. There is evidence for the rapid passage of materials through intermediate cyclic C_4 stages in the course of some condensations. Three- and four-membered rings must be made by internal alkylation (page 225) and addition reactions (Chap. 15) which are essentially irreversible.

2. C_5 and C_6 rings are formed rapidly (perhaps not as rapidly as C_3) and are stable when formed.

3. The *stability* of medium and large rings favors their formation, but the *rates* of formation fall off. The most important factor in this decrease in rate is the improbability of finding the two ends of a randomly coiled chain close together. In all cases, cyclization competes with intermolecular condensation to form polymeric materials.

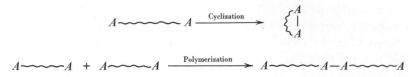

4. Some additional effect must account for the minimum yield at C_{10}. The phenomenon has been explained by reference to interactions between hydrogens in a cycloalkane. In cyclopentane, the hydrogen atoms would be completely eclipsed (page 123) in the plane pentagonal structure permitted by the tetrahedral C—C—C bond angles. Repulsion between hydrogen atoms is sufficient to account for a slight puckering of the cyclopentane ring.

In cyclohexane, staggering of methylene groups is perfect in the chair form. As a consequence of perfect staggering and strainless internal bond angles, the cyclohexane structure is very stable. In cycloheptane, a considerable amount of hydrogen-hydrogen interference is again found, and the effect increases to a maximum in cyclodecane. The relatively slow rates of cyclization to medium-sized rings are due to the twofold problems of overcoming H—H repulsions and the necessity that the two ends of a long chain come in contact with each other. The latter "hunting" problem persists in the formation of large rings, but the **H—H** repulsions disappear because of the great flexibility of large cycles.

Various techniques have been brought to bear on the problem of overcoming unfavorable competition with intermolecular reactions in the synthesis of medium and large rings.   The first success with the pyrolysis of salts of divalent metals is probably due to the fact that some cyclic salt structures are formed in the solid mixture, thus bringing two functional ends together.

Success with the Thorpe cyclization is due to the choice of a reaction that can be run at very high dilution in homogeneous solutions.   The intermolecular reaction of a cyano carbanion is bimolecular, so that the rate of polymerization depends upon the concentration of both the anion and the dinitrile.

Rate of polymerization $= k_P[\overline{R}CHCN][RCN]$

On the other hand, the rate of cyclization is unimolecular.

Rate of cyclization $= k_C[\overline{R}CHCN]$

Therefore, the ratio of the two reaction rates depends on the concentration of the nitrile, and cyclization is favored by high dilution.

$$\frac{\text{Rate of cyclization}}{\text{Rate of polymerization}} = \frac{k_C}{k_P[RCN]}$$

Despite the success of the high-dilution technique, a dramatic improvement was made with the cyclic acyloin condensation.   The reaction occurs in a *dilute layer* of ester molecules adsorbed on the surface of sodium metal.   Not all surface reactions simulate high-dilution conditions, but in the present case, the ester is only weakly adsorbed on the surface. As a result, ester molecules are unlikely to be close enough together to permit intermolecular coupling to compete with cyclization.   Yields in the cyclic acyloin condensation fall to a minimum at C_{10}, but the minimum is a respectable 55%.   Large rings, such as C_{16}, can be made in almost quantitative yield.

Dimethyl sebacate   Sebacoin 55%

Syntheses of cyclic compounds are often cumulative schemes of considerable complexity. The following synthesis of dimethyldihydroresorcinol (dimedone) makes the end product a readily available chemical. The variety of condensations involved is instructive. The last three steps occur without isolation of intermediates.

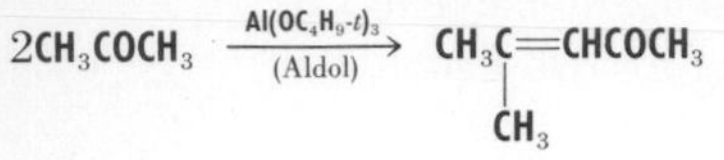

$$2CH_3COCH_3 \xrightarrow[\text{(Aldol)}]{Al(OC_4H_9\text{-}t)_3} CH_3C{=}CHCOCH_3$$

(with CH$_3$ substituent)

Mesityl oxide

$$CH_2(CO_2C_2H_5)_2 + CH_3C{=}CHCOCH_3 \xrightarrow[\text{(Michael)}]{C_2H_5ONa}$$

(with CH$_3$ substituent)

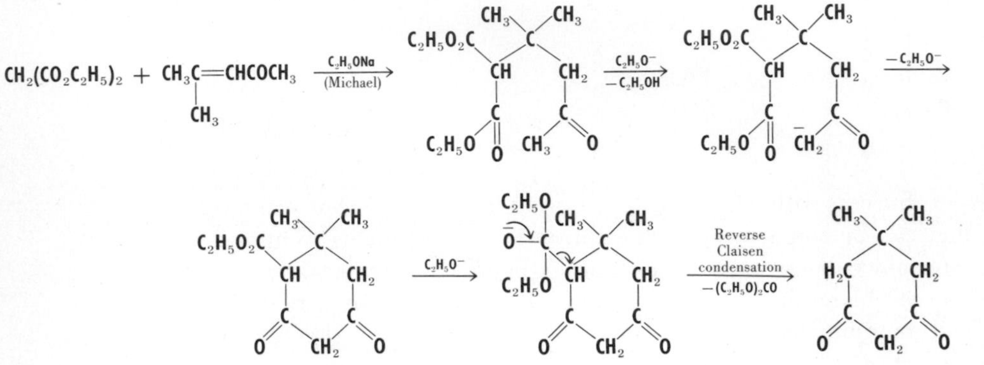

Dimedone
(Dimethyldihydro-
resorcinol)
76%

Application of the Claisen condensation to a diester of a six or seven carbon diacid is called a Dieckmann reaction.

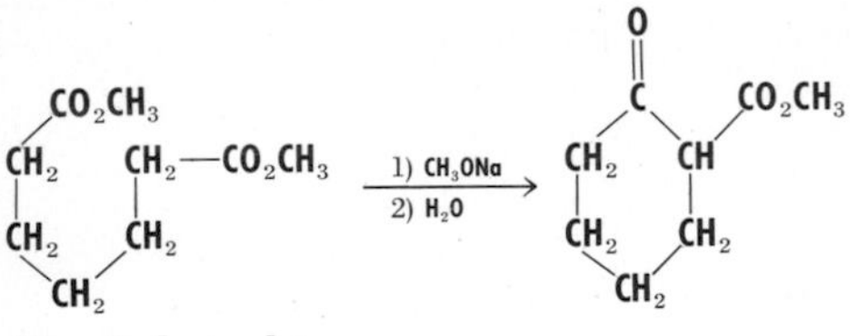

Dimethyl pimelate

The following is an example of the synthesis of an aliphatic compound from an aromatic system. The ring is opened by an interesting cleavage of a β-ketoester.

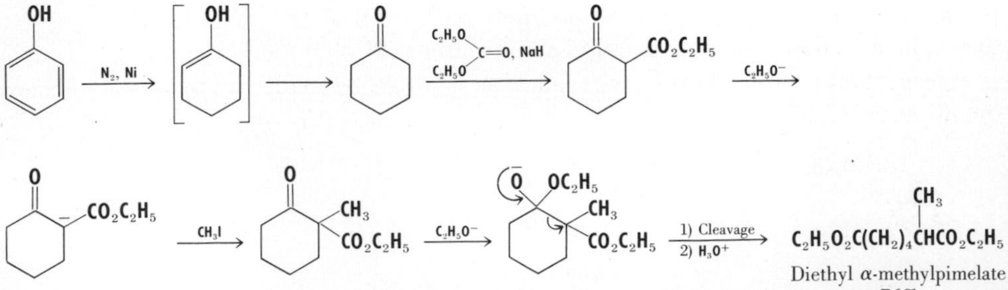

$$\xrightarrow[\text{2) H}_3\text{O}^+]{\text{1) Cleavage}} C_2H_5O_2C(CH_2)_4CHCO_2C_2H_5$$

(with CH$_3$ substituent)

Diethyl α-methylpimelate
76%

Acid-catalyzed Acylation

A few acid-catalyzed acylations have been used successfully for synthetic purposes. Unsymmetrical ketones frequently give products in acid-catalyzed condensations that are different from those formed under basic conditions.

$$CH_3CH_2COCH_3 + (CH_3CO)_2O \xrightarrow{BF_3} CH_3COCHCOCH_3$$
$$\underset{CH_3}{|}$$

3-Methylacetylacetone
30%

$$CH_3CH_2COCH_3 + CH_3CO_2C_2H_5 \xrightarrow{C_2H_5ONa} CH_3CH_2COCH_2COCH_3$$

Propionylacetone
60%

Acid-catalyzed reactions depend upon enolization. Enols are sufficiently nucleophilic to be acylated by very reactive substrates such as anhydride-boron trifluoride addition compounds.

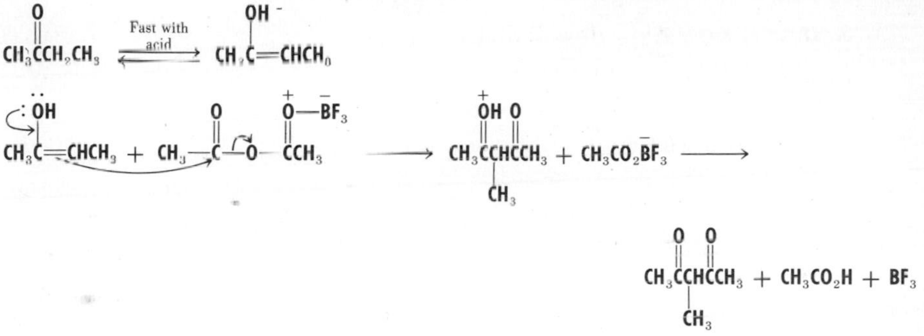

Acylation of enol esters is a strictly analogous reaction.

$$\underset{O_2CCH_3}{\overset{}{C_6H_5C-CH_2}} + (CH_3CO)_2O \xrightarrow{BF_3} C_6H_5COCH_2COCH_3$$

Benzoyl acetone
68%

A good β-diketone synthesis utilizes the nucleophilic character of eneamines.

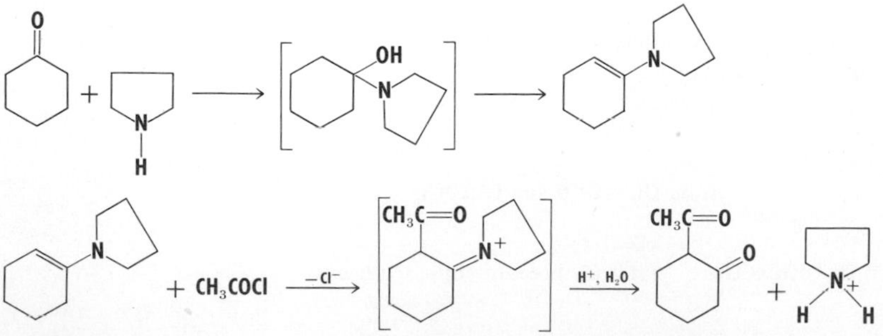

Problems

1. Write equations for the following transformations:

a. Benzamide is hydrolyzed, and the acid produced is then esterified with phenol, trifluoroacetic anhydride being used as a condensing agent.

b. *n*-Butyl mercaptan is acylated with propionic anhydride.

c. Diethyl adipate is subjected to the Dieckmann condensation, and the product is alkylated with ethyl bromide.

d. *n*-Valeronitrile is condensed in the Thorpe reaction, and the product is converted to a ketone.

e. *p*-Chlorotoluene is made by a Sandmeyer reaction and is then aminated by treatment with sodamide in liquid ammonia.

f. Methyl *n*-propyl ketone is converted to several characteristic derivatives.

g. Dimethyl pimelate is cyclized by the acyloin condensation. The product is reduced to a mixture of stereoisomeric diols, which are converted to dibenzoates.

h. *n*-Butyl methyl ketone is acetylated under acidic and basic conditions.

i. 4-Methylcyclohexanone is recovered from its semicarbazone.

j. Nitromethane is acylated with *p*-nitrobenzoyl chloride.

2. Devise syntheses of the following compounds from the starting materials indicated and compounds containing no more than three carbon atoms.

a. $CH_3CHOHCH_2CH_2OH$ from $CH_3CO_2C_2H_5$

b. $C_6H_5COCH_2COCH_3$ from C_6H_5Cl

c.

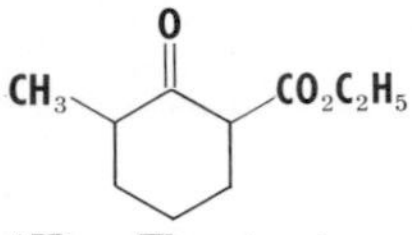

from

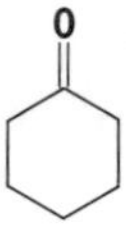

(*Hint:* The ring is opened and closed again.)

d. $(CH_3CO)_3CH$

e. $(CH_3)_3CC-CC(CH_3)_3$ (with two O above)

f.

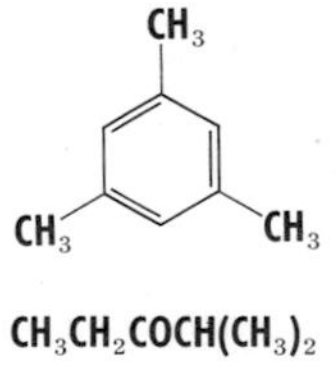

g. $CH_3CH_2COCH(CH_3)_2$

h.

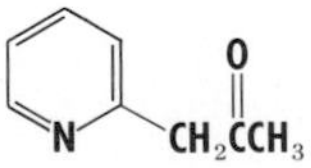

from

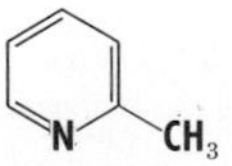

i.

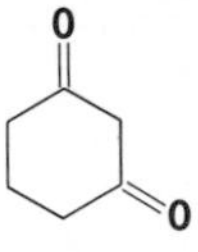

from $CH_2{=}CHCN$ and CH_3COCH_3

j. $CH_3CH_2COCH_2COCH_3$ (at least three different syntheses)

3. Write mechanisms for each of the following reactions:

a. $CH_3CO_2H \xrightarrow{\text{HCl, } C_2H_5OH} CH_3CO_2C_2H_5$

b. $C_6H_5COCl + (CH_3)_2Cd \longrightarrow C_6H_5COCH_3$

c. $CH_3COCl + KCN \longrightarrow CH_3COCN + KCl$

d. 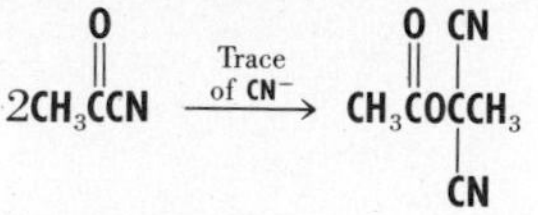 $2CH_3\overset{O}{\overset{\|}{C}}CN \xrightarrow[\text{of CN}^-]{\text{Trace}} CH_3\overset{O}{\overset{\|}{C}}\overset{CN}{\underset{CN}{\overset{|}{\underset{|}{C}}}}CH_3$

e. 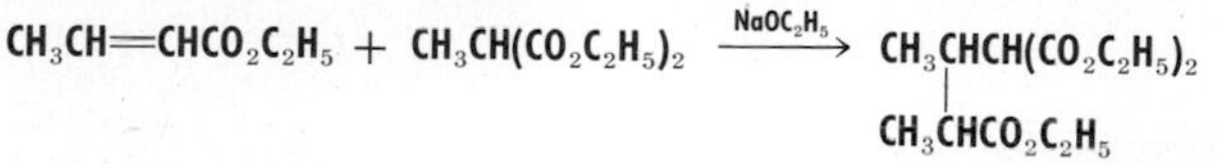 $CH_3CH{=}CHCO_2C_2H_5 + CH_3CH(CO_2C_2H_5)_2 \xrightarrow{\text{NaOC}_2H_5}$

$$CH_3\underset{\underset{CH_3\overset{|}{C}HCO_2C_2H_5}{|}}{\overset{|}{C}}HCH(CO_2C_2H_5)_2$$

(A cyclobutanone
derivative is an intermediate)

f. $(CH_3CO)_2O + CH_3COCH_2CO_2C_2H_5 \xrightarrow{\text{BF}_3} (CH_3CO)_2CHCO_2C_2H_5$

g. 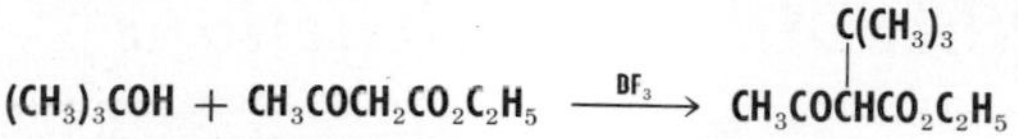 $(CH_3)_3COH + CH_3COCH_2CO_2C_2H_5 \xrightarrow{\text{BF}_3} CH_3CO\overset{C(CH_3)_3}{\overset{|}{C}}HCO_2C_2H_5$

h. 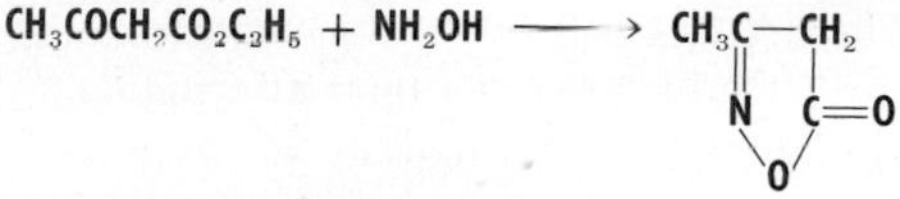 $CH_3COCH_2CO_2C_2H_5 + NH_2OH \longrightarrow CH_3\underset{\underset{O}{N}}{C}{-}\underset{C=O}{CH_2}$

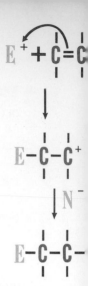

15

Electrophilic and Other Addition Reactions

Most reactions of alkenes and alkynes are additions. Electrophilic reagents usually initiate the attack; therefore addition reactions can usually be formulated as stepwise processes involving the intermediate formation of carbonium ions or other cations. The two-step ionic mechanism leads to many correct predictions about electrophilic addition. However, related mechanisms, involving cyclic intermediates or concerted addition, may also occur. The most likely possibilities are illustrated in Fig. 15.1.

This chapter first considers electrophilic additions. It then deals with free-radical additions and, finally, with miscellaneous nonpolar additions that do not involve free radicals.

Carbon-Halogen Bond Formation

Both halogens and hydrogen halides add readily to alkenes and their derivatives unless the latter are heavily substituted with electron-withdrawing groups. Rates of electrophilic additions are increased by electron-donating substituents. Since alkyl groups are electron-donors, alkenes that are highly branched at the seat of unsaturation are particularly reactive.

Hydrogen halide addition:

$$HBr + CH_3CH_2CH{=}CH_2 \xrightarrow{\text{Acetic acid}} CH_3CH_2CHCH_3$$
$$\underset{\text{Br}}{|}$$

sec-Butyl bromide
80%

$$HCl + (CH_3)_2C{=}CH_2 \xrightarrow{\text{Conc. HCl}} (CH_3)_3CCl$$

tert-Butyl chloride
100%

Halogen and hypohalous acid addition:

$$Br_2 + CH_2{=}CH_2 \longrightarrow BrCH_2CH_2Br$$

Ethylene dibromide
100% (by titration)

$$Br_2 + CH_2{=}CHCH_2Br \xrightarrow[-20°]{CHCl_3} BrCH_2CHBrCH_2Br$$

1,2,3-Tribromopropane
98%

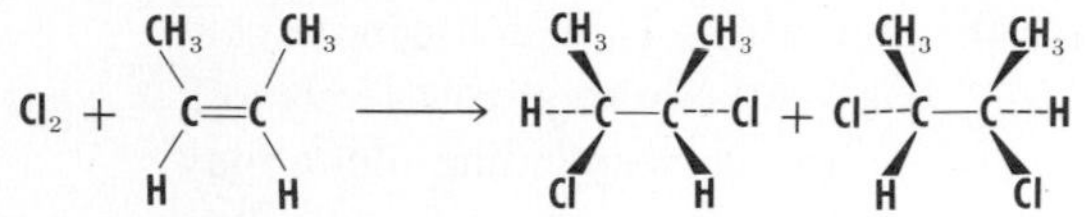

cis-2-Butene   (±)2,3-Dichlorobutane

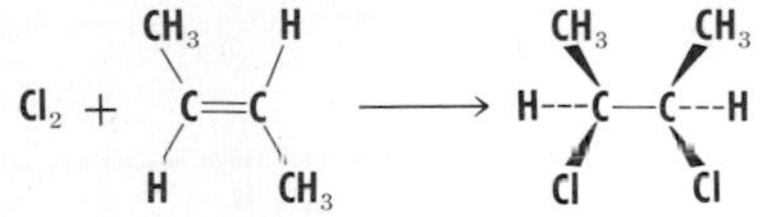

trans-2-Butene   *meso*-2,3-Dichlorobutane
61%

$$I{-}Cl + (CH_3)_2C{=}CH_2 \xrightarrow{HgCl_2} (CH_3)_2CCH_2I$$
$$\mid$$
$$Cl$$

Iodine   2-Chloro-1-iodo-2-methylpropane
monochloride   (Isobutylene iodochloride)
67%

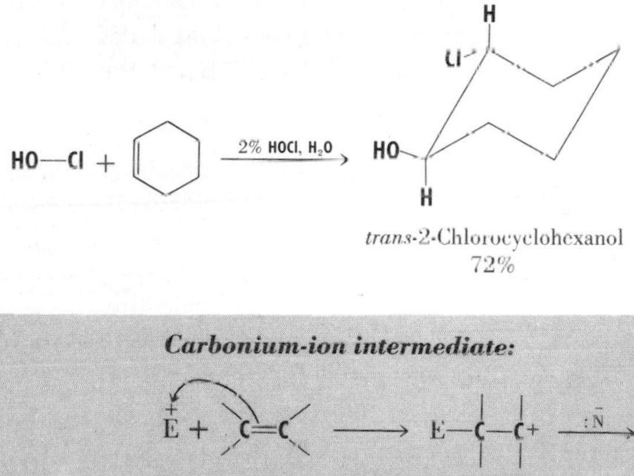

$$HO{-}Cl + \text{(cyclohexene)} \xrightarrow{2\% \ HOCl, \ H_2O} HO$$

trans-2-Chlorocyclohexanol
72%

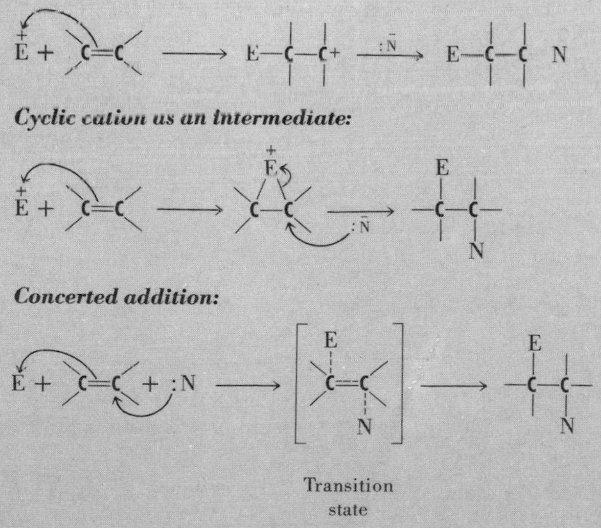

Carbonium-ion intermediate:

Cyclic cation as an intermediate:

Concerted addition:

Transition
state

FIG. 15.1   *Electrophilic addition mechanisms.*

Addition of hydrogen halides to alkenes has some preparative value in the conversion of unsaturated natural products and petroleum alkenes to halides. The reaction is not often used in synthesis, since the best synthetic route to most olefins leads through alcohols, which can be converted directly to halides (page 216). If a synthetic sequence leads to a primary alcohol, dehydration (Chap. 17) to the corresponding olefin may precede conversion to the nonterminal halide.

$$CH_3CH_2CH_2CH_2CH_2OH \xrightarrow{\hspace{1cm}} \begin{array}{l} \xrightarrow{\text{Conc. HCl}} CH_3CH_2CH_2CH_2CH_2Cl \\[2em] \xrightarrow[-H_2O]{P_2O_5} CH_3CH_2CH_2CH=CH_2 \xrightarrow{\text{HCl}} CH_3CH_2CH_2CHCH_3 \\ \hspace{8cm} | \\ \hspace{8cm} Cl \end{array}$$

The above examples illustrate two outstanding characteristics of electrophilic addition reactions: (1) Addition of unsymmetrical reagents is unidirectional. (2) Halogen addition is stereospecific.

Markownikoff's rule, which was first stated, on empirical grounds, in 1871, predicts the direction of addition to alkenes and vinyl halides. The rule simply states that in the addition of HX to a double bond the hydrogen becomes attached to that carbon atom which already bears the largest number of hydrogen atoms.

$$CH_3CH=CH_2$$
$$(X\!-\!H)$$

The rule and many of its useful extensions are readily derivable from the stepwise addition mechanism. A hydrogen ion is added first to give the most stable possible carbonium ion. Study of the reactivity of halides and other substrates in nucleophilic substitution by the carbonium-ion mechanism (Chap. 11) established the order of stability of carbonium ions as tertiary > secondary > primary. Application of the same relationships to hydrogen halide addition leads to the same predictions as Markownikoff's rule.

$$CH_3CH=CH_2 \xrightarrow{H^+} \begin{array}{l} \xrightarrow{\hspace{0.5cm}} CH_3\overset{+}{C}HCH_3 \xrightarrow{X^-} CH_3CHXCH_3 \\ \hspace{3.5cm} \text{Secondary carbonium ion} \\[1.5em] \xrightarrow{X} CH_3CH_2\overset{+}{C}H_2 \\ \hspace{2cm} \text{Primary carbonium ion} \end{array}$$

Addition of hydrogen halides to conjugated dienes involves intermediate allylic cations which add halide ions to give mixtures of products (Fig. 15.2).

Addition to conjugated systems is very rapid, because of the stability of the intermediate ions.

The carbonium-ion mechanism also predicts that rearrangements will occur in the course of hydrogen halide addition (Chaps. 11 and 20).

$$(CH_3)_3CCH{=}CH_2 \xrightarrow{H^+} (CH_3)_3C\overset{+}{C}HCH_3 \xrightarrow{CH_3\ shift} (CH_3)_2\overset{+}{C}CH(CH_3)_2 \xrightarrow{Cl^-} (CH_3)_2CCH(CH_3)_2$$

The first step in halogen additions is the transfer of a halogen cation to the unsaturated substrate. The reaction is really a nucleophilic displacement on the halogen, or a complex of the halogen with a Lewis acid. The nucleophile is the alkene with its loosely bound π electrons. A cyclic bromonium ion rather than a carbonium ion is formed. Attack of

$$\overset{+}{H} + CH_2{=}CH{-}CH{=}CH_2 \longrightarrow CH_3\overset{+}{C}H{-}CH{=}CH_2 \longleftrightarrow$$

$$CH_3CH{=}CH{-}\overset{+}{C}H_2 \xrightarrow{Cl^-} CH_3CHClCH{=}CH_2 \ + \ CH_3CH{=}CHCH_2Cl$$

Methylvinylcarbinyl   Crotyl-chloride
chloride

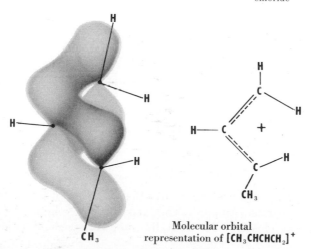

Molecular orbital
representation of $[CH_3CHCHCH_2]^+$

FIG. 15.2   *Addition to a conjugated diene.*

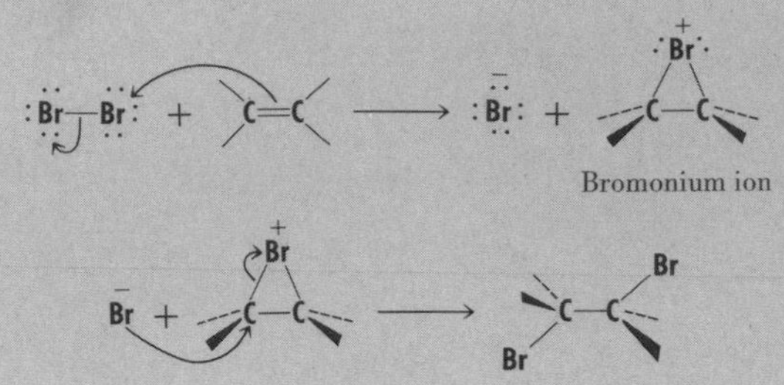

FIG. 15.3 *Trans addition of bromine to a double bond.*

halide ion on a bromonium ion occurs with inversion of configuration. The over-all steric course of the reaction is such that the two halogen atoms add from opposite sides of the plane of the olefinic substrate. Such a *trans addition* is outlined in Fig. 15.3.

Bromonium ions were discussed previously in connection with neighboring-group participation in S_N1 reactions (page 240). Nucleophilic attack on unsymmetrical bromonium ions occurs at that carbon atom which is best able to support a positive charge (most highly substituted position).

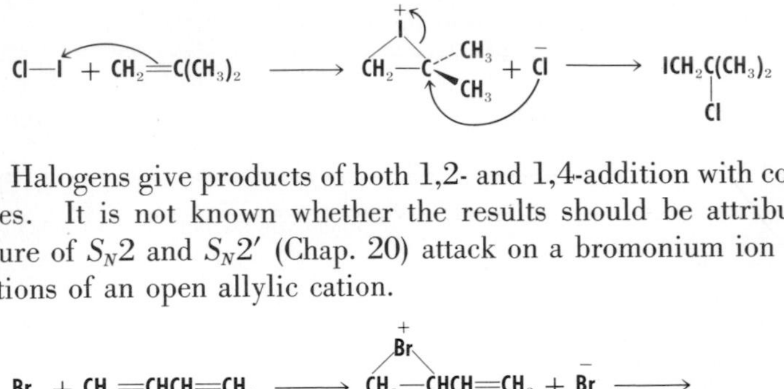

Halogens give products of both 1,2- and 1,4-addition with conjugated dienes. It is not known whether the results should be attributed to a mixture of S_N2 and S_N2' (Chap. 20) attack on a bromonium ion or to the reactions of an open allylic cation.

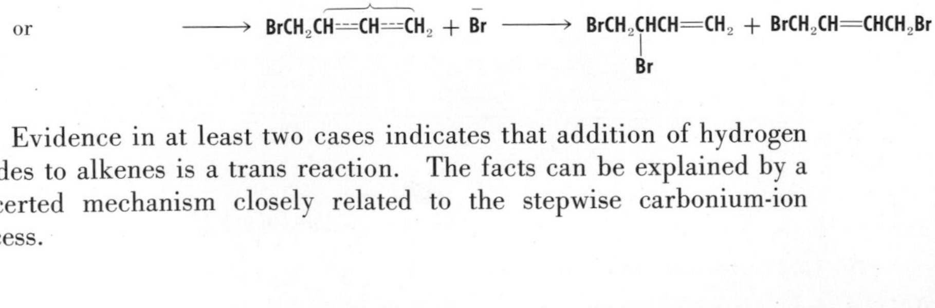

Evidence in at least two cases indicates that addition of hydrogen halides to alkenes is a trans reaction. The facts can be explained by a concerted mechanism closely related to the stepwise carbonium-ion process.

† The term π complex is applied to loose complexes between unsaturated compounds and electron-deficient compounds. The name derives from the view that the π electrons are only slightly polarized to form a weak bond.

Carbon-Oxygen Bond Formation

Virtually all hydroxylic compounds can be added to alkenes under acidic conditions. *Hydration* (addition of water) is a very important process, used commercially for preparation of alcohols from petroleum by-products. The synthesis of esters, especially *tert*-alkyl carboxylates, frequently utilizes this reaction, as does the synthesis of diethyl ether by the addition of water and ethanol to ethylene. Conditions required to effect the transformations vary considerably with alkene structure. Reactivity is increased by attachment of electron-donor substituents, such as alkyl, to alkene linkages.

The reactions are proton-initiated and, therefore, follow Markownikoff's rule. Since capture of the intermediate carbonium ion is a matter of competition among the various nucleophiles in the system, hydrogen halides cannot be used as catalysts when the object is to add a molecule of a weakly nucleophilic solvent. Sulfuric acid produces only weakly nucleophilic bisulfate ions, which are not good competitors. Furthermore, acid sulfates formed as intermediates are readily solvolyzed. Figure 15.4 shows the competition for capture of carbonium ions in an acidic solution of an alkene.

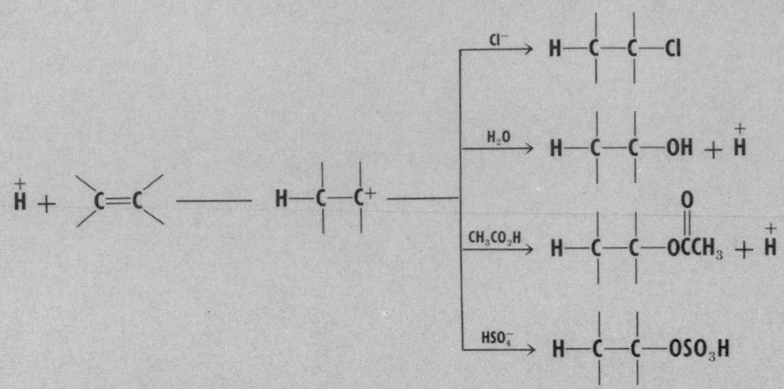

$$\overset{+}{H} + \overset{\diagdown}{\underset{\diagup}{C}}=\overset{\diagup}{\underset{\diagdown}{C}} \longrightarrow H-\underset{|}{\overset{|}{C}}-\overset{|}{C}{}^{+} \longrightarrow \begin{cases} \xrightarrow{Cl^-} H-\underset{|}{\overset{|}{C}}-\underset{|}{\overset{|}{C}}-Cl \\[2mm] \xrightarrow{H_2O} H-\underset{|}{\overset{|}{C}}-\underset{|}{\overset{|}{C}}-OH + \overset{+}{H} \\[2mm] \xrightarrow{CH_3CO_2H} H-\underset{|}{\overset{|}{C}}-\underset{|}{\overset{|}{C}}-OCCH_3 + \overset{+}{H} \\[2mm] \xrightarrow{HSO_4^-} H-\underset{|}{\overset{|}{C}}-\underset{|}{\overset{|}{C}}-OSO_3H \end{cases}$$

FIG. 15.4   *Competition in alkene addition.*

Hydration of alkynes produces carbonyl compounds. The reaction is catalyzed by mercuric salts, which are known to form complexes with acetylenes. The formal similarity to alkene hydration may be illusory, but the over-all consequences are exactly those expected from hydration according to Markownikoff's rule, followed by tautomerization of the resulting enol.

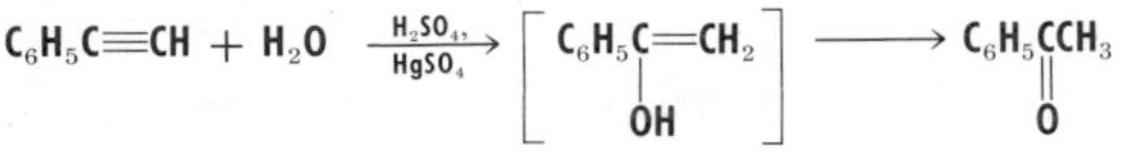

$$C_6H_5C{\equiv}CH + H_2O \xrightarrow[HgSO_4]{H_2SO_4} \left[\underset{\underset{OH}{|}}{C_6H_5C}{=}CH_2 \right] \longrightarrow \underset{\underset{O}{\|}}{C_6H_5CCH_3}$$

Phenylacetylene   α-Phenylvinyl   Acetophenone
                      alcohol

Coupling of acetylene hydration with acetylene alkylation (page 223) provides an interesting method for extending carbon chains to give products with nonterminal functional groups.

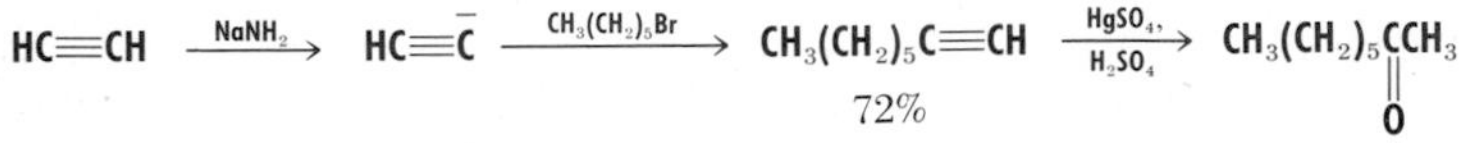

$$HC{\equiv}CH \xrightarrow{NaNH_2} HC{\equiv}\bar{C} \xrightarrow{CH_3(CH_2)_5Br} \underset{72\%}{CH_3(CH_2)_5C{\equiv}CH} \xrightarrow[H_2SO_4]{HgSO_4} \underset{\underset{O}{\|}}{CH_3(CH_2)_5CCH_3}$$

n-Hexyl methyl ketone
91%

Hydration of the products of condensation of acetylenes with carbonyl compounds is also an excellent synthetic procedure.

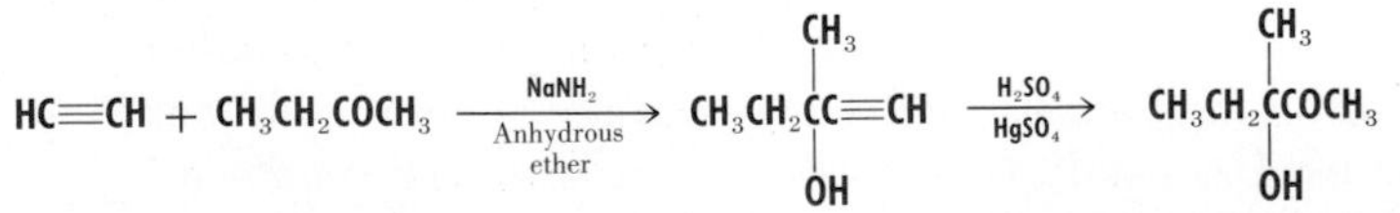

$$HC{\equiv}CH + CH_3CH_2COCH_3 \xrightarrow[\underset{ether}{Anhydrous}]{NaNH_2} \underset{\underset{OH}{|}}{CH_3CH_2\overset{\overset{CH_3}{|}}{C}C{\equiv}CH} \xrightarrow[HgSO_4]{H_2SO_4} \underset{\underset{OH}{|}}{CH_3CH_2\overset{\overset{CH_3}{|}}{C}COCH_3}$$

3-Hydroxy-3-methyl-2-pentanone

Addition of carboxylic acids to acetylenes leads to alkenyl esters, a versatile class of compounds. Vinyl esters undergo polymerization (Chap. 25), and all alkenyl esters may be further modified by a host of reactions.

$$CH_3CO_2H + CH{\equiv}CH \xrightarrow{BF_3,\ HgO} CH_2{=}CHO_2CCH_3$$

Vinyl acetate

$$CH_3CO_2H + CH_3(CH_2)_3C \equiv CH \xrightarrow{BF_3, HgO} CH_3(CH_2)_3C = CH_2$$
$$\underset{O_2CCH_3}{|}$$

31%

$$CH_3(CH_2)_3C = CH_2 \xrightarrow{Br_2} \left[CH_3(CH_2)_3CBrCH_2Br \right] \xrightarrow[-Br^-]{Spontaneous} \left[CH_3(CH_2)_3\overset{+}{C}CH_2Br \right] \longrightarrow$$

$$CH_3(CH_2)_3CCH_2Br + \overset{+}{CH_3CO} \xrightarrow{Br^-} CH_3COBr$$

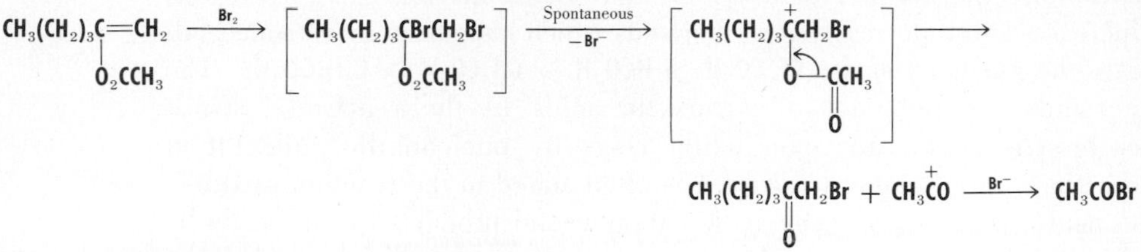

1-Bromo-2-hexanone
67%

Hypohalous Acid Addition. Dilute solutions of halogens in water attack alkenes with the formation of halohydrins. The reaction is a halogen addition that has been diverted by the capture of the intermediate ion by the solvent. Dihalides are usually formed as by-products.

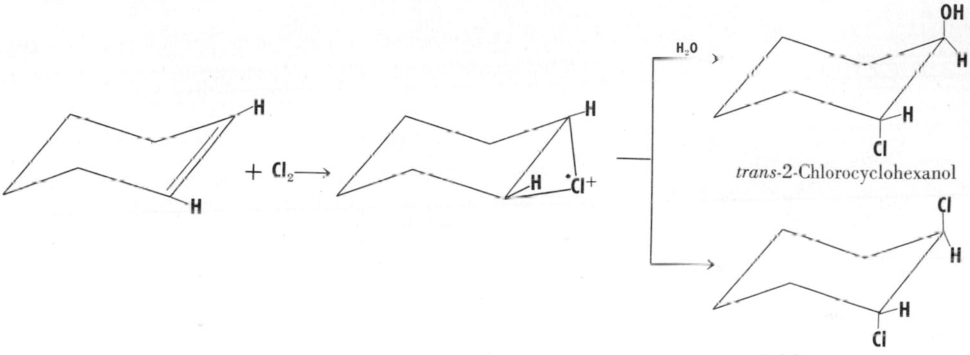

trans-2-Chlorocyclohexanol

trans-1,2-Dichlorocyclohexane

An alternative method of adding the elements of **HOX** or **ZOX** to an olefin is through the use of compounds, other than molecular halogen, which are positive halogen-donors. The *N*-haloamides have been used for this purpose.

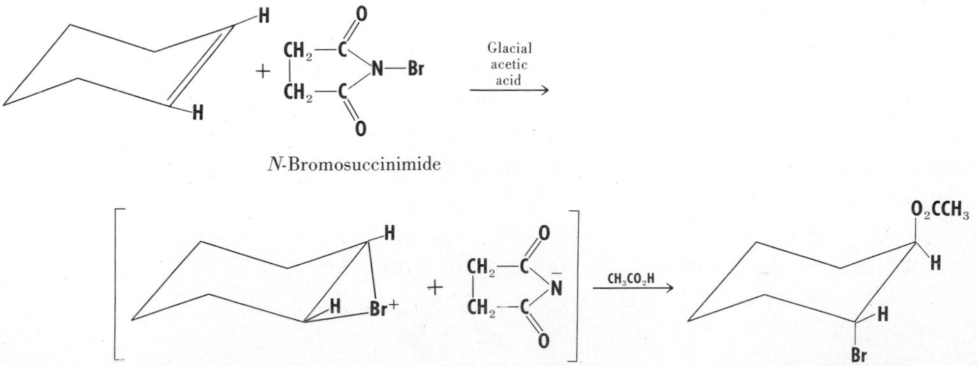

N-Bromosuccinimide

trans-2-Bromocyclohexyl acetate

Peracid Oxidations. Conversion of an alkene to an epoxide (oxirane) by oxidation with percarboxylic acids shows the variations in reactivity with varying alkene structure that are characteristic of electrophilic addition. Substitution of alkyl or alkoxyl groups for vinyl hydrogens increases substrate reactivity. Peracids which have been investigated fall into the reactivity series $CF_3CO_3H \gg HCO_3H > CH_3CO_3H > C_6H_5CO_3H$. The peracids are reduced to carboxylic acids in the reaction. Since carboxylic acids can open oxide rings by nucleophilic substitution reactions, an insoluble weak base is often added to the reaction mixtures to neutralize the carboxylic acid. Many useful products can be made by opening the three numbered rings of epoxides with various nucleophilic reagents.

$$CH_2{=}CHCO_2C_2H_5 + CF_3CO_3H \xrightarrow{\ CH_2Cl_2,\ NaH_2PO_4\ } CH_2{-}CHCO_2C_2H_5$$
$$O$$

Ethyl acrylate   Ethyl glycidate
                                                        80%

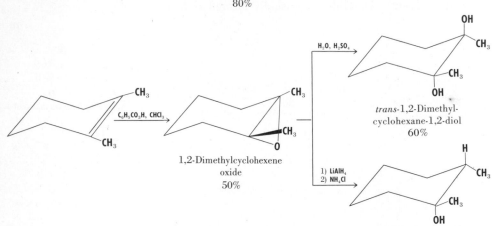

1,2-Dimethylcyclohexene oxide
50%

trans-1,2-Dimethyl-cyclohexane-1,2-diol
60%

trans-1,2-Dimethylcyclohexanol

Oxidation with osmium tetroxide is an alternative method for hydroxylation of carbon-carbon double bonds. Because of the expense and toxicity of the reagent, the procedure is used only in the synthesis of fine chemicals, such as pharmaceuticals, and for degradative studies. To conserve the reagent, it is used only in minor catalytic amounts, with hydrogen peroxide available to reoxidize osmium in its lower valence states to OsO_4. A striking feature of the reaction is that the hydroxyl groups are introduced cis to each other.

Oleic acid

erythro-9,10-Dihydroxystearic acid

Hydroxylation of a double bond by either of the above procedures, followed by cleavage of the product with a specific reagent for glycols, such as lead tetraacetate or periodic acid (Chap. 19), provides an elegant method for the degradation of unsaturated compounds. Identification of the simpler cleavage fragments constitutes presumptive evidence for the structure of the original compound. In the following example, it was necessary to establish the structure of an olefin formed by a reaction involving a rearrangement. The degradation products were both converted to characteristic derivatives.

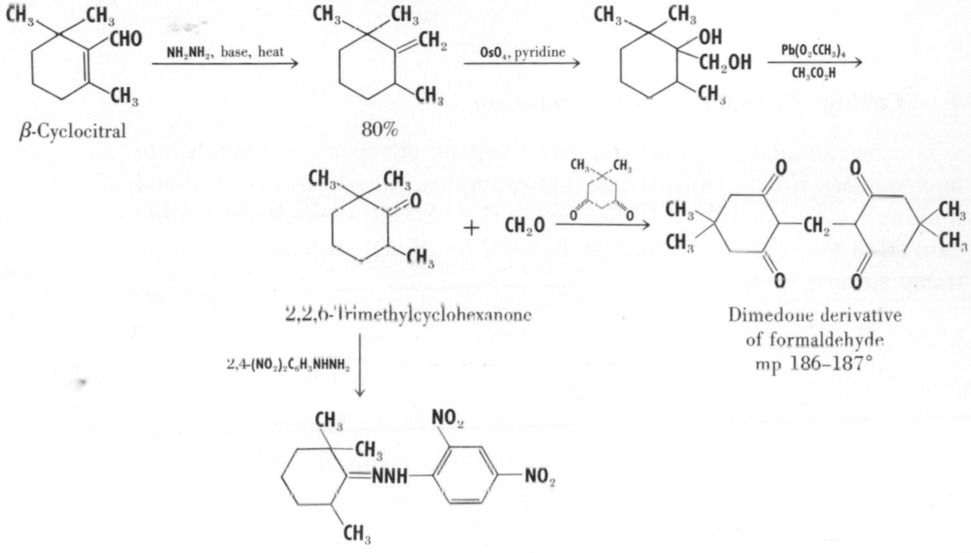

β-Cyclocitral

80%

2,2,6-Trimethylcyclohexanone

+ CH_2O

Dimedone derivative
of formaldehyde
mp 186–187°

2,4-Dinitrophenylhydrazone of
2,2,6-trimethylcyclohexanone
mp 121–122°

Ozone. Cleavage of alkenes with ozone is another, much used, degradative procedure. This very potent reagent breaks both carbon-carbon bonds with the formation of cyclic peroxides known as ozonides. If the peroxide is decomposed under oxidative conditions, carboxylic acids are produced. Reductive cleavage leads to aldehydes and (or) ketones. Ozonides themselves are usually not isolated, because of their explosive character. In addition to degradative uses, ozonolysis has occasionally been used for preparation of aldehydes and ketones from readily available alkenes.

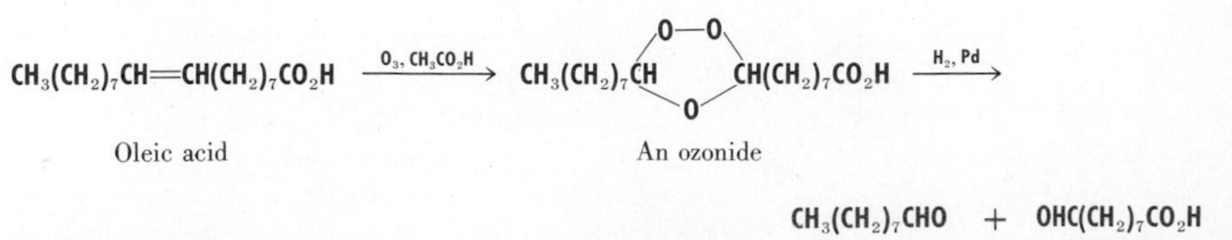

Oleic acid

An ozonide

$CH_3(CH_2)_7CHO$ + $OHC(CH_2)_7CO_2H$

Nonanal   Azeleic half aldehyde

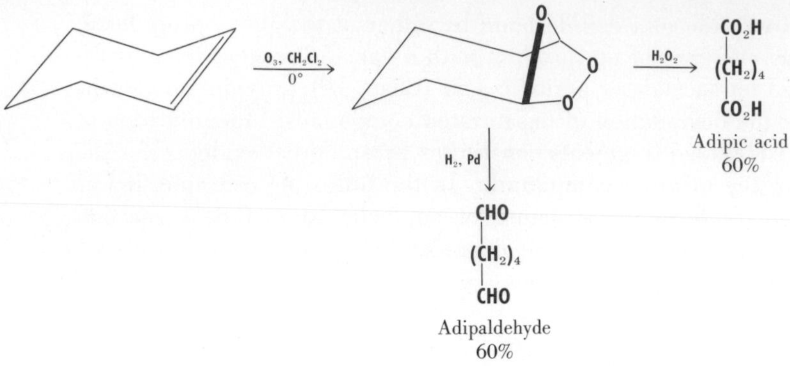

Adipic acid
60%

Adipaldehyde
60%

Carbon-Nitrogen Bond Formation

Since amines, the most important organo-nitrogen compounds, are nucleophilic, it is not surprising that examples of carbon-nitrogen bond making by electrophilic addition are rare. Alkenes which are readily converted to carbonium ions may be used to alkylate nitriles in concentrated sulfuric acid.

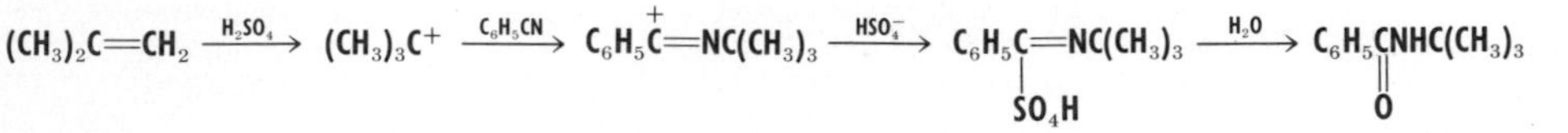

$$(CH_3)_2C{=}CH_2 \xrightarrow{H_2SO_4} (CH_3)_3C^+ \xrightarrow{C_6H_5CN} C_6H_5\overset{+}{C}{=}NC(CH_3)_3 \xrightarrow{HSO_4^-} C_6H_5\underset{SO_4H}{C}{=}NC(CH_3)_3 \xrightarrow{H_2O} C_6H_5\underset{O}{\overset{\|}{C}}NHC(CH_3)_3$$

N-tert-Butylbenzamide
90%

Nitration (introduction of nitro groups) is primarily of importance in the aromatic field (Chap. 16). Concentrated nitric acid reacts readily with alkenes, but the products are usually mixtures. Like other nitrating agents, concentrated nitric acid produces the electrophilic ion NO_2^+ by complex ionization.

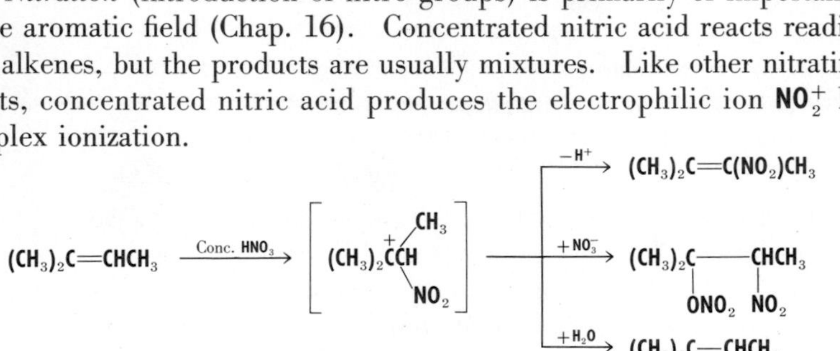

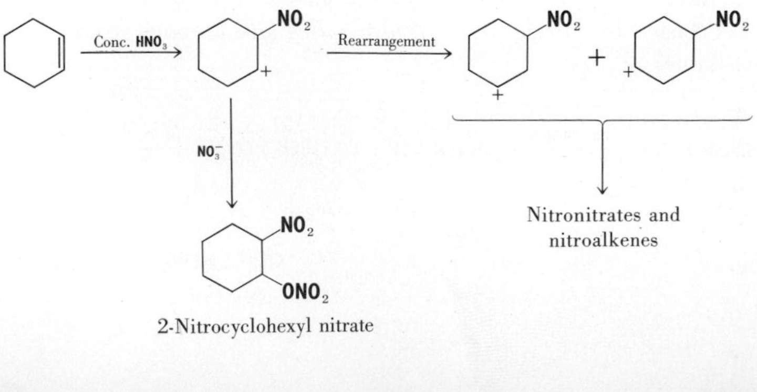

$$(CH_3)_2C{=}CHCH_3 \xrightarrow{Conc. HNO_3} \left[(CH_3)_2\overset{+}{C}\overset{CH_3}{\underset{NO_2}{C}H} \right]$$

$$\xrightarrow{-H^+} (CH_3)_2C{=}C(NO_2)CH_3$$

$$\xrightarrow{+NO_3^-} (CH_3)_2\underset{ONO_2}{C}{-}\underset{NO_2}{C}HCH_3$$

$$\xrightarrow{+H_2O} (CH_3)_2\underset{OH}{C}{-}\underset{NO_2}{C}HCH_3$$

Nitronitrates and
nitroalkenes

2-Nitrocyclohexyl nitrate

Addition of nitrosyl chloride to olefins has been used to characterize alkenes and, occasionally, for specialized preparative purposes.

$$(CH_3)_2C{=}CHCH_3 \xrightarrow[\text{n-C$_5$H$_{11}$ONO + HCl)}]{\text{NOCl (from}} (CH_3)_2\overset{\displaystyle NO}{\underset{\displaystyle Cl}{C}}CHCH_3 \longrightarrow (CH_3)_2\overset{\displaystyle NOH}{C}ClCCH_3$$

Trimethylethylene
nitroso chloride
30%

The reaction of phenylazides with alkenes produces triazoles. Although the products are an interesting group of 1,2-bifunctional compounds, they have attracted little attention and are mainly known as characteristic derivatives of alkenes.

2,3(2,2,1)Bicycloheptene
(Norbornylene)

Diazo compounds react with unsaturated compounds in a manner formally similar to phenyl azide addition. However, the former reagent is most reactive toward electrophilic centers, such as double bonds conjugated with carbonyl groups. The first products are pyrazolines, which can be pyrolyzed to give cyclopropane derivatives.

$$[\overset{-}{:}\overset{..}{N}{=}\overset{+}{N}{=}CHCO_2C_2H_5 \longleftrightarrow :N{\equiv}\overset{+}{N}{-}\overset{..}{\overset{-}{C}}HCO_2C_2H_5] + CH_2{=}CH{-}\overset{\displaystyle O}{\overset{\displaystyle \|}{C}}OC_2H_5 \longrightarrow$$

Carbon-Hydrogen Bond Formation

All electrophilic additions initiated by protons are carbon-hydrogen bond-making processes. Because of their very large number, they are classified on the basis of the second bond-making step. Electrophilic hydrogenation sequences such as that shown in the example below can be visualized, but have never been subjected to systematic study. Catalytic hydrogenation is so successful for preparative purposes that there is little stimulus for the development of alternative procedures.

$$(C_6H_5)_2C{=}CH_2 \xrightarrow{\text{Acid}} (C_6H_5)_2\overset{+}{C}CH_3 \xrightarrow[\text{(e.g., R$_2$CHOH)}]{\text{H$^-$ donor}} (C_6H_5)_2CHCH_3$$

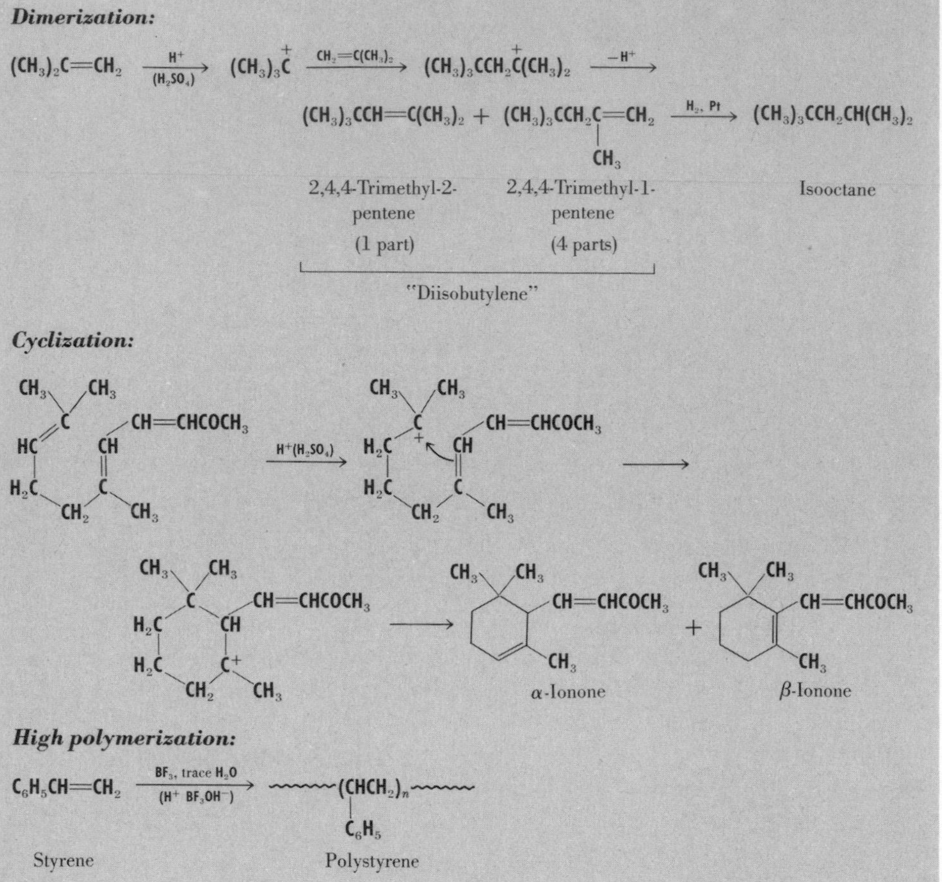

Dimerization:

$$(CH_3)_2C=CH_2 \xrightarrow[(H_2SO_4)]{H^+} (CH_3)_3\overset{+}{C} \xrightarrow{CH_2=C(CH_3)_2} (CH_3)_3CCH_2\overset{+}{C}(CH_3)_2 \xrightarrow{-H^+}$$

$$(CH_3)_3CCH=C(CH_3)_2 + (CH_3)_3CCH_2\underset{\underset{CH_3}{|}}{C}=CH_2 \xrightarrow{H_2, Pt} (CH_3)_3CCH_2CH(CH_3)_2$$

2,4,4-Trimethyl-2-pentene	2,4,4-Trimethyl-1-pentene	Isooctane
(1 part)	(4 parts)	

"Diisobutylene"

Cyclization:

High polymerization:

$$C_6H_5CH=CH_2 \xrightarrow[(H^+ BF_3OH^-)]{BF_3,\ trace\ H_2O} \sim\sim\sim(\underset{\underset{C_6H_5}{|}}{CHCH_2})_n\sim\sim\sim$$

Styrene   Polystyrene

FIG. 15.5   *Acid-catalyzed reactions of alkenes.*

Carbon-Carbon Bond Formation

Alkene polymerization heads the list of reactions that make carbon-carbon bonds by addition reactions. The scope of the general process runs the gamut from cyclization and dimerization reactions to the formation of high polymers (Fig. 15.5).

Carbon Monoxide Addition. During World War II, a group of German chemists developed a number of remarkable procedures for addition of carbon monoxide to alkenes and alkynes. The reactions are catalyzed by nickel and cobalt carbonyls in conjunction with mineral acids. Aldehydes are produced from alkenes, carbon monoxide, and hydrogen (*hydroformylation*). Water or alcohols, carbon monoxide, and unsaturated compounds give acids or esters. The process is now the basis of a commercial synthesis of acrylate esters, which are in demand for the plastics industry.

$$\bigcirc + CO + H_2 \xrightarrow{Co(CO)_4,\ pressure} \bigcirc\!\!\!\text{CHO}$$

Cyclopentanealdehyde

$$HC\!\equiv\!CH + CO + C_2H_5OH \xrightarrow{Ni(CO)_4,\ H_2SO_4} CH_2\!=\!CHCO_2C_2H_5$$

Ethyl acrylate
(almost quantitative)

Alkylation and Acylation. In the presence of Lewis acids, alkenes are sufficiently nucleophilic to take part in substitutions at both saturated and unsaturated carbon atoms. The reactions are best known as Friedel-Crafts alkylation and acylation substitution reactions of aromatic compounds, but a limited number of additions to alkenes have also been effected. The catalyst functions by polarizing, and perhaps ionizing, the alkylating or acylating agent.

$$C_2H_5COCl \xrightarrow{AlCl_3} \left[C_2H_5C\!\overset{+}{=}\!\overset{-}{O}AlCl_4 \right] \xrightarrow{CH_2=CH_2} C_2H_5COCH_2CH_2AlCl_4 \longrightarrow C_2H_5COCH_2CH_2Cl + AlCl_3$$

β-Chloroethyl ethyl ketone
45%

$$(CH_3)_3CCl + CH_2\!=\!CH_2 \xrightarrow[0°]{SnCl_4} (CH_3)_3CCH_2CH_2Cl$$

Neohexyl chloride

Similar alkylation reactions are an important feature of the reforming process for the production of synthetic gasoline (Chap. 26).

Free-radical Addition

Many alkene additions can be effected by small amounts of peroxides, by thermally labile azo compounds, or by irradiation by ultraviolet light. Reactions occurring under such conditions are nearly always *free-radical chain reactions*. They are perhaps best illustrated by the *abnormal addition of hydrogen bromide to alkenes*.

$$C_6H_5CH\!=\!CH_2 + HBr \xrightarrow{Peroxide} C_6H_5CH_2CH_2Br$$

β-Phenylethyl bromide
85%

The reaction is termed "abnormal," since it does not follow Markownikoff's rule. The steps in addition by a free-radical chain mechanism are illustrated in Fig. 15.6.

Since the chain-propagating reactions recur again and again, the decomposition of a single initiator molecule may produce a large number of molecules of product. The chains eventually end when two of the active chain-carrying intermediates meet and destroy each other.

Hydrogen chloride and hydrogen iodide do not undergo abnormal addition to olefins under normal circumstances. The reasons for failure

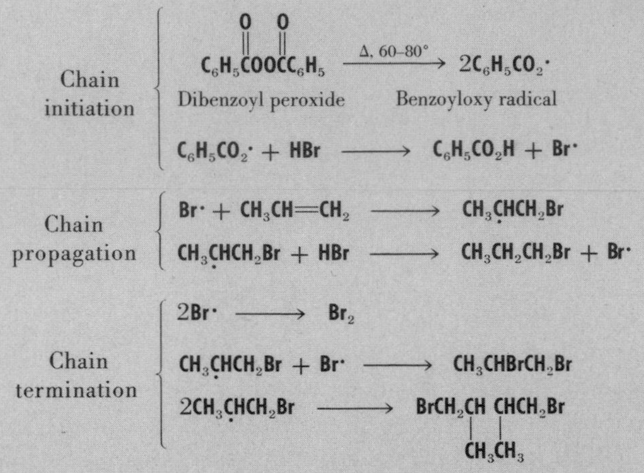

$$
\begin{matrix}
& & \overset{O}{\overset{\|}{C_6H_5COOC}}\overset{O}{\overset{\|}{C_6H_5}} & \xrightarrow{\Delta,\ 60-80°} & 2C_6H_5CO_2\cdot \\
& & \text{Dibenzoyl peroxide} & & \text{Benzoyloxy radical}
\end{matrix}
$$

Chain initiation

$$C_6H_5CO_2\cdot + HBr \longrightarrow C_6H_5CO_2H + Br\cdot$$

Chain propagation

$$Br\cdot + CH_3CH=CH_2 \longrightarrow CH_3\overset{\cdot}{C}HCH_2Br$$

$$CH_3\overset{\cdot}{C}HCH_2Br + HBr \longrightarrow CH_3CH_2CH_2Br + Br\cdot$$

Chain termination

$$2Br\cdot \longrightarrow Br_2$$

$$CH_3\overset{\cdot}{C}HCH_2Br + Br\cdot \longrightarrow CH_3CHBrCH_2Br$$

$$2CH_3\overset{\cdot}{C}HCH_2Br \longrightarrow \underset{\underset{CH_3}{|}}{BrCH_2CH}\ \underset{\underset{CH_3}{|}}{CHCH_2Br}$$

FIG. 15.6 *Addition of hydrogen bromide to propylene by a peroxide-initiated radical reaction.*

are different for the two compounds. The hydrogen-chlorine bond is too strong to be broken readily in the *atom-abstraction* reaction. Hydrogen iodide gives up a hydrogen atom very readily, but iodine atoms do not add rapidly to double bonds.

$$R\cdot + HCl \xrightarrow{\text{Slow}} RH + Cl\cdot$$

$$R\cdot + HI \xrightarrow{\text{Fast}} RH + I\cdot$$

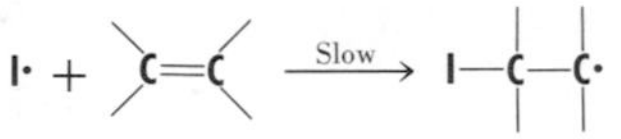

$$I\cdot + \ \underset{}{>}C=C\underset{}{<} \ \xrightarrow{\text{Slow}} \ I\overset{|}{\underset{|}{C}}\overset{|}{\underset{|}{C}}\cdot$$

The structure of the product is determined in the addition step. The results show that orientation in radical addition to a double bond is the same as in proton addition. The final products of hydrogen bromide addition by ionic and radical reactions are different because in one case hydrogen enters first, in the other bromine is added first. Secondary and tertiary radicals may be somewhat stabilized by hyperconjugation.

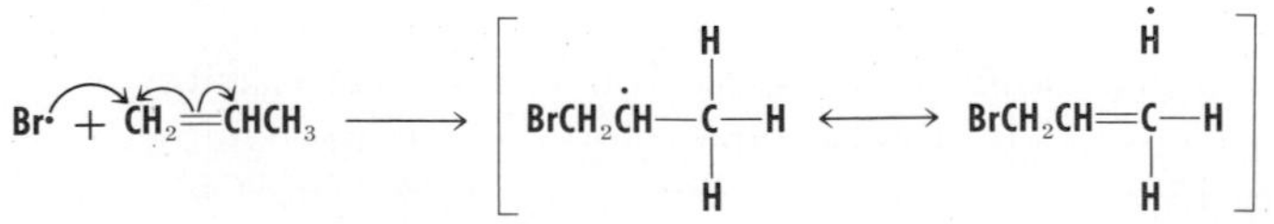

$$Br\cdot + CH_2 = CHCH_3 \longrightarrow \left[BrCH_2\overset{\cdot}{C}H - \underset{\underset{H}{|}}{\overset{\overset{H}{|}}{C}} - H \longleftrightarrow BrCH_2CH = \underset{\underset{H}{|}}{\overset{\overset{\cdot H}{|}}{C}} - H \right]$$

Not:

$$Br\cdot + CH_2 = CHCH_3 \longrightarrow \cdot CH_2CHBrCH_3$$

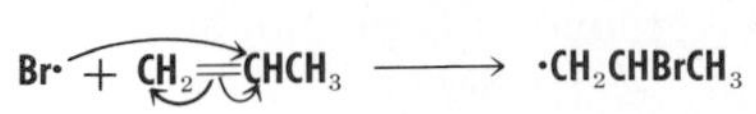

Abnormal addition of hydrogen bromide is a useful means of preparing primary bromides from terminal olefins.

$$\text{HBr} + \text{CH}_2\text{=CHCH}_2\text{Br} \xrightarrow{\text{Peroxides}} \text{BrCH}_2\text{CH}_2\text{CH}_2\text{Br}$$

Allyl bromide · · · · · · · · · · · · · · · · 1,3-Dibromopropane

$$\text{HBr} + (\text{CH}_3)_3\text{CCH}_2\text{C=CH}_2 \xrightarrow{\text{Peroxides}} (\text{CH}_3)_3\text{CCH}_2\text{CHCH}_2\text{Br}$$
$$\qquad\qquad\qquad |\qquad\qquad\qquad\qquad\qquad\qquad |$$
$$\qquad\qquad\qquad \text{CH}_3 \qquad\qquad\qquad\qquad\qquad \text{CH}_3$$

Wittig and coworkers have developed an interesting synthesis of terminal alkenes from ketones. The products should be easily converted to primary bromides by the abnormal addition reaction.

$$(\text{C}_6\text{H}_5)_3\overset{+}{\text{P}}\text{CH}_3\overset{-}{\text{Br}} \xrightarrow{\text{C}_6\text{H}_5\text{Li}} (\text{C}_6\text{H}_5)_3\overset{+}{\text{P}}\text{—}\overset{-}{\text{CH}}_2 + \text{C}_6\text{H}_6 + \text{LiBr}$$

Methyltriphenylphosphonium
bromide

CH₂ + HBr → CH₂Br

A host of other radical additions, many of them carbon-carbon bond-making processes, have been carried out successfully. In many cases, it is necessary to use the addend in large excess in order to inhibit polymerization, which arises from the addition of radicals from the alkene to a second alkene molecule (Chap. 25). Table 15.1 shows

TABLE 15.1   *Free-radical Addition to Alkenes*

Reagent	Atom abstracted	Product from RCH=CH₂ (or ArCH=CH₂)
R'SH	H	RCH₂CH₂SR'
CCl₄	Cl	RCHClCH₂CCl₃
CBr₄	Br	RCHBrCH₂CBr₃
CHBr₃	Br	RCHBrCH₂CHBr₂
CCl₃Br	Br	RCHBrCH₂CCl₃
BrCH₂CO₂C₂H₅	Br	RCHBrCH₂CH₂CO₂C₂H₅
R'CHO	H	RCH₂CH₂COR'
(C₆H₅)₃SiH	H	RCH₂CH₂Si(C₆H₅)₃
CO(Cl)₂	Cl	RCHClCH₂COCl

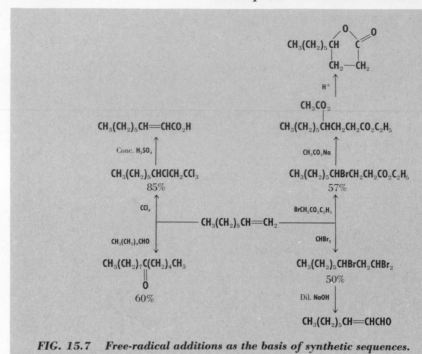

FIG. 15.7   *Free-radical additions as the basis of synthetic sequences.*

reagents that have been used, the adding entities, and the structures of the products expected in addition to unsymmetrical olefins.   Figure 15.7 provides illustrations of the possibilities, using as examples products from various radical additions to 1-octene.

Cyclic Additions

In a number of addition reactions, two unsaturated molecules unite directly to form a ring without passing through discrete intermediate stages.   The best known is the *Diels-Alder reaction,* in which a six-membered ring is formed by 1,4-addition of an olefinic unit to a conjugated diene (Fig. 15.8).

The *dienophile* is activated by electron-withdrawing substituents such as —CO_2H, —CO_2R, —CHO, —COR, —NO_2, —CN, and —SO_2—.   Some reactive dienes do not require activated dienophiles, as is illustrated by the dimerization of cyclopentadiene.   Dienes are activated by electron-donor substituents.   For example, 1,3-butadiene is less reactive than its mono-, di-, and trimethyl derivatives.   However, in the case of the tetramethylbutadienes, steric hindrance asserts itself and reactivity decreases.

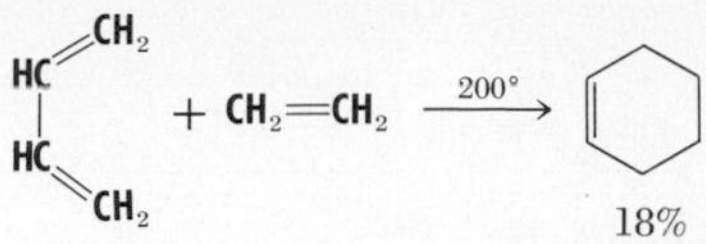

HC⟨CH₂ + CH₂=CH₂ →(200°) ⬡

18%

2 ⬠ →(25°)

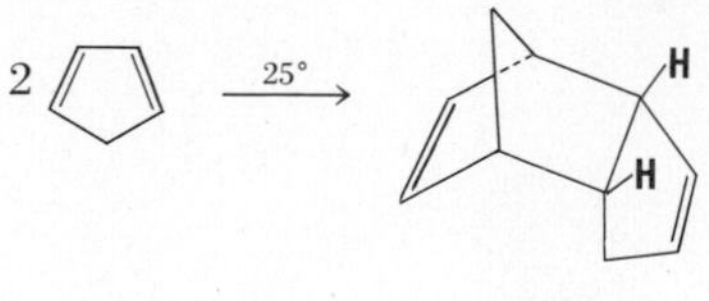

Cyclopentadiene   Dicyclopentadiene
95%

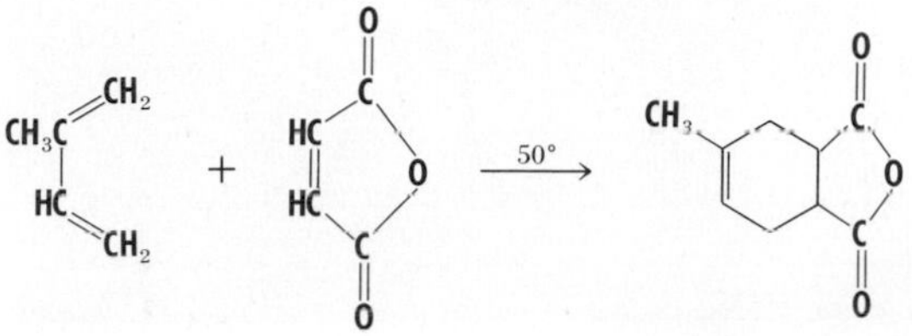

CH₃C⟨CH₂ + Maleic anhydride →(50°) 4-Methyl-1,2,3,6-tetrahydrophthalic anhydride

Isoprene   Maleic anhydride   4-Methyl-1,2,3,6-tetrahydro-
phthalic anhydride
97%

Diels-Alder reactions are highly stereospecific, as is illustrated by the reactions of furan and cyclopentadiene. The structures of products can nearly always be predicted by placing the reactants in two parallel planes in such a way as to obtain maximum overlapping of double bonds (Fig. 15.8). Diels-Alder reactions sometimes provide excellent methods for synthesis of aromatic compounds from aliphatic starting materials, as is illustrated by the following examples.

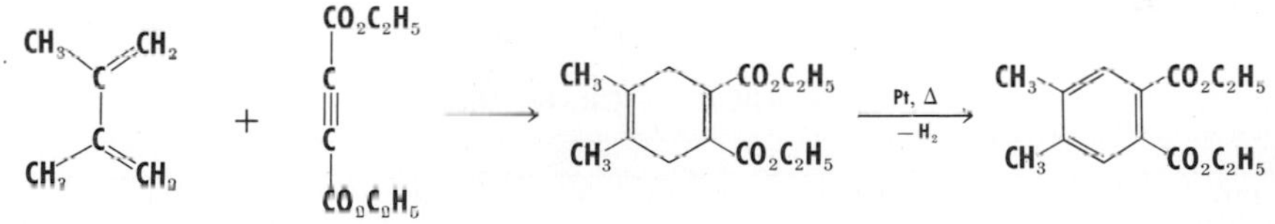

CH₃—C(=CH₂), CH₃—C(—CH₂) + Diethyl acetylenedicarboxylate ($CO_2C_2H_5$) → CH_3 ... $CO_2C_2H_5$ →(Pt, Δ; −H₂) Diethyl 4,5-dimethylphthalate

2,3-Dimethyl-
1,3-butadiene   Diethyl
acetylene-
dicarboxylate   Diethyl 4,5-
dimethylphthalate

CH_3—furan—CH_3 + maleic anhydride → (Stereochemistry not definitely established) →(Conc. H₂SO₄, −10°; −H₂O) 3,6-Dimethylphthalic anhydride

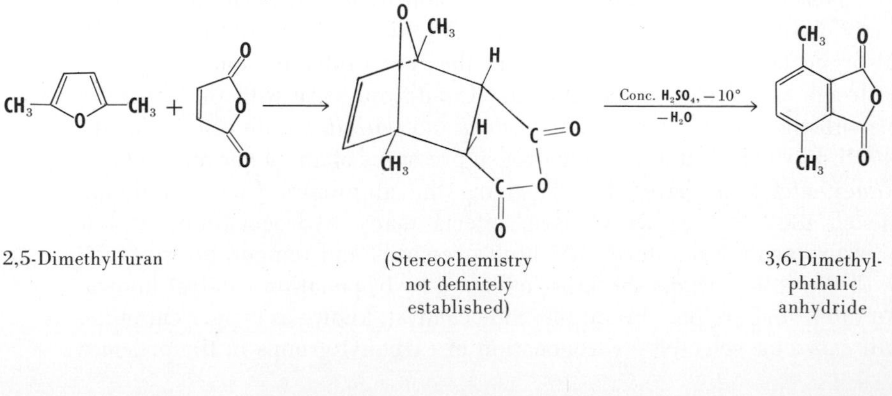

2,5-Dimethylfuran   (Stereochemistry
not definitely
established)   3,6-Dimethyl-
phthalic
anhydride

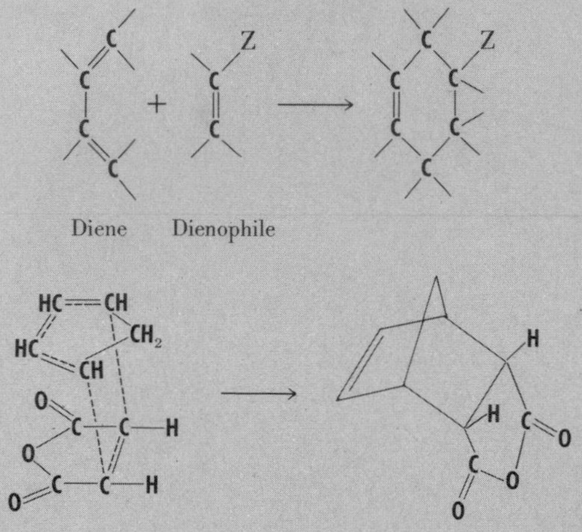

FIG. 15.8   Diels-Alder reaction.

A number of other reactions resemble the Diels-Alder reaction. Olefins which are heavily substituted with halogen and other electron-attracting substituents dimerize to form cyclobutanes at high temperatures, and some compounds dimerize to four-member rings when irradiated by ultraviolet light.

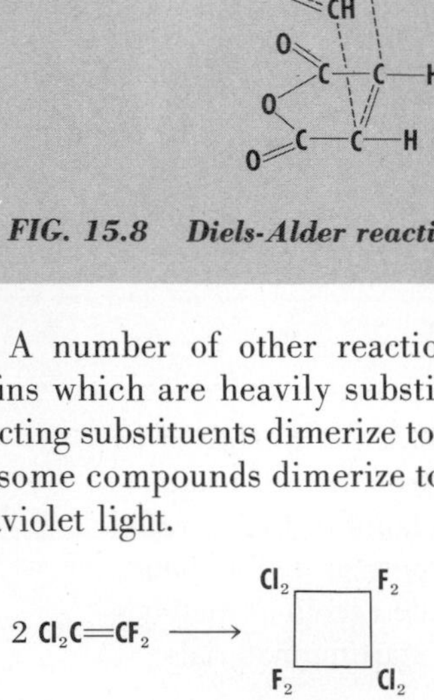

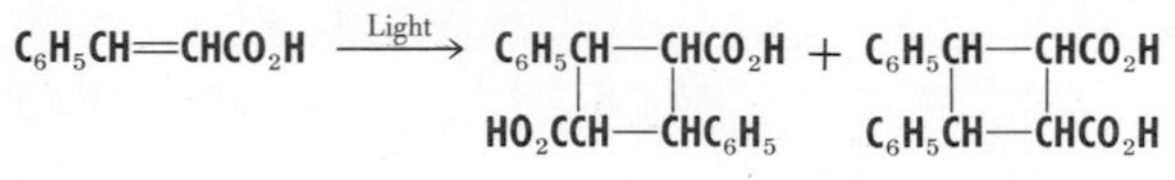

Catalytic Hydrogenation

Nearly all unsaturated compounds add hydrogen in the presence of finely divided metals or metal oxides. Addition occurs with the reactants adsorbed on the solid surface, where they are probably bound by metal-hydrogen and metal-carbon bonds. Conditions vary with the nature of the substrates and catalysts. *Platinum* and *palladium* are often effective at ordinary temperatures and hydrogen pressures of about one atmosphere. *Raney nickel,* prepared by dissolving the aluminum from aluminum-nickel alloy with aqueous base, effects many hydrogenations at low pressure and temperature. At high pressures and temperatures of 150 to 200°, it is perhaps the most effective hydrogenation catalyst known. An interesting copper-chromium oxide catalyst, known as copper chromite, will cause the selective hydrogenation of carbonyl groups in the presence of carbon-carbon double bonds. Alkenes are hydrogenated in the presence of copper chromite, but at a slow rate.

Hydrogenation of Carbon-Carbon Double Bonds. Catalytic hydrogenation of alkenes is the most general synthetic procedure for preparation of pure alkanes. The reaction is usually stereospecific, and cis addition of hydrogen often occurs with both alkenes and alkynes.

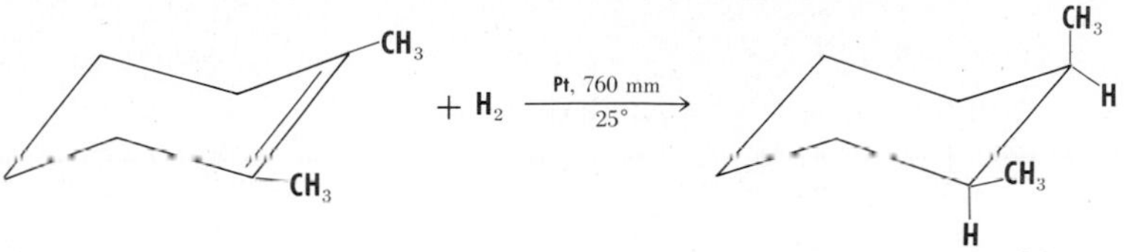
CH3
CH3
+ H2
Pt, 760 mm
25°
CH3
H
CH3
H

cis-1,2-Dimethylcyclohexane

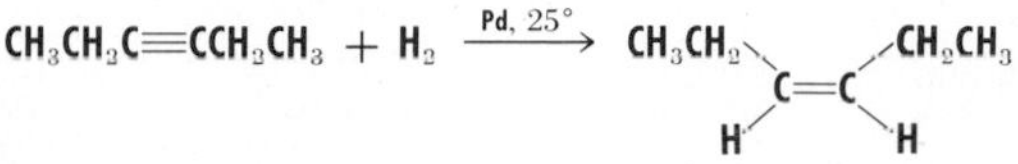
CH3CH2C≡CCH2CH3 + H2
Pd, 25°
CH3CH2
CH2CH3
C=C
H
H

cis-3-Hexene

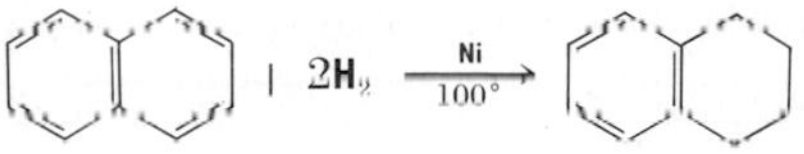
+ 2H2
Ni
100°

Tetralin
(Tetrahydronaphthalene)
100%

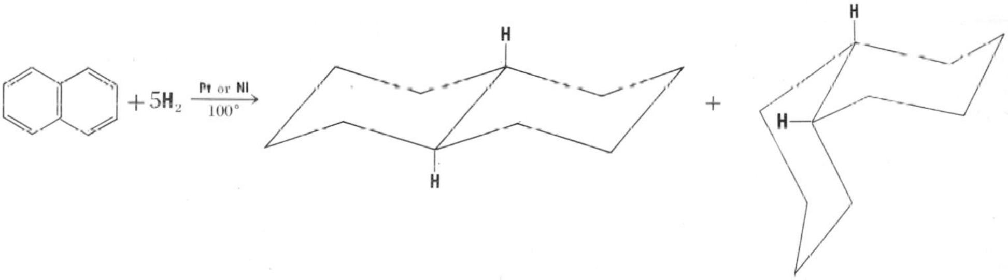
+ 5H2
Pt or Ni
100°
H
H
+
H
H

trans-Decalin *cis*-Decalin

A familiar application of catalytic hydrogenation is the process of "hardening" of vegetable oils. All fats and vegetable oils are mixtures of the esters of long-chain fatty acids and glycerol (Chap. 24). The glycerides from plants, such as soybean, peanut, and soybean oils, contain relatively large amounts of unsaturated acyl groups. Hydrogenation produces saturated esters, which are solids at room temperature.

Carbonyl and Similar Groups. The carbonyl groups of *aldehydes, ketones, and esters and carbon-nitrogen double and triple bonds all undergo catalytic hydrogenation.* Catalysts used in hydrogenation of alkenes and alkynes are all effective in reduction of unsaturated polar groups, but copper chromite is particularly useful because of its selective action. The selectivity probably arises from the strong adsorption of the polar functions on the metal oxide surface.

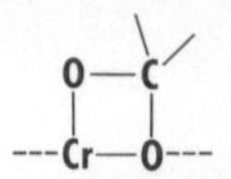

Carbonyl group adsorbed on
a chromium oxide surface

$$CH_3COCH_3 + H_2 \xrightarrow{Ni} CH_3CHOHCH_3$$

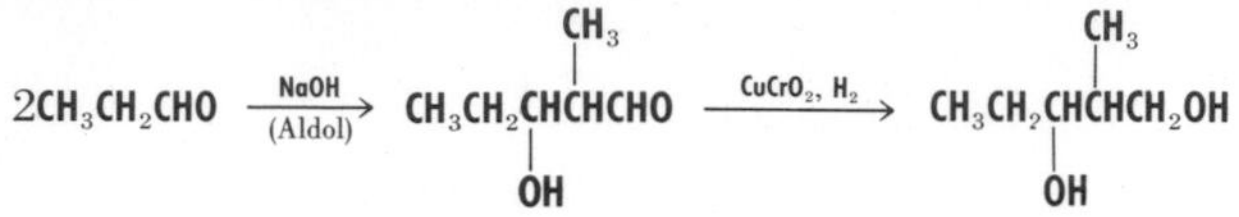

$$2CH_3CH_2CHO \xrightarrow[\text{(Aldol)}]{NaOH} CH_3CH_2\underset{OH}{\underset{|}{CH}}\overset{CH_3}{\overset{|}{CH}}CHO \xrightarrow{CuCrO_2, H_2} CH_3CH_2\underset{OH}{\underset{|}{CH}}\overset{CH_3}{\overset{|}{CH}}CH_2OH$$

2-Methyl-1,3-
pentanediol
60% over-all

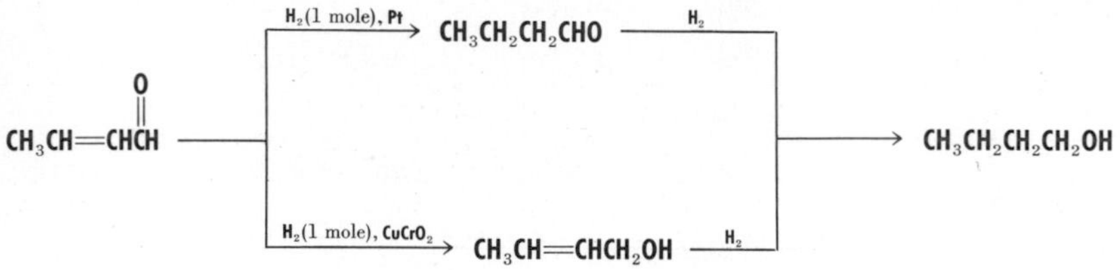

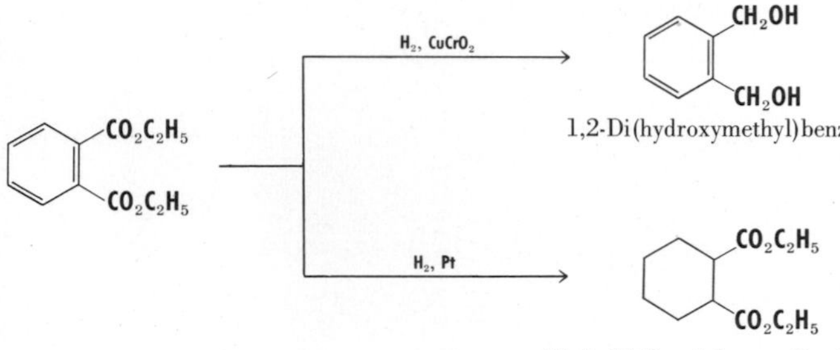

$$CH_3CH{=}CHCH \xrightarrow{H_2(1\ mole),\ Pt} CH_3CH_2CH_2CHO \xrightarrow{H_2} CH_3CH_2CH_2CH_2OH$$

$$\xrightarrow{H_2(1\ mole),\ CuCrO_2} CH_3CH{=}CHCH_2OH \xrightarrow{H_2}$$

$$\xrightarrow{H_2,\ CuCrO_2}$$ CH$_2$OH CH$_2$OH

1,2-Di(hydroxymethyl)benzene

CO$_2$C$_2$H$_5$ CO$_2$C$_2$H$_5$

$$\xrightarrow{H_2,\ Pt}$$ CO$_2$C$_2$H$_5$ CO$_2$C$_2$H$_5$

Diethyl 1,2-cyclohexanedicarboxylate
95%

Hydrogenation of esters involves an intermediate elimination reaction of the first-formed products, which are hemiacetals.

$$\underset{RCOR'}{\overset{O}{\overset{\|}{}}} \xrightarrow{H_2,\ catalyst} \underset{RCHOR'}{\overset{OH}{\overset{|}{}}} \xrightarrow{-R'OH} RCHO \longrightarrow RCH_2OH$$

$$C_2H_5O_2C(CH_2)_4CO_2C_2H_5 \xrightarrow{H_2,\ CuCrO_2} HO(CH_2)_6OH$$

Diethyl adipate   Hexamethylene glycol
100%

Nitriles, oximes, and nitro compounds are reduced smoothly to amines.

$$NC(CH_2)_4CN + 4H_2 \xrightarrow{Ni} H_2N(CH_2)_6NH_2$$

Hexamethylenediamine
85%

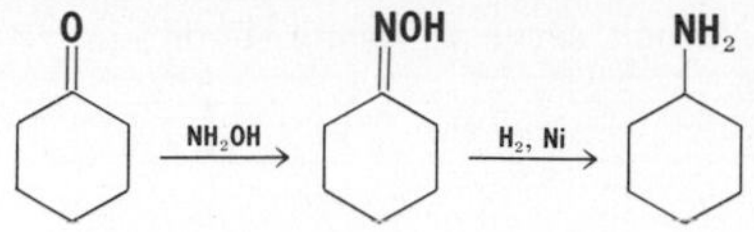

Cyclohexylamine
80%

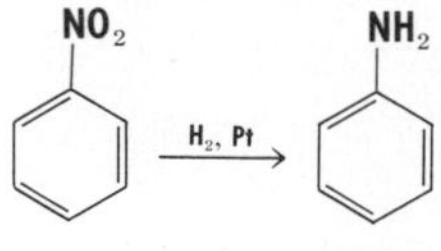

≈ 100%

Hydrogenation of ketones in the presence of excess ammonia results in *reductive amination*. The reaction probably involves hydrogenation of imines, which are in equilibrium with the ketones and ammonia. The procedure is an excellent method for synthesis of amines. Yields are sometimes reduced because of the formation of secondary amines.

$$RCR \overset{NH_3}{\underset{H_2O}{\rightleftharpoons}} R_2C—NH \xrightarrow{H_2, \text{ catalyst}} R_2CHNH_2 \xrightarrow{R_2CO} R_2CHN=CR_2 \xrightarrow{H_2} R_2CHNHCHR_2$$

$$CH_3COCH_2CH(CH_3)_2 \xrightarrow[NH_3]{H_2, \text{ Ni}} CH_3CHCH_2CH(CH_3)_2$$
$$\underset{NH_2}{|}$$

2-Amino-4-methylpentane

Problems

1. Write equations for the reactions of 1,3-butadiene with each of the following reagents:

a. Br_2
b. HCl
c. ICl
d. $CH_2=CHCN$
e. $C_6H_5CO_3H$ (one equivalent)
f. HBr (with and without added peroxides)

g. D_2 in the presence of finely divided platinum
h. A trace of concentrated H_2SO_4
i. OsO_4
j. A dilute solution of bromine in methanol
k. $C_6H_5COCl + AlCl_3$ at $-50°$

2. Devise syntheses of the following compounds, utilizing the starting materials indicated and compounds containing no more than two carbon atoms. Do not repeat the preparation of a given intermediate within the problem set.

a. $(CH_2)_7\genfrac{}{}{0pt}{}{CHOH}{CHOH}$ from $CH_3(CH_2)_7CH=CH(CH_2)_7CO_2H$

b. $(CH_3)_2CHCH_2CO_2H$ from CH_3COCH_3

c. 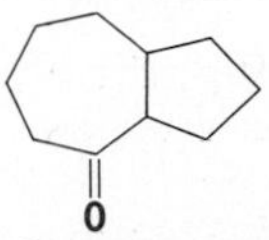 from

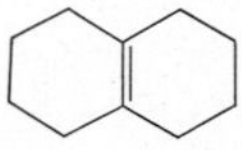

(Open a ring and then close again.)

d. $(CH_3)_2CHCH_2CHCH_3$ from CH_3COCH_3
$\underset{NH_2}{|}$

e. from $\genfrac{}{}{0pt}{}{CH—C}{CH—C}\genfrac{}{}{0pt}{}{}{}$ (with O's)

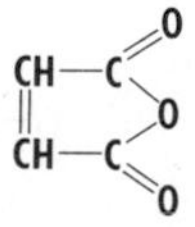

f. 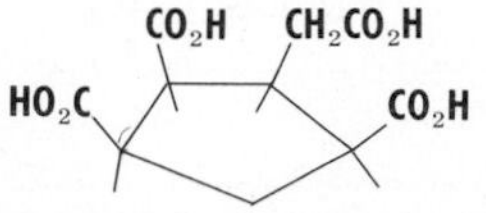 HO_2C CO_2H from

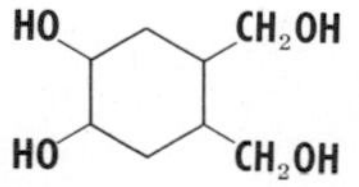

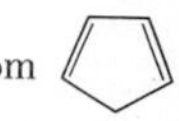

g. $(CH_3)_3CCH_2CCH_3$ (with O) from $(CH_3)_2C=CH_2$

3. Write equations for the following reactions, which serve to establish the structure of compound *A*.

$$C_7H_{10} \xrightarrow{Br_2} C_7H_{10}Br_4$$
$$A$$

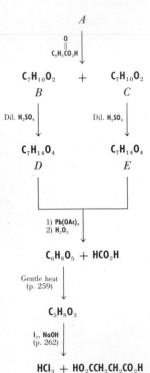

$$A$$

$$\xdownarrow{\overset{\overset{O}{\parallel}}{C_6H_5CO_3H}}$$

$$\underset{B}{C_7H_{10}O_2} \quad + \quad \underset{C}{C_7H_{10}O_2}$$

Dil. H$_2$SO$_4$ ↓   Dil. H$_2$SO$_4$ ↓

$$\underset{D}{C_7H_{14}O_4} \qquad \underset{E}{C_7H_{14}O_4}$$

1) Pb(OAc)$_4$
2) H$_2$O$_2$ ↓

$$C_6H_8O_5 + HCO_2H$$

Gentle heat
(p. 259) ↓

$$C_5H_8O_3$$

I$_2$, NaOH
(p. 262) ↓

$$HCl_3 + HO_2CCH_2CH_2CO_2H$$

4. Some of the following reactions cannot be carried out; some are possible under conditions other than those indicated; others are reasonable as written. Indicate the category into which each falls, and supply proper conditions where necessary.

a. $CH_3CH{=}CH_2 \xrightarrow{HCl,\ Pt} CH_3\underset{\underset{Cl}{|}}{C}HCH_3$

b. $(CH_3)_2C{=}CH_2 \xrightarrow{HCl,\ peroxide} (CH_3)_2CHCH_2Cl$

c.

$\xrightarrow{Br_2,\ conc.\ H_2SO_4}$

d. $CH_3CH{=}CH_2 \xrightarrow{BF_3,\ NaOCH_3} CH_3CH{=}CHCH(CH_3)_2$

e.

$\xrightarrow[{-75°}]{NaOH}$

f. $CH_3CH_2CH{=}CHCH_2CO_2C_2H_5 \xrightarrow{H_2,\ CuCrO_2} CH_3(CH_2)_4CO_2C_2H_5$

g. $(CH_3)_2C{=}CHCH_3 \xrightarrow{Br_2,\ CH_3OH} (CH_3)_2\underset{\underset{OCH_3}{|}}{C}CHBrCH_3$

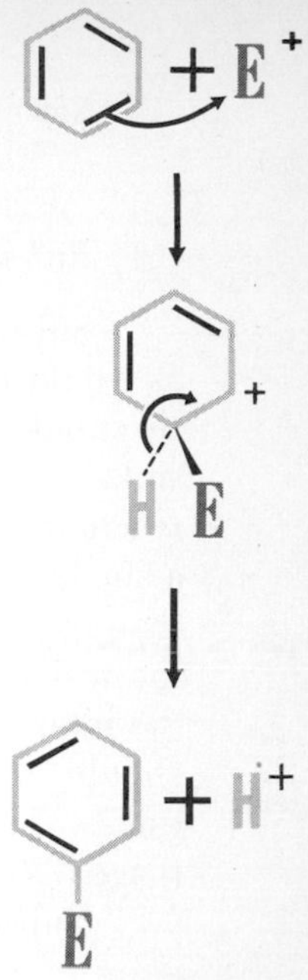

16

Electrophilic Substitution

at Unsaturated Carbon

In Chap. 14, a correlation was noted between nucleophilic substitution reactions of aromatic substrates and nucleophilic additions at aliphatic unsaturated carbon atoms. A similar close relationship exists between the reactions of alkenes and aromatic compounds. *Both classes of compounds are sensitive to electrophilic reagents* and are therefore prone to undergo reactions in the presence of *acid catalysts*. Differences between the behavior of the two classes are associated with the stability of aromatic systems. More drastic conditions are required to initiate reactions of aromatic compounds, and the tendency to restore the aromatic systems leads, ultimately, to substitution rather than addition products. Figure 16.1 is a schematic comparison of the usual consequence of electrophilic reactions of alkenes and aromatic substrates.

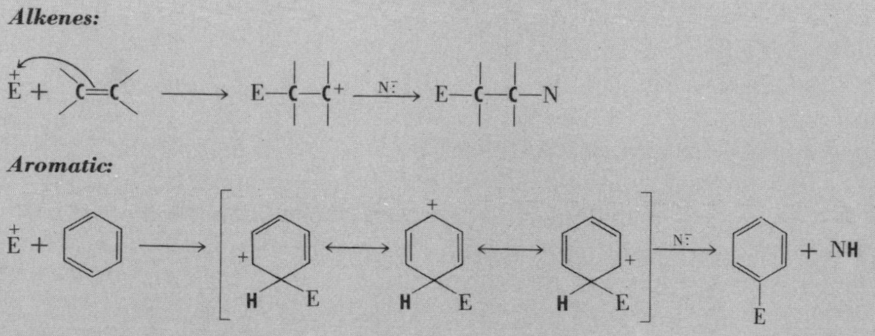

FIG. 16.1 *Reactions of electrophilic reagents with alkenes and aromatic compounds.*

Substituent Effects

Substituent effects in electrophilic aromatic substitution are about as would be expected by comparison with electrophilic alkene addition reactions. Electron-donor substituents speed up reaction, and "electron sinks" inhibit substitution. The effects are seen both in the relative reactivities of different substrates and in the orientation in attack on a single substrate. For example, electrophilic attack on toluene is easier than on benzene and predominantly gives substitution ortho and para to the resident methyl group. Examination of the resonance structures of the intermediate carbonium ion (Fig. 16.2) shows that hyperconjugation should be an important aid in substitution at the ortho and para positions. The analogy to the electronic statement of Markownikoff's rule (page 336) is obvious.

Substituent groups, such as **OH, OR, NH₂**, etc., which have unshared pairs of electrons available to lend to the intermediate ion have very strong activating and orienting influences. The behavior of amino substituents is somewhat ambiguous, however, since in strongly acidic solutions aromatic amines may essentially be completely protonated to form arylammonium ions, $ArNH_3^+$, which are very inert toward electrophilic attack.

Electron-withdrawing substituents deactivate aromatic nuclei, but the effect is smallest at the meta position. Figure 16.3 shows the principal resonance structures of the intermediate ions that could be formed by electrophilic attack on nitrobenzene. Attack at the ortho and para positions places part of the positive charge adjacent to the electron-deficient substituent group. This arrangement gives rise to electrostatic repulsions larger than those involved in meta attack. The structures in question are labeled *A* and *B* in Fig. 16.3.

There is a further barrier to attack on nitrobenzene. Formation of the intermediate cation requires sacrifice of some of the resonance energy of the substrate. The interaction between the substituent and the ring removes π electrons from the ring, as is shown in Fig. 16.4. Since electrophilic substitution also withdraws electrons from the ring, interaction between the ring and the nitro group must be decreased in the transition state for substitution.

The effects of halogens as substituents were long considered anomalous. Chloro-, bromo-, and iodobenzene are less reactive than benzene itself, but give predominantly ortho and para substitution. Fluorobenzene orients ortho-para and is about equal in reactivity to benzene. All other groups which orient ortho-para also activate aromatic rings. The curious effects of the halogens are due to the interplay between inductive effects and weak resonance effects. Halobenzenes have dipole moments with halogen negative, but the moments are smaller than those of aliphatic halides. An oversimplified explanation of the effect attrib-

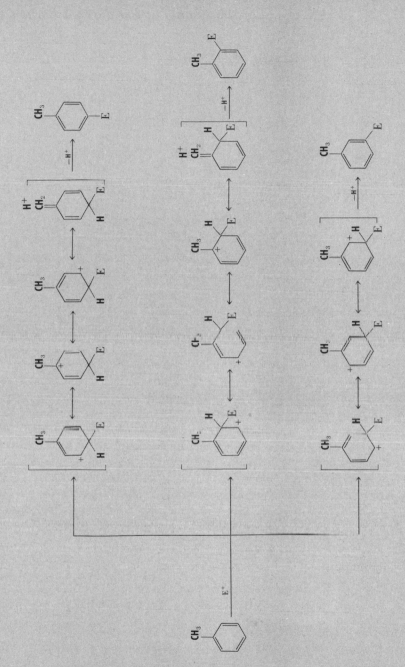

FIG. 16.2   *Effect of a methyl group in an electrophilic substitution reaction of toluene.*

359

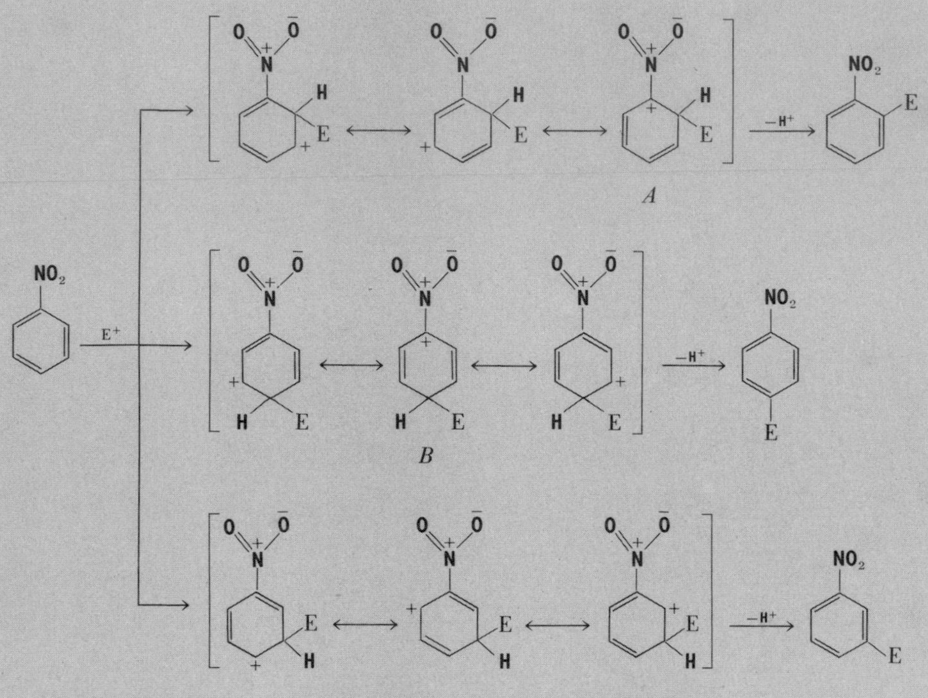

FIG. 16.3   Effect of a nitro group on electrophilic substitution.

utes the result to partial compensation of the polarity of the C—X σ
bonds by some feedback of nonbonding halogen *p* electrons by π bonding
(see Fig. 16.5). The π bonding must be increased in the electron-
deficient intermediates formed in electrophilic substitution. The π-elec-

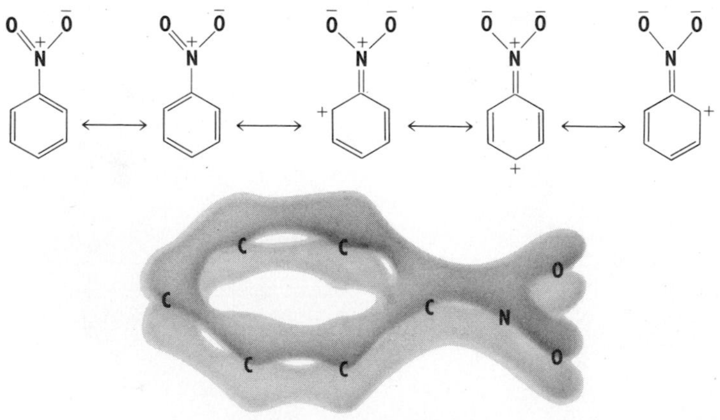

Schematic representation of a
π orbital of nitrobenzene

FIG. 16.4   Resonance in nitrobenzene.

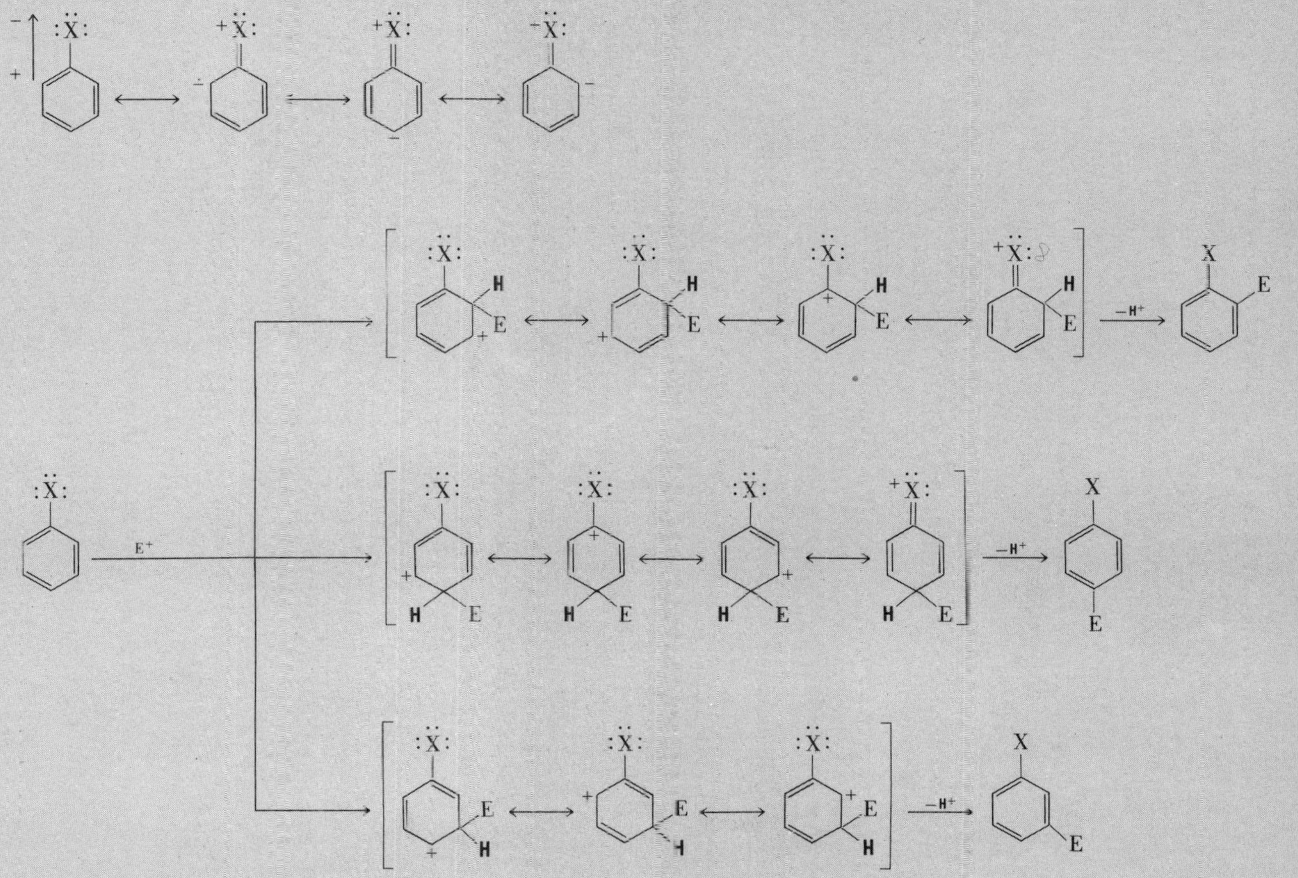

FIG. 16.5   Electronic structure of halobenzenes and their behavior in electrophilic substitution.

tron feedback is greatest if attack occurs at the ortho and para positions and this effect provides preferential attack at those positions. However, the unfavorable electrostatic interaction between the polar C—X bond and the positive charge is still sufficient to make the halobenzenes less reactive than benzene. The interactions are all summarized in Fig. 16.5. Although the duality of effects makes the phenomenon of ortho-para orientation by deactivating groups understandable, there is no a priori basis for prediction of the actual balance of effects.

Polynuclear aromatic compounds are more reactive than benzene derivatives. Such a result would be expected from consideration of the extensive delocalization of electrons in the cations formed by adding electrophiles to polynuclear systems.

Conjugated arylalkenes are highly reactive, but are attacked both in the side chain and on the nucleus, as is illustrated by the nitration of styrene.

Quantitatively, relative reactivities and orienting influences in aromatic substitutions vary considerably from one reaction to another. Toluene is about 200 times as reactive as benzene in bromination in acetic acid solution, but is only 30 times as reactive in nitration in nitromethane solution. The reasons for such variations are not reflected in the simplified discussion presented. Error arises in treating a reaction intermediate as though it were actually the transition state in the rate-determining step of the substitution. While the transition states are probably similar to the intermediates, they are not identical with them. In the actual transition states, the extent to which π electrons have been withdrawn from the aromatic systems probably varies with the nature of the incoming reagent.

Carbon-Halogen Bond Formation

Halogenation is one of the most useful methods for introduction of substituents in an aromatic system. Reactive substrates are substituted very readily, as is illustrated by the following examples.

With less reactive substrates, Lewis acid catalysts of varying activity are used to accelerate reactions. The function of the catalysts is to complex with, and polarize, the halogen, rendering it a better electrophile.

$$X_2 + I_2 \rightleftharpoons \overset{+}{X} I_2 \overset{-}{X}$$

$$X_2 + FeX_3 \rightleftharpoons \overset{+}{X} Fe \overset{-}{X}_4$$

$$X_2 + AlX_3 \rightleftharpoons \overset{+}{X} Al \overset{-}{X}_4$$

Acid catalysis is used even with alkylbenzenes to allow a more favorable competition between electrophilic substitution, which gives nuclear attack, and free-radical halogenation, which results in side-chain attack (Chap. 18).

The above examples demonstrate that direct halogenation is not a feasible way to produce all isomers of a given di- or polysubstituted benzene.　Various artifices are employed to produce derivatives which cannot be formed by direct introduction of a second substituent.　Sometimes different compounds are formed by simply reversing the order of substitution.　For example, *o*- and *p*-nitrohalobenzenes are formed by nitration of halobenzenes, since the halogens orient ortho-para.　Such a procedure would not suffice for the production of an *m*-halotoluene, since both halogen and methyl orient ortho-para.

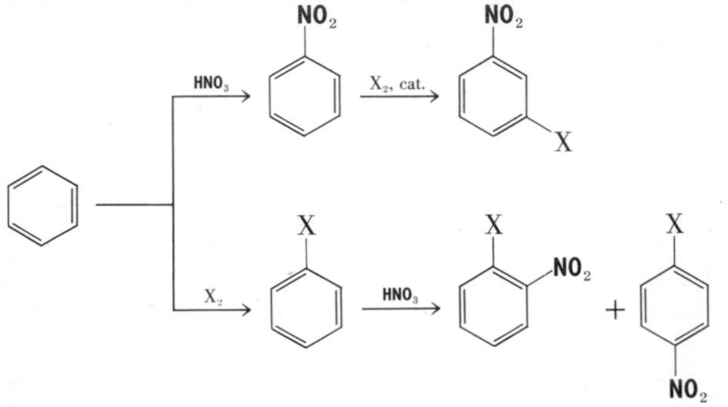

A number of general procedures are available for the synthesis of an "abnormal" substitution product.

1. Synthesis of one of the groups from a group having a different orienting influence.

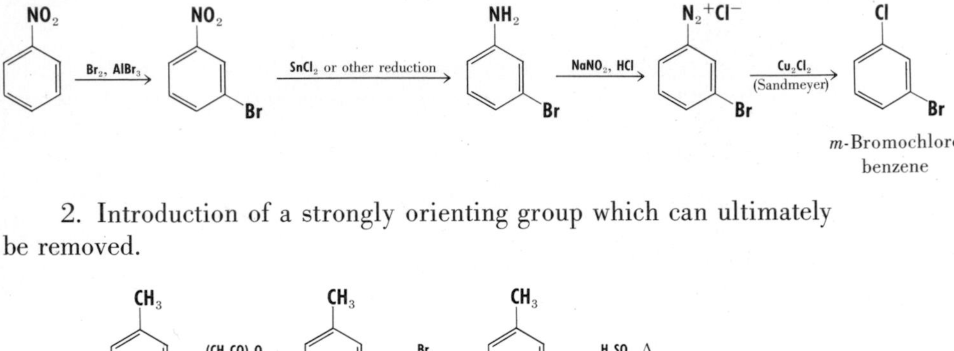

m-Bromochloro-
benzene

2. Introduction of a strongly orienting group which can ultimately be removed.

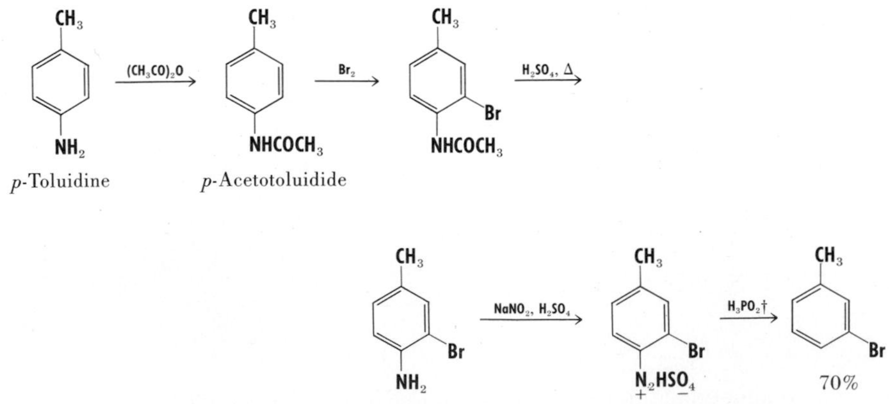

p-Toluidine　　　　　*p*-Acetotoluidide

70%

† Diazonium ions are reduced smoothly by *hypophosphorous acid*.　The *deamination reaction* is carried out in strong sulfuric acid solution.　The reaction is a chain reaction involving free radicals as intermediates.

3. Nucleophilic or other substitution reactions (occasional).

Carbon-Oxygen Bond Formation

Except for a few reactions classified as molecular rearrangements (Chap. 20), there are no useful electrophilic substitution reactions which attach oxygen to aromatic nuclei. Peracids, especially peroxytrifluoroacetic acid, hydroxylate aromatic compounds, but each new hydroxyl group increases the reactivity of the substrate, so that the products are nondescript mixtures of polyhydroxy compounds and other oxidation products. Phenols are made almost exclusively by nucleophilic substitution reactions (page 311).

Carbon-Sulfur Bond Formation

Sulfonation is one of the most important aromatic substitution reactions.

$$\text{ArH} + \text{H}_2\text{SO}_4 \longrightarrow \text{Ar}-\text{SO}_3\text{H} + \text{H}_2\text{O}$$

Sulfonic acids are intrinsically important and can be converted to a host of important derivatives. The reactive electrophile in sulfonation is either SO_3 or SO_3H^+, species which are present in fuming sulfuric acid, the reagent generally used in sulfonation. In the following equations, the yield data in **boldface** type show *isomer distribution* rather than isolable yields.

Benzenesulfonic acid

p-Chlorobenzenesulfonic acid
100%

62%   **32%**   **6%**

Since sulfonation is reversible, sulfonic acid groups are removed if the acids are heated with sulfuric acid of 50 to 60% concentration. Because of the powerful meta-directing influence of the sulfonic acid function, sulfonic acid groups are often introduced for blocking and orienting purposes. After other substituents have been introduced, the sulfonate group is removed by hydrolysis.

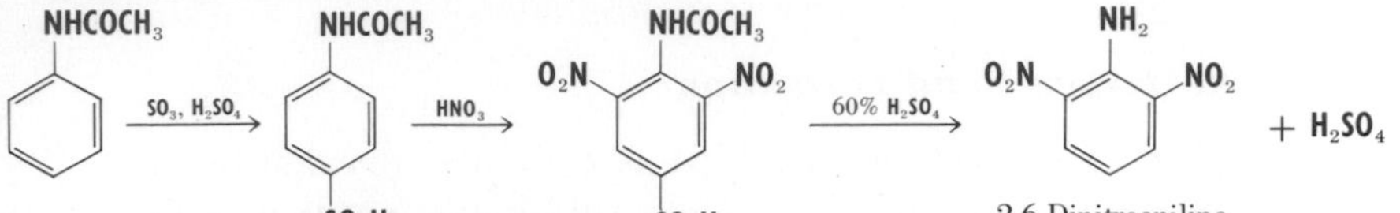

2,6-Dinitroaniline

The reversibility of the reaction is also demonstrated by a tendency for initially formed products to revert to more stable isomers at high temperatures.

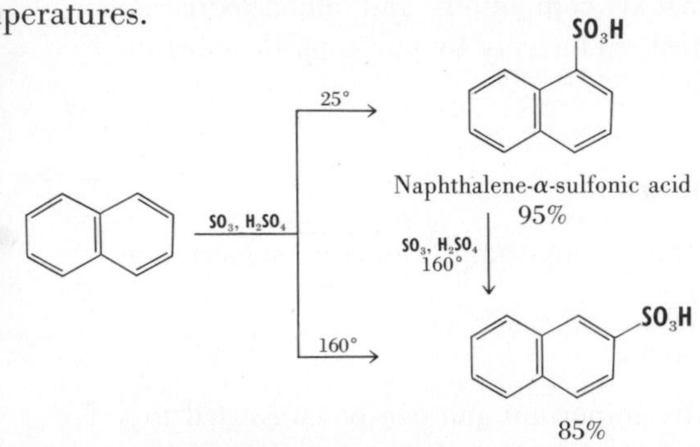

Naphthalene-α-sulfonic acid
95%

85%

Rapid formation of the α-isomer in the sulfonation of naphthalene reflects the greater stabilization of the intermediate carbonium ion. However, the α-sulfonic acid group is sterically hindered by the hydrogen in the 8- (or *peri*) position. The unhindered β-isomer is the more stable of the two compounds.

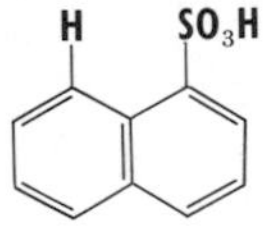

peri-Steric hindrance

Disulfonation is very slow, because of the strong electron-withdrawing influence of —SO_3H, and requires forcing conditions. Note the extensive reversion to the stable para isomer in the following example.

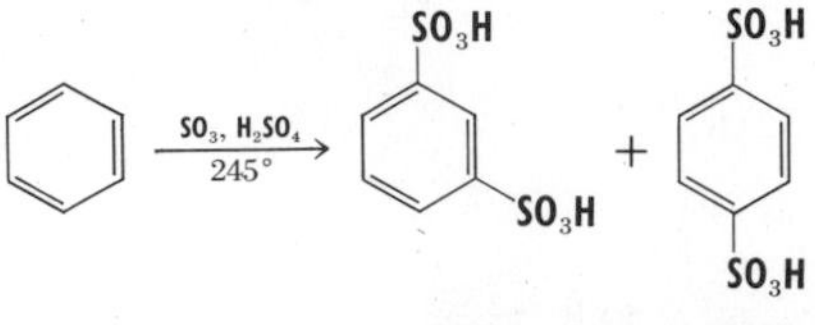

75%   25%

Sulfonic acids are useful as cheap strong acids which are more soluble than strong mineral acids in organic solvents. Their chief chemical importance is conversion to phenols by alkaline fusion. In addition, they are readily converted to sulfonyl chlorides, the precursors of sulfonate esters, sulfonamides, and mercaptans.

Sulfonyl chlorides are made directly by treatment of aromatics with chlorosulfonic acid. Sulfonation probably occurs first and is followed by conversion of the sulfonic acid to the acid chloride by reaction with excess reagent. As is true in most electrophilic substitutions, the actual reagent is produced by a complex ionization reaction.

$$2ClSO_2OH \rightleftharpoons HCl + HO\overset{+}{S}O_2 + Cl\overset{-}{SO_3}$$

Chlorosulfonic
acid

$$HO\overset{+}{S}O_2 + ArH \longrightarrow ArSO_2OH + \overset{+}{H}$$

$$ArSO_2OH + ClSO_2OH \rightleftharpoons ArSO_2Cl + H_2SO_4$$

Carbon-Nitrogen Bond Formation

Nitration.   Aromatic nitration provides a basis for a large mosaic of chemical syntheses.   Polynitro compounds themselves are used as high explosives.   Reduction of nitro groups leads to a variety of functional groups (Chap. 20), the most important of which is the amino group. Reduction to amines converts a strongly deactivating meta-directing substituent into a powerful ortho-para orienting group.   Since the Sandmeyer reaction permits replacement of the amino group with many other groups, a synthesis of virtually any polysubstituted aromatic compound can be based upon nitration as a first (or early) step.

Conditions for accomplishing the nitration reaction, $ArH + HNO_3 \longrightarrow ArNO_2 + H_2O$, vary greatly with the reactivity of the aromatic substrate. Conditions appropriate for the introduction of a second nitro group in benzene would lead to an uncontrollable exothermic reaction with phenol. Nearly all nitrations involve electrophilic attack by the *nitronium ion*, NO_2^+.   Consequently, reactions can be regulated by controlling the concentration of nitronium ion in solution.   In 95% sulfuric acid, the ionization of dissolved nitric acid is complete.

$$H_2SO_4 + HONO_2 \rightleftharpoons H_2\overset{+}{O}NO_2 + HS\bar{O}_4$$

$$H_2\overset{+}{O}NO_2 \rightleftharpoons H_2O + \overset{+}{N}O_2$$

$$H_2O + H_2SO_4 \rightleftharpoons H_3\overset{+}{O} + HS\bar{O}_4$$

$$\overline{}$$

$$2H_2SO_4 + HNO_3 \rightleftharpoons H_3\overset{+}{O} + \overset{+}{N}O_2 + 2HS\bar{O}_4$$

In concentrated nitric acid, a small amount of NO_2^+ is present, and even less is formed in solutions of nitric acid in solvents such as acetic acid, acetic anhydride, and nitromethane.

88%   7%   1%

(+ isomers)

Trinitrotoluene
(TNT)

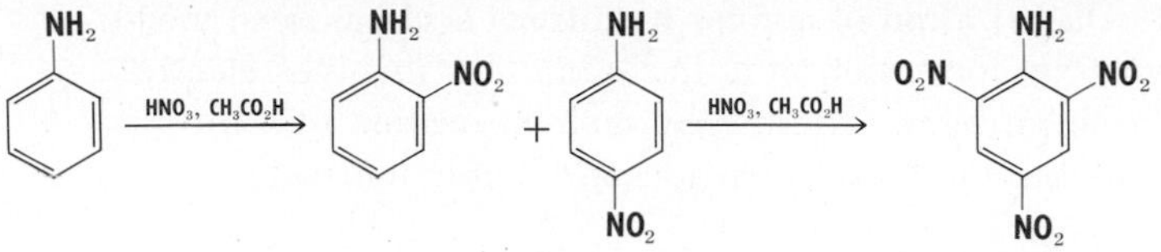

Picramide
(low yield)

Compare

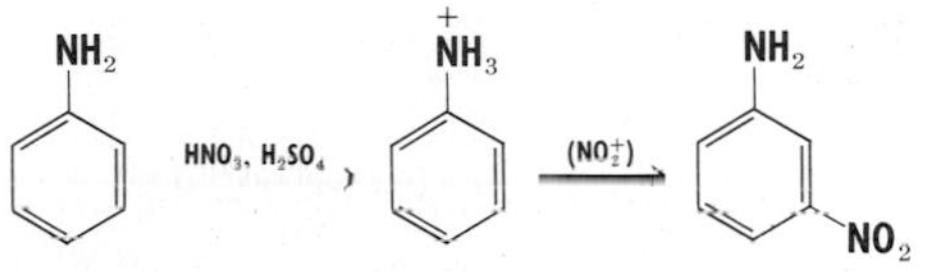

and

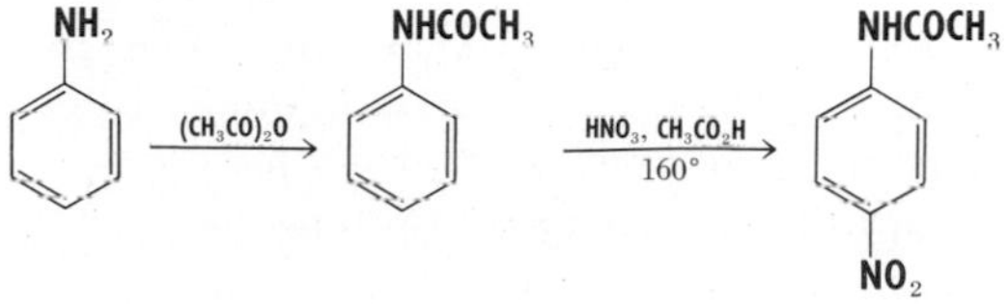

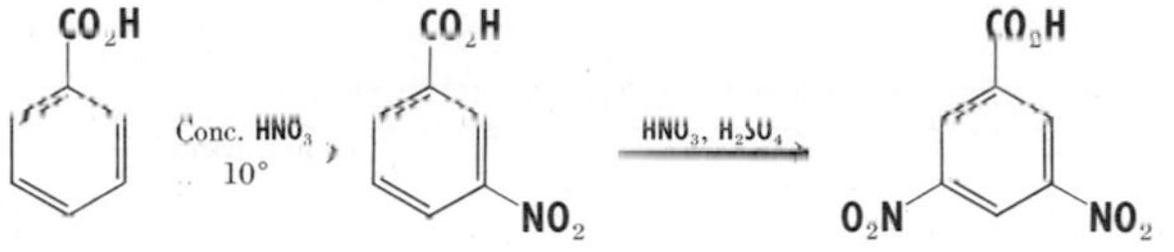

The synthesis of *m*-nitrobenzoic acid is illustrated above. Indirect syntheses of the ortho and para isomers, chosen to illustrate methods, are shown below. Many others can be devised.

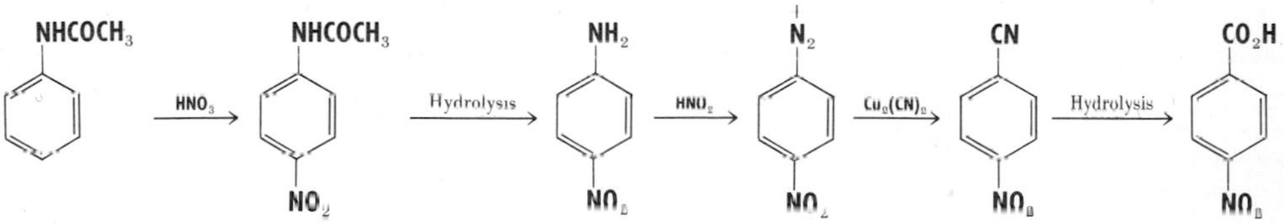

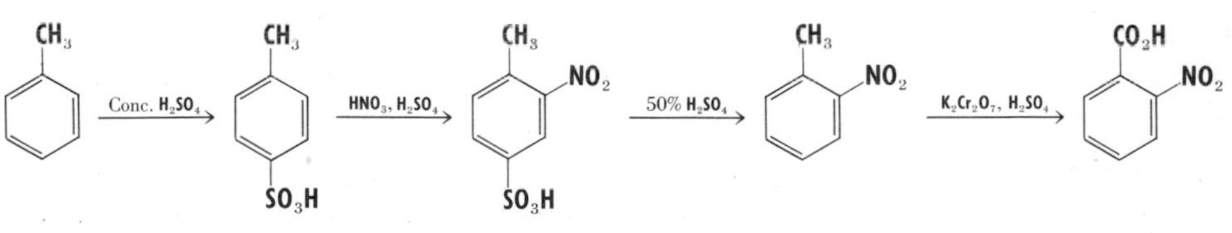

Nitration, as well as other electrophilic substitutions, is subject to steric hindrance, and substitution ortho to a large group may become difficult, as is illustrated by the isomer distribution in the mononitration of alkyl benzenes.

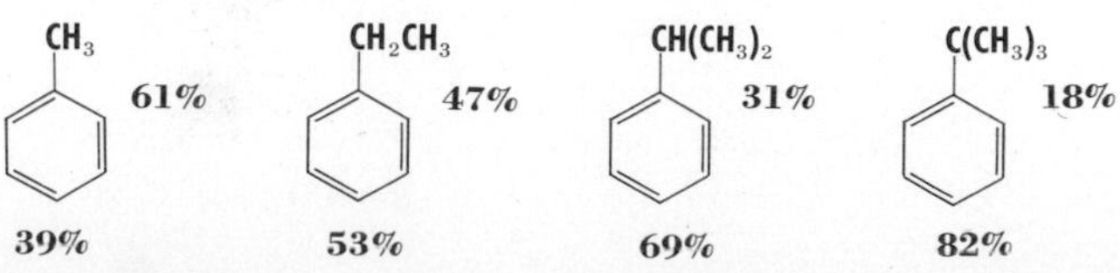

Azo Coupling.   Diazotization of amines by nitrous acid has been mentioned frequently.   The formation of a diazonium ion involves electrophilic substitution on nitrogen followed by tautomerization of a nitrosamine.   In acid solution, the diazohydroxides are highly ionized.

$$ArNH_2 + HON=O \longrightarrow Ar-\underset{H}{\overset{H}{N}}-\overset{+}{\underset{}{N}}-OH \longrightarrow ArNHNO \longrightarrow ArN=NOH \xrightarrow{H^+} Ar\overset{+}{N_2} + H_2O$$

As has been mentioned previously (page 207), aliphatic diazonium ions are unstable.   Solutions of aromatic diazonium salts can be preserved reasonably well at 0°, but are hydrolyzed to phenols on warming (page 311).   Salts of very weakly nucleophilic ions such as fluoroborate (**BF$_4^-$**) and perchlorate can be isolated and dried.   Diazonium ions are sufficiently electrophilic to couple with reactive aromatic nuclei to give azo compounds.   An enormous number of dyestuffs have been prepared by the reaction.   Since diazonium ions are not destroyed by weak alkali, coupling with phenols is strongly accelerated by base.

Primary amines couple through nitrogen to form diazoamino compounds which are isolable but rearrange easily to give azo compounds.

Diazoamino benzene

An interesting phenomenon concerning the reactivity of the naphthalene nucleus has been studied by means of the coupling reactions of α- and β-naphthol.   The former gives a mixture of products, whereas the latter couples only in the α-position adjacent to the hydroxyl group.   If the α-position is blocked, no reaction takes place.

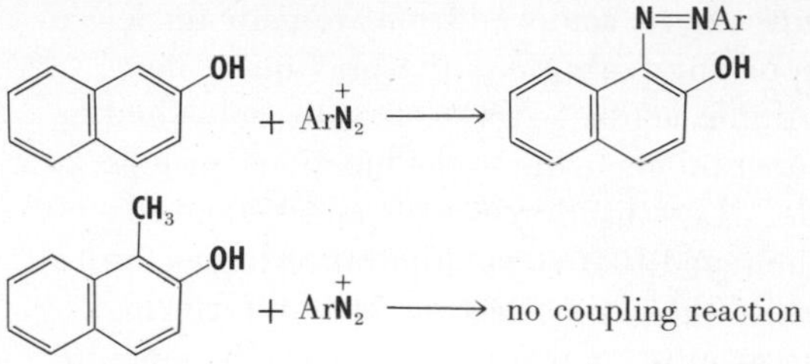

The lack of reactivity of the 3-position in 2-naphthol led at one time to the view that the bonds in naphthalene are "fixed." Such fixation would be contrary to quantum-mechanical indication that the 10 π electrons should be spread over the entire system (although not exactly uniformly). The real difference between 1- and 3-positions in 2-naphthol seems to be due primarily to differences in the transition states which would lead to substitution at the two positions. If the adduct ion is taken as a model for the transition state, the problem can be analyzed by the resonance method.

1-Substitution:

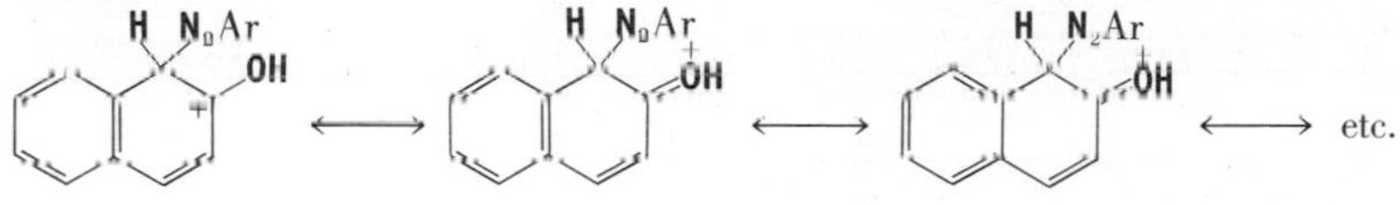

3-Substitution:

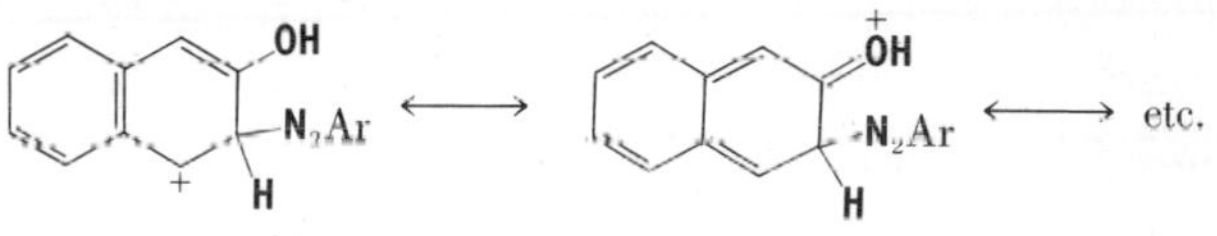

The transition state for substitution in the 3-position has only one structure in which the electron deficiency is assigned to oxygen, whereas the isomeric transition state has two such structures.

Carbon-Hydrogen Bond Formation

Electrophilic substitution by protons can be observed in isotopic exchange reactions. Treatment of benzene with D_2SO_4 results in slow exchange, and, as would be expected, toluene undergoes fairly rapid exchange in the ortho and para positions.

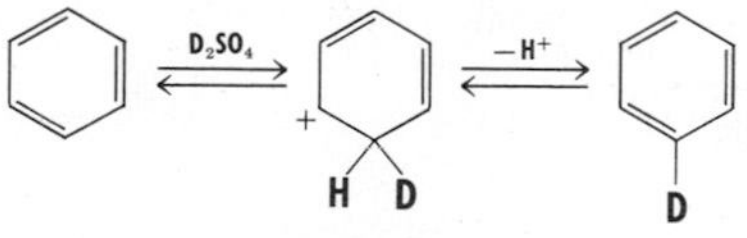

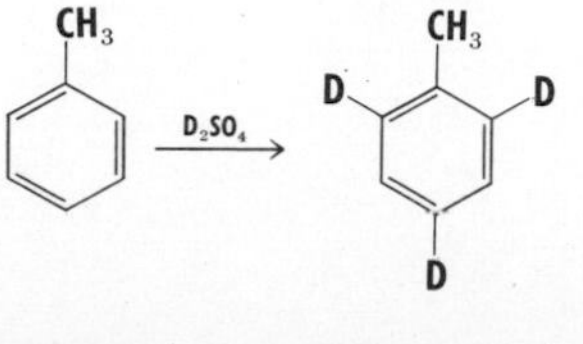

A number of functional groups can be removed from aromatic nuclei by acid cleavage. The most important example is the previously mentioned hydrolysis of aromatic sulfonic acids. Arylcarboxylic acids and aryl ketones that have two alkyl substituents ortho to the functional groups are cleaved by concentrated acids. Less hindered acids and ketones do not undergo the reaction. It is believed that steric hindrance forces the carbonyl groups out of the plane of the aromatic ring, thus interfering with the normal interaction of the groups. Cleavage occurs easily, since electrophilic attack does not involve as much loss of resonance energy as would be the case with unhindered carbonyl compounds.

Carbon-Carbon Bond Formation

Generation of carbonium ions, or very reactive carbonium-ion donors, in the presence of reactive aromatic compounds leads to the alkylation and acylation of the aromatic nuclei. The entire group of reactions is known as the *Friedel-Crafts reaction,* although the name was originally applied only to alkylations by alkyl halides catalyzed by aluminum chloride. All the reactions may be formulated in terms of carbonium-ion intermediates, although the attacking electrophile may often be a highly polarized complex. A few of the many procedures are illustrated.

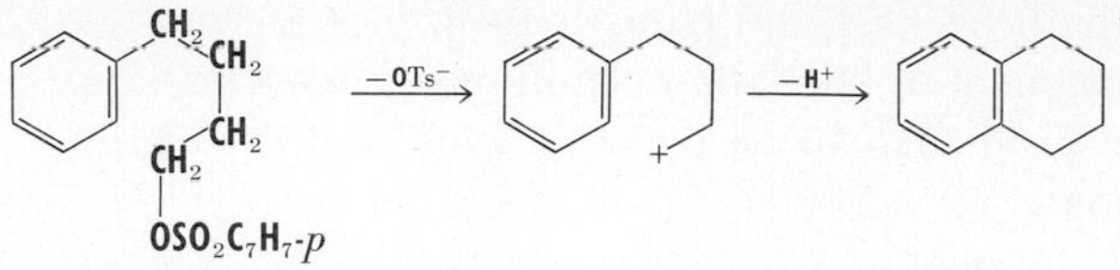

4-Phenylbutyl
p-toluenesulfonate

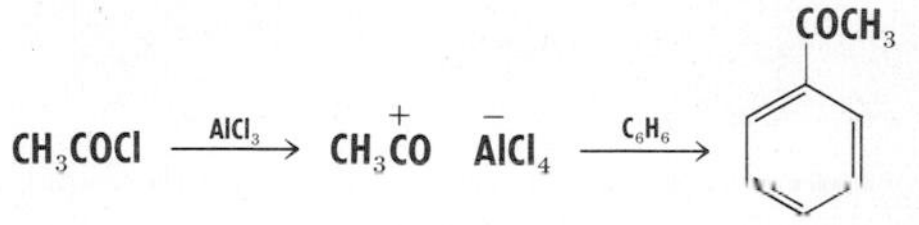

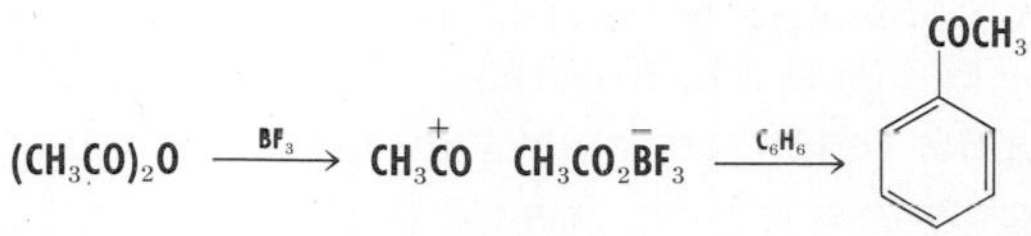

Alkylation. Alkylation reactions are complicated by several factors. First, alkyl groups activate aromatic nuclei, so that mixtures of polyalkylated products are formed.

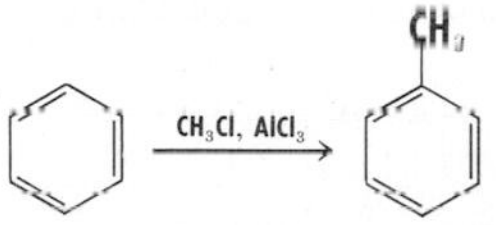

+ dimethylbenzenes + trimethylbenzenes +

tetramethylbenzenes + +

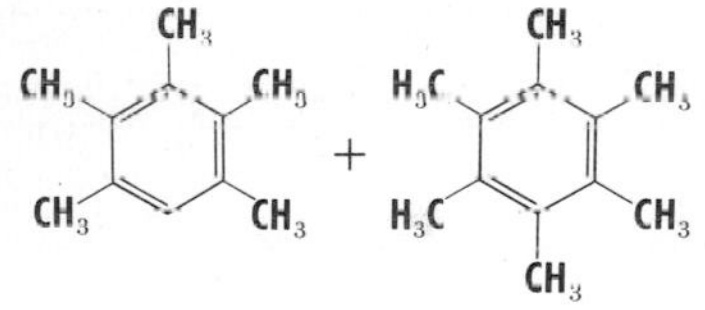

Relative amounts of products depend upon the ratios of reactants used and contact times. Toluene can be made in high yield by using a high ratio of benzene to methyl chloride. If four equivalents of methyl chloride are used, a significant yield (10%) of durene may be isolated by distillation and freezing of the tetramethylbenzene fraction. Since *polyalkylbenzenes rearrange under the reaction conditions*, the yield is increased to 25% by treating the liquid mixture of the other tetramethyl benzenes with aluminum chloride and freezing out more durene from the equilibrated mixture.

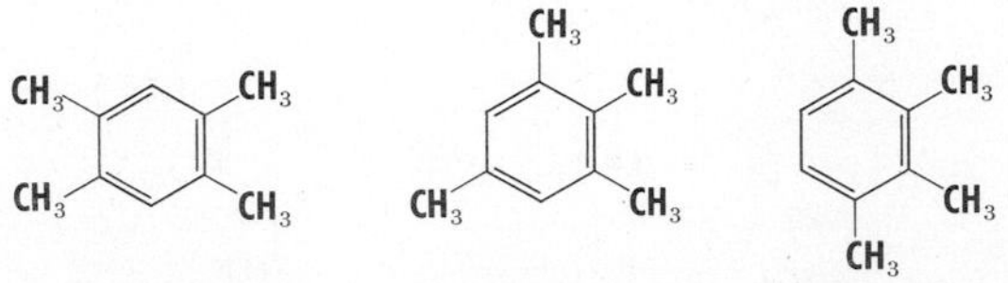

Durene
mp 80°

Isodurene
mp −24°

Prehnitine
mp −4°

Mixed xylenes (dimethylbenzenes) and trimethylbenzenes are produced commercially by adjustment of alkylation conditions. Rearrangement of primary alkylation products can be partially avoided by using very gentle reaction conditions.

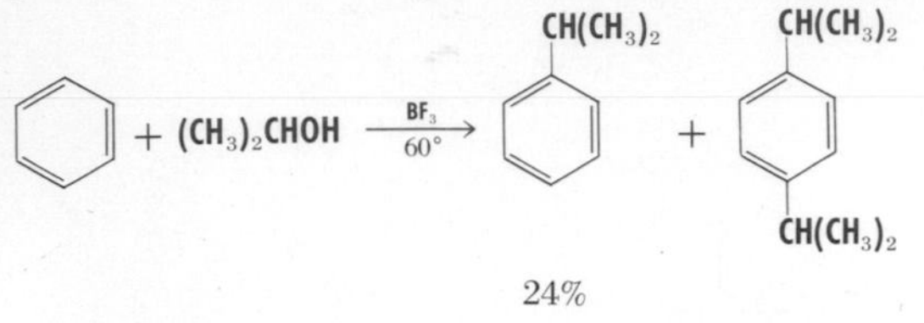

24%

Para substitution may also be obtained by acylation of an alkyl benzene followed by reduction of the ketone to a hydrocarbon. Rearrangements of ketones under Friedel-Crafts conditions usually do not occur.

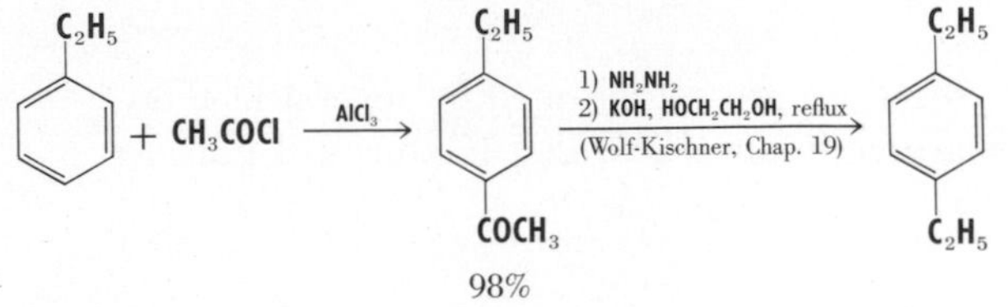

98%

Rearrangement of alkyl groups can be depended upon to give *sym*-trisubstituted benzenes when alkyl groups larger than methyl are introduced. Under equilibrating conditions, steric hindrance forces the system toward configurations having no two adjacent alkyl groups. Oxidation of the alkyl groups in such a product permits the synthesis of a variety of *sym*-trisubstituted compounds.

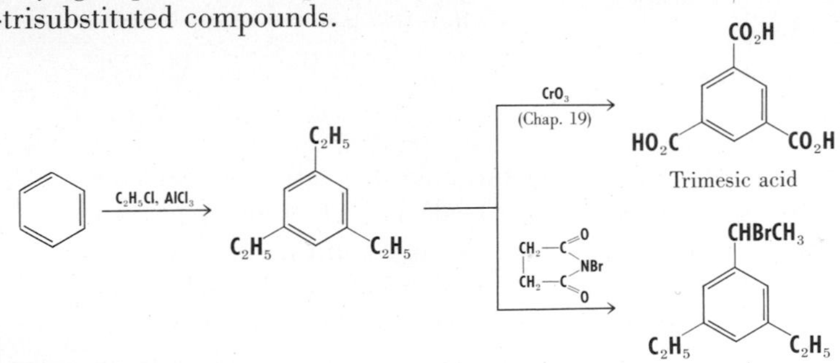

Trimesic acid

Rearrangement of alkyl groups may occur by way of cleavage followed by realkylation in a less active, meta position. Direct intramolecular transfer from one position to another is also believed to occur.

Dealkylation:

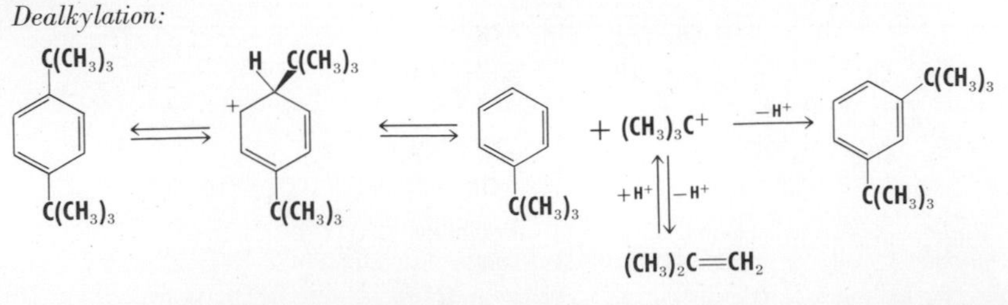

Intramolecular rearrangement:

Pseudocumene   Mesitylene

Another undesirable feature of Friedel-Crafts alkylations is rearrangement of alkyl groups themselves during the reaction. Low yields of *n*-alkyl derivatives may be obtained by using carefully controlled conditions, but usually the products obtained are those derived from the most stable carbonium ion having the skeleton of the original alkyl group.

Cumene
(Isopropylbenzene)

Details of rearrangement are, at least in some instances, more complex than is indicated by the above formulation. Alkylation with *n*-propanol and boron trifluoride at low temperature gives some *n*-propylbenzene, but the reaction is not recommended for the synthesis of *n*-alkyl aromatics. Large alkyl groups also undergo extensive fragmentation (cf. page 404) under alkylation conditions.

Commercial syntheses are frequently based upon alkylation of aromatic hydrocarbons with ethylene, propylene, and isobutene, because of the low cost of the olefins. Ethylation, followed by dehydrogenation, is used in the industrial synthesis of styrene.

Acylation. The Friedel-Crafts ketone synthesis is one of the most useful of all aromatic substitution reactions. Because of the electron-withdrawing effect of a carbonyl group, polysubstitution and reshuffling of groups occur only rarely, and substitution takes place without rearrangement. Since carbonyl groups are easily reduced to methylene groups by the Clemmensen (page 447) and Wolf-Kischner (page 447) methods, acylation followed by reduction is an excellent procedure for introduction of alkyl side chains. Secondary alkyl groups can be constructed by adding organometallic reagents to acylation products.

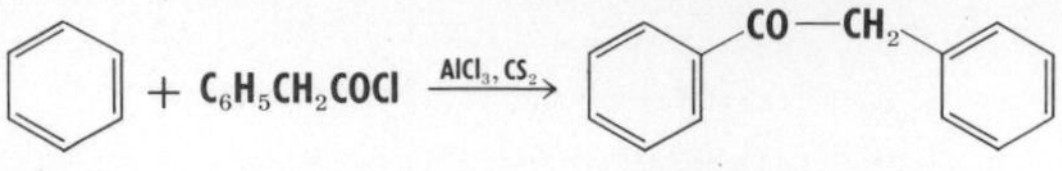

$\bigcirc$ + $C_6H_5CH_2COCl$ $\xrightarrow{AlCl_3, CS_2}$ phenyl—CO—CH₂—phenyl

Phenyl benzyl ketone
83%

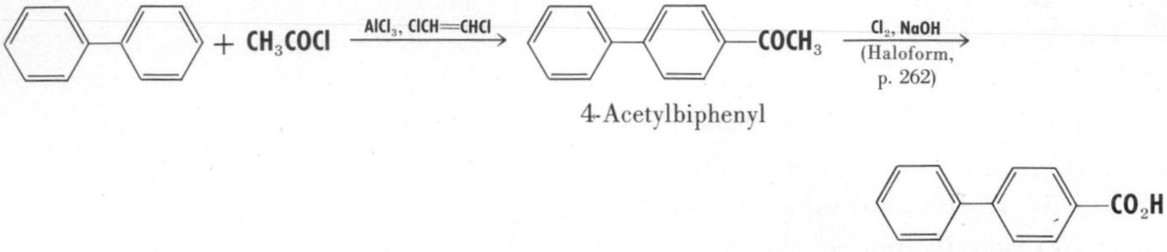

biphenyl + CH_3COCl $\xrightarrow{AlCl_3, ClCH=CHCl}$ biphenyl—$COCH_3$ $\xrightarrow[\text{(Haloform, p. 262)}]{Cl_2, NaOH}$

4-Acetylbiphenyl

biphenyl—CO_2H

p-Phenylbenzoic acid
80%

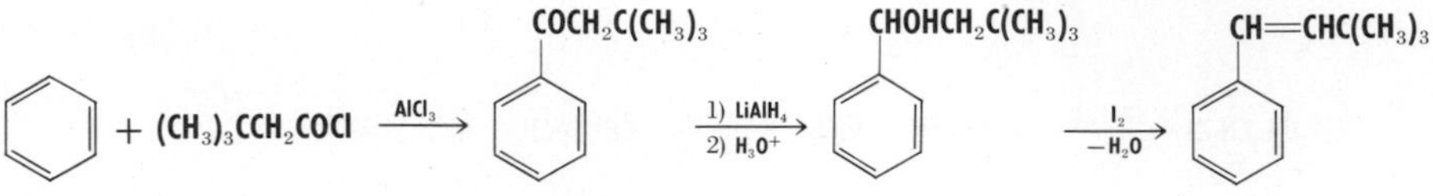

$\bigcirc$ + $(CH_3)_3CCH_2COCl$ $\xrightarrow{AlCl_3}$ phenyl—$COCH_2C(CH_3)_3$ $\xrightarrow[\text{2) H}_3O^+]{\text{1) LiAlH}_4}$ phenyl—$CHOHCH_2C(CH_3)_3$ $\xrightarrow[-H_2O]{I_2}$ phenyl—$CH=CHC(CH_3)_3$

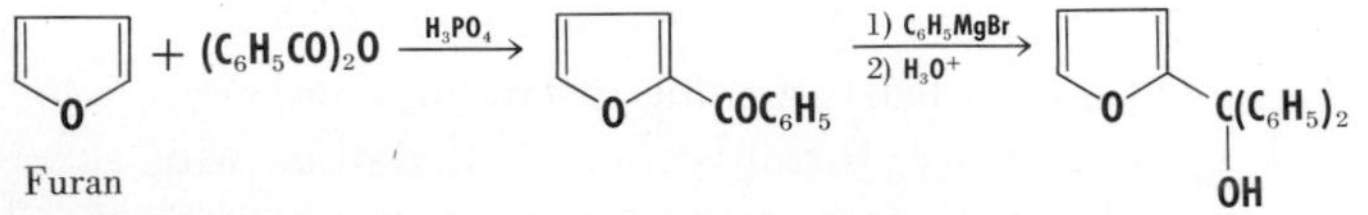

87%

Furan + $(C_6H_5CO)_2O$ $\xrightarrow{H_3PO_4}$ furan—COC_6H_5 $\xrightarrow[\text{2) H}_3O^+]{\text{1) C}_6H_5MgBr}$ furan—$C(C_6H_5)_2$—OH

Aromatic rings with meta-directing substituents are not sufficiently reactive to undergo ready acylation; meta-substituted ketones must frequently be made by indirect procedures.

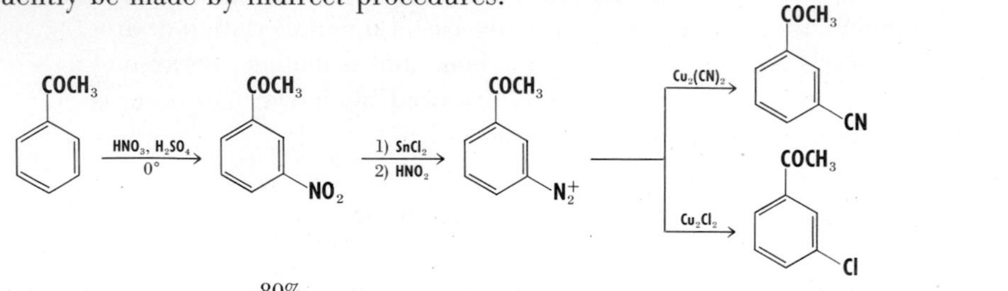

phenyl—$COCH_3$ $\xrightarrow[0°]{HNO_3, H_2SO_4}$ $COCH_3$/NO_2 $\xrightarrow[\text{2) HNO}_2]{\text{1) SnCl}_2}$ $COCH_3$/N_2^+

$\xrightarrow{Cu_2(CN)_2}$ $COCH_3$/CN

$\xrightarrow{Cu_2Cl_2}$ $COCH_3$/Cl

80%   83%

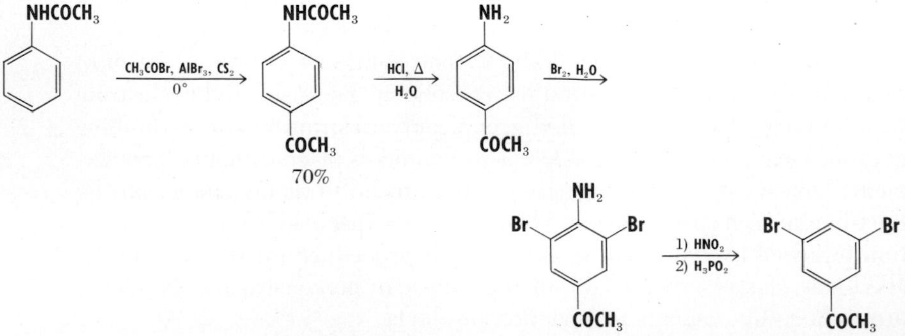

phenyl—$NHCOCH_3$ $\xrightarrow[0°]{CH_3COBr, AlBr_3, CS_2}$ $NHCOCH_3$/$COCH_3$ $\xrightarrow[H_2O]{HCl, \Delta}$ NH_2/$COCH_3$ $\xrightarrow{Br_2, H_2O}$

70%

Br—(ring, NH_2 top, $COCH_3$ bottom)—Br $\xrightarrow[\text{2) H}_3PO_2]{\text{1) HNO}_2}$ Br—(ring, $COCH_3$ bottom)—Br

Cyclization. Cyclization of β- and γ-arylalkanoic acids (and acid chlorides) under acid conditions is an elegant method for synthesis of carbocyclic rings fused to aromatic nuclei. A multitude of reaction conditions have been investigated in the course of syntheses of polycyclic systems.

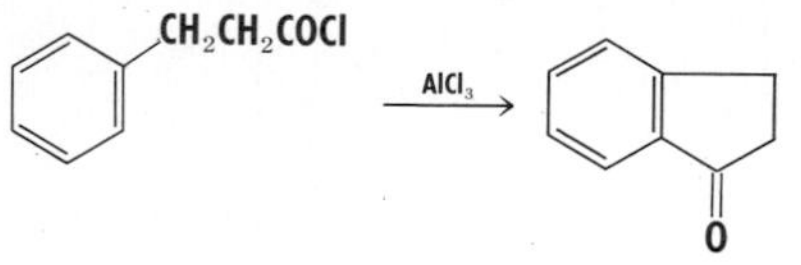

1-Hydrindone
90%

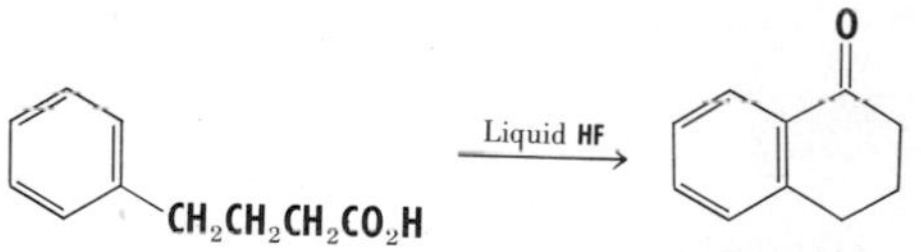

α-Tetralone

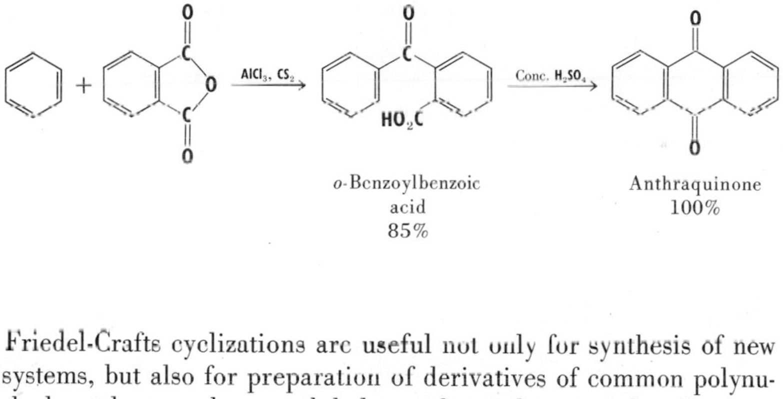

o-Benzoylbenzoic
acid
85%

Anthraquinone
100%

Friedel-Crafts cyclizations are useful not only for synthesis of new ring systems, but also for preparation of derivatives of common polynuclear hydrocarbons such as naphthalene, phenanthrene, and anthracene. Monosubstituted naphthalenes are nearly all made from naphthalene, but the isomer mixtures obtained in attempting disubstitution are often too complex for practical separation. Even monosubstitution of phenanthrene often gives complex mixtures. The structures of substitution products must be established by unambiguous syntheses which usually involve cyclization. Succinic anhydride and its derivatives are particularly useful in ring-building sequences. Combinations of Friedel-Crafts acylation reactions with Clemmensen reductions, with Grignard additions, with simple reductions of carbonyl groups, and with dehydrogenation reactions of alicyclic compounds provide routes to a large variety of substituted polycyclic compounds. Some possibilities are shown by the following examples.

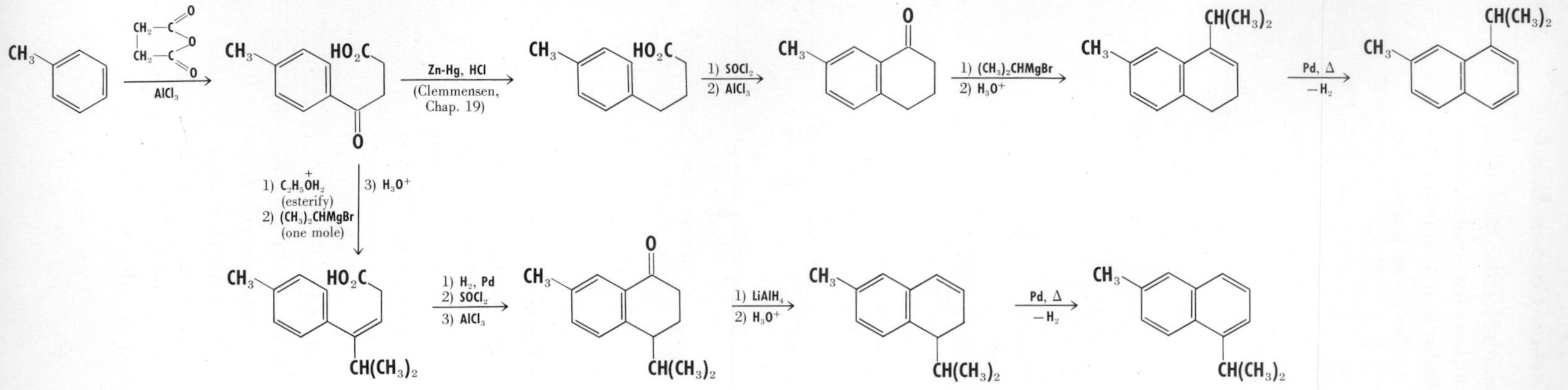

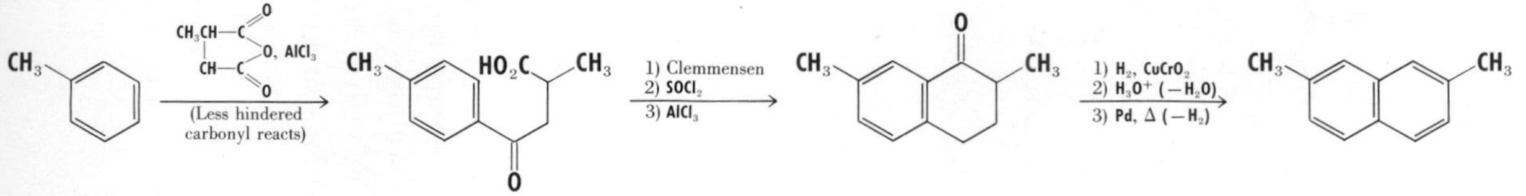

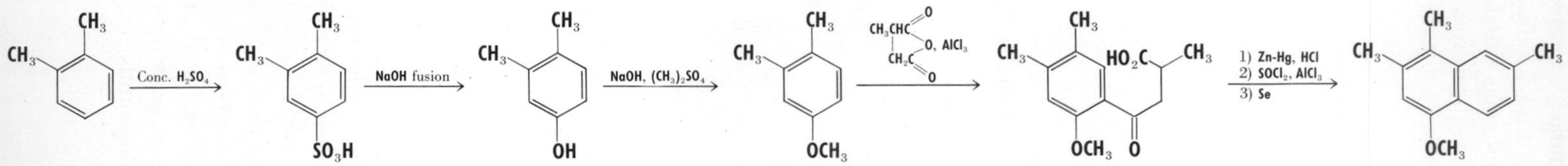

AlCl₃

Zn-Hg, HCl (Clemmensen, Chap. 19)

1) SOCl₂ 2) AlCl₃

1) (CH₃)₂CHMgBr 2) H₃O⁺

Pd, Δ −H₂

1) C₂H₅OH⁺ (esterify) 2) (CH₃)₂CHMgBr (one mole) 3) H₃O⁺

1) H₂, Pd 2) SOCl₂ 3) AlCl₃

1) LiAlH₄ 2) H₃O⁺

Pd, Δ −H₂

(Less hindered carbonyl reacts)

1) Clemmensen 2) SOCl₂ 3) AlCl₃

1) H₂, CuCrO₂ 2) H₃O⁺ (−H₂O) 3) Pd, Δ (−H₂)

Conc. H₂SO₄

NaOH fusion

NaOH, (CH₃)₂SO₄

1) Zn-Hg, HCl 2) SOCl₂, AlCl₃ 3) Se

378

Acylation of naphthalene is subject to an interesting solvent effect. Reaction in carbon disulfide or halogenated solvents gives predominant attack in the α-position. However, in nitrobenzene solution, the bulk of the attacking electrophile is increased by solvation with nitrobenzene, so that the less hindered, β-position is attacked.

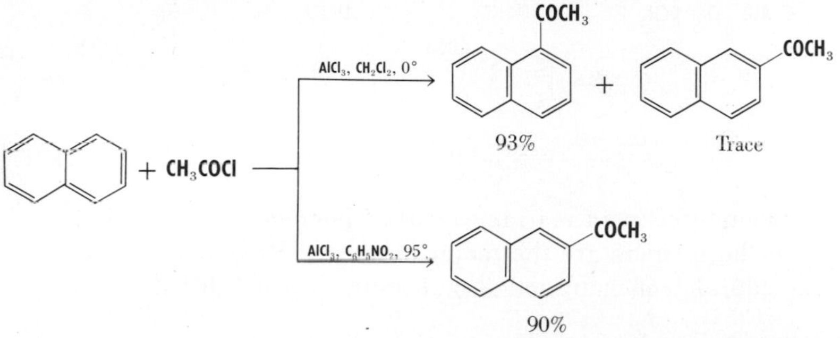

Succinoylation of naphthalene in nitrobenzene gives a separable mixture of α- and β-isomers, both of which are useful in the synthesis of phenanthrene derivatives.

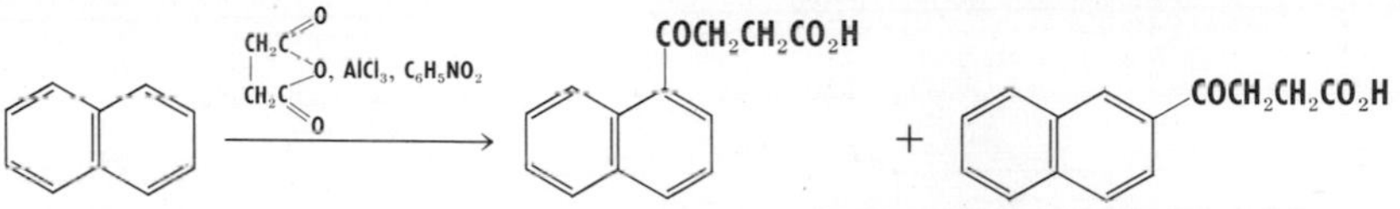

Tetralin is acylated exclusively in the β-position.

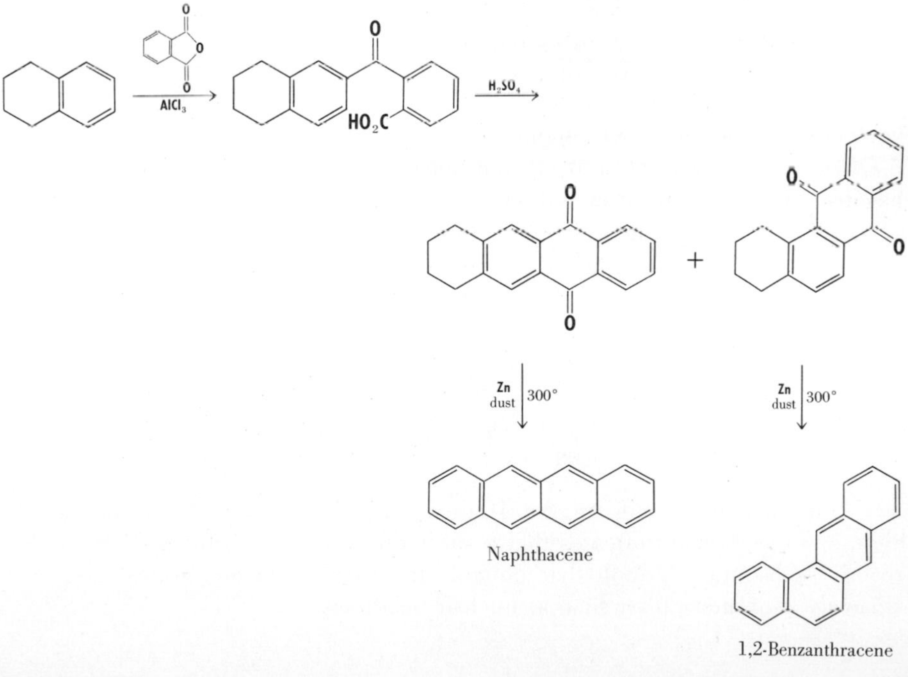

Naphthacene

1,2-Benzanthracene

The above example illustrates the *reluctance of 2-naphthoyl derivatives to cyclize to the 3-position* to give linearly condensed products.

Other Ketone Syntheses.   Phenolic ketones are often prepared by the Fries rearrangement of aryl esters (Chap. 20).   The reaction is a self-acylation.

At low temperatures, para rearrangement predominates, and at high temperatures, ortho isomers are the major product.   Solvent variation and aluminum chloride concentration also affect the product distribution.

The Fries rearrangement is rather useful, since direct acylation of phenols is complicated by formation of aluminum phenoxides, which are sometimes insoluble.   Attempts at direct acylation may go through the ester as an intermediate, but cannot be relied upon to do so.   Monoacylation of a polyhydroxy phenol is not conveniently accomplished by the Fries rearrangement, and is even more susceptible to complication, because of the formation of polymeric aluminum phenoxides.   For the acylation of such compounds, the *Hoesch reaction* is preferred.   The process consists of substitution by the conjugate acid of a nitrile.   The first product is an imine, which is hydrolyzed during isolation.

Unfortunately, yields in the Hoesch reaction are not consistently high, and experience indicates that a successful reaction requires a very reactive substrate.   Monohydric phenols are usually attacked almost exclusively at oxygen rather than at nuclear positions.

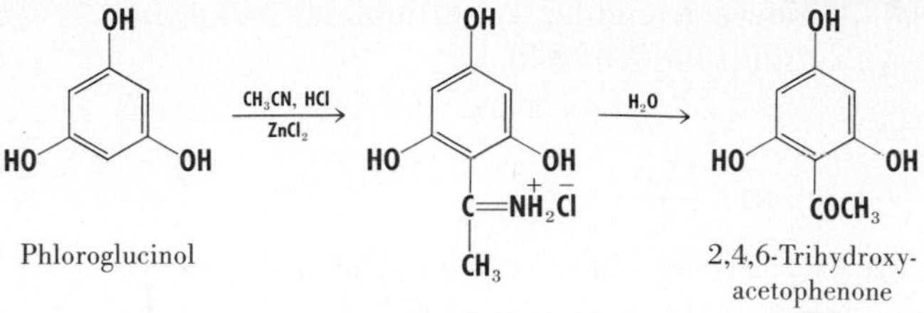

Phloroglucinol

2,4,6-Trihydroxy-
acetophenone
87%

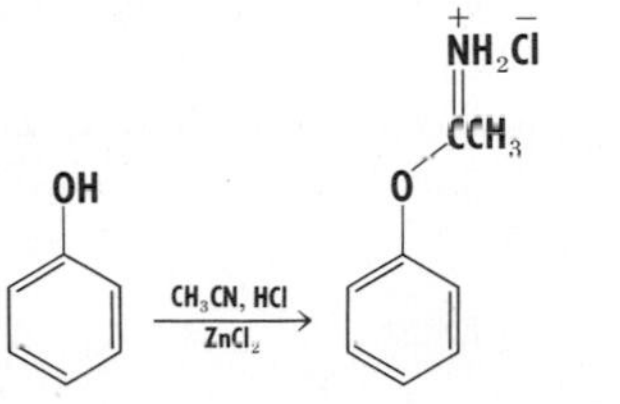

Hydrochloride of
phenyliminoacetate

When evaluating various procedures for synthesis of a given aryl ketone, one must bear in mind that methods other than electrophilic substitution will occasionally be of service. The alternatives include reaction of an organometallic with an acid chloride, oxidation of a secondary alcohol (page 73), and addition of an organometallic reagent to a nitrile. Direct oxidation of the methylene groups in a side chain is also occasionally possible (Chap. 19).

$$2\ C_6H_5COCl + (n\text{-}C_4H_9)_2Cd \longrightarrow 2\ C_6H_5COC_4H_9\text{-}n + CdCl_2$$

$$C_6H_5CN + (CH_3)_2CHMgBr \longrightarrow \underset{\underset{NMgBr}{\|}}{C_6H_5CCH(CH_3)_2} \xrightarrow{H_2O} \underset{\underset{O}{\|}}{C_6H_5CCH(CH_3)_2}$$

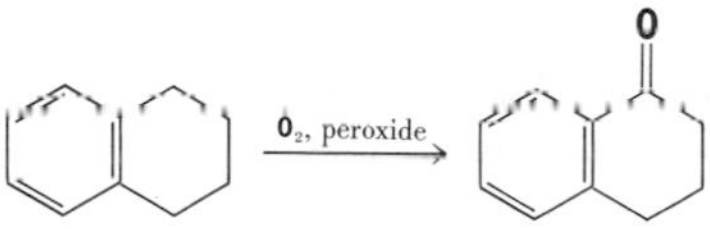

Formylation. Although formyl chloride (**HCOCl**) and formic anhydride [**(HCO)$_2$O**] are unknown compounds, the ion, **HC≡O$^+$**, needed for formylation can be produced by protonation of carbon monoxide. In the presence of **HCl, CO**, and **AlCl$_3$**, aldehydes are produced from substrates which are ordinarily subject to acylation.

$$:C{=}O + HCl + AlCl_3 \rightleftharpoons \overset{+}{HC}{=}O\overset{-}{AlCl_4}$$

$$\overset{+}{HC}{=}O + ArH \longrightarrow ArCHO$$

Protonation of **HCN** produces a similar electrophile. Solid zinc cyanide is often used as an *in situ* source of **HCN**.

$$HC\equiv N \xrightarrow{\text{ZnCl}_2,\ \text{HCl}} H\overset{+}{C}=NH$$

$$H\overset{+}{C}=NH + ArH \longrightarrow ArCH=\overset{+}{N}H_2 \xrightarrow{\text{H}_2\text{O}} ArCHO$$

Even though they are virtually the same reaction, the aldehyde synthesis with **CO** and **HCl** is known as the *Gatterman-Koch method* and that with **HCN** is called the *Gatterman synthesis*.

Gatterman-Koch:

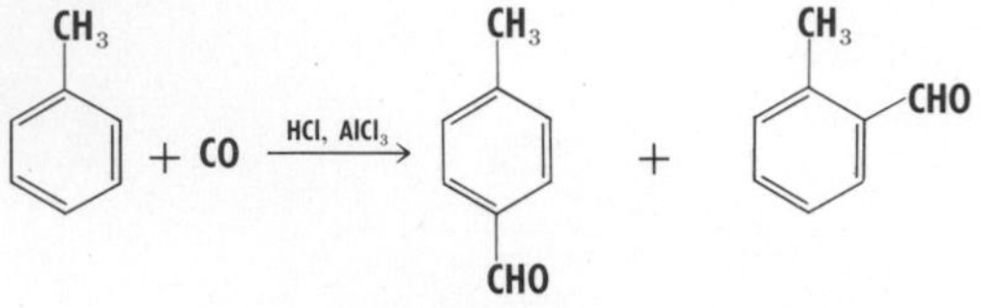

     p-Tolualdehyde   Small amount
          51%

Gatterman:

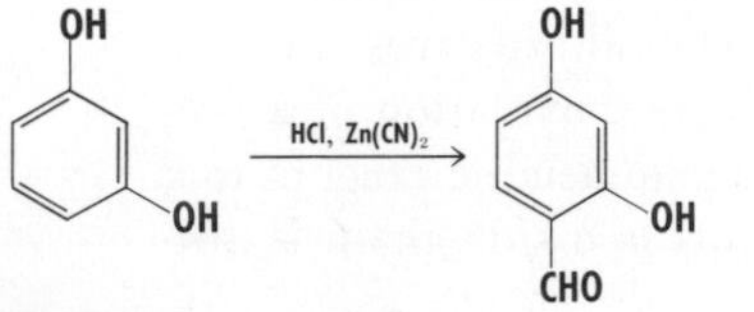

  Resorcinol   Resorcyl aldehyde
               95%

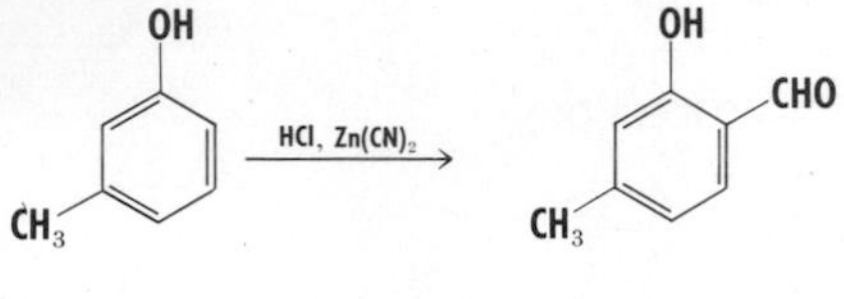

N-Methylformanilide is a source of $HC\equiv O^+$ ion that can be used to formylate *moderately reactive* aromatic substrates. The reagent is prepared from *N*-methylaniline and formic acid. Formylation is usually promoted by phosphorus oxychloride, although other Lewis acids have been used successfully.

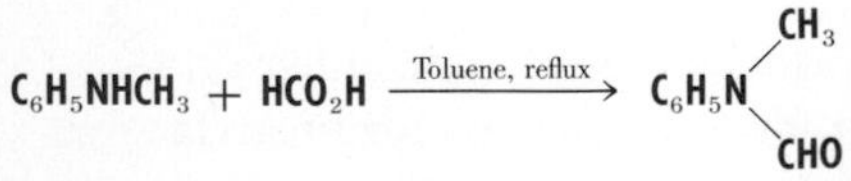

$$C_6H_5NHCH_3 + HCO_2H \xrightarrow{\text{Toluene, reflux}} C_6H_5N\begin{smallmatrix}CH_3\\CHO\end{smallmatrix}$$

                           N-methylformanilide
                               95%

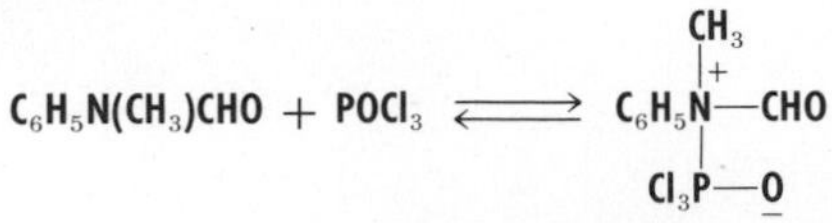

$$C_6H_5N(CH_3)CHO + POCl_3 \rightleftharpoons C_6H_5\overset{CH_3}{\underset{Cl_3P-O}{\overset{+}{N}-CHO}}$$

(Expanded phosphorus valence shell)

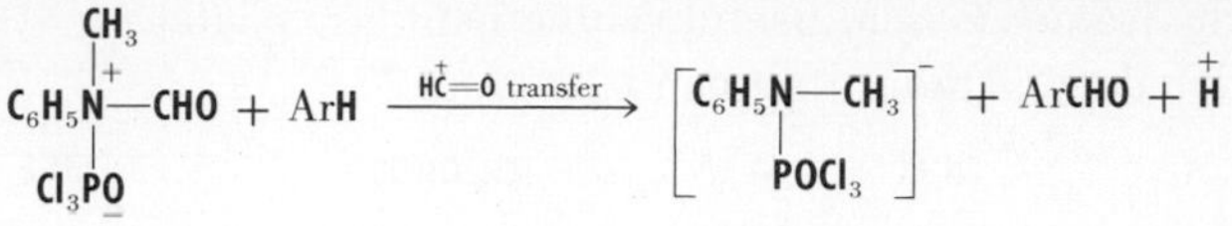

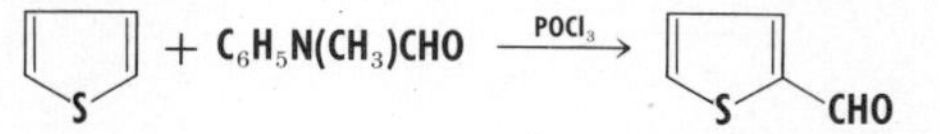

$$\underset{\underset{\text{Cl}_3\text{PO}}{|}}{\overset{\overset{\text{CH}_3}{|}}{\text{C}_6\text{H}_5\overset{+}{\text{N}}}}-\text{CHO} + \text{ArH} \xrightarrow{\text{H}\overset{+}{\text{C}}=\text{O transfer}} \left[\underset{\underset{\text{POCl}_3}{|}}{\text{C}_6\text{H}_5\overset{+}{\text{N}}}-\text{CH}_3\right]^{-} + \text{ArCHO} + \overset{+}{\text{H}}$$

Thiophene   + $\text{C}_6\text{H}_5\text{N(CH}_3)\text{CHO} \xrightarrow{\text{POCl}_3}$ 2-Thiophene aldehyde
76%

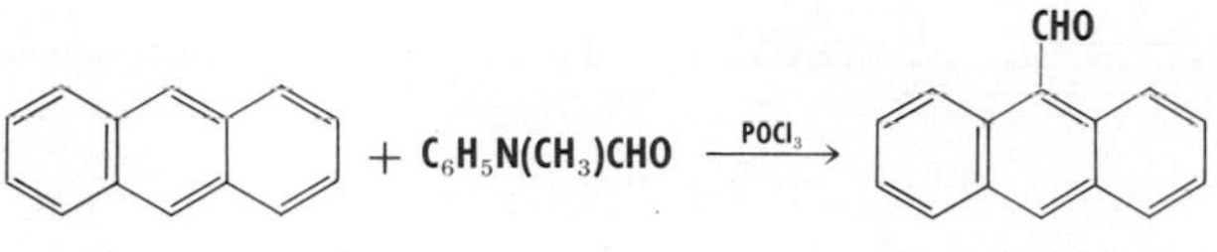

+ $\text{C}_6\text{H}_5\text{N(CH}_3)\text{CHO} \xrightarrow{\text{POCl}_3}$

9 Anthraldehyde
84%

Synthesis of aromatic aldehydes is of considerable importance, because of the use of the compounds in side-chain building through carbonyl condensations (page 321). Benzaldehyde itself is made commercially by hydrolysis of benzal chloride.

$$\text{C}_6\text{H}_5\text{CH}_3 \xrightarrow{\text{Cl}_2,\text{ light}} \text{C}_6\text{H}_5\text{CHCl}_2 \xrightarrow{\text{H}_2\text{O}} \text{C}_6\text{H}_5\text{CHO}$$

A general route to meta-substituted benzaldehydes is available through nitration. The reaction is carried out very carefully to avoid oxidation of the aldehyde group.

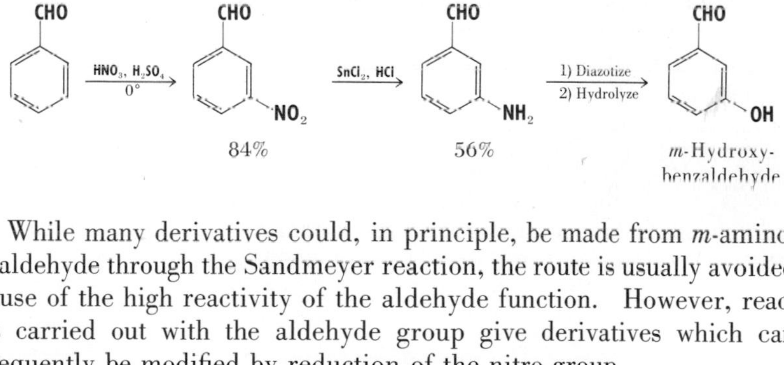

84%   56%   *m*-Hydroxy-
benzaldehyde

While many derivatives could, in principle, be made from *m*-aminobenzaldehyde through the Sandmeyer reaction, the route is usually avoided because of the high reactivity of the aldehyde function. However, reactions carried out with the aldehyde group give derivatives which can subsequently be modified by reduction of the nitro group.

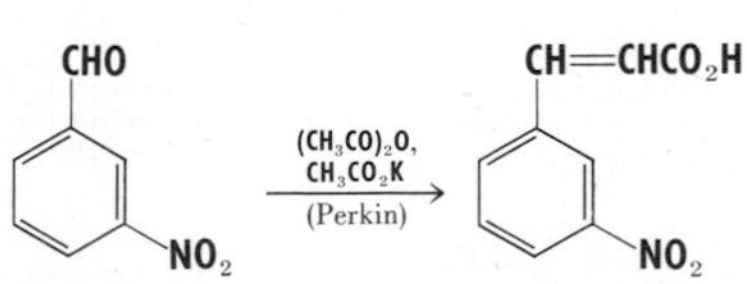

m-Nitrocinnamic acid
77%

Ortho- and *para*-nitrobenzaldehyde are made by oxidation of nitrobenzyl chlorides (obtained as a separable mixture in the nitration of

benzyl chloride).   The ortho isomer (a very useful synthetic intermediate)
is also made by an oxidative degradation of cinnamic acid.

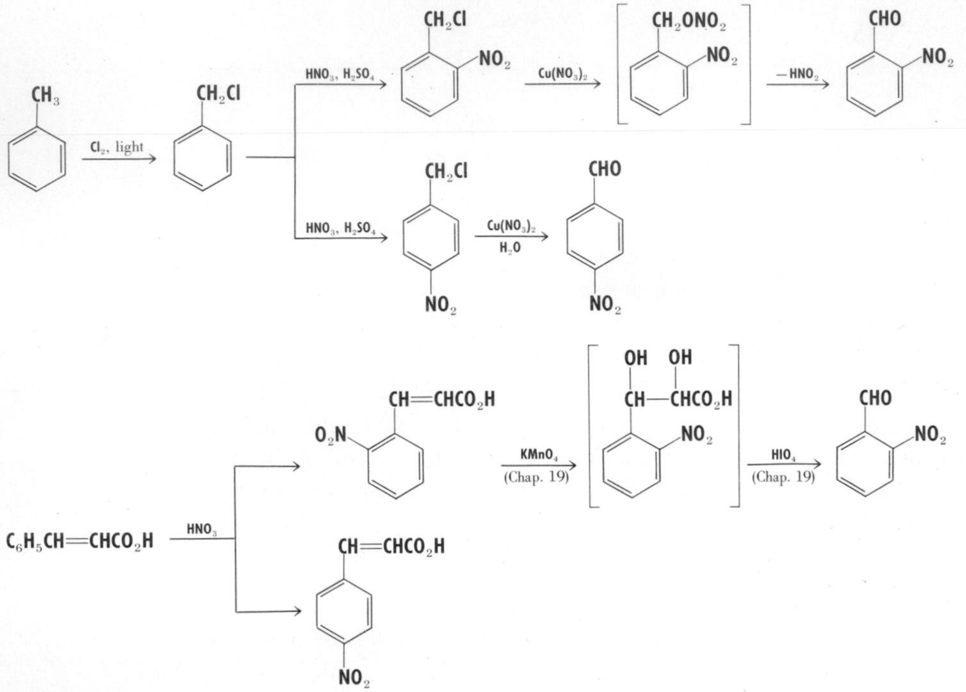

The syntheses of various halobenzaldehydes provide an instructive
study, since the compounds cannot be made directly.   The formylation
of halobenzenes is not successful, because of the low reactivity of the
aromatic nuclei.   Direct halogenation of benzaldehyde is seriously complicated by oxidation of the aldehyde function to a carboxyl group.   A
variety of indirect syntheses have been developed, some of which are
illustrated below.   Development from original starting materials is
included for the sake of illustration and because many important (for
other purposes) intermediates are included in the schemes.   Synthesis of
ortho-disubstituted compounds from phthalic anhydride is especially
important.

Ortho:

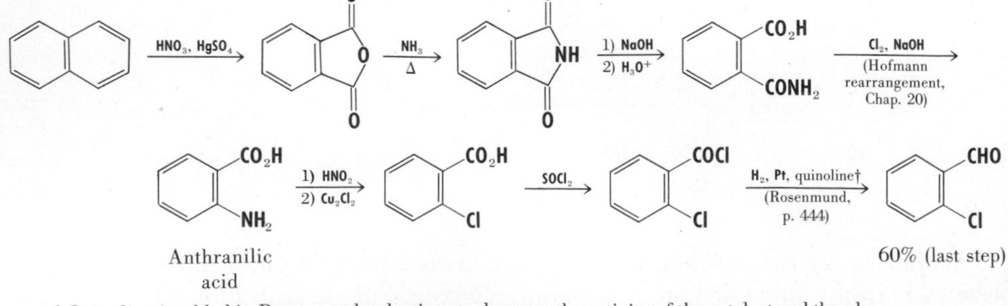

† Quinoline is added in Rosenmund reductions to decrease the activity of the catalyst and thereby
prevent reduction of the aldehyde produced in the reaction.

Meta:

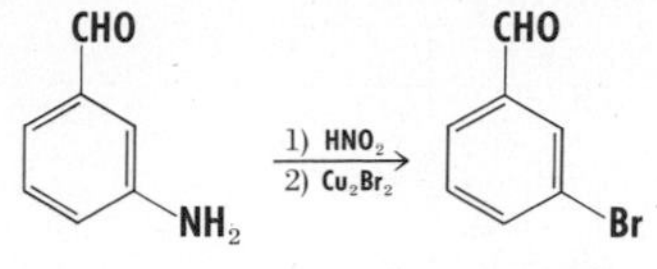

67%

Para:

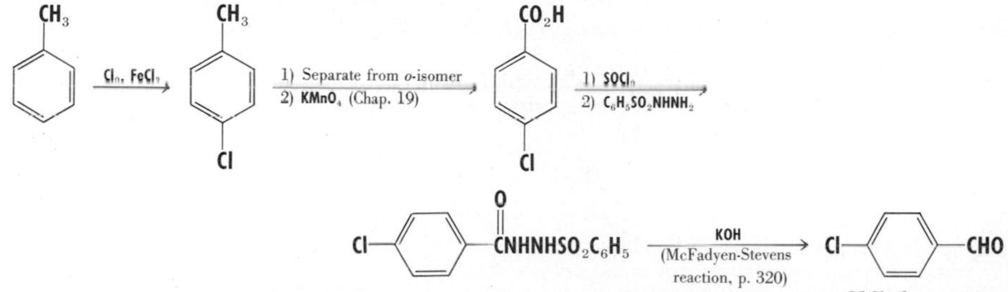

81% (last step)

Condensation of Aldehydes and Ketones with Aromatic Substrates. In the presence of strong acid, carbonyl compounds are converted to their powerfully electrophilic conjugate acids, $>C=OH^+$. Examples of the condensation of these conjugate acids with the enols of the parent carbonyl compounds in acid-catalyzed aldol condensations have been encountered earlier.

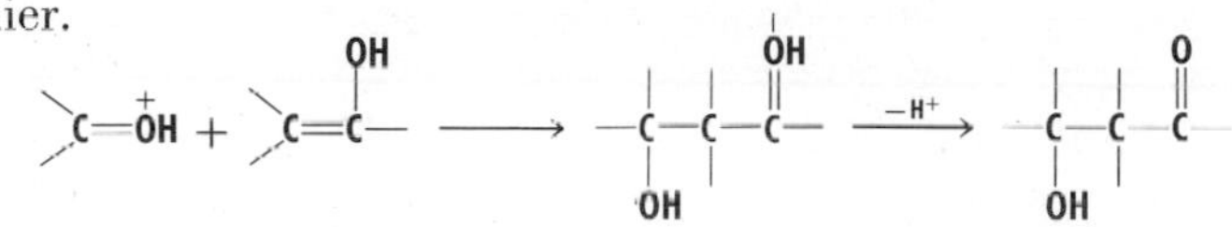

In a completely analogous reaction, aldehydes and ketones condense with reactive aromatic nuclei.

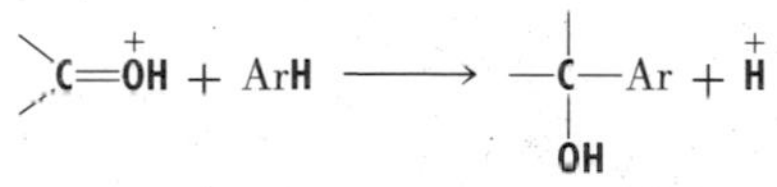

Since the products are benzyl alcohols, they are readily converted to carbonium ions, which may alkylate another nucleus.

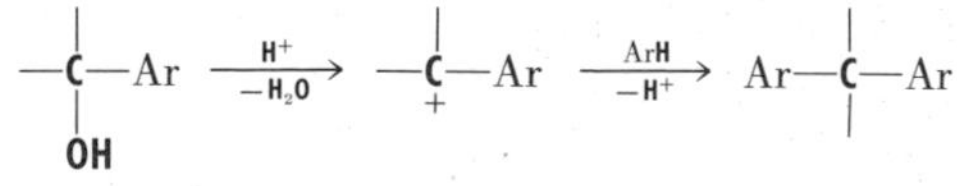

The activated nucleus is ordinarily still subject to further attack, so that the process generally leads to the formation of high polymers such as *phenol-formaldehyde resins.*

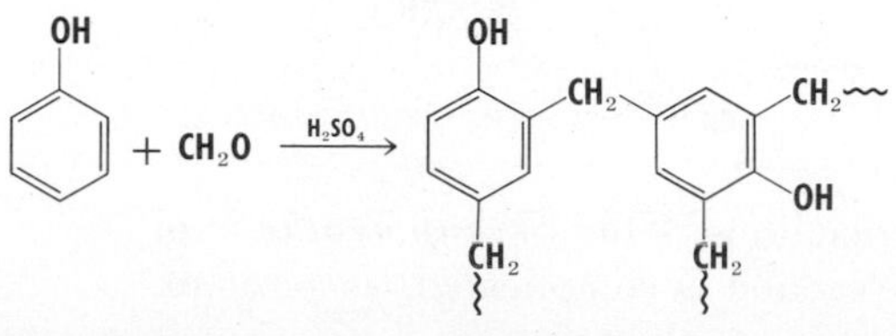

Bakelite structure

A phenol which is already dialkylated can be converted to a *bisphenol.*

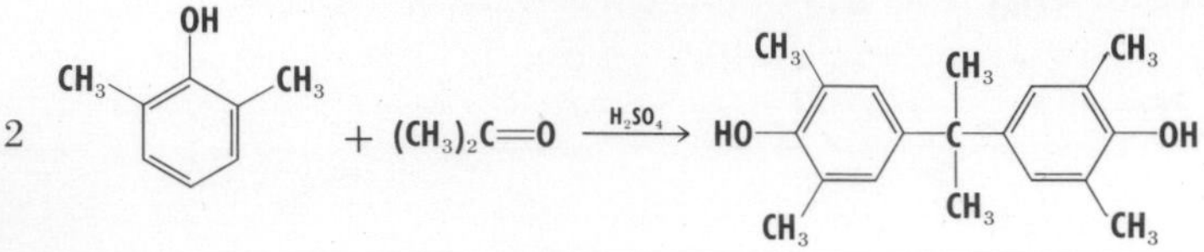

If the reaction mixture contains a high concentration of a nucleophilic ion, such as halide, the benzyl alcohols may be intercepted and converted to halides. The combination of formaldehyde with hydrogen chloride introduces the —CH_2Cl group, a process known as *chloromethylation.*

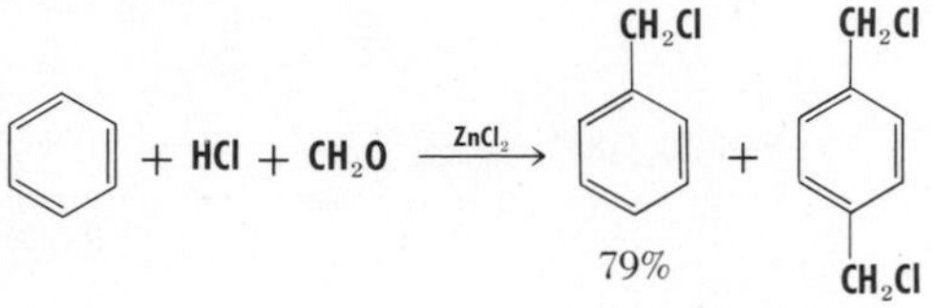

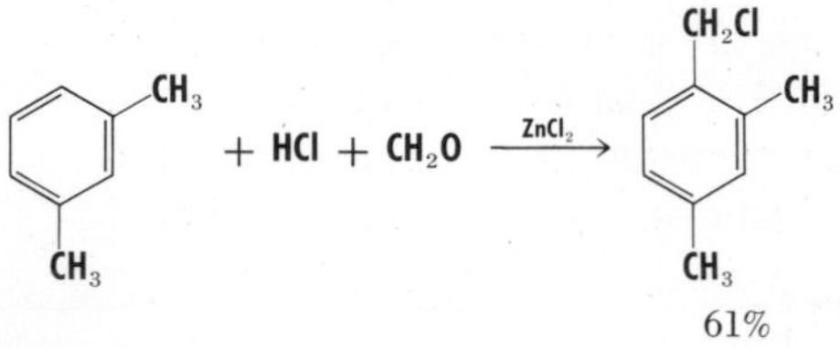

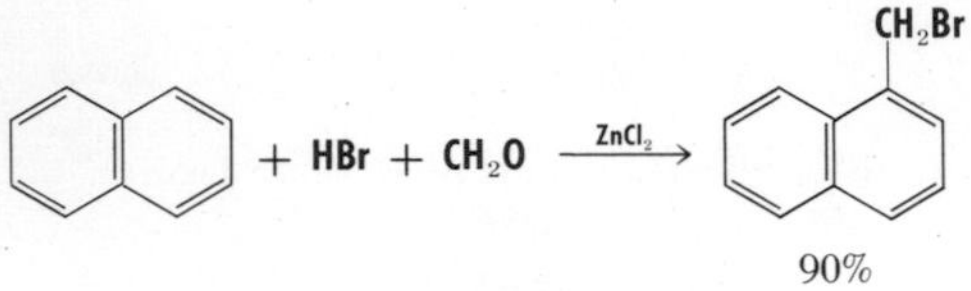

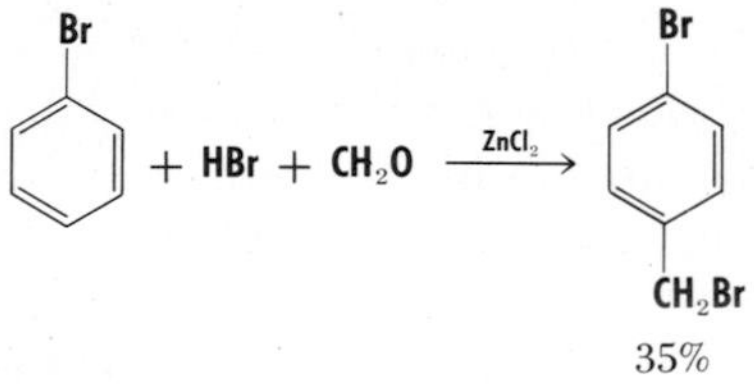

79%

61%

90%

35%

In the presence of secondary amines, the intermediate can be captured to give aminomethyl compounds. Little is known about the scope of the reaction.

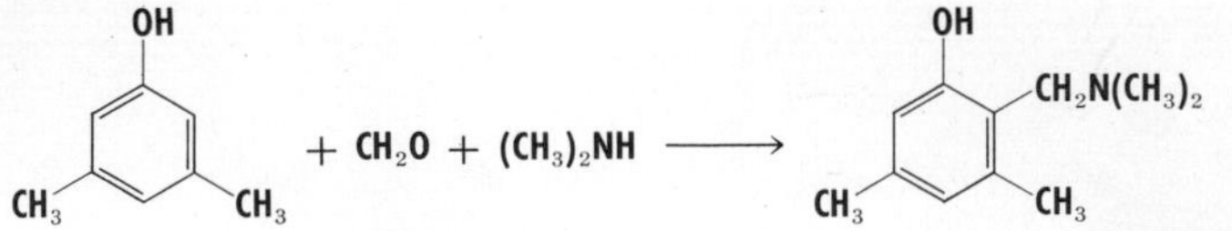

A close relative of the above reactions is the *Skraup synthesis* of quinoline and its derivatives. The reaction is complicated, as acrolein, the reactive intermediate, is generated *in situ* from glycerol, and an oxidant is included to dehydrogenate the first cyclization product. The reaction is strongly exothermic and is characterized by almost explosive violence after an induction period. The term "witch's brew," which has often been used to characterize organic reaction mixtures, might well have been inspired by Skraup reactions.

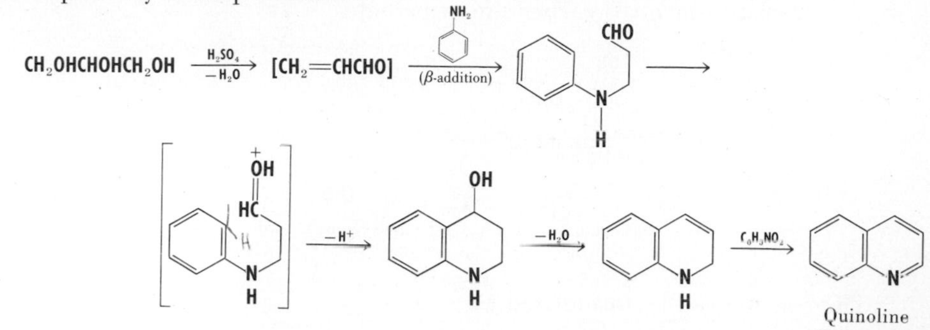

Quinoline
85% over-all

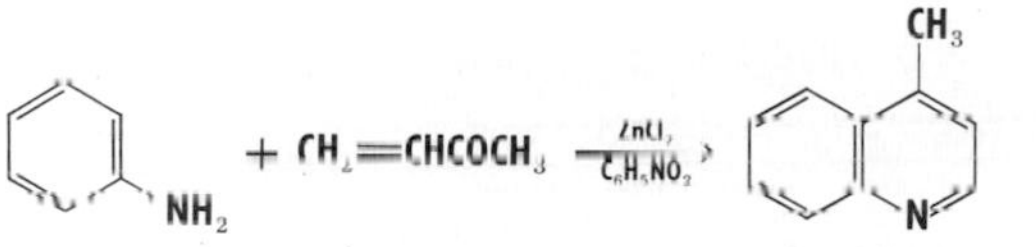

Lepidine
(4-Methylquinoline)
75%

Variation of the amine and carbonyl compound allows the synthesis of nearly any quinoline derivative.

Carbenes as Electrophiles

Thermal or photochemical decomposition of diazo compounds gives divalent carbon compounds (*carbenes*) which attack unsaturated compounds quite indiscriminately. The classification of the reagents as electrophilic is a moot question and is, for present purposes, a matter of convenience. The first step is addition, to give cyclopropanes that can be opened to give products in which the ring is expanded.

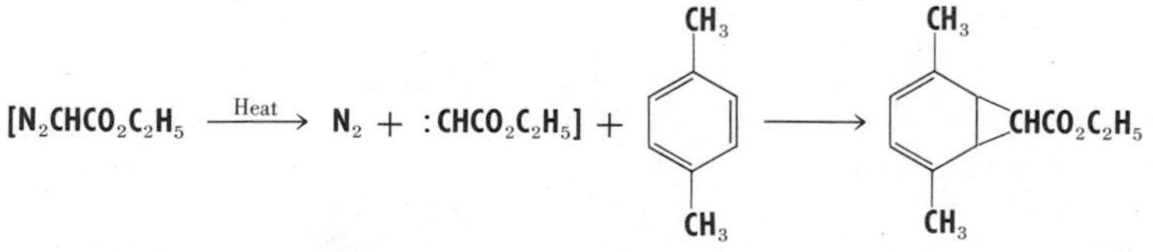

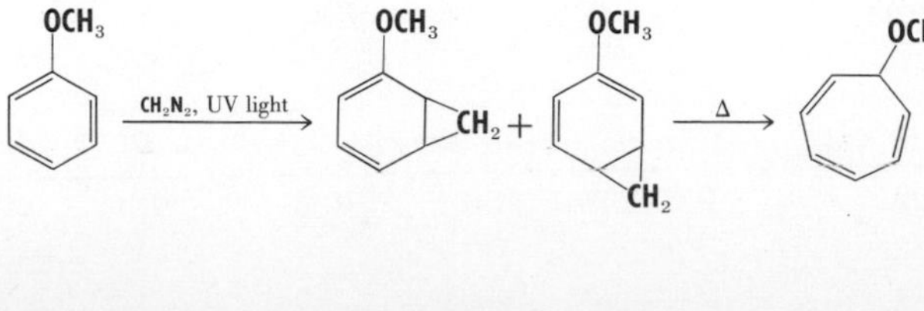

Chloroform is converted to dichlorocarbene when treated with base.

$$HCCl_3 + \bar{O}H \rightleftharpoons H_2O + \bar{C}Cl_3$$

$$\bar{C}Cl_3 \longrightarrow :CCl_2 + \bar{Cl}$$

It is likely that the *Reimer-Tiemann synthesis* of aldehydes from activated aromatics involves carbene intermediates.

Salicylaldehyde	*p*-Hydroxybenzaldehyde
40%	10%

The reaction can be formulated as:

Salicylaldehyde

"Abnormal" products are produced when the dienone cannot tautomerize to regenerate a phenolic system.

2,4,5-Trimethylphenol	2-Hydroxy-3,5,6-	2,4,5-Trimethyl-
(Pseudocumenol)	trimethylbenzaldehyde	4-dichloromethyl-
		cyclohexadiene-1-one

Thiophene undergoes the normal Reimer-Tiemann reaction, but pyrrole undergoes ring expansion.

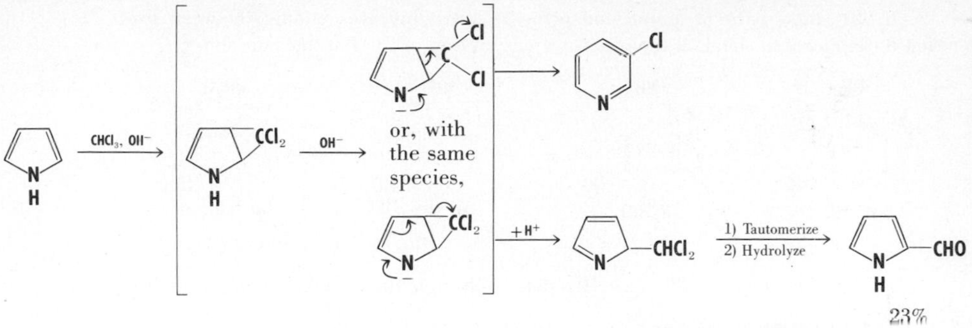

23%

Kolbe Synthesis. Salicylic acid is made by the Kolbe reaction. Sodium phenoxide and sodium hydroxide are heated under a high pressure of carbon dioxide. Carbonation occurs in a step similar to the carbonation of organometallic compounds (page 263). The reaction is also similar to the reverse of decarboxylation of the anion of a β-keto acid. Polyhydric phenols usually give good yields in the reaction under relatively mild conditions.

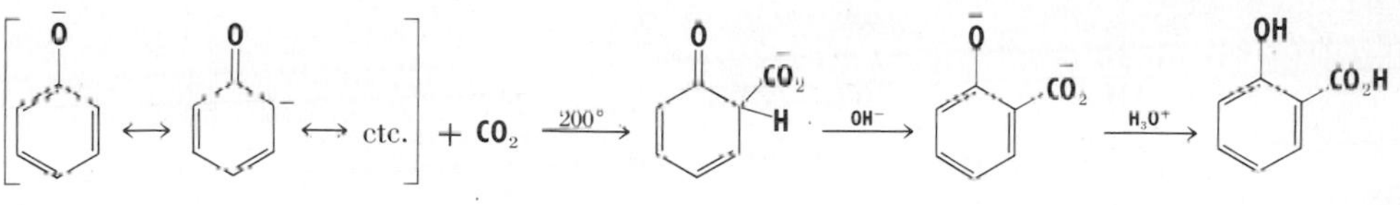

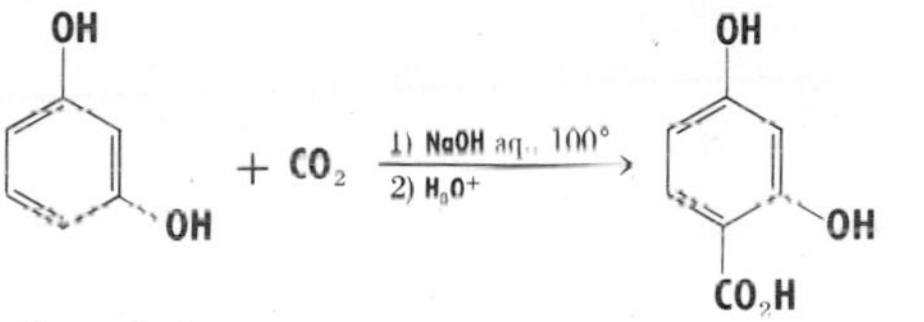

Resorcinol

β-Resorcylic acid
60%

Problems

1. The following reactions have been observed. Make a careful analysis of the substitution process in each case, and give an explanation of the observations.
Example:

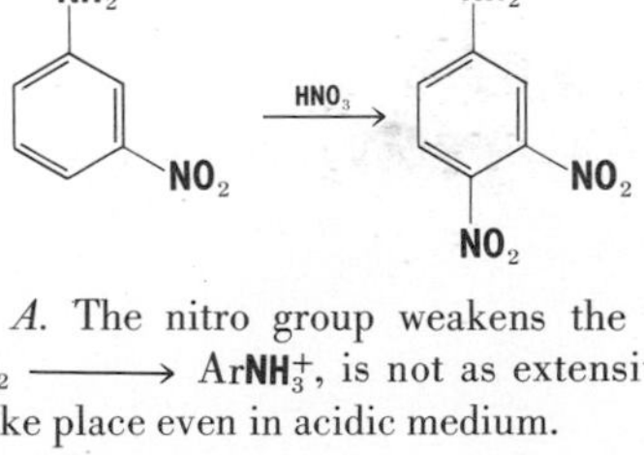

+ smaller amounts of 2,3- and 3,6-isomers

A. The nitro group weakens the basicity of the amine, so that the ionization, $ArNH_2 \longrightarrow ArNH_3^+$, is not as extensive as with aniline. Nitration of the free base can take place even in acidic medium.

B. Nitration para to amino and ortho to nitro involves conflict between two orienting influences. Look at the resonance description of the intermediate ion.

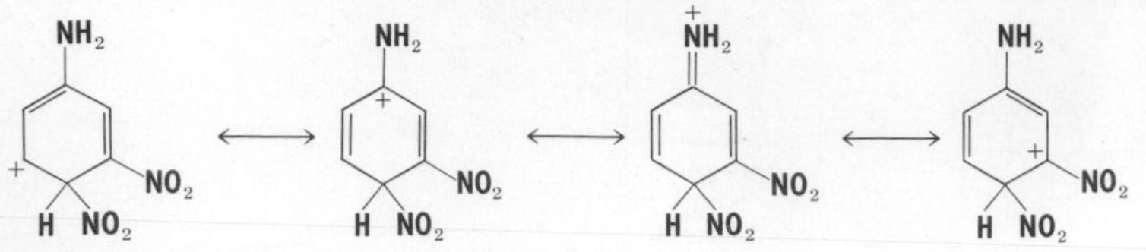

I   II   III   IV

The specific help of NH_2 (see III) must outweigh the specific influence of NO_2 (see IV).†

a.

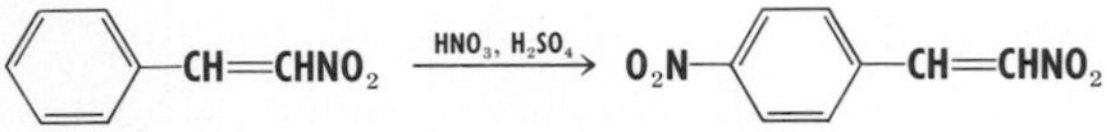

b.

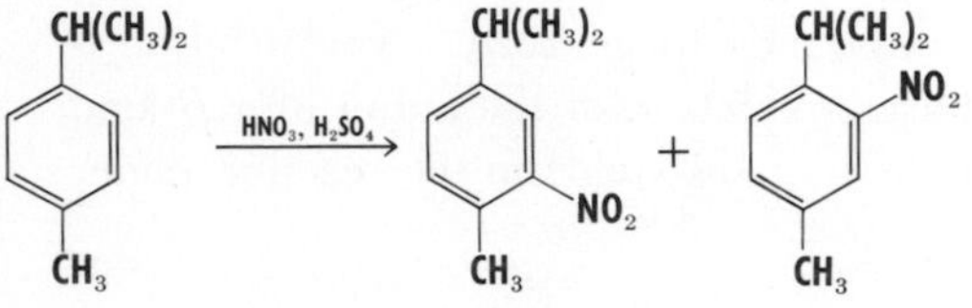

90%   Trace

c.

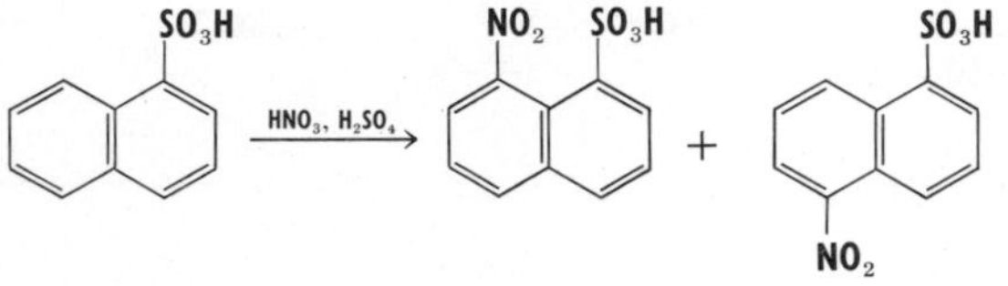

d.

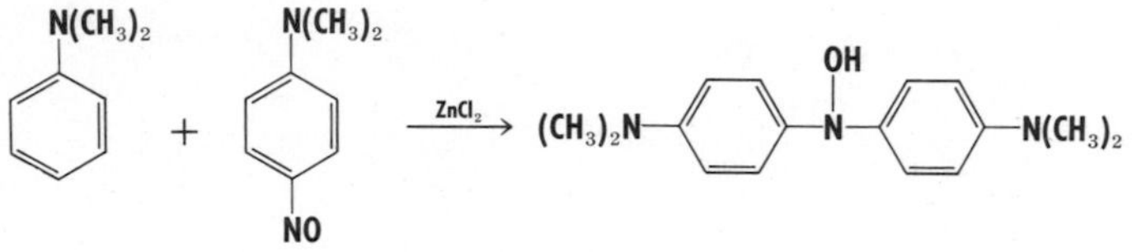

e. Attempts to use esters for Friedel-Crafts acylation, $ArH + RCO_2R' \xrightarrow[\text{or AlCl}_3]{\text{FeCl}_3} ArCOR$, always lead to a complex mixture of *alkylated and acylated* products.

f.

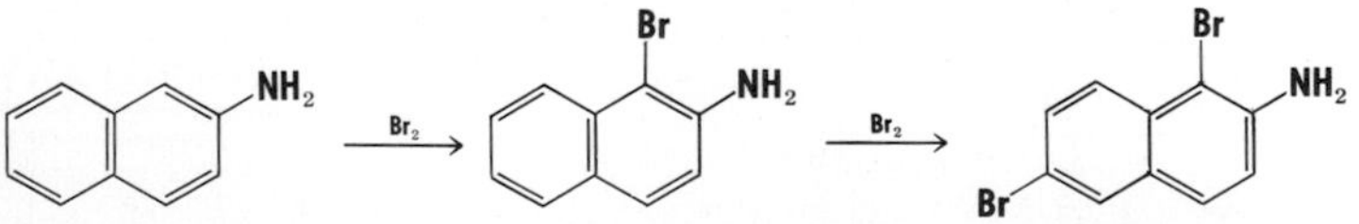

90% for the step

g.

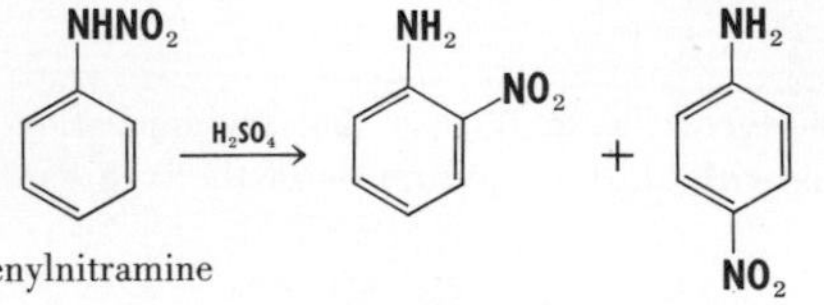

Phenylnitramine

† When they are brought into conflict, the influence of an activating group virtually always outweighs the effect of a deactivating substituent.

h.

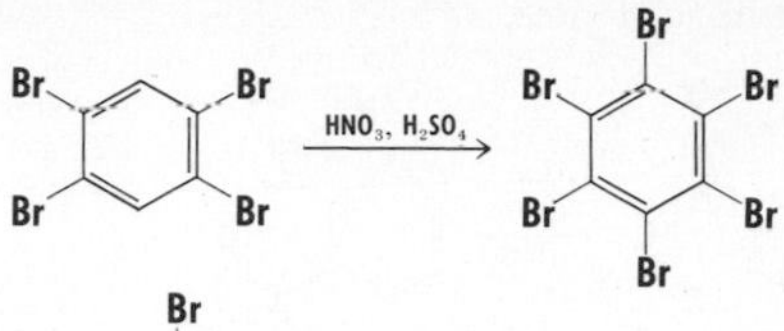

$\xrightarrow{\text{HNO}_3,\ \text{H}_2\text{SO}_4}$ + many other products

i.

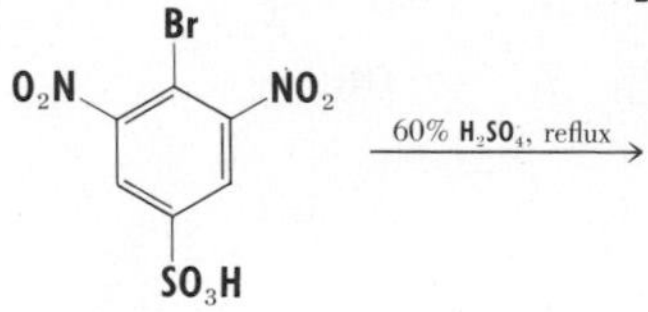

$\xrightarrow{60\%\ \text{H}_2\text{SO}_4,\ \text{reflux}}$ no reaction

Compare with:

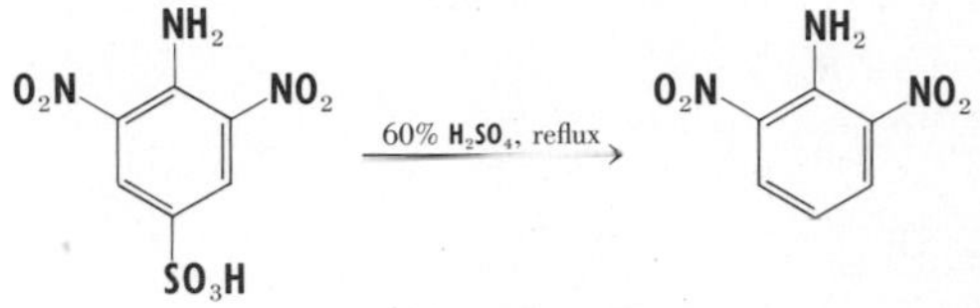

$\xrightarrow{60\%\ \text{H}_2\text{SO}_4,\ \text{reflux}}$

j.

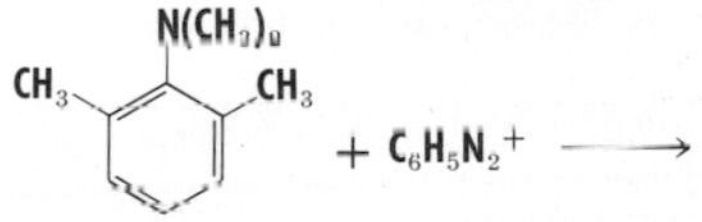

+ $C_6H_5N_2^+$ ⟶ no reaction

Compare with:

+ $C_6H_5N_2^+$ $\xrightarrow{\text{Very fast}}$ $(CH_3)_2N$——$N{=}N$—

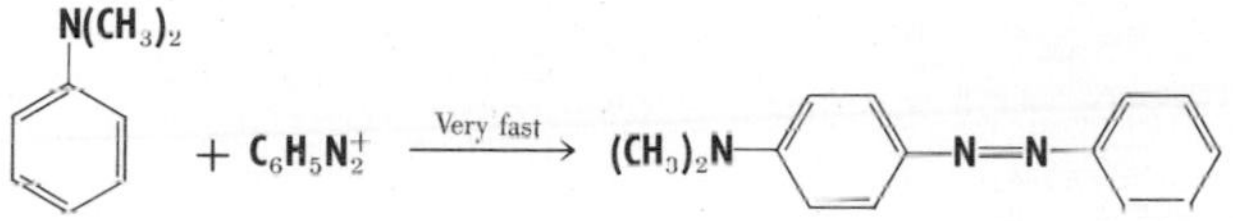

2. Devise suitable synthetic sequences to accomplish the following transformations:

a. 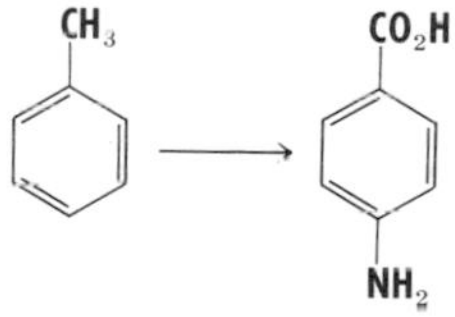 ⟶

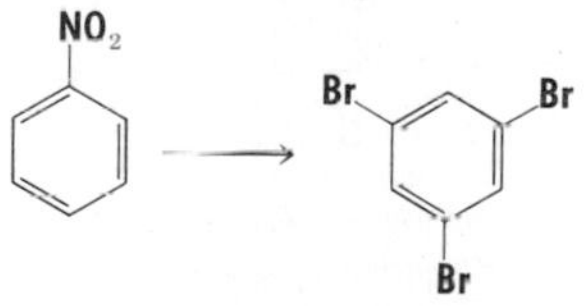

b. 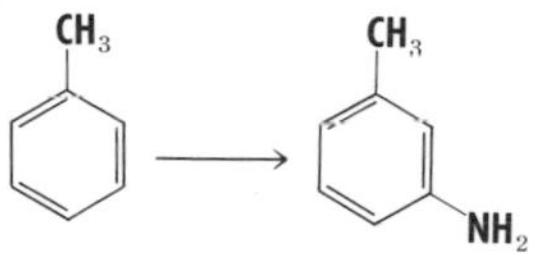 ⟶

c. ⟶

d. ⟶

e. ⟶

f. 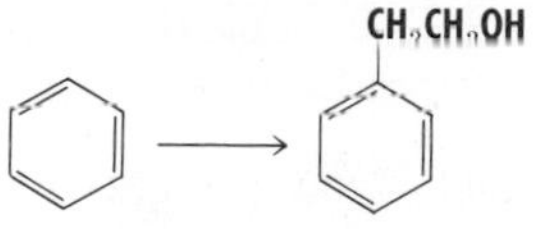 ⟶

(At least two methods, including one that utilizes $CH_2{-}CH_2$ with O)

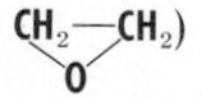

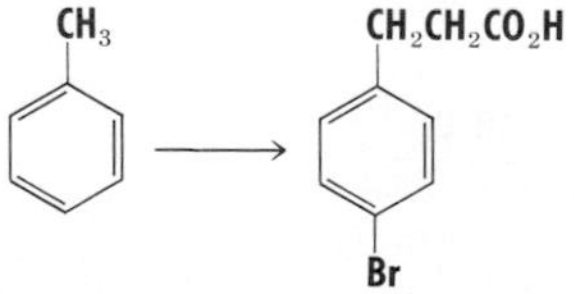

g. 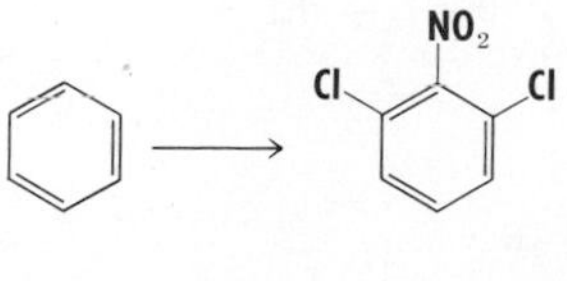 ⟶

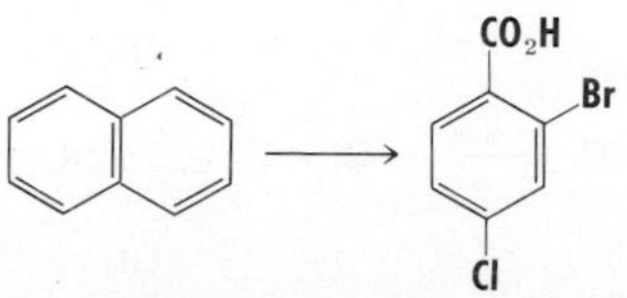

h. 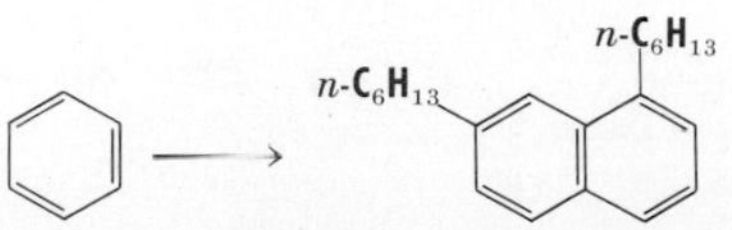 ⟶

i. The following reactions can be carried out in good yield:

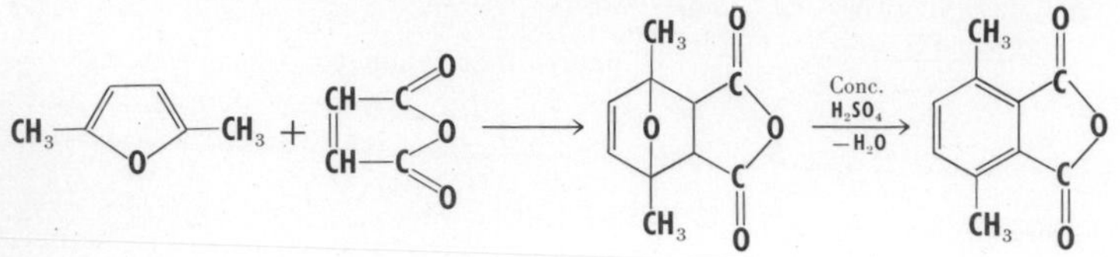

[reaction scheme: methyl-furan-methyl (CH₃ ... CH₃) + maleic/fumaric dianhydride-type reagent → bicyclic adduct → (Conc. H₂SO₄, −H₂O) → 3,6-dimethylphthalic anhydride]

3,6-Dimethylphthalic
anhydride

Using the product as a starting material, devise syntheses of several 1,2,3,4-tetrasubstituted benzenes having four different substituents.

3. Formulate reasonable mechanisms for each of the following reactions:

a. 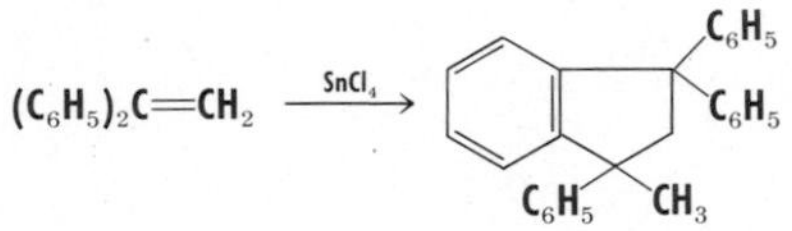 $(C_6H_5)_2C=CH_2$ $\xrightarrow{\text{SnCl}_4}$ [indane derivative bearing C_6H_5, C_6H_5, C_6H_5, CH_3 substituents]

b. [phenol, OH] $+ \text{Hg}(O_2CCH_3)_2 \longrightarrow$ [o-(HgOCCH₃ with C=O) phenol, OH]

c. [salicylic acid: OH, CO₂H] $\xrightarrow{\text{Br}_2}$ [2,4,6-tribromophenol: OH with Br, Br, Br]

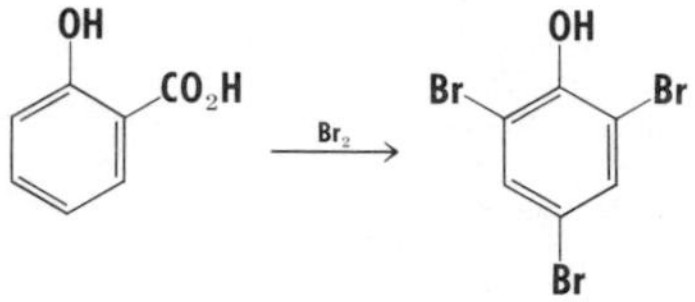

d. 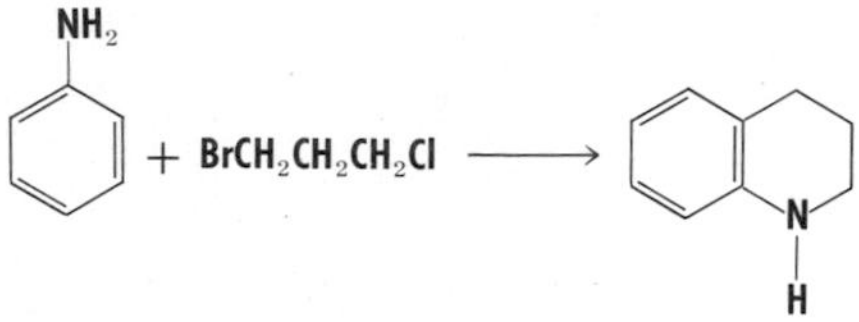 [aniline, NH₂] $+ \text{BrCH}_2\text{CH}_2\text{CH}_2\text{Cl} \longrightarrow$ [1,2,3,4-tetrahydroquinoline, N–H]

e. 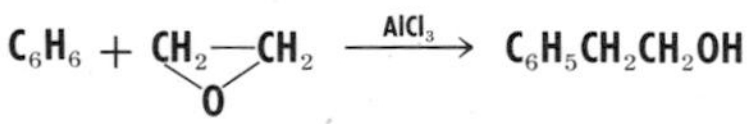 $C_6H_6 + \text{CH}_2\overset{\displaystyle O}{-}\text{CH}_2 \xrightarrow{\text{AlCl}_3} C_6H_5\text{CH}_2\text{CH}_2\text{OH}$

f. $C_6H_5\text{CHO} + 2C_6H_6 \xrightarrow{\text{H}_2\text{SO}_4} (C_6H_5)_3\text{CH}$

g. 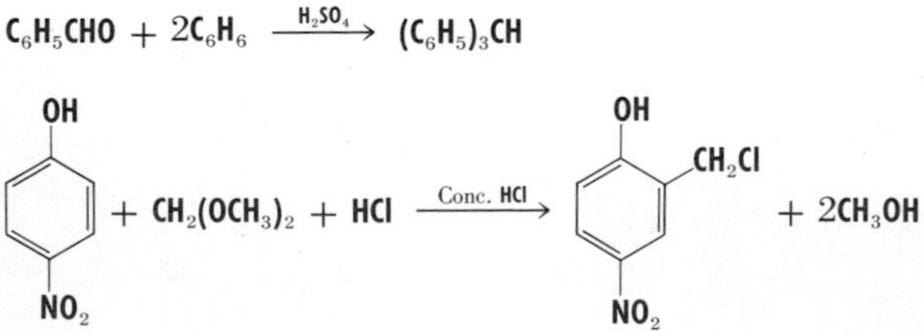 [phenol with OH, NO₂] $+ \text{CH}_2(\text{OCH}_3)_2 + \text{HCl} \xrightarrow{\text{Conc. HCl}}$ [phenol with OH, CH₂Cl, NO₂] $+ 2\text{CH}_3\text{OH}$

h. 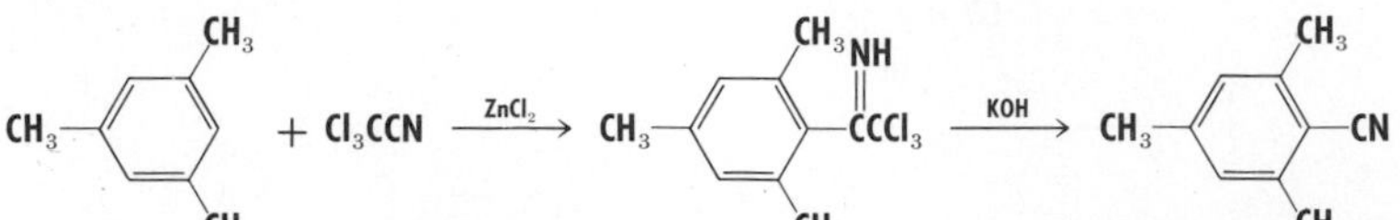 CH_3–[3,5-dimethylphenyl, CH₃, CH₃] $+ \text{Cl}_3\text{CCN} \xrightarrow{\text{ZnCl}_2}$ CH₃–[ring with CH₃, CH₃, and $\overset{NH}{C}\text{Cl}_3$ group] $\xrightarrow{\text{KOH}}$ CH₃–[ring with CH₃, CH₃, CN]

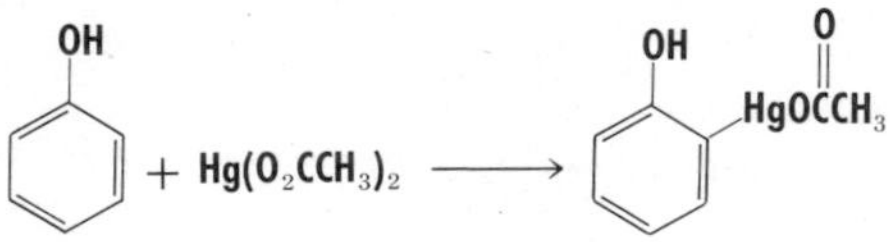

i. [structure: 2,5-dimethoxyaniline with OCH₃ groups and NH₂] + $CH_2=C\!-\!O$ / $CH_2\!-\!C\!=\!O$ (Ketene dimer) →[1) Mix / 2) Add H_2SO_4] [structure: quinoline with OCH₃, CH₃, OCH₃ substituents, N, OH]

Ketene
dimer

j. Cl–[benzene ring] + CCl_3CHO →[Conc. H_2SO_4] Cl–[benzene]–CH–[benzene]–Cl with CCl_3

α,α-[Di-p-chlorophenyl]
β,β,β-trichloroethane
(DDT)

4. Devise syntheses of the following compounds from readily available aromatic and aliphatic chemicals.

a. [benzene ring with NH₂, CH₃, NO₂]

f. [benzene ring with CO₂H, HO₂C, CO₂H, HO₂C, CO₂H, CO₂H] Mellitic acid

b. [phenanthrene-type tricyclic with two CH₃ groups]

g. [benzene ring with $C_2H_5\!-\!N\!-\!CH_3$ and $OC_3H_7\text{-}n$]

c. [naphthalene with COCH₃ and OH]

h. [quinoline with Br and CH₃, N]

d. [benzene ring with $CH_2CH_2C(OH)(CH_3)_2$ and NO_2]

i. [two benzene rings connected by CH_2 groups forming a ring, CH_2 groups]

e. [benzene ring with CH_2CH_2Br, HO_2C, Br]

j. [benzene ring with cyclopropyl group]

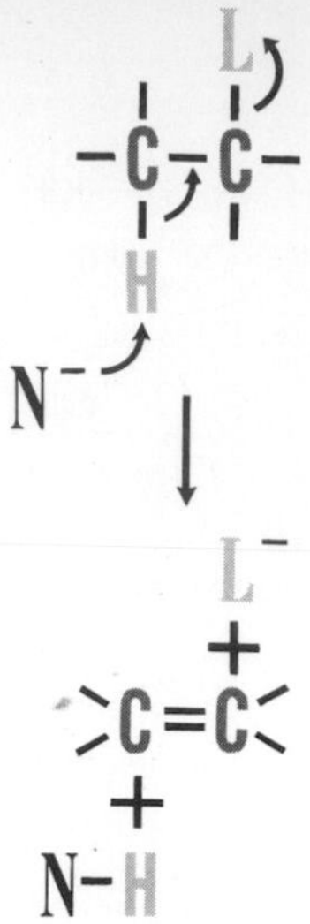

$$-\overset{|}{\underset{|}{C}}\overset{\overset{\displaystyle L}{|}}{\underset{|}{C}}-$$

$$\overset{|}{\underset{H}{}}$$

$$N \curvearrowright \qquad \downarrow$$

$$\overset{\displaystyle L^-}{\underset{+}{}}$$

$$\overset{}{\underset{}{>}}C=C\overset{}{\underset{}{<}}$$

$$\overset{+}{\underset{}{}}$$

$$N-H$$

17

Elimination Reactions

Elimination reactions are formally the reverse of the addition reactions discussed in Chaps. 13 and 15. Usually two atoms attached to adjacent centers are removed from the molecule with the formation of a double or triple bond. Less frequently, nonadjacent centers are involved, and a ring is formed. Generalized examples are shown in Fig. 17.1.

Two leaving groups are involved in elimination reactions. One is usually a neutral molecule or an anion, like the leaving groups in nucleophilic substitutions, and the other is often a proton. There is a close relationship between nucleophilic substitutions at saturated carbon and elimination reactions, and the two processes are often competitive.

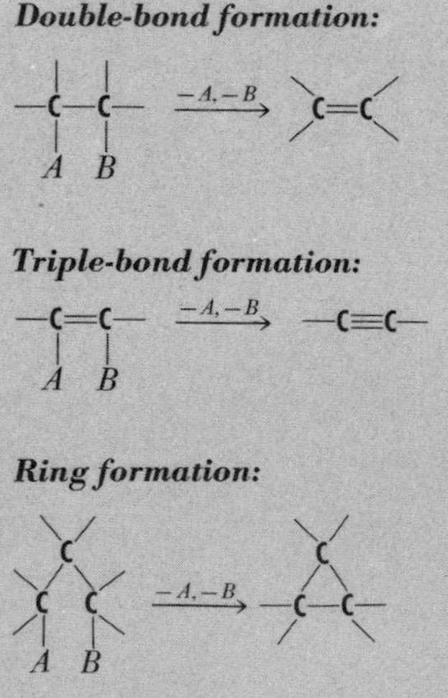

Double-bond formation:

$$-\overset{|}{\underset{\overset{|}{A}}{C}}-\overset{|}{\underset{\overset{|}{B}}{C}}-\quad\xrightarrow{-A,-B}\quad \overset{}{>}C=C\overset{}{<}$$

Triple-bond formation:

$$-\overset{}{\underset{\overset{|}{A}}{C}}=\overset{}{\underset{\overset{|}{B}}{C}}-\quad\xrightarrow{-A,-B}\quad -C\equiv C-$$

Ring formation:

$$\underset{\overset{|}{A}}{C}\quad\underset{\overset{|}{B}}{C}\quad\xrightarrow{-A,-B}\quad -\overset{}{\underset{}{C}}-\overset{}{\underset{}{C}}-$$

FIG. 17.1   *Elimination reactions.*

Each of the mechanistic variations in substitution reactions has its counterpart in an elimination mechanism.

Carbon-Carbon Double-bond Formation

The $E2$ Reaction. Strong bases cause bimolecular elimination ($E2$) reactions with substrates that have a reactive leaving group and β-hydrogens. The reaction is competitive with S_N2 reactions which involve similar reactants (Fig. 17.2).

In general, the elimination reaction is favored by high reaction temperatures, by increase of the basic strength of the nucleophile, and by increase of steric hindrance in the substrate. Attachment of electron-withdrawing substituents to C_β increases the acidity of the proton to be removed and accelerates elimination very strongly.

Nucleophiles used in elimination reactions include H_2O, R_3N, $CH_3CO_2^-$, HO^-, RO^-, H_2N^-, $CO_3^=$, and H^--donors. The leaving groups include all those involved in nucleophilic substitutions, such as Cl^-, Br^-, I^-, RSO_3^-, RCO_2^-, R_3N, R_3P, R_2S, HO^-, and others such as RO^- and enolate ions. Variation in the reactivity of leaving groups is qualitatively the same as in nucleophilic substitution; i.e., reactivity is increased with increasing polarizability and decreasing basicity of the group. The reactivity of nucleophiles in elimination reactions parallels the basicity of the nucleophiles in proton-transfer reactions. As a consequence, nucleophiles such as RS^-, which owe much of their reactivity to high polarizability, tend to bring about substitution rather than elimination. Very strong bases, such as H_2N^-, give elimination predominantly, even with primary substrates. Some of the trends are illustrated by the following examples.

$$C_2H_5\overset{-}{O}\overset{+}{Na} + CH_3CH_2Br \xrightarrow[-NaBr]{C_2H_5OH,\ 55°} CH_3CH_2OCH_2CH_3 + CH_2\!=\!CH_2 + C_2H_5OH$$
$$\phantom{C_2H_5ONa + CH_3CH_2Br \xrightarrow[-NaBr]{}}90\% 10\%$$

$$C_2H_5\overset{-}{O}\overset{+}{Na} + \underset{\underset{Br}{|}}{CH_3CHCH_3} \xrightarrow[-NaBr]{C_2H_5OH,\ 55°} (CH_3)_2CHOC_2H_5 + CH_2\!-\!CHCH_3 + C_2H_5OH$$
$$\phantom{C_2H_5ONa + CH_3CHCH_3 \xrightarrow[-NaBr]{}}21\% 79\%$$

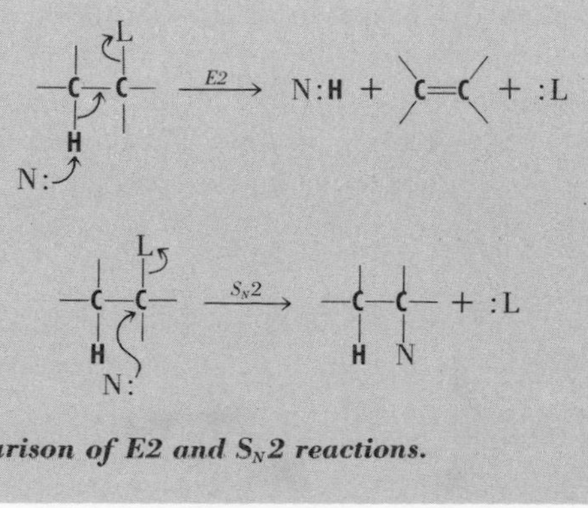

FIG. 17.2 *Comparison of $E2$ and S_N2 reactions.*

$$C_2H_5\overset{-}{O}\overset{+}{Na} + (CH_3)_3CBr \xrightarrow[-NaBr]{C_2H_5OH,\ 55°} CH_2=C(CH_3)_2 + C_2H_5OH$$
$$100\%$$

$$C_2H_5OH + \underset{\underset{Br}{|}}{CH_3CHCH_3} \xrightarrow{Neutral\ C_2H_5OH,\ 55°} (CH_3)_2CHOC_2H_5 + CH_2=CHCH_3 + HBr$$
$$\qquad\qquad 97\% \qquad\qquad 3\%$$

$$C_2H_5\overset{-}{O}\overset{+}{Na} + C_2H_5\overset{+}{S}(CH_3)_2 \xrightarrow[-(CH_3)_2S]{C_2H_5OH,\ 45°} C_2H_5OC_2H_5 + CH_2=CH_2 + C_2H_5OH$$
$$\qquad\qquad 88\% \qquad\quad 12\%$$

$$C_2H_5\overset{-}{O}\overset{+}{Na} + C_2H_5\overset{+}{S}(CH_3)_2 \xrightarrow[-(CH_3)_2S]{C_2H_5OH,\ 64°} C_2H_5OC_2H_5 + CH_2=CH_2 + C_2H_5OH$$
$$\qquad\qquad 85\% \qquad\quad 15\%$$

$$\text{(pyridine)} + \underset{\underset{Br}{|}}{CH_3CHCH_3} \xrightarrow{C_2H_5OH,\ 80°} \text{(pyridinium)} \quad Br^-$$
$$\underset{CH(CH_3)_2}{|}$$
$$\sim 100\%$$

Dehydrohalogenation and Related Reactions. Eliminations with halide and sulfonate ions as leaving groups are usually encountered as side reactions in nucleophilic substitution. Elimination reactions of alkyl halides seldom have preparative value, because the best synthetic precursors of the substrates are alcohols which can be dehydrated directly to olefins. Exceptions are found in systems that contain functional groups sensitive to acid (required in dehydration) and those which are not very reactive in dehydration.

$$CH_2=CH_2 + Cl_2 \longrightarrow ClCH_2CH_2Cl \xrightarrow[Reflux]{NaOH,\ C_2H_5OH} CH_2=CHCl$$
$$\qquad\qquad\qquad\qquad\qquad\qquad\qquad\qquad\qquad Vinyl\ chloride$$

$$CH_3CH_2CH_2CO_2H \xrightarrow[(p.\ 255)]{Br_2,\ PBr_3} \underset{\underset{Br}{|}}{CH_3CH_2CHCO_2H} \xrightarrow[Reflux]{Pyridine} CH_3CH=CHCO_2H$$
$$\qquad\qquad\qquad\qquad\qquad\qquad\qquad\qquad\qquad Crotonic\ acid$$

An important halide elimination is found in the preparation of ketenes from acid chlorides.

$$(C_6H_5)_2CHCOCl + (CH_3CH_2CH_2)_3N \xrightarrow{Ether} (C_6H_5)_2C=C=O + (CH_3CH_2CH_2)_3\overset{+}{N}H\overset{-}{Cl}$$
$$\text{Diphenylacetyl chloride} \qquad\qquad\qquad \text{Diphenylketene}$$

Direction of Elimination. Unsymmetrical secondary and tertiary substrates give mixtures of elimination products. The *Saytzeff rule* states that *neutral substrates give a predominance of the most highly substituted ethylene.* The rule is fairly reliable, but the predominance of the predicted product is usually not large, and exceptions are noted if the approach of a base to the predicted point of attack is sterically hindered.

$$C_2H_5\overset{-}{O}\overset{+}{Na} + \underset{\underset{Br}{|}}{CH_3CH_2CHCH_3} \xrightarrow{C_2H_5OH} CH_3CH=CHCH_3 + CH_3CH_2CH=CH_2 + \underset{\underset{CH_3}{|}}{CH_3CHOC_2H_5}$$
$$\qquad\qquad\qquad\qquad\qquad\qquad\qquad 4\ parts \qquad\qquad 1\ part$$

$$(CH_3)_3\overset{-}{C}\overset{+}{O}K + \underset{\underset{Br}{|}}{CH_3CH_2CH_2CHCH_3} \longrightarrow CH_3CH_2CH=CHCH_3 + CH_3CH_2CH_2CH=CH_2$$
$$\qquad\qquad\qquad\qquad\qquad\qquad\qquad\qquad 3\ parts \qquad\qquad 1\ part$$

Stereochemistry. Most *E*2 reactions appear to be stereospecific. When such an arrangement is permitted by the geometry of the molecule, the elements being removed prefer to arrange themselves as far apart as possible at the time of their departure.

One diastereoisomer   *cis*-α-Methylstilbene
of 1-bromo-1,2-diphenylpropane

Other diastereomer   *trans*-α-Methylstilbene
of 1-bromo-1,2-diphenylpropane

The process is known as *trans elimination*, with the term *trans* referring to the disposition of the leaving groups at the time of the reaction and *not to the configuration of the olefinic product*. This orientation rule, when applied to cyclohexane derivatives, means that both leaving groups must be able to enter axial positions for a facile elimination. The preference is shown by the diastereoisomeric 4-*tert*-butylcyclohexyl *p*-toluenesulfonates, in which the bulky *tert*-butyl group always assumes an equatorial position, locking the ring in a single conformation. The cis isomer, in which the tosylate group is axial, undergoes bimolecular elimination very easily. Under the same reaction conditions, the trans isomer undergoes no bimolecular reactions, even in the presence of strong base.

cis-4-*tert*-Butylcyclohexyl tosylate   *trans*-4-*tert*-Butylcyclohexyl tosylate
(undergoes *E*2 reaction with 0.02 *M* C₂H₅ONa   (undergoes only first-order elimination and
in C₂H₅OH at 75°)   solvolysis with 0.02 *M* C₂H₅ONa in C₂H₅OH at 75°)

Another fine example of stereospecificity in the *E*2 reaction is furnished by the stereoisomeric mixture of benzene hexachlorides formed by the photochemical addition of chlorine to benzene. The crude mixture is a potent insecticide, although the activity is due to the γ-isomer, which constitutes 10 to 12% of the mixture. The β-isomer, which has been shown by X-ray diffraction studies with the crystal to be the all-trans

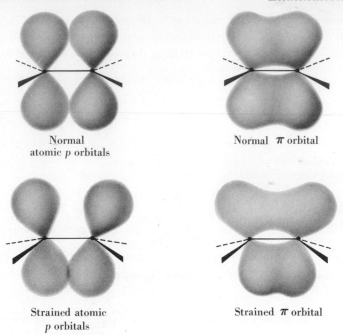

Normal
atomic *p* orbitals

Normal π orbital

Strained atomic
p orbitals

Strained π orbital

Atomic orbitals in a strained double bond at a bridgehead

$\Delta^{1,2}$(2.2.1)Bicycloheptene
(has never been prepared)

$\Delta^{1,9}$(4.3.1)Bicyclodecene
(known compound)

FIG. 17.3   *Steric strain in π bonding.*

compound, reacts with alcoholic sodium hydroxide at a rate which is
7,000 to 24,000 times as slow as those of its isomers.

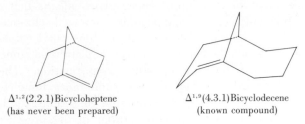

γ-Hexachlorocyclohexane
(active insecticide)

β-Hexachlorocyclohexane
(very slow cis elimination)

Bredt's Rule.   Elimination reactions designed to produce double
bonds to the bridgehead atoms in bicyclic systems are either entirely
unsuccessful or very slow.   The $\Delta^{1,2}$[2.2.1]bicycloheptene system has never

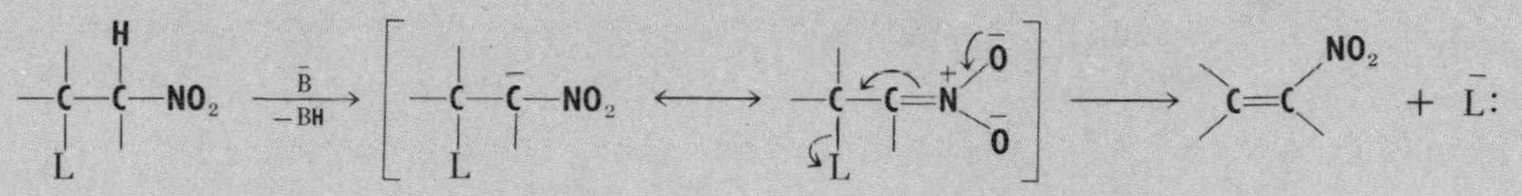

FIG. 17.4 *Stepwise β-elimination.*

been prepared. Presumably this failure is due to the fact that a rigid ring system requires acute bond angles at the bridgeheads. As a consequence, the planar configuration required for strong π bonding to an adjacent carbon atom cannot be achieved (Fig. 17.3). The smallest ring system that has been prepared with a bridgehead double bond is $\Delta^{1,9}(4.3.1)$ bicyclo-decene.

β-Elimination. Elimination reactions of β-substituted esters, acids, ketones, aldehydes, and nitro compounds are very rapid. The electron-withdrawing groups have strong acid-strengthening effects on the proton, which is removed by nucleophiles during the reaction. The reactions may be formulated as involving anionic intermediates (Fig. 17.4), although it is doubtful that such intermediates are *always* involved.

Even leaving groups, such as amino, hydroxyl, and enolate ions, which are not ordinarily lost in either nucleophilic eliminations or substitutions leave readily in β-elimination. These reactions will be recognized as the reverse of Michael additions to α,β-unsaturated systems (page 292).

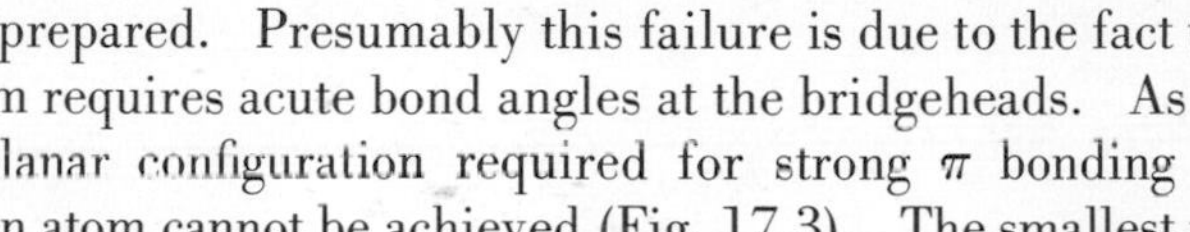

$$C_6H_5COCH_2CH_2-N\big\langle \quad\rangle \xrightarrow{\text{NaOH}} C_6H_5COCH=CH_2 \quad + \quad \big\langle N\big\rangle_{H}$$

β-Piperidinopropiophenone   Phenyl vinyl ketone   Piperidine

$$C_2H_5ONa + C_6H_5\underset{\underset{CH(CO_2C_2H_5)_2}{|}}{CHCH_2CO_2C_2H_5} \longrightarrow C_6H_5CH=CHCO_2C_2H_5 + NaCH(CO_2C_2H_5)_2$$

The second of the above reactions is known as a *retrograde Michael reaction.* Driving force is supplied by formation of the stable diethyl malonate ion.

The Hofmann Elimination. Pyrolysis of quaternary ammonium hydroxides leads to elimination reactions if β-hydrogen atoms are available.

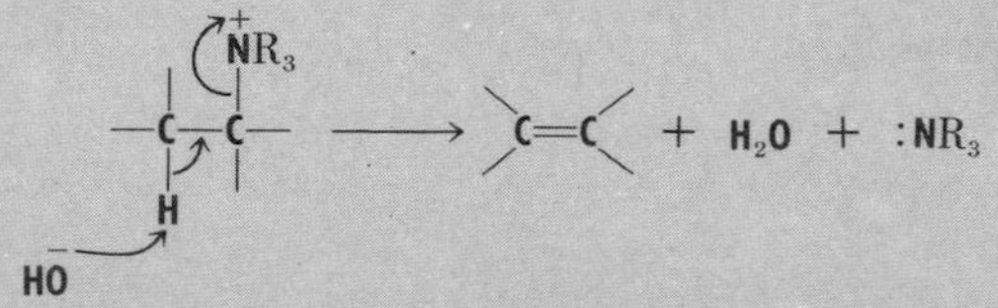

FIG. 17.5 *Hofmann elimination.*

The hydroxides are usually prepared by addition of silver oxide to a water solution of a quaternary ammonium halide. The mixture is then heated to distill off the water. Continued heating of the residue causes elimination to occur. The reaction has been much used in the stepwise degradation of naturally occurring amines in the course of structure determination. Amines to be degraded in this manner are quaternized by alkylation with methyl iodide.

Piperidine   N,N-Dimethyl-
                          piperidinium iodide

In unsymmetrical quaternary systems, competition occurs both among the four alkyl groups and within secondary and tertiary groups. The Hofmann rule states that quaternary ions will give a predominance of the least substituted ethylene in elimination reactions. The predominance is usually more pronounced than in eliminations from neutral substrates, although mixtures are ordinarily produced in competitive situations. The same rules apply to trialkyl sulfonium ions, another group of positively charged substrates.

$$(CH_3)_3C-\overset{\overset{\displaystyle CH_3}{|}}{\underset{\underset{\displaystyle CH_3}{|}}{N^+}}-CH_2CH_3 \quad \bar{O}H \xrightarrow{150°} CH_2{=}CH_2 + (CH_3)_2C{=}CH_2$$

                                                                       99%   1%

$$\underset{+\ N(CH_3)_3}{CH_3CH_2\underset{|}{C}HCH_3} \quad \bar{O}H \xrightarrow{150°} CH_3CH{=}CHCH_3 + CH_3CH_2CH{=}CH_2$$

                              cis-2-Butene 3%   1-Butene
                              trans-2-Butene 2%   95%

$$\underset{+\ S(CH_3)_2}{CH_3CH_2\underset{|}{C}HCH_3} \quad \bar{O}C_2H_5 \longrightarrow CH_3CH{=}CHCH_3 + CH_3CH_2CH{=}CH_2$$

                                       26%   74%

Reactivity in eliminations from onium ions is a function of the acidity of the hydrogen removed as a proton. Acidity is lowered by substitution of alkyl groups for hydrogen at the point of reaction. Other groups that have acid-strengthening inductive or resonance effects increase ease of elimination. As with neutral substrates, onium ions give trans elimination in the *E2* reaction.

$$C_6H_5CH_2CH_2-\overset{\overset{\displaystyle CH_3}{|}}{\underset{\underset{\displaystyle CH_3}{|}}{N^+}}CH_2CH_3 \quad \bar{O}H \xrightarrow{150°} C_6H_5CH{=}CH_2 + CH_2{=}CH_2$$

                              Styrene   0.4%
                               93%

Dehalogenation. Reactive metals remove halogens from *vic*-dihalides and also cause similar elimination reactions with related compounds, such as 1,2-haloesters and 1,2-haloethers.   Zinc is generally used in preparative work, although other metals effect the same reaction. Grignard and lithium reagents cannot be made from *vic*-dihalides because of this reaction.   As in *E*2 reactions, trans elimination occurs in dehalogenation.

Threo-2,3-dibromobutane   *cis*-2-Butene

Erythro-2,3-dibromobutane   *trans*-2-Butene

$$\text{Mg} + \text{BrCH}_2\text{CH}_2\text{Br} \xrightarrow{\text{Ether}} \text{MgBr}_2 + \text{CH}_2\!\!=\!\!\text{CH}_2$$

The Boord synthesis, which makes available pure alkenes, uses the 1,2-bromoether elimination.

$$\text{CH}_3\text{CH}_2\text{CH}_2\text{CHO} \xrightarrow{\text{C}_2\text{H}_5\text{OH, HCl}} \text{CH}_3\text{CH}_2\text{CH}_2\text{CHOC}_2\text{H}_5 \xrightarrow{\text{Pyridine}} \text{CH}_3\text{CH}_2\text{CH}\!\!=\!\!\text{CHOC}_2\text{H}_5 \xrightarrow{\text{Br}_2}$$
$$\overset{|}{\text{Cl}}$$

$$\underset{\text{Br Br}}{\text{CH}_3\text{CH}_2\text{CHCHOC}_2\text{H}_5} \xrightarrow{\text{CH}_3\text{MgI}} \underset{\text{Br CH}_3}{\text{CH}_3\text{CH}_2\text{CHCHOC}_2\text{H}_5} \xrightarrow{\text{KOH}} \underset{\text{CH}_3}{\text{CH}_3\text{CH}_2\text{CH}\!\!=\!\!\text{COC}_2\text{H}_5} \xrightarrow{\text{Br}_2}$$

$$\underset{\text{Br CH}_3}{\text{CH}_3\text{CH}_2\text{CHCOC}_2\text{H}_5} \xrightarrow{\text{CH}_3\text{MgI}} \underset{\text{Br CH}_3}{\text{CH}_3\text{CH}_2\text{CHCOC}_2\text{H}_5} \xrightarrow{\text{Zn, (CH}_3)_2\text{CHCH}_2\text{OH}} \text{CH}_3\text{CH}_2\text{CH}\!\!=\!\!\text{C(CH}_3)_2$$

Iodide ion causes the same sort of elimination from 1,2-dibromides. The reaction is stereospecific, but eliminations that appear to be cis may occur as a consequence of halide exchange reactions which give trans compounds.

trans-1,2-Dibromocyclohexane

cis-1,2-Dibromocyclohexane   *trans*-1-Bromo-2-iodocyclohexane

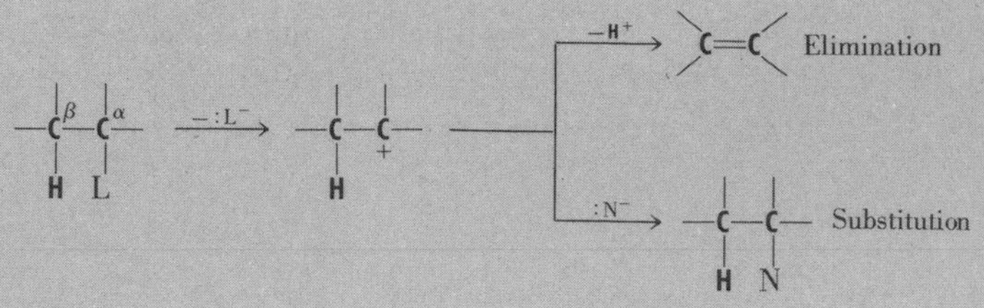

FIG. 17.6   *The relationship between E1 and S_N1 reactions.*

Decarboxylative Elimination. β-Haloacids may undergo elimination reactions in which the carboxyl group is lost.   The reaction usually occurs with di-α-substituted acids, in which the β-elimination reaction is impossible.

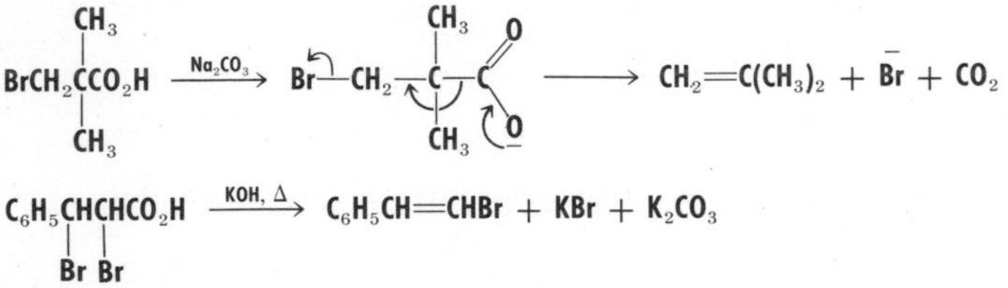

Cinnamic acid
dibromide

β-Bromostyrene

The E1 Reaction.   Carbonium ions formed in solvolysis reactions often undergo elimination reactions as well as nucleophilic substitution as is shown in Fig. 17.6.

Since ionization is the rate-determining step in both reactions, the general reactivity relationships are the same in E1 reactions as in S_N1 reactions (Chap. 11).   Competition between elimination and substitution is determined largely by the basicity of the solvent and the reactivity of nucleophiles present in solution.   For example, solvolysis in pyridine, a basic solvent, usually gives a good deal of elimination, and solvolysis in the presence of thiosulfate $(S_2O_3^=)$ ions usually leads to capture of the carbonium ion to form a substitution product.   Branching at the β-carbon atom increases the amount of elimination, as does raising the reaction temperature.

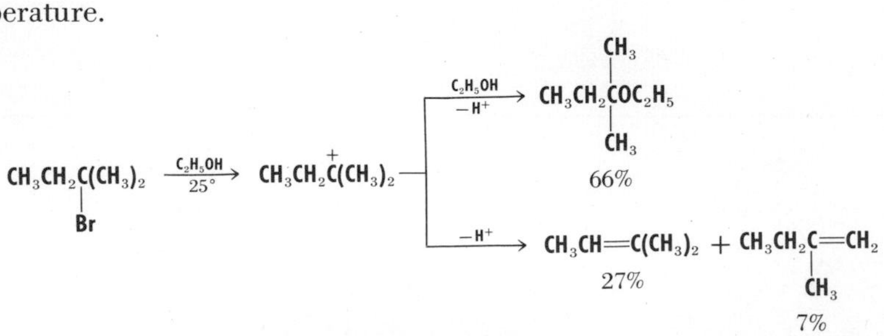

As demonstrated by the above example, $E1$ reactions tend to give the most highly substituted ethylene in predominance (Saytzeff rule). Since the leaving group is not involved in the product-determining steps, the product distribution in $E1$ reactions is the same for halides, sulfonates, ammonium ions, and sulfonium ions.

$$(CH_3)_3CBr \xrightarrow[65°]{80\% \ C_2H_5OH, \ 20\% \ H_2O} CH_2=C(CH_3)_2 + \underbrace{(CH_3)_3COH + (CH_3)_3COC_2H_5}$$

$$36\% \qquad\qquad 64\%$$

$$(CH_3)_3C\overset{+}{S}(CH_3)_2 \xrightarrow[65°]{80\% \ C_2H_5OH, \ 20\% \ H_2O} CH_2=C(CH_3)_2 + \underbrace{(CH_3)_3COH + (CH_3)_3COC_2H_5} \ | \ (CH_3)_2S$$

$$36\% \qquad\qquad 64\%$$

Steric hindrance in the vicinity of the β-hydrogen can shift the preferred course of elimination to favor the least substituted ethylene.

$$(CH_3)_3CCH_2C(CH_3)_2 \xrightarrow{CH_3OCH_2CH_2OCH_3 \cdot H_2O} (CH_3)_3CCH_2C=CH_2 + (CH_3)_3CCH=C(CH_3)_2$$
$$\overset{|}{Cl} \qquad\qquad\qquad\qquad\qquad\qquad\qquad \overset{|}{CH_3}$$

Isooctyl chloride $\qquad\qquad\qquad\qquad$ 4 parts $\qquad$ 1 part

$$\underbrace{\qquad\qquad\qquad\qquad}$$
65% combined yield

Dehydration. The $E1$ reaction with halides and sulfonates is little used for preparative purposes, because of the undesirable complexity of the product mixtures. However, a reaction very commonly used in synthesis of alkenes is the acid-catalyzed dehydration of alcohols. Reaction conditions vary widely, depending on the reactivity of the substrate. The role of acid catalysts is the same as in acid-catalyzed nucleophilic substitution reactions of alcohols and ethers. Primary alcohols probably react by bimolecular attack of anions or nucleophilic solvent molecules on conjugate acids of the alcohols. The over-all reactivity relationships in dehydration reactions are those expected from carbonium-ion reactions.

$$CH_3CH_2OH \xrightarrow[180°]{Conc. \ H_2SO_4} CH_2=CH_2$$

85%

$$CH_3\overset{\overset{\displaystyle OH}{|}}{C}CH_2CH_3 \xrightarrow[90-100\%]{I_2 \ (trace)} CH_3\overset{\overset{\displaystyle OI}{|}}{C}CH_2CH_3 \xrightarrow{-HOI} CH_3C=CHCH_3 + CH_2=CCH_2CH_3$$
$$\overset{|}{CH_3} \qquad\qquad\qquad \overset{|}{CH_3} \qquad\qquad\qquad \overset{|}{CH_3} \qquad\qquad \overset{|}{CH_3}$$

tert-Amyl alcohol $\qquad\qquad\qquad\qquad\qquad\qquad\qquad$ 85% $\qquad\qquad$ 15%
(*tert*-Pentyl alcohol)

$$(C_6H_5)_2CCH_3 \quad \xrightarrow[100°]{H_2SO_4} \quad (C_6H_5)_2C{=}CH_2$$
$$\underset{OH}{|}$$

Diphenylmethylcarbinol　　　　1,1-Diphenylethylene
　　　　　　　　　　　　　　　　80%

$$CH_3CHCH_2CH_2OH \quad \xrightarrow[\text{Vapor phase}]{\substack{\text{Tantalum-silica}\\ \text{catalyst}}} \quad CH_2{=}CHCH{=}CH_2$$
$$\underset{OH}{|}$$

　　　　　　　　　　　　　　　　1,3-Butadiene

A carbonium ion formed in the course of dehydration reactions will rearrange if a more stable ion can be formed by the migration of a group from an adjacent atom (Chap. 20).

$$\overset{OH}{\underset{|}{}}$$
$$(CH_3)_3CCHCH_3 \quad \xrightarrow{H_2SO_4} \quad (CH_3)_3C\overset{+}{C}HCH_3 \quad \xrightarrow{CH_3 \text{ migration}} \quad (CH_3)_2\overset{+}{C}CH(CH_3)_2 \quad \xrightarrow{-H^+} \quad (CH_3)_2C{=}C(CH_3)_2$$

tert-Butylmethylcarbinol

Elimination of Carbon. Fragmentation of carbonium ions and other cations is especially well known as a step in the cracking of petroleum products (Chap. 26), but there are also a number of well-known **C—C** bond cleavages of other aliphatic compounds. Driving force may be supplied by formation of carbon-oxygen double bonds and by relief of strain in a highly branched system.

$$C_6H_5\overset{CH_3}{\underset{O}{C}}{-}CHCO_2H \xrightarrow{HCl} C_6H_5\overset{CH_3}{\underset{O^+}{C}}{-}\overset{O}{\underset{H}{C}}{-}\overset{O}{O}{-}H \longrightarrow \overset{C_6H_5}{\underset{CH_3}{}}C{=}CHOH + CO_2 + H^+$$

$$\downarrow$$
$$C_6H_5CHCHO$$
$$\underset{CH_3}{|}$$
2-Phenylpropanal

$$(CH_3)_2CC(CH_3)_2C(CH_3)_2 \xrightarrow[-H_2O]{H_2SO_4} (CH_3)_2C{-}\overset{CH_3}{\underset{}{C}}{-}\overset{+}{C}(CH_3)_2 \longrightarrow (CH_3)_2C{=}O + (CH_3)_2C{=}C(CH_3)_2$$
$$\underset{OH}{|} \quad \underset{OH}{|} \qquad\qquad H{-}O \ CH_3$$

2,3,3,4-Tetramethyl-2,4-pentanediol

$$C_6H_5C(CH_3)_2CO_2H \xrightleftharpoons{H_2SO_4} C_6H_5C(CH_3)_2C{-}\overset{+}{O}H_2 \xrightarrow{-H_2O} C_6H_5C(CH_3)_2\overset{+}{C}{\equiv}O \xrightarrow{-CO}$$
$$\underset{O}{\|}$$

$$C_6H_5\overset{CH_3}{\underset{CH_3}{C^+}} \xrightarrow{-H^+} C_6H_5\overset{CH_3}{\underset{}{C}}{=}CH_2$$
　　　　　　　　　　　　α-Methylstyrene

These reactions bear a close relationship to the decarboxylation of β-ketoacids, discussed in Chap. 12.

$$CH_3\overset{CH_2}{\underset{O}{C}}\overset{}{\underset{O}{C}}{=}O \xrightarrow{-CO_2} CH_3C{=}CH_2 \longrightarrow CH_3CCH_3$$
$$\underset{H}{} \qquad\qquad \underset{OH}{|} \qquad\qquad \underset{O}{\|}$$

Acetoacetic acid

Internal Eliminations. A group of pyrolytic elimination reactions might be called *Ei* reactions by analogy with the term S_Ni, used to designate substitutions in which the nucleophile is part of the leaving group (page 237). The mechanistic analogy is not complete, however, as the substitution reactions are believed to involve ion pairs as intermediates, whereas internal eliminations are regarded as concerted cyclic processes. The best evidence for the cyclic mechanism is that the reactions show a *high preference for cis elimination*. One of the chief advantages of internal eliminations as preparative procedures for olefins is *freedom from molecular rearrangements*.

In the Chugaev reaction, xanthate esters are pyrolyzed at 140 to 200°. As in nearly all elimination reactions, unsymmetrical substrates give mixtures of products, although there is a tendency for the more highly substituted ethylenes to predominate.

Xanthate pyrolysis is typical of a large number of internal elimination reactions of esters, thioesters, carbamates, etc. The group can be represented by the following general formulation:

A = O, S, or N
B = O or S
Z = R, Ar, SR, OR, NHC$_6$H$_5$, or Cl

Pyrolysis of acetate esters, which requires temperatures of 400 to 500°, has been much used in olefin synthesis, because the starting materials are readily prepared. Although there have been reports of highly selective reactions which give the least substituted olefin, the more common experience is that the abstraction of various β-hydrogen atoms is nearly a random process. Since the reactions are carried out by passing the vapor of the ester through a hot tube packed with glass helices or beads, it is possible that subtle changes in the surface of the packing material will have a profound influence on the course of the reaction.

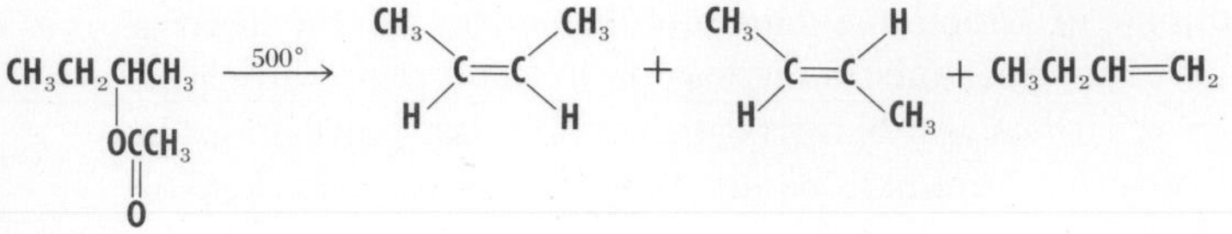

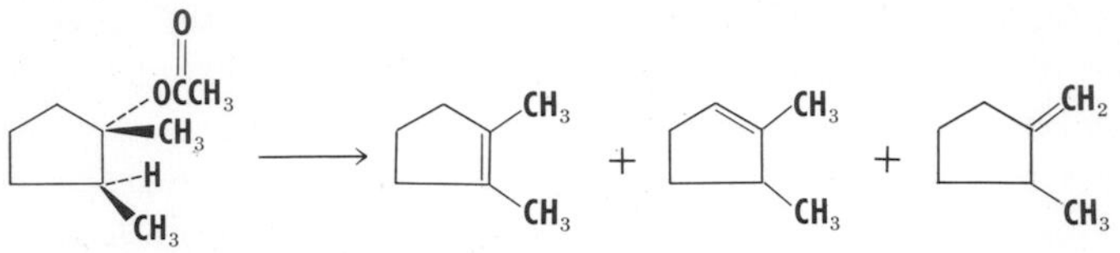

cis-1,2-Dimethylcyclopentyl
acetate

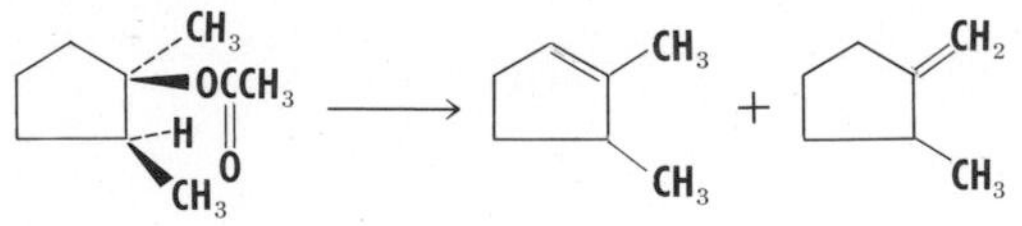

trans-1,2-Dimethylcyclopentyl acetate

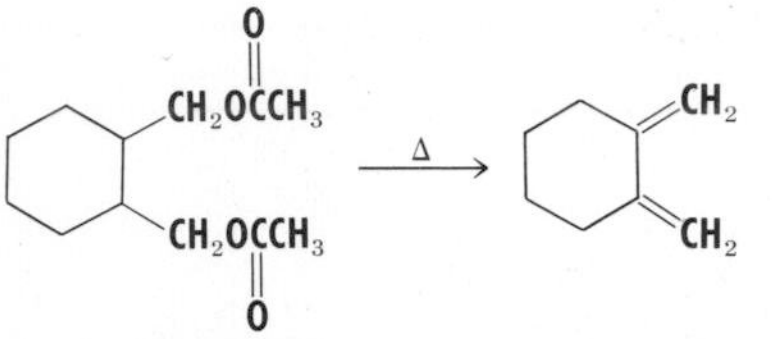

Carbon suboxide, a novel and highly reactive compound (bp 7°), is formed by pyrolysis of either diacetyl tartaric anhydride or α-acetoxy-maleic anhydride. The compound is also obtained by dehydration of malonic acid.

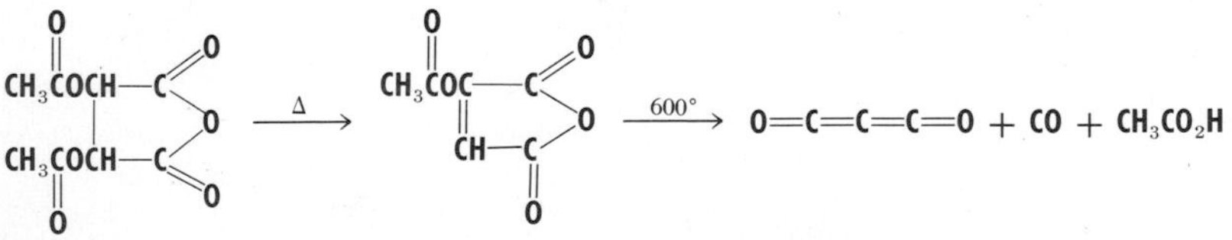

Diacetyltartaric
anhydride

α-Acetoxymaleic
anhydride

Carbon suboxide

$$CH_2(CO_2H)_2 \xrightarrow[\Delta]{P_2O_5} C_3O_2 + 2H_2O$$

Pyrolysis of amine oxides affords an elegant alkene synthesis. The reaction occurs at relatively low temperatures but, as usual, gives mixtures when the elimination can take two alternative paths, unless there is a pronounced stereochemical advantage for some particular route.

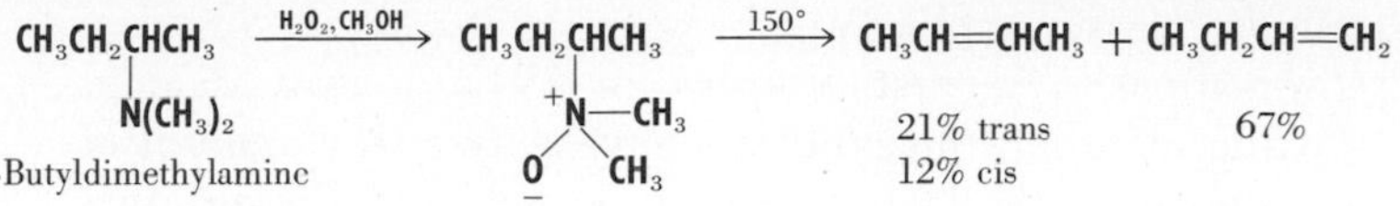

$$CH_3CH_2CHCH_3 \xrightarrow{H_2O_2, CH_3OH} CH_3CH_2CHCH_3 \xrightarrow{150°} CH_3CH=CHCH_3 + CH_3CH_2CH=CH_2$$

CH₃CH₂CHCH₃ with N(CH₃)₂ below — *sec*-Butyldimethylamine

middle structure with N⁺—CH₃ / O⁻ / CH₃

21% trans   67%
12% cis

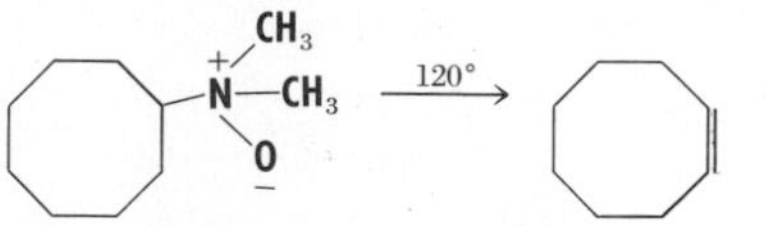

Cyclooctyldimethylamine oxide $\xrightarrow{120°}$ *cis*-Cyclooctene 81%

Compare with:

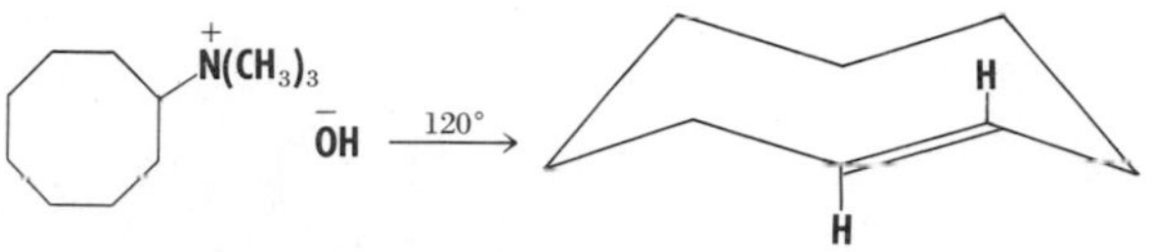

Cyclooctyltrimethylammonium hydroxide $\xrightarrow{120°}$ *trans*-Cyclooctene 60%   + 40% cis isomer

Olefin Synthesis

The general problem of olefin synthesis is instructive because of the variety of reactions available for introducing olefinic groups. Choices are often dictated by the problems involved in building up the carbon skeleton prior to the final elimination step. Carbinols are often subjected to dehydration with acid if highly branched olefins are desired, since the acidic conditions equilibrate the olefinic products. Branched alkenes usually predominate in mixtures of equilibrated products.

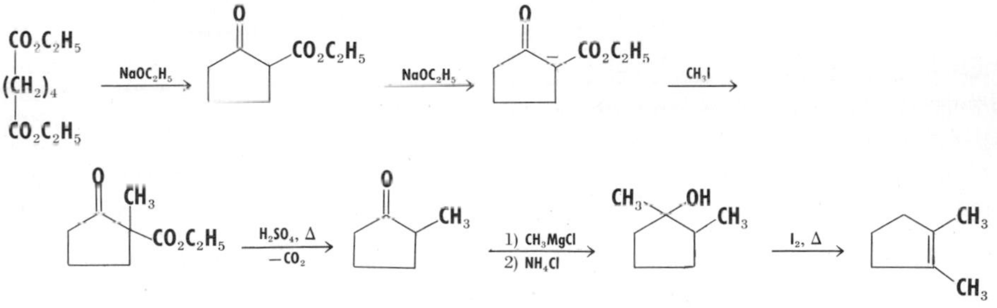

CO₂C₂H₅ / (CH₂)₄ / CO₂C₂H₅ $\xrightarrow{NaOC_2H_5}$ (cyclic structure with C=O and CO₂C₂H₅) $\xrightarrow{NaOC_2H_5}$ (structure with CO₂C₂H₅) $\xrightarrow{CH_3I}$

(structure with CH₃, CO₂C₂H₅) $\xrightarrow[-CO_2]{H_2SO_4, \Delta}$ (structure with CH₃) $\xrightarrow[2) NH_4Cl]{1) CH_3MgCl}$ (structure CH₃, OH, CH₃) $\xrightarrow{I_2, \Delta}$ (structure CH₃, CH₃)

cis- and *trans-* 1,2-Dimethylcyclopentanol   1,2-Dimethylcyclopentene

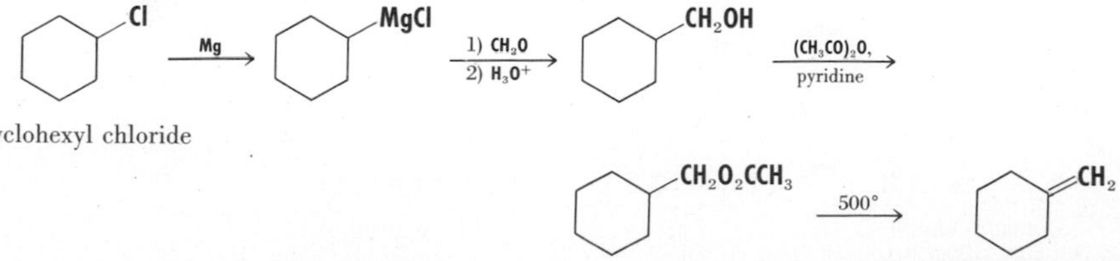

Cyclohexyl chloride (with Cl) $\xrightarrow{Mg}$ (with MgCl) $\xrightarrow[2) H_3O^+]{1) CH_2O}$ (with CH₂OH) $\xrightarrow[pyridine]{(CH_3CO)_2O,}$

(with CH₂O₂CCH₃) $\xrightarrow{500°}$ (with =CH₂)

Methylenecyclohexene

Willstaetter's classic synthesis of cyclooctatetraene involved a variety of eliminations. As first reported in 1913, a rare alkaloid serving as starting material, the synthesis gave only a tiny amount of product. The entire synthesis has been repeated, and the original observations were completely verified.

Pseudopelletierine   84%   86%

96%   83%   1,3,5-Cyclooctatriene
66%

47%   Cyclooctatetraene
6–8%

Carbon-Carbon Triple-bond Formation

Treatment of vinyl halides or *gem-* or *vic-*dihalides with strong bases effects eliminations, with formation of acetylenes. Nonterminal acetylenes are isomerized to terminal acetylenes with strong base; therefore direct synthesis by elimination is usually restricted to the latter type or to structures in which rearrangement is blocked by phenyl or vinyl groups.

$$CH_3CH_2CH_2CCl_2CH_3 + 2NaNH_2 \xrightarrow[\substack{-NaCl \\ -NH_3}]{Toluene} CH_3CH_2CH_2C{\equiv}\overset{-+}{C}Na \xrightarrow{H_3O^+} CH_3CH_2CH_2C{\equiv}CH$$

1-Pentyne

$$CH_3(CH_2)_4CBr{=}CHCH_3 \xrightarrow[\text{2) } H_3O^+]{\text{1) } NaNH_2} CH_3(CH_2)_5C{\equiv}CH$$

$$C_6H_5CHBrCH_2Br \xrightarrow[\text{2) } H^+]{\text{1) } NaNH_2} C_6H_5C{\equiv}CH$$

Styrene dibromide   Phenylacetylene
50%

$$C_6H_5CHBrCHBrCO_2H \xrightarrow{KOH} C_6H_5C{\equiv}CCO_2K \xrightarrow{H^+} C_6H_5C{\equiv}CCO_2H$$

Cinnamic acid   Phenylpropiolic
dibromide   acid
80%

The base-catalyzed rearrangement involves allenes as intermediates. Although rearrangement is not complete with bases such as sodium ethoxide, mixtures are obtained as reaction products.

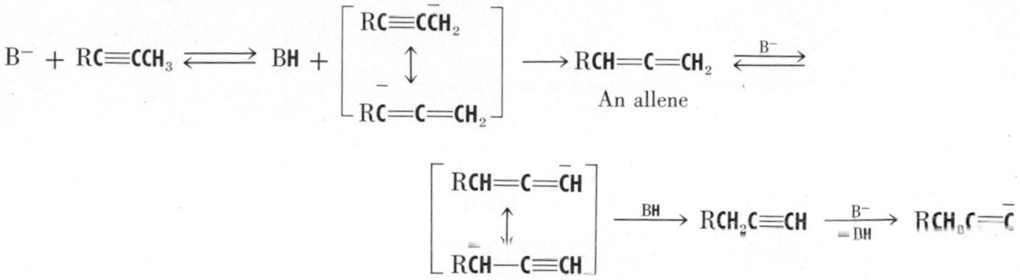

$$B^- + RC{\equiv}CCH_3 \rightleftharpoons BH + \left[\begin{array}{c} RC{\equiv}\overset{-}{C}CH_2 \\ \updownarrow \\ RC{=}C{=}CH_2 \end{array} \right] \longrightarrow RCH{=}C{=}CH_2 \xrightarrow{B^-}$$

An allene

$$\left[\begin{array}{c} RCH{=}C{=}\overset{-}{C}H \\ \updownarrow \\ \overset{-}{RCH}{-}C{\equiv}CH \end{array} \right] \xrightarrow{BH} RCH_2C{\equiv}CH \xrightarrow[-BH]{B^-} RCH_2C{\equiv}\overset{-}{C}$$

By combination of the synthesis of terminal acetylenes with use of acetylide ions as nucleophiles in substitution reactions (page 223), non-terminal acetylenes can be made. Starting materials for the synthesis are obtained by addition of halogens to double bonds (page 334) or by the reaction of phosphorus pentachloride with aldehydes or ketones (page 270).

The formation of acetylenes is an *E2* reaction and shows the same preference for trans eliminations as the corresponding olefin-producing eliminations.

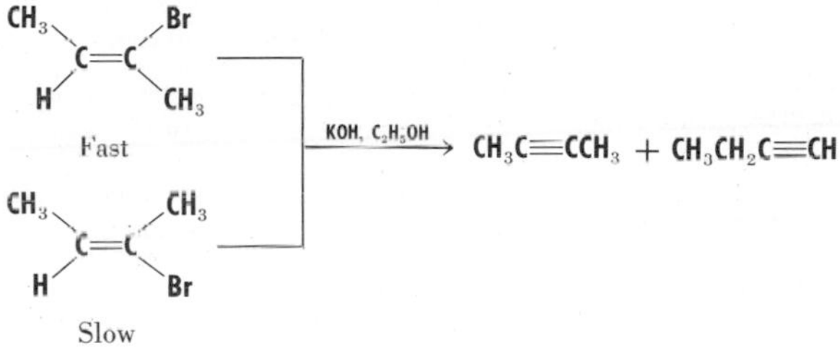

$$\xrightarrow{\text{KOH, } C_2H_5OH} CH_3C{\equiv}CCH_3 + CH_3CH_2C{\equiv}CH$$

Active metals dehalogenate 1,2-dihaloethenes with ease. The reaction has little preparative value, however, because of the inaccessibility of the dihalides. Decarboxylative eliminations to give acetylenes are also known. Both reactions are facilitated if trans elimination can occur

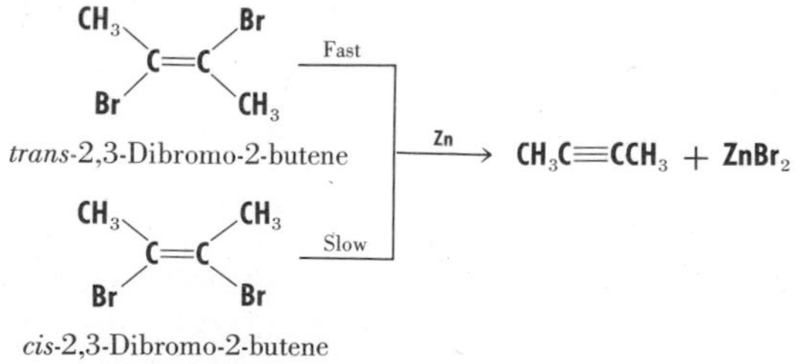

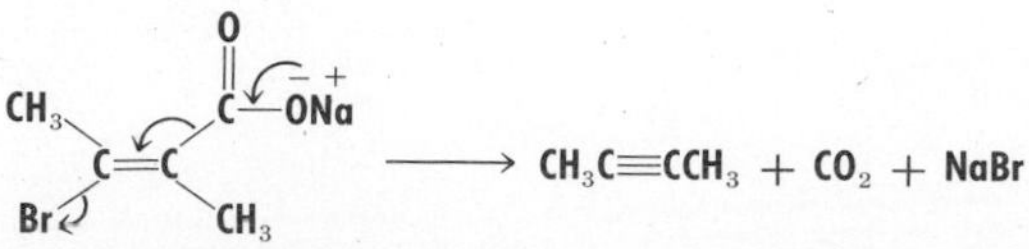

trans-2,3-Dibromo-2-butene

$$\xrightarrow{Zn} CH_3C{\equiv}CCH_3 + ZnBr_2$$

cis-2,3-Dibromo-2-butene

$$\longrightarrow CH_3C{\equiv}CCH_3 + CO_2 + NaBr$$

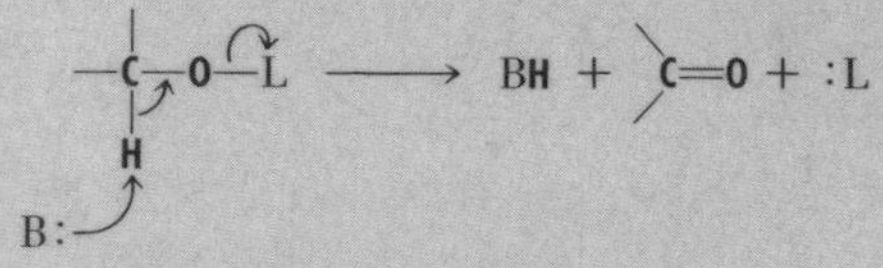

FIG. 17.7 Oxidative elimination reactions.

Carbon-Oxygen Bond Formation

The two principal groups of reactions which form **C=O** bonds by eliminations are discussed in detail elsewhere. Those which exchange a **C—H** bond for the second **C—O** bond are classified as oxidations. A general formulation is shown in Fig. 17.7, and the group will be discussed in full in Chap. 19.

Reactions which break **C—C** bonds with the formation of carbonyl groups are almost always electrophilic substitutions (Chap. 12) at the carbon atom which is eliminated. These reactions will be recognized as the reverse of nucleophilic additions to carbonyl groups. Other fast reactions which equilibrate carbonyl groups with noncarbon adducts were treated in connection with nucleophilic addition reactions (Chap. 13). Representative examples of the various types of reaction are given below.

Oxidative eliminations:

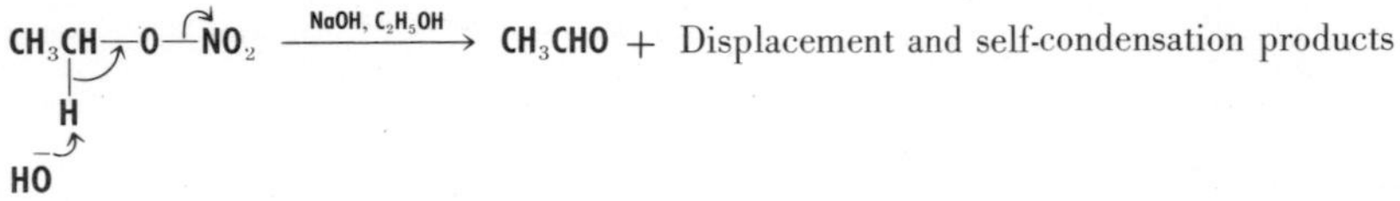

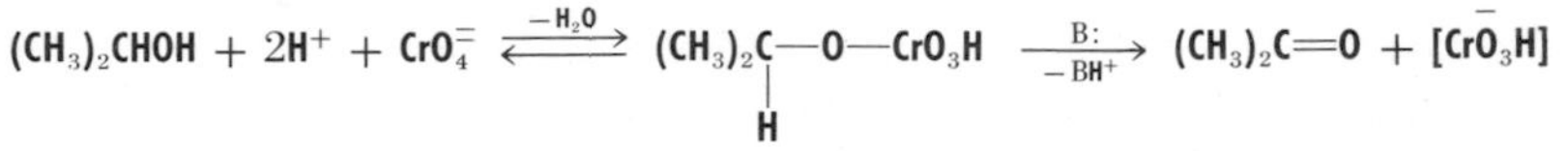

Chromic acid Isopropyl chromate

Retrograde aldol:

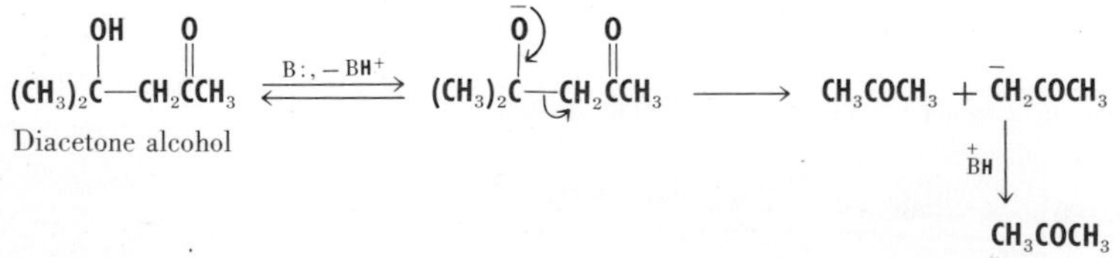

Diacetone alcohol

Rapid addition-elimination:

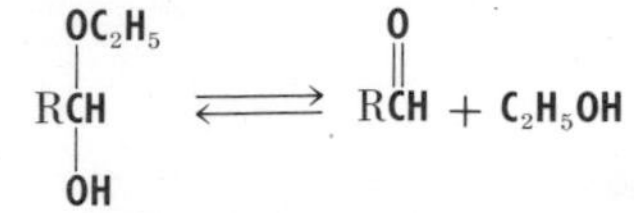

Hemiacetal

Carbon-Nitrogen Triple-bond Formation

Dehydration of aldoximes gives nitriles. This reaction, when coupled with the hydrolysis of the nitrile, provides a reaction sequence for oxidation of an aldehyde to an acid without recourse to use of strong oxidizing agents.

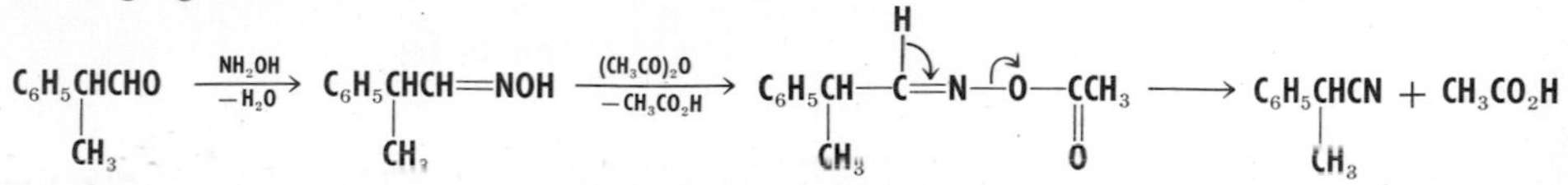

$$C_6H_5CHCHO \xrightarrow[-H_2O]{NH_2OH} C_6H_5CHCH=NOH \xrightarrow[-CH_3CO_2H]{(CH_3CO)_2O} C_6H_5CH-C\equiv N-O-CCH_3 \longrightarrow C_6H_5CHCN + CH_3CO_2H$$

2-Phenylpropanal   2-Phenylpropanaldoxime   2-Phenylpropanaldoxime acetate   2-Phenylpropionitrile

$$CH_3CH_2CH_2CH=NOH \xrightarrow{(CH_3CO)_2O} CH_3CH_2CH_2CN$$

Butyraldoxime   Butyronitrile

Amides are dehydrated in good yields with thionyl chloride, phosphorus oxychloride, or phosphorus pentoxide.

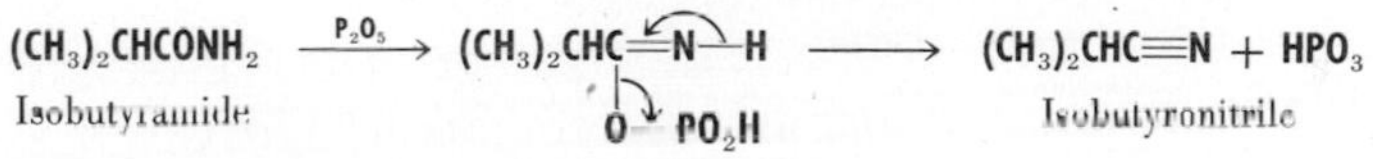

$$(CH_3)_2CHCONH_2 \xrightarrow{P_2O_5} (CH_3)_2CHC\equiv N-H \longrightarrow (CH_3)_2CHC\equiv N + HPO_3$$

Isobutyramide   Isobutyronitrile

N-Substituted amides of aromatic acids are also degraded to nitriles by phosphorus pentahalides (*von Braun reaction*). This reaction also involves nucleophilic substitution at the carbon atoms which are removed from nitrogen. Some use has been made of von Braun reactions for degradation of heterocyclic nitrogen compounds in the course of structure studies.

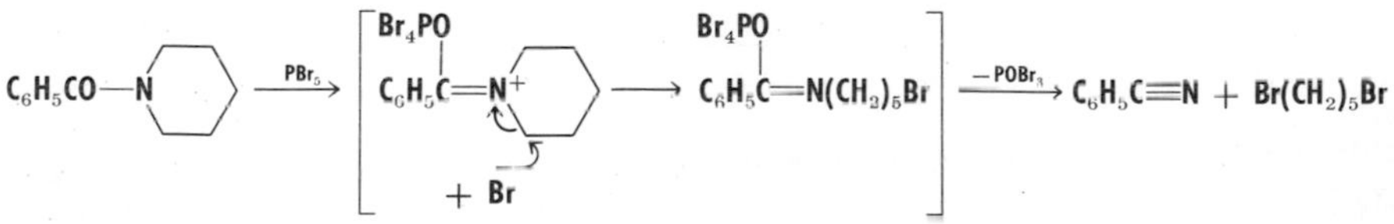

$$C_6H_5CO-N\langle\rangle \xrightarrow{PBr_5} \left[C_6H_5\overset{Br_4PO}{C}=N^+\langle\rangle \longrightarrow C_6H_5\overset{Br_4PO}{C}=N(CH_2)_5Br \right] \xrightarrow{-POBr_3} C_6H_5C\equiv N + Br(CH_2)_5Br$$

$$+ Br$$

Problems

1. Write out 10 base-catalyzed olefin-forming eliminations, each of which leads to a different olefin, and in which the same combination of base and leaving groups is never employed.

2. Indicate the major olefinic products of each of the following reactions, and state the reasons for your choices.

a. 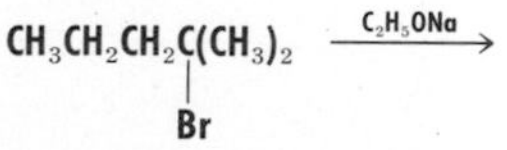 $CH_3CH_2CH_2\underset{\underset{Br}{|}}{C}(CH_3)_2 \xrightarrow{C_2H_5ONa}$

c. $CH_3CH_2\underset{\underset{OTs}{|}}{C}HCH_3 \xrightarrow{\text{Acetic acid, }\Delta}$

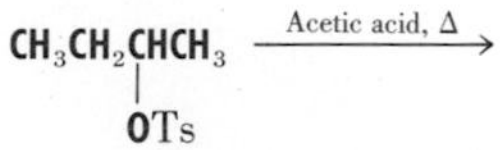

b. 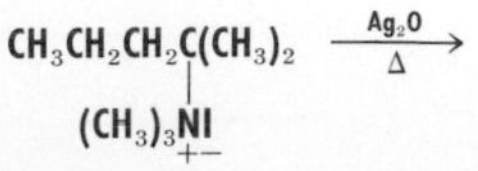 $CH_3CH_2CH_2\underset{\underset{(CH_3)_3\overset{+}{N}I^-}{|}}{C}(CH_3)_2 \xrightarrow{Ag_2O \atop \Delta}$

d. 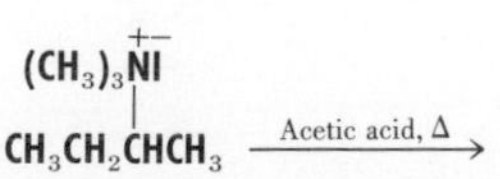 $CH_3CH_2\underset{\underset{(CH_3)_3\overset{+}{N}I^-}{|}}{C}HCH_3 \xrightarrow{\text{Acetic acid, }\Delta}$

$(CH_3)_3\overset{+}{N}-\overset{-}{O}$

e. 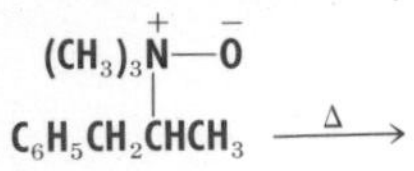 $C_6H_5CH_2\overset{|}{C}HCH_3$ $\xrightarrow{\Delta}$

f. 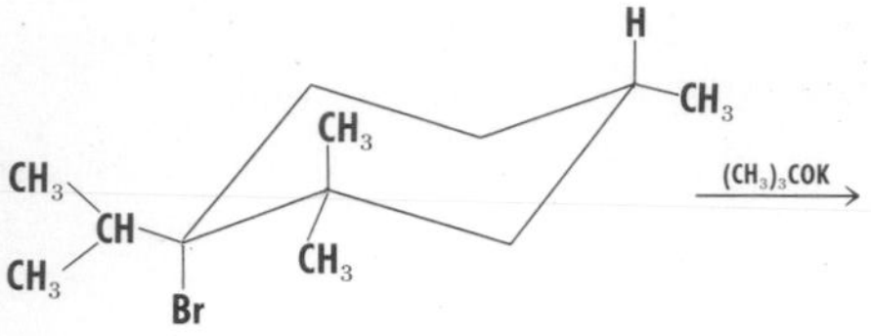 $\xrightarrow{(CH_3)_3COK}$

g. 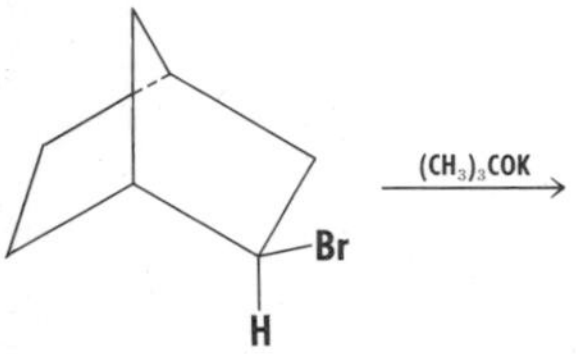 $\xrightarrow{(CH_3)_3COK}$

h. 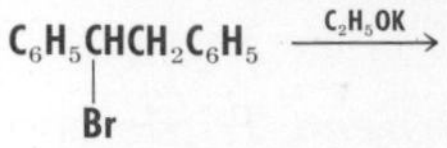 $C_6H_5CHCH_2C_6H_5 \xrightarrow{C_2H_5OK}$
    |
    Br

(*Hint:* Minimize the steric repulsions in the transition state.)

i. 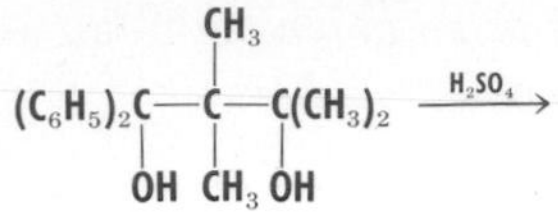 $(C_6H_5)_2C-\overset{CH_3}{\underset{CH_3}{\overset{|}{C}}}-C(CH_3)_2 \xrightarrow{H_2SO_4}$
    | |
    OH   CH$_3$ OH

3. Write out reactions for the following conversions:
a. Propionaldehyde and other organic materials to *pure* 2-butene
b. Propionaldehyde and other organic materials to 2-methyl-2-butene
c. Acetylene to crotonaldehyde ($CH_3CH=CHCHO$)
d. *n*-Butanol to 1-butyne
e. *n*-Pentanol to 2-pentyne
f. Acetophenone and other organic materials to benzalacetophenone
g. Benzophenone [$(C_6H_5)_2CO$] and other materials to 1,1-diphenyl-1-butene
h. 3-Phenylpropionic acid to cinnamic acid
i. Stilbene to α-bromostilbene
j. *o*-Methoxychlorobenzene to *m*-methoxyaniline
k. 3-Octene to 2-octanone
l. Methyl *n*-propyl ketone to *n*-butylmethylacetylene
m. Acetaldehyde to crotononitrile
n. Propionic acid to propionitrile

4. Deduce the structures of the following compounds, and write out the transformations involved.

a. A compound when treated with acid gave one mole of benzaldehyde and one mole of α-methylstilbene.

b. A compound when heated with base gave a mole of carbon dioxide and a mole of 1-methylcyclohexene.

c. A compound when treated with acid gave one mole of acetic acid and one mole of 3,5-dimethylanisole.

5. With three-dimensional formulas, work out the probable steric course of the following reaction for each of the two diastereomeric starting materials.

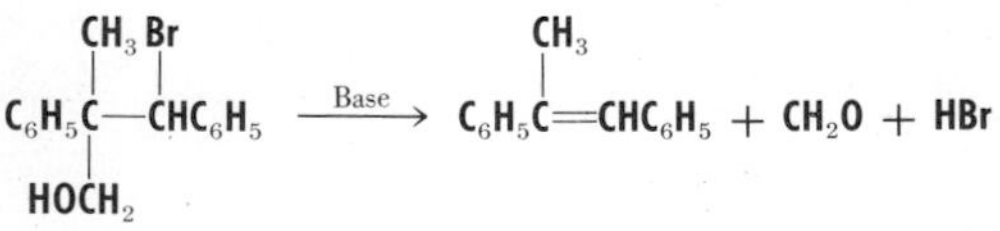

$$C_6H_5\overset{\overset{\displaystyle CH_3}{|}\,\overset{\displaystyle Br}{|}}{\underset{\underset{\displaystyle HOCH_2}{|}}{C}}-CHC_6H_5 \xrightarrow{\text{Base}} C_6H_5\overset{\overset{\displaystyle CH_3}{|}}{C}=CHC_6H_5 + CH_2O + HBr$$

6. Suggest mechanisms to explain the following transformations:

a.

b. $C_6H_5CHCH_2CH_2CHC_6H_5$ $\xrightarrow{Zn}$ $2C_6H_5CH{=}CH_2 + ZnBr_2$
    | |
    Br   Br

7. With three-dimensional structures, trace the following transformations:

$$Cl \cdot + H - R$$

$$\downarrow$$

$$Cl - H + R \cdot$$

$$\downarrow Cl_2$$

$$R - Cl + Cl \cdot$$

18

Homolytic Substitution Reactions

Thus far, no difficulty has been encountered in the classification of reactions, because the reagents involved had structural characteristics that immediately stamped them as either electrophilic or nucleophilic. However, the operational characteristics of homolytic reactions are more subtle. The reactions are usually recognized as occurring under conditions conducive to the dissociation of reagents or *initiators* into atoms or free radicals. In other cases, the key to recognition may be found in the nature of the reaction products. When such guides are lacking, it becomes necessary *to base classification upon studies of reaction mechanism.* Since opinions as to mechanism are subject to modification, occasionally a reaction is discovered to have been misclassified.

Stable Free Radicals

In the period between 1840 and 1865, many reports appeared in the literature on the preparation of "free radicals," such as methyl and ethyl. However, after Cannizzaro's suggestions in 1860 led to the development of methods for the assignment of molecular weights, chemists came to recognize that the so-called radicals isolated by earlier workers were invariably dimers, such as ethane (methyl "radical") and butane (ethyl "radical"). The 1896 pronouncement of Ostwald, "It took a long time before it was finally recognized that the very nature of organic radicals is inherently such as to preclude the possibility of isolating them," was accepted and considered final by most workers in the field. Curiously, this dogmatic statement and its acceptance barely preceded Gomberg's announcement in 1900 of the preparation of the free triphenylmethyl radical. Since that time, many compounds have been shown, by magnetic measurements,† to exist as free radicals either in solution or as pure crystalline solids. "Stable" carbon radicals always contain extensive unsaturated systems, so that the unpaired electron is free to spread throughout a large volume, as in triphenylmethyl. Furthermore, the dimers that would be formed by the *coupling* of the radicals are ordinarily subject to great steric strain.

$$(C_6H_5)_3C—C(C_6H_5)_3 \underset{}{\overset{Solvents}{\rightleftharpoons}} 2(C_6H_5)_3C\cdot \longleftrightarrow \text{[structure]} =C(C_6H_5)_2 \longleftrightarrow \text{etc.}$$

Hexaphenylethane   Triphenylmethyl

The classic example of a stable free radical, triphenylmethyl, barely meets the requirements for independent characterization. In solutions, the radical exists in appreciable concentrations in equilibrium with its dimer. However, it is rapidly destroyed by various reagents, including atmospheric oxygen, and concentration of its solutions leads to the separation of crystals of hexaphenylethane which are not paramagnetic.

Preparation. Gomberg's method, which consists of the treatment of a halide with a metal, remains one of the standard procedures for production of stable radicals. If sodium is employed to abstract the halogen, an exactly equivalent amount must be used, because an excess reduces the radical, producing trityl sodium.

$$(C_6H_5)_3CCl \xrightarrow[\text{Na; benzene}]{\text{Ag. Hg. Zn, or}} (C_6H_5)_3C\cdot + AgCl, HgCl_2, ZnCl_2, \text{ or NaCl}$$

Triphenylmethyl
chloride
(Trityl chloride)

$$(C_6H_5)_3C\cdot + Na\cdot \longrightarrow (C_6H_5)_3\overset{-}{C}\overset{+}{Na}$$

Triphenylmethyl sodium
(Trityl sodium)

Triphenylmethane dyes, which are really substituted triphenylcarbonium ion salts, are reduced to free radicals by inorganic reductants such as titanous and vanadous salts.

$$(C_6H_5)_3COH \underset{}{\overset{Conc. H_2SO_4}{\rightleftharpoons}} (C_6H_5)_3\overset{+}{C} \xrightarrow{VCl_2} (C_6H_5)_3C—C(C_6H_5)_3$$

A third method of synthesis is used if the related halide cannot be prepared. An ether is cleaved by potassium metal, and the resulting organometallic compound is oxidized by reaction with a *vicinal* dibromide.

$$cyclo\text{-}C_6H_{11}\overset{\overset{C_6H_5}{|}}{\underset{\underset{C_6H_5}{|}}{C}}OCH_3 \xrightarrow{K, \text{ ether}} cyclo\text{-}C_6H_{11}\overset{\overset{C_6H_5}{|}}{\underset{\underset{C_6H_5}{|}}{\overset{-}{C}}}\overset{+}{K} \xrightarrow{(CH_3)_2CBrCBr(CH_3)_2} cyclo\text{-}C_6H_{11}\overset{\overset{C_6H_5}{|}}{\underset{\underset{C_6H_5}{|}}{C}}\cdot \rightleftharpoons \text{dimer}$$

Diphenylcyclo-
hexylmethyl radical

---

† Free radicals have magnetic moments because of the spins of the unpaired electrons. As a consequence, a solution or solid that contains a free radical is drawn into the magnetic field when placed between the poles of a powerful magnet. Such material is said to be paramagnetic.

Oxidation of certain highly substituted phenols, aryl amines, and hydrazines produces free radicals that are usually classified as oxygen or nitrogen radicals by reference to the structures of parent compounds. However, the odd electrons in the radicals are spread over extensive conjugated systems.

2,4,6-Tri-*tert*-butyl phenol   2,4,6-Tri-*tert*-butylphenoxy radical

α,α-Diphenyl-β-picrylhydrazine

α,α-Diphenyl-β-picrylhydrazyl radical

Tetraphenylpyrrole   Tetraphenylpyrrolyl radical

Generation of Transient Radicals

Short-lived free radicals are produced by three principal methods:

1. *Thermal decomposition of compounds containing weak bonds* often gives free radicals. Simple free radicals, such as methyl and ethyl, were first detected in the vapor-phase decomposition of lead and mercury alkyls.

$$(CH_3)_4Pb \xrightarrow{600°} Pb + 4CH_3· \longrightarrow 2C_2H_6$$

Peroxides, which contain weak $O—O$ bonds, and aliphatic azo compounds serve as convenient sources of free radicals at relatively low temperatures.

$(CH_3)_3COOC(CH_3)_3 \xrightarrow{\ 100\text{--}130° \ } 2(CH_3)_3CO\cdot$

    Di-*tert*-butyl   *tert*-Butoxy radical
    peroxide

$(C_6H_5CO_2)_2 \xrightarrow{\ 60\text{--}100° \ } 2C_6H_5CO_2\cdot$

    Dibenzoyl   Benzoyloxy radical
    peroxide

$\underset{\text{$\alpha,\alpha'$-Azo-bis-}}{\overset{\displaystyle \ \ \ \ \overset{CN}{|} \ \ \ \ \ \overset{CN}{|}}{(CH_3)_2CN=NC(CH_3)_2}} \xrightarrow{\ 60\text{--}100° \ } 2(CH_3)_2\overset{\cdot}{C}CN + N_2$

    α,α'-Azo-bis-   2-Cyanoiso-
    isobutyronitrile   propyl radical

2. Photochemical reactions of two types form radicals. Absorption of visible or ultraviolet light gives molecules with sufficient energy to break chemical bonds, and dissociation to give radicals may occur. The wavelength of the light must correspond to an absorption band of the substance to be decomposed.

$Cl_2 \xrightarrow{\ \text{Sunlight} \ } 2Cl\cdot$

          Chlorine atoms

$CH_3COCH_3 \xrightarrow[\text{Vapor phase}]{\ \lambda \sim 3,000\ \text{Å} \ } CH_3\overset{\cdot}{C}O + CH_3\cdot$

                    Acetyl   Methyl
                    radical   radical

In solution, acetone and other ketones do not break down to give radicals, but may produce radicals by the reaction of photochemically excited molecules with solvents.

$C_6H_5COCH_3 \xrightarrow{\ \lambda = 3,000\text{--}3,500\ \text{Å} \ } C_6H_5COCH_3{}^* \xrightarrow{\ RH\ \text{(solvent)} \ } R\cdot + C_6H_5\overset{\overset{\textstyle OH}{|}}{\underset{\cdot}{C}}CH_3$

                             Excited state α-Hydroxy-α-phenyl-
                         of acetophenone   ethyl radical

3. Oxidation-reduction reactions with inorganic ions that can change their valence state by the gain or loss of a single electron can be used for generation of radicals.

$H_2O_2 + Fe^{++} \longrightarrow HO\cdot + Fe(OH)^{++}$

      Ferrous   Hydroxyl   Ferric
      ion   radical   ion

$(CH_3)_3COOH + Co^{3+} \longrightarrow (CH_3)_3COO\cdot + Co^{++} + H^+$

    tert-Butyl   Cobaltic   *tert*-Butylperoxy   Cobaltous   H+
    hydroperoxide   ion   radical   ion

Radicals made by the above procedures undergo rapid reactions in solution. Within their short lifetime, they may initiate important reactions of other constituents of the solution. Sometimes a radical produced in the primary process undergoes a fragmentation reaction to produce a smaller radical and a stable molecule.

$$(CH_3)_3CO\cdot \longrightarrow CH_3COCH_3 + CH_3\cdot$$

$$C_6H_5CO_2\cdot \longrightarrow C_6H_5\cdot + CO_2$$

Carbon-Halogen Bond Formation

The action of light on halogens produces halogen atoms. The latter easily abstract hydrogen atoms from saturated carbon atoms to initiate *chain reactions* that lead to the *photochemical halogenation* of hydrocarbons. The steps of the chain reaction are illustrated with methane as an example (cf. alkene addition by homolytic chain reactions, Chap. 26).

Initiation $\qquad Cl_2 \xrightarrow{\text{Sunlight}} 2Cl\cdot$

Propagation $\begin{cases} Cl\cdot + CH_4 \longrightarrow HCl + CH_3\cdot \\ CH_3\cdot + Cl_2 \longrightarrow CH_3Cl + Cl\cdot \end{cases}$

Termination $\begin{cases} 2Cl\cdot \longrightarrow Cl_2 \\ 2CH_3\cdot \longrightarrow C_2H_6 \\ Cl\cdot + CH_3\cdot \longrightarrow CH_3Cl \end{cases}$

Photochlorination is used industrially for production of mixtures of alkyl halides from petroleum hydrocarbons and for chlorination of aromatic side chains. Attack of chlorine atoms on an alkane shows little discrimination, although *tertiary* C—H bonds are slightly more susceptible to attack than secondary and primary positions. Aromatic side chains, on the other hand, are specifically activated in the positions adjacent to the ring.

$$CH_4 \xrightarrow[-HCl]{Cl_2, \text{ light}} \underset{\substack{\text{Methyl}\\\text{chloride}}}{CH_3Cl} \xrightarrow[-HCl]{Cl_2} \underset{\substack{\text{Methylene}\\\text{chloride}}}{CH_2Cl_2} \xrightarrow[-HCl]{Cl_2} \underset{\text{Chloroform}}{HCCl_3} \xrightarrow[-HCl]{Cl_2} \underset{\substack{\text{Carbon}\\\text{tetrachloride}}}{CCl_4}$$

$$\underset{\substack{|\\CH_3\\\text{Isopentane}}}{CH_3CHCH_2CH_3} \xrightarrow{Cl_2, \text{ light}} \left[\begin{array}{l} \underset{\substack{|\\CH_3}}{ClCH_2CHCH_2CH_3} + (CH_3)_2CClCH_2CH_3 \\[2mm] + (CH_3)_2CHCHClCH_3 + (CH_3)_2CHCH_2CH_2Cl \end{array} \right]$$

$$C_6H_5CH_3 \xrightarrow[-HCl]{Cl_2, \text{ light}} \underset{\substack{\text{Benzyl}\\\text{chloride}}}{C_6H_5CH_2Cl} \xrightarrow[-HCl]{Cl_2} \underset{\substack{\text{Benzal}\\\text{chloride}}}{C_6H_5CHCl_2} \xrightarrow[-HCl]{Cl_2} \underset{\text{Benzotrichloride}}{C_6H_5CCl_3}$$

$$\underset{\text{Ethylbenzene}}{C_6H_5CH_2CH_3} + Cl_2 \xrightarrow{\text{Light}} \underset{\substack{|\\Cl\\\alpha\text{-Phenylethyl chloride}}}{C_6H_5CHCH_3} + HCl$$

Benzene, which has no hydrogen attached to saturated carbon atoms, exclusively undergoes *addition* of chlorine in photochemical experiments. The resulting mixture of stereoisomers is used as an insecticide, known as Gammexane (page 398). The activity is due to the γ-isomer, which constitutes 10 to 12% of the mixture.

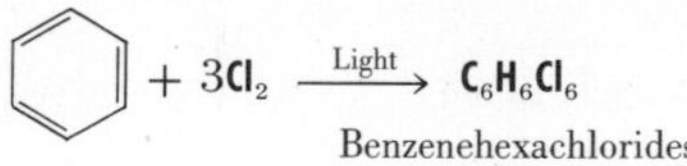

Benzenehexachlorides

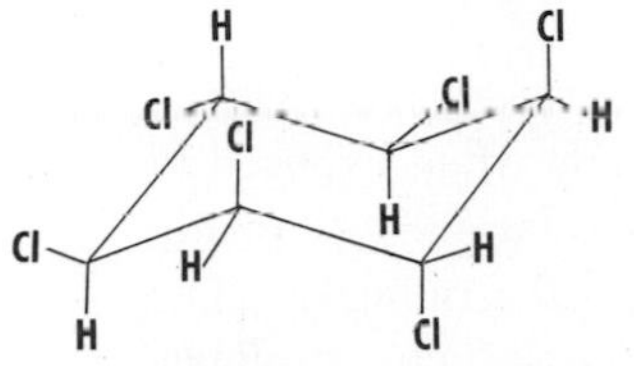

γ-Benzenehexachloride

Photochemical bromination occurs in a manner analogous to chlorination, but the reactions are slow because the reaction chains are rather short. Bromination with *N*-bromosuccinimide has found extensive use in the laboratory for introduction of halogen in positions adjacent to olefinic, aromatic, and carbonyl groups. The reaction has characteristics of a radical-chain process, since it is initiated by light absorbed by the reagent or by the decomposition of labile azo compounds and peroxides. The reaction is also *inhibited* by addition of small amounts of materials, such as benzoquinone, that react readily with free radicals.

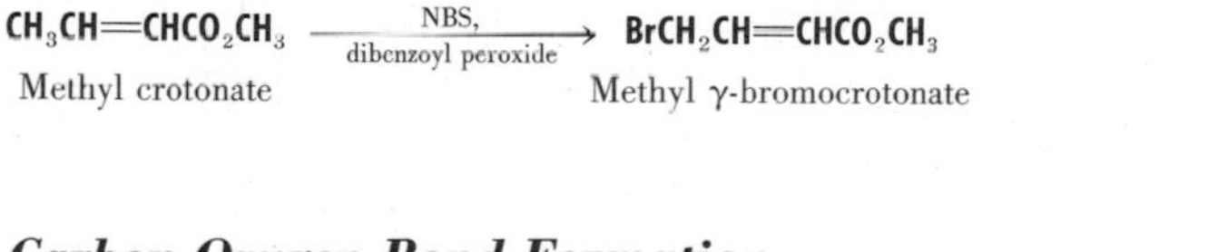

N-Bromosuccinimide
(NBS)

3-Cyclohexenyl
bromide
70%

$$CH_3CH{=}CHCO_2CH_3 \xrightarrow[\text{dibenzoyl peroxide}]{\text{NBS,}} BrCH_2CH{=}CHCO_2CH_3$$

Methyl crotonate   Methyl γ-bromocrotonate

Carbon-Oxygen Bond Formation

In the presence of free-radical initiators, oxygen attacks saturated hydrocarbon structures, especially at allylic positions. The reactions are chain processes, and the first products are hydroperoxides.

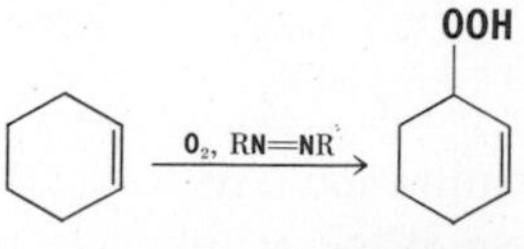

3-Cyclohexenyl
hydroperoxide

Tetralin   α-Tetralyl
                                  hydroperoxide

The chain-carrying steps of the reaction are as follows:

$RO_2\cdot + RH \longrightarrow RO_2H + R\cdot$

$R\cdot + O_2 \longrightarrow RO_2\cdot$

The slow deterioration of most organic materials when exposed to air and sunlight is due largely to photosensitized oxidation. Aromatic amines and phenols *inhibit* oxidation by destroying $RO_2\cdot$ radicals. The inclusion of such *antioxidants* in rubber, gasoline, plastics, etc., prolongs the useful lifetime of such materials.

Activation of allylic and benzylic hydrogen atoms toward abstraction is associated with the fact that removal of hydrogen from such a position leaves a resonance-stabilized allylic radical.

Cyclohexenyl radical

Hydroperoxides decompose to give radicals capable of initiating oxidation when heated to $100°$ or higher. As a consequence, high-temperature oxidation is autocatalytic and leads to extensive degradation or complete combustion.

Carbon-Nitrogen Bond Formation

Very few homolytic substitutions produce **C—N** bonds. A possible example is the vapor-phase nitration of alkanes. The reaction with higher alkanes is accompanied by extensive degradation, and nitromethane can be isolated as a product of the nitration of any member of the series.

$CH_3CH_3 \xrightarrow[450°]{HNO_3} CH_3CH_2NO_2 + CH_3NO_2$

   Nitroethane   Nitromethane
   80–90%   10–20%

$(CH_3)_3CH \xrightarrow[450°]{HNO_3} (CH_3)_2CHCH_2NO_2 + (CH_3)_3CNO_2 + CH_3CHNO_2CH_3 + CH_3NO_2$

primary-Nitroisobutane   *tert*-Nitroisobutane   2-Nitropropane   3%
        65%   7%   20%

The lower nitroalkanes produced by vapor-phase nitration are a very useful group of synthetic starting materials. Because of the acidity of their α-hydrogen atoms, the compounds undergo many base-catalyzed addition and condensation reactions. Unfortunately, attempts to alkylate nitroalkide anions usually give only unstable nitronate esters (**O**-alkylation).

$$CH_3COCH_3 + CH_3CH_2NO_2 \xrightarrow{\text{NaOH}} CH_3\overset{\overset{\displaystyle OH}{|}}{\underset{\underset{\displaystyle CH_3}{|}}{C}}\!-\!\overset{\overset{\displaystyle CH_3}{|}}{C}HNO_2$$

$$CH_3CH\!\!=\!\!CHCO_2C_2H_5 + CH_3NO_2 \xrightarrow{\text{NaOH}} CH_3\overset{|}{\underset{\underset{\displaystyle CH_2NO_2}{|}}{C}}HCH_2CO_2C_2H_5$$

$$C_6H_5CHO + CH_3NO_2 \xrightarrow{\text{NaOH}} C_6H_5CH\!\!=\!\!CHNO_2$$
$$\text{β-Nitrostyrene}$$

Nitroalkanes are easily reduced to amines (Chap. 19). The procedure makes many aliphatic amines readily available.

$$CH_2O + CH_3NO_2 \xrightarrow{\text{NaOH}} HOCH_2CH_2NO_2 \xrightarrow{\text{H}_2,\ \text{Pt}} HOCH_2CH_2NH_2$$
$$\text{2-Nitroethanol} \qquad\qquad \text{Ethanolamine}$$

Salts of primary and secondary nitro compounds are hydrolyzed to carbonyl compounds when treated with concentrated sulfuric acid (*Nef reaction*). This interesting reaction is of limited synthetic value, because the reaction conditions cause extensive side reactions with polyfunctional molecules. Hydrolysis of 1-nitropropane is the basis of an industrial process for production of hydroxylamine.

$$(CH_3)_2CHNO_2 \xrightarrow{\text{NaOH}} \left[(CH_3)_2\bar{C}\!-\!NO_2 \longleftrightarrow (CH_3)_2C\!\!=\!\!\overset{+}{N}\overset{\displaystyle O}{\underset{\displaystyle \underline{O}}{}} \right] \xrightarrow{\text{Conc. H}_2\text{SO}_4} (CH_3)_2C\!\!=\!\!\overset{+}{N}\overset{\displaystyle OH}{\underset{\displaystyle O}{}} \xrightarrow{\text{H}_2\text{O}}$$
$$\text{2-Nitropropane} \qquad\qquad\qquad\qquad\qquad\qquad \text{An } \textit{aci}\text{-nitro compound}$$

$$(CH_3)_2C\!-\!\overset{\displaystyle OH}{\underset{\underset{\displaystyle +}{\overset{|}{O}H_2}}{N}}\overset{}{O} \longrightarrow (CH_3)_2C\!-\!\overset{\displaystyle OH}{\underset{\underset{\displaystyle OH}{|}}{N}}OH \longrightarrow (CH_3)_2C\!-\!O + N_2O + H_2O$$

$$CH_3CH_2CH_2NO_2 \xrightarrow{\text{Conc. H}_2\text{SO}_4} CH_3CH_2CH\!-\!\overset{\displaystyle OH}{\underset{\underset{\displaystyle OH}{|}}{N}}OH \xrightarrow{-\text{H}_2\text{O}} CH_3CH_2C\!\!=\!\!\overset{|}{\underset{\underset{\displaystyle OH}{|}}{N}}OH \xrightarrow{+\text{H}_2\text{O}} CH_3CH_2CO_2H + NH_2OH$$
$$\text{1-Nitropropane}$$

Carbon-Hydrogen Bond Formation

Catalytic hydrogenations (page 352) have been regarded as reactions of hydrogen atoms adsorbed on a catalyst surface, and it is conceivable that some of the reduction reactions discussed in Chap. 19 involve homolytic mechanisms. Since mechanistic details are in doubt, discussion would be unprofitable.

Carbon-Carbon Bond Formation

Coupling of free radicals produced by thermal decompositions and atom-abstraction reactions leads to a number of interesting syntheses. Such reactions are not chain processes, and a two-to-one equivalence exists between radicals produced and carbon-carbon bonds made. A variety of substrates have been coupled, although there have been relatively few examples of applications in syntheses. Typical reaction steps are illustrated by the coupling of acetone to form a 1,4-diketone in the presence of decomposing diacetyl peroxide.

$$(CH_3CO_2)_2 \xrightarrow{100°} 2CH_3CO_2· \longrightarrow 2CH_3· + 2CO_2$$

$$CH_3· + CH_3COCH_3 \longrightarrow CH_4 + ·CH_2COCH_3$$

$$2CH_3COCH_2· \longrightarrow CH_3COCH_2CH_2COCH_3$$
$$\text{2,5-Hexanedione}$$

$$C_6H_5CH(CH_3)_2 \xrightarrow[120°]{(CH_3)_3COOC(CH_3)_3} \underset{\underset{CH_3\ CH_3}{|}}{\overset{\overset{CH_3\ CH_3}{|}}{C_6H_5C-CC_6H_5}}$$

$$BrCH_2CO_2C_2H_5 \xrightarrow{(CH_3CO_2)_2} \underset{BrCHCO_2C_2H_5}{\overset{|}{BrCHCO_2C_2H_5}} + CH_4 + CO_2$$

Aromatic compounds undergo substitution by some radicals. Most of the examples involve substitution by an aryl radical with formation of biaryls. Many sources of aryl radicals have been investigated, as is illustrated by the following preparations of the phenyl radical. Some details of the decomposition reactions remain uncertain.

$$(C_6H_5CO_2)_2 \longrightarrow 2C_6H_5CO_2· \longrightarrow C_6H_5· + CO_2$$

$$C_6H_5N{=}NC(C_6H_5)_3 \longrightarrow C_6H_5· + (C_6H_5)_3C· + N_2$$
Phenylazotri-
phenylmethane

$$\underset{\underset{O}{\overset{||}{}}}{\overset{\overset{NO}{|}}{C_6H_5NCCH_3}} \longrightarrow C_6H_5{\overset{\frown}{N}}{\overset{\frown}{=}}{N}{\overset{\frown}{O}}{\overset{\overset{O}{||}}{C}}CH_3 \longrightarrow C_6H_5· + CH_3CO_2· + N_2$$

N-Nitroso-   Benzene
acetanilide   diazoacetate

$$C_6H_5\overset{+}{N}_2\overset{-}{Cl} \xrightarrow{OH^-} C_6H_5N{=}NOH \longrightarrow C_6H_5· + HO· + N_2$$
Benzenediazonium   Benzenediazo
chloride   hydroxide

$$Pb(O_2CC_6H_5)_4 \longrightarrow Pb(O_2CC_6H_5)_2 + 2C_6H_5CO_2· \longrightarrow 2C_6H_5· + 2CO_2$$
Lead tetrabenzoate

Although the timing of the substitution reaction is not understood, material conservation demands that two radicals must sooner or later be involved in the substitution, one to take the displaced hydrogen atom and one to form the new carbon-carbon bond.

$$Ar\cdot + Ar'H + R\cdot \longrightarrow Ar—Ar' + RH$$

Substituent effects are much smaller in aromatic substitutions by free radicals than in electrophilic aromatic substitutions (Chap. 16). Both electron-withdrawing and electron-donating substituents on Ar'H have a very mild tendency to direct the incoming substituent to the ortho positions, and, unless the substituent is quite large, ortho substitution predominates. Although yields in the reaction are never high (maximum of about 70% on the basis of the stoichiometry indicated above), the reactions have been useful in the synthesis of the derivatives of biphenyl.

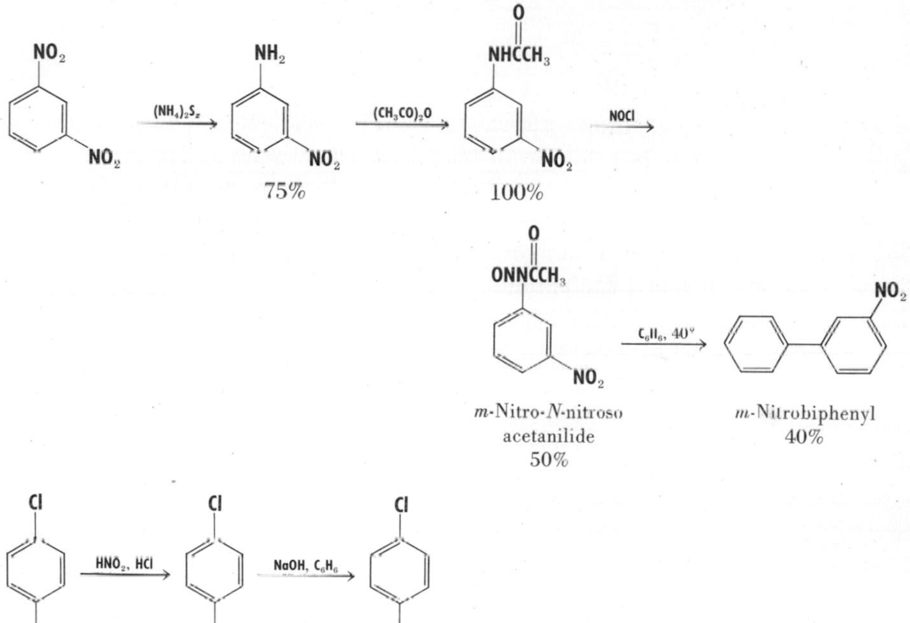

m-Nitro-*N*-nitroso acetanilide 50%

m-Nitrobiphenyl 40%

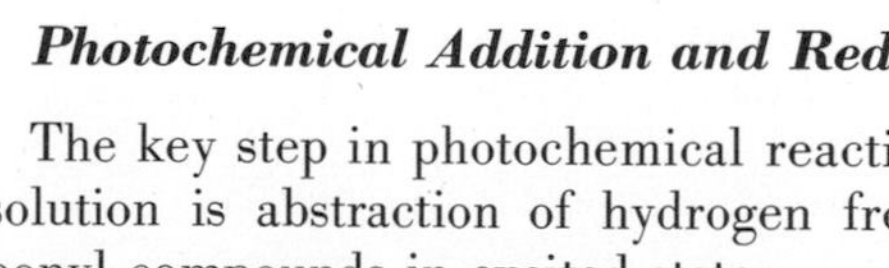

28%

Photochemical Addition and Reduction

The key step in photochemical reactions of aldehydes and ketones in solution is abstraction of hydrogen from *hydrogen atom donors* by carbonyl compounds in excited states.

Both symmetrical and unsymmetrical coupling products are formed from R· and $\overset{\cdot}{\underset{}{C}}$OH. Radicals produced in the initial hydrogen abstraction may initiate chain reactions such as polymerization of olefins and oxidation. In the absence of reactive radical scavengers, the products obtained are derived from the coupling of pairs of the above radicals and further hydrogen abstractions.

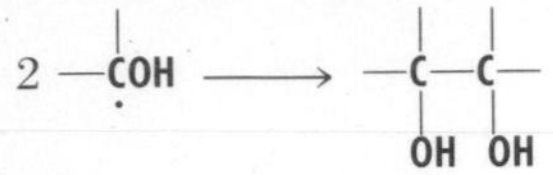

$$2 \ -\overset{|}{\underset{\cdot}{C}}OH \ \longrightarrow \ -\overset{|}{C}-\overset{|}{C}- \\ \quad\quad\quad\quad \underset{OH\ OH}{}$$

Pinacol

$$2R\cdot \ \longrightarrow \ R-R$$

$$R\cdot \ + \ -\overset{|}{\underset{\cdot}{C}}OH \ \longrightarrow \ -\overset{|}{\underset{OH}{C}}-R$$

$$-\overset{|}{\underset{\cdot}{C}}-OH \ + \ RH \ \longrightarrow \ -\overset{|}{\underset{H}{C}}OH \ + \ R\cdot$$

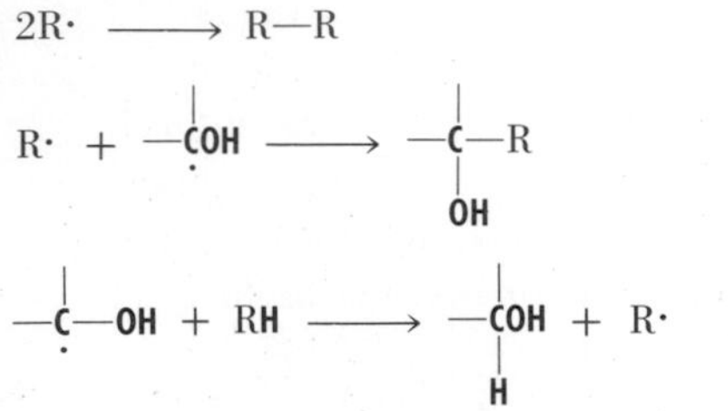

A hydrogen-donor, **RH**, is often used as solvent, and the products derived from it are sometimes not isolated. The most extensive investigation of the synthetic possibilities of photoreactions has been carried out in Egypt, where the ultraviolet components of sunlight are not filtered by passage through a thick layer of particle-laden atmosphere. The following are examples of typical conversions. Yields, where indicated, are based upon the carbonyl compound.

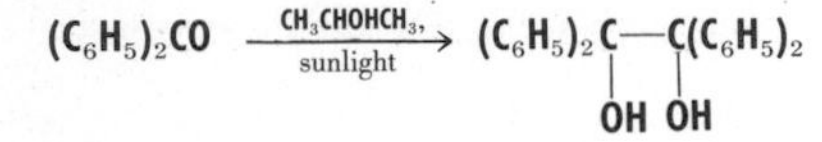

$$(C_6H_5)_2CO \ \xrightarrow[\text{sunlight}]{CH_3CHOHCH_3,} \ (C_6H_5)_2\overset{|}{C}-\overset{|}{C}(C_6H_5)_2 \\ \quad\quad\quad\quad\quad\quad\quad \underset{OH\ OH}{}$$

Benzophenone Benzpinacol
100%

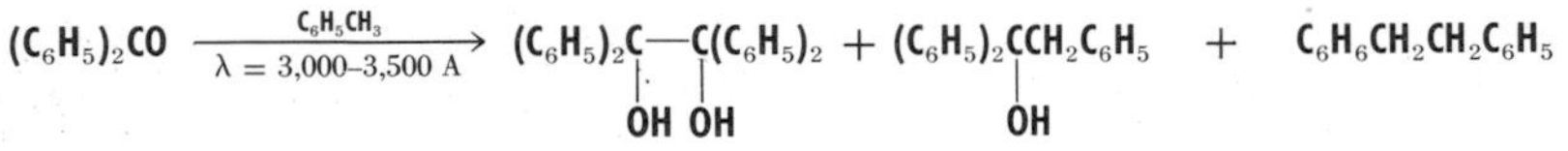

$$(C_6H_5)_2CO \ \xrightarrow[\lambda\,=\,3{,}000-3{,}500\ A]{C_6H_5CH_3} \ (C_6H_5)_2\overset{|}{C}-\overset{|}{C}(C_6H_5)_2 \ + \ (C_6H_5)_2\overset{|}{C}CH_2C_6H_5 \ + \ C_6H_6CH_2CH_2C_6H_5 \\ \quad\quad\quad\quad\quad\quad\quad\quad \underset{OH\ OH}{} \quad\quad\quad \underset{OH}{}$$

65% Benzyldiphenyl carbinol 1,2-Diphenylethane (Bibenzyl)
35% 35%

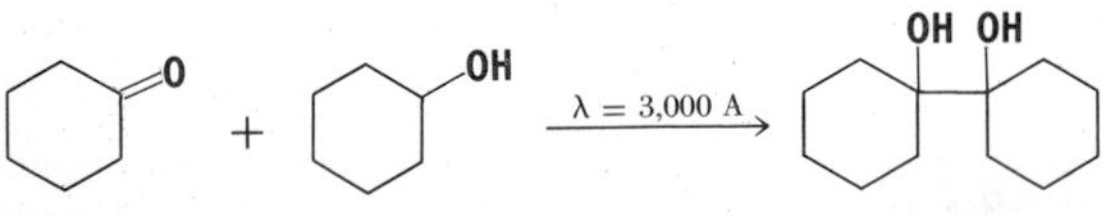

~100%

Problems

1. Write equations for the following reactions:
a. Oxidation of hexaphenylethane to ditrityl peroxide
b. Preparation of hexaphenylethane
c. Reaction of hydrogen peroxide with ferrous ions
d. Low-temperature oxidation of tetralin

e. Formation of a diketone by the coupling of diethyl ketone
f. A synthesis of 2,4-dimethylbiphenyl
g. Nitration of isopentane
h. Photochemical addition of toluene to *p,p'*-dichlorobenzophenone

2. Formulate reasonable mechanisms for the following reactions:

a.

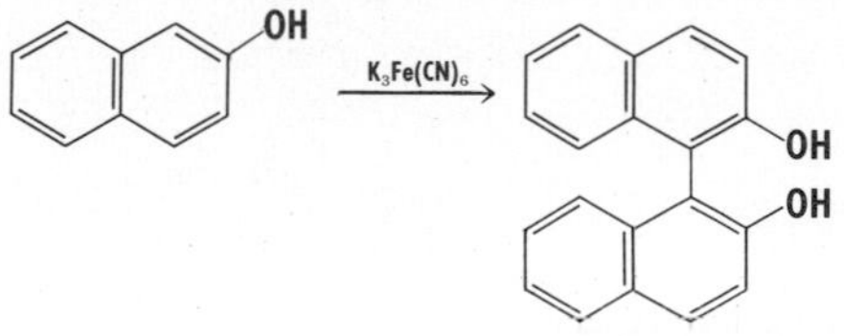

b.

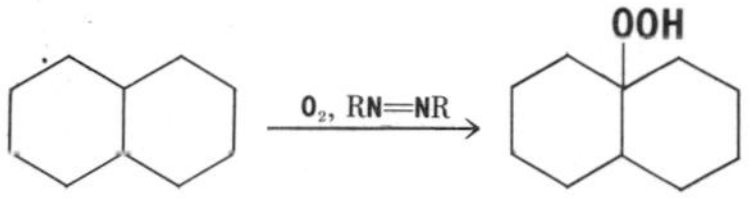

c.

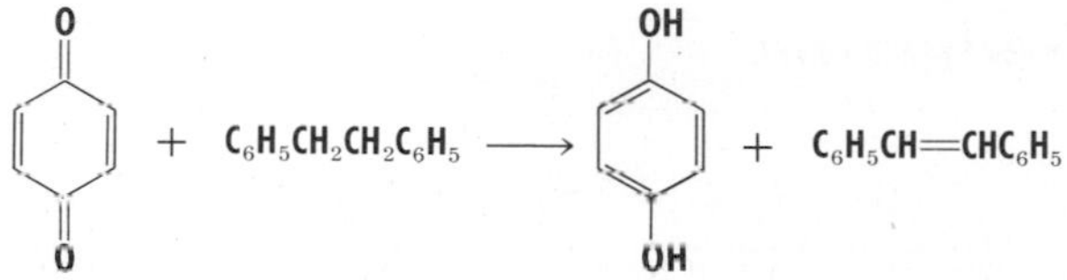

d. (CH$_3$)$_2$C—N=N—C(CH$_3$)$_2$ $\xrightarrow{80°}$ (CH$_3$)$_2$C=C=NC(CH$_3$)$_2$ $\xrightarrow{80°}$ (CH$_3$)$_2$CCN
                                                                                      (CH$_3$)$_2$CCN

with CN groups on the first carbons.

e. CH$_3$CH=CHCH$_3$ + Cl$_2$ $\xrightarrow{\text{Sunlight}}$ CH$_3$CHCH=CH$_2$ + other compounds
                                                                            Cl

3. A hydrocarbon, C$_6$H$_{14}$, gives a mixture containing only two monochlorides in photochemical chlorination. One of these compounds solvolyzes very rapidly in ethanol, whereas the other is very slow. What is the hydrocarbon? (See Chap. 11.)

4. Devise suitable reactions for carrying out the following transformations:

a.

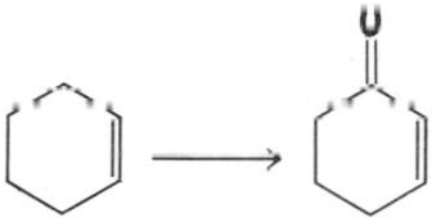

b.

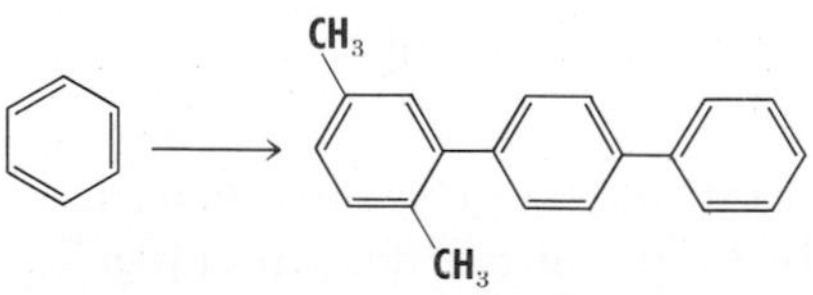

c. CH$_3$COCH$_3$ $\longrightarrow$ CH$_3$C=CHCH=CCH$_3$
                                          | |
                                         CH$_3$ CH$_3$

d. CH$_3$CH$_3$ $\longrightarrow$ CH$_3$CHCH$_2$CH$_2$NH$_2$
                                        |
                                       OH

19

Oxidation and Reduction

The terms *oxidation* and *reduction* do not have the same precise significance in organic chemistry as in the inorganic field. It is nevertheless possible to relate a few general concepts to these terms. Reactions that make new bonds to hydrogen are almost always spoken of as reduction reactions. Removal of hydrogen to form multiple bonds or to make new bonds between carbon and electronegative elements such as oxygen, nitrogen, sulfur, and the halogens is usually called oxidation. Thus primary alcohols are said to be oxidized to carboxylic acids and acids to be reduced to alcohols.

Even though carbon has no fixed average valence number in organic compounds, the ion-electron method of balancing oxidation-reduction reactions is entirely valid for balancing equations for organic *redox* reactions.

$$3 \text{ (H}_2\text{O} + \text{CH}_3\text{CH}_2\text{OH} \longrightarrow \text{CH}_3\text{CO}_2\text{H} + 4\text{H}^+ + 4e)$$
$$\underline{2 \text{ (6}e + 14\text{H}^+ + \text{Cr}_2\text{O}_7^= \longrightarrow 2\text{Cr}^{3+} + 7\text{H}_2\text{O)}}$$
$$3\text{CH}_3\text{CH}_2\text{OH} + 16\text{H}^+ + 2\text{Cr}_2\text{O}_7^= \longrightarrow 3\text{CH}_3\text{CO}_2\text{H} + 4\text{Cr}^{3+} + 11\text{H}_2\text{O}$$

Oxidation and reduction reactions all fall into large groups such as substitution, addition, and elimination. Two types of reactions are often involved in one over-all transformation. Many useful oxidation and reduction reactions have not been studied carefully from the mechanistic point of view, and relatively little can be said about intimate details in many cases.

Oxidation

Many of the oxidizing agents familiar from inorganic chemistry will, under suitable conditions, effect more or less drastic oxidation of organic materials. Carbon-hydrogen bonds can always be broken by oxidative procedures, although the nature of the substituents in the vicinity of a particular bond has a strong influence on reactivity. Carbon-carbon multiple bonds are attacked readily by many oxidants, but there are only a few oxidative procedures which allow selective breaking of particular carbon-carbon single bonds without at the same time destroying the entire molecule.

Elimination of Hydrogen to Make Carbon-Carbon Double Bonds. Specially prepared solid catalysts cause *dehydrogenation* of alkanes. High temperatures are required, and provision must be made for continuous removal of hydrogen. The reactions are frequently carried out by passage of vapor of the substrate over a hot catalyst bed.

$$(CH_3)_2CHCH_3 \xrightarrow[500°]{Cr_2O_3\text{-}Al_2O_3} (CH_3)_2C{=}CH_2$$

$$CH_2{=}CHCH_2CH_3 \xrightarrow[\Delta]{\text{Oxide catalyst}} CH_2{=}CHCH{=}CH_2$$

1,3-Butadiene

Alkanes containing chains of six or more carbon atoms undergo *dehydrocyclization* to aromatics. At the present time, more toluene is produced commercially by this method than is obtained from coal tar.

$$CH_3(CH_2)_5CH_3 \xrightarrow[450°]{Cr_2O_3\text{-}Al_2O_3}$$

n-Heptane

Alicyclics that already contain six-membered rings are *aromatized* when heated in the presence of hydrogenation catalysts, such as platinum or palladium, or easily reducible substances such as selenium, sulfur, or chloranil (tetrachlorobenzoquinone).

$$\xrightarrow[200°]{\text{Pd-charcoal}} \quad + \quad 2H_2$$

Tetralin

$$\xrightarrow[230°]{S} \quad + \quad 5H_2S$$

1,3-Dimethyldecalin

Aromatization is frequently the last step in synthetic sequences in which complex aromatic systems are built up from aliphatic or alicyclic starting materials.

p-Terphenyl   Tetrachloro-
                                        hydroquinone

An interesting application of dehydrocyclization is found in the synthesis of polynuclear aromatic hydrocarbons.

o-Terphenyl   Triphenylene
                                      15%

Oxidative Coupling. The union of a pair of free radicals to form a coupling product is part of an oxidative sequence if the radicals are produced by oxidation reactions.   A number of examples of such procedures have already been discussed as homolytic substitution reactions (page 422).   Another way of forming radicals that can be coupled is by electrolytic oxidation.   Although organic electrochemistry is a relatively undeveloped field, there is at least one very old example of oxidative coupling at an anode.   In the *Kolbe electrolysis,* salts of carboxylic acids are electrolyzed and coupled with loss of the carboxyl groups as carbon dioxide.

$$RC\bar{O}_2 \xrightarrow[-e]{\text{Anode}} RCO_2\cdot \longrightarrow CO_2 + R\cdot \xrightarrow{R\cdot} R\text{---}R$$

$$2CH_3(CH_2)_2C\bar{O}\overset{+}{O}K \xrightarrow[-e]{\text{Anode}} CH_3(CH_2)_4CH_3$$
Potassium butyrate   *n*-Hexane

$$CH_3O_2C(CH_2)_4CO_2Na \quad + \quad NaO_2C(CH_2)_4CH_3 \xrightarrow{\text{Electrolysis}} CH_3O_2C(CH_2)_8CH_3$$
Monomethyl sodium   Sodium caproate   Methyl decanoate
     adipate   58%

Formation of Carbon-Oxygen Bonds. Organic compounds containing carbon-oxygen bonds form a continuous series with respect to oxidation level, as is shown in Fig. 19.1.

Carbon-oxygen bonds are fairly readily made by substitution reactions in which $C—H$ bonds are broken and, under forcing conditions, by degradative reactions which break carbon-carbon bonds. Addition reactions, such as hydration of alkenes to give alcohols, are not considered oxidative processes, but alkene addition reactions that form two new $C—O$ bonds are called oxidations.

Oxidation of Hydrocarbons. Complete oxidation of hydrocarbons results in combustion to carbon dioxide and water.

$$CH_3CH_2CH_3 + 5O_2 \longrightarrow 3CO_2 + 4H_2O$$

Low-temperature air oxidation of hydrocarbons is difficult to control. The process is a free-radical chain reaction, and the first products are hydroperoxides. The reaction is occasionally used to make tertiary hydroperoxides.

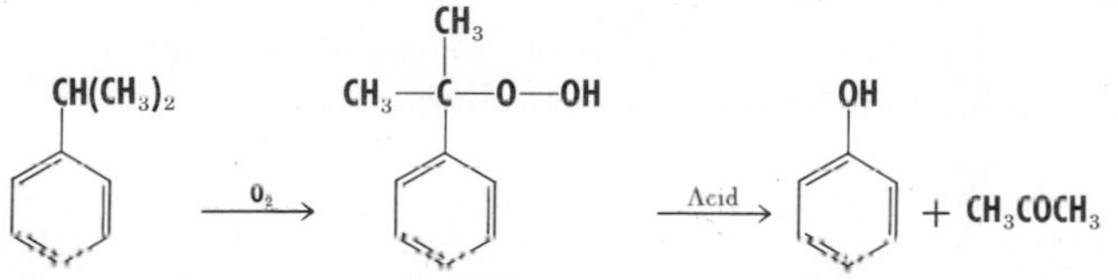

Cumene   Cumyl hydroperoxide   Phenol

Potentially, air oxidation of hydrocarbons is a rich source of chemicals, because of the low cost of petroleum hydrocarbons. Only a few examples of controlled oxidations of simple hydrocarbons have been reported.

$$CH_2{=}CHCH_3 \xrightarrow[\substack{CuCl_2, \\ catalyst}]{O_2} CH_2{=}CHCHO$$

The ease of oxidation of aromatic rings varies considerably. Benzene is oxidized to maleic anhydride under drastic conditions; one ring of the naphthalene system is much more readily oxidized; and anthracene is very easily oxidized to 9,10-anthraquinone.

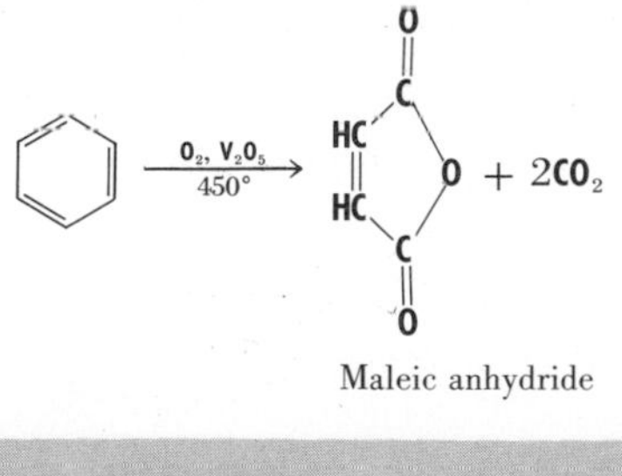

Maleic anhydride

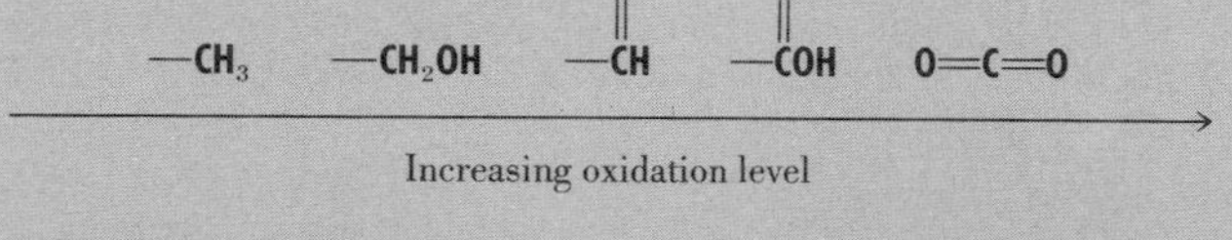

Increasing oxidation level

FIG. 19.1   *Oxidation levels of oxygen-containing functional groups.*

Phthalic anhydride

9,10-Anthraquinone
Quantitative yield

Electron-withdrawing substituents deactivate aromatic nuclei toward oxidation, and electron-donors have the opposite effect. These facts were used in a classic proof that naphthalene contains two fused aromatic rings.

1-Nitronaphthalene   3-Nitrophthalic anhydride

1-Aminonaphthalene   Phthalic anhydride

Aliphatic side chains attached to aromatic ring systems are much more readily oxidized than are the nuclei themselves. Drastic oxidation degrades a side chain to a carboxyl group, a useful step in proof of the structures of certain aromatic compounds.

Mesitylene   Trimesic acid

o-Chlorotoluene   o-Chlorobenzoic acid

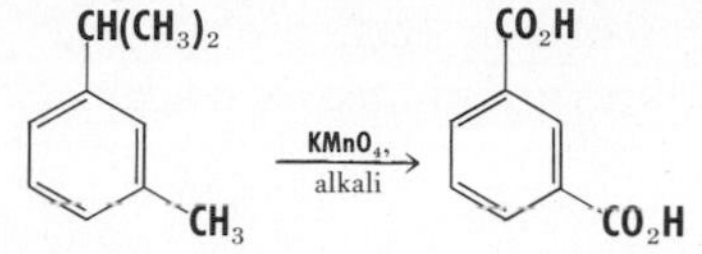

m-Isopropylmethylbenzene

Alkyl side chains are specifically activated toward oxidation at the position adjacent to the aromatic nucleus. Several reagents are capable of oxidizing benzyl positions without causing extensive degradation of the carbon skeleton. A remarkable example of selective oxidation is the Étard reaction, in which a methyl group is oxidized to an aldehyde group by chromyl chloride.

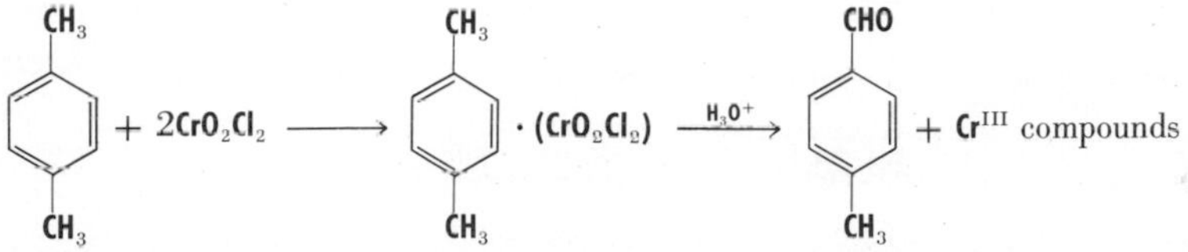

p-Xylene   Complex of unknown   *p*-Tolualdehyde
                  structure   75%

The most convenient method for introduction of an alcoholic hydroxyl group in positions α to an aromatic nucleus employs side-chain bromination followed by hydrolysis.

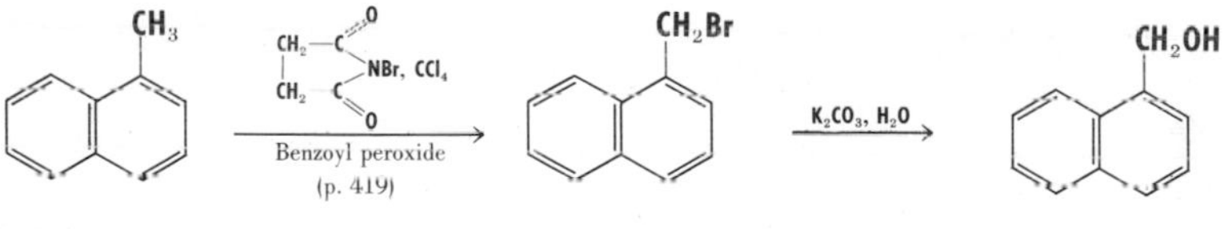

1-Methylnaphthalene   1-Bromomethylnaphthalene   1-Hydroxymethylnaphthalene
                            70%

$CH_2=CHCH_2CH_2CH=CH_2 \longrightarrow BrCH_2CH=CHCH=CHCH_2Br$

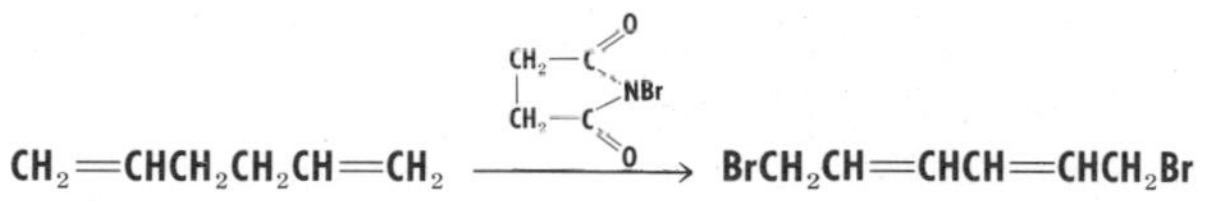

1,6-Dibromo-2,4-hexadiene

Low-temperature air oxidation of alkenes also occurs selectively at positions adjacent to the double bonds. The first products are hydroperoxides, which are seldom isolated but are further oxidized with ease.

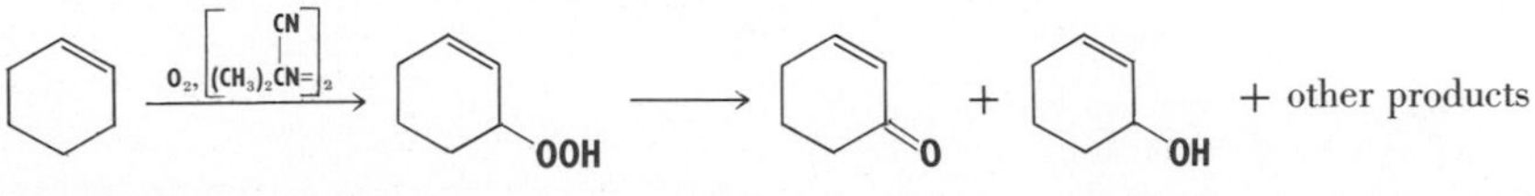

Oxidation of Olefinic Linkage. Because of their importance in synthetic and degradative sequences, many reactions that specifically oxidize carbon-carbon double bonds have been mentioned in earlier chapters. For the sake of continuity, the principal procedures are summarized again.

Ozonolysis (page 343):

$$\mathrm{C}{=}\mathrm{C} + \mathrm{O_3} \longrightarrow \quad \xrightarrow[\text{Reductive hydrolysis}]{\text{H}^+,\ \text{Zn}} \quad \mathrm{C}{=}\mathrm{O} + \mathrm{O}{=}\mathrm{C}$$

Peroxidation (page 342):

$$\mathrm{C}{=}\mathrm{C} + \overset{\text{O}}{\underset{}{\mathrm{R}\mathrm{C}}}\mathrm{OOH} \longrightarrow \quad + \ \overset{\text{O}}{\underset{}{\mathrm{R}\mathrm{C}}}\mathrm{OH}$$

Hydroxylation (page 342):

$$\mathrm{C}{=}\mathrm{C} \xrightarrow{\text{Neutral KMnO}_4} \underset{\overset{|}{\text{OH}}}{-\mathrm{C}}-\underset{\overset{|}{\text{OH}}}{\mathrm{C}}-$$

$$\mathrm{C}{=}\mathrm{C} \xrightarrow{\text{OsO}_4,\ \text{H}_2\text{O}_2} \underset{\overset{|}{\text{OH}}}{-\mathrm{C}}-\underset{\overset{|}{\text{OH}}}{\mathrm{C}}-$$

Destructive oxidation:

$$\underset{\mathrm{R}'}{\overset{\mathrm{R}}{\diagdown}}\mathrm{C}{=}\mathrm{C}\underset{\mathrm{R}}{\overset{\mathrm{R}}{\diagup}} \xrightarrow{\text{Alkaline KMnO}_4} \underset{\mathrm{R}'}{\overset{\mathrm{R}}{\diagdown}}\mathrm{C}{=}\mathrm{O} + \mathrm{O}{=}\mathrm{C}\underset{\mathrm{R}}{\overset{\mathrm{R}}{\diagup}}$$

$$\underset{\mathrm{R}'}{\overset{\mathrm{R}}{\diagdown}}\mathrm{C}{=}\mathrm{C}\underset{\mathrm{H}}{\overset{\mathrm{R}}{\diagup}} \xrightarrow{\text{Alkaline KMnO}_4} \underset{\mathrm{R}'}{\overset{\mathrm{R}}{\diagdown}}\mathrm{C}{=}\mathrm{O} + \mathrm{RCO}_2\mathrm{H}$$

Alcohols as Substrates.   Oxidative replacement of α-hydrogen atoms of primary and secondary alcohols is accomplished by many reagents. Chromic acid is frequently used in laboratory procedures, as is the Oppenauer method, in which an excess of some inexpensive ketone is equilibrated with a secondary alcohol (page 280). Catalytic dehydrogenation is the usual industrial procedure for conversion of alcohols to aldehydes and ketones. Atmospheric oxygen converts primary alcohols to acids and secondary alcohols to ketones. The reaction is very slow unless free-radical initiators are added.

$$\mathrm{CH_3CH_2OH} \xrightarrow{\text{H}_2\text{Cr}_2\text{O}_7} \underset{\substack{\text{Isolated only if} \\ \text{removed by continuous} \\ \text{distillation}}}{\mathrm{CH_3CHO}} \xrightarrow{\text{H}_2\text{Cr}_2\text{O}_7} \mathrm{CH_3CO_2H}$$

Cyclohexanol   Cyclohexanone

$$(CH_3)_2CHCH_2CH_2OH \xrightarrow[275°]{CuCrO_2} (CH_3)_2CHCH_2CHO + H_2$$
Isoamyl alcohol   Isovaleraldehyde

$$O_2 + 2CH_3OH \xrightarrow[250°]{Ag} 2CH_2O + 2H_2O$$

$$2CH_3CHO \xrightarrow[\text{(Aldol cond.)}]{NaOH} CH_3\overset{OH}{\underset{|}{C}}HCH_2CHO \xrightarrow[\text{(Acetal formation)}]{(CH_3)_2CCH_2CHCH_3, HCl}$$

3-Ketobutyraldehyde

Oxidation of ethanol by atmospheric oxygen is responsible for formation of the acetic acid in vinegar. The reaction is catalyzed by enzymes produced by the metabolism of certain bacteria. If wine or cider is left exposed to the atmosphere, the beverage is inoculated by air-borne cultures of the organism, and oxidation occurs. Fortified wines, such as sherry, are not oxidized, because the enzyme is inactivated by high concentrations of ethanol. Dilute solutions of pure ethanol in water are stable because the microorganism needs other nutrients, present in fermentation mixtures.

Chromic acid oxidation of secondary alcohols has been studied in detail. The oxidation step is an elimination reaction of an alkyl ester of chromic acid. The reaction produces a chromium IV species which reacts with chromate to give chromium V. The latter is rapidly consumed in oxidation of more of the alcohol.

$$R_2CHOH + Cr\overset{=}{O}_4 + 2\overset{+}{H} \rightleftharpoons R_2CHOCrO_3H + H_2O$$
Alkyl chromic acid

$$B: + H\text{—}C\text{—}O\text{—}CrO_3H \longrightarrow \overset{+}{B}H + R_2C{=}O + HOCrO_2^-$$
(Usually a nucleophilic solvent) (Cr^{IV})

$$Cr^{IV} + Cr^{VI} \xrightarrow{Fast} 2Cr^V$$

$$Cr^V + R_2CHOH \xrightarrow{Fast} Cr^{III} + R_2CO$$

Similar elimination steps are probably involved in many other oxidation reactions. Di-*tert*-butyl chromate is a useful oxidizing agent that can be employed in organic solvents. Ester interchange reactions produce chromates of the alcohols which are to be oxidized.

Glycol Cleavage. Two reagents, metaperiodic acid and lead tetra-acetate, cleave 1,2-diols smoothly to form carbonyl compounds. The reactions have been formulated as passing through cyclic esters as intermediates, but the belief has recently been expressed that lead tetraacetate oxidations may involve noncyclic, heterolytic mechanisms.

$$-\underset{OH}{\underset{|}{C}}-\underset{OH}{\underset{|}{C}}- + H_5IO_6 \longrightarrow -\underset{O}{\underset{|}{C}}\underset{O}{\underset{|}{C}}- \longrightarrow \;\;\underset{}{>}C=O \quad O=C< + HIO_3$$

Iodic acid

$$-\underset{OH}{\underset{|}{C}}-\underset{OH}{\underset{|}{C}}- + Pb(O_2CCH_3)_4 \xrightarrow{-2CH_3CO_2H} -\underset{O}{\underset{|}{C}}\underset{O}{\underset{|}{C}}- \longrightarrow \;\;>C=O + O=C< + Pb(O_2CCH_3)_2$$

CH_3CO_2   O_2CCH_3

As reagents for the cleavage of glycols, lead tetraacetate and metaperiodic acid complement each other, since the former is soluble in organic solvents and the latter is water-soluble. In addition to oxidizing glycols, metaperiodic acid also oxidizes α-dicarbonyl, α-hydroxycarbonyl compounds and α-amino alcohols. The scope of lead tetraacetate oxidations has not been as thoroughly investigated. The reagent is known to oxidize α-hydroxy acids and oxalic acid smoothly. One example is known of the cleavage of a highly branched tertiary alcohol by lead tetraacetate under conditions usually associated with specific glycol cleavage.

$$HOCH_2CH_2OH + H_5IO_6 \longrightarrow 2CH_2O + HIO_3 + 3H_2O$$

Metaperiodic acid   Iodic acid

$$HOCH_2CHNH_2CO_2H \xrightarrow{H_5IO_6} HCO_2H + CH_2O + CO_2 + NH_3$$

$$CH_3(CH_2)_7CH=CH(CH_2)_7CO_2H \xrightarrow{HCOOH} CH_3(CH_2)_7\underset{O}{\overset{O}{CH-CH}}(CH_2)_7CO_2H \xrightarrow{H_3O^+}$$

$$CH_3(CH_2)_7\underset{OH}{\underset{|}{CH}}-\underset{OH}{\underset{|}{CH}}(CH_2)_7CO_2H \xrightarrow{H_5IO_6} CH_3(CH_2)_7CHO + OCH(CH_2)_7CO_2H$$

Nonaldehyde   Azelaic half-
89%   aldehyde
76%

$$CH_3COCHO \xrightarrow{H_5IO_6} CH_3CO_2H + HCO_2H$$

$$(C_6H_5)_2\underset{OH}{\underset{|}{C}}-\underset{OH}{\underset{|}{C}}(C_6H_5)_2 + Pb(O_2CCH_3)_4 \xrightarrow{Toluene} 2(C_6H_5)_2CO + Pb(O_2CCH_3)_2 + 2CH_3CO_2H$$

Benzpinacol   Benzophenone
95%

$$C_6H_5\underset{CH_3}{\overset{CH_3}{\underset{|}{\overset{|}{C}}}}-\underset{}{\overset{OH}{\underset{|}{C}}}(C_6H_5)_2 \xrightarrow{Pb(O_2CCH_3)_4} (C_6H_5)_2CO + C_6H_5\underset{CH_3}{\overset{CH_3}{\underset{|}{\overset{|}{C}}}}O_2CCH_3$$

1,1,2-Triphenyl-2-methyl-   95%   Cumyl acetate
1-propanol

Tertiary Alcohols as Substrates. Drastic conditions are required for oxidation of tertiary alcohols, since carbon-carbon bond cleavage must occur. The products are acids or ketones resulting from oxidative replacement of all hydrogen atoms attached to the carbon atoms involved in the cleavage. Hot chromium trioxide solutions are frequently used in these degradative cleavages. A few applications have been made in synthesis.

1-Phenylcyclohexanol   δ-Benzoylvaleric acid   81%   6-Phenylpentanoic acid

Chromic acid oxidations are a key step in the *Barbier-Wieland method* for the stepwise degradation of carboxylic acids.

$$RCH_2CO_2H \xrightarrow{\text{H}^+,\ C_2H_5OH} RCH_2CO_2C_2H_5 \xrightarrow[\text{2) H}_2\text{O}]{\text{1) C}_6\text{H}_5\text{MgBr}} RCH_2\overset{\overset{\displaystyle OH}{|}}{C}(C_6H_5)_2 \xrightarrow{\text{H}^+}$$

$$RCH = C(C_6H_5)_2 \xrightarrow{CrO_3} RCO_2H + (C_6H_5)_2CO$$

Aldehydes as Substrates. Aldehydes are very easily oxidized to carboxylic acids by most oxidizing agents, including air. Air oxidation is a chain reaction which proceeds by way of peracids as intermediates. Free-radical traps, such as aromatic amines and phenols, inhibit air oxidation and are added to aldehydes in small amounts to preserve them during storage.

Net reaction: $C_6H_5CHO + \frac{1}{2}O_2 \longrightarrow C_6H_5CO_2H$

The rapid oxidation of aldehydes lends itself to the development of convenient characteristic tests for the aldehyde group. Two frequently used tests are oxidation with alkaline solutions containing complex copper II ions and oxidation by ammoniacal silver solutions. The products, cuprous oxide and metallic silver, are deposited as easily recognizable solids. Deposition of silver on a glass surface by reduction with formaldehyde is used in making mirrors.

Fehling's test:

$$RCHO + 2Cu(Tart\dagger)_2^= + 5OH^- \longrightarrow Cu_2O\downarrow + RCO_2^- + 4\,Tart^= + 3H_2O$$

Cuprous
oxide
(red)

$$\dagger\,Tart = tartrate = \bar{O}_2CCHOHCHOHC\bar{O}_2.$$

Tollens' test:

$$RCHO + 2Ag(NH_3)_2^+ + 3\bar{O}H \longrightarrow 2Ag\downarrow + RC\bar{O}_2 + 4NH_3 + 2H_2O$$

$$CH_2O + 4Ag(NH_3)_2^+ + 4\bar{O}H \longrightarrow 4Ag\downarrow + CO_2 + 8NH_3 + 3H_2O$$

Mirror

Ketones as Substrates. The behavior of ketones with respect to oxidation is very similar to that of tertiary alcohols. Hot nitric acid and alkaline or acid permanganate have often been used to cleave ketones. The commercial preparation of adipic acid by oxidation of cyclohexanone is an example. It is likely that the initial attack is on an enol rather than on the ketone itself.

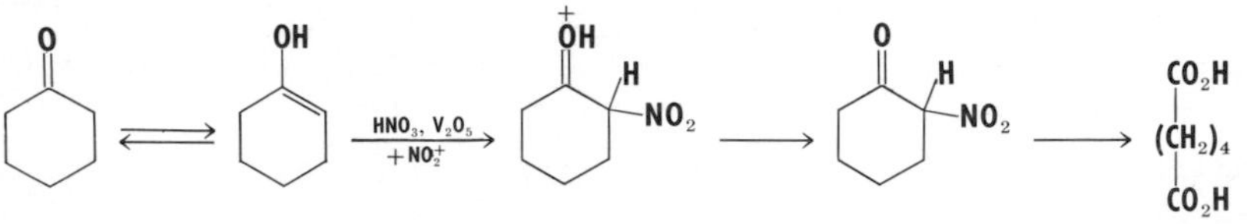

Adipic acid
60%

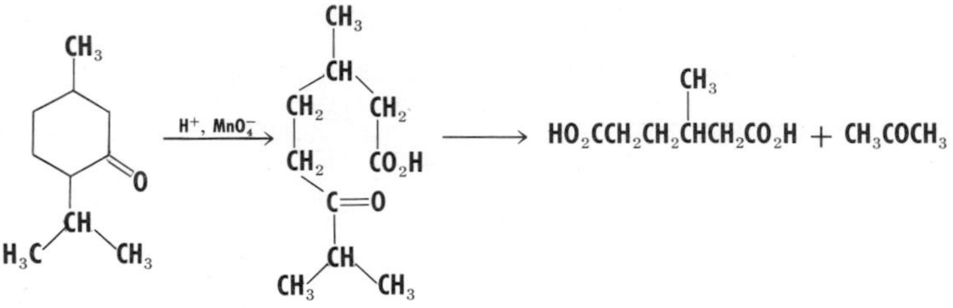

The smooth oxidation of ketones by peracids in the *Baeyer-Villiger reaction* will be discussed in detail in the next chapter.

$$\overset{O}{\overset{\|}{R C R}} + R'\overset{O}{\overset{\|}{C}}OOH \longrightarrow R\overset{O}{\overset{\|}{C}}OR + R'CO_2H$$

The hypohalite reaction (page 262) is an oxidative procedure which degrades methyl ketones to carboxylic acids with one less carbon atom. Some *methylene ketones* have been similarly degraded.

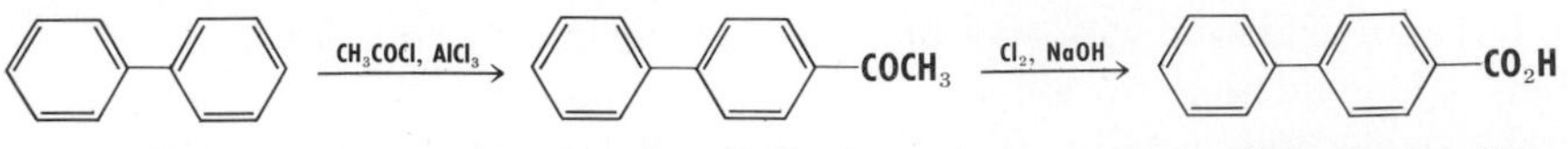

Biphenyl   *p*-Acetylbiphenyl   *p*-Biphenylcarboxylic
acid

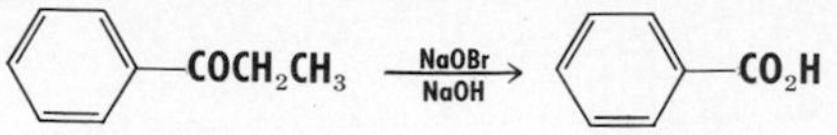

Propiophenone → Benzoic acid
64%

Methylene ketones are subject to specific oxidative attack at the
α-positions. The *Reilly oxidation* with selenium dioxide leads to α-
diketones, and nitrous acid and its esters convert methylene ketones to
α-ketooximes.

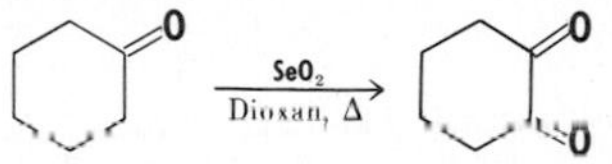

1,2-Cyclohexanedione
60%

$$CH_3COCH_3 \xrightarrow{SeO_2} CH_3COCHO$$

Pyruvaldehyde
60%

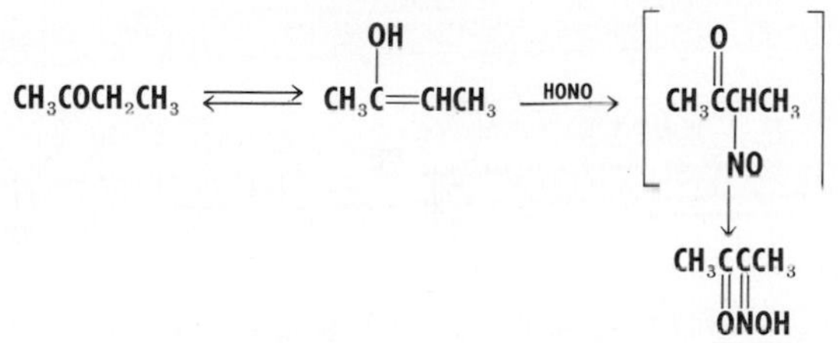

2,3-Butanedione monooxime

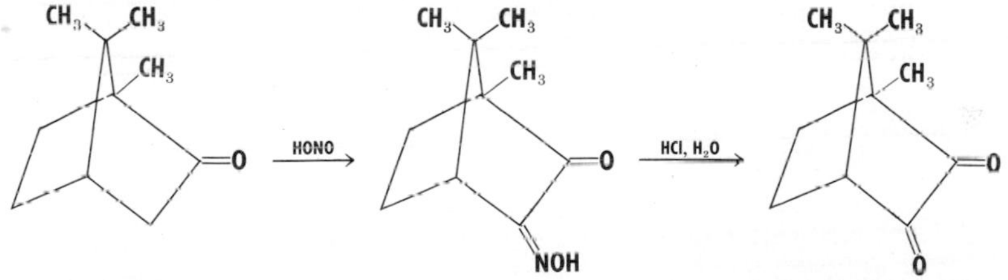

Camphor → → 3-Ketocamphor
("Camphorquinone")

Synthesis of Quinones. Methods for synthesis of quinones vary with
their structure. Benzoquinone is prepared by oxidation of aromatic
amines or phenols. Naphthalene and the larger linear polynuclear
aromatic hydrocarbons are oxidized directly to form quinones. Ortho-
quinones are usually prepared from ortho-disubstituted derivatives of the
corresponding aromatic systems.

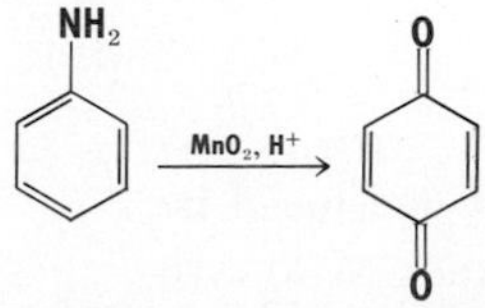

Benzoquinone

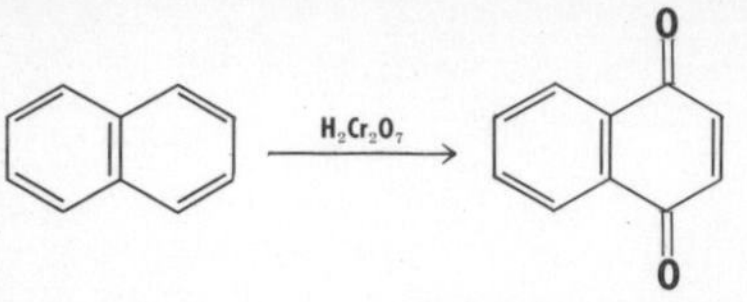

1,4-Naphthoquinone
35%

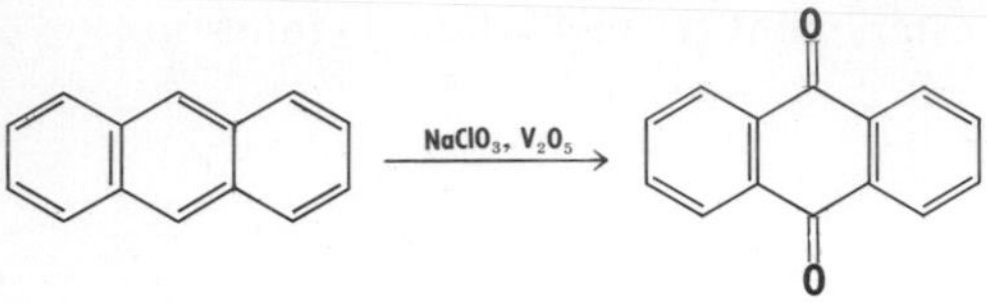

Anthraquinone

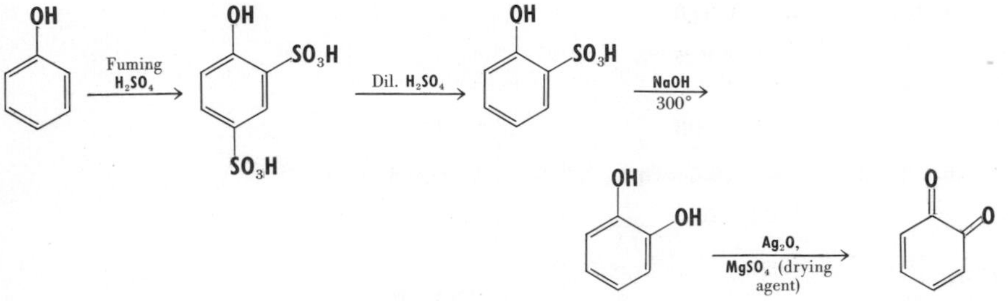

Catechol   *o*-Benzoquinone

The stable radical nitrosyldisulfonate has been used in synthesis of quinones difficult to prepare by other methods.

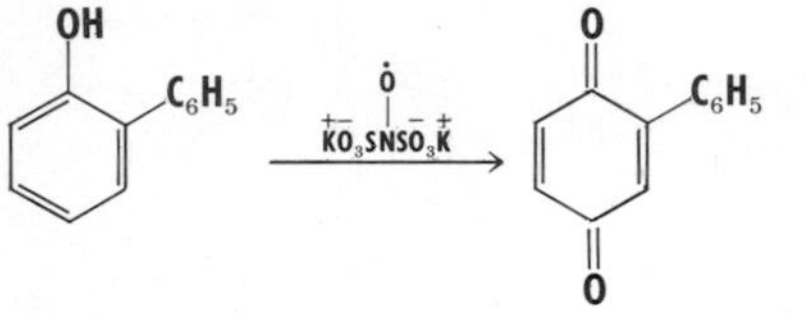

2-Phenylphenol   2-Phenylbenzoquinone
                                    85%

Quinones and the corresponding hydroquinones form oxidation-reduction couples which give reproducible electrode potentials.

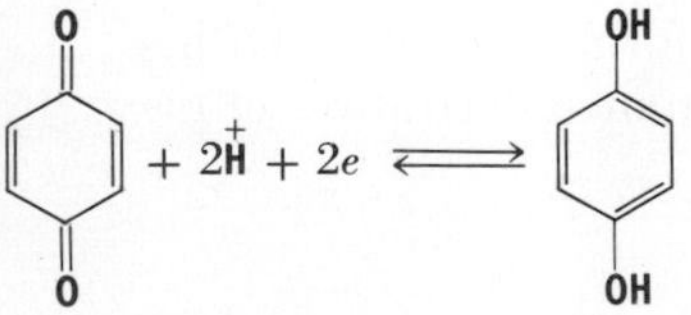

The oxidation potentials of many quinones have been measured by potentiometric titration of the hydroquinones with oxidants of known oxidation potential. Electron-withdrawing substituents, such as —NO₂, —CN, —SO₂Ar, —COAr, —CO₂H, and halogens, raise the oxidation potentials, making quinones more powerful oxidants. Electron-donor substituents, such as —NHCH₃, —NH₂, —N(CH₃)₂, —OH, —OCH₃, —CH₃, —NHCOCH₃, —C₆H₅, and —OCOCH₃, have the opposite effect. Since reduction of a quinone involves hydrogen ions, the quinone-hydroquinone system is used as an indicator electrode for measurement of the hydrogen-ion activities of water solutions. The system is known as the *quinhydrone electrode,* because hydroquinone and quinone combine to form a molecular compound called quinhydrone. The molecular complex has a characteristic black color.

Oxidation of Atoms Other than Carbon. Oxidizing agents add oxygen atoms to nitrogen, phosphorus, sulfur, and iodine. Figure 19.2 contains a summary of the known oxidation states of each of these atoms in organic compounds. The compounds cannot, in all cases, be made by direct oxidative procedures.

Direct oxidation of amines with most oxidants leads to tars, but peracids and hydrogen peroxide convert tertiary amines to amine oxides,

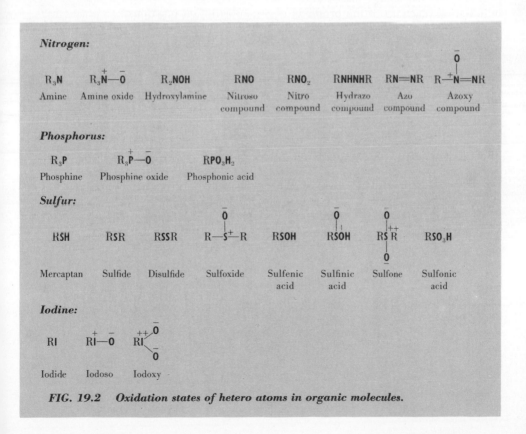

FIG. 19.2 *Oxidation states of hetero atoms in organic molecules.*

and peroxytrifluoroacetic acid has been used successfully for oxidation of some primary amines to nitro compounds.

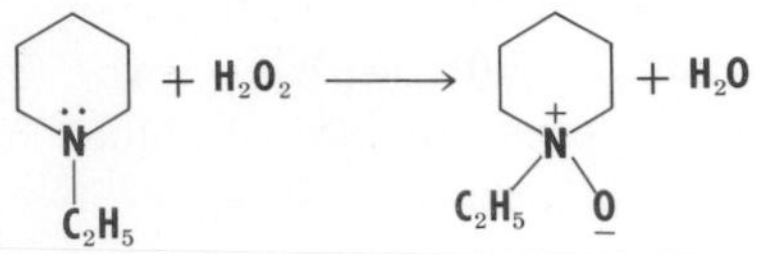

N-Ethylpiperidine   *N*-Ethylpiperidine oxide

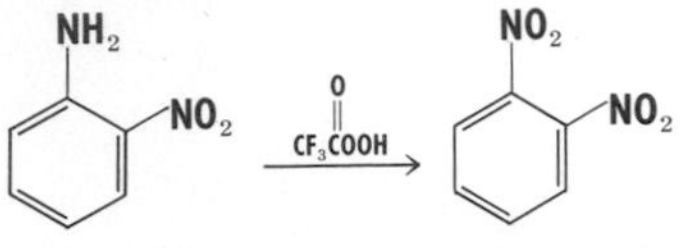

o-Nitroaniline   *o*-Dinitrobenzene

Amine oxides are of some interest, since they are easily pyrolyzed to give olefins (page 406), and because they have some potential value as specific oxidants. The oxygen atom of an amine oxide is sufficiently nucleophilic to effect displacement of halide and sulfonate ions from primary and secondary substrates. Carbonyl groups are formed by elimination reactions of the products of the substitution reactions.

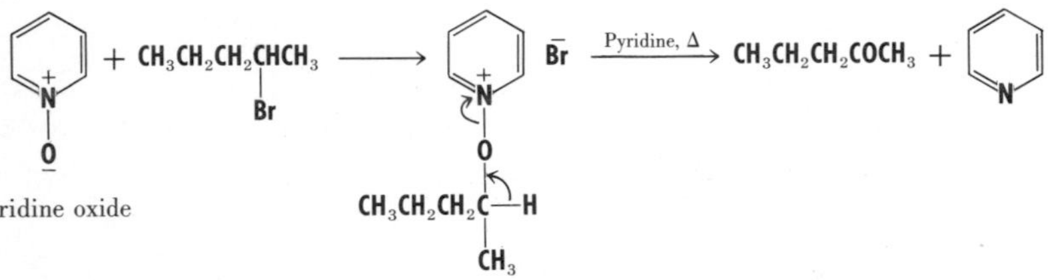

Pyridine oxide

Mercaptans are very rapidly oxidized to disulfides by many oxidants, including ferric salts, iodine, and oxygen. The reverse reaction is also easily accomplished by reducing agents.

$$2C_6H_5SH \underset{Zn, CH_3CO_2H}{\overset{O_2 \ (air)}{\rightleftarrows}} C_6H_5SSC_6H_5$$

Thiophenol   Diphenyl
                          disulfide

Sulfides can be oxidized in steps to sulfoxides and sulfones by a variety of strong oxidants. Hydrogen peroxide is usually the reagent of choice. It is difficult to interrupt the oxidation of mercaptans at any stage intermediate between the disulfide and the sulfonic acid. High yields of sulfonic acids are obtained through the action of nitric acid on lead mercaptides.

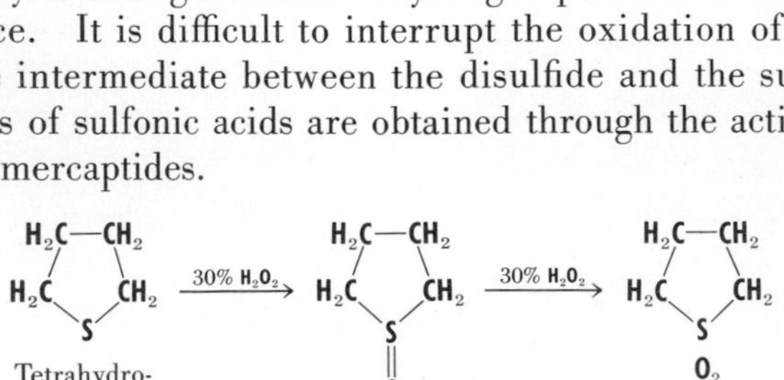

Tetrahydro-
thiophene

$$CH_3(CH_2)_3SH \xrightarrow{Pb(NO_3)_2} [CH_3(CH_2)_3S]_2 Pb \xrightarrow{HNO_3} CH_3(CH_2)_3SO_3H$$

Butyl mercaptan	Lead	1-Butane-
(Butanethiol)	dibutyl mercaptide	sulfonic acid

Sulfinic acids are made by reduction of sulfonyl chlorides. Sulfenic acids are virtually unknown, but their derivatives are obtained from sulfenyl chlorides which are, in turn, produced by chlorinolysis of disulfides.

$$p\text{-}CH_3C_6H_4SO_3H \xrightarrow{PCl_5} p\text{-}CH_3C_6H_4SO_2Cl \xrightarrow[\text{2) Na}_2\text{CO}_3]{\text{1) Zn, H}_2\text{O}} p\text{-}CH_3C_6H_4SO_2Na \xrightarrow{HCl} p\text{-}CH_3C_6H_4\overset{\text{O}}{\overset{\|}{S}}OH$$

p Toluenesulfinic
acid

$$CH_3(CH_2)_4SH \xrightarrow{Cl_2} [CH_3(CH_2)_4S]_2 \xrightarrow{Cl_2} CH_3(CH_2)_4SCl$$

Amyl mercaptan	1-Pentanesulfenyl chloride	
(Pentanethiol)	78%	

$$CH_3(CH_2)_4SCl \begin{cases} \xrightarrow{ROH} CH_3(CH_2)_4SOR & \text{Sulfenate ester} \\ \xrightarrow{RNH_2} CH_3(CH_2)_4SNHR & \text{Sulfenamide} \\ \xrightarrow{\;C=C\;} \underset{CH_3(CH_2)_4S}{-\overset{\overset{Cl}{\|}}{C}-\overset{\|}{C}-} \end{cases}$$

Reduction

Virtually all common inorganic reducing agents have been used in organic chemistry, but the most useful are hydrogen (with solid catalysts), metal hydrides, and active metals, especially zinc and sodium. The majority of organic reductions involves saturation of unsaturated functional groups, but a number of useful reductive substitution reactions are also known.

Reduction of Carbon-Carbon Multiple Bonds. The most generally applicable procedure for reducing alkenes, alkynes, aromatic compounds, and their derivatives is catalytic hydrogenation, which has been discussed frequently in earlier chapters (see page 352). Metal hydrides do not generally attack alkene linkages under usual reaction conditions. Occasionally, α,β-unsaturated linkages are reduced as a side reaction in lithium aluminum hydride reductions of other functional groups. Aluminum hydride has been found to add smoothly to terminal alkenes in benzene solutions at reflux temperature.

$$C_6H_5CH{=}CHCO_2H \xrightarrow[\text{2) H}_3\text{O}^+]{\text{1) LiAlH}_4} C_6H_5CH{=}CHCH_2OH \;+\; C_6H_5CH_2CH_2CH_2OH$$

Cinnamic acid	Cinnamyl alcohol	3-Phenyl-1-propanol

$$n\text{-}C_4H_9CH{=}CH_2 \xrightarrow{AlH_3,\ C_6H_6} (n\text{-}C_6H_{13})_3Al \xrightarrow{H_3O^+} n\text{-}C_6H_{14}$$

Diborane (**B₂H₆**) adds reversibly to alkenes, and the adduct when heated in acetic acid gives the saturated compound. Borane adducts also can be oxidized to alcohols, and the over-all reaction provides a method for preparing alcohols from alkenes by non-Markownikoff addition of the elements of water. Acetylenes can be reduced to olefins with diborane. The reaction assumes a cis steric course.

$$6CH_3(CH_2)_2CH{=}CH_2 + B_2H_6 \xrightarrow{CH_3O(CH_2CH_2O)_2CH_3} 2[CH_3(CH_2)_4]_3B \xrightarrow{CH_3CO_2H}_{\Delta} CH_3(CH_2)_3CH_3$$

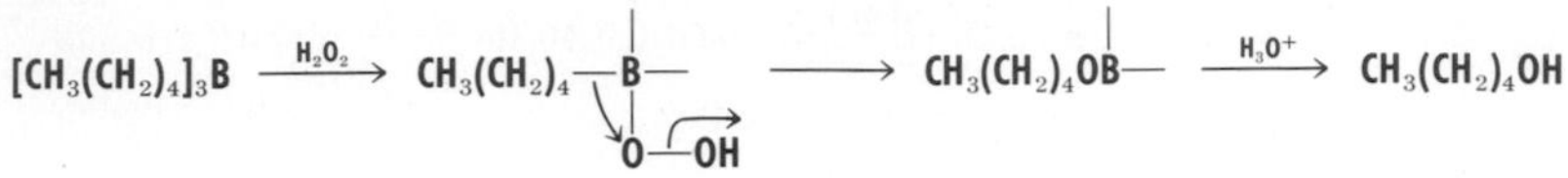

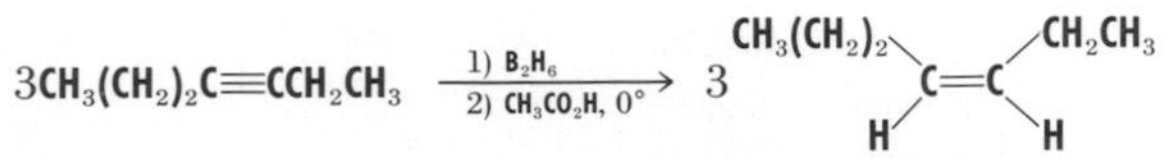

$$3CH_3(CH_2)_2C{\equiv}CCH_2CH_3 \xrightarrow[\text{2) }CH_3CO_2H,\,0°]{\text{1) }B_2H_6} 3$$

98%

Reduction of aromatic rings with solutions of sodium or lithium in liquid ammonia or amines has become a useful means of producing certain alicyclic compounds. The last double bond is frequently left in the ring system since it reduces with more difficulty than the others. The first steps produce radical-anions and dianions, species which are stable in aprotic solvents such as ether.

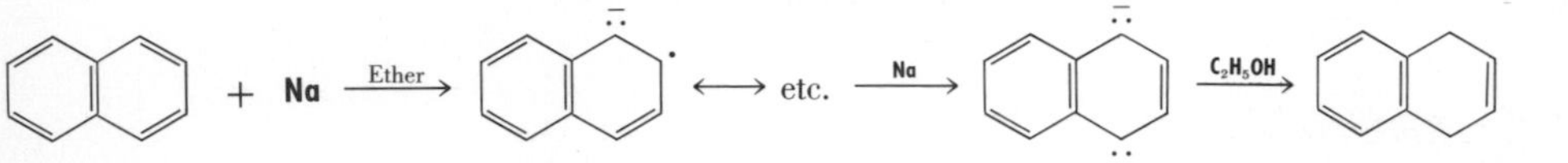

Sodium
naphthalene

1,4-Dihydronaphthalene

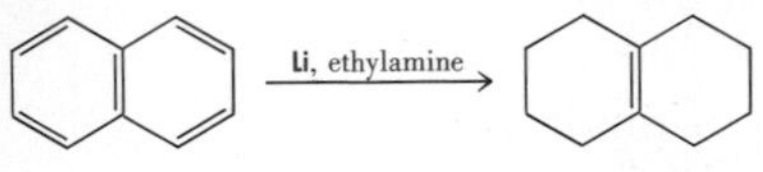

9,10-Octalin
90%

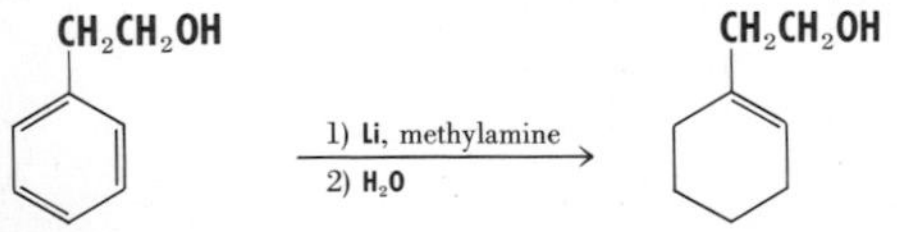

1-(2-Hydroxyethyl)-cyclohexene

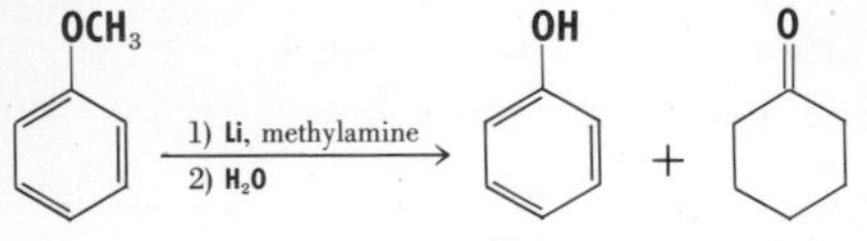

48%   40%

Sodium in liquid ammonia reduces alkynes stereospecifically to trans alkenes. The reaction assumes this course since the negative charges

in the dianion intermediate distribute themselves as far from one another
as possible.

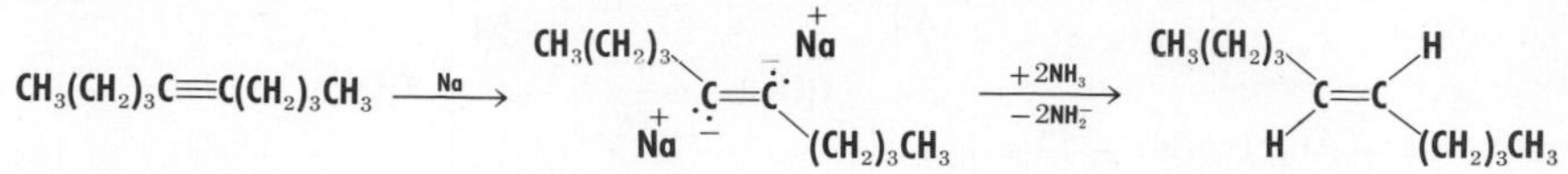

CH$_3$(CH$_2$)$_3$C≡C(CH$_2$)$_3$CH$_3$ $\xrightarrow{\text{Na}}$ [structure] $\xrightarrow[\text{− 2NH}_2^-]{\text{+ 2NH}_3}$ [structure]

trans-5-Decene
85%

Compare with:

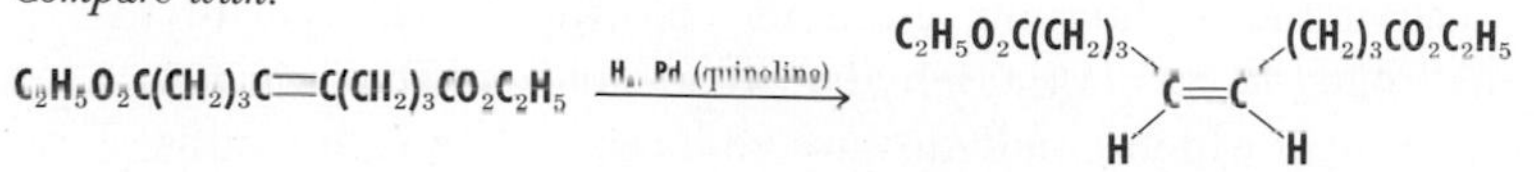

C$_2$H$_5$O$_2$C(CH$_2$)$_3$C≡C(CH$_2$)$_3$CO$_2$C$_2$H$_5$ $\xrightarrow{\text{H}_2, \text{ Pd (quinoline)}}$ [structure]

95%

Halogen Compounds as Substrates. Hydrogen may be substituted for
halogens by a variety of procedures. The methods include reduction
with active metals, nucleophilic substitution reactions of reactive halides
with lithium aluminum hydride (page 218), catalytic hydrogenolysis, and
reduction of alkyl iodides with hydrogen iodide.

A stepwise procedure in which a Grignard reagent is first formed
and then hydrolyzed can be used to reduce halides. A more common
procedure consists of treating a halide with zinc in acetic acid.

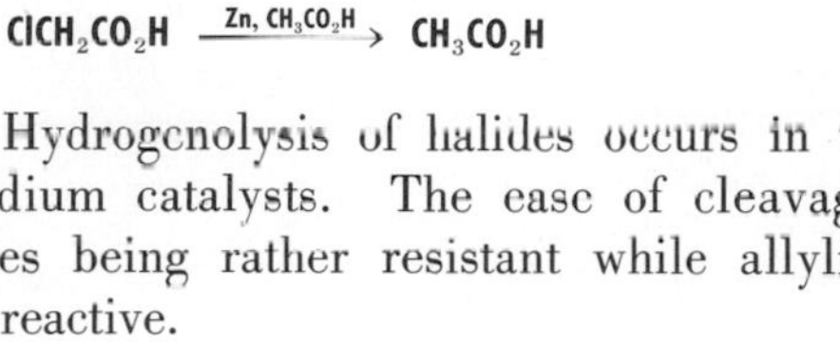

[reaction scheme: toluene with Br → Mg, ether → MgBr → D$_2$O → D]

Toluene-4-*d*

ClCH$_2$CO$_2$H $\xrightarrow{\text{Zn, CH}_3\text{CO}_2\text{H}}$ CH$_3$CO$_2$H

Hydrogenolysis of halides occurs in the presence of platinum or
palladium catalysts. The ease of cleavage varies a great deal, aryl
halides being rather resistant while allylic and benzylic halides are
very reactive.

C$_6$H$_5$Br + H$_2$ $\xrightarrow[\text{Alcoholic KOH}]{\text{Pd-CaCO}_3}$ C$_6$H$_6$ + HBr

C$_6$H$_5$Br $\xrightarrow[200°]{\text{H}_2, \text{ Pt}}$ C$_6$H$_6$ + C$_6$H$_5$—C$_6$H$_5$ + C$_6$H$_{12}$

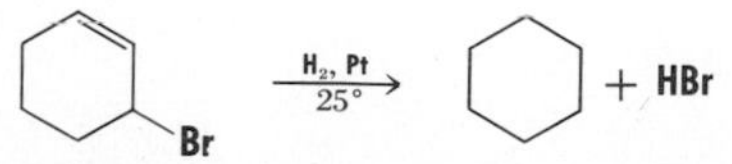

[structure: 3-bromocyclohexene] $\xrightarrow[25°]{\text{H}_2, \text{ Pt}}$ [structure: cyclohexane] + HBr

3-Bromocyclohexene   Cyclohexane

Nickel-aluminum alloy is sometimes used directly as a reducing
agent. The alloy is treated with aqueous base in the presence of the

compound to be reduced. Aluminum dissolves, leaving nickel hydride as in the preparation of Raney nickel catalyst.

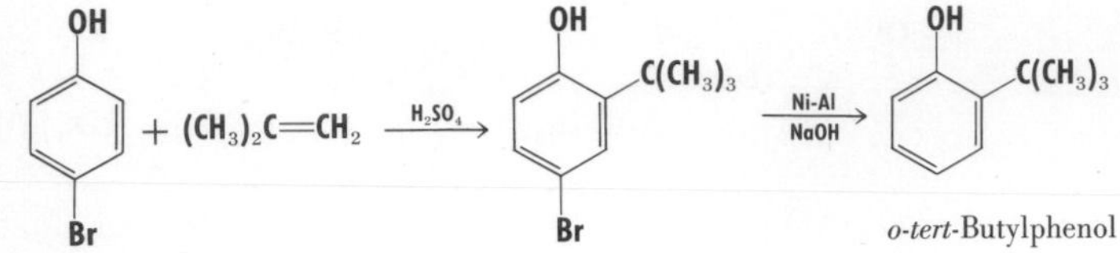

o-tert-Butylphenol

In the Rosenmund reduction, an acid chloride is catalytically reduced with hydrogen to give an aldehyde. The chief drawback of the method is the ease with which aldehydes are reduced. Although results are somewhat erratic, considerable success has attended use of supported platinum and palladium catalysts partially inactivated by sulfur or quinoline.

$$C_6H_5CH_2CH_2COCl \xrightarrow[\text{Refluxing xylene}]{H_2,\ Pd\text{-}BaCO_3} C_6H_5CH_2CH_2CHO$$

β-Phenylpropionyl   β-Phenylpropionaldehyde
chloride

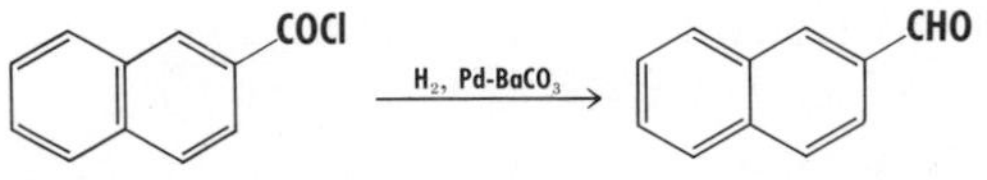

β-Naphthoyl chloride   β-Naphthaldehyde

Oxygen Compounds as Substrates. All saturated oxygen-containing functional groups can be reduced to alcoholic hydroxyl groups by suitable procedures. Although many special cases of the hydrogenolysis of alcohols and ethers are known, there is no general method for direct reduction of saturated oxygen compounds to hydrocarbons.

Benzyl alcohols and α-hydroxy ketones are readily cleaved by chemical reduction or by catalytic hydrogenation.

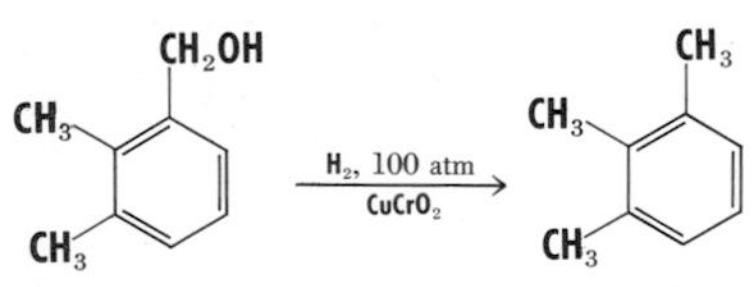

2,3-Dimethylbenzyl   Hemimellitine
alcohol   92%

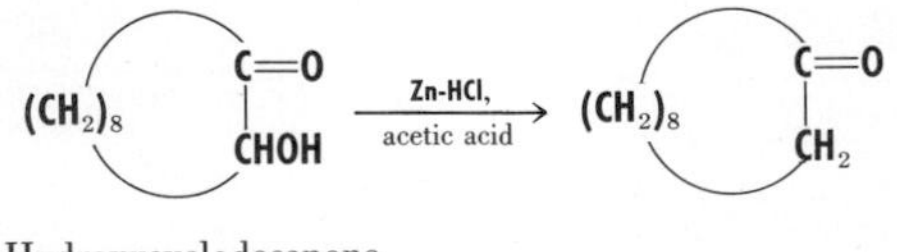

2-Hydroxycyclodecanone

Benzoins are easily reduced by a number of special methods. Activation by the two aryl groups is responsible for the lability of the compounds.

$$C_6H_5CHOHCOC_6H_5 \text{ (Benzoin)}$$

- $\xrightarrow[\text{HCl}]{\text{Sn-Hg,}}$ $C_6H_5CH_2COC_6H_5$ Desoxybenzoin
- $\xrightarrow[\text{Ether}]{\text{Na-Hg,}}$ $C_6H_5\overset{\text{OH}}{\underset{\text{OH}}{C}}HCHC_6H_5$ Hydrobenzoin 75%
- $\xrightarrow{\text{Zn-Hg}}$ $C_6H_5CH{=}CHC_6H_5$ Stilbene 55%

Benzyl esters and ethers are often made in the course of synthetic sequences to protect sensitive functional groups in polyfunctional molecules. The benzyl group may be removed by catalytic hydrogenolysis at the end of the synthesis. For example, primary amino groups can be masked by conversion to *carbobenzoxy* derivatives, as is done in one method for synthesis of *peptides* (Chap. 23).

$$\xrightarrow[\text{pyridine}]{C_6H_5CH_2Cl,} \xrightarrow{\text{Alkaline KMnO}_4} \xrightarrow{H_2, Pt} HO_2CCHOH(CH_2)_3CO_2H + C_6H_5CH_3$$

α Hydroxyadipic acid

$$C_6H_5CH_2OH + COCl_2 \longrightarrow C_6H_5CH_2O\overset{O}{\overset{\|}{C}}Cl$$

Phosgene   Carbobenzoxy chloride

$$HO_2CCH_2CH_2\overset{}{\underset{NH_2}{CH}}CO_2H \xrightarrow{C_6H_5CH_2OCOCl} HO_2CCH_2CH_2\overset{}{\underset{NHCOCH_2C_6H_5}{CH}}CO_2H \xrightarrow{(CH_3CO)_2O} \cdots \xrightarrow{} \cdots$$

Glutamic acid

$$HO_2CCH_2CH_2\overset{CO_2C_2H_5}{\underset{NHCOCH_2C_6H_5}{CHCONHCHCH_2CH_2CO_2C_2H_5}} \xrightarrow[\text{2) } H_2,\text{ Pt}]{\text{1) Ester hydrolysis}} HO_2CCH_2CH_2\overset{CO_2H}{\underset{NH_2}{CHCONHCHCH_2CH_2CO_2H}}$$

Glutamyl glutamic acid (a dipeptide)

Oxygen is removed from aromatic nuclei by dry distillation with zinc dust. The procedure has been useful in determination of the structures of natural products containing polycyclic ring systems related to aromatic compounds. Results are sometimes misleading, since rearrangements frequently occur under the drastic reaction conditions. A more gentle procedure for removing phenolic hydroxyl groups is hydrogenolysis of aryl sulfonate esters.

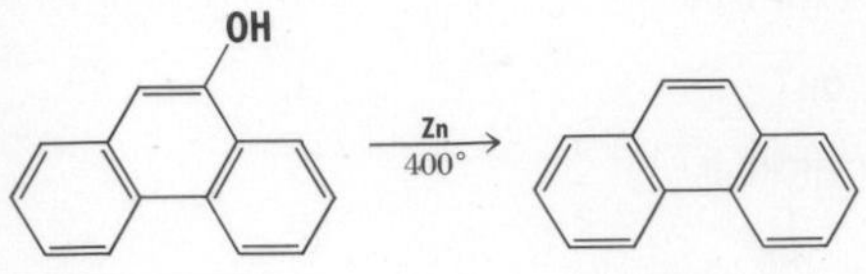

9-Phenanthrol

Phenanthrene
72%

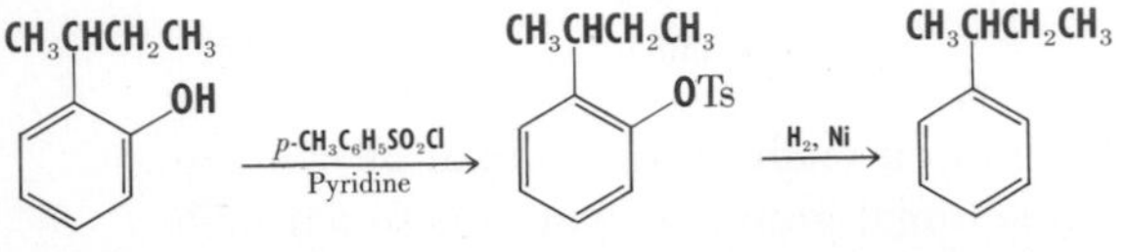

Reduction of Aldehydes and Ketones.
The carbonyl groups of aldehydes and ketones are very easily reduced to hydroxyl groups by catalytic hydrogenation (page 353) or with metal hydrides (page 278). The choice of procedure is likely to be dictated by considerations of convenience and cost. Hydrogen is much less expensive than metal hydrides, but the latter are somewhat more convenient to use on a small scale in the research laboratory. The high selectivity of sodium borohydride makes it the reagent of choice for reduction of carbonyl groups in sensitive polyfunctional molecules.

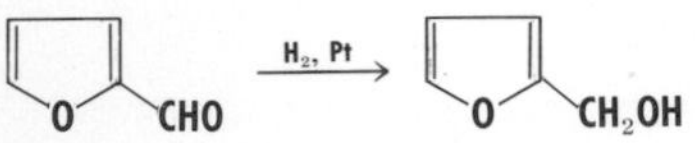

Furfural

Furylcarbinol
90%

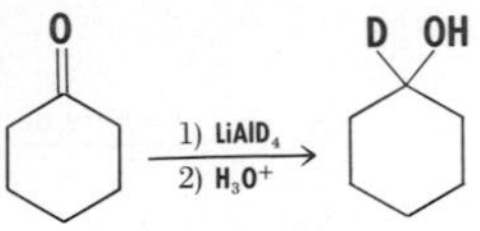

Cyclohexanol-1-*d*

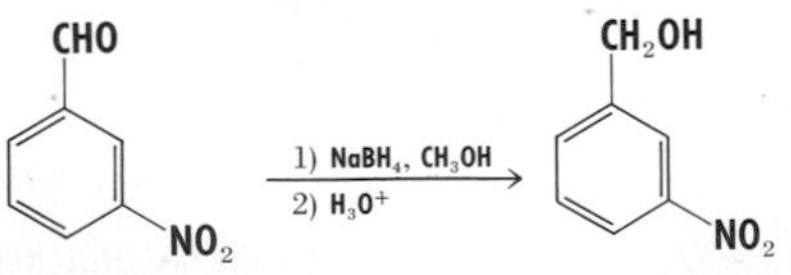

m-Nitrobenzaldehyde

m-Nitrobenzyl alcohol

The Ponndorf reduction with aluminum isopropoxide (page 280) has also been employed frequently to convert ketones to alcohols.

There are two excellent procedures for reduction of carbonyl groups to methylene groups. Alcohols, which are not reduced under the conditions of either reaction, cannot be intermediates in either case. In the *Wolf-Kishner reduction*, a ketone or aldehyde is first converted to a hydrazone, which is subsequently decomposed by heating with strong base.

The *Clemmensen reduction* involves use of zinc amalgam and hydrochloric acid. Examples of the application of both methods in syntheses were presented in Chap. 16.

Wolf-Kishner reduction:

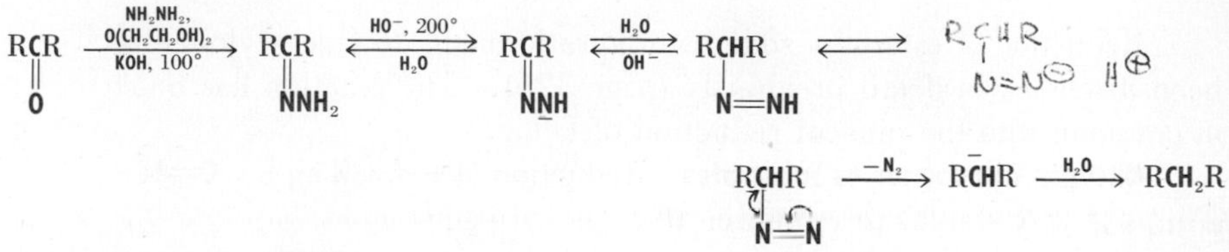

$$RCR \xrightarrow[\text{KOH, }100°]{\substack{NH_2NH_2, \\ O(CH_2CH_2OH)_2}} RCR \underset{H_2O}{\overset{HO^-, 200°}{\rightleftharpoons}} RCR \underset{OH^-}{\overset{H_2O}{\rightleftharpoons}} RCHR \rightleftharpoons \; \begin{matrix} RCHR \\ | \\ N \equiv N \end{matrix} H^{\oplus}$$

with the O, NNH_2, NNH, $N{=}NH$ groups shown below the structures.

$$\begin{matrix} RCHR \\ | \\ N = N \end{matrix} \xrightarrow{-N_2} \overset{-}{R}CHR \xrightarrow{H_2O} RCH_2R$$

$$C_6H_5CH_2COCH_2C_6H_5 \xrightarrow[\text{KOH, }200°]{\substack{NH_2NH_2, \\ O(CH_2CH_2OH)_2}} C_6H_5CH_2CH_2CH_2C_6H_5$$

Dibenzyl ketone   1,3-Diphenyl propane
                                      93%

Clemmensen reduction:

$$C_6H_5COCH_2CH_2CH_3 \xrightarrow[\text{HCl}]{\text{Zn-Hg}} C_6H_5CH_2CH_2CH_2CH_3$$

Butyrophenone   *n*-Butylbenzene

Pinacol Reduction. Reduction of ketones with magnesium amalgam or a mixture of magnesium and magnesium iodide yields *pinacols*. Symmetrical coupling can also be accomplished electrolytically with magnesium anodes, and is believed to involve monovalent magnesium.

$$Mg + MgI_2 \rightleftharpoons 2MgI \quad \text{or} \quad Mg \xrightarrow{\text{Electrolysis}} \overset{+}{Mg}\cdot + e$$

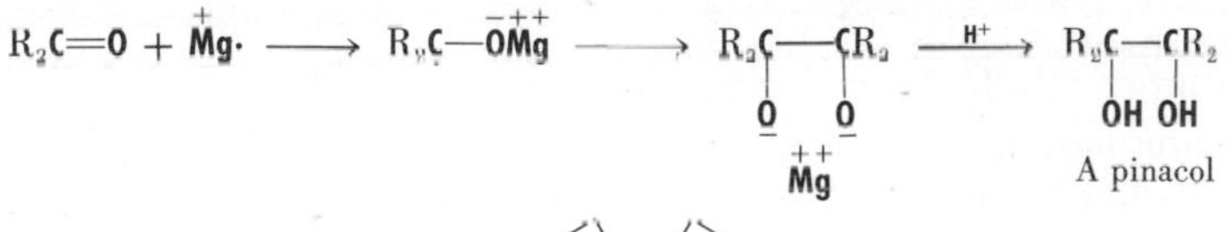

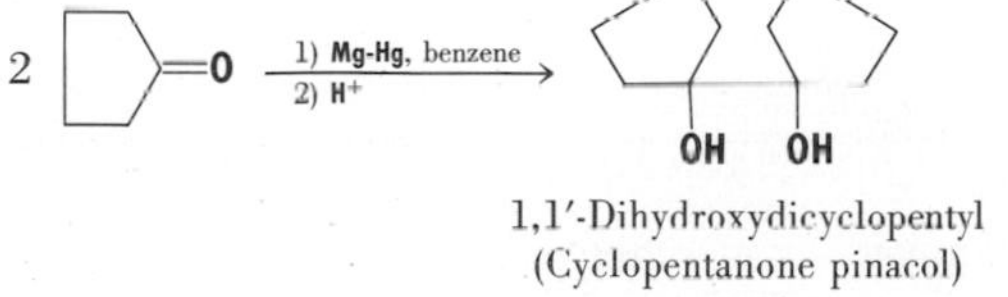

$$R_2C{=}O + \overset{+}{Mg}\cdot \longrightarrow R_2C \overset{-++}{-}OMg \longrightarrow \underset{\substack{O \quad O \\ ++ \\ Mg}}{R_2C{-}CR_2} \xrightarrow{H^+} \underset{OH \; OH}{R_2C{-}CR_2}$$

A pinacol

$$2 \; \bigcirc{=}O \xrightarrow[\text{2) H}^+]{\text{1) Mg-Hg, benzene}} \underset{OH \quad OH}{\text{(dicyclopentyl)}}$$

1,1'-Dihydroxydicyclopentyl
(Cyclopentanone pinacol)

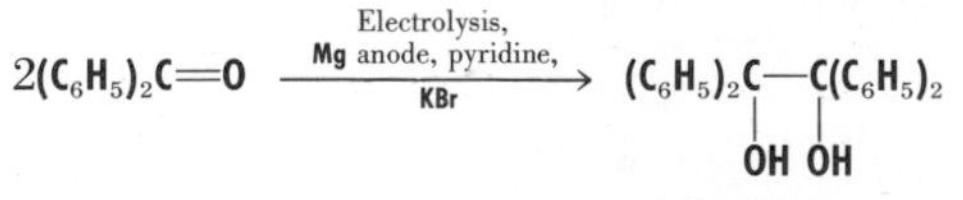

$$2(C_6H_5)_2C{=}O \xrightarrow[\text{KBr}]{\substack{\text{Electrolysis,} \\ \text{Mg anode, pyridine,}}} \underset{OH \; OH}{(C_6H_5)_2C{-}C(C_6H_5)_2}$$

Benzpinacol

Reduction of Carboxyl Groups. Carboxylic acids and all their derivatives can be reduced by lithium aluminum hydride, the only reagent which reduces acids themselves (page 279). Esters are much more readily attacked and undergo both catalytic hydrogenation (page 353) and reduction with metallic sodium and alcohol.

$$(CH_3)_3CCO_2H \xrightarrow[\text{2) H}^+]{\text{1) LiAlH}_4, \text{ ether}} (CH_3)_3CCH_2OH$$

Trimethylacetic   Neopentyl alcohol
acid

$$C_2H_5O_2C(CH_2)_8CO_2C_2H_5 \xrightarrow{\text{Na, } C_2H_5OH} HO(CH_2)_{10}OH$$

Diethyl sebacate   Decamethylene glycol
75%

$$CH_3(CH_2)_7CH\!=\!CH(CH_2)_7CO_2C_2H_5 \xrightarrow[150°]{H_2, \text{ CuCrO}_2} CH_3(CH_2)_7CH\!=\!CH(CH_2)_8OH + C_2H_5OH$$

Ethyl oleate   Oleyl alcohol

Reduction of esters by sodium in aprotic media to give acyloins has been discussed in detail previously (page 325). The reaction has much in common with the pinacol reduction of ketones.

Nitrogen Compounds as Substrates. Reduction of —C≡N and >C=N— groups is very similar to reduction of carbonyl compounds.

$$CH_3(CH_2)_4C\!\equiv\!N \xrightarrow{\text{Na, } C_2H_5OH} CH_3(CH_2)_4CH_2NH_2$$

Capronitrile

$$C_6H_5C\!\equiv\!N \xrightarrow[\text{2) } H_2O]{\text{1) LiAlH}_4} C_6H_5CH_2NH_2$$

Benzonitrile   Benzylamine

$$C_6H_5CHO \xrightarrow{CH_3(CH_2)_4NH_2} C_6H_5CH\!=\!N(CH_2)_4CH_3 \xrightarrow{H_2, \text{ Pt}} C_6H_5CH_2NH(CH_2)_4CH_3$$

A Schiff base   Benzylpentylamine,
high yield

$$\underset{\underset{\text{NOH}}{\|}}{CH_3(CH_2)_4CCH_3} \xrightarrow[1,000 \text{ psi}]{H_2, \text{ Ni}} \underset{\underset{\text{NH}_2}{|}}{CH_3(CH_2)_4CHCH_3}$$

Methyl pentyl   2-Heptylamine
ketoxime   80%

Nitro compounds and their relatives are very readily reduced by many reagents. In acidic media, nitro groups are converted smoothly to primary amino groups. Reduction in alkaline solutions is complicated by condensations among the various species present. Catalytic hydrogenation causes complete reduction very smoothly.

$$RNO_2 \xrightarrow[\text{acid}]{\text{Reducing agent,}} RNH_2$$

$$RNO_2 \xrightarrow{H_2, \text{ Pt, Pd, or Ni}} RNH_2$$

$$RNO_2 \xrightarrow[\text{alkali}]{\text{Reducing agent,}} RNO \longrightarrow RNHOH \longrightarrow RNH_2$$

Nitro   Nitroso   Hydroxylamine   Amine

$$\begin{array}{ccc}
\downarrow RNO & & \downarrow RNO \\
\left[\underset{\underset{\text{OH OH}}{|\quad|}}{RN\!-\!NR}\right] & & \left[\underset{\underset{\text{OH}}{|}}{RN\!-\!NHR}\right] \\
\downarrow -H_2O & & \downarrow -H_2O \\
\underset{\underset{\text{O}}{|}}{\overset{+}{RN}\!=\!NR} & & RN\!=\!NR \longrightarrow RNHNHR \\
\text{Azoxy} & & \text{Azo} \qquad\qquad \text{Hydrazo}
\end{array}$$

Since aromatic nitro compounds are easily made by nitration reactions, they are used as starting materials in syntheses of virtually all aryl-nitrogen compounds.

Ammonium polysulfide reduces many dinitro compounds selectively to nitroamines.

m Dinitrobenzene   *m*-Nitroaniline

Nitroalkanes can be reduced to amines either by catalytic hydrogenolysis or with lithium aluminum hydride. This reaction, coupled with base-catalyzed condensation reactions of nitroalkanes (page 286), provides a good synthetic route to amino alcohols.

$$CH_3CH_2\underset{\underset{NO_2}{|}}{C}HCH_3 \xrightarrow[\text{2) } H_2O]{\text{1) LiAlH}_4} CH_3CH_2\underset{\underset{NH_2}{|}}{C}HCH_3$$

2-Nitrobutane   2-Aminobutane
                        85%

$$CH_3CH_2CH_2NO_2 + CH_2O \xrightarrow{\text{NaOH}} CH_3CH_2\underset{\underset{NO_2}{|}}{C}HCH_2OH \xrightarrow[\text{2) Ca(OH)}_2]{\text{1) Fe, H}_2\text{SO}_4} CH_3CH_2\underset{\underset{NH_2}{|}}{C}HCH_2OH$$

                       2-Nitro-1-butanol   2-Amino-1-butanol
                                                      90%

Reduction of Sulfur Compounds. Hydrogenolysis of carbon-sulfur bonds is carried out with excess Raney nickel. Catalytic hydrogenolysis is not successful, because catalysts are poisoned by sulfur compounds. Nickel desulfurization is frequently used in indirect reductive procedures.

$C_6H_5CH_2CH_2OH \xrightarrow{SOCl_2} C_6H_5CH_2CH_2Cl \xrightarrow{Na_2S_2O_3} C_6H_5CH_2CH_2S-\overset{-}{S}O_3\overset{+}{Na} \xrightarrow[NaOD]{Ni-Al} C_6H_5CH_2CH_2D$

β-Phenylethanol   1-Phenylethane-1-*d*

Problems

1. Make a list of all oxidizing and reducing agents mentioned in this chapter, and give one example of a use for each.

2. With starting materials containing no more than six carbon atoms, write equations for syntheses of the following substances:

a. Cyclohexanone

b. $C_6H_5CH_2CH_2N(CH_3)_2$

c. $C_6H_5CH_2CHO$

d. 1,2-Cyclodecanedione

e. 1-Methylnaphthalene

f. *m*-Aminotoluene

g. 1,6-Cyclodecanedione

h.

i. $C_6H_5CHOHCHNH_2CH_2CH_2CH_3$

j.

k. $CH_3(CH_2)_5CH_2\overset{+}{N}(CH_3)_2$
                      |
                      $\overset{-}{O}$

l. $C_6H_5CH_2SO_3H$

m. $CH_3CH_2CH_2CHCH_2CH_2CH_3$
                            |
                            NH_2

n.

o. 4,5-Nonanedione

p. $C_6H_5(CH_2)_5CHO$

q. $CH_3(CH_2)_{10}CO_2H$

r. $[CH_3(CH_2)_4]_2SO_2$

s. *trans*-4-Octene

t. Cyclodecane

3. Formulate examples of the following:

a. A quinone with a higher and one with a lower oxidation potential than methylbenzoquinone.

b. Five separate methods for conversion of a ketone to a hydrocarbon.

c. Three methods for introduction of a blocking group in an aromatic ring and its subsequent removal.

d. Five reactions or processes for degradation of a carbon chain by one carbon atom.

e. Three ways of making aromatic compounds from saturated hydrocarbons.

f. Four ways of converting an alcohol to a hydrocarbon having the same number of carbon atoms.

g. Two compounds in which iodine has a valence of more than one.

h. All compounds that can be prepared from aniline or nitrobenzene through use of either oxidizing or reducing agents.

i. A compound which would give a positive Tollens' test, would give between one and two moles of acetic acid in a terminal-methyl determination (page 28), and which would react with one mole of periodic acid to give one mole of formic acid and an aldehyde.

j. Three reactions making use of metals in either liquid ammonia or primary amine solutions.

4. An unknown compound, $C_{10}H_{12}O$, when treated with $(NaSO_3)_2NO\cdot$ gave a quinone. The original substance, when heated with zinc, gave a new substance $C_{10}H_{12}$, which, when treated with palladium at $210°$, gave two moles of hydrogen and a new compound $C_{10}H_8$. Write equations for the reactions.

5. Phenanthrene, when catalytically reduced with only one mole of hydrogen, added hydrogen in the 9,10-positions. Careful oxidation of the product with nitric acid introduced a carbonyl group into the 9-position. Write equations for these reactions, and indicate with additional equations how the following compound could be prepared.

6. Formulate mechanisms for the reduction reactions of benzoin shown on page 445.

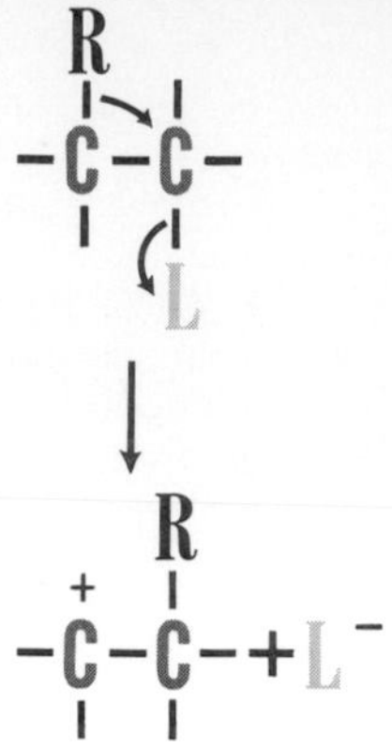

20

Molecular Rearrangements

A vastly simplifying assumption in the study of organic chemistry is that reactions occur at various functional groups and leave carbon skeletons unchanged. However, many reactions are encountered in which functional groups migrate within molecules, or carbon skeletons are modified. Examples of *molecular rearrangements* have been mentioned in earlier chapters, since the entities which rearrange are usually intermediates encountered in the course of ordinary functional-group transformations.

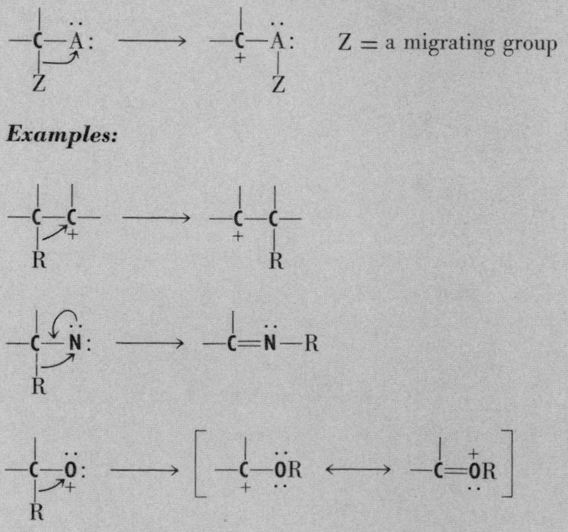

Z = a migrating group

Examples:

FIG. 20.1 *Rearrangement of an electron-deficient system.*

Rearrangement of Electron-deficient Systems

A large family of molecular rearrangements involve the migration of a group from carbon to an adjacent atom which has only six electrons in its valence shell. The rearranging entity may be either a cation or a neutral molecule.

The migrating group, Z, in 1,2-shifts may be halogen, oxygen, sulfur, nitrogen, carbon, or hydrogen. The migrating group never leaves the molecule. If Z has nonbonding electrons, they are used in the migration, and metastable cyclic intermediates are formed during the reaction.

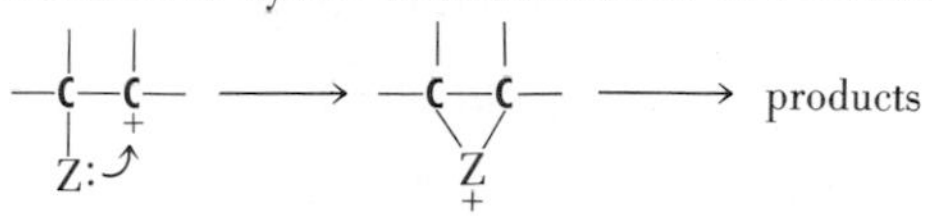

$$-\overset{|}{\underset{\underset{Z:}{\overset{|}{+}}}{C}}-\overset{|}{\underset{|}{C}}- \longrightarrow -\overset{|}{C}\underset{\underset{Z}{\overset{}{+}}}{\diagup\diagdown}\overset{|}{C}- \longrightarrow \text{products}$$

In these cases, the cyclic ions are often formed as the first intermediates by neighboring-group participation in a solvolytic substitution or in electrophilic addition reactions. The ions are opened directly by nucleophilic substitution.

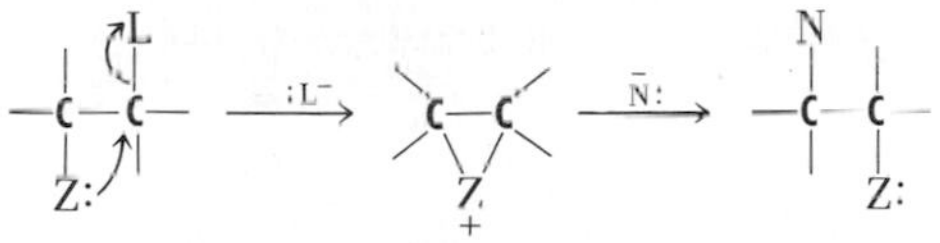

$$-\overset{|}{\underset{Z:}{C}}-\overset{L}{\underset{|}{C}}- \xrightarrow{:L^-} \underset{\underset{Z}{\overset{}{+}}}{\diagup\diagdown}\overset{}{C}\!\!-\!\!C \xrightarrow{\bar{N}:} -\overset{N}{\underset{}{C}} \overset{}{\underset{Z:}{C}}-$$

If the migrating group is saturated carbon or hydrogen, the transition state for the rearrangement step has only the electrons from the bond being broken to bind the system together. The intermediate stage is then best described by a molecular-orbital picture in which one pair of electrons forms three bonds. Such *bridge bonds* are well known in the boron hydrides, a group of stable electron-deficient compounds (Fig. 20.2).

Halogen, Oxygen, Sulfur, and Nitrogen Migration. Hetero-atom migration is commonly encountered in solvolysis reactions, and the neighboring nucleophilic atom usually participates directly in the first ionization step (page 240). The three-membered ring that is formed may be opened at C_α, which gives over-all substitution with retention of configuration, or at

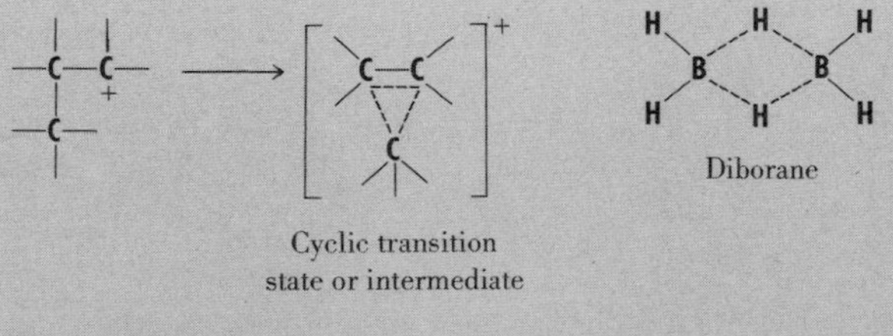

FIG. 20.2   Bridge bonds.

C_β, which gives rearrangement. If the intermediate ions are unsymmetrical, they are opened at whatever center tolerates a positive charge most easily.†

$$(CH_3)_2\underset{CH_3O\colon}{C_\beta}\!\!-\!\!C_\alpha HCH_3 \xrightarrow[-\,AgBr]{Ag^+} (CH_3)_2C_\beta\!\!-\!\!C_\alpha HCH_3 \xrightarrow[-\,H^+]{H_2O} (CH_3)_2C\!\!-\!\!CHCH_3$$

An ethylene
oxonium ion

$$CH_3CHCH_2OH \underset{C_2H_5S}{\overset{HCl}{\rightleftharpoons}} CH_3CH\!\!-\!\!CH_2 \xrightarrow{-H_2O} CH_3CH\!\!-\!\!CH_2 \xrightarrow{Cl^-} CH_3CHCH_2SC_2H_5$$

| 2-[Ethylmercapto]-1-propanol | An ethylene sulfonium ion | 2-Chloro-1-propyl ethyl sulfide |

$$C_6H_5CH\!\!-\!\!CHCOCH_3 \xrightarrow{-Br^-} C_6H_5CH\!\!-\!\!CHCOCH_3 \xrightarrow{HN\,O} C_6H_5CH\!\!-\!\!CHCOCH_3$$

| 3-Bromo-4-piperidino-4-phenyl-2-butanone | A cyclic immonium ion | 3-Piperidino-4-morpholino-4-phenyl-2-butanone |

| 2-[Chloromethyl]-1-ethyl-pyrolidine | | 3-Chloro-1-ethylpiperidine |

† The opening of small positively charged ring systems was not well understood for a long time. The direction of opening suggested that the ions were opened by an S_N1 mechanism.

However, the stereochemistry and very fast rate of the reaction indicate that it must involve direct attack by a nucleophile. It is now recognized that some S_N2 reactions involve transition states which have a distinct "S_N1 character." Such a description implies that structures such as II make a very important contribution to the transition state.

Stable cyclic compounds may be produced if the migrating hetero atom carries a hydrogen atom which can be eliminated as a proton.

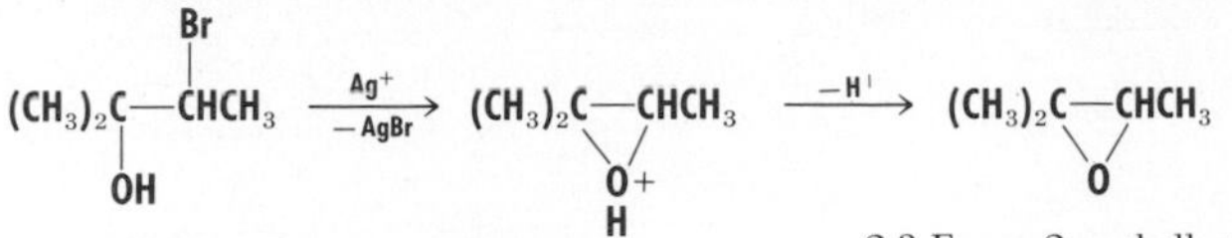

$$(CH_3)_2\underset{\underset{OH}{|}}{C}\!-\!\overset{\overset{Br}{|}}{C}HCH_3 \xrightarrow[-\,AgBr]{Ag^+} (CH_3)_2C\!-\!CHCH_3 \xrightarrow{-H^+} (CH_3)_2C\!-\!CHCH_3$$

2,3-Epoxy-2-methylbutane

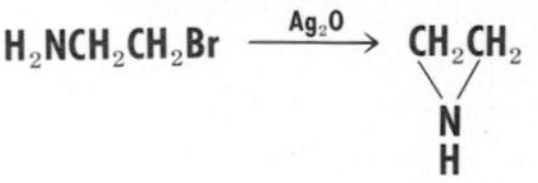

$$H_2NCH_2CH_2Br \xrightarrow{Ag_2O} CH_2CH_2$$

Ethyleneimine

Acyl and Related Migrating Groups. Rearrangements by way of five-membered cyclic ions are exemplified by the migration of acetoxyl groups in solvolysis reactions (see Fig. 20.3).

Five-membered rings may be opened with inversion of configuration at the carbon atom that can best support a positive charge. They are also opened by an entirely different mechanism, which involves attack at the carbonyl group.

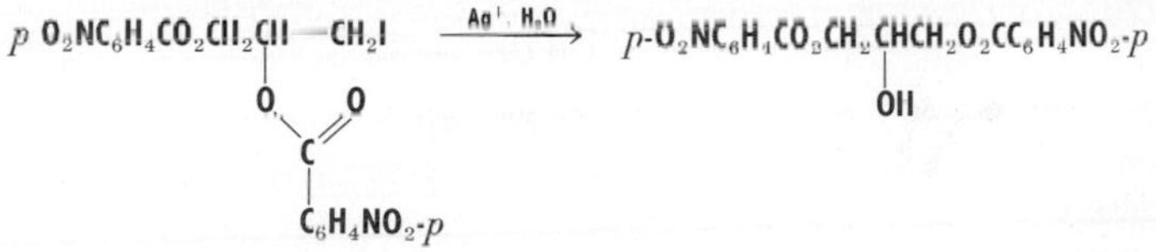

$$p\text{-}O_2NC_6H_4CO_2CH_2CH\!-\!CH_2I \xrightarrow{Ag^+,\ H_2O} p\text{-}O_2NC_6H_4CO_2CH_2CHCH_2O_2CC_6H_4NO_2\text{-}p$$

1-Iodo-2,3-di-[*p*-nitrobenzoyloxy]propane   1,3-Di-[*p*-nitrobenzoyloxy]-2-propanol

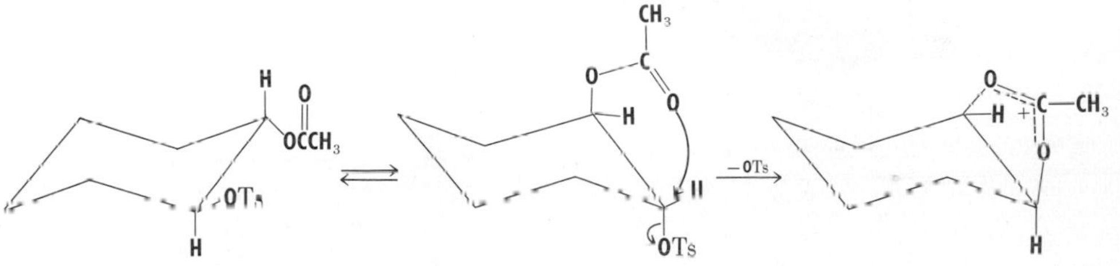

trans-2-Acetoxycyclohexyl
tosylate

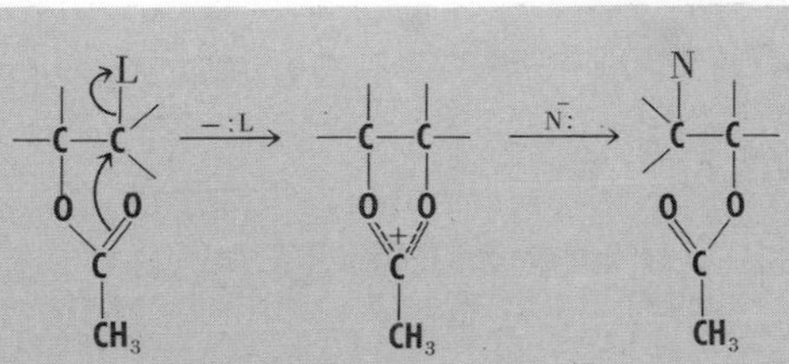

FIG. 20.3 *Acetoxyl migration.*

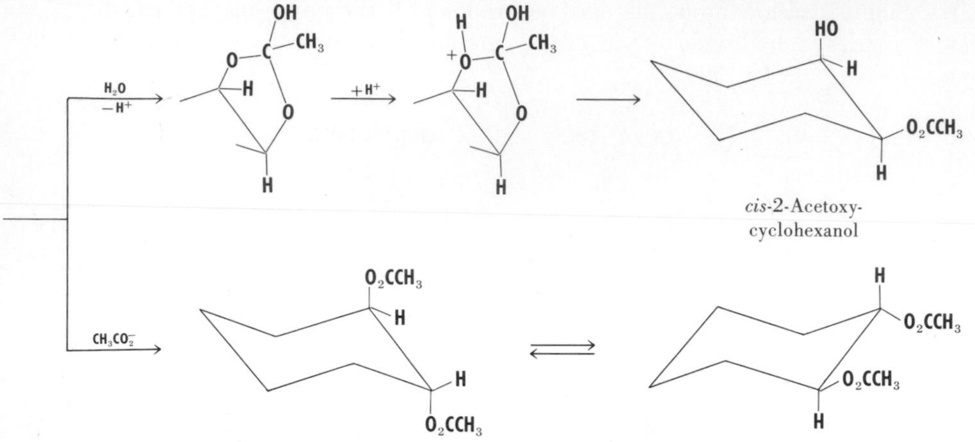

cis-2-Acetoxy-
cyclohexanol

trans-1,2-Diacetoxycyclohexane

In a second family of rearrangements, acyl groups migrate from one hetero atom to another. The benzoyl substituent of ephedrine migrates from nitrogen to oxygen, or in the reverse direction, depending on the acidity of the medium in which the compound is dissolved.

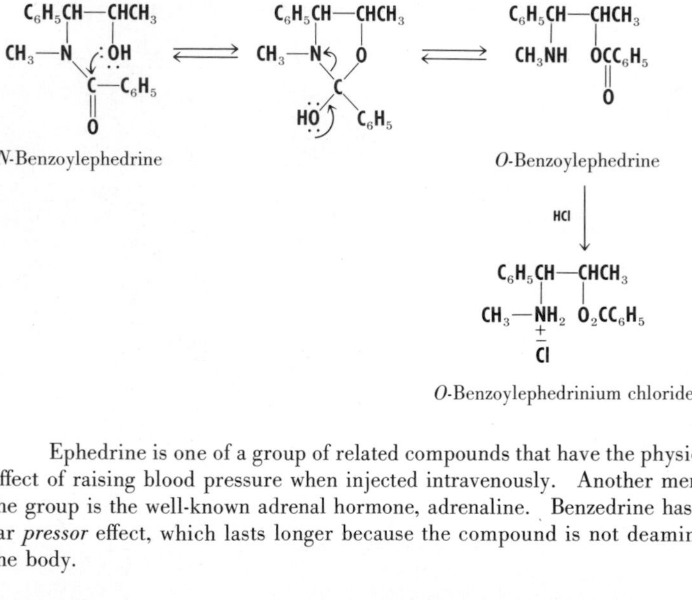

N-Benzoylephedrine

O-Benzoylephedrine

O-Benzoylephedrinium chloride

Ephedrine is one of a group of related compounds that have the physiological effect of raising blood pressure when injected intravenously. Another member of the group is the well-known adrenal hormone, adrenaline. Benzedrine has a similar *pressor* effect, which lasts longer because the compound is not deaminated in the body.

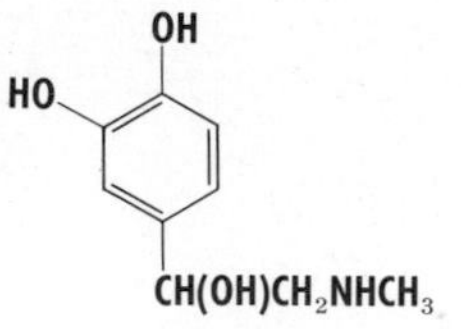

Adrenaline

$C_6H_5CH(OH)CH(CH_3)NHCH_3$

Benzedrine

If the geometry of a system is favorable, 1,3-acyl migrations occur. The rearrangements have been carefully studied with the acetyl derivatives of the alkaloid degradation products, nortropine and ψ-nortropine. The results have been used to establish the stereochemistry of the parent alkaloids.

ψ-Tropine $\xleftarrow{CH_3I}$ ψ-Nortropine $\underset{(CH_3CO)_2O}{\overset{HCl,\ H_2O}{\rightleftharpoons}}$ N-Acetyl-ψ-nortropine $\underset{OH^-}{\overset{H^+}{\rightleftharpoons}}$ O-Acetyl-ψ-nortropinium cation

Tropine $\xleftarrow{CH_3I}$ Nortropine $\underset{HCl,\ H_2O}{\overset{(CH_3CO)_2O}{\rightleftharpoons}}$ N-Acetylnortropine $\xrightarrow{HCl}$ no reaction

Migration to Oxygen. In the *Baeyer-Villiger oxidation*, a ketone is converted to an ester by reaction with a peracid. The reaction has been studied carefully, and evidence indicates that the key step in the mechanism is heterolytic dissociation of the **O—O** bond of an adduct formed from a peracid and a carbonyl compound.

$$RCR + R'COOH \rightleftharpoons \cdots \xleftarrow{H^+} \cdots \longrightarrow$$

$$\left[RCOR \longleftrightarrow RCOR \longleftrightarrow RC{=}OR \right] \xrightarrow{-H^+} RCOR$$

Over-all reaction: $R_2CO + R'CO_3H \longrightarrow RCO_2R + R'CO_2H$

The *migratory aptitudes* of various groups have been studied by internal-competition experiments with unsymmetrical ketones. The groups best able to support a positive charge move most easily. This shows that *the migrating group must acquire some of the character of a carbonium ion in the transition state of the rearrangement step*. The point is noteworthy because a rather different set of migratory aptitudes are observed in the rearrangements of alkyl groups to electron-deficient

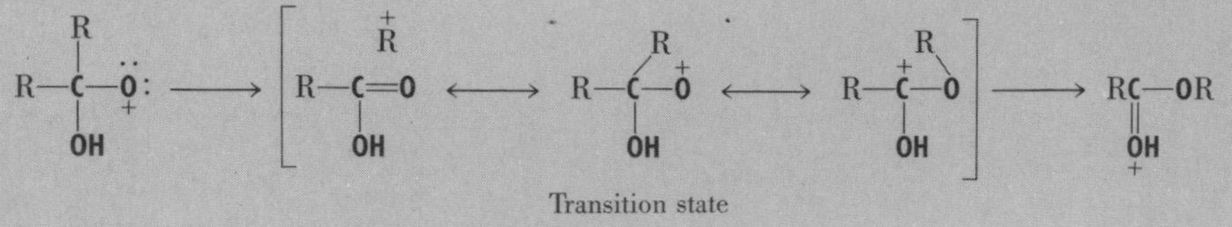

FIG. 20.4   *Rearrangement to a positive oxygen atom.*

carbon.   The difference arises from the fact that oxygen has a higher electron affinity than carbon (see Fig. 20.4).

$$C_6H_5COCH_3 \quad + \quad CF_3CO_3H \xrightarrow{CH_2Cl_2,\ CF_3CO_2H} C_6H_5O_2CCH_3 + CF_3CO_2H$$

Acetophenone   Peroxytrifluoracetic
                                    acid

$$(CH_3)_3CCOCH_3 + CF_3CO_3H \xrightarrow{CH_2Cl_2,\ CF_3CO_2H} CH_3CO_2C(CH_3)_3 + CF_3CO_2H$$

Pinacalone
(*t*-Butyl methyl ketone)

Peroxytrifluoroacetic acid is the most reactive peracid known, but both peracetic acid and perbenzoic acid have been used with good results. A related transformation is the *Dakin oxidation* of *o*- and *p*-hydroxybenz-aldehydes or phenyl ketones by the action of alkaline hydrogen peroxide. The esters are usually hydrolyzed under the reaction conditions.

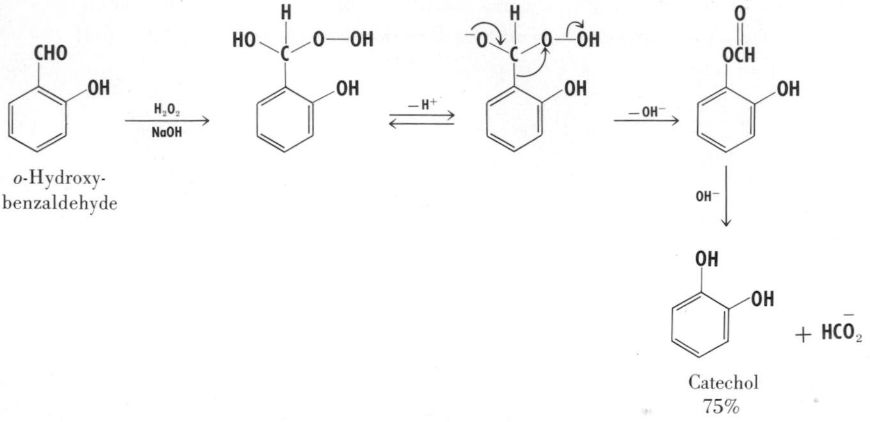

o-Hydroxy-
benzaldehyde

Catechol
75%

Migration to Nitrogen.   The *Beckmann rearrangement* is an acid-catalyzed transformation of a ketoxime to an amide.   The reaction is highly stereospecific in that the group which is anti (trans) to the hydroxyl group always migrates.

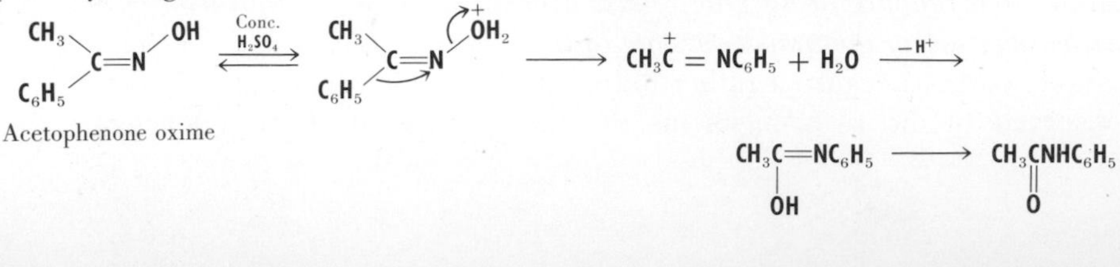

Acetophenone oxime

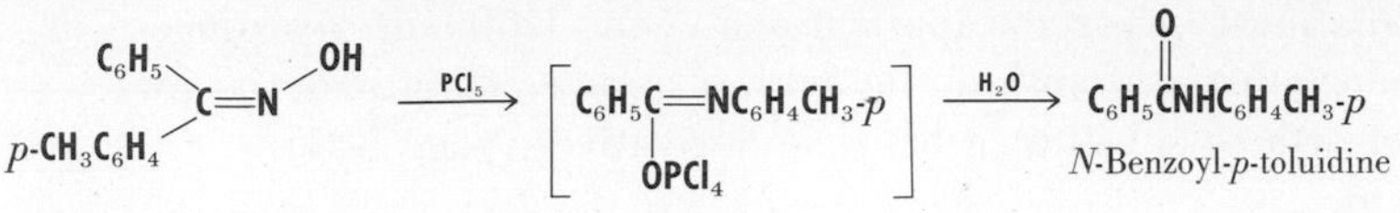

$$p\text{-}CH_3C_6H_4 \overset{C_6H_5}{\underset{}{>}}C=N\overset{OH}{} \xrightarrow{PCl_5} \left[C_6H_5C=NC_6H_4CH_3\text{-}p \atop OPCl_4 \right] \xrightarrow{H_2O} C_6H_5\overset{O}{\overset{\|}{C}}NHC_6H_4CH_3\text{-}p$$

N-Benzoyl-*p*-toluidine

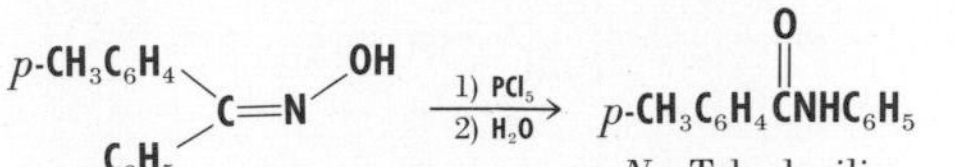

$$p\text{-}CH_3C_6H_4 \overset{}{\underset{C_6H_5}{>}}C=N\overset{OH}{} \xrightarrow[\text{2) }H_2O]{\text{1) }PCl_5} p\text{-}CH_3C_6H_4\overset{O}{\overset{\|}{C}}NHC_6H_5$$

N-*p*-Toluylaniline

The Beckmann rearrangement has interesting synthetic applications, including the preparation of ε-caprolactam. The lactam in turn is polymerized to a linear polyamide, which may be spun into a synthetic fiber known as Perlon.

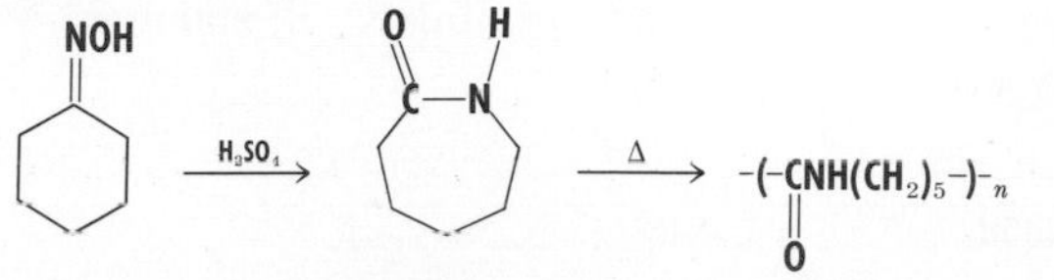

Cyclohexanone   ε-Caprolactam   Perlon
oxime   65%

A group of reactions which are closely related to the Beckmann transformation convert *N*-substituted amides to isocyanates. If the reactions are carried out in water solution, the isocyanate is hydrolyzed to give a primary amine. The *Hofmann rearrangement* of *N*-haloamides is the most frequently used of the group. The reactions are useful for conversion of carboxylic acids and their derivatives to amines that contain one less carbon atom than the starting materials. Such a procedure is useful if the amine cannot be made directly by a nucleophilic substitution reaction.

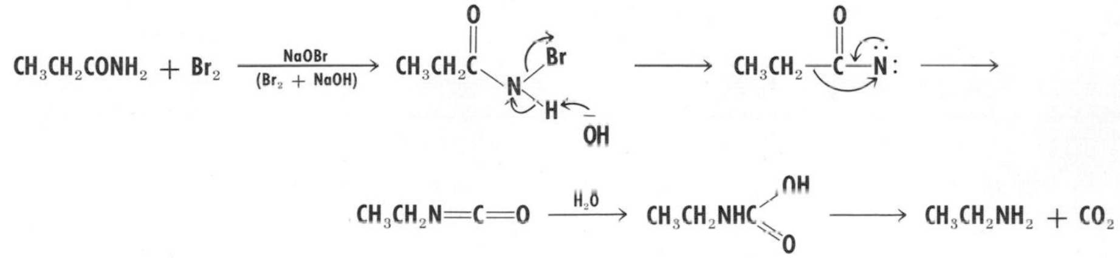

Ethylisocyanate   *N*-Ethylcarbamic acid   Ethylamine
90%

$$(CH_3)_3CCH_2CONH_2 \xrightarrow{NaOBr} (CH_3)_3CCH_2NH_2$$

β,β-Dimethylbutyramide   Neopentylamine
94%

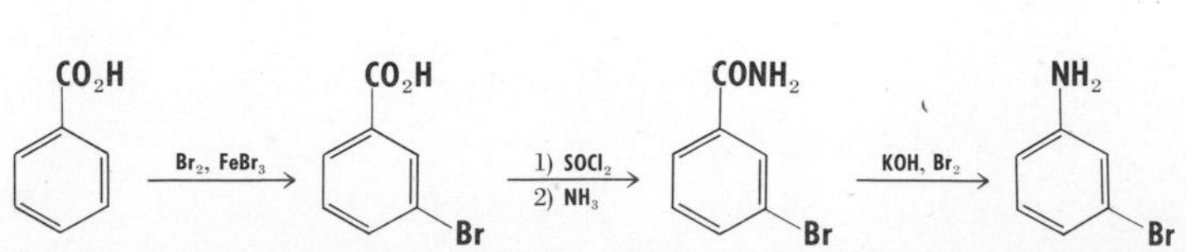

m-Bromobenzamide   *m*-Bromoaniline
87% (last step)

One of the most important applications of the Hofmann rearrangement is in the synthesis of anthranilic acid, a basic starting material for preparation of ortho-disubstituted benzene derivatives (page 384).

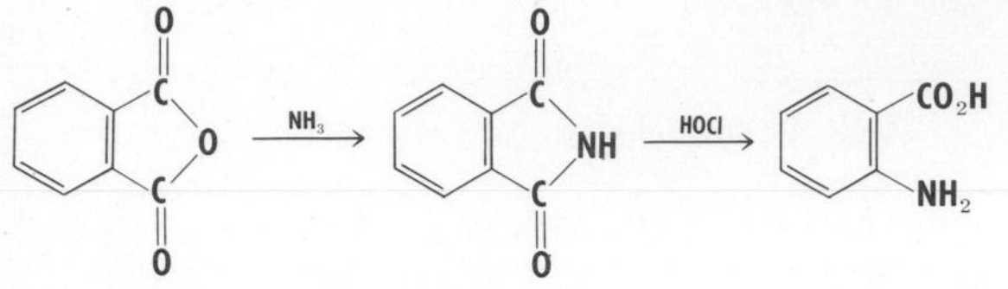

Phthalic anhydride   Phthalimide   Anthranilic acid

In the *Lossen rearrangement*, a salt of a hydroxamic acid or a related compound is decomposed in a manner strictly analogous to N-haloamide decomposition. The relative inaccessibility of starting materials has limited synthetic use of the reaction.

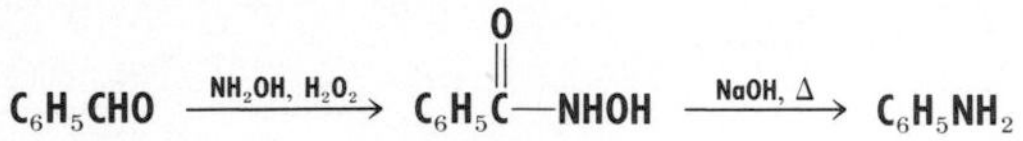

$$C_6H_5CHO \xrightarrow{NH_2OH, \ H_2O_2} C_6H_5\overset{O}{\overset{\|}{C}}-NHOH \xrightarrow{NaOH, \ \Delta} C_6H_5NH_2$$

Phenylhydroxamic
acid

The *Curtius rearrangement* results from the thermal decomposition of an acyl azide. The reaction can be carried out in inert solvents, which favor isolation of the isocyanates. The azides required as starting materials may be made by the reaction of acid chlorides with sodium azide or by the reaction of acyl hydrazides with nitrous acid.

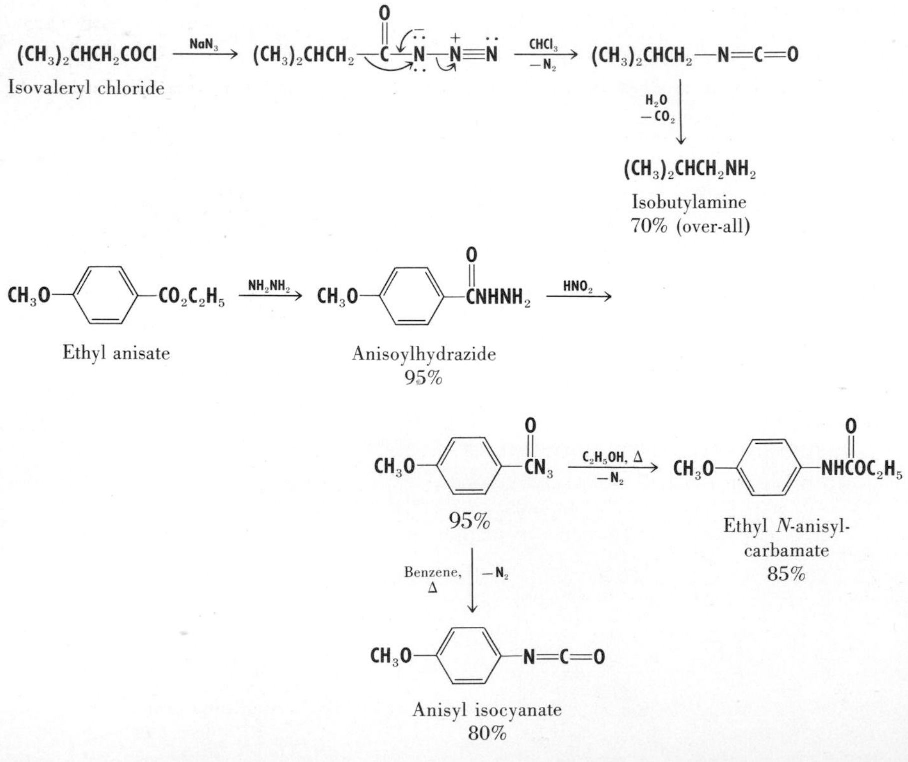

$(CH_3)_2CHCH_2COCl \xrightarrow{NaN_3} (CH_3)_2CHCH_2-\overset{O}{\overset{\|}{C}}-\ddot{N}-\overset{+}{N}\equiv\ddot{N} \xrightarrow[-N_2]{CHCl_3} (CH_3)_2CHCH_2-N=C=O$
Isovaleryl chloride

$\xrightarrow[-CO_2]{H_2O}$

$(CH_3)_2CHCH_2NH_2$
Isobutylamine
70% (over-all)

Ethyl anisate   Anisoylhydrazide
95%

95%   Ethyl N-anisyl-
carbamate
85%

Benzene, | $-N_2$
Δ

Anisyl isocyanate
80%

The reactions of hydrazoic acid with carboxylic acids and ketones in the presence of concentrated sulfuric acid are known as *Schmidt rearrangements*. The reaction with acids is similar to the Curtius and Hofmann rearrangements, and the reaction with ketones resembles the Beckmann transformation. Yields are usually high, and sterically hindered acids react very smoothly. The rate-determining step in the reaction is the formation of an acyl cation, a process accelerated by bulky groups.

Schmidt reaction with acids:

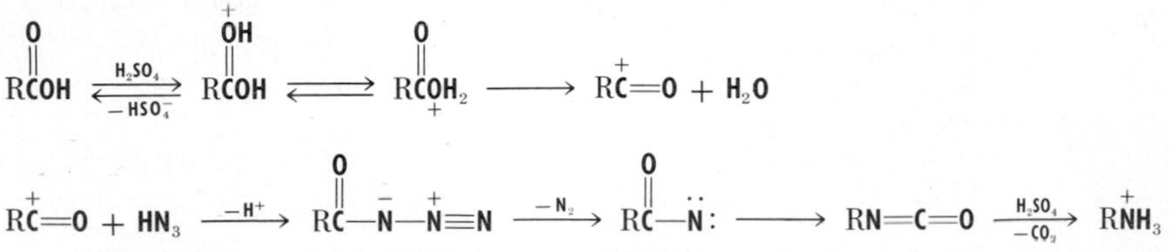

$$RCOH \xrightleftharpoons[-HSO_4^-]{H_2SO_4} R\overset{+}{C}OH \rightleftharpoons R\overset{+}{C}OH_2 \longrightarrow R\overset{+}{C}{=}O + H_2O$$

$$R\overset{+}{C}{=}O + HN_3 \xrightarrow{-H^+} RC{-}\overset{-}{N}{-}\overset{+}{N}{\equiv}N \xrightarrow{-N_2} RC{-}\overset{..}{N}: \longrightarrow RN{=}C{=}O \xrightarrow[-CO_2]{H_2SO_4} R\overset{+}{N}H_3$$

Hydrazoic acid

Schmidt reaction with ketones:

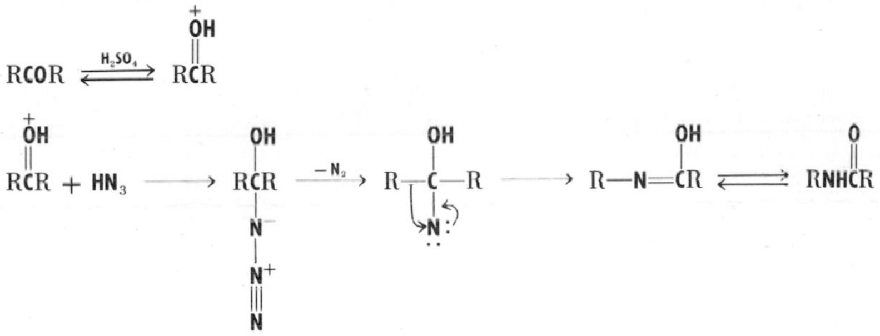

$$RCOR \xrightleftharpoons{H_2SO_4} R\overset{+}{\underset{}{C}}R\,\overset{\overset{+}{O}H}{}$$

$$R\overset{+}{C}R + HN_3 \longrightarrow RCR \xrightarrow{-N_2} R{-}\underset{}{C}{-}R \longrightarrow R{-}N{=}CR \rightleftharpoons RNHCR$$

$$CH_3(CH_2)_4CO_2H + HN_3 \xrightarrow{H_2SO_4} CH_3(CH_2)_4NH_2$$
Hexanoic acid   *n* Pentylamine
70–75%

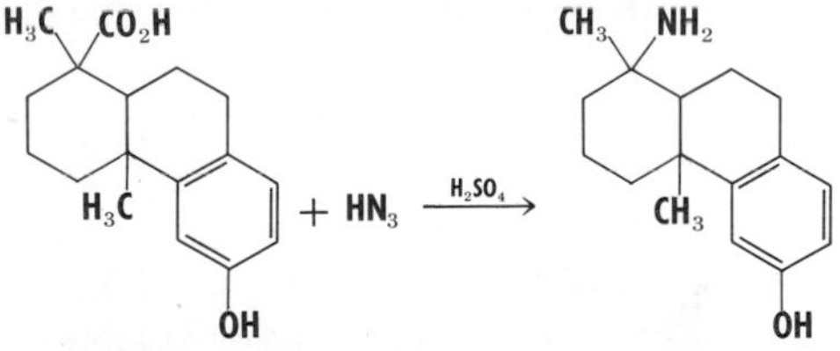

Podocarpic acid   73%

$$C_6H_5COCH_3 + HN_3 \xrightarrow{H_2SO_4} CH_3CONHC_6H_5$$
Acetophenone   Acetanilide
77%

In all rearrangements of electron-deficient nitrogen compounds, the steric configuration of the migrating group is retained. The fact was

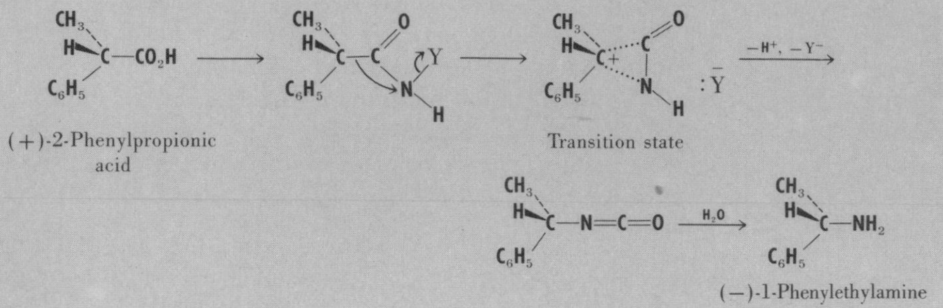

CH$_3$
H—C—CO$_2$H $\longrightarrow$
C$_6$H$_5$

(+)-2-Phenylpropionic
acid

CH$_3$ O
H—C—C$\diagdown$Y $\longrightarrow$
C$_6$H$_5$ N—H

CH$_3$ O
H—C$^+$···C
C$_6$H$_5$ N   :Ȳ $\xrightarrow{-H^+,\ -Y^-}$
H

Transition state

CH$_3$
H—C—N=C=O $\xrightarrow{H_2O}$
C$_6$H$_5$

CH$_3$
H—C—NH$_2$
C$_6$H$_5$

(−)-1-Phenylethylamine

FIG. 20.5 *Steric course of rearrangements to an electron-deficient nitrogen atom. Retention of configuration has been demonstrated in the Beckmann, Hofmann, Lossen, Curtius, and Schmidt rearrangements.*

established by conversion of derivatives of (+)-2-phenylpropionic acid to either (−)-α-phenylethylamine or to amides which can be hydrolyzed to give the latter. The acid and amine are known to have the same relative configurations from independent correlation studies. Figure 20.5 shows the mechanism of rearrangement in detail.

Migration to Carbon. Electron-deficient carbon atoms are produced in the course of solvolytic substitution and elimination reactions, and by electrophilic addition to olefins and acetylenes. Rearrangements occur regularly in the course of such reactions if the intermediate carbonium ions can be converted to more stable ions by 1,2-shifts of hydrogen atoms or alkyl or aryl groups. In some instances, rearrangement is initiated before a carbonium ion is formed, and in some solvolytic reactions acceleration of rate is attributed to driving force supplied by the migrating group. The rearrangements of neopentyl compounds under conditions designed to effect substitution or electrophilic additions are representative.

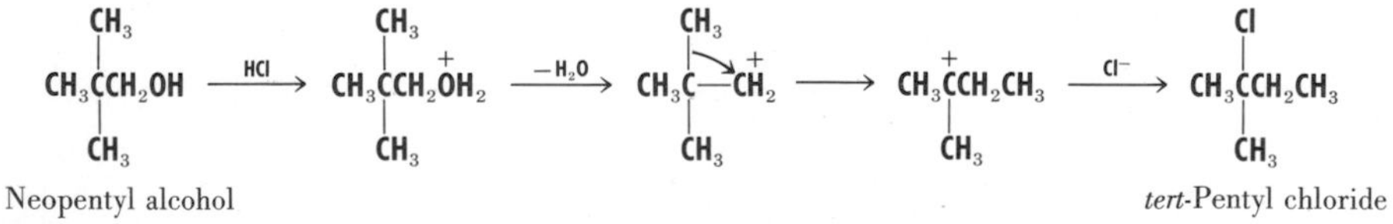

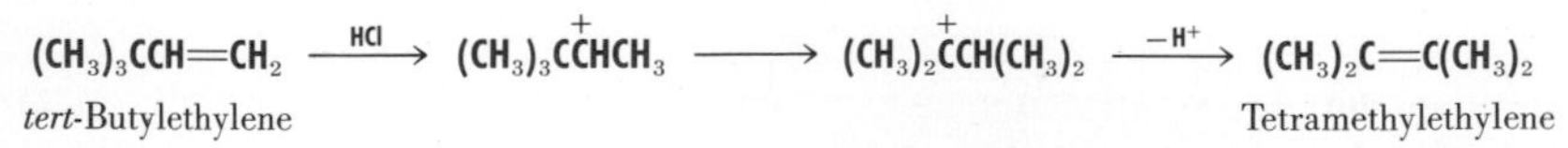

CH$_3$
CH$_3$CCH$_2$OH $\xrightarrow{HCl}$
CH$_3$

CH$_3$
CH$_3$CCH$_2$OH$_2^+$ $\xrightarrow{-H_2O}$
CH$_3$

CH$_3$
CH$_3$C$-^+$CH$_2$ $\longrightarrow$
CH$_3$

CH$_3$CCH$_2$CH$_3$ $\xrightarrow{Cl^-}$
CH$_3$

Cl
CH$_3$CCH$_2$CH$_3$
CH$_3$

Neopentyl alcohol   *tert*-Pentyl chloride

(CH$_3$)$_3$CCH=CH$_2$ $\xrightarrow{HCl}$ (CH$_3$)$_3$CCHCH$_3$ $\longrightarrow$ (CH$_3$)$_2$CCH(CH$_3$)$_2$ $\xrightarrow{-H^+}$ (CH$_3$)$_2$C=C(CH$_3$)$_2$

tert-Butylethylene   Tetramethylethylene

Pinacol Rearrangements. Attempts to dehydrate *vic*-diols (pinacols) usually lead to rearrangements with formation of ketones. Because the highly branched structures of the products are not easily constructed by other reactions, the rearrangement has found interesting applications in synthesis. Pinacols themselves are made by reduction of ketones with bivalent metals, usually magnesium, under anhydrous conditions (page 447).

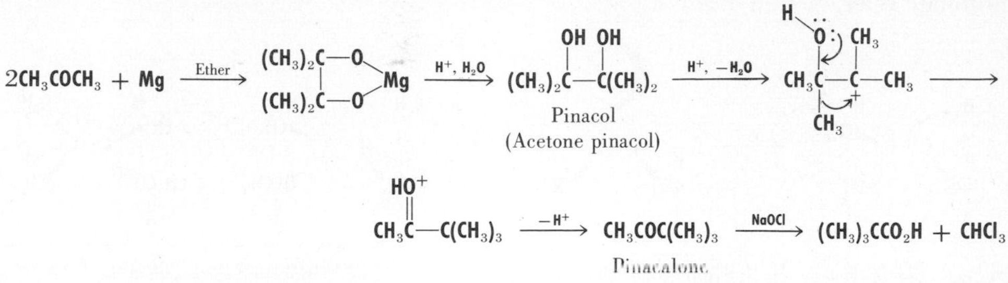
Ether
H⁺, H₂O
Pinacol
(Acetone pinacol)
H⁺, −H₂O
−H⁺
NaOCl
Pinacolone

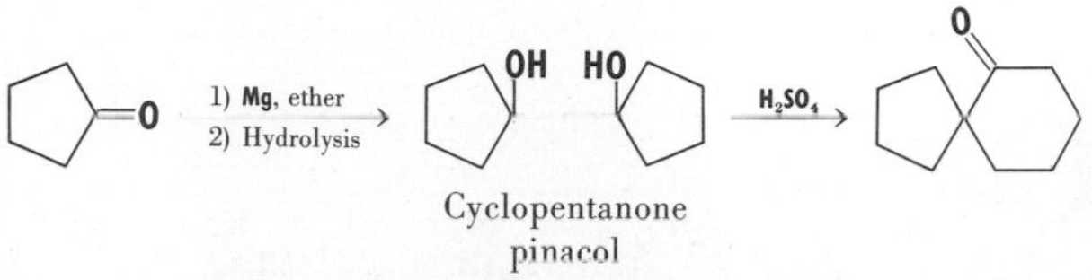
1) Mg, ether
2) Hydrolysis
H₂SO₄
Cyclopentanone
pinacol

Wagner-Meerwein Rearrangements. Rearrangement of alcohols under acidic conditions was originally known as the Wagner-Meerwein rearrangement, but the term has been broadened to include rearrangements which involve many other leaving groups. A wide variety of substrates and electrophilic reagents are involved.

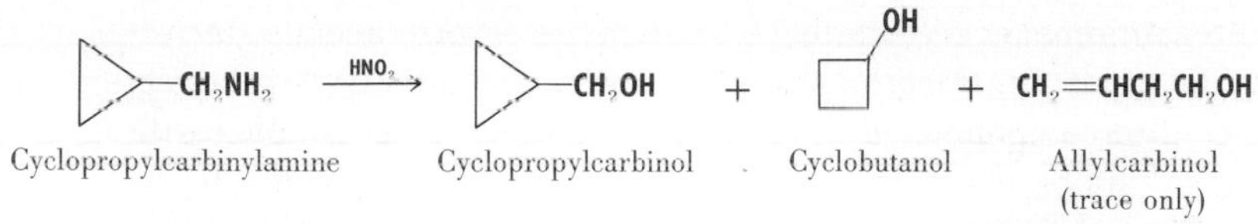
HNO₂
Cyclopropylcarbinylamine
Cyclopropylcarbinol
Cyclobutanol
Allylcarbinol
(trace only)

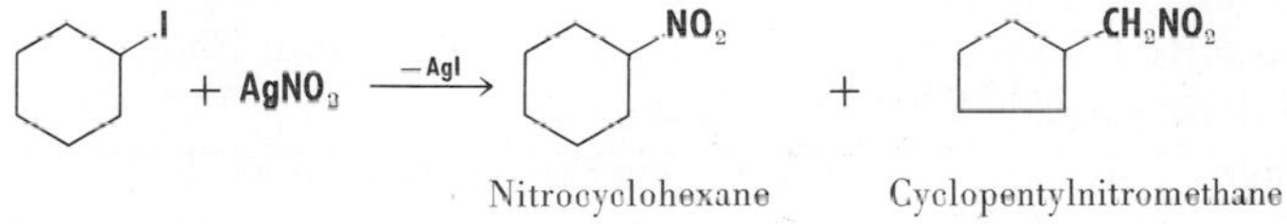
−AgI
Nitrocyclohexane
Cyclopentylnitromethane

$$CH_3CH_2CH_2Br + AlBr_3 \rightleftharpoons CH_3CH_2\overset{+}{C}H_2 \quad \overset{-}{AlBr_4} \rightleftharpoons CH_3\overset{+}{C}HCH_3 \quad \overset{-}{AlBr_4}$$

$$\updownarrow$$

$$CH_3CHBrCH_3 + AlBr_3$$

Stereochemistry of Wagner-Meerwein Rearrangements. All rearrangements have been formulated as stepwise processes. Careful studies of the stereochemistry of the reactions show that, in some cases, rearrangement must be initiated before free carbonium ions are formed. The best-documented example is found in the solvolysis of the diastereoisomeric 3-phenyl-2-butyl tosylates. The over-all results indicate that the first intermediate is probably a symmetrical *phenonium ion*,† formed by participation of the neighboring phenyl group in the ionization of the sulfonate ester.

Optically active *threo*-3-phenyl-2-butyl tosylate   Symmetrical phenonium ion   Racemic *threo* acetate

Optically pure *erythro*-3-phenyl-2-butyl tosylate   Asymmetric phenonium ion   Optically pure *erythro* acetate

Each enantiomeric *erythro* tosylate gives its *erythro* acetate derivative. The fact that the *threo* tosylates gave racemic solvolysis products while the erythro compounds gave optically active products, coupled with the failure to interconvert the *threo* and *erythro* series, seems to be uniquely explained by the assumption that the phenyl group participates in the ionization process. In certain other Wagner-Meerwein rearrangements, evidence is equally convincing that free, planar carbonium ions are formed prior to migration of β-aryl and -alkyl groups.

Migratory Aptitudes. Wagner-Meerwein rearrangements may be regarded as electrophilic substitutions at the migrating carbon atoms. As a consequence, one expects that those groups which are most susceptible to electrophilic attack will migrate most readily. Experiments with

---

† In a symmetrical phenonium ion, the positive charge is probably largely concentrated in the aromatic system. The plane of the aromatic ring should be perpendicular to the plane of the three carbon atoms which form the bridge. The rearrangement is really an electrophilic substitution reaction of the migrating aromatic nucleus. The intervention of an intermediate in this aromatic substitution suggests that similar intermediates exist in ordinary aromatic substitutions.

symmetrical pinacols, RR'C(OH)C(OH)RR', have established the following series of relative migratory aptitudes:

$$\text{Ar} > \text{R} > \text{H}$$

and, among aryl groups:

$$p\text{-CH}_3\text{OC}_6\text{H}_4 > p\text{-CH}_3\text{C}_6\text{H}_4 > \text{C}_6\text{H}_5 > p\text{-ClC}_6\text{H}_4$$

As is indicated by the following example, the differences between various migrating groups are somewhat smaller than the differences observed in electrophilic substitution reactions (Chap. 16).

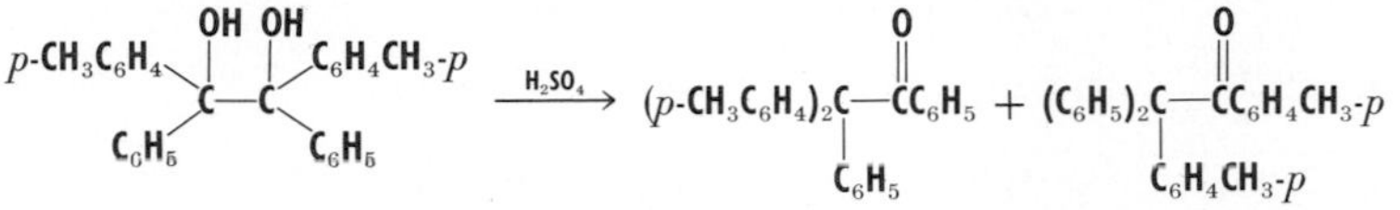

94%   6%

In unsymmetrical pinacols, the direction of rearrangement is largely determined by the relative ease of removal of hydroxyl groups from the two possible positions. The hydroxyl group is usually lost from that center which is more easily converted to a carbonium ion.

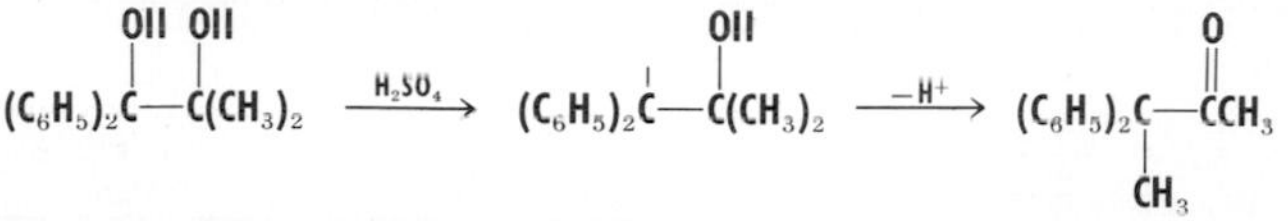

3,3-Diphenyl-2-
butanone

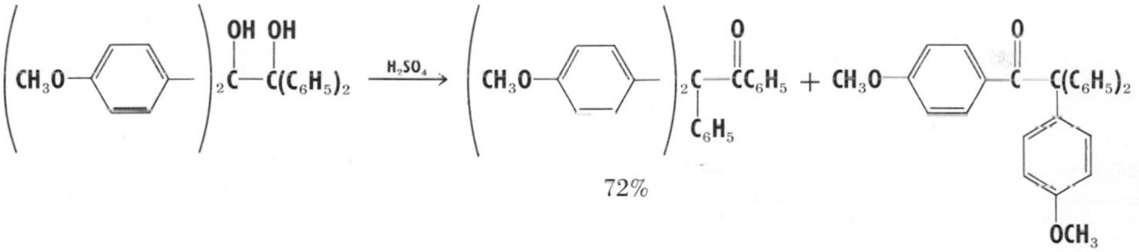

72%

The Wolff Rearrangement. α-Diazoketones lose nitrogen and rearrange to ketenes in the presence of solid silver oxide. The reaction is ordinarily carried out in the presence of water or alcohols, which convert the ketenes to carboxylic acids or their esters.

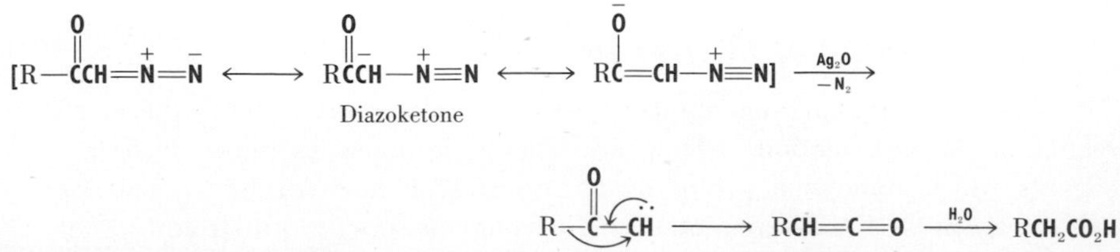

Diazoketone

A ketene

The Wolff rearrangement has been incorporated in a general sequence, the *Arndt-Eistert synthesis*, in which an acid is converted to its next-higher homologue.

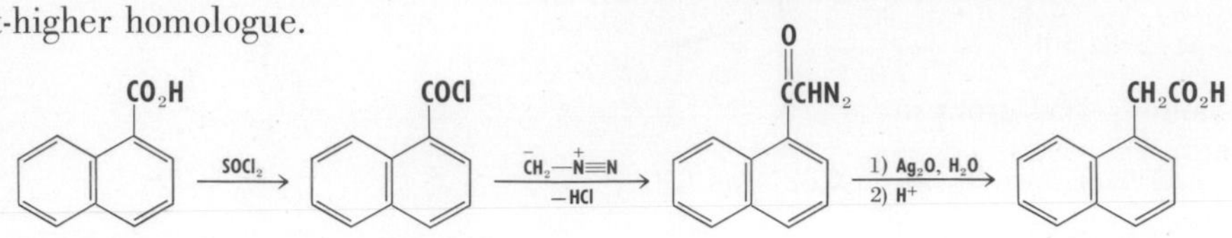

α-Naphthoic
acid

α-Naphthylacetic
acid
45% over-all

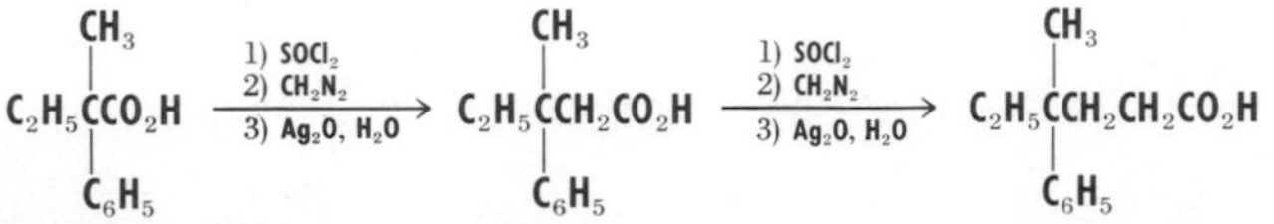

2-Methyl-2-
phenylbutyric acid

3-Methyl-3-phenyl-
valeric acid
52%

4-Methyl-4-phenyl-
caproic acid

Diazomethane is also used in a reaction which converts ketones to higher homologues. The process has been used for expansion of cycloalkanone rings. A ring closure to form ethylene oxides competes with the rearrangement step and often becomes the principal reaction.

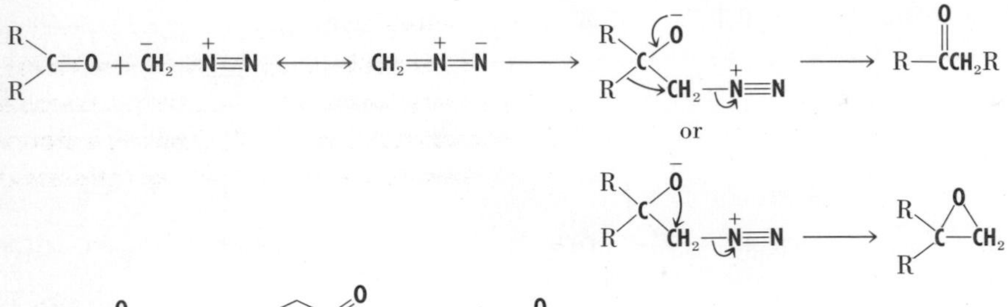

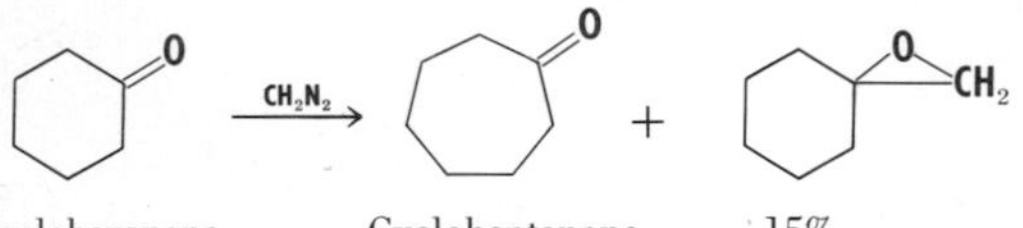

Cyclohexanone

Cycloheptanone
63%

15%

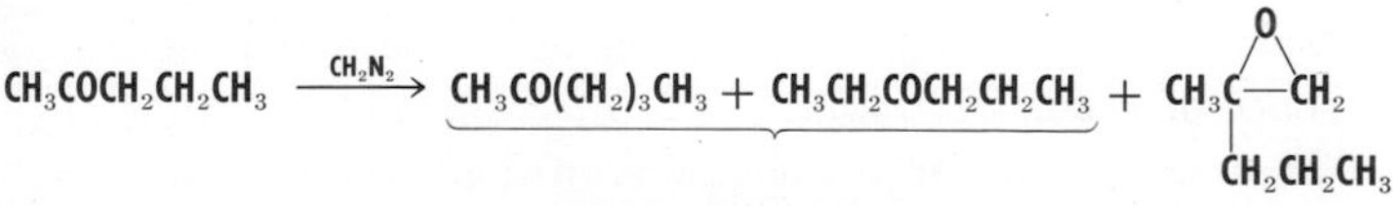

$CH_3COCH_2CH_2CH_3 \xrightarrow{CH_2N_2} CH_3CO(CH_2)_3CH_3 + CH_3CH_2COCH_2CH_2CH_3 +$

2-Pentanone

18% total

55%

Rearrangement of Electron-rich Systems

This group of rearrangements is the electronic counterpart of those treated in the last section. They are usually initiated by those basic reagents which remove a group or an atom, such as hydrogen. The residual anion then stabilizes itself by rearrangement, as is illustrated in Fig. 20.6.

An acid-strengthening substituent, which stabilizes the first ionic center, Z, by conjugation or electrostatic effects, is usually required in order to start the process.

In the *Stevens rearrangement,* keto-quaternary ammonium or sulfonium salts are rearranged to amino ketones under the influence of strong base.

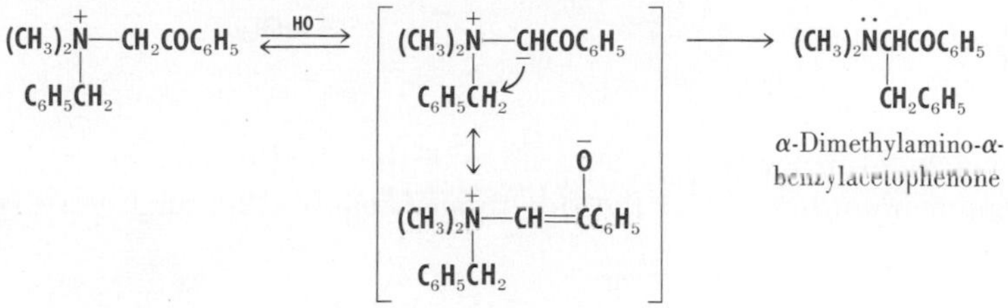

$$(CH_3)_2\overset{+}{N}-CH_2COC_6H_5 \underset{C_6H_5CH_2}{} \overset{HO^-}{\rightleftharpoons} \left[(CH_3)_2\overset{+}{N}-CHCOC_6H_5 \underset{C_6H_5CH_2}{} \right] \longrightarrow (CH_3)_2\overset{..}{N}CHCOC_6H_5 \underset{CH_2C_6H_5}{}$$

α-Dimethylamino-α-benzylacetophenone

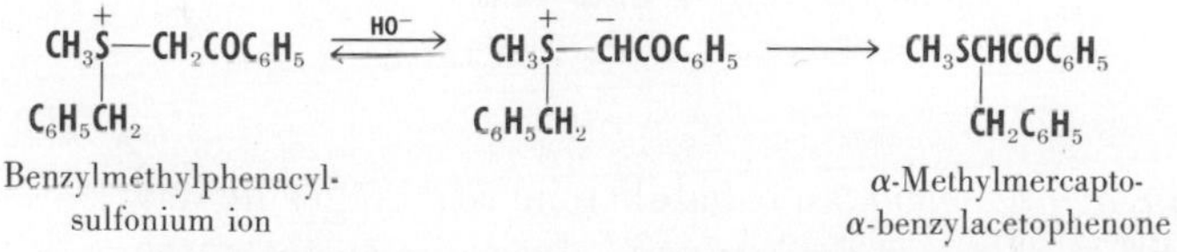

$$(CH_3)_2\overset{+}{N}-CH=\overset{O}{C}C_6H_5 \underset{C_6H_5CH_2}{}$$

$$CH_3\overset{+}{S}-CH_2COC_6H_5 \underset{C_6H_5CH_2}{} \overset{HO^-}{\rightleftharpoons} CH_3\overset{+}{S}-CHCOC_6H_5 \underset{C_6H_5CH_2}{} \longrightarrow CH_3SCHCOC_6H_5 \underset{CH_2C_6H_5}{}$$

Benzylmethylphenacyl-sulfonium ion

α-Methylmercapto-α-benzylacetophenone

Proton removal in the first step of a Stevens rearrangement is facilitated both by the positive charge in the cationic substrates and by virtue of the delocalization energy of the enolate ions. Migrating groups are usually either benzyl or allyl systems. The reaction is actually a nucleophilic substitution at the migrating center. As would be expected, electron-withdrawing substituents in the benzyl group facilitate rearrangement.

The *Wittig rearrangement* follows a similar path. Since the substrates are much less acidic than those encountered in the Stevens transformation, powerful basic reagents are required to cause the Wittig reaction.

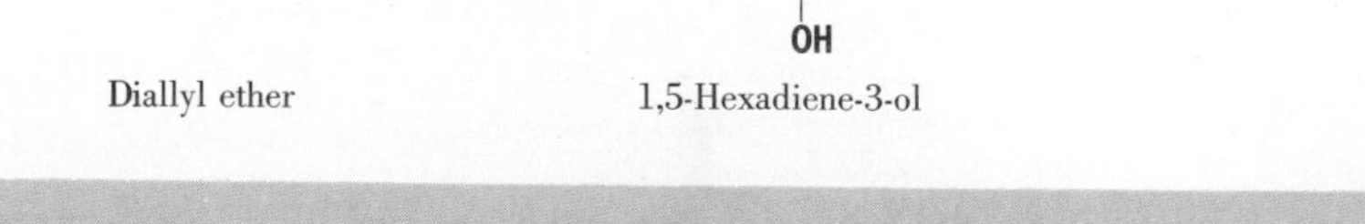

$$\underset{CH_3}{}O-CH_2C_6H_5 \xrightarrow[-C_6H_6]{C_6H_5Li} \underset{CH_3}{}\overset{\overset{+}{Li}}{C}OCHC_6H_5 \longrightarrow \underset{CH_3}{Li}\overset{+-}{O}CHC_6H_5 \xrightarrow{H_3O^+} \underset{CH_3}{HO}CHC_6H_5$$

Benzyl methyl ether

α-Phenylethanol

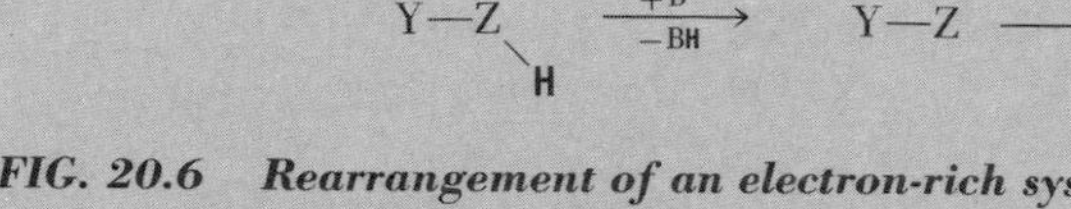

$$CH_2=CHCH_2OCH_2CH=CH_2 \xrightarrow[2)\ H_3O^+]{1)\ C_6H_5Li} CH_2=CHCH_2CHCH=CH_2 \underset{OH}{}$$

Diallyl ether

1,5-Hexadiene-3-ol

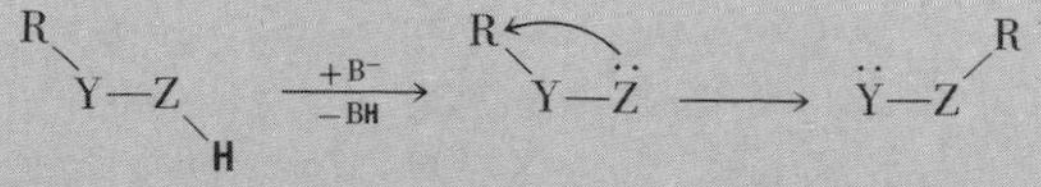

FIG. 20.6 *Rearrangement of an electron-rich system.*

Sommelet rearrangements involve the nucleophilic alkylation of the aromatic ring of a benzyltrimethylammonium ion. Protons are first removed from the more acidic benzyl position and subsequently from a methyl group.

The rearrangement occurs only where none of the alkyl groups of the quaternary ammonium ion carries the β-hydrogen required for an E_2 reaction (page 395).

$$C_6H_5CH_2\overset{+}{N}(CH_2CH_2CH_3)_3 \xrightarrow[-NH_3]{NaNH_2} C_6H_5N(CH_2CH_2CH_3)_2 + CH_3CH{=}CH_2$$

Benzyl tri-*n*-propyl-
ammonium ion

In the *Favorskii rearrangement,* an α-haloketone rearranges by way of intermediate formation of a cyclopropanone. In cyclic systems, the process leads to over-all ring contraction.

$$C_2H_5ONa + (CH_3)_3CCHCCH_3 \longrightarrow (CH_3)_3CCH_2CH_2CO_2H + NaBr$$

2-Chlorocyclohexanone   Carbethoxycyclopentane

In the *Neber reaction,* azacyclopropenes† are produced as inter-mediates by base-catalyzed elimination reactions of oxime tosylates.

†Azacyclopropenes are CH$=$CH and CH—CH$_2$.

$$C_6H_5CH_2CCH_3 \xrightarrow[\text{pyridine}]{p\text{-}CH_3C_6H_4SO_2Cl,} C_6H_5CH_2CCH_3 \xrightarrow{C_2H_5ONa} \left[C_6H_5CHCCH_3 \right] \xrightarrow{-OTs^-}$$

with N–OH and N–OTs groups shown on the respective structures, and N→OTs on the bracketed intermediate.

$$\left[C_6H_5CH\!-\!CCH_3 \right] \xrightarrow{H_2O} \underset{\underset{NH_2}{|}}{C_6H_5CHCCH_3} \overset{O}{\underset{\|}{}}$$
with N bridging in the bracketed ring structure.

2-Methyl-3-phenyl-   1-Amino-1-phenyl-2-propanone
1-azacyclopropene   65% over-all

The Benzilic Acid Rearrangement. The base-catalyzed rearrangement of 1,2-diketones takes its name from the leading example of the reaction.

$$C_6H_5\overset{O}{\underset{\|}{C}}\overset{O}{\underset{\|}{C}}C_6H_5 \xrightarrow[\text{Reflux}]{\text{KOH, ethanol}} (C_6H_5)_2\overset{OH}{\underset{|}{C}}CO_2H$$

Benzil   Benzilic acid

Driving force for the reaction is provided by addition of hydroxide ions to one of the carbonyl groups.

$$ArCCAr + \bar{O}H \rightleftharpoons Ar\overset{O}{\underset{\underset{Ar}{|}}{C}}\overset{\bar{O}}{\underset{|}{C}}OH \longrightarrow Ar\overset{O}{\underset{\underset{Ar}{|}}{-C}}\overset{O}{\underset{}{-COH}} \longrightarrow Ar_2\overset{OH}{\underset{|}{C}}CO_2^-$$

Application of the benzilic acid rearrangement has been limited almost exclusively to aromatic diketones. Several examples of the rearrangement of aliphatic diketones are known, but condensations involving α-hydrogens usually compete with rearrangement and keep yields low.

9,10-Phenanthrenequinone → 9-Hydroxy-9-fluorenecarboxylic acid
with reagent KOH, C₂H₅OH over the arrow; product shows HO and CO₂H groups.

$$HO_2CCH_2\overset{O}{\underset{\|}{C}}\overset{O}{\underset{\|}{C}}CH_2CO_2H \xrightarrow[\text{2) H}^+]{\text{1) KOH, H}_2\text{O, reflux}} HO_2CCH_2\underset{\underset{CO_2H}{|}}{\overset{\overset{OH}{|}}{C}}CH_2CO_2H$$

Ketopinic acid   Citric acid

Migration of Double and Triple Bonds

Allylic Rearrangements. Substitution reactions at *allylic positions* often involve migration of the double bond from its original position in the carbon skeleton to an adjacent site. Figure 20.7 shows the general formulations of allylic rearrangements.

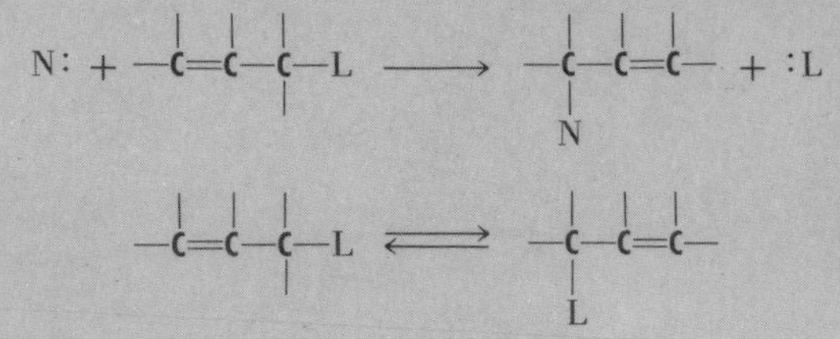

$$N: + -\overset{|}{C}=\overset{|}{C}-\overset{|}{C}-L \longrightarrow -\overset{|}{C}-\overset{|}{C}=\overset{|}{C}- + :L$$
$$\underset{N}{|}$$

$$-\overset{|}{C}=\overset{|}{C}-\overset{|}{C}-L \rightleftharpoons -\overset{|}{C}-\overset{|}{C}=\overset{|}{C}-$$
$$\underset{L}{|}$$

FIG. 20.7   Allylic rearrangements.

The most widely recognized examples of allylic rearrangements occur in the course of the nucleophilic substitution reactions of allylic compounds.   Rearrangement may involve either monomolecular (S_N1) or bimolecular (S_N2') mechanisms.

Rearrangement by the S_N1 mechanism:

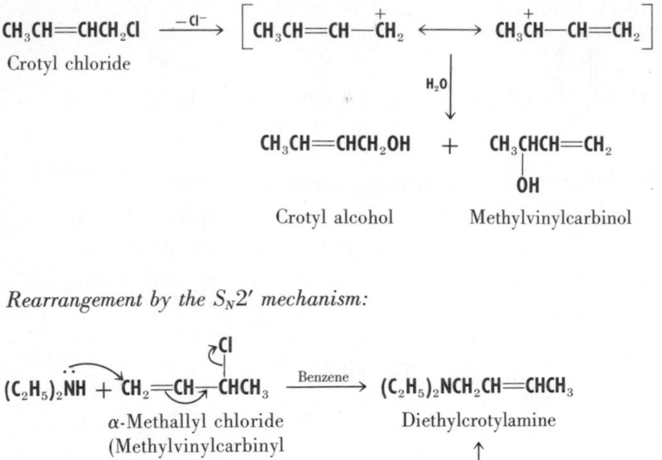

$$CH_3CH=CHCH_2Cl \xrightarrow{-Cl^-} \left[CH_3CH=CH-\overset{+}{C}H_2 \longleftrightarrow CH_3\overset{+}{C}H-CH=CH_2 \right]$$

Crotyl chloride

$$\downarrow H_2O$$

$$CH_3CH=CHCH_2OH \quad + \quad CH_3CHCH=CH_2$$
$$\underset{OH}{|}$$

Crotyl alcohol   Methylvinylcarbinol

Rearrangement by the S_N2' mechanism:

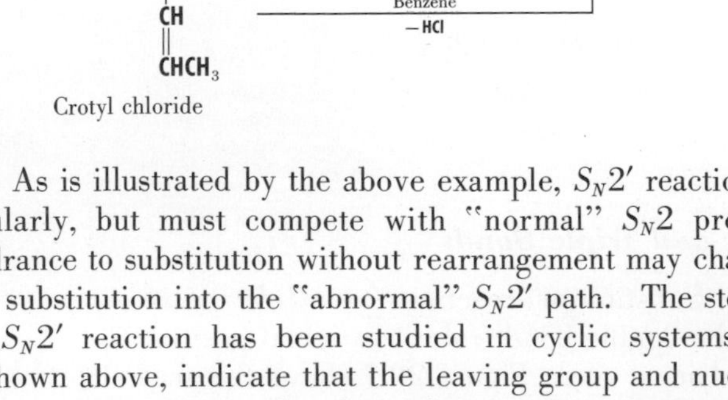

$$(C_2H_5)_2\overset{..}{N}H + CH_2=CH-CHCH_3 \xrightarrow{\text{Benzene}} (C_2H_5)_2NCH_2CH=CHCH_3$$

α-Methallyl chloride
(Methylvinylcarbinyl
chloride)   Diethylcrotylamine

$$(C_2H_5)_2\overset{..}{N}H + CH_2-Cl$$
$$\underset{\overset{\|}{CHCH_3}}{CH}$$

Crotyl chloride

Benzene
− HCl

As is illustrated by the above example, S_N2' reactions do not occur regularly, but must compete with "normal" S_N2 processes.   Steric hindrance to substitution without rearrangement may channel a bimolecular substitution into the "abnormal" S_N2' path.   The stereochemistry of the S_N2' reaction has been studied in cyclic systems.   The results, as shown above, indicate that the leaving group and nucleophile are on the same side of the molecule in the transition state.

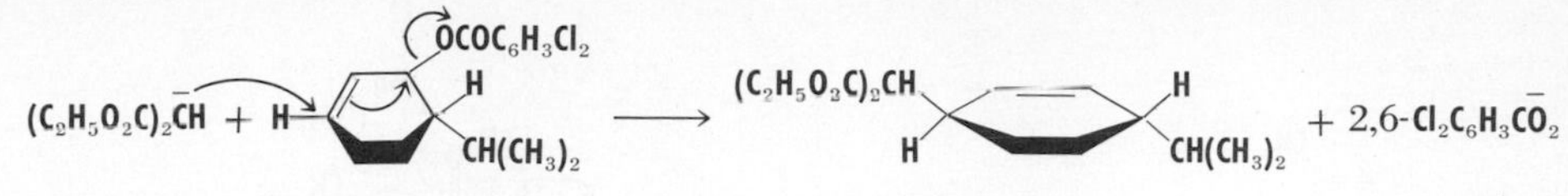

Diethyl malonate anion	*trans*-4-Isopropyl-3-cyclohexenyl 2,6-dichlorobenzoate	Diethyl *trans*-3-isopropyl-6-cyclohexenylmalonate

An interesting approach was used in the study shown above. A compound of known configuration, *trans*-4-isopropyl-3-cyclohexenol, was available as a starting material. For the preparation of a suitable substrate for the substitution reaction, it was necessary to convert the hydroxyl group to some group which could be displaced as a negative ion in nucleophilic substitution reactions. Cyclohexenyl tosylates are so reactive that they are unstable, and would be quite likely to undergo substitution by the S_N1 mechanism under most reaction conditions. Carboxylate esters are usually not suitable leaving groups in nucleophilic substitutions, because of the preferential attack of nucleophiles at the carbonyl group of the ester function (page 305). The problem was solved by use of the 2,6-dichlorobenzoate in which the carbonyl group is protected by steric hindrance.

Electrophilic substitution reactions with allylic organometallic compounds usually give mixtures of products. Furthermore, when organometallic reagents are made from isomeric allylic halides, the same metal derivative is obtained from both isomers,

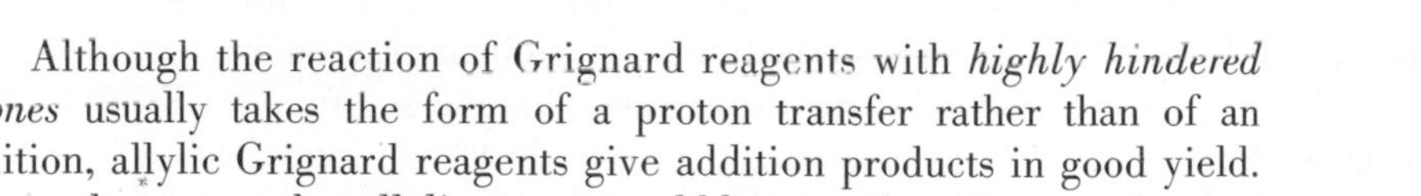

Butenyl Grignard reagent

Although the reaction of Grignard reagents with *highly hindered ketones* usually takes the form of a proton transfer rather than of an addition, allylic Grignard reagents give addition products in good yield. The results suggest that allylic reagents add by way of a unique mechanism which is probably a cyclic process.

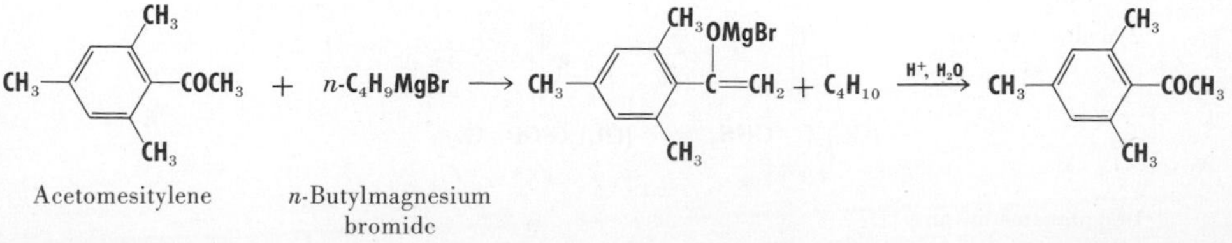

Acetomesitylene	*n*-Butylmagnesium bromide	

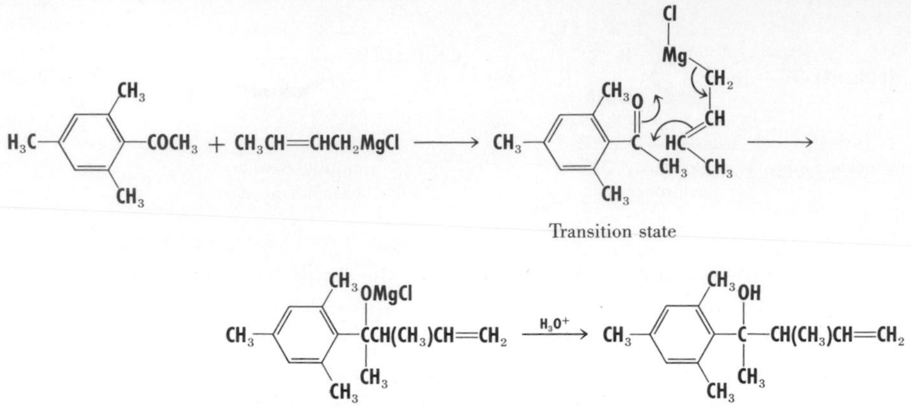

Transition state

2-Mesityl-3-methylpent-4-ene-2-ol

In the presence of strong bases, double bonds will migrate within carbon skeletons by the removal and readdition of protons. The rigor of the reaction conditions required to cause the change depends upon the effects of other substituents on the acidity of the hydrogen first involved.

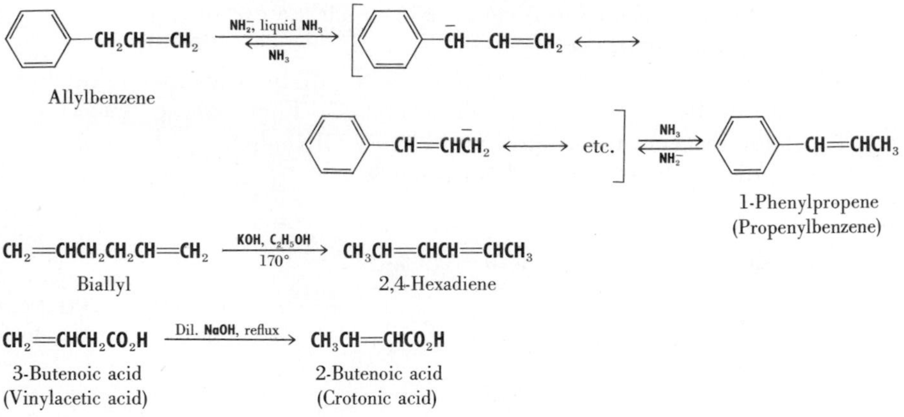

Allylbenzene

1-Phenylpropene
(Propenylbenzene)

$CH_2=CHCH_2CH_2CH=CH_2 \xrightarrow[170°]{KOH, C_2H_5OH} CH_3CH=CHCH=CHCH_3$
          Biallyl   2,4-Hexadiene

$CH_2=CHCH_2CO_2H \xrightarrow{\text{Dil. NaOH, reflux}} CH_3CH=CHCO_2H$

3-Butenoic acid   2-Butenoic acid
(Vinylacetic acid)   (Crotonic acid)

Double-bond migrations are also easily induced by acid. However, competition from addition, polymerization, and skeletal rearrangements limits the use of the method. Equilibration of isomers often occurs during acid-catalyzed dehydration of alcohols. Related isomerization reactions of alkenes and alkanes are discussed in Chap. 26.

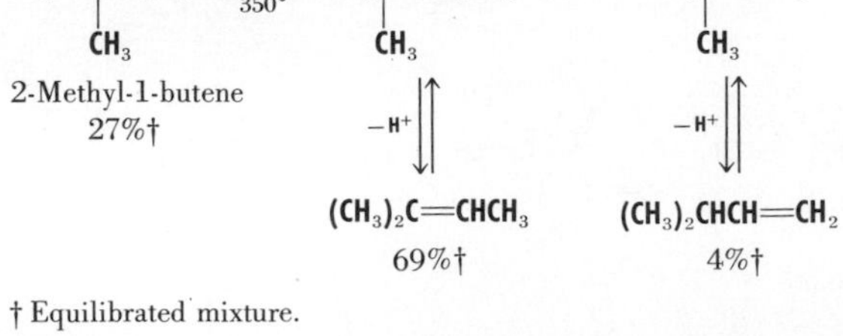

2-Methyl-1-butene
27%†

(CH$_3$)$_2$C=CHCH$_3$ (CH$_3$)$_2$CHCH=CH$_2$
69%†   4%†

† Equilibrated mixture.

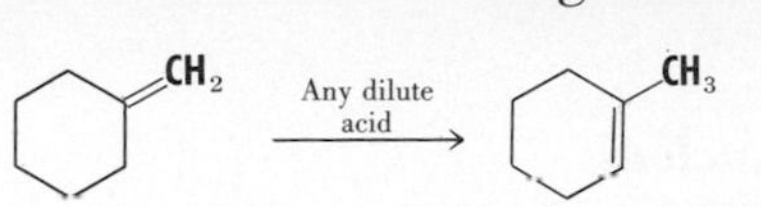

Methylenecyclohexane   1-Methylcyclohexene

Acetylenic Rearrangements. Migration of acetylenic linkages to terminal positions has been discussed earlier (page 409). The *Rupe rearrangement* of acetylenic alcohols, which are readily available from addition of acetylenes to ketones, converts the acetylenes to α,β-unsaturated ketones.

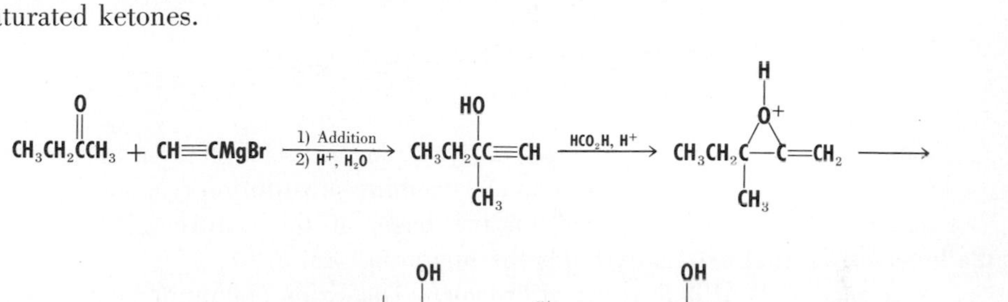

ıne Willgerodt Reaction. The Willgerodt reaction is a remarkable rearrangement in which a functional group migrates from one internal position to the end of a carbon chain. Aryl alkyl ketones undergo a combined oxidation and rearrangement to ω-arylthioamides when heated with ammonium polysulfide or sulfur and a secondary amine.

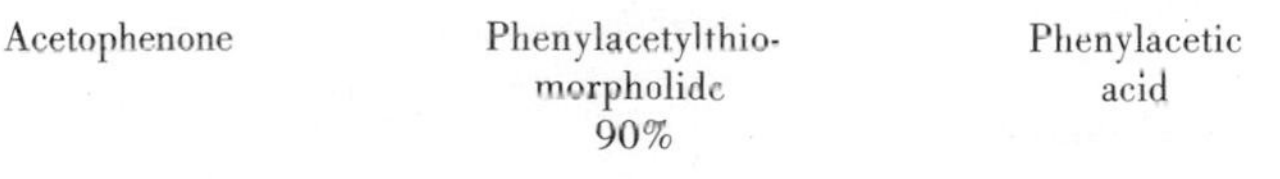

Acetophenone   Phenylacetylthio-   Phenylacetic
                      morpholide   acid
                      90%

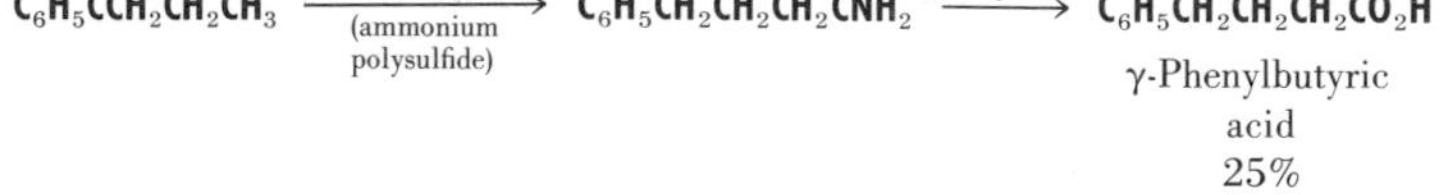

γ-Phenylbutyric
acid
25%

Olefins and acetylenes can be substituted for ketones in the Willgerodt reaction.

80%

Rearrangement to an Aromatic Nucleus

In a large number of reactions a group, A, migrates from a substituted hetero atom, Z, and becomes directly attached to an ortho or para position of an aromatic nucleus.

The reactions are nearly all *acid-catalyzed;* hence attack of Z on the nucleus has some of the character of an electrophilic substitution reaction. The reactions are best classified on the basis of the nature of A, the hetero atom that originally holds the migrating group.

Rearrangements of Derivatives of Phenols.   The Fries rearrangement of aryl esters to phenolic ketones was discussed earlier (page 380).

$$\text{ArOCCH}_3 \xrightarrow{\text{AlCl}_3} \textit{o-} \text{ and } \textit{p-}\text{CH}_3\text{COArOH}$$

The *Claisen rearrangement* of aryl allyl ethers to allylphenols has been studied carefully and can be described with great precision.   If there is an open ortho position, only ortho rearrangement occurs.   However, if both ortho positions are blocked, rearrangement to an open para position takes place.

Phenyl allyl ether   *o*-Allylphenol
                                         90%

Allyl 2,6-dimethylphenyl   4-Allyl-2,6-dimethylphenol
        ether

Studies with allylic groups labeled with substituents or carbon-14 (Fig. 20.8) show that the allylic group is inverted during the ortho rearrangement, but maintains its structure (or is inverted twice) during migration to a para position.   These and other data virtually necessitate

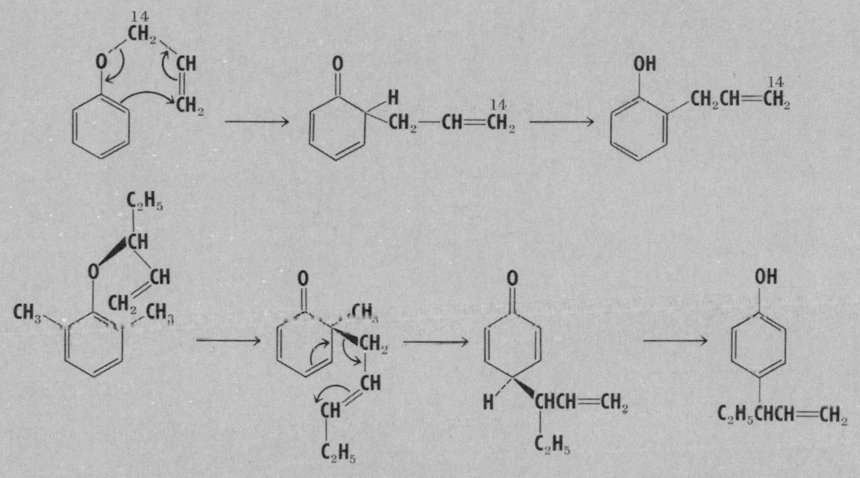

FIG. 20.8 *Mechanism of the Claisen rearrangement.*

the view that the rearrangements have cyclic mechanisms and involve dienones as intermediates.

Rearrangements of Derivatives of Aniline. *N*-Haloacetanilides rearrange to *o*- and *p*-haloanilides when treated with mineral acid. In this reaction, halogen becomes detached from the molecule and then reenters in an ordinary electrophilic substitution reaction.

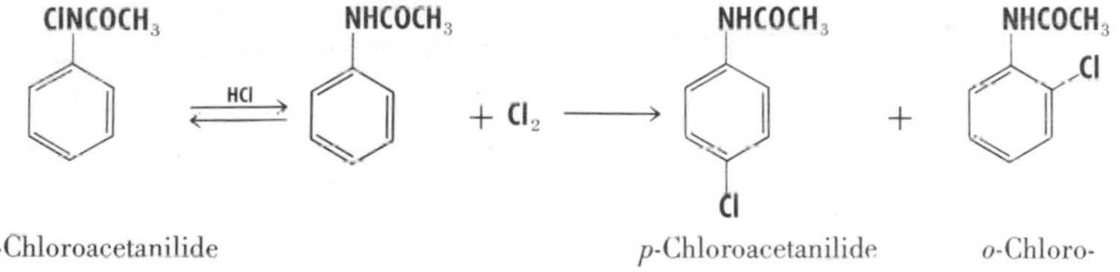

N-Chloroacetanilide   *p*-Chloroacetanilide   *o*-Chloro-acetanilide

The *N*-haloamide rearrangement is one of a group of formally similar rearrangements. Several of the group are believed to involve *intermolecular* mechanisms, but in three cases (nitramine, *N*-sulfonic acid, and benzidine rearrangements), all available evidence points to *intramolecular* mechanisms in which the migrating group never becomes completely detached from the substrate.

Intermolecular:

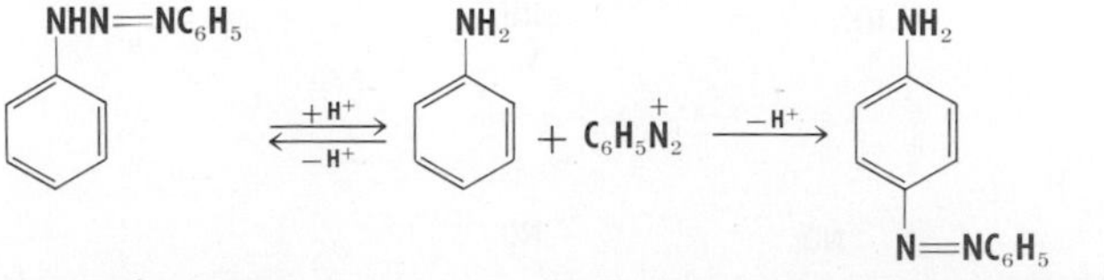

Diazoaminobenzene   *p*-Aminoazobenzene

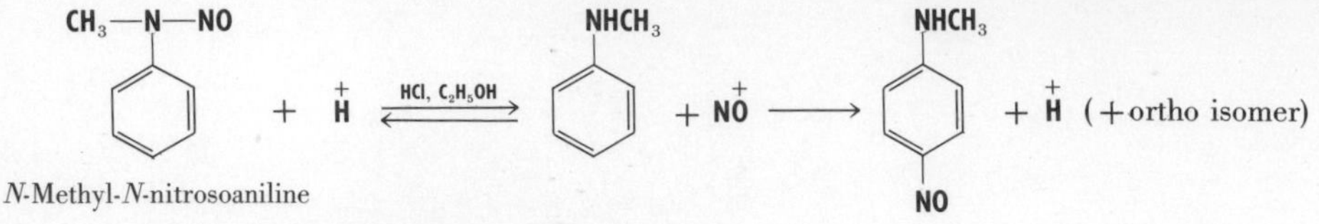
CH3—N—NO
+ H
HCl, C2H5OH
NHCH3
+ NO
NHCH3
NO
+ H (+ortho isomer)
N-Methyl-N-nitrosoaniline

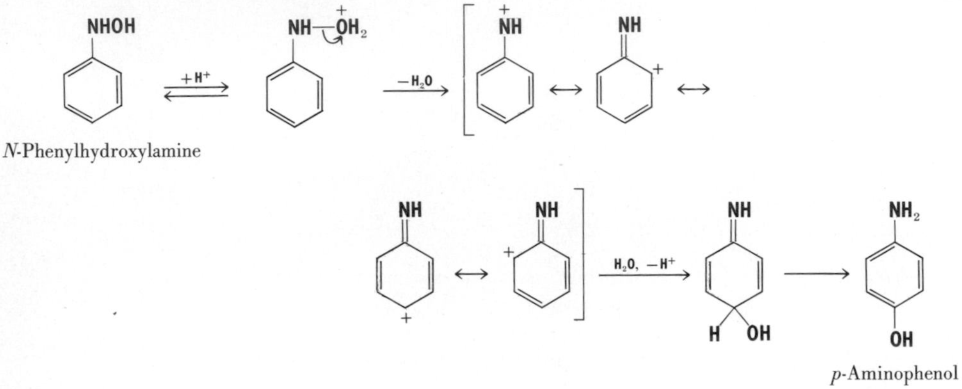
NHOH
+H+
NH—OH2
−H2O
NH
NH
H2O, −H+
NH
H OH
NH2
OH
N-Phenylhydroxylamine
p-Aminophenol

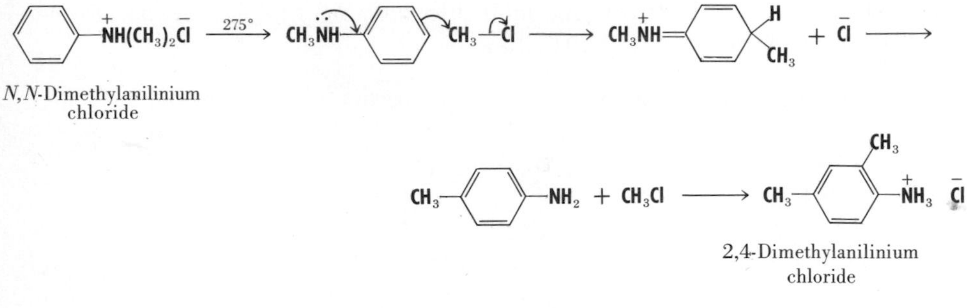
NH(CH3)2Cl
275°
CH3NH
CH3—Cl
CH3NH
H
CH3
+ Cl
CH3
NH2
+ CH3Cl
CH3
CH3
NH3 Cl
N,N-Dimethylanilinium chloride
2,4-Dimethylanilinium chloride

Intramolecular:

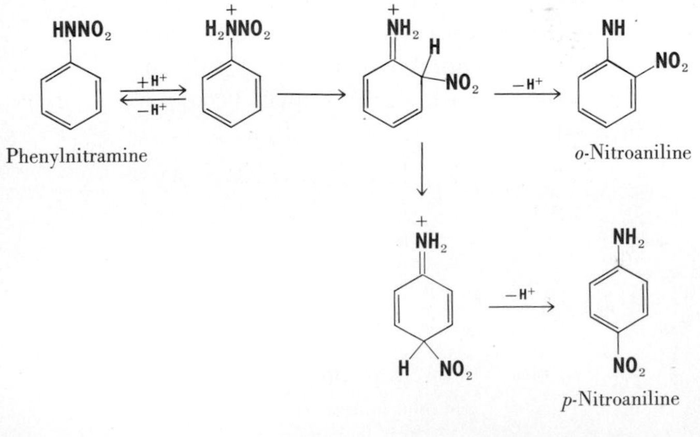
HNNO2
+H+
−H+
H2NNO2
NH2
H
NO2
−H+
NH
NO2
NH2
H NO2
−H+
NH2
NO2
Phenylnitramine
o-Nitroaniline
p-Nitroaniline

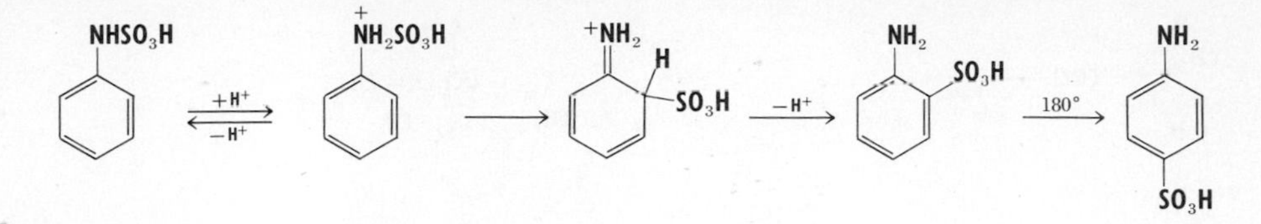

Phenylsulfamic acid   Orthanilic acid   Sulfanilic acid

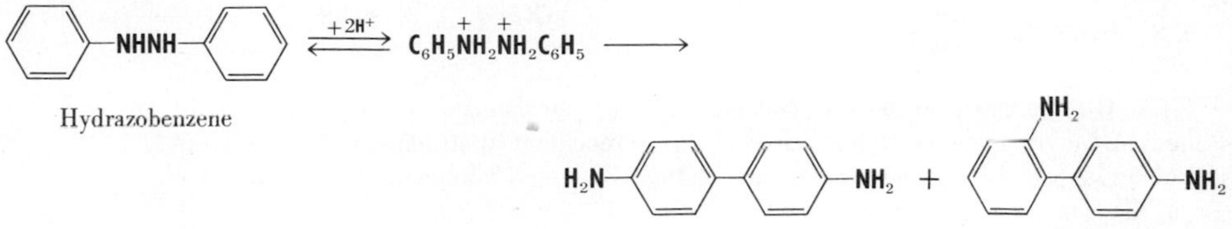

Hydrazobenzene

Benzidine   Diphenylene

Problems

1. Devise syntheses of the following compounds, using no organic starting materials except benzene and any substances containing three carbons or less. Make a given compound only once for the whole problem set.

a. $(CH_3)_3CCOCH_3$

b. $(CH_3)_3CCO_2H$

c. $(CH_3)_3CCH_2CO_2H$

d. $C_6H_5CH_2CH_2CO_2H$

e. $(C_6H_5)_2CCO_2H$
$\quad\quad OH$

f. Cycloheptanone

g. $NH_2(CH_2)_5CO_2H$

h. $(C_6H_5)_3CCHOHC_6H_5$

i.

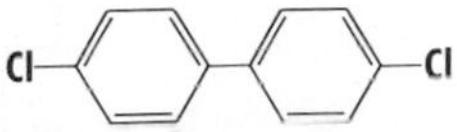

j.

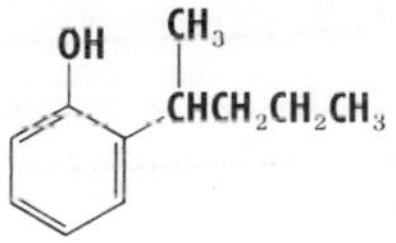

k. 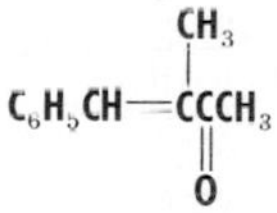 $C_6H_5CH=CCCH_3$ (with CH_3 on middle carbon and O below)

l.

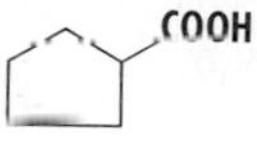

2. With three-dimensional formulas, where required, represent structurally the products of the following reactions:

a.

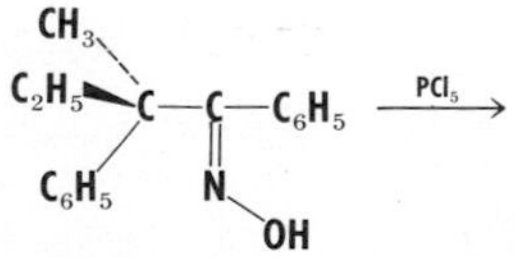

b. 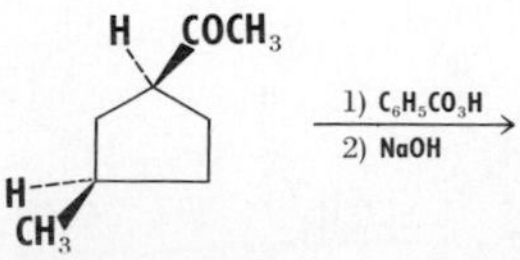
$\quad$ 1) $C_6H_5CO_3H$
$\quad$ 2) $NaOH$

c. $(CH_3)_2\overset{+}{N}CH_2COC_2H_5$ $\xrightarrow{\text{Base}}$

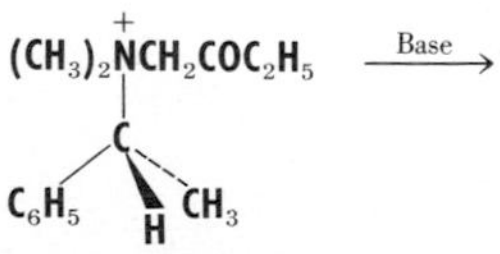

(Predict on geometric grounds.)

d. 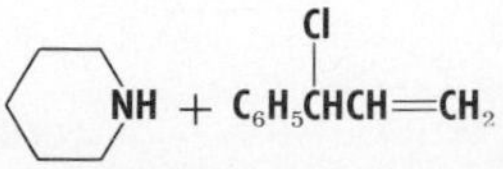 NH + $C_6H_5CHCH=CH_2$ (with Cl)

e.
$$CH_3\overset{H}{\underset{C_6H_5}{\overset{|}{C}}}\text{—COCl} \xrightarrow[\text{2) CH}_3\text{OH,}\ \text{Ag}_2\text{O}]{\text{1) CH}_2\text{N}_2}$$

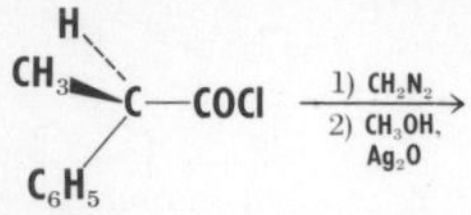

h.
CH_3 ... $OCHCH{=}CH_2$ (with C_6H_5), CH_3

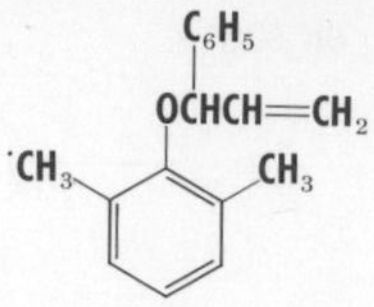

f.
$$CH_3\overset{H}{\underset{C_2H_5}{\overset{|}{C}}}\text{—CONH}_2 \xrightarrow{\text{NaOBr}}$$

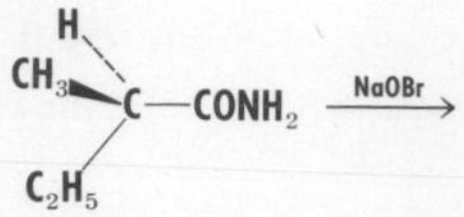

g. $C_6H_5CH{=}CHCH_2Cl \xrightarrow[\text{2) CH}_3\text{CHO}]{\text{1) Mg}}$

i. CH_3—⟨⟩—$NHNH$—⟨⟩(CH_3) $\xrightarrow{\text{HCl}}$

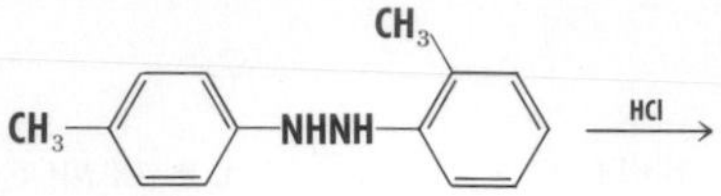

3. On the basis of the stereochemistry and mechanism of the acetolysis of 3-phenyl-2-butyl *p*-toluenesulfonate, predict the stereochemical structures of the isomers of 3-phenyl-2-pentyl *p*-toluenesulfonate and 2-phenyl-3-pentyl *p*-toluenesulfonate that give rise to the same mixture of acetates.

4. Explain the following observations:

a. In the synthesis of 2-acetamido-1-propylamine, the final step involved the treatment of 2-acetamido-1-propyl chloride with ammonia. The product was a mixture of two amino amides instead of the single substance expected.

b.

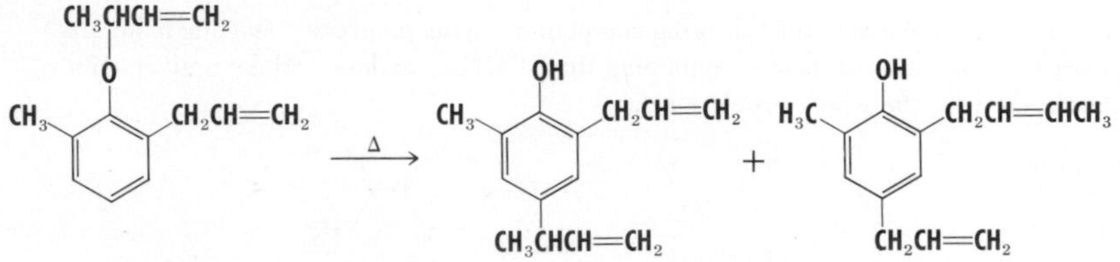

c. When subjected to the reaction conditions of a Favorskii rearrangement, 1,3-dibromo-3-methyl-2-butanone gave *β*-methylcrotonic acid.

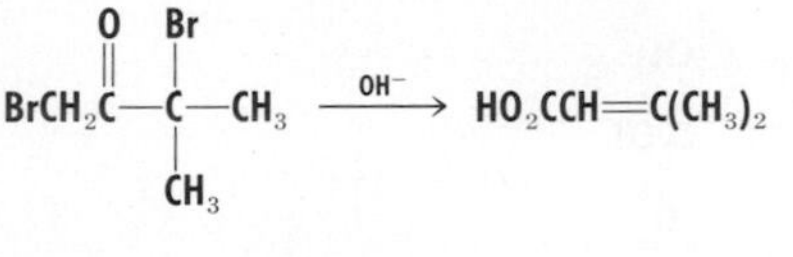

$$BrCH_2\text{—}\overset{O}{\overset{||}{C}}\text{—}\underset{CH_3}{\overset{Br}{\overset{|}{\underset{|}{C}}}}\text{—CH}_3 \xrightarrow{\text{OH}^-} HO_2CCH{=}C(CH_3)_2$$

d. When treated with base, the oxime tosylate drawn below gave an unstable substance with the molecular formula $C_9H_7N_3O_4$.

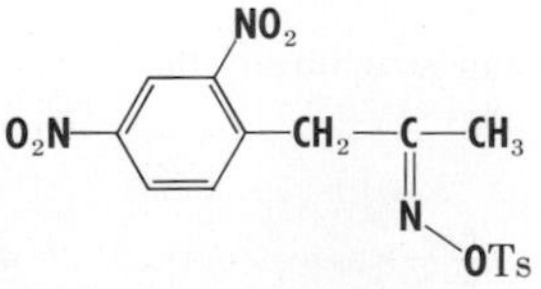

e.

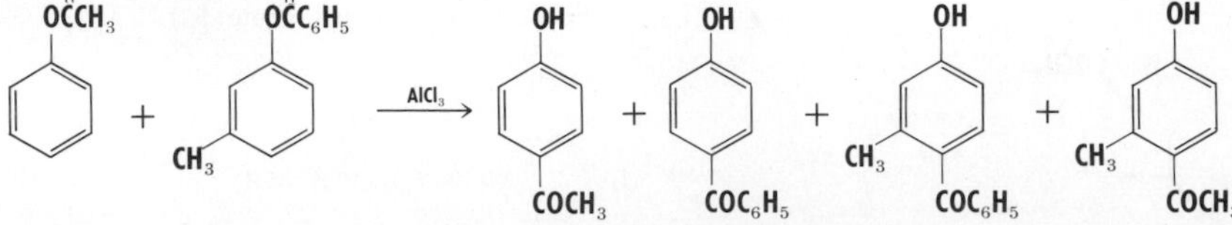

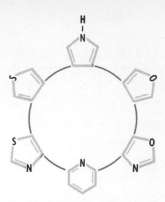

21

Heterocyclic Compounds

A number of special properties appear when oxygen, sulfur, or nitrogen is contained in a five- or six-membered ring system, particularly when the maximum number of double bonds is also incorporated in the ring. Such compounds, known as heterocycles, are often found in natural products, and the important role played by these substances in the biochemistry of plants and animals makes their treatment in a special chapter desirable. The subject also provides a good vehicle for developing synthetic sequences with the reactions discussed in previous chapters.

Heterocyclic compounds such as ethylene oxide and butyrolactone have been treated earlier in the text, and only their five- and six-membered homologues will be discussed here.

Five-membered Rings

Table 21.1 lists the unsaturated five-membered heterocyclic compounds. These ring systems display varying degrees of resemblance to benzene in their physical and chemical properties, with thiophene occupying the position closest to that of benzene. Thus thiophene and benzene boil at 84 and 80°, respectively. They both undergo addition and electrophilic substitution reactions.

These similarities and others are rationalized as follows: (1) Unsaturated five-membered ring compounds all possess molecular weights close to that of benzene. (2) They are planar, and their molecular volumes and shapes resemble those of benzene. (3) The p orbitals of the double bonds (page 105) and those of the hetero atoms overlap to form doughnut-shaped molecular orbitals above and below the plane of the nuclei (Fig. 21.1). The resulting resonance of stabilization amounts to 23, 31, and

479

TABLE 21.1   Five-membered Heterocycles

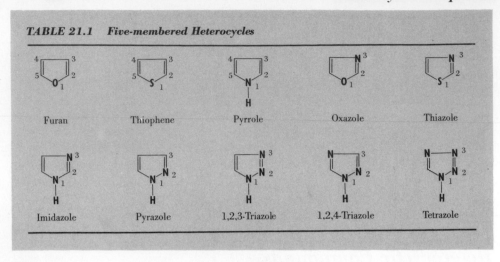

Furan   Thiophene   Pyrrole   Oxazole   Thiazole

Imidazole   Pyrazole   1,2,3-Triazole   1,2,4-Triazole   Tetrazole

31 kcal/mole for furan, pyrrole, and thiophene, respectively, as compared to 39 kcal/mole for benzene.

Dipolar structures make important contributions to the resonance hybrids of these substances. The charge distribution provides the carbon portion of the nucleus with partial negative charge in those cycles which contain one hetero atom.

$$\text{(resonance structures)} \qquad A = \text{O, S, or N}$$

Preparation of Furan, Thiophene, and Pyrrole.   Succinaldehyde is a key intermediate in the preparation of these heterocyclic compounds. Diketones such as 2,5-hexanedione undergo similar reactions to provide substituted heterocycles. In the reaction sequence formulated below, acrolein diacetate is converted to 4,4-diacetoxybutanal. This conversion is an example of the *oxo reaction,* which constitutes an important industrial method for converting alkenes to aldehydes.

$$CH_2{=}CHCHO \xrightarrow{(CH_3CO)_2O} CH_2{=}CHCH(O_2CCH_3)_2 \xrightarrow[\substack{[Co(CO)_4]_2 \\ 125°}]{CO,\ H_2} OCHCH_2CH_2CH(O_2CCH_3)_2 \xrightarrow{HCl}$$

$$\text{Acrolein diacetate} \qquad\qquad\qquad \text{4,4-Diacetoxybutanal}$$

$$OCHCH_2CH_2CHO$$
Succinaldehyde

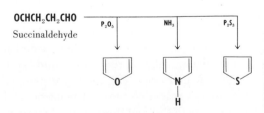

A number of special methods are available for preparing individual cycles. Pyrrole can be prepared from ammonium salts of saccharic acids, which are obtained by oxidation of certain carbohydrates (Chap. 22). A second method involves acetylene and formaldehyde as starting materials.

$$\underset{\substack{\text{Ammonium salts}\\\text{of saccharic acids}}}{\overset{\overset{\displaystyle\text{HOCH--CHOH}}{\underset{\text{OH\ \ OH}}{\text{H}_4\text{NO}_2\text{CCH}\ \ \text{CHCO}_2\text{NH}_4}}{}}} \xrightarrow{\Delta}\quad \underset{\substack{\ \\\text{H}}}{\overset{}{\boxed{}}}\ \ +\ 2\text{CO}_2\ +\ 4\text{H}_2\text{O}\ +\ \text{NH}_3$$

$$\text{HC}\equiv\text{CH}\ +\ 2\text{CH}_2\text{O}\ \longrightarrow\ \underset{\text{Butyne 1,4 diol}}{\text{HOCH}_2\text{C}\equiv\text{CCH}_2\text{OH}}\ \xrightarrow{\text{NH}_3}\ \underset{\substack{\ \\\text{H}}}{\boxed{}}$$

A commercial preparation of thiophene involves butane and sulfur as starting materials.

$$\text{CH}_3\text{CH}_2\text{CH}_2\text{CH}_3\ +\ 4\text{S}\ \xrightarrow{650°}\ \underset{\text{S}}{\boxed{}}\ +\ 3\text{H}_2\text{S}$$

Furfural is a commercially important aldehyde, which serves as solvent for certain petrochemical processes and as raw material for preparation of polymers, plastics, and the commercial solvent tetrahydrofuran. This aldehyde is prepared by a threefold elimination reaction from aldopentoses (Chap. 22), which are made from agricultural waste products such as corn cobs and oat hulls.

$$\underset{\substack{\text{An aldopentose}}}{\overset{\overset{\displaystyle\text{HOCH--CHOH}}{\underset{\text{OH\ \ OH}}{\text{CH}_2\ \ \text{CHCHO}}}{}}} \xrightarrow[\text{distill.}]{\text{Dilute acid}} \underset{\text{Furfural}}{\boxed{}\!\text{CHO}} \xrightarrow[\substack{\text{MnCrO}_2\\400°}]{\text{ZnCrO}_2} \underset{\text{Furan}}{\boxed{}} \xrightarrow[\text{Ni}]{\text{H}_2} \underset{\text{Tetrahydrafuran}}{\boxed{}}$$

The reactions of furfural that involve the carbonyl group resemble those of benzaldehyde and other aldehydes without hydrogen at the

FIG. 21.1 *π-Molecular orbital of thiophene, furan, and pyrrole.*

α-position.   Levulinic acid represents one of a number of useful open-chain substances that are prepared from furfural, whose very low price makes it an attractive starting material for chemical industry.   One of the stages in the transformation involves a hydride shift reminiscent of that in the Cannizzaro reaction (page 281).

Furfural   Furfuryl
                  alcohol

Levulinic acid

Reactions of Furan, Thiophene, and Pyrrole.   The reactions of thiophene show a marked resemblance to those of benzene with respect to electrophilic substitution (page 357), except that the heterocycle undergoes substitution under milder conditions.   The 2,5-positions are more amenable to electrophilic attack than the 3,4-positions, and substitution occurs at the latter places only if the other two are blocked.

2-Chlorothiophene   2-Nitrothiophene

2-Acetylthiophene   2-Thiophenesulfonic
                           acid

Pyrrole is a weaker base than aniline.   The aromatic character of the substance is destroyed by addition of acids, and the diene produced polymerizes.   This fact prohibits application of many of the common electrophilic substitution reactions to pyrrole.

Pyrrole is also a weak acid, whose conjugate base is stabilized by delocalization of negative charge, in much the same way as in the phthalimide anion (page 173).   A number of *nucleophilic substitutions* of pyrrole are observed which probably involve this anion as an intermediate.

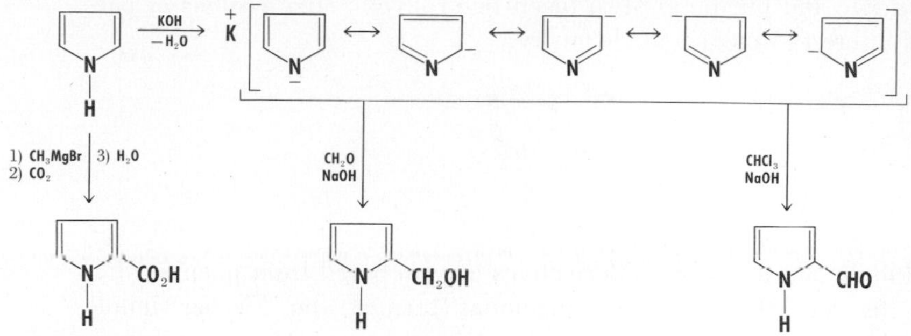

2-Pyrrolecarboxylic acid	2-Pyrrolyl alcohol	2-Pyrrolaldehyde
Carbon dioxide as an electrophile	Nucleophilic addition to carbonyl group	Nucleophilic substitution at saturated carbon (resembles Reimer-Tiemann reaction)

When treated with hydrogen and platinum, pyrrole gives tetrahydropyrrole.   An alternate synthesis involves 4-chlorobutylamine as starting material.

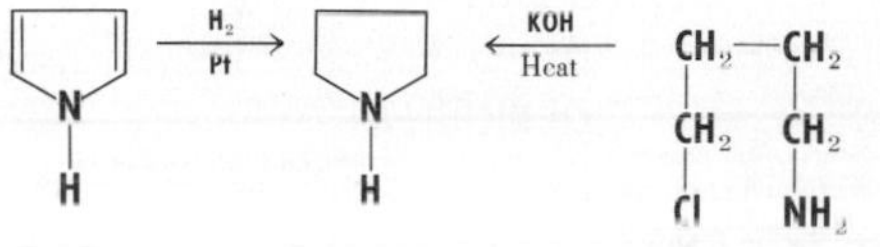

Pyrrolidine
(Tetrahydropyrrole)   4-Chlorobutylamine

Furan responds to the electrical demands of a variety of reagents, behaving in some cases as a diene, in others as an aromatic system, and occasionally as an ether.

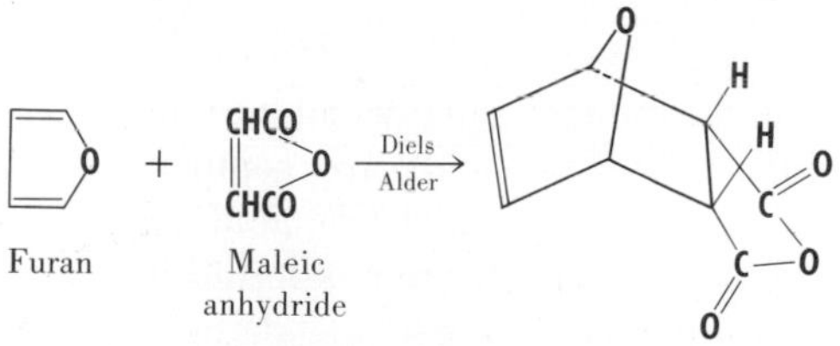

Furan   Maleic anhydride

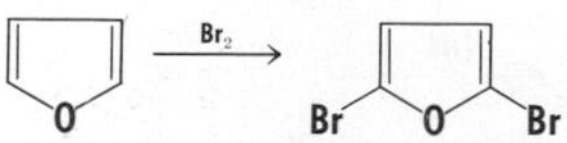

2,5-Dibromofuran

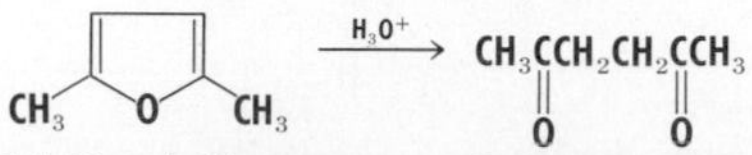

2,5-Dimethylfuran   2,5 Hexanedione

Fused Systems with Five-membered Rings

Indole and purine are two fused heterocyclic ring systems of particular interest to medicinal chemistry.

Indole   Purine

Indole and many of its derivatives are prepared from phenylhydrazones by an interesting rearrangement termed the Fischer indole synthesis.

Phenylhydrazone of   Indole-2-carboxylic acid   Indole
pyruvic acid

The first step in the synthesis of the important amino acid, tryptophan, illustrates that many of the reactions of indole involve carbon 3 acting as a nucleophile in addition reactions to unsaturated carbon (Mannich reaction, page 293).

Tryptophan

The purine ring system is found in compounds such as adenosine, obtained by hydrolysis of nucleic acids. Nucleic acids are complex materials which occur in the nuclei of cells. Caffeine and uric acid are two additional members of the purine family. The former is found in tea and coffee; the latter is the end product of nitrogen metabolism. Both are stimulants.

Adenosine   Caffeine   Uric acid

A number of vitamins contain five-membered heterocyclic rings. Thiamin (vitamin B$_1$) is composed of a pyrimidine (page 490) coupled through a methylene bridge to a thiazole ring system. This substance, which is necessary for the maintenance of good health in human beings, is found in meat and many vegetables. Biotin is a material necessary to the normal growth of yeasts and other microorganisms. The compound contains two fused five-membered rings.

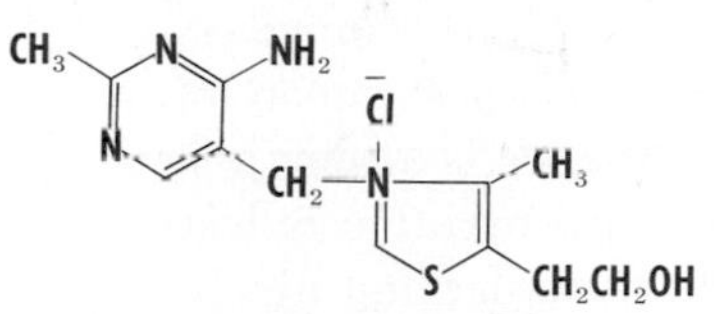

Thiamin (vitamin B$_1$)

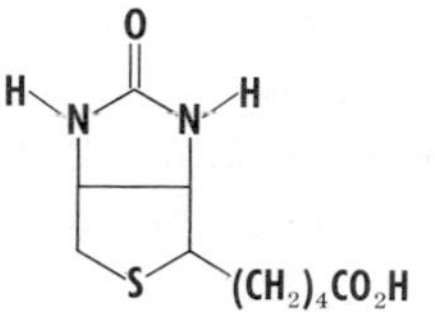

Biotin

Chlorophyll and hemin contain four pyrrole-derived nuclei incorporated in a *porphyrin* ring system carrying a complexed metal ion in the center. Chlorophyll, the green plant pigment, occurs in nature bound to a complex protein molecule. It functions as a vehicle for conversion of light into chemical energy in the photosynthetic process so important to plants. Hemoglobin, one of the components of red corpuscles in the blood of mammals, is composed of hemin (a red pigment) attached to protein. It acts as a carrier of oxygen from the lungs to tissues in animal organisms. This function involves the iron portion of the complex. The poisonous character of carbon monoxide is associated with its ability to substitute for oxygen in this process—suffocation of the organism being the ultimate result. Figure 21.2 contains the formulas of chlorophyll a and hemin.

O$_2$ + hemoglobin $\rightleftharpoons$ oxyhemoglobin

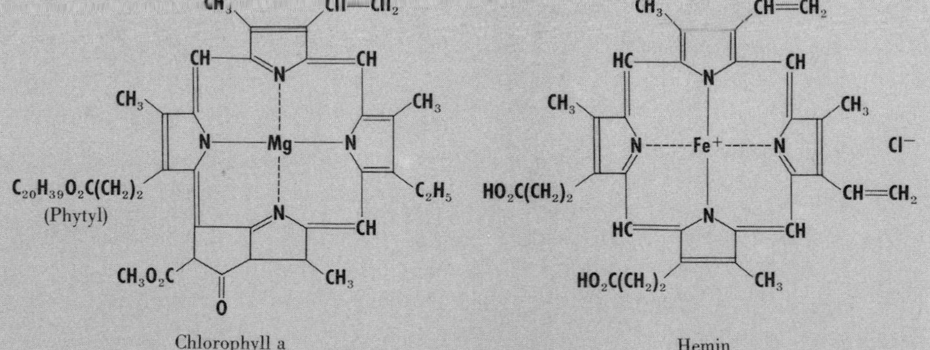

Chlorophyll a

Hemin

FIG. 21.2   Structures of the plant and blood pigments.

Six-membered Rings

A large variety of six-membered heterocyclic compounds are known. Many are found in natural products, while others have been made only in the laboratory. Table 21.2 lists the most important ring systems, each one of which possesses a rather specialized chemistry. Only pyridine and pyrimidine will be discussed in any detail.

Chemistry of Pyridine. Of heterocyclic compounds containing six-membered rings, pyridine and derived substances are the most important. The pyridine ring is extremely stable, and the substance is aromatic in character. The resonance energy of 43 kcal/mole in pyridine reflects the contributions to the resonance hybrid of both nonpolar and dipolar structures.

Pyridine as a resonance hybrid

Pyridine is a much weaker base than ordinary tertiary amines ($pK_b \sim 4$) and possesses a pK_b of 8.8. When a hetero atom becomes multiply bonded in an unsaturated system, the unshared electrons associated with the atom are relegated to orbitals that have more s character than do singly bonded hetero atoms in like structures. As a result, these electrons are less available for forming bonds with protons. The compound is used extensively as a basic catalyst and solvent in preparation of esters and amides, and in other nucleophilic substitution reactions at unsaturated carbon.

Pyridine occurs in coal tar along with α-, β-, and γ-picoline, its three monomethyl derivatives.

α-Picoline β-Picoline γ-Picoline

Pyridine enters into a number of reactions, some of which are similar to those of other tertiary amines. For instance, it reacts with hydrogen peroxide to give an amine oxide, and when treated with alkyl halides, quaternary ammonium salts are formed. Pyridine is readily reduced to piperidine either with hydrogen and the usual catalysts or with sodium and ethanol.

N-Methylpyridinium iodide

Pyridine oxide

Piperidine

The presence of a basic nitrogen in the nucleus of pyridine greatly inhibits electrophilic substitution of the ring. The cations (Br^+, SO_3H^+, NO_2^+, and RCO^+) normally involved in substitution of aromatic nuclei place a formal charge on nitrogen. As a result, the ring is deactivated with respect to electrophilic substitution.

Such interference is avoided through use of pyridine oxide as a starting material. This substance undergoes substitution predominantly

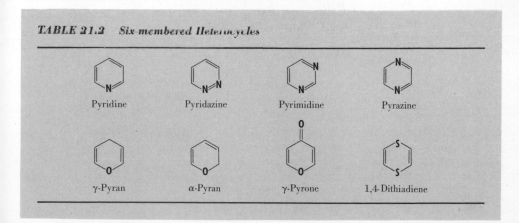

TABLE 21.2   Six-membered Heterocycles

Pyridine	Pyridazine	Pyrimidine	Pyrazine
γ-Pyran	α-Pyran	γ-Pyrone	1,4-Dithiadiene

in the 4-position, and to some extent in position 2. The intermediates produced by reactions at these positions are more resonance-stabilized than those involving the β-position. Thus pyridine oxide can be nitrated to give products that can be reduced to nitropyridines.

| γ-Nitro- | α-Nitropyri- |
| pyridine | dine |

A striking example of steric hindrance which illustrates the same principles is the direct sulfonation of 2,6-di-*tert*-butylpyridine in the γ-position. Although the 2,6-di-*tert*-butyl groups play little or no electronic role in promoting this reaction, they cover up the nitrogen atom so completely that the usual acid-base reaction is eliminated, and the compound readily substitutes at carbon.

2,6-Di-*tert*-butylpyridine   2,6-Di-*tert*-butylpyridine-4-
                                          sulfonic acid

Pyridine, like pyrrole, is subject to nucleophilic substitution by such reagents as sodamide and other organometallic substances. Reactions occur at either the α- or γ-positions, and an addition-elimination mechanism is involved. In some cases, the addition compounds have been isolated.

2-Aminopyridine

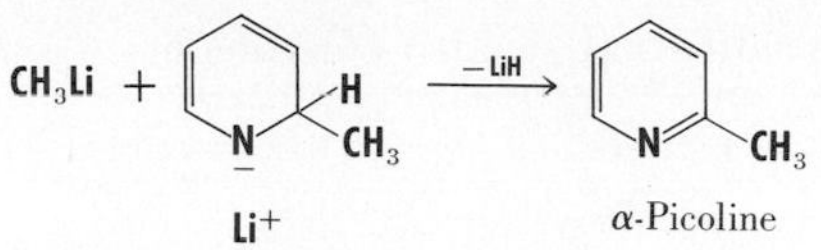

CH$_3$Li + [structure] $\xrightarrow{-\text{LiH}}$ [structure] α-Picoline

Methyl groups attached to the pyridine nucleus in the α- or γ-positions are more acidic than the methyl group in toluene, and the derived anions are nucleophiles which resemble other organometallic compounds in their behavior.

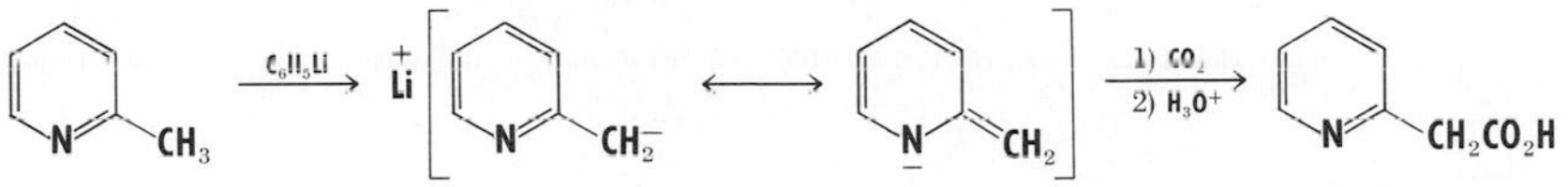

[structure] $\xrightarrow{C_6H_5Li}$ [structures] $\xrightarrow[\text{2) H}_3\text{O}^+]{\text{1) CO}_2}$ [structure] CH$_2$CO$_2$H

α-Pyridinoacetic
acid

B + [structures] $\underset{+\text{BH}}{\overset{-\text{BH}}{\rightleftarrows}}$ [structures] $\xrightarrow{C_6H_5CHO}$ [structure] $\xrightarrow[-\text{H}_2\text{O}]{+\text{H}^+}$ CH=CHC$_6$H$_5$

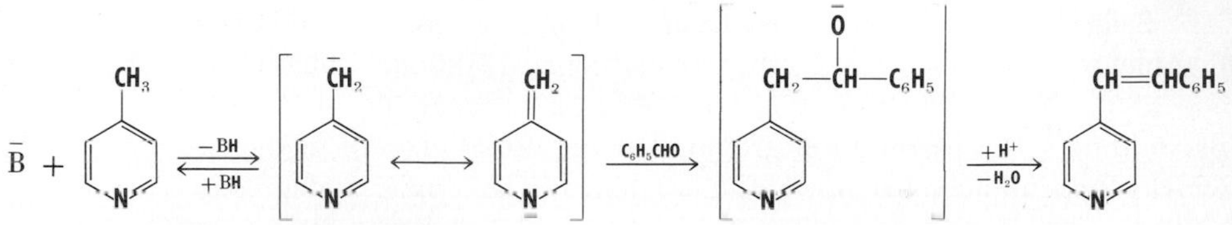

Like the benzene nucleus, that of pyridine resists oxidation, as shown by the conversion of the three picolines into the corresponding pyridine-carboxylic acids with potassium permanganate. The α- and γ-picolinic acids decarboxylate rather readily, probably by a mechanism involving reversible protonation of the aromatic ring. The β-isomer resists the reaction.

[structure] CH$_3$ $\xrightarrow{\text{KMnO}_4}$ [structure] CO$_2$H

α , β , or γ Picolines   α-, β-, or γ Picolinic acids

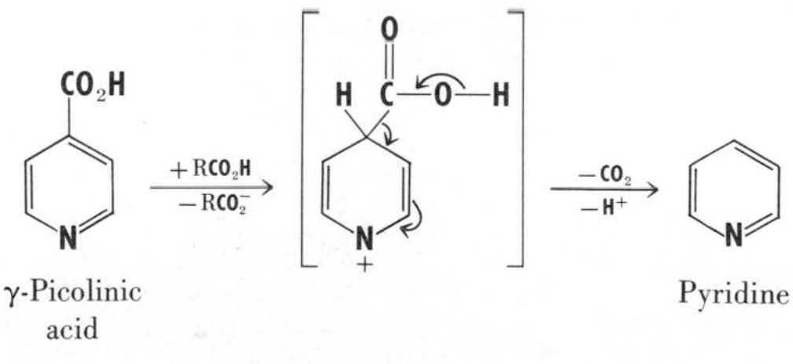

[structure] $\xrightarrow[-\text{RCO}_2^-]{+\text{RCO}_2\text{H}}$ [structure] $\xrightarrow[-\text{H}^+]{-\text{CO}_2}$ [structure] Pyridine

γ-Picolinic
acid

A number of important natural products contain the pyridine nucleus. Nicotine, a stimulant and poison found in the tobacco leaf, may also be oxidized with preservation of the aromatic nucleus. The product, β-picolinic acid (nicotinic acid), is an antipellagra vitamin. It is produced on a large scale and is used along with other vitamins to "fortify" wheat flour. A second vitamin, pyridoxin (B_6), also contains a pyridine nucleus.

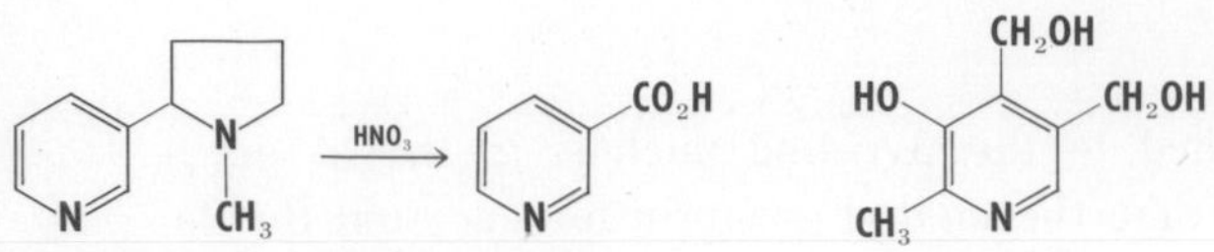

| Nicotine | Nicotinic acid (β-Picolinic acid) | Pyridoxine |

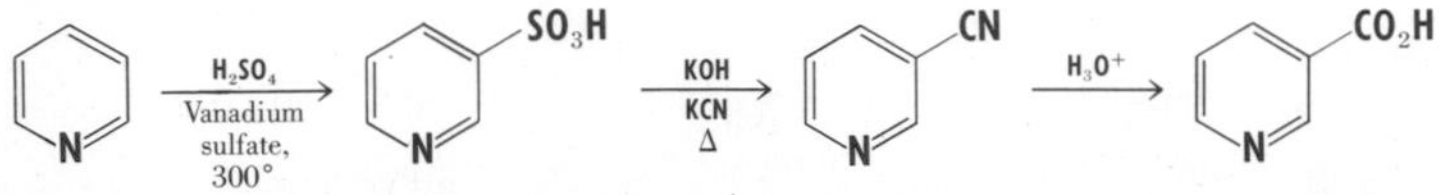

Nicotinic acid

Pyrimidine and Derived Compounds. A number of compounds of therapeutic importance contain the pyrimidine ring system. Sulfadiazine, one of the best sulfa drugs (antibiotics), is a sulfonamide of 2-amino-pyrimidine. The barbiturates are another important class of medicinals which contain the pyrimidine ring system. They have a depressant action on the central nervous system (sedative or soporific action) and are widely and often indiscriminately used in sleeping pills. Pheno-barbital is a representative of this class of compound. A third important group of pyrimidines (cytosine, uracil, and thymine) is obtained by hydrolysis of nucleic acids.

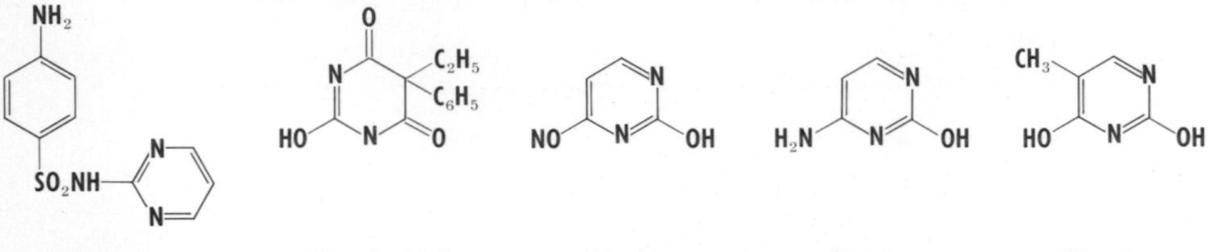

| Sulfadiazine | Phenobarbital | Uracil | Cytosine | Thymine |

The synthesis of sulfadiazine illustrates the construction of a pyrimidine ring system.

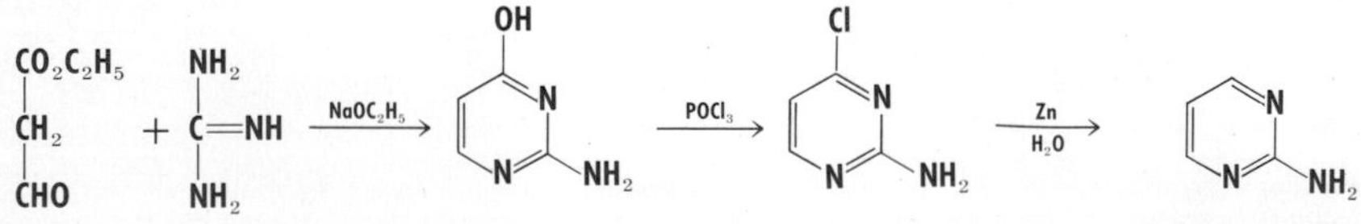

Guanidine

2-Aminopyrimidin

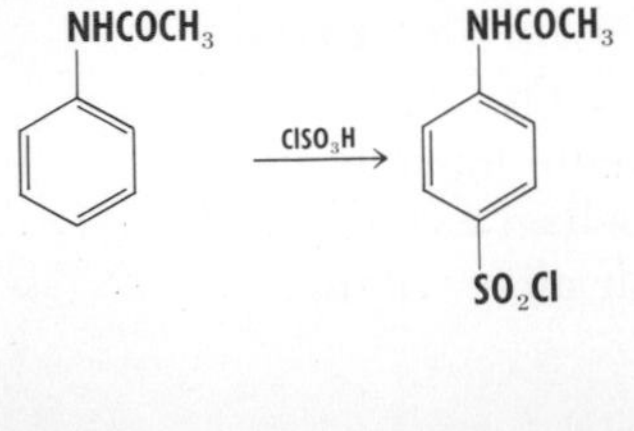

Sulfadiazine

Fused Six-membered Ring Systems

From the large variety of fused heterocycles that contain six-membered rings, the chemistry of only quinoline, isoquinoline, and pterin will be treated. These three ring systems are widely distributed in nature, the first two in the plant kingdom in alkaloids (Chap. 23), the third in the animal kingdom in pigments and vitamins. Quinoline and isoquinoline, found in the basic fraction from coal tar, are commercial chemicals. Pterin itself has little commercial importance. Table 21.3 gives the structures of these and other common heterocyclic fused six-membered ring systems.

Chemistry of Quinoline. The Skraup synthesis of the quinoline ring system is a multistage reaction that involves aniline or substituted anilines as starting materials. If glycerine or acrolein is employed as the

TABLE 21.3   Fused Six-membered Heterocycles

Quinoline	Isoquinoline	Cinnoline	Quinazoline
Quinoxaline	Phthalazine	Pterin	Acridine
Phenazine	Chroman	Chromone	Xanthone

second component, an unsubstituted nitrogen-containing ring is produced (page 387). If methyl vinyl ketone is employed, lepidine is the product.

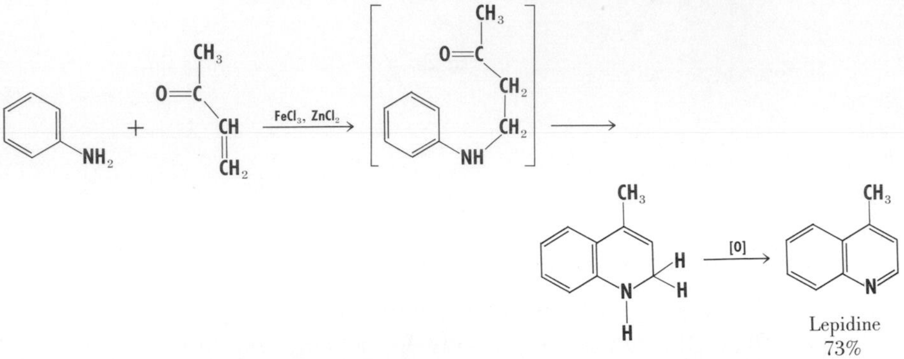

A second general synthesis of the quinoline ring system employs aniline or substituted anilines and an aldehyde containing α-hydrogens as starting materials. The reaction is mechanistically complex, and yields are low.

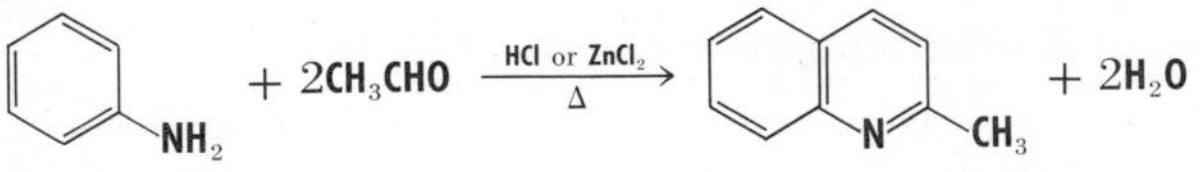

Aniline

The heterocyclic ring of quinoline is more stable toward oxidizing agents but more amenable to reduction than the carbocyclic ring, as is illustrated in the following transformations:

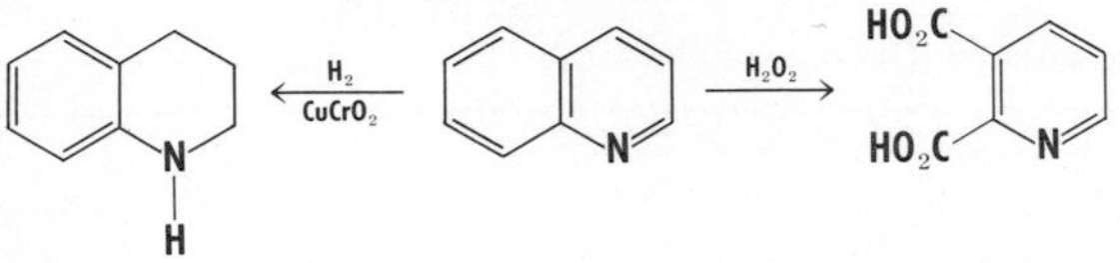

Tetrahydroquinoline   Quinoline   Quinolinic acid
95%   65%

Electrophilic substitution reactions of quinoline occur only under rather drastic conditions, as was the case with pyridine. In nitration and sulfonation, the carbocyclic ring is attacked, and in bromination, the heterocyclic ring is substituted.

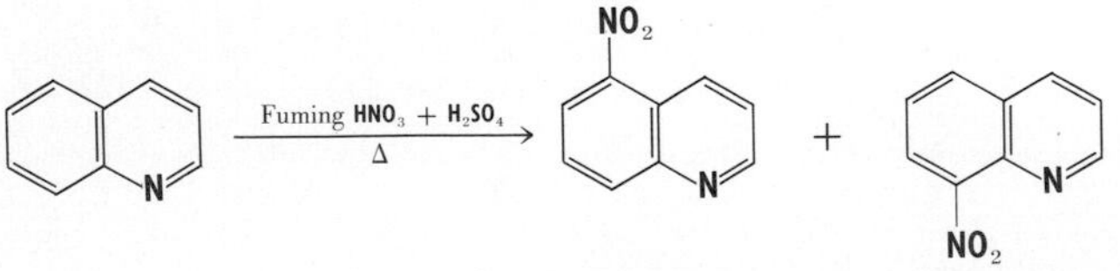

5-Nitroquinoline   8-Nitroquinoline
37%   27%

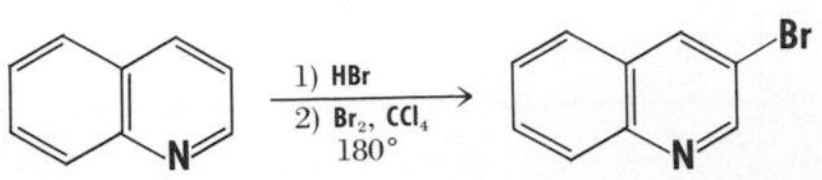

3-Bromoquinoline

Nucleophilic substitutions occur readily, as in the case of pyridine, and the substituent enters the 2- or 4-position.

2-Aminoquinoline

Isoquinoline, Pterin, and Related Compounds. This section is limited to illustrations of the synthesis of compounds of medicinal importance that incorporate fused six-membered ring systems. Papaverine, one of the constituents of opium, is used as an antispasmodic; it is produced industrially from vanillin (Chap. 22). Other important pharmaceuticals containing the isoquinoline ring system are discussed in the section on alkaloids (Chap. 23).

The pterin ring system is found in a number of pigments isolated from extracts of butterfly wings, and less lovely parts of other insects. Xanthopterin and leucopterin are examples of this class of compound. A more complex group of pterins has been isolated from liver, yeast, and spinach. Some of these substances have been found necessary for the growth of microorganisms. One of the most active compounds contains a pterin ring system attached to *p*-aminobenzoic acid, which in turn is

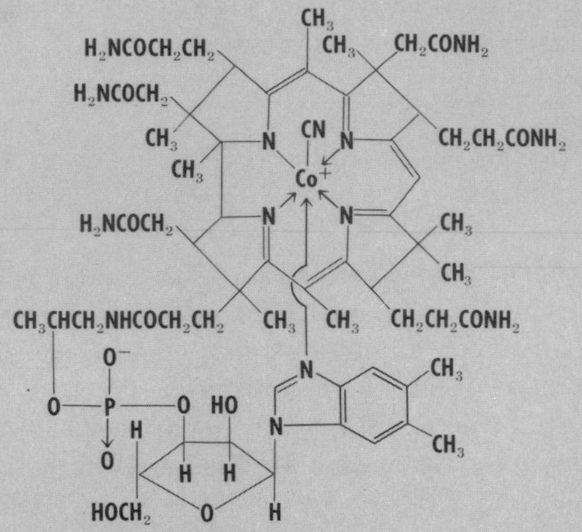

FIG. 21.3   Structure of vitamin B_{12}.

tied to glutamic acid. This substance has some value in the treatment of pernicious anemia, but is inferior to vitamin B_{12}. The structure of the latter molecule was elucidated largely through use of digital computers in interpreting the X-ray diffraction patterns of crystals of vitamin B_{12} and its degradation products. Figure 21.3 records the structure of the substance.

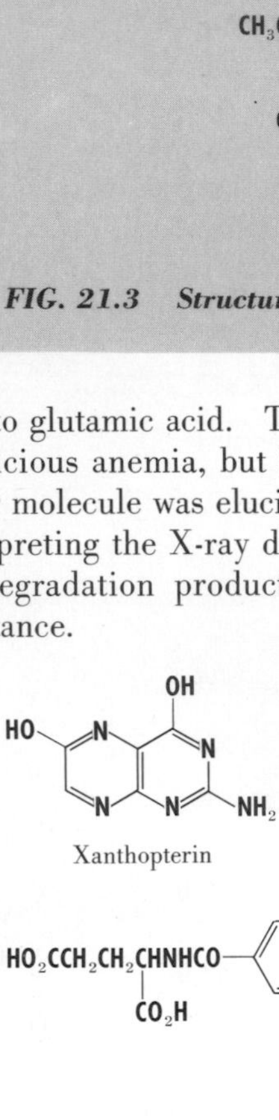

Xanthopterin

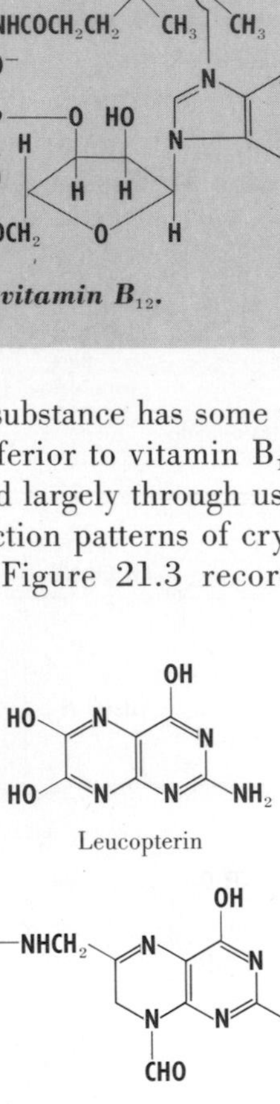

Leucopterin

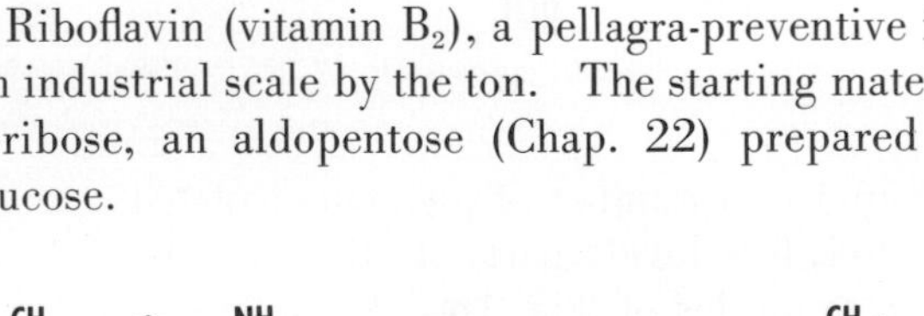

8-Formyl-7,8-dihydropteroylglutamic acid

Riboflavin (vitamin B_2), a pellagra-preventive factor, is synthesized on an industrial scale by the ton. The starting materials are 3,4-xylidine and ribose, an aldopentose (Chap. 22) prepared by the degradation of glucose.

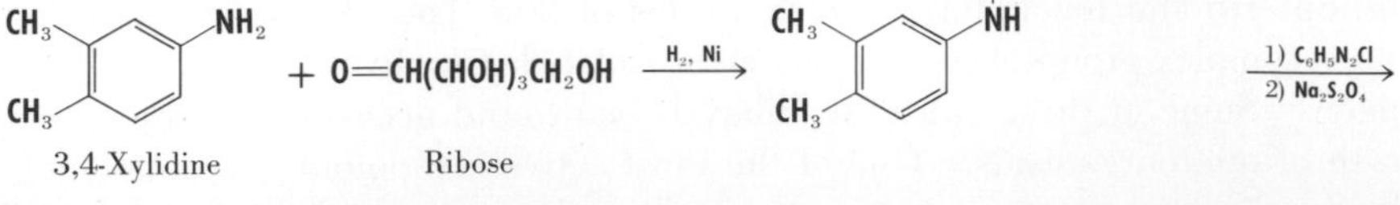

3,4-Xylidine   Ribose

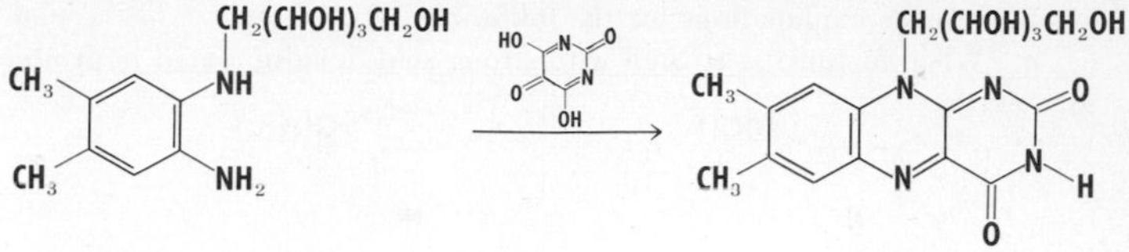

$$CH_2(CHOH)_3CH_2OH$$

[structures depicting reaction forming Riboflavin]

Riboflavin

Problems

1. Classify each reaction in this chapter in terms of the classes of reaction described in the titles of Chaps. 10 through 20.

2. The furan ring system is stable to most bases and to weak acids, and furfural does not possess any α-hydrogens. Write 10 reactions that you predict would work well for furfural (reactions of benzaldehyde can serve as models).

3. With only open-chain starting materials, write syntheses of the following substances:

a.

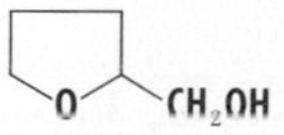

[structure: tetrahydrofuran-CH₂OH]

b.

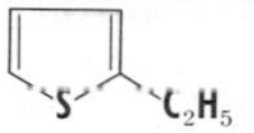

[structure: thiophene-C₂H₅]

c.

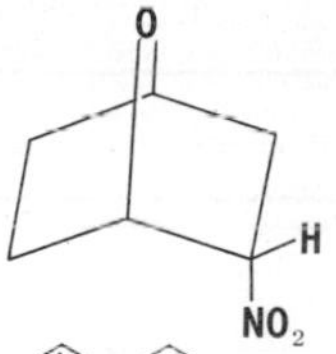

[bicyclic ketone structure with —H, NO₂]

d.

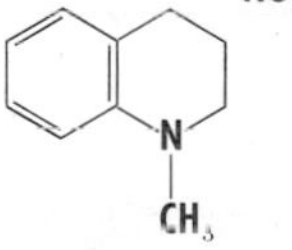

[structure: N-methyl tetrahydroquinoline, CH₃]

e.

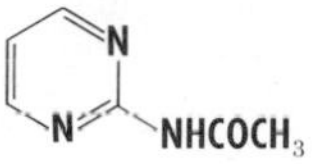

[structure: pyrimidine-NHCOCH₃]

f.

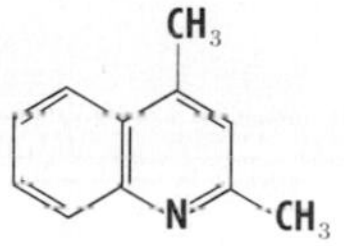

[structure: 4-methyl-2-methyl quinoline with CH₃ groups]

g.

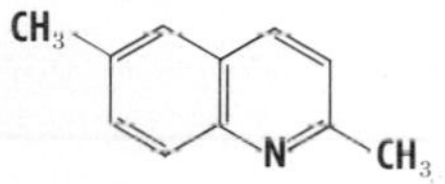

[structure: 6-methyl-2-methyl quinoline with CH₃ groups]

h.

[structure: N-methyl pyridine N-oxide, CH₃]

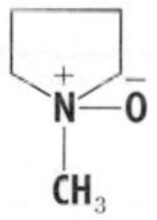

i.

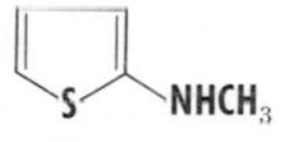

[structure: thiophene-NHCH₃]

j.

[structure: pyrrole-N-D]

D

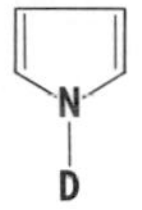

4. Write syntheses of the following compounds with commercially available heterocycles as starting materials.

a. 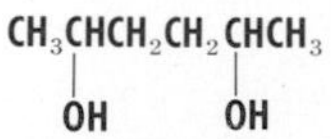 $CH_3CHCH_2CH_2CHCH_3$ with OH OH groups

b.

[structure: pyridine dicarboxylic anhydride]

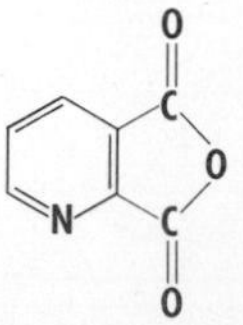

c. $CH_2=CHCH_2CH_2CH_2N(CH_3)_2$

d.

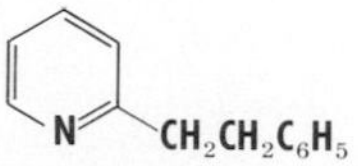

[structure: pyridine-CH₂CH₂C₆H₅]

e.

[structure: pyridine-NH₂]

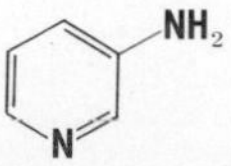

5. Provide explanations for the following facts:

a. When furfural is treated with strong acid, levulinic acid is produced.

b.

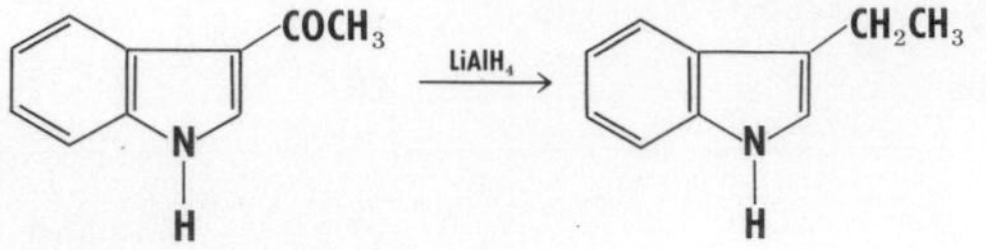

c.

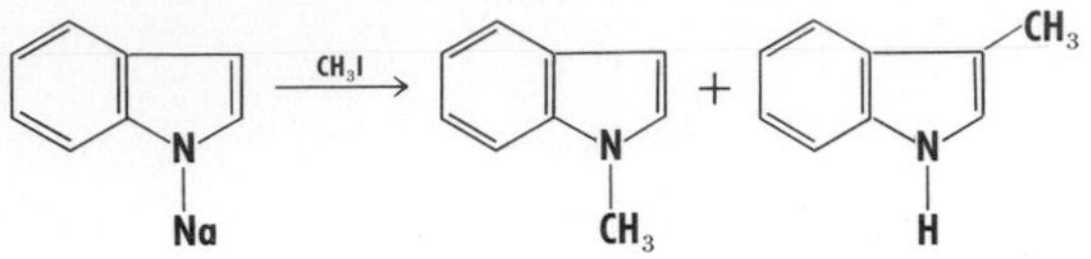

d. Although biotin has three asymmetric centers, only a few of the theoretically possible stereoisomers can exist. What are their structures?

e. The Fischer indole synthesis.

$$\begin{array}{c} \text{O} = \text{C} \begin{array}{c} \nearrow \text{H} \\ \searrow \text{C} \begin{array}{c} \text{OH} \\ \text{H} \end{array} \\ \text{HO} \cdots \text{C} \begin{array}{c} \text{H} \\ \text{C} \begin{array}{c} \text{OH} \\ \text{H} \end{array} \\ \text{H} \cdots \text{C} \begin{array}{c} \text{H} \\ \text{HO} \nearrow \text{C} \begin{array}{c} \text{H} \\ \text{HO} \nearrow \text{H} \end{array} \end{array}$$

22

Carbohydrates and Phenolic Plant Products

The term *carbohydrate* arose historically from the observation that a group of compounds isolated from natural sources possessed molecular formulas which could be fitted to the general formula $C_x(H_2O)_y$. After the structures of these compounds were elucidated, many other substances were discovered whose constitution placed them within the carbohydrate family, but whose molecular formulas were in conflict with the implications of the term. Carbohydrates are now classified as polyhydroxylated compounds, many of which contain aldehydic or ketonic groups, or yield such groups on hydrolysis. The importance of carbohydrates lies in the vital role they play in the metabolism of living organisms.

Simple carbohydrates are referred to as sugars, or saccharides, because they are sweet to the taste. Usually their names end in *-ose*. Sugars are classified as *monosaccharides, oligosaccharides, or polysaccharides*, depending on the number of simple sugar units linked together in the molecule. Monosaccharide units usually consist of chains of five or six carbon atoms, and are called *pentoses* and *hexoses*, respectively. If monosaccharides contain an aldehyde function, they are classified as *aldoses*; if a ketonic group, as *ketoses*. Thus a monosaccharide might be any one of the following: *aldopentose, aldohexose, ketopentose,* or *ketohexose*. Monosaccharides that contain from three to eight carbon atoms are found in nature. Oligosaccharides yield a few monosaccharide units upon hydrolysis, whereas polysaccharides yield many such units when hydrolyzed.

The really distinguishing feature of carbohydrates is that in most of the substances each carbon atom carries a hydroxyl group or a function derived from a hydroxyl. This multitude of substituents gives rise to a large number of asymmetric centers in each molecule. As a result, formulation of stereochemical principles, use of protective groups, and discovery of specific reagents which can distinguish between functional groups have been the great contributions made by carbohydrate chemists to the general science. This chapter deals with monosaccharides, disaccharides, and related compounds; polysaccharides are discussed in Chap. 25.

Monosaccharides

Structures and Configurations of Glucose and Other Monosaccharides. Many of the principles associated with the simple sugars, and many of their reactions, can be illustrated by an argument for the structure of the most common aldohexose, glucose. This substance is readily obtained by acid hydrolysis of starch, cellulose, cane sugar (sucrose), and a host of other natural products. Glucose, in free or combined state, is one of the most plentiful of all organic compounds.

The molecular formula of glucose is $C_6H_{12}O_6$. The gross structure of the sugar is established by the following facts:

1. Reduction of the substance with hydrogen iodide and red phosphorus gives *n*-hexane and reveals an unbranched chain of six carbon atoms.

2. Glucose reacts with reagents such as hydroxylamine and phenylhydrazine, which are used to characterize aldehydes and ketones (page 315).

3. Oxidation of the compound with bromine water gives gluconic acid $(C_5H_{11}O_5CO_2H)$, a monocarboxylic acid. This fact and fact 2 establish that glucose is an aldehyde.

4. Reduction of the aldehyde with sodium amalgam gives *sorbitol*, $C_6H_{14}O_6$, which upon acetylation gives a hexaacetate.

Thus sorbitol must contain six hydroxyl groups, one due to reduction of the aldehyde and five originating in glucose. Each of the six carbon atoms of sorbitol would appear to be linked to one hydroxyl group.† If the structural formula of glucose is assigned as $HOCH_2(CHOH)_4CHO$, all the reactions can be readily formulated. In these and subsequent formulas, $Ac = CH_3CO$.

---

† Examples have been given of compounds which contain two hydroxyl groups per carbon atom. In each case, however, strong electron-withdrawing groups occupy adjacent carbon atoms, as in chloral hydrate and ninhydrin.

$CCl_3CH(OH)_2$

Chloral hydrate   Ninhydrin

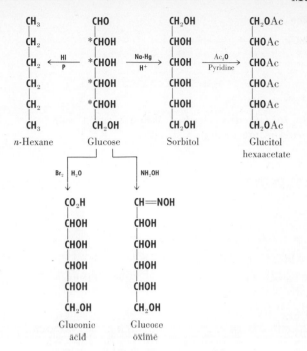

n-Hexane   Glucose   Sorbitol   Glucitol hexaacetate

Gluconic acid   Glucose oxime

Four asymmetric centers are found in the glucose molecule, and the number of possible stereoisomeric structures is 2^4, or 16. The task of relating the configurations of these four asymmetric centers to one another was completed by Emil Fischer in 1896, and the essential portions of the work are reproduced here.

At that time, three aldohexoses, (+)-glucose, (+)-mannose, and (+)-gulose, were known, together with the aldopentose, (−)-arabinose, and the ketohexose, (−)-fructose. The gross structures of these substances were known, but their relative configurations were not established. Three general reaction sequences were available for interrelating and characterizing monosaccharides.

1. *Osazone Formation.* Compounds containing the group **CHOHCO**, when treated with three moles of hydrazine or phenyl hydrazine, produce *bis*-1,2-hydrazones, known as osazones, which are usually nicely crystalline compounds. One mole of hydrazine is involved in oxidizing a hydroxyl to a carbonyl group, and the other two moles give the osazone.

$$
\begin{array}{ccccc}
\text{CHO} & & \left[\text{CH}=\text{NNHC}_6\text{H}_5\right] & & \text{CH}=\text{NNHC}_6\text{H}_5 & & \text{CH}=\text{NNHC}_6\text{H}_5 \\
\text{CHOH} & \xrightarrow{\text{C}_6\text{H}_5\text{NHNH}_2} & \text{CHOH} & \xrightarrow[-\text{NH}_3]{\substack{\text{C}_6\text{H}_5\text{NHNH}_2 \\ -\text{C}_6\text{H}_5\text{NH}_2}} & \text{C}=\text{O} & \xrightarrow[-\text{H}_2\text{O}]{\text{C}_6\text{H}_5\text{NHNH}_2} & \text{C}=\text{NNHC}_6\text{H}_5 \\
(\text{CHOH})_n & & (\text{CHOH})_n & & (\text{CHOH})_n & & (\text{CHOH})_n \\
\text{CH}_2\text{OH} & & \text{CH}_2\text{OH} & & \text{CH}_2\text{OH} & & \text{CH}_2\text{OH} \\
\text{An} & & & & & & \text{An} \\
\text{aldose} & & & & & & \text{osazone}
\end{array}
$$

$$
\begin{array}{ccc}
\text{CH}_2\text{OH} & & \text{CH=NNHC}_6\text{H}_5 \\
| & & | \\
\text{C=O} & \xrightarrow{3\text{C}_6\text{H}_5\text{NHNH}_2} & \text{C=NNHC}_6\text{H}_5 \\
| & & | \\
\text{(CHOH)}_n & & \text{(CHOH)}_n \\
| & & | \\
\text{CH}_2\text{OH} & & \text{CH}_2\text{OH}
\end{array}
$$

A ketose   An osazone

2. *Oxidation of Aldoses to Glycaric Acids.* When treated with nitric acid, aldoses are converted to glycaric acids.

$$
\begin{array}{ccc}
\text{CHO} & & \text{CO}_2\text{H} \\
| & & | \\
\text{(CHOH)}_n & \xrightarrow{\text{HNO}_3} & \text{(CHOH)}_n \\
| & & | \\
\text{CH}_2\text{OH} & & \text{CO}_2\text{H}
\end{array}
$$

An   A glycaric
aldose   (saccharic)
    acid

3. *Chain Extension.* Aldoses or ketoses when subjected to the cyanohydrin reaction (page 282) give a mixture of diastereomeric nitriles, which may be hydrolyzed to a mixture of diastereomeric carboxylic acids.

$$
\begin{array}{ccccccccc}
\text{CHO} & & \text{CN} & & \text{CN} & & \text{CO}_2\text{H} & & \text{CO}_2\text{H} \\
| & & | & & | & & | & & | \\
\text{(CHOH)}_n & \xrightarrow{\text{HCN}} & \text{H--C--OH} & + & \text{HO--C--H} & \xrightarrow{\text{H}_3\text{O}^+} & \text{H--C--OH} & + & \text{HO--C--H} \\
| & & | & & | & & | & & | \\
\text{CH}_2\text{OH} & & \text{(CHOH)}_n & & \text{(CHOH)}_n & & \text{(CHOH)}_n & & \text{(CHOH)}_n \\
& & | & & | & & | & & | \\
& & \text{CH}_2\text{OH} & & \text{CH}_2\text{OH} & & \text{CH}_2\text{OH} & & \text{CH}_2\text{OH}
\end{array}
$$

Diastereomeric nitriles   Diastereomeric acids

At the time Fischer did this work, *no absolute configurations* were known, and he assumed (and by chance correctly) that the *absolute configuration* about carbon 5 in (+)-glucose was as written. For the sake of simplicity, he wrote projection formulas in such a way as to place the carbon chain in a vertical line in the plane of the page, with the horizontal bonds carrying the attached substituents (page 135). This projection may be transformed into a three-dimensional structure by lifting the horizontally bonded substituents above, and allowing the extremities of the chain to coil below, the plane of the page. The configurations about carbons 2, 3, and 4 in relation to the assumed configuration about carbon 5 were demonstrated as follows:

$$
\begin{array}{l}
^1\text{CHO} \\
| \\
^2\text{CHOH} \\
| \\
^3\text{CHOH} \\
| \\
^4\text{CHOH} \\
| \\
\text{H--}^5\text{C--OH} \\
| \\
^6\text{CH}_2\text{OH}
\end{array}
$$

(+)-Glucose

The compounds (+)-mannose and (+)-glucose were found to yield the same osazone. This fact demonstrates that the two compounds are *epimers* and *differ only in their configurations* at carbon 2. The same osazone was formed from (−)-fructose. This experiment shows that the latter substance has a carbonyl group at carbon 2, and that carbons 3, 4, and 5 possess configurations like those of (+)-mannose and (+)-glucose.

$$
\begin{array}{ccc}
^1CHO & CH\!\!=\!\!NNHC_6H_5 & ^1CH_2OH \\
^2CHOH & C\!\!=\!\!NNHC_6H_5 & ^2C\!\!=\!\!O \\
^3CHOH & CHOH & ^3CHOH \\
^4CHOH & CHOH & ^4CHOH \\
H\!-\!{}^5C\!-\!OH & H\!-\!C\!-\!OH & H\!-\!{}^5C\!-\!OH \\
^6CH_2OH & CH_2OH & ^6CH_2OH \\
\end{array}
$$

(+)-Glucose or   Glucosazone   (−)-Fructose
(+)-mannose

Configurations about carbons 3–5 are the same

When (+)-mannose and (+)-glucose were oxidized with nitric acid, two different optically active glycaric acids, *mannaric* and *glucaric acids*, were produced. Because these glycaric acids have identical terminal groups, the total number of stereoisomers is reduced to ten, two meso forms and four enantiomeric pairs (see Table 22.1). The fact that mannaric and glucaric acid are optically active indicates that neither one can correspond to structures I and II. Structure III is also eliminated, since mannaric and glucaric acid, like their parents, glucose and mannose, differ in configuration only at carbon 2. Should structure III apply to either mannaric or glucaric acid, the structure of the other would have to correspond to I or II, both of which are optically inactive. Since both mannaric and glucaric acid are optically active, they must possess one of the last three structures, IV, V, or VI.

$$
\begin{array}{cccc}
CHO & CO_2H & CO_2H & CHO \\
(CHOH)_3 & (CHOH)_3 & (CHOH)_3 & (CHOH)_3 \\
H\!-\!C\!-\!OH & H\!-\!C\!-\!OH & H\!-\!C\!-\!OH & H\!-\!C\!-\!OH \\
CH_2OH & CO_2H & CO_2H & CH_2OH \\
\end{array}
$$

(+)-Glucose   Glucaric   Mannaric   (+)-Mannose
           acid   acid

The aldopentose (−)-arabinose was subjected to the cyanohydrin reaction, and the cyanohydrins produced were hydrolyzed to give two glyconic acids. These substances were found to be identical with the *two glyconic acids* obtained by oxidation of (+)-glucose and (+)-mannose with bromine water. Thus the configurations about carbons 2,

TABLE 22.1   *Glycaric Acids*

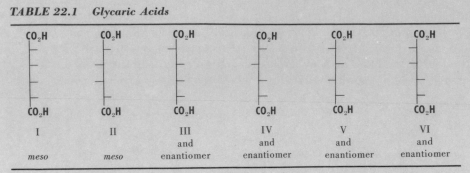

I	II	III	IV	V	VI
		and	and	and	and
meso	*meso*	enantiomer	enantiomer	enantiomer	enantiomer

Horizontal bonds stand for positions of hydroxyl groups.

3, and 4 of (−)-arabinose must be the same as the configurations about carbons 3, 4, and 5, respectively, of (+)-glucose and (+)-mannose.

When (−)-arabinose was oxidized to the corresponding dicarboxylic acid, an optically active product was obtained. The two possible meso structures for this acid were thus eliminated, and only the asymmetric structure remained.

This chain of interlocking configurational relationships eliminated configuration V for either glucaric or mannaric acid, and limited the configurations available for these two acids to IV and VI. Hence only two configurations, VII and VIII, remained for (+)-glucose and (+)-mannose, and the structure of (−)-fructose was established.

CHO	CHO	CH₂OH
HCOH	HOCH	C=O
HOCH	HOCH	HOCH
HCOH	HCOH	HCOH
HCOH	HCOH	HCOH
CH₂OH	CH₂OH	CH₂OH
VII	VIII	(−)-Fructose

A final experiment distinguished between configurations VII and VIII for (+)-glucose. The third available aldohexose, (+)-gulose, was not enantiomerically related to either (+)-glucose or (+)-mannose. This substance when oxidized with nitric acid gave glucaric acid, which was identical with a sample of the substance similarly obtained from glucose. Hence (+)-glucose and (+)-gulose must differ only in that their aldehyde and hydroxymethylene groups are interchanged. Such a relationship is incompatible with structure VIII for (+)-glucose, and structure VII remains for the substance. Thus (+)-mannose must have structure VIII.

CHO	CO₂H	CH₂OH		CHO
HCOH	HCOH	HCOH		HOCH
HOCH	HOCH	HOCH		HOCH
HCOH	HCOH	HCOH		HCOH
HCOH	HCOH	HCOH		HOCH
CH₂OH	CO₂H	CHO		CH₂OH
(+)-Glucose	Glucaric acid		(+)-Gulose	

With experiments of the above type and similar reasoning, investigators have established the relative configurations of a multitude of compounds, including all the aldoses (see Table 22.2). Since the absolute configuration of (+)-glyceraldehyde is now established (page 142), the absolute configurations of the compounds in Table 22.2 are known.

TABLE 22.2   *Configurations of the D-Aldoses*

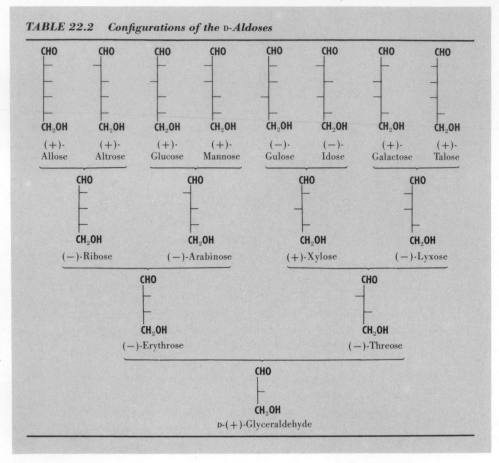

Structures of Methyl Glucosides.   When treated with hot methanolic hydrogen chloride, glucose gives two mixed acetals that involve the hydroxyl group of one methanol molecule and one of the hydroxyl groups of the chain. These compounds, called methyl glucosides, differ only in their configurations at the new asymmetric carbon atom.

The great usefulness of periodic acid (page 433) for deciding between possible structures of sugars is demonstrated in the application of this oxidizing agent to the problem of the structures of the methyl glucosides. Table 22.3 lists the five possible structures for these mixed acetals. Each of the five compounds associated with these structures would consume a predictable number of moles of periodic acid when titrated with that reagent, and would give a predictable number of moles of formaldehyde or formic acid or both as products. A unique combination of numbers characterizes each structure. Actual titrations of each of the two methyl glucosides revealed that two moles of periodic acid were consumed, one mole of formic acid was produced, and no formaldehyde was generated in the reaction. Clearly, gross structure XII must apply to both acetals formed from glucose.

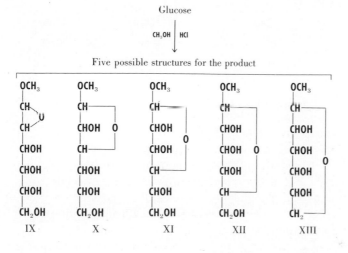

This conclusion was verified by an examination of the larger fragments formed in this reaction. Oxidative hydrolysis of the acetal-dialdehyde gave (−)-glyceric acid and oxalic acid. Since D-(+)-glyceraldehyde had been oxidized to give (−)-glyceric acid in other studies, this chain of reactions demonstrated that the configurations at carbon 5 of glucose and D-(+)-glyceraldehyde are the same. By convention, projection formulas in which the hydroxyl farthest removed from the carbonyl group is written on the right designate sugars that possess the D-configuration (see Table 22.2).

TABLE 22.3 *Predicted Behavior of Compounds IX–XIII When Titrated with Periodic Acid*

Structure	Number of moles		
	HIO_4 consumed	HCO_2H formed	CH_2O formed
IX	3	2	1
X	2	1	1
XI	2	0	1
XII	2	1	0
XIII	3	2	0

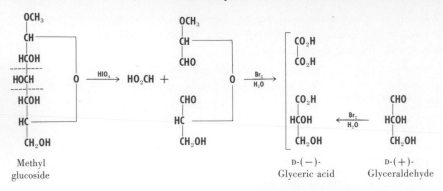

Methyl glucoside   D-(−)-   D-(+)-
                                                    Glyceric acid   Glyceraldehyde

The two methyl glucosides differ only in their configurations at carbon 1, the new asymmetric center. These isomers are diastereomers but are also designated as *anomers,* and the carbon atom responsible for the existence of *anomers* is called the *anomeric carbon.* These acetals are referred to as methyl α- and β-D-glucopyranosides, the Greek letters referring to the configuration of the anomeric carbon. The α-configuration requires that the methoxyl group be written on the same side in the Fischer projection formulas as the oxygen of the carbon determining the configurational family (carbon 5 of the hexoses). The β-configuration specifies the opposite configuration. Thus in all D sugars, the methoxyl is written on the right to indicate an α-anomeric carbon, and in L sugars, the methoxyl is written on the left for an α-anomeric carbon.

Formulas written in perspective are superior for configurational designation to the flat Fischer formulas. Ring size is indicated in names by the suffix *-pyranoside,* which relates to the parent heterocycle, pyran. This term is necessary, since five-membered acetal rings are also encountered, and these are designated as *furanosides.* The class name *glycoside* has been given to mixed acetals of aldoses, irrespective of ring size or the nature of the group attached to the noncyclic ether oxygen.

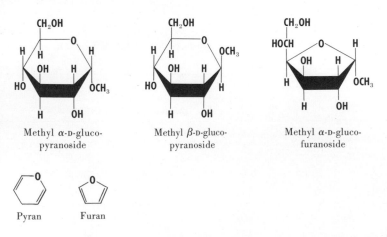

Methyl α-D-gluco-   Methyl β-D-gluco-   Methyl α-D-gluco-
pyranoside   pyranoside   furanoside

Pyran   Furan

Although glucose itself has been represented as an aldehyde, a more stable form of the substance in either solution or the solid state contains a pyranose structure. Both the α- and β-isomers of glucose have been isolated in crystalline form. When dissolved in water, these anomers equilibrate both with the open aldehyde form and with each other. These changes are followed by observation of change in rotation with time, the equilibrium value being $[\alpha]_D + 52°$. The change in rotation that occurs when either the α- or the β-isomer goes to the equilibrium mixture is called *mutarotation*. Configurational assignments given to the anomeric carbon in these cyclic hemiacetals and to the methylglucosides depend partly on physical measurements, partly on enzymatic reactions, and partly on chemical syntheses.

α-D-Glucopyranose
$[\alpha]_D + 113°$

Aldehyde form

β-D-Glucopyranose
$[\alpha]_D + 19°$

Although with glucose only a small amount of the aldehyde form is present in an equilibrated mixture, equilibrium is established rapidly enough to allow the compound to behave very much like an ordinary aldehyde. Thus glucose reduces silver ion complexed with ammonia (Tollens' reagent) or cupric ion complexed with citrate ion (Benedict's solution). Sugars that reduce cupric ion are referred to as *reducing sugars*. Under the basic conditions of the test, even ketoses give the reaction, either because they undergo alkali-caused fragmentation or rearrangements to give aldehydes, or because the α-ketol group itself is susceptible to oxidation.

Reactions of Monosaccharides. When acetylated, glucose forms one of two anomeric pentaacetates. With an acid catalyst such as zinc chloride, the anomers equilibrate, and equilibrium favors the α-form by a factor of 10 (thermodynamic control of products). With a basic catalyst, although α- and β-glucose can equilibrate, the acetates, once formed, maintain their integrity. The β-anomer, which is formed faster, predominates in the product (kinetic control of products). Frequently kinetically controlled processes lead to the thermodynamically unstable isomer.

α-D-Glucopyranosyl
pentaacetate

β-D-Glucopyranosyl
pentaacetate

A special method is employed to prepare the acyclic pentaacetate of glucose. The superiority of sulfur over oxygen as a nucleophile (page 241) is demonstrated by the fact that an open-chain thioacetal (unlike an acetal) of glucose can be prepared directly. This material is then acetylated, and the thioacetal group is removed by hydrolysis.

Although simple sugars are unstable in alkaline solution, the methyl glycosides are stable enough to permit formation of ethers from the hydroxyl groups by means of the Williamson synthesis (page 208). The ring structure of methyl α-D-glucofuranoside was demonstrated through use of the reaction. The completely methylated derivative was partially hydrolyzed to give a tetramethyl etheraldehyde. The selectivity of this reaction indicates that the glycosidic (acetal) linkage is more susceptible to hydrolysis than ordinary ether bonds. The aldehyde was oxidized to a carboxylic acid which spontaneously formed a lactone. Treatment of the lactone with nitric acid gave two fragments, whose structures identify the ring system of the starting material.

α-D-Methyl glucofuranoside

CH$_2$OCH$_3$

CH$_3$OCH   OH

OCH$_3$ H   CO$_2$H

H

H   OCH$_3$

$\longrightarrow$

CH$_2$OCH$_3$

CH$_3$OCH   O

OCH$_3$ H   =O

H

H   OCH$_3$

Tetra-*o*-methyl-D-glucono-
γ-lactone

$\xrightarrow{HNO_3}$

CO$_2$H
CO$_2$H

+ HO$_2$C   OCH$_3$ H   CO$_2$H

H   OCH$_3$

(+)-Dimethoxysuccinic
acid

Triphenylmethyl chloride (trityl chloride) is a selective reagent which reacts much faster with the less sterically hindered primary hydroxyl groups than with secondary hydroxyl groups. Use of this property is made in reactions of the saccharides in which hydroxymethylene groups (**CH$_2$OH**) are selectively converted to some other groups, as in the following example.

CH$_2$OH

H   H   O   H

OH   H

HO   OCH$_3$

H   OH

$\xrightarrow[\text{Pyridine}]{(C_6H_5)_3CCl}$

CH$_2$OC(C$_6$H$_5$)$_3$

H   H   O   H

OH   H

HO   OCH$_3$

H   OH

$\xrightarrow[\text{AcONa}]{Ac_2O}$

CH$_2$OC(C$_6$H$_5$)$_3$

H   H   O   H

OAc   H

AcO   OCH$_3$

H   OAc

$\xrightarrow{PBr_3}$

CH$_2$Br

H   H   O   H

OAc   H

AcO   OCH$_3$

H   OAc

$\xrightarrow[\text{AcOH}]{Zn}$

CH$_3$

H   H   O   H

OAc   H

AcO   OCH$_3$

H   OAc

Carbohydrates also react with such reagents as acetone or benzaldehyde and dry hydrogen chloride to form isopropylidene (ketals of acetone) or benzylidene derivatives, respectively. In some cases, these derivatives are used as protective groups which are easily and sometimes selectively removed (dilute acid), in others for purposes of obtaining furanosides difficult to prepare by other means. The hydroxyl group on the anomeric carbon sometimes participates in the reaction. Usually, hydroxyl groups on adjacent carbon atoms that are cis to each other become involved in the same acetal function. Frequently one isopropylidene group can be hydrolytically removed under conditions that leave a second group undisturbed. Carbonate derivatives of the sugars serve very much the same purpose, and possess the complementary virtue of being relatively stable to acid hydrolysis but readily subject to

basic hydrolysis.   Use of these types of derivatives is made in the preparation of methyl α-D-glucofuranoside from D-glucose.

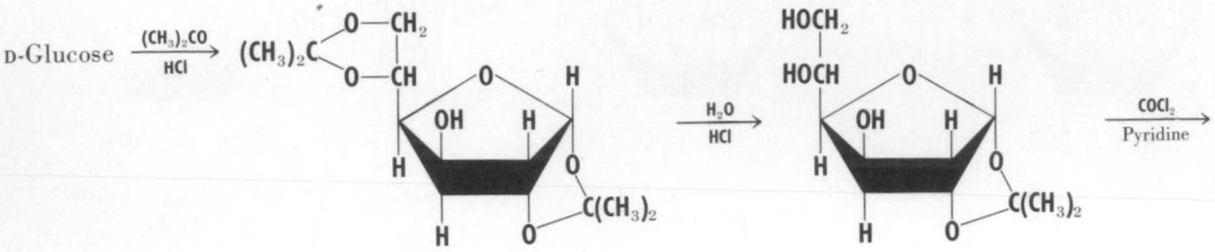

1,2:5,6-Di-o-isopropylidene-
α-D-glucofuranose

1,2-Isopropylidene-
D-glucofuranose

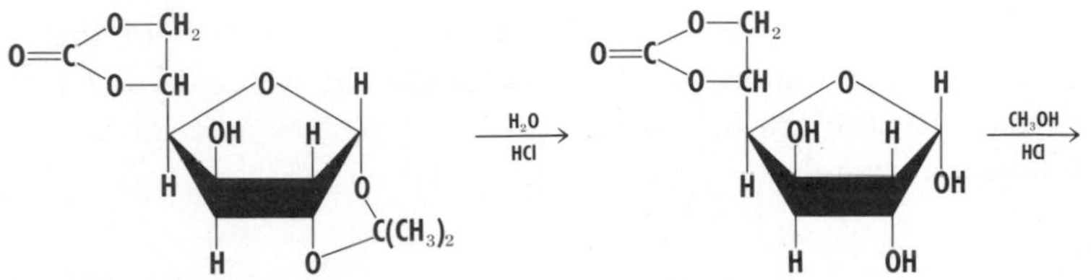

1,2-Isopropylidene-D-
glucofuranose 5,6-carbonate

D-Glucose
5,6-carbonate

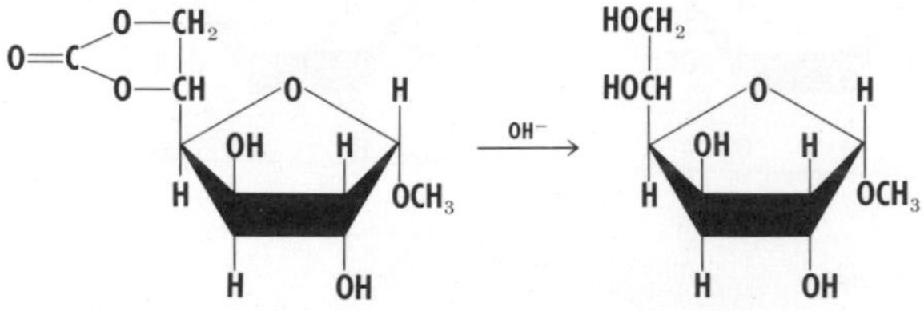

Methyl α-D-glucofuranoside
5,6-carbonate

Methyl α-D-
glucofuranoside

A characteristic reaction of the glyconic acids (or their lactones) is
epimerization of the asymmetric carbon atom in the 2-position.   When
heated in pyridine, these acids lose protons reversibly from the carbon
α to the carboxyl group, and an equilibrium between diastereomers is
established.   The reaction has proved useful for producing relatively
unavailable sugars from their more plentiful isomers.   In some cases, the
conversion can be accomplished simply by heating the calcium salt of
the acid to 120°.

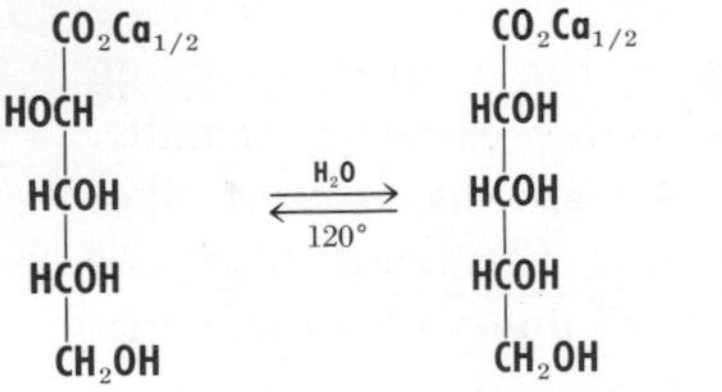

Calcium D-arabonate   Calcium D-ribonate

Epimers

A number of other methods are available for changing one sugar into another. The Wohl degradation is one of a number of means of converting an aldose to its next-lower homologue. The reaction makes use of the reversibility of the cyanohydrin reaction.

$$
\begin{array}{cccc}
\text{CHO} & \text{CH}=\text{NOH} & \text{CN} & \\
| & | & | & \\
\text{HCOH} & \text{HCOH} & \text{H}-\text{C}-\text{OAc} & \text{CHO} \\
| & | & | & | \\
\text{(CHOH)}_3 & \text{(CHOH)}_3 & \text{(CHOAc)}_3 & \text{(HCOH)}_3 \\
| & | & | & | \\
\text{CH}_2\text{OH} & \text{CH}_2\text{OH} & \text{CH}_2\text{OAc} & \text{CH}_2\text{OH} \\
\text{D-Glucose} & \text{D-Glucose oxime} & & \text{D-Arabinose}
\end{array}
$$

with reagents $\xrightarrow{\text{NH}_2\text{OH}}$, $\xrightarrow[\text{ZnCl}_2]{\substack{\text{Ac}_2\text{O} \\ \text{AcONa}}}$, $\xrightarrow{\text{NaOCH}_3}$

When treated with either strong acids or bases, the monosaccharides suffer rather profound chemical modification. In strong base, a series of reverse and forward aldol condensations (page 284) occur which lead to very complicated mixtures. Similarly when formaldehyde, glycolic aldehyde, and glyceraldehyde are treated with strong alkali, complex mixtures of sugars arise from which racemic glucose has been isolated in very low yields. In strong hot acid, the pentoses give furfural in a dehydration reaction. Hexoses also undergo a ring-closing dehydration reaction, but the products are more complex.

Disaccharides

Disaccharides consist of two simple sugar units bound together by a glycosidic linkage. Of the four common disaccharides (see Table 22.4), sucrose is the most important, because of its extensive use as a food. This material is widely distributed in nature and is commercially prepared by the extraction of either sugar cane or sugar beet. Table sugar is pure sucrose and is one of the cheapest pure chemicals prepared in large quantities.

Sucrose is composed of a D-glucose and a D-fructose unit, as demonstrated by the fact that these two substances are produced in equal amounts by hydrolysis of the disaccharide with either dilute acid or an enzyme (*invertase*).

$$
\underset{\text{Sucrose}}{\text{C}_{12}\text{H}_{22}\text{O}_{11}} + \text{H}_2\text{O} \xrightarrow{\text{HCl}} \underset{\text{D-Glucose}}{\text{C}_6\text{H}_{12}\text{O}_6} + \underset{\text{D-Fructose}}{\text{C}_6\text{H}_{12}\text{O}_6}
$$

The positions of attachment of glucose and fructose units to one another have been demonstrated by methylation of all free hydroxyls of sucrose. Hydrolysis of the glycosidic linkage of the product gives two partially methylated monosaccharides. The positions of the free hydroxyl groups in these compounds reveal the positions of attachment of the two units in the disaccharide.

TABLE 22.4   *Common Disaccharides*

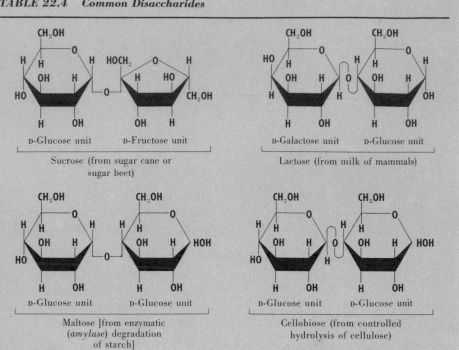

Sucrose (from sugar cane or sugar beet)

Lactose (from milk of mammals)

Maltose [from enzymatic (*amylase*) degradation of starch]

Cellobiose (from controlled hydrolysis of cellulose)

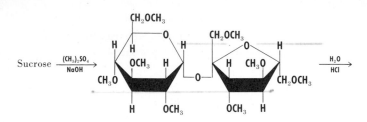

Sucrose $\xrightarrow[\text{NaOH}]{\text{(CH}_3\text{)}_2\text{SO}_4}$ ... $\xrightarrow[\text{HCl}]{\text{H}_2\text{O}}$

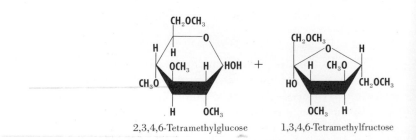

2,3,4,6-Tetramethylglucose   1,3,4,6-Tetramethylfructose

Glycosides

A relatively small number of naturally occurring monosaccharides are found in an uncombined state. Most carbohydrates occur as oligosaccharides, polysaccharides, or glycosides. Individual glycosides are designated as glucosides, galactosides, mannosides, etc. When the second group is not itself a monosaccharide, it is known as an *aglycone*. Thus methanol is the aglycone of methyl glucoside.

Glucosides readily hydrolyze with hot dilute acid or with enzymes such as *emulsin* or *maltase*. These protein catalysts, which are widely distributed in nature, exhibit a remarkable specificity with regard to the configuration of the glycosides whose hydrolyses they catalyze. Thus emulsin hydrolyzes β-glycosides and maltase cleaves α-glycosides. Table 22.5 lists some of the common glycosides.

The usual method of synthesis of a glycoside is illustrated by preparation of methylarbutin, found in the bearberry plant. An inversion of configuration occurs at the glycosidic linkage during the substitution of bromine for acetoxyl, and a second inversion occurs in the substitution of the aglycone for halogen.

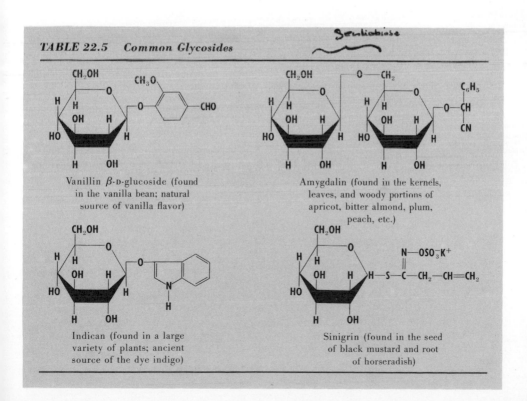

TABLE 22.5   *Common Glycosides*

Vanillin β-D-glucoside (found in the vanilla bean; natural source of vanilla flavor)

Amygdalin (found in the kernels, leaves, and woody portions of apricot, bitter almond, plum, peach, etc.)

Indican (found in a large variety of plants; ancient source of the dye indigo)

Sinigrin (found in the seed of black mustard and root of horseradish)

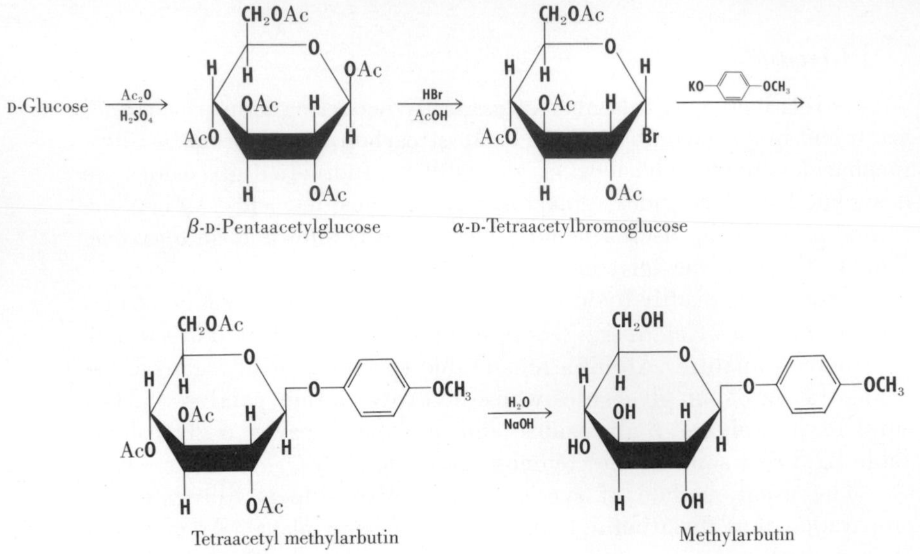

D-Glucose $\xrightarrow[\text{H}_2\text{SO}_4]{\text{Ac}_2\text{O}}$

β-D-Pentaacetylglucose

$\xrightarrow[\text{AcOH}]{\text{HBr}}$

α-D-Tetraacetylbromoglucose

$\xrightarrow{\text{KO}\!\!-\!\!\bigcirc\!\!-\!\!\text{OCH}_3}$

Tetraacetyl methylarbutin

$\xrightarrow[\text{NaOH}]{\text{H}_2\text{O}}$

Methylarbutin

Natural Products Related to Saccharides

Ascorbic Acid. This simple substance found in fresh fruit and vegetables is an important dietary factor (vitamin C). Absence of this compound in the diet causes scurvy, an ancient disease most prevalent among sailors who on long sea voyages were prevented from eating fresh food. The disease is marked by tendencies to hemorrhage and by abnormal changes in cartilage, bone, and teeth. Vitamin C is synthesized on a large scale industrially with glucose as starting material. Bacterial oxidation is employed in one of the critical steps in the synthesis. The substance is a lactone, and the hydroxyl groups of the enediol are acidic.

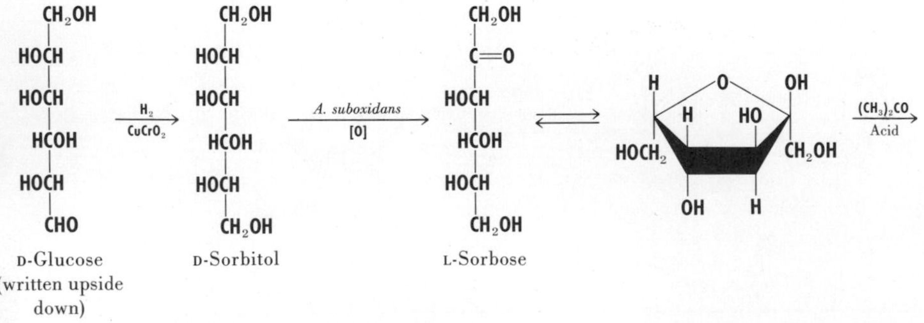

D-Glucose
(written upside down)

$\xrightarrow[\text{CuCrO}_2]{\text{H}_2}$

D-Sorbitol

$\xrightarrow[\text{[O]}]{\textit{A. suboxidans}}$

L-Sorbose

$\xrightarrow[\text{Acid}]{\text{(CH}_3\text{)}_2\text{CO}}$

Diacetone-L-sorbose   2-Keto-L-gulonic
                                              acid

Ascorbic acid

Antibiotics. A number of compounds produced in the metabolism of *molds* and *actinomyces* are remarkably efficient in preventing bacteria from multiplying. Compounds of this type, some of which are nontoxic to mammals, have been dramatically successful in preventing and curing many infectious diseases of mankind. Some of these substances are related chemically to carbohydrates, others to amino acids. Most antibiotics contain unique structural features, not found in other classes of natural products.

Streptomycin is a trisaccharide derivative which has found important use in tuberculosis therapy and the treatment of other infections such as tularemia and plague. *Chloramphenicol* is effective against certain viral and rickettsial infections. It was the first organic compound found in nature which contains a nitro group. *Novobiocin* is a glycoside useful in the treatment of a wide variety of bacterial infections. *Tetracycline* represents a family of antibiotics whose structures differ in only minor details, and which are effective chemotherapeutic agents in the treatment of bacterial, viral, and rickettsial infections.

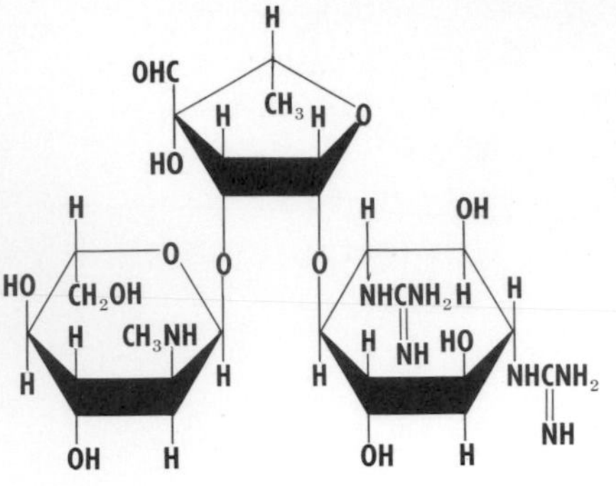

Streptomycin

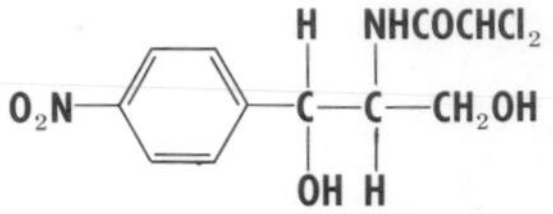

Chloramphenicol

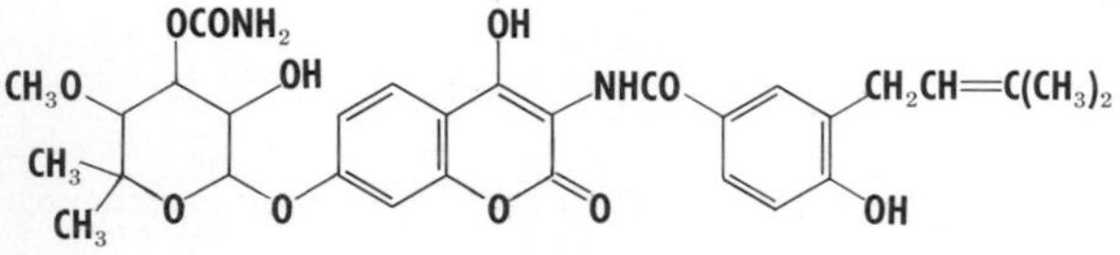

Novobiocin

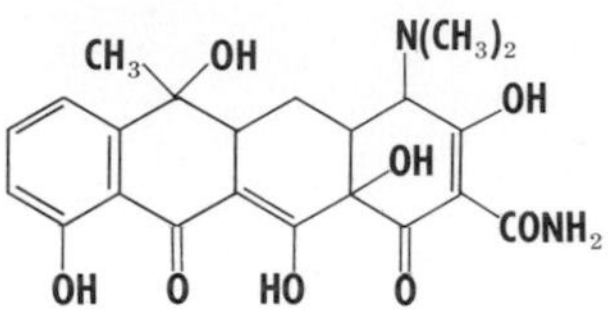

Tetracycline

The relative simplicity of chloramphenicol has led to its synthesis on an industrial scale by a variety of means. The other antibiotics are grown by vast fermentation processes from such agricultural waste products as corn steep.

Inositols. A group of compounds occur in nature whose structures in a sense are intermediate between carbohydrates on the one hand and many of the phenolic plant products on the other. Hexahydroxycyclohexanes or *inositols* are the first link in the chain. All possible nine stereoisomers of hexahydroxycyclohexane are known (two optically active, seven inactive). Only myoinositol is found widely distributed in nature. The substance occurs in microorganisms, plants, and in many of the organs and fluids of animals. The substance is probably required in the diet of higher forms of life, and thus should be designated as a vitamin. *Scyllitol*, the all-trans isomer, is found in certain fish and plants. Racemic inositol occurs in mistletoe berries and blackberries.

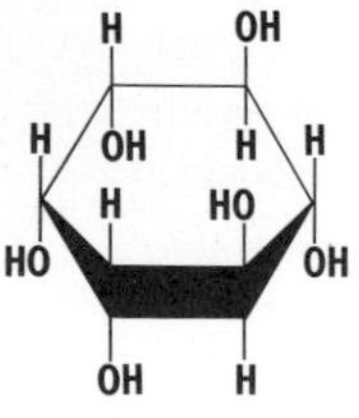

Myoinositol

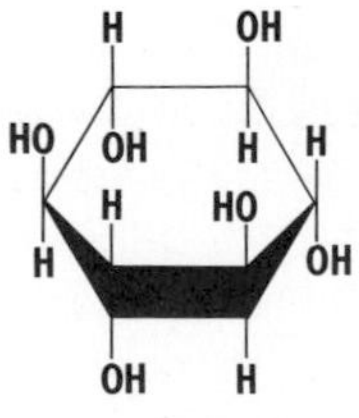

Scyllitol

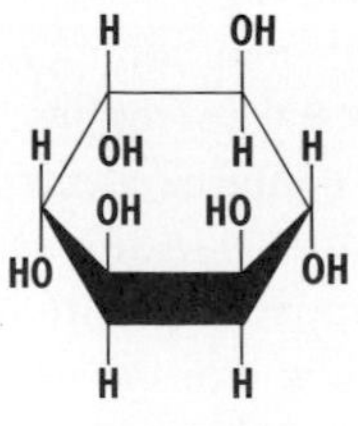

One enantiomer
of racemic inositol

A series of compounds are intermediate in structure between inositols and phenols. *Tetrahydroxybenzoquinone, spinulosin,* and *fumigatin* are representatives of a family of pigments produced by molds. The first of these is related in structure to the inositols, the second and third to mytilitol, which has been isolated from the muscle of a mussel, *Mytilus edilis.*

Tetrahydroxy-   Mytilitol   Spinulosin   Fumigatin
benzoquinone

Another series of compounds with related structures include quinic, shikimic, and gallic acid. Quinic acid is found in cinchona bark (source of quinine), meadow hay, and the leaves of berries. Shikimic acid is isolated from the star anise. Gallic acid occurs in the free form in sumac, tea, and a variety of plants, and can be obtained by hydrolysis of *tannin (tannic acid)*, a complex of esters and ethers of various carbohydrates. Tannic acid is used to cure leather, since the compound makes the gelatin (protein) of hides insoluble.

Quinic acid   Shikimic acid   Gallic acid

Phenolic Plant Products

Simple Phenols. Although carbohydrates are aliphatic or heterocyclic and phenols are aromatic, a biogenetic relationship between these classes is very probable, with the former as precursors of the latter. A large number of phenols and phenol derivatives occur in nature, particularly in the plant world. Many of these substances have fragrant odors and pleasant flavors, properties frequently put to commercial use. Table 22.6 lists the more important compounds, along with their natural sources.

Chroman Derivatives. The *chroman* ring system is found in a large group of plant products. Many of the plant and flower pigments, as well

TABLE 22.6　　Simple Phenols Found in Nature

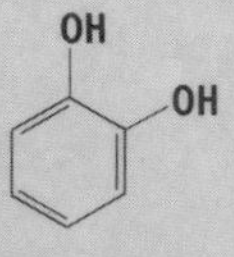

Catechol (from
horse urine and a
variety of plants)

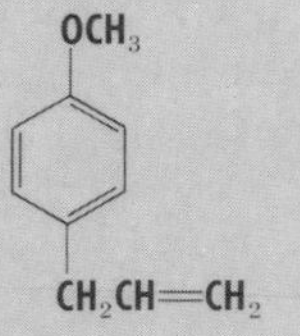

Anethole (from
anise seed)

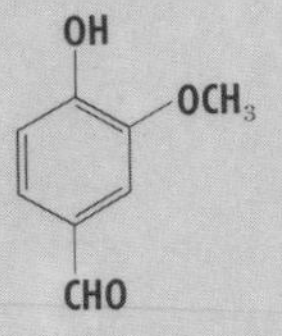

Vanillin (fragrant
component of
vanilla bean)

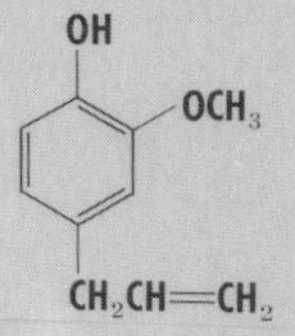

Eugenol (found
in cloves)

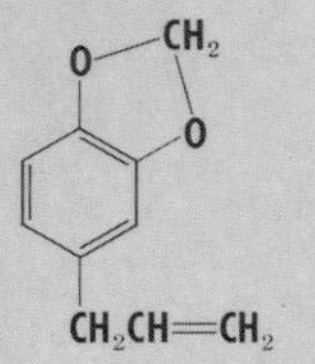

Safrole (chief
constituent of oil
of sassafras)

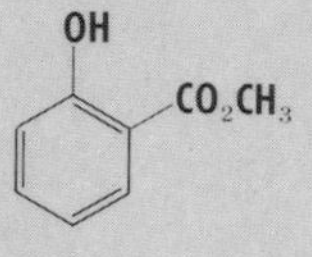

Methyl salicylate
(fragrant principle
in wintergreen)

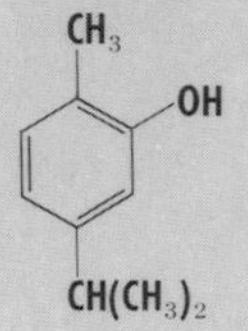

Carvacrol

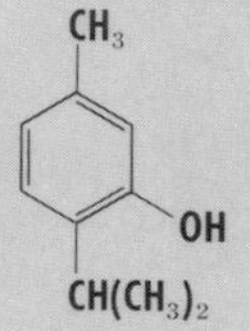

Thymol

(essential oils found
in many plants; related
to terpenes)

as some of the colored components produced by molds, are derived
from this parent ring system. The *coumarin* and *chromone* ring systems
are the most important.

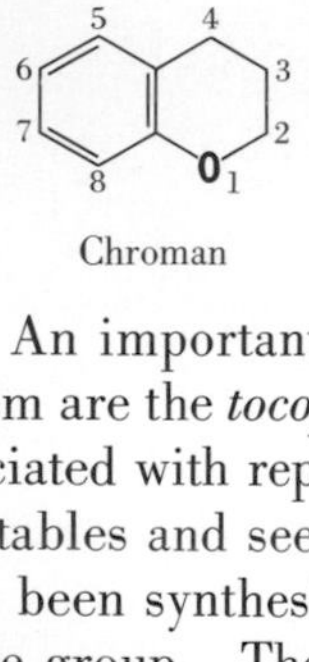

Chroman

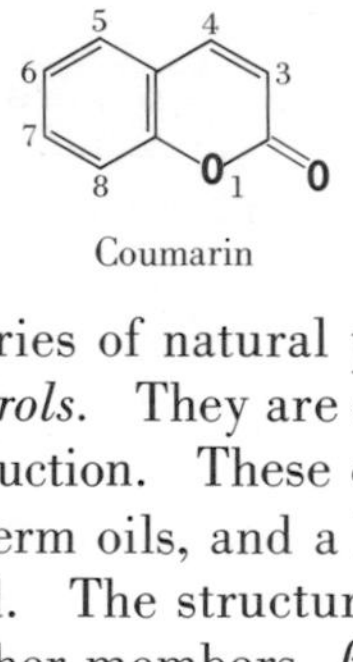

Coumarin

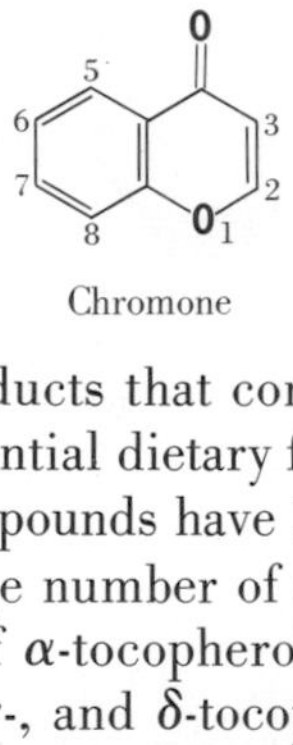

Chromone

An important series of natural products that contain the chroman
system are the *tocopherols*. They are essential dietary factors (vitamin E)
associated with reproduction. These compounds have been isolated from
vegetables and seed-germ oils, and a large number of structural variants
have been synthesized. The structure of α-tocopherol is representative
of the group. The other members, β-, γ-, and δ-tocopherol, differ only
in position and number of methyl and hydroxyl groups on the benzenoid
ring. The substances are powerful antioxidants and provide protection
both *in vivo* and *in vitro* for natural products against indiscriminate
oxidation.

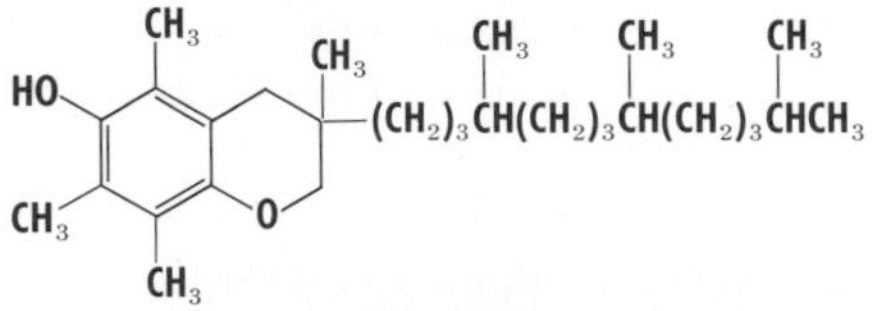

α-Tocopherol

Anthocyanins are one of the main classes of plant pigments. They occur in flowers and fruit as glycosides, hydrolysis of which provides colored aglycones known as *anthocyanidins*. The vivid blues and reds of anthocyanins are associated with the distribution of positive charge throughout an aryl-substituted chroman ring system.

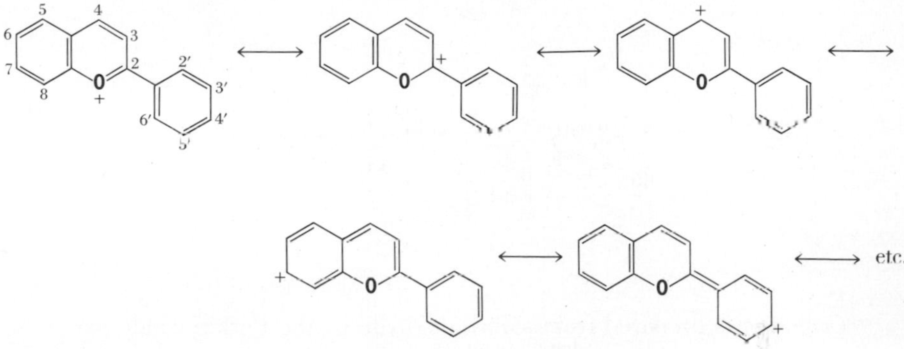

Anthocyanidins are usually isolated in the form of chloride salts and are frequently hydroxylated in the 5-, 7-, 3'-, 4'-, and 5'-positions. The character of the resonating system is seriously affected by the presence of mineral salts and by the pH of the environment. Consequently colors of the pigments of flowers sometimes vary markedly with type of soil. Thus cyanin, the pigment of the red rose and blue cornflower, is pale violet in neutral solution, red in dilute acid, and blue in dilute base. Other cyanins differ only in number and position of hydroxyl groups and in the character of the sugars to which they are attached.

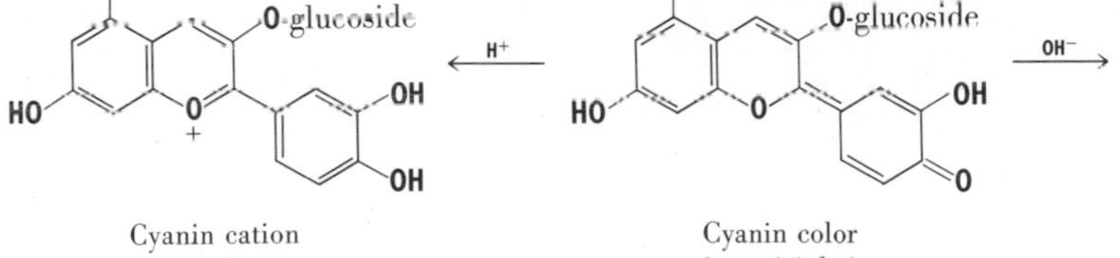

Cyanin cation
(red)

Cyanin color
base (violet)

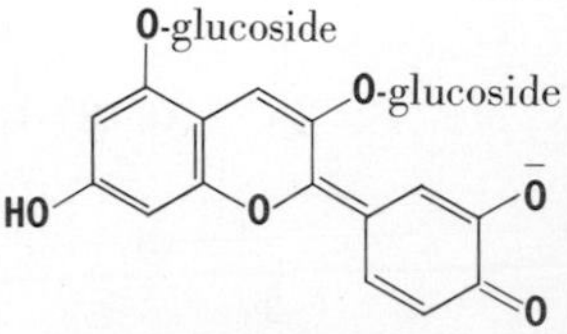

Cyanin anion
(blue)

The synthesis of cyanin is representative of methods applied to the preparation of a number of these plant pigments.

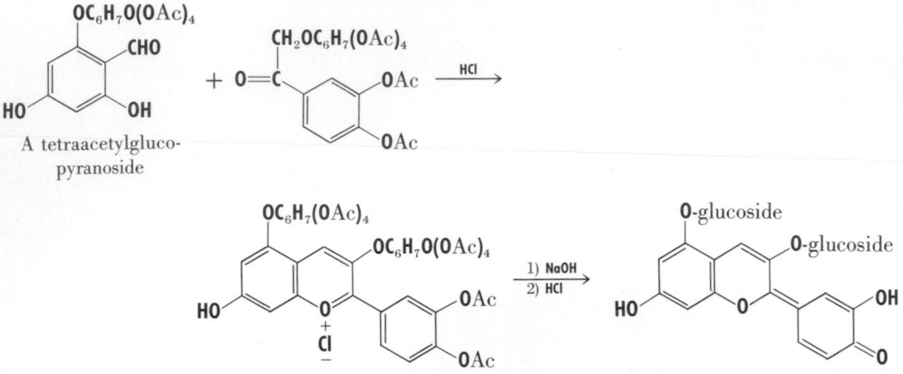

A tetraacetylgluco-
pyranoside

Cyanin

Coumarin is prepared from salicylaldehyde by the Perkin condensation reaction (page 289). The substance resembles new-mown hay in fragrance and is employed in the perfume industry.

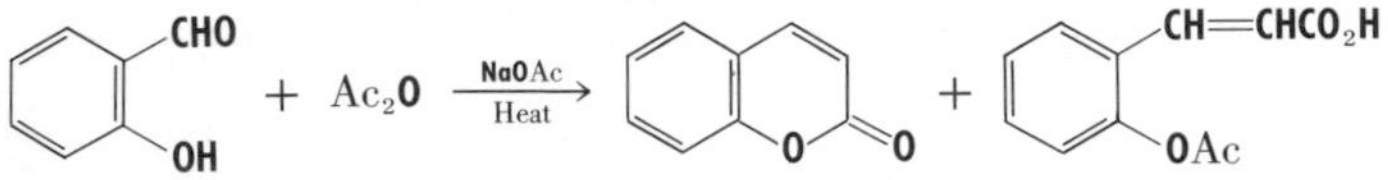

Coumarin   Acetyl coumaric
acid

Dicoumarol and *umbelliferone* are representative of coumarins that have been isolated from natural sources. Dicoumarol prevents coagulation of blood and is used in medicine in connection with vitamin K therapy. Vitamin K (blood-clotting vitamin) is a 1,4-naphthoquinone that occurs in green plants and has been isolated from alfalfa. This substance contains an isoprenoid side chain (Chap. 24) similar to that of α-tocopherol.

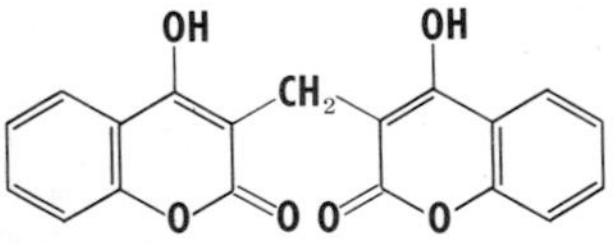

Dicoumarol
(from spoiled sweet-
clover hay)

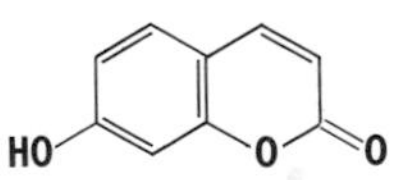

Umbelliferone
(from spurge-laurel bark)

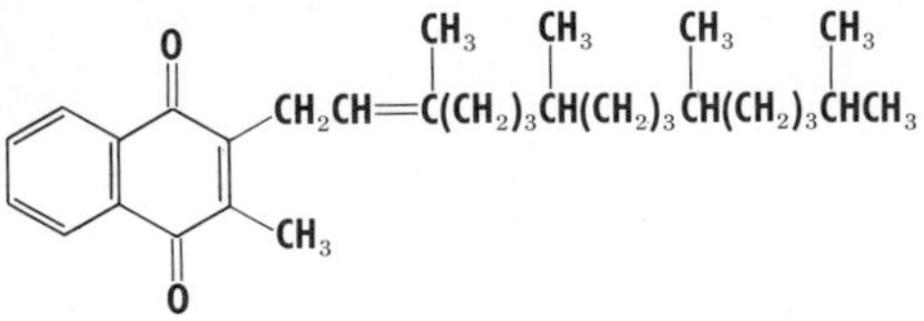

Vitamin K$_1$

Chromone is synthesized by condensation of *o*-hydroxyacetophenone with oxalic ester. The product is hydrolyzed and decarboxylated to give chromone.

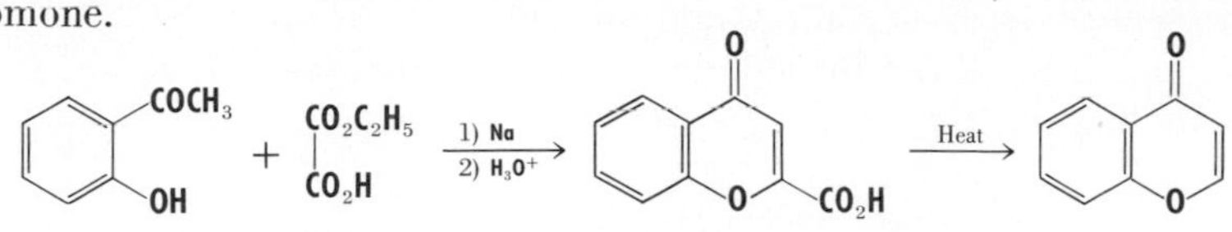

Flavones and isoflavones are 2-phenyl- and 3-phenylchromones, respectively, which usually contain hydroxyl groups in either or both benzene rings. These substances are usually pale yellow and are widely distributed in nature as glycosides.

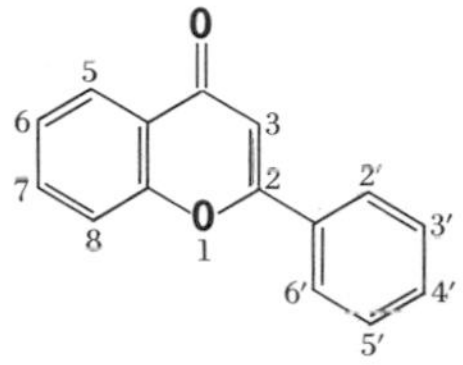

Flavone 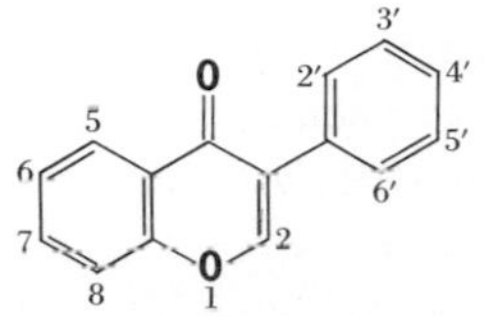   Isoflavone

Synthesis of flavones is usually effected through condensation reactions of the type involved in the preparation of fisetin, a pigment of yellow cedar and sumac. The steps of the synthesis are recorded in Fig. 22.1.

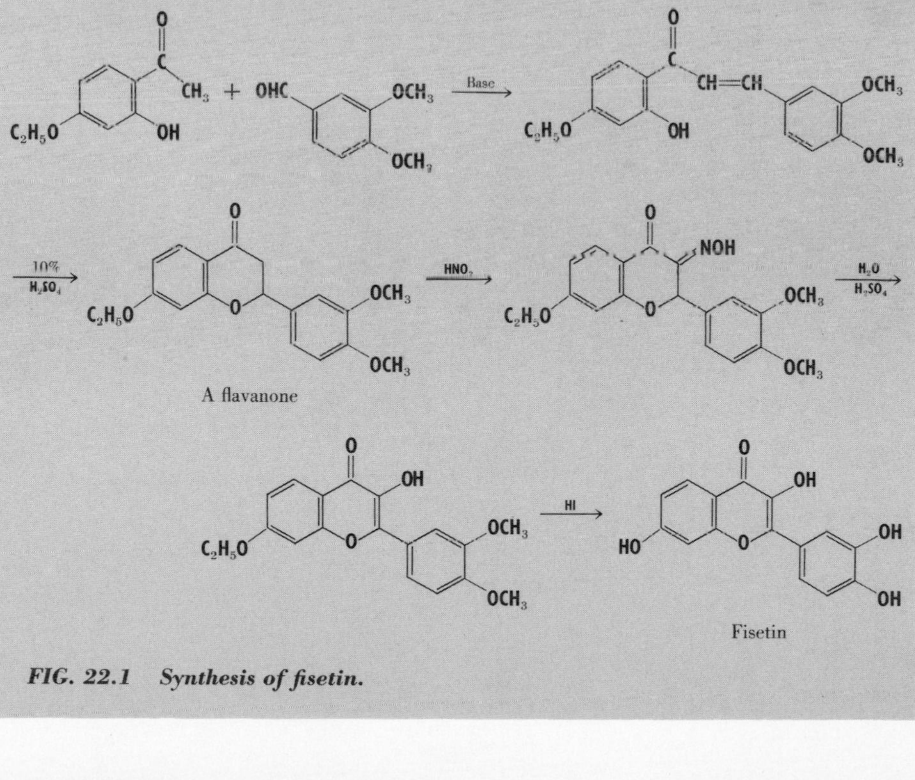

A flavanone

FIG. 22.1   Synthesis of fisetin.

Interesting variants of these ring systems are found in *khellin* and *citrinin*. Khellin (colorless), which has the ability to increase coronary flow, has been isolated from a plant found in Egypt. Citrinin is an orange-yellow pigment produced by several species of mold, as well as by a certain Australian plant.

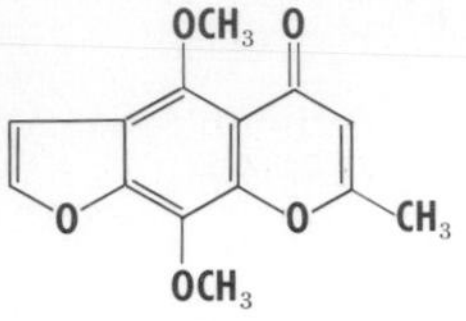

Khellin 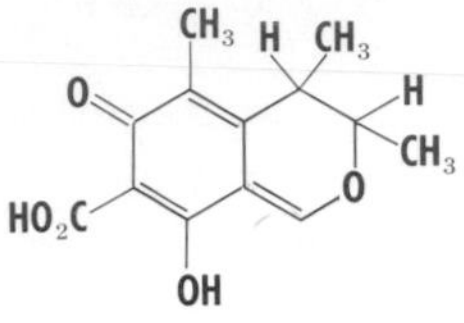   Citrinin

Tropolones. A group of natural products found in plants and produced by certain molds contain a pseudoaromatic and planar seven-membered unsaturated carbocyclic ring, known as the *tropolone ring system*. Representative natural products which contain this ring system are *hinokitol, puberulic acid,* and *colchicine.* Hinokitol is found in the essential oil of the Japanese hinoki tree; puberulic acid is a mold metabolite; and colchicine occurs in the autumn crocus. This last substance possesses the interesting property of arresting cell division in plants and animals.

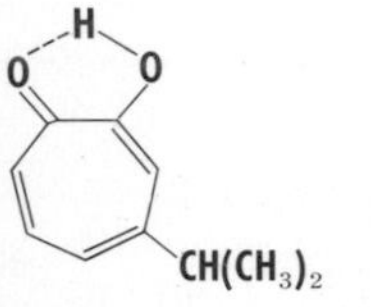

Hinokitol 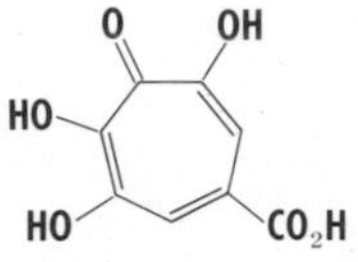   Puberulic acid 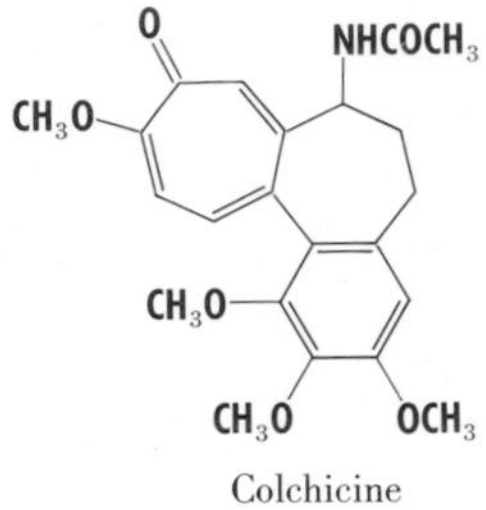   Colchicine

A fourth compound, *stipitatic acid,* is also produced by a mold. This compound has been synthesized by a sequence that involves as a key step the destruction of an aromatic system by an addition reaction.

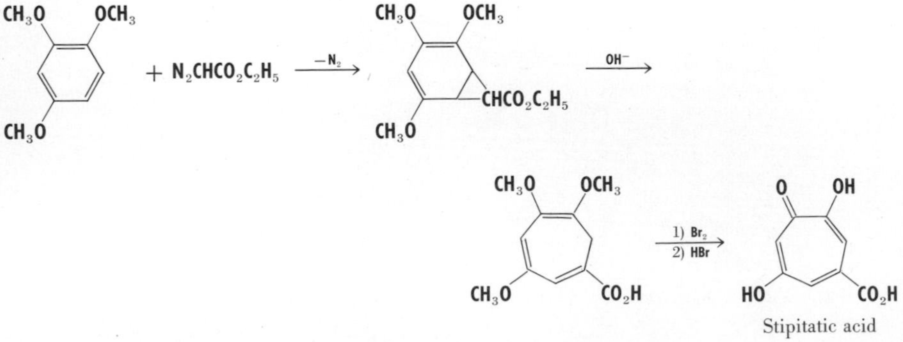

Stipitatic acid

Problems

1. With structures for actual compounds, formulate the following:

a. An epimerization reaction.

b. Formation of an osazone from a ketohexose.

c. Conversion of an aldose to its next-higher homologue.

d. Degradation of an aldose to its next-lower homologue.

e. A glyconic and a glycaric acid.

f. An α- and β-methyl pyranoglycoside and an α- and β-methyl furanoside.

g. Five oxidizing agents used in sugar chemistry and examples of their use.

h. Preparation of a cyclic and a noncyclic pentaacetate of glucose

ι. A reaction involving an inversion of configuration at the anomeric carbon of a sugar.

j. The structure of octamethyllactose.

k. Three aglucones.

l. Preparation of an isopropylidene derivative of a monosaccharide.

m. The structures of three vitamins and their names.

n. The structures of four antibiotics and their names.

o. The structures of all isomers of inositol. Which are optically active?

p. The structures of all the ketohexoses.

q. The structures of four naturally occurring quinones with their names.

r. The structures and names of four pigments found in nature.

s. Three dimensional structures for all the stereoisomers of chloramphenicol.

t. The periodic oxidation products of methyl α-D-mannofuranoside. How many moles of oxidizing agent would be consumed?

2. Devise synthetic schemes for the following:

a. Preparation of mannonic lactone from glucose.

b. Preparation of the pentaacetate of galactonic acid from galactose (simple acetylation of galactonic acid leaves one hydroxyl unacetylated owing to the lactone).

c. Preparation of 3,5,6-triacetylglucose from glucose.

d. Preparation of phenyl β-D-glucopyranoside from glucose and phenol.

e. Conversion of D-gulose into

f. Conversion of D-allose into

g. Conversion of D-mannose into

CHO

CH₃

h. Preparation of 3-methyl-D-glucose from glucose.
i. Preparation of 6-methylcoumarin from *p*-methylphenol.
j. Synthesis of

from resorcinol and anisole.

k. Synthesis of the following flavanone from resorcinol and phenol:

l. Synthesis of the following natural product with vanillin as starting material:

3. Interchange the functions on the ends of the eight D-aldohexoses without otherwise disturbing the configurations of the asymmetric centers, and name the products of this operation.

4. A ketohexose of D, but otherwise unknown, configuration upon oxidation gave a mixture of (+)- and (−)-tartaric acid. What is the total structure of the ketohexose?

5. Assume you have four bottles whose labels have been lost, each containing one of the following compounds. What are the simplest tests that would allow you to label the bottles correctly?

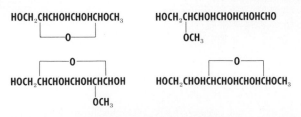

6. Two different aldohexoses gave the same optically active glycaric acid (six-carbon dicarboxylic acid) when oxidized. Degradation of the aldohexoses to their aldopentoses and oxidation of these substances gave two different five-carbon dicarboxylic acids, of which one was optically active, the other inactive. Both aldohexoses were converted to their methyl glycopyranosides, which when oxidized with periodic acid gave the same compound as that obtained from similar treatment of methyl α-D-glucopyranoside. With the correct formulas, trace the above reactions.

7. Design a series of experiments which would differentiate L-arabinose from the other L-aldopentoses.

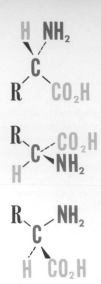

23

Amino Acids, Peptides, and Alkaloids

In the same sense that polymeric carbohydrates (polysaccharides) provide structural material for plants, *proteins* make up much of the structural material for animals. Proteins are polymers of α-amino acids which sometimes contain an additional amino or carboxyl group. Amide linkages bind the amino acid units together in polymers of extremely high molecular weight. Such large molecules constitute a large portion of the skin, flesh, muscle, blood, and organs of members of the animal kingdom. *Peptides* are polymers that contain only a small number of amino acid units.

Section of a protein

Proteins, peptides, and amino acids are all synthesized in plants and constitute one of the three major classes of foods. Plants construct these substances, combining photosynthesized compounds made from water, oxygen, and carbon dioxide with nitrogen taken from the soil in the form of ammonia or nitrate. These forms of "fixed nitrogen" are created from nitrogen of the air by soil bacteria. Such organisms are often associated with the roots of certain plants, notably legumes.

Proteins are classified as either simple proteins, which give only α-amino acids when hydrolyzed, or conjugate proteins, which provide both α-amino acids and one or more compounds of a different nature. The latter substances, when bound to protein, are known as *prosthetic groups* and include such varied structural classes as nucleic acids and hemes. This chapter is concerned with the chemistry of amino acids obtained by protein hydrolysis, with simpler peptides, and with plant products related to amino acids. The structures and properties of proteins are treated in Chap. 25.

Amino Acids

Structures. Most of the naturally occurring amino acids have their amino group α to the carboxyl function. In a few cases a second amino group is found elsewhere in the molecule, and in even fewer cases a single amino group is found in the β or γ position. Amino acids are classified as neutral (one carboxyl, one amino group), acidic (two carboxyls, one amino group), or basic (one carboxyl, two amino groups). Neutral amino acids exist as inner salts with dipolar structures. These saltlike compounds are high-melting (with decomposition), relatively nonvolatile, water-soluble, and ether-insoluble.

$$\text{R—CH—CO}_2\text{H} \rightleftharpoons \text{R—CH—CO}_2^- \overset{\text{OH}^-}{\rightleftharpoons} \text{R—CH—CO}_2^-$$
$$\underset{\text{NH}_2}{|} \qquad \underset{\overset{+}{\text{NH}_3}}{|} \qquad \underset{\text{NH}_2}{|}$$

$$\text{H}^+ \Big\updownarrow$$

$$\text{R—CH—CO}_2\text{H}$$
$$\underset{\overset{+}{\text{NH}_3}}{|}$$

The lowest solubility of neutral amino acids in water occurs at that acidity level which provides the highest concentration of inner salt. This pH, called the *isoelectric point*, ranges from 4.8 to 6.3 for neutral amino acids and varies according to the relative effect of structural features on the acidity and basicity of the two functions (Chap. 8). Above the isoelectric point, amino acids are converted to anions; below the critical pH, they add protons forming cations. Isoelectric points for acidic amino acids are at lower pH's and range from about 2.7 to 3.2. Those of basic amino acids are at higher pH's and range from 7.6 to 10.8. Table 23.1 records structures and common names of most amino acids derived from protein hydrolysates.

All these amino acids except glycine possess asymmetric centers and are optically active. The configurations of amino acids obtained from protein hydrolysates are all similar to one another and belong to the same configurational family as L-(−)-glyceraldehyde.

$$\begin{array}{ccc}
\text{CHO} & \text{CO}_2\text{H} & \text{CO}_2\text{H} \\
| & | & | \\
\text{HO—C—H} & \text{H}_2\text{N—C—H} & \text{H}_2\text{N—C—H} \\
| & | & | \\
\text{CH}_2\text{OH} & \text{CH}_2\text{OH} & \text{R}
\end{array}$$

L-(−)-Glyceraldehyde   L-(−)-Serine   Generalized naturally occurring amino acid

TABLE 23.1   *Amino Acids from Protein Hydrolysates*

Neutral amino acids

Glycine	$CH_2(NH_2)CO_2H$	Serine	$HOCH_2CH(NH_2)CO_2H$
Alanine	$CH_3CH(NH_2)CO_2H$	Threonine	$CH_3CH(OH)CH(NH_2)CO_2H$
Valine	$(CH_3)_2CHCH(NH_2)CO_2H$	Methionine	$CH_3SCH_2CH_2CH(NH_2)CO_2H$
Leucine	$(CH_3)_2CHCH_2CH(NH_2)CO_2H$	Cysteine	$HSCH_2CH(NH_2)CO_2H$
Isoleucine	$CH_3CH_2CH(CH_3)CH(NH_2)CO_2H$	Cystine	$SCH_2CH(NH_2)CO_2H$
Phenylalanine	$C_6H_5CH_2CH(NH_2)CO_2H$		$SCH_2CH(NH_2)CO_2H$

Tyrosine   HO—⟨ ⟩—$CH_2CH(NH_2)CO_2H$ Proline

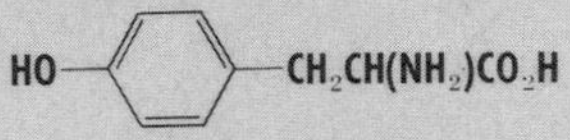

Diiodotyrosine   HO—⟨ ⟩—$CH_2CH(NH_2)CO_2H$ Hydroxyproline   HO—

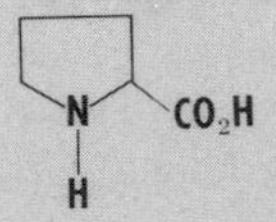

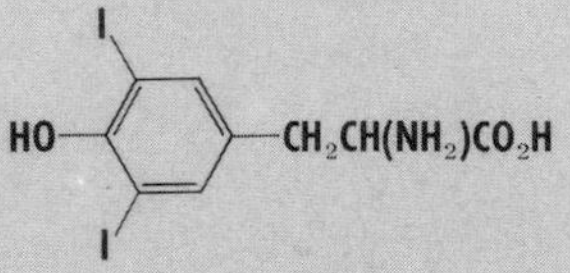

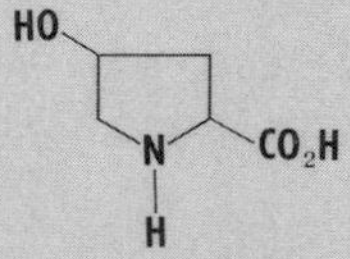

Thyroxine   HO—⟨ ⟩—O—⟨ ⟩—$CH_2CH(NH_2)CO_2H$

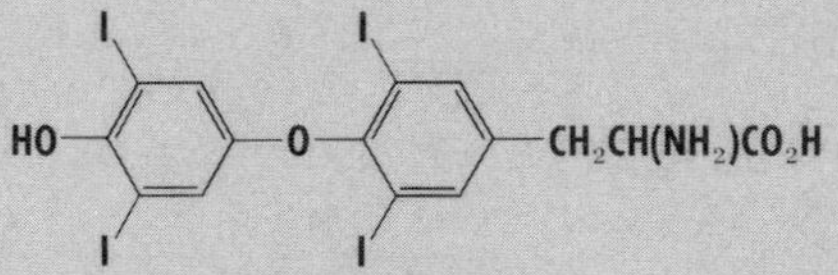

Tryptophan $CH_2CH(NH_2)CO_2H$

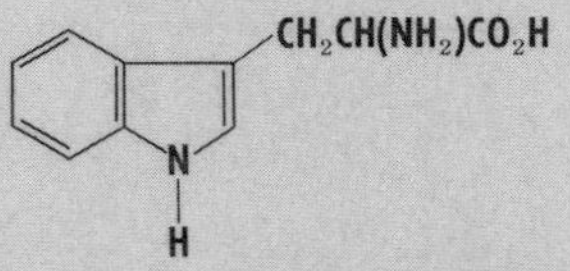

Acidic amino acids

Aspartic acid	$HO_2CCH_2CH(NH_2)CO_2H$	Glutamic acid	$HO_2CCH_2CH_2CH(NH_2)CO_2H$

Basic amino acids

Lysine	$H_2N(CH_2)_4CH(NH_2)CO_2H$		
Arginine	$H_2NCNH(CH_2)_3CH(NH_2)CO_2H$	Histidine	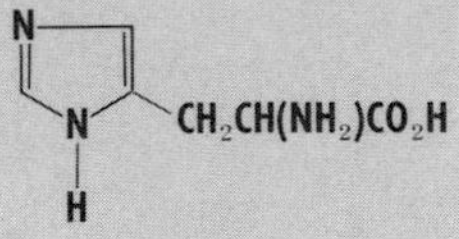 $CH_2CH(NH_2)CO_2H$
	$\overset{\parallel}{NH}$		
Ornithine	$H_2N(CH_2)_3CH(NH_2)CO_2H$		

The above relationships have been established by the principle "Two compounds whose configurations are established in relation to that of a third become known in relation to each other." The configurations of lactic acid and alanine are key links in the chain of structural relationships recorded in Fig. 23.1. Only two of these ten reactions involve the making or breaking of bonds to the asymmetric carbon atom. Reactions of ($+$)-α-bromopropionic acid with either hydroxide or azide ion were found by rate measurements to belong to the S_N2 reaction-mechanism family, and these transformations have been demonstrated to occur with inversion of configuration (page 235).

Characterization. Treatment of proteins with hot acid gives mixtures of amino acids whose character can be determined either indirectly or by actual isolation techniques. The component amino acids can be separated with the aid of selective precipitants, ion exchange resins (which utilize the small differences in acidity or basicity of the amino acids), and paper chromatography (page 150). This last technique provides a powerful tool for identifying components in a mixture of amino acids when only small amounts of material are available. Each amino acid has a characteristic rate of travel (R_f value) on a paper chromatogram. Even homologous acids may be differentiated. After "development," a chromatogram is dried and sprayed with ninhydrin reagent. Characteristic colored spots develop on those sections of the paper which contain an amino acid. When control and parallel chromatograms of mixtures of known and unknown amino acids are carried out, the relative positions of spots allow an identification of components in the unknown mixture.

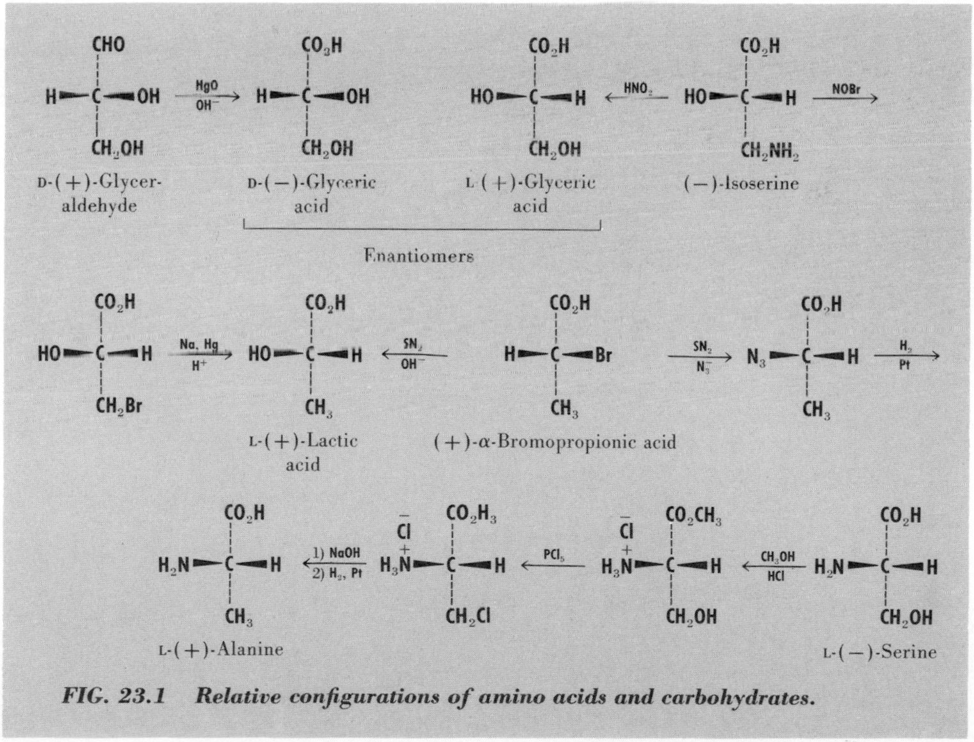

FIG. 23.1 *Relative configurations of amino acids and carbohydrates.*

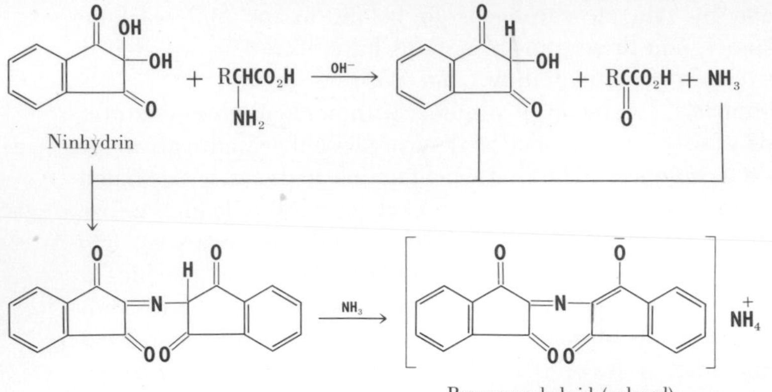

Resonance hybrid (colored)

A number of other analytical techniques are useful in amino acid chemistry. A *Kjeldahl determination* gives a measure of the total nitrogen content present in a protein or protein hydrolysate. In this determination, the organic compound is decomposed by digestion with a mixture of concentrated sulfuric acid and a catalyst such as selenium dioxide. The resulting ammonium salts are converted to ammonia, which is distilled and titrated. The total nitrogen content varies considerably with the character of the amino acids in the protein. The amount of nitrogen present in the form of primary amino groups is determined by the *Van Slyke method*. The unknown substance is treated with nitrous acid, and the volume of nitrogen evolved is measured.

Van Slyke determination:

$$\underset{\underset{NH_2}{|}}{RCHCO_2H} + HNO_2 \longrightarrow \underset{\underset{OH}{|}}{RCHCO_2H} + N_2$$

A number of syntheses of amino acids are discussed elsewhere in the text (e.g., page 283).

Peptides

Structure. Peptides are polyamides of amino acids, arbitrarily defined as possessing molecular weights of less than 10,000. These substances have been isolated from extracts of cells such as those of the pituitary gland and those of certain types of soil bacteria. One of the simplest peptides is *glutathione*, a tripeptide present in many living cells. More complex examples include *gramicidin S*, an antibiotic, and *oxytocin*, a hormone isolated from the posterior pituitary gland. The elucidation of the structure of the last substance and its synthesis represent one of the great triumphs of the techniques of organic chemistry in the natural-product field.

Structures of these complex substances are frequently written with abbreviations of the names (Table 23.1) of the amino acids. In these formulas, arrows symbolize *bonds from a carbonyl group of one unit to an amino group of a second.* Unless otherwise specified, *amide* linkages are assumed to be of the type shown below. Figure 23.2 lists the structures of typical peptides.

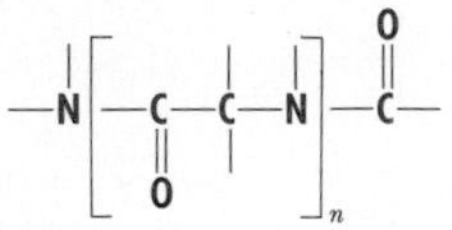

Naturally occurring peptides from sources other than microorganisms appear to contain amino acid residues belonging to the L-configurational family. Thus *oxytocin*, which is a posterior pituitary gland hormone (stimulates contraction of the uterus), is composed of only L-amino acid residues. Some of the amino acid groups found in antibiotics possess the D configuration. For example, a D-phenylalanine residue is found in gramicidin S (Fig. 23.2).

Penicillin is a second example of a peptidelike substance made up of amino acid groups, some of which possess the D configuration. This substance may be considered as derived from an amino acid, penicillamine, which resembles both alanine and cysteine in structure, but possesses the D configuration. Penicillin was the first of the naturally occurring antibiotics to be discovered, and it is still the most important. The substance in very small amounts inhibits the growth of a variety of pathological bacteria, gonococci, meningococci, pneumococci, streptococci, staphylococci, and the spirochete responsible for syphilis.

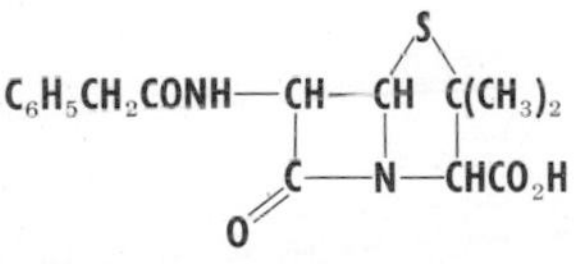

Penicillin G 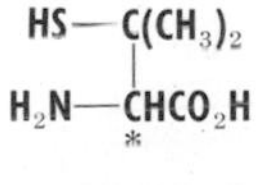 · D-Penicillamine

Synthesis. Syntheses of peptides feature numerous selective reagents and protective groups. The multiplicity of functional groups in amino acids renders amide formation an unusually complex operation. Thus when an α-amino acid is heated, a cyclic diamide is formed.

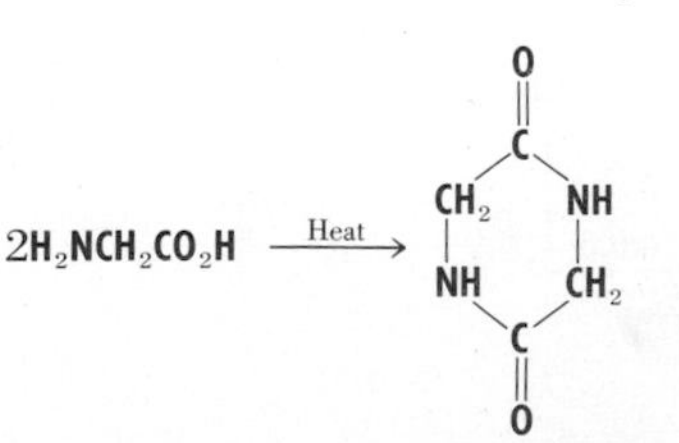

Diketopiperazine

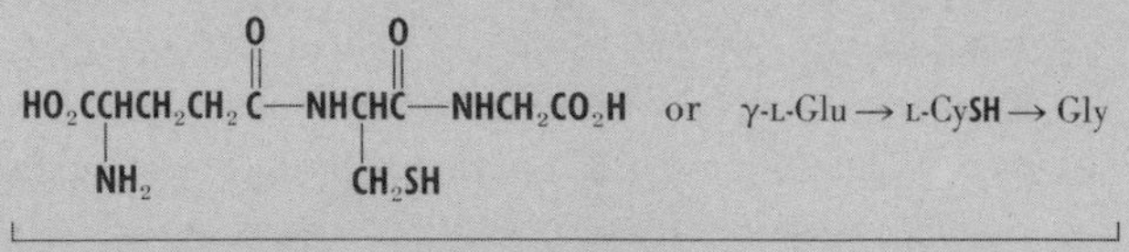

$$HO_2CCHCH_2CH_2 \overset{O}{\underset{NH_2}{C}}-NHCH\overset{O}{\underset{CH_2SH}{C}}-NHCH_2CO_2H \quad \text{or} \quad \gamma\text{-L-Glu} \rightarrow \text{L-CySH} \rightarrow \text{Gly}$$

γ-L-Glutamyl-L-cysteinylglycine   or   Glutathione

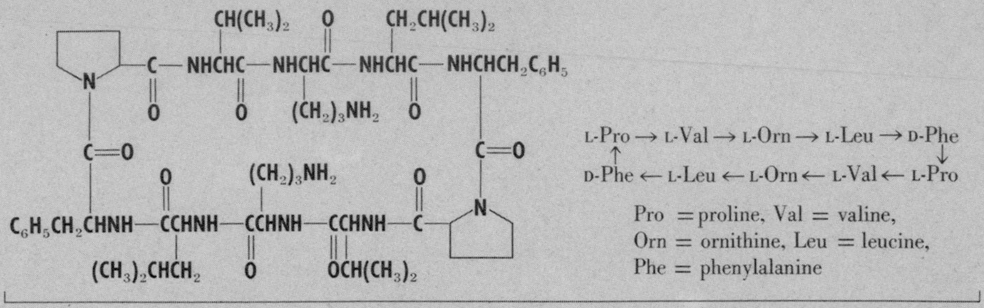

L-Pro → L-Val → L-Orn → L-Leu → D-Phe

D-Phe ← L-Leu ← L-Orn ← L-Val ← L-Pro

Pro = proline, Val = valine,
Orn = ornithine, Leu = leucine,
Phe = phenylalanine

Gramicidin S

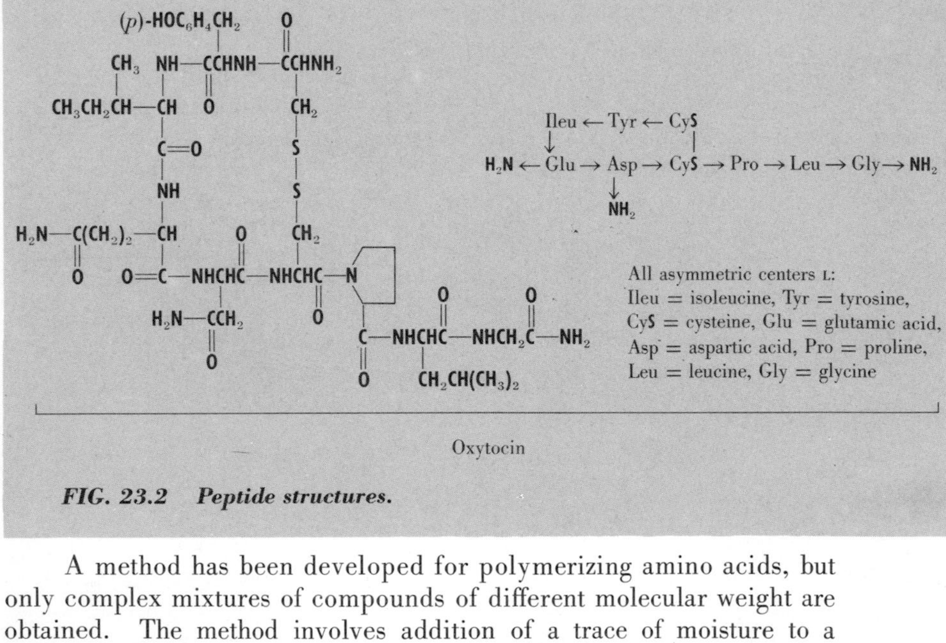

Ileu ← Tyr ← CyS

H_2N ← Glu → Asp → CyS → Pro → Leu → Gly → NH_2

NH_2

All asymmetric centers L:
Ileu = isoleucine, Tyr = tyrosine,
CyS = cysteine, Glu = glutamic acid,
Asp = aspartic acid, Pro = proline,
Leu = leucine, Gly = glycine

Oxytocin

FIG. 23.2   Peptide structures.

A method has been developed for polymerizing amino acids, but only complex mixtures of compounds of different molecular weight are obtained. The method involves addition of a trace of moisture to a cyclic amide-anhydride. The trace of amino acid liberated reacts at the carbonyl group of anhydride, and a second amino group is liberated, which in turn reacts with a third anhydride molecule, etc.

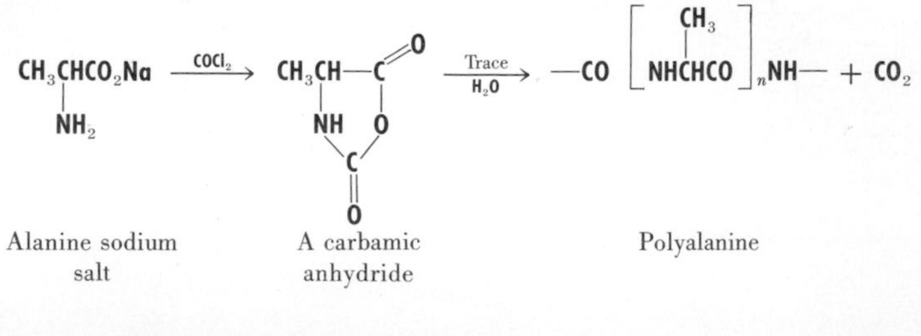

$$CH_3CHCO_2Na \xrightarrow{COCl_2} CH_3CH-C \xrightarrow[H_2O]{Trace} -CO\left[NHCHCO\right]_nNH- + CO_2$$

Alanine sodium   A carbamic   Polyalanine
salt   anhydride

More effective synthetic methods make use of covering groups, usually for the amino function of the amino acid. The carbobenzoxy group is particularly good, since it can readily be attached to an amine, and readily removed by hydrogenolysis, under mild conditions (page 445).

The phthalyl group has also been used to cover amine functions while peptide linkages are made. The reagent *N,N*-dicyclohexyl-carbodiimide causes amide formation at room temperature from amino and carboxyl groups. The reaction may even be conducted in the presence of moisture. These methods are illustrated as follows:

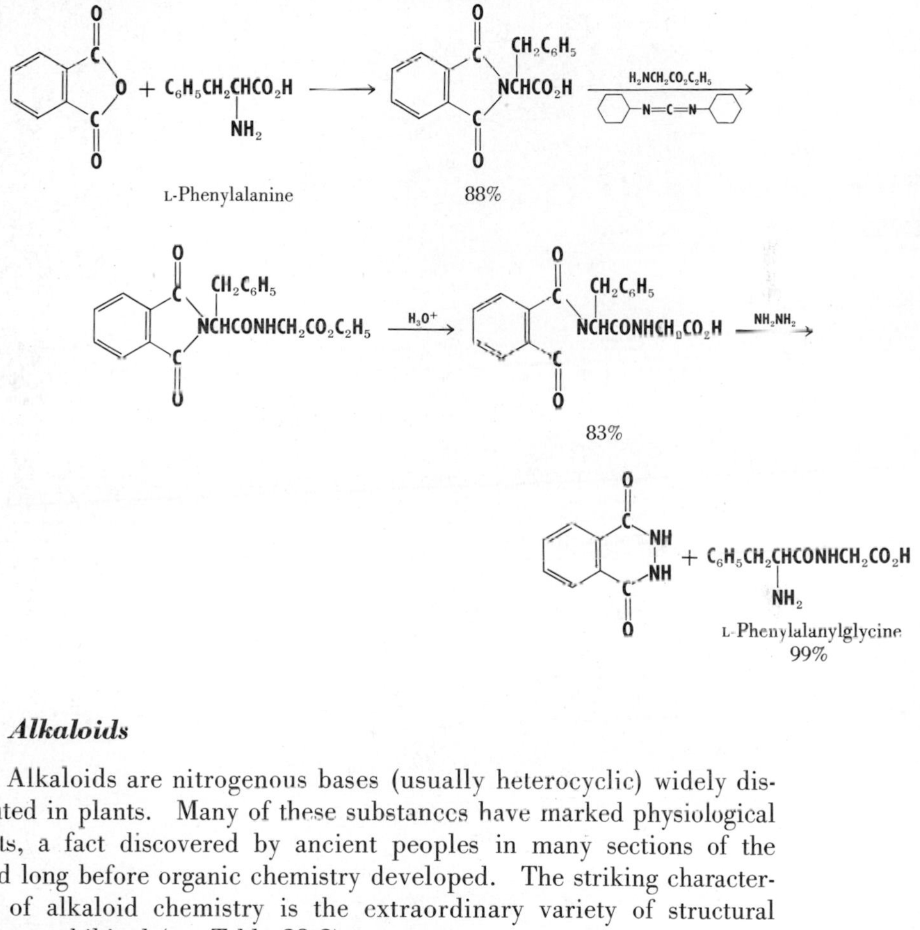

L-Phenylalanine   88%

83%

L-Phenylalanylglycine
99%

Alkaloids

Alkaloids are nitrogenous bases (usually heterocyclic) widely distributed in plants. Many of these substances have marked physiological effects, a fact discovered by ancient peoples in many sections of the world long before organic chemistry developed. The striking characteristic of alkaloid chemistry is the extraordinary variety of structural features exhibited (see Table 23.2).

The challenge presented by the elaborate ring systems, from the point of view both of elucidation of structure and of synthesis, has absorbed the efforts of some of the most talented researchers of the century. These substances are discussed in the same chapter with amino acids, since the two classes of compounds are biogenetically associated with each other in their elaboration in plants. This section is divided into three parts, each of which illustrates a type of research effort that has occupied organic chemists working with natural products.

TABLE 23.2   Representative Alkaloids

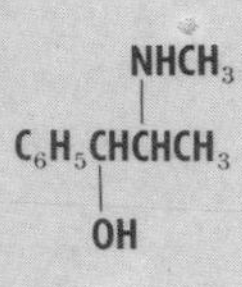

Ephedrine
(*Ephedra vulgaris*),
increases blood
pressure

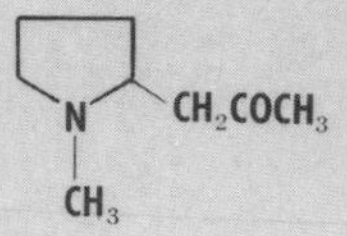

Hygrine
(Peruvian coca leaf)

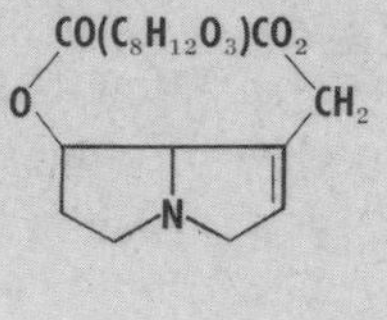

Grantianine
(*Senecio* genus),
creates liver cirrhosis,
hallucinations

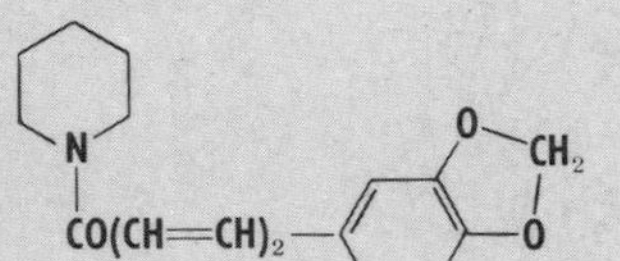

Piperine
(kernel of white pepper),
possesses sharp taste

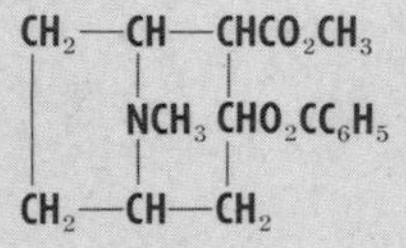

Cocaine
(coca leaves),
powerful anesthetic,
produces fever, stimulant

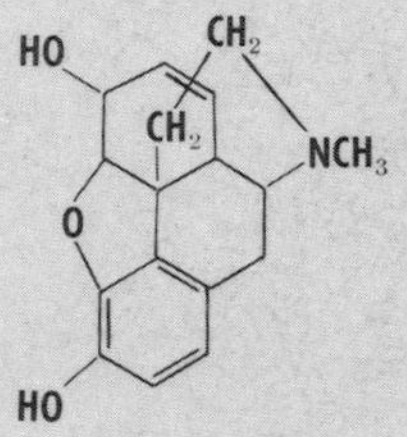

Morphine
(opium from poppy),
powerful analgesic,
producer of dreams

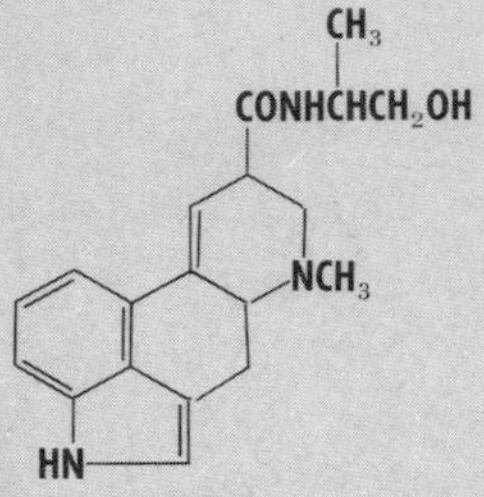

Ergonovine
(parasitic fungus),
uterotonic activity

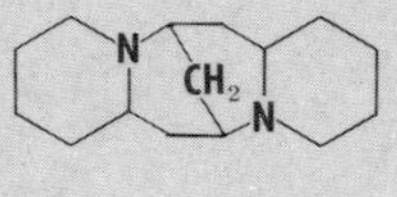

Sparteine
(e.g., *Lupinus arboreus*),
toxic

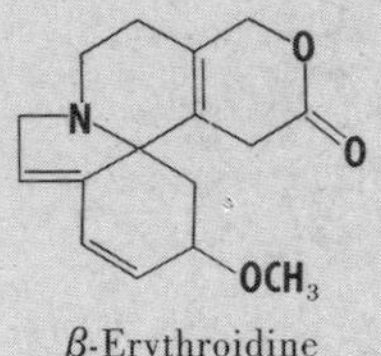

β-Erythroidine
(*Erythrina* genus),
curarizing agent

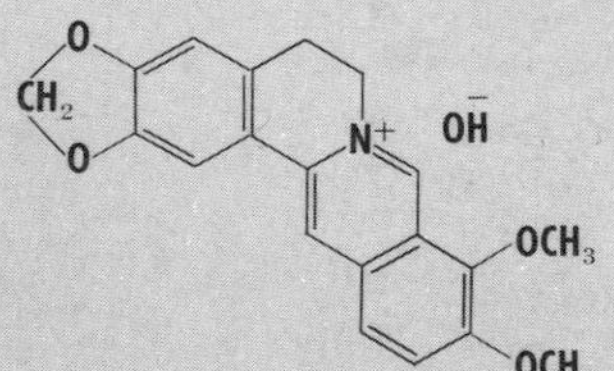

Berberine
(barberry root),
paralytic effect,
increases blood
pressure

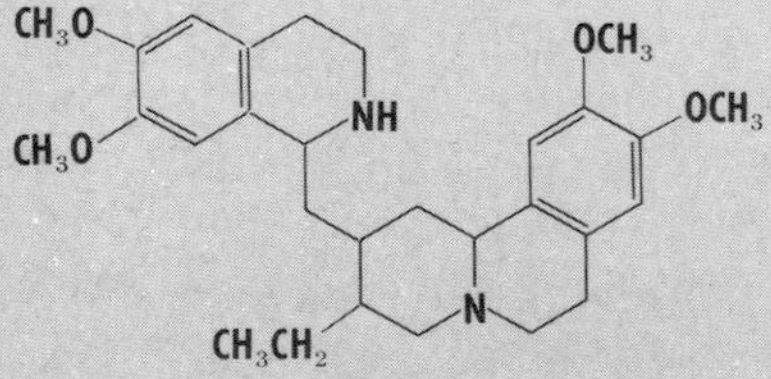

Emetine
(South American creeping
plant), emetic used in
amebic dysentery

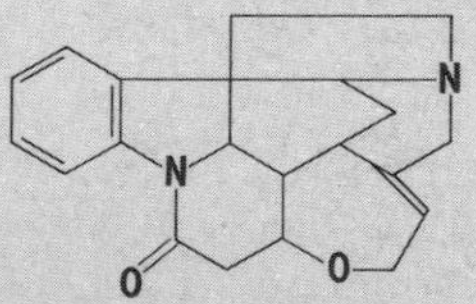

Strychnine
(*Strychnos nux-vomica*),
poison, used to exter-
minate rodents

Elucidation of Structures of Quinine and Cinchonine. Elucidation of the structures of unknown compounds developed historically through the degradation of complex molecules into simpler molecules, which in turn were further fragmented until substances of known structure were obtained. The structure of the original substance was then inferred from the structures of the fragments and from their mode of formation. As an example of the method, determination of the structures of quinine and cinchonine is presented. Cinchona alkaloids occur in the bark of *Cinchona* and *Remijia* species, indigenous to the high eastern slopes of the Andes. Quinine is one of the chief constituents and the active principle of the bark extract, which was found in 1639 to be an effective antimalarial, a fact that led to extensive cultivation of cinchona trees in the Dutch East Indies. Elucidation of the structures of quinine and cinchonine (a companion substance) was one of the classic problems of the last quarter of the nineteenth century.

Quinine and cinchonine were demonstrated to possess the molecular formulas $C_{20}H_{24}N_2O_2$ and $C_{19}H_{22}N_2O$ through elemental analysis and molecular weight determinations. These two formulas differ only by CH_2O. The alkaloids form double salts with acids, which indicates that both nitrogen atoms are basic. Both substances possess 10 sites of unsaturation (page 28), a fact that suggests unsaturated ring systems.

Treatment of the compounds with ethyl iodide gave quaternary ammonium salts, each with only one ethyl group on nitrogen. Thus both amino groups in each molecule are tertiary. Both compounds when warmed with acetic anhydride gave monoacetyl derivatives, hydrolysis of which gave back the original alkaloids. Since the two amino groups are tertiary and are therefore incapable of acylation, the monoacetyl derivatives must have involved hydroxyl groups. Treatment of the alkaloids with phosphorus pentachloride in chloroform gave monochlorides, a fact that confirms the presence of one hydroxyl group in both quinine and cinchonine. Both alkaloids rapidly decolorize solutions of permanganate and bromine. These results suggest the presence of double bonds in the molecules. Oxidation of the substances gave formic acid and carboxylic acids whose molecular formulas indicated that a vinyl group had been cleaved. Thus one of the sites of unsaturation in each alkaloid was accounted for. The above transformations are summarized with part structures as follows:

Cinchonine was cleaved by fusion with sodium hydroxide to produce quinoline, a compound of known structure. The same treatment of quinine gave a base similar to quinoline, but which differed from quinoline by the elements of CH_2O, in the same way that quinine and cinchonine differ. The chemical inertness of this oxygen-containing group in both quinine and the $C_{10}H_9NO$ degradation product suggested that the group was CH_3O and that the $C_{10}H_9NO$ molecule was a methoxyquinoline.

$C_{19}H_{22}N_2O$ $\xrightarrow{KOH}$

Cinchonine   Quinoline, C_9H_7N

$C_{20}H_{24}N_2O_2$ $\xrightarrow{KOH}$ $C_{10}H_9NO$

Quinine   Possibly a
                          methoxyquinoline

The presence of a methoxyl group in the $C_{10}H_9NO$ molecule was confirmed as follows: When quinine and cinchonine were oxidized with chromic acid, cinchoninic and quinic acids were obtained. When oxidized with potassium permanganate, both acids gave the same pyridine tricarboxylic acid. Thus the methoxyl group, if present, had to be in the benzenoid ring of quinine.

$C_{19}H_{22}N_2O$ $\xrightarrow{H_2Cr_2O_7}$ CO_2H $\xrightarrow{KMnO_4}$ CO_2H

Cinchonine   Cinchoninic acid   A pyridine
                                                                 tricarboxylic acid

                                                            $KMnO_4$ $\uparrow$

$C_{20}H_{24}N_2O_2$ $\xrightarrow{H_2Cr_2O_7}$ CO_2H $\xrightarrow{HCl}$ CO_2H
                                                  OCH_3 OH

Quinine   Quinic acid

All four methoxyquinolines in which the methoxyl group was in the benzenoid ring were prepared by the Skraup method (page 387). Direct comparison showed that the degradation product ($C_{10}H_9NO$) was identical with synthetic 6-methoxyquinoline.

CH_3O $CH_2OHCHOHCH_2OH$ CH_3O
                          $\xrightarrow[H_2SO_4]{p\text{-}CH_3OC_6H_4NO_2}$

        NH_2

                          6-Methoxyquinoline

Isolation of a pyridine tricarboxylic acid by the oxidative sequences indicated that the carboxyl groups of quinic and cinchoninic acid were in the heterocyclic ring of the quinoline system. The position of this carboxyl group was demonstrated by synthesis.

Isatin   Cinchoninic acid

The above conclusions are summarized below with part structures for quinine and cinchonine.

Cinchonine   Quinine

When the chlorides derived from quinine and cinchonine were treated with alkali, an elimination reaction occurred to give quinene and cinchene. These substances were heated with acid, and the resulting hydrolytic cleavage reaction gave fragments which accounted for all the atoms of the original alkaloids. One fragment (meroquinene) was the same for each alkaloid, and the other two fragments (one from each alkaloid) differed in molecular formula only by CH_2O.

$$C_{20}H_{24}N_2O_2 \xrightarrow{PCl_5} C_{20}H_{23}N_2OCl \xrightarrow{KOH} C_{20}H_{22}N_2O \xrightarrow[\substack{(H_3PO_4) \\ 175°}]{2H_2O} C_{11}H_{11}NO + C_9H_{15}NO_2$$

Quinine   Quinene   6-Methoxy-   Meroquinene
                                                           lepidine

$$C_{19}H_{22}N_2O \xrightarrow{PCl_5} C_{19}H_{21}N_2Cl \xrightarrow{KOH} C_{19}H_{20}N_2 \xrightarrow[\substack{(H_3PO_4) \\ 175°}]{2H_2O} C_{10}H_9N + C_9H_{15}NO_2$$

Cinchonine   Cinchene   Lepidine   Meroquinene

The above facts, coupled with the structure of cinchoninic acid and the molecular formulas, made lepidine structures reasonable for $C_{11}H_{11}NO$

and $C_{10}H_9N$. This hypothesis was confirmed by synthesis (not recorded here).

CH₃O— [structure] 4-methyl ... N

6-Methoxylepidine   Lepidine

Meroquinene contained the terminal double bond originally found in the alkaloids, and was demonstrated to possess a secondary amino and carboxyl group as well. When treated with dilute hydrochloric acid at high temperatures, this substance gave β-collidine in low yields. The loss of the carbon atom of the carboxyl group from meroquinene was the only change in carbon content that occurred in the transformation. This reaction established the ring structure of meroquinene, and the points of attachment of the two hydrocarbon chains to the ring.

$$\left[C_4H_{10} \begin{array}{c} CH=CH_2 \\ C \\ \diagdown NH \\ C \\ CO_2H \end{array} \right] \xrightarrow[240^\circ]{HCl} \begin{array}{c} CH_3 \\ C_2H_5 \\ N \end{array}$$

$$C_8H_{11}N$$

Meroquinene β-Collidine

When oxidized with potassium permanganate, meroquinene gave cincholoiponic acid, which contained a secondary amino and two carboxyl groups. This reaction established that the terminal double bond of meroquinene was contained in a vinyl group, and that this was converted to an ethyl group in the production of β-collidine.

$$\left[C_4H_{10} \begin{array}{c} CH=CH_2 \\ C \\ \diagup NH \\ C \\ CO_2H \end{array} \right] \xrightarrow{KMnO_4} \left[C_4H_{10} \begin{array}{c} CO_2H \\ C \\ \diagdown NH \\ C \\ CO_2H \end{array} \right]$$

Meroquinene   Cincholoiponic acid

When oxidized further with potassium permanganate, cincholoiponic acid gave a second amino-dicarboxylic acid that differed from the starting material by one methylene group. Apparently the chain containing one of the carboxyl groups was degraded by one carbon atom in the oxidation reaction.

$$\left[C_3H_8 \begin{array}{c} CO_2H \\ C \\ \diagup NH \\ C \\ CH_2CO_2H \end{array} \right] \xrightarrow{KMnO_4} \left[C_3H_8 \begin{array}{c} CO_2H \\ C \\ \diagup NH \\ C \\ CO_2H \end{array} \right]$$

Cincholoiponic acid   Loiponic acid

When put together, the above evidence strongly supported the following structures for the three acids:

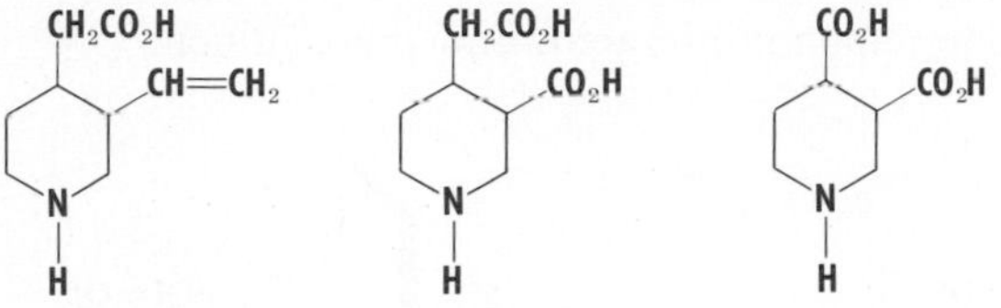

Meroquinene   Cincholoiponic acid   Loiponic acid

These deductions were proved valid by synthesis of cincholoiponic acid.

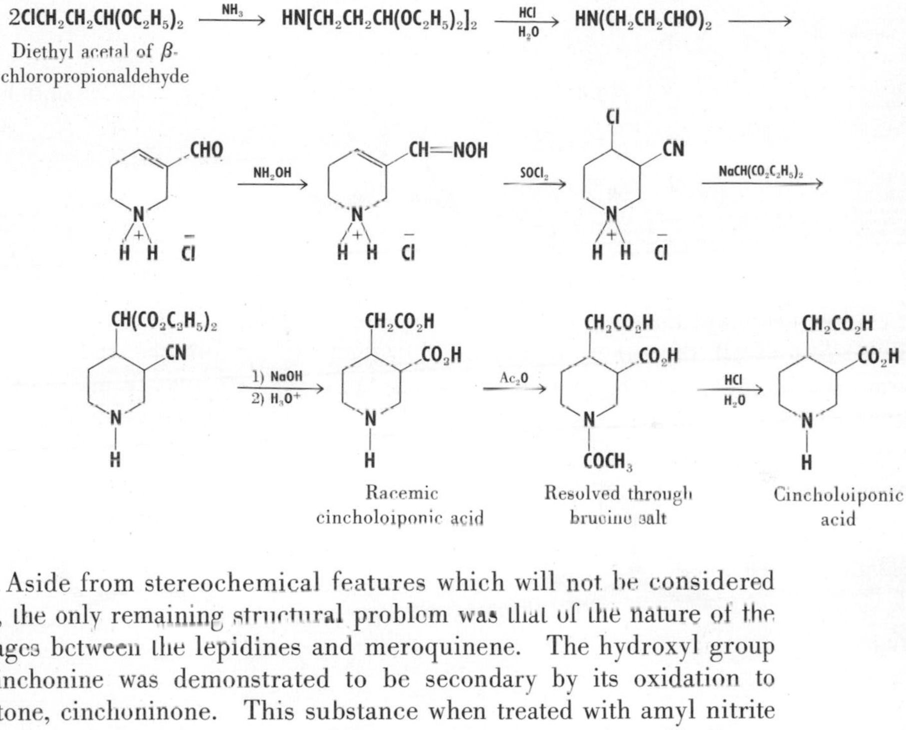

$$2ClCH_2CH_2CH(OC_2H_5)_2 \xrightarrow{NH_3} HN[CH_2CH_2CH(OC_2H_5)_2]_2 \xrightarrow[H_2O]{HCl} HN(CH_2CH_2CHO)_2 \longrightarrow$$

Diethyl acetal of β-
chloropropionaldehyde

Racemic   Resolved through   Cincholoiponic
cincholoiponic acid   brucine salt   acid

Aside from stereochemical features which will not be considered here, the only remaining structural problem was that of the nature of the linkages between the lepidines and meroquinene. The hydroxyl group of cinchonine was demonstrated to be secondary by its oxidation to a ketone, cinchoninone. This substance when treated with amyl nitrite and base was cleaved to give cinchoninic acid and an oxime. The latter hydrolyzed readily to give meroquinene and hydroxylamine.

These reactions found their most reasonable interpretation in terms of structures for quinine and cinchonine in which the nonaromatic portion of the molecules consisted of a bicyclic system, with nitrogen occupying the bridgehead position. This deduction rested on the following facts:

1. Cinchonine and cinchinone were shown to contain two tertiary amino groups, whereas meroquinene contained a secondary amino group.

2. The molecular formulas of cinchoninic acid and meroquinene accounted for all the carbons originally present in cinchonine.

3. The number of sites of unsaturation in cinchinone indicated the presence of two rings in the portion of the molecule found in the side chain of the quinoline nucleus.

The formation of cinchinone, cinchoninic acid, and meroquinene could now be written.

Cinchonine $\xrightarrow{[0]}$ Cinchinone $\xrightarrow[n\text{-}C_5H_{11}ONO]{C_2H_5ONa}$

Cinchoninic
acid   Meroquinene

Elucidation of the structures of quinene and cinchonene allowed the structures of all the other degradation products (e.g., quinene and cinchene) to be assigned. About forty years later, the last links in the total synthesis of quinine were forged, and the structure proposed by the early investigators was thereby confirmed.

Quinine   Quinene

Synthesis of Reserpine. Reserpine is one of a family of *Rauwolfia* alkaloids whose remarkable physiological properties have led to its extensive use in treatment of hypertensive, nervous, and mental disorders.

Elucidation of the structure of quinine took about twenty-five years, and its synthesis was spread over a period of about fifty years. In contrast, reserpine, an alkaloid of comparable complexity, was isolated in 1952. Its structure was determined, and the compound was synthesized (R. B. Woodward) within a span of five years.

Much of the incentive to synthesize natural products has come from the traditional assumption that the structure of a compound is not established with certainty unless the substance is prepared by a rational series of reactions. The synthesis of reserpine provides an instructive example of the construction of an involved ring system. The stereochemical features of the compound were neatly mastered at appropriate stages in the sequence.

The scaffold of rings *D* and *E* was constructed with a Diels-Alder reaction (page 351) between *p*-benzoquinone and vinylacrylic acid. The reaction assumed the usual steric course to give that diastereomer which contains the largest possible number of hydrogens oriented cis to one another. The *less hindered carbonyl group* of the adduct (I) was reduced with sodium borohydride (page 280), the hydride coming in from the *less hindered side* of the molecule to give alcohol II. When treated with perbenzoic acid (page 342), II gave epoxide III, the reagent having donated an oxygen atom to the molecule from the *less hindered side*. In reactions of this type, isolated double bonds are more readily attacked than double bonds conjugated with a carbonyl group. When subjected to dehydrating conditions, hydroxy acid (III) gave a δ-lactone (page 67). Formation of this lactone depends on the favorable configuration of the four asymmetric centers at the α-, β-, γ-, and δ-positions that intervene between the carboxyl and hydroxyl groups of III.

p-Benzoquinone   Vinylacrylic acid   I

II   III   IV

When subjected to the reducing action of isopropanol-aluminum isopropoxide (page 280), the carbonyl of IV was reduced to a hydroxyl group. As in the other reactions, hydride entered the molecule from the less hindered "underside." The alkoxide base in the reaction mixture caused three other transformations to occur.

1. The original lactone opened and a new γ-lactone ring closed on the new hydroxyl group.

2. The alcohol anion liberated in this transfer opened the epoxide ring, an inversion occurring in the process (page 209).

3. The hydroxyl created from the epoxide underwent a β-elimination (page 39) to give a double bond conjugated with the lactone function.

Compound V was the product. In the next step, elements of methanol were added to the conjugated double bond (page 275) to give VI. Addition occurred from the less hindered "underside" of the system.

IV   V   VI

Hypobromous acid made from *N*-bromosuccinimide and acid was added to the double bond of VI. In this reaction, positive bromine added to the double bond from the least hindered side, and the resulting bromonium ion (page 338) was opened trans (over-all trans addition) by water to give VII. Chromic acid oxidation of the hydroxyl group of VII gave ketone VIII. When treated with zinc and acetic acid, VIII underwent a twofold reaction.

1. The bromine and ether link trans to each other (axial-axial relationship, page 400) underwent elimination to give an α,β-unsaturated ketone.

2. The hydroxyl originally bound in the lactone function underwent hydrogenolysis, a reaction promoted by the neighboring ketone function.

Compound IX was the product.

VI   VII

VIII   IX

The carboxyl group of IX was then esterified with diazomethane (page 211), and the free hydroxyl group was acetylated with acetic anhydride and pyridine to produce X. With these groups covered, the double bond of X was hydroxylated with osmium tetroxide (page 342) in a cis addition. In this reaction, the oxidizing agent approached the double bond from the least hindered side of the molecule. The resulting diol (XI) was cleaved with periodate (page 433) to produce aldehyde-acid XII, which was converted to ester XIII.

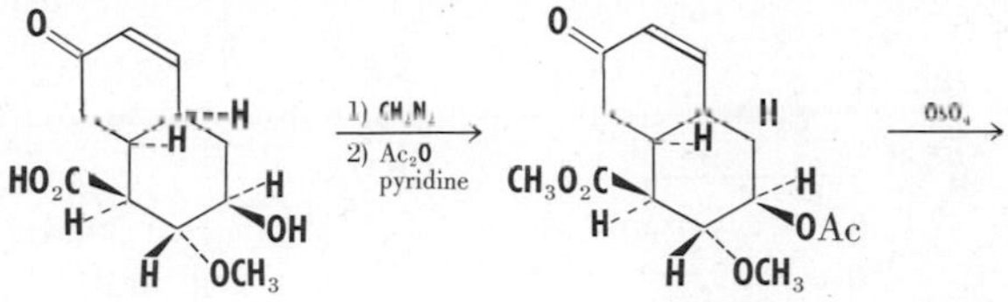

IX   X

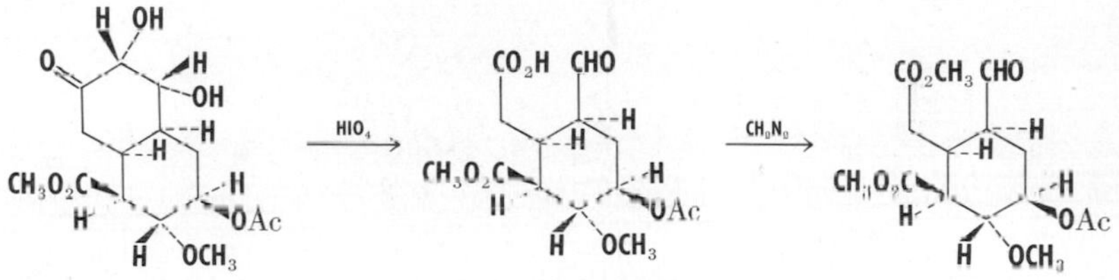

XI   XII   XIII

At this point in the sequence, amine XIV was prepared. This compound contains two rings which eventually became rings *A* and *B* of reserpine. In the first step, 6-methoxyindole was metalated (page 250). The product was employed as a nucleophile in substitution of α-chloro-acetonitrile (page 489). The resulting nitrile was reduced with sodium and ethanol to give amine XIV.

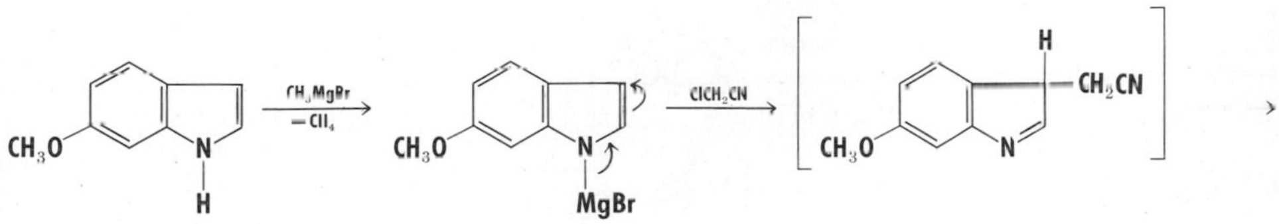

6-Methoxyindole

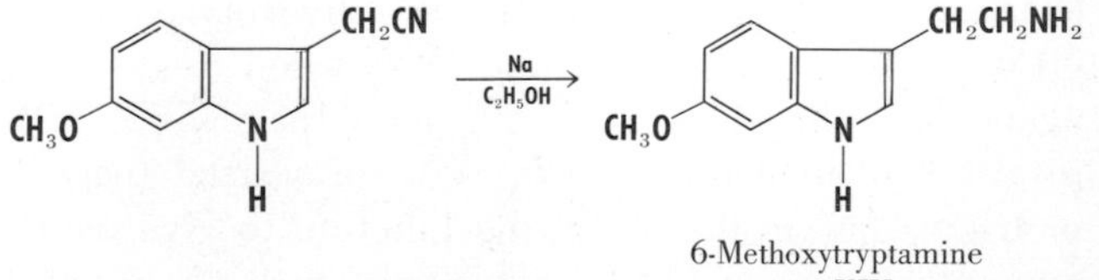

6-Methoxytryptamine
XIV

The elements of rings *A, B, C, D,* and *E* were now put together through condensation of amine XIV with aldehyde XIII. The imine linkage in the product (XV) was reduced selectively with sodium borohydride (page 280). As the reaction proceeded, sodium borohydride catalyzed an amide-ester interchange (page 313) which led to lactam XVI. When treated with phosphorus oxychloride, this substance underwent ring closure to give imine XVII, which contained the full ring system of reserpine. Reduction of the imine linkage with sodium borohydride led to XVIII, formed by approach of the hydride from the least hindered "underside" of the ring system. This compound was resolved, and the (−)-rotating antipode was isolated in optically pure form.

XIV   XIII   XV (not isolated)

(Not isolated)   XVI

XVII (not isolated)   XVIII, resolved through optically active di-*p*-toluyl-*l*-tartaric acid

The remaining steps of the synthesis were relatively simple. The two ester functions of XVIII were hydrolyzed to give hydroxy acid XIX, which formed a γ-lactone (XX) when treated with the dehydrating agent *N,N'*-dicyclohexylcarbodiimide (page 533). When treated with pivalic acid in boiling xylene, XX epimerized (page 137) at the asymmetric carbon of the *C–D* ring junction to give the thermodynamically more stable isomer (XXI). This substance possessed the stereochemical structure found in reserpine. Epimerization probably involved reversible tautomeric shifts of hydrogen on the asymmetric carbon atom into the 3-position of the indole nucleus. Lactone XXI was subjected to methanolysis to give XXII, which was esterified with 3,4,5-trimethoxybenzoyl chloride in pyridine to give reserpine. This substance was identical in all respects with the naturally occurring alkaloid. The fact that many false starts and blind alleys are encountered in syntheses as complex as this does not detract from the beauty of design of the sequence that is finally found to work.

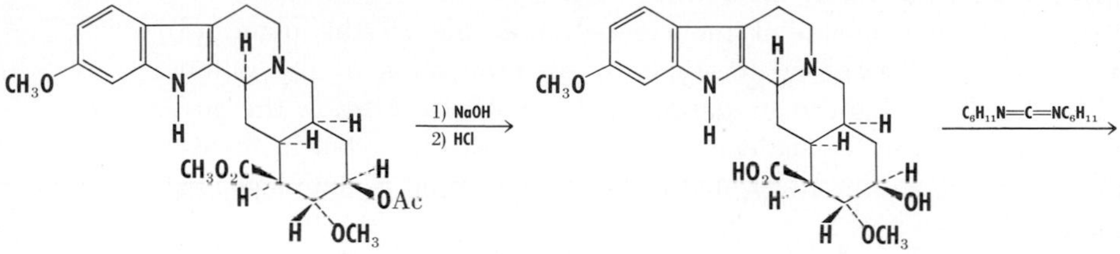

XVIII

XIX

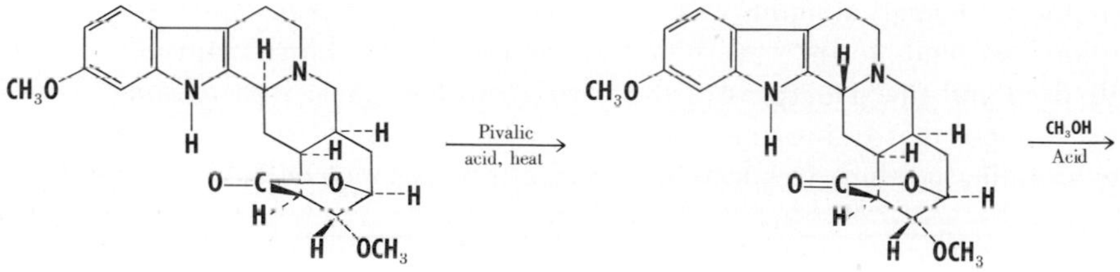

XX

XXI

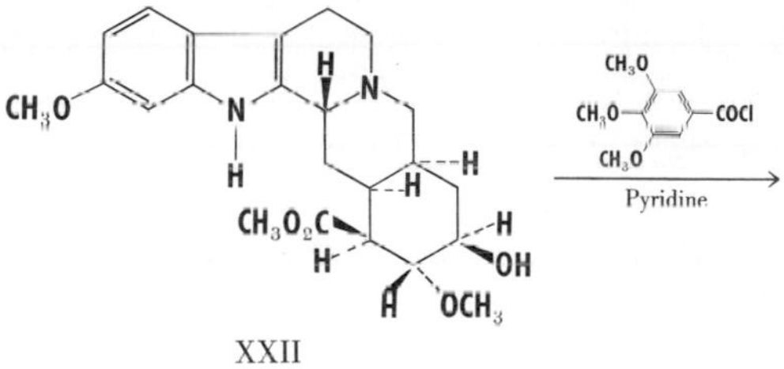

XXII

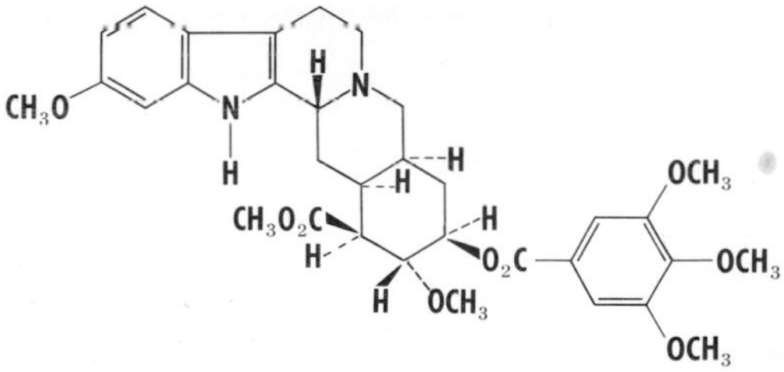

Reserpine

Use of Isotopes in Study of Biogenesis. Elucidation of structures of families of natural products has provided a basis for conjecture with respect to the types of synthetic sequences carried out by enzyme systems in organisms. Inspection of relationships between structures of compounds frequently suggests that one compound is an intermediate in the biogenetic synthesis of a more complex substance. In this section, an example of the experimental approach to the problem of biogenesis is presented. The reasonable and long-held opinion that amino acids are precursors of alkaloids in plant metabolism has been substantiated in recent times through use of molecules that contain isotopes of carbon, nitrogen, oxygen, or hydrogen. The technique involves the following steps: (1) synthesis of the amino acid with isotopes in known positions of the molecule; (2) metabolism of the labeled molecule by the plant; (3) isolation of the alkaloid in question; (4) determination of the isotope level in the alkaloid and degradation of the molecule to show the positions of the tracer in the molecule. The principles involved in the use of this technique will be illustrated in their application to the biogenesis of nicotine.

Nicotine is one of a group of alkaloids which occur in the tobacco plant. The substance is highly toxic and is extensively used as a contact insecticide. In small amounts (e.g., cigarette smoke), the substance is a stimulant and tends to increase blood pressure. From the structure of the alkaloid and the structures of the various amino acids, it is reasonable to suppose that lysine and ornithine are precursors of the pyridine and pyrrolidine portions (respectively) of the nicotine molecule.

Lysine   Nicotine   Ornithine

Ornithine labeled at its asymmetric center with carbon-14 was prepared from acetic-2-C-14 acid as follows:

$$C^{14}H_3CO_2H \xrightarrow[P]{Br_2} BrC^{14}H_2CO_2H \xrightarrow[\text{2) } C_2H_5OH_2]{\text{1) NaCN}} N\equiv CC^{14}H_2CO_2C_2H_5 \xrightarrow{HNO_2}$$

Ethyl cyanoacetate-2-C-14

Ethyl isonitrosocyanoacetate-2-C-14   Ethyl acetamidocyanoacetate-2-C-14

Potassium   N-(γ-Bromopropyl)-
phthalimide   phthalimide

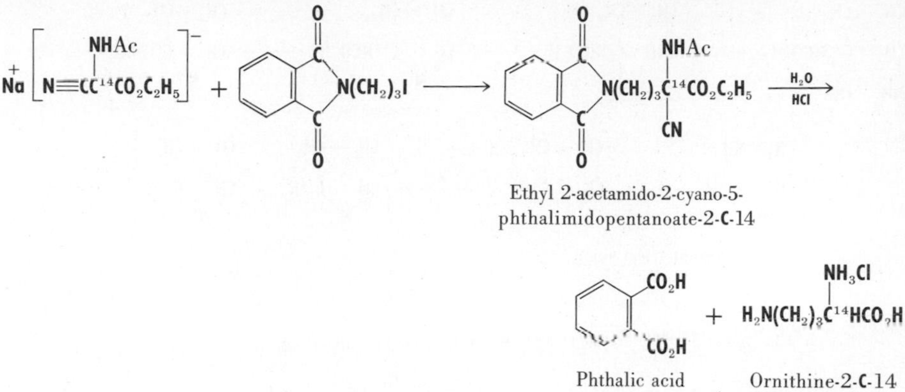

Ethyl 2-acetamido-2-cyano-5-
phthalimidopentanoate-2-C-14

Phthalic acid   Ornithine-2-C-14
hydrochloride

Labeled ornithine was fed to a young tobacco plant, and nicotine isolated from leaves of the mature plant was found to contain radioactive carbon (carbon-14). The radioactivity was located in the pyrrolidine portion of the molecule by the following degradation experiments:

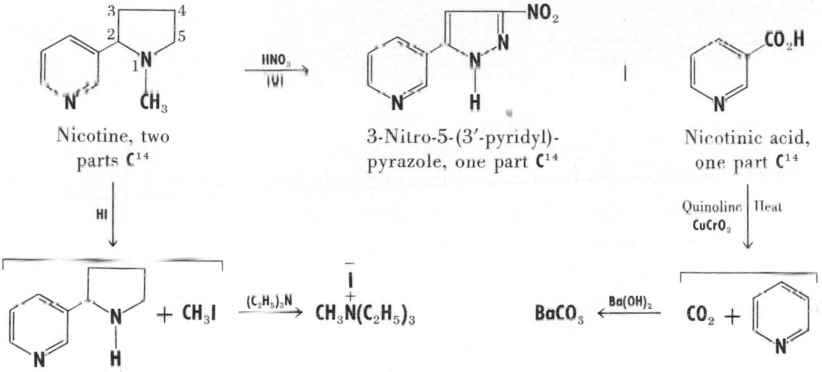

Nicotine, two
parts C^{14}

3-Nitro-5-(3'-pyridyl)-
pyrazole, one part C^{14}

Nicotinic acid,
one part C^{14}

2-(3'-Pyridyl)-
pyrrolidine

No C^{14}

One part
C^{14}

Pyridine

The carbon dioxide obtained by decarboxylation of the nicotinic acid contained all the C^{14} originally present in the nicotinic acid. Thus all the C^{14} present in nicotine must have been associated with the pyrrolidine portion of the alkaloid. The methyl group attached to the nitrogen of the pyrrolidine ring of nicotine was demonstrated to be free of C^{14}. Accordingly all the radiocarbon had to be localized in C-2, C-4, or C-5 of nicotine. The level of radiocarbon in 3-nitro-5-(3'-pyridyl)-pyrazole was only half that in the starting nicotine, although this oxidation product contained C-2, C-3, and C-4 (but not C-5) of the original nicotine molecule. It was concluded that half of the C^{14} present in nicotine was present in C-2 and half in C-5. This fact suggested that conversion of ornithine to the pyrrolidine portion of nicotine in the plant involved a symmetrical intermediate.

$$\begin{array}{c} \text{CH}_3\text{—CH}_2 \\ | \\ \text{CH}_2 \quad \text{C}^{14}\text{HCO}_2\text{H} \\ | \\ \text{NH}_2 \quad \text{NH}_2 \end{array} \longrightarrow \begin{array}{c} \text{CH}_2\text{—CH}_2 \\ | \\ \text{CHO} \quad \text{C}^{14}\text{HCO}_2\text{H} \\ | \\ \text{NH}_2 \end{array} \longrightarrow \begin{array}{c} \text{CH}_2\text{—CH}_2 \\ | \\ \text{CH} \quad \text{C}^{14}\text{HCO}_2\text{H} \\ \diagdown\text{N}\diagup \end{array} \longrightarrow \begin{array}{c} \text{CH}_2\text{—CH}_2 \\ | \\ \text{CH} \quad \text{C}^{14}\text{HCO}_2^{-} \\ \diagdown\text{N}\diagup \end{array} \xrightarrow{-\text{CO}_2}$$

$$\left\{ \begin{array}{c} \text{CH}_2\text{—CH}_2 \\ | \\ \text{CH} \quad \text{C}^{14}\text{H} \\ \diagdown\text{N}\diagup \end{array} \longleftrightarrow \begin{array}{c} \text{CH}_2\text{—CH}_2 \\ | \\ {}^{-}\text{CH} \quad \text{C}^{14}\text{H} \\ \diagdown\text{N}\diagup \end{array} \right\} \xrightarrow{\text{H}^+} \left\{ \begin{array}{c} \text{CH}_2\text{—CH}_2 \\ | \\ \text{CH} \quad \text{C}^{14}\text{H}_2 \\ \diagdown\text{N}\diagup \end{array} + \begin{array}{c} \text{CH}_2\text{—CH}_2 \\ | \\ \text{CH}_2 \quad \text{C}^{14}\text{H} \\ \diagdown\text{N}\diagup \end{array} \right\} \xrightarrow[\text{steps}]{\text{Many}}$$

Symmetrical anion

In a different set of experiments, the methyl group of nicotine was demonstrated to originate in the methyl group of methionine. Thus a *transmethylation* must have occurred at some stage in the biogenetic process.

$$\text{C}^{14}\text{H}_3\text{SCH}_2\text{CH}_2\underset{\underset{\text{NH}_2}{|}}{\text{CHCO}_2\text{H}} \xrightarrow[\text{plant}]{\text{Tobacco}}$$

C¹⁴-Methyl methionine   C¹⁴-Methyl nicotine

The idea that amino acids are precursors of alkaloids has been very profitable as applied to elucidation of the structures of the latter substances. Frequently identification of part of the structure of an alkaloid, coupled with a knowledge of the structures of amino acids, allows hypothetic total structures to be drawn for the substance in question.

Problems

1. Assume that the alkaloids of Table 23.2 are made in the plant from amino acids (Table 23.1). Indicate with formulas which parts of which amino acids you think went to make up six alkaloids of your own selection.

2. Write out series of reactions which could be utilized for relating the configurations of the following substances to one of the compounds whose configuration was related to that of D-glyceraldehyde in this chapter.

a. $\overset{*}{\text{CH}_3\text{CHCH}_2\text{CH}_3}$
$\quad\quad |$
$\quad\quad \text{OCH}_3$

b. $\overset{*}{\text{CH}_3\text{CHCH}_2\text{OH}}$
$\quad\quad |$
$\quad\quad \text{OH}$

c. $\overset{*}{\text{CH}_3\text{CHC}_6\text{H}_5}$
$\quad\quad |$
$\quad\quad \text{OH}$

d. $\overset{*}{\text{CH}_3\text{CH}_2\text{CHCH}_3}$
$\quad\quad\quad |$
$\quad\quad\quad \text{NH}_2$

e. $\overset{*}{\text{HO}_2\text{CCHCH}_2\text{CO}_2\text{H}}$
$\quad\quad |$
$\quad\quad \text{OH}$

f. $\text{C}_2\text{H}_5\underset{*}{\text{CHCH}_2\text{OH}}$
$\quad\quad\overset{\text{CH}_3}{|}$

3. Write out syntheses of the following compounds from substances ordinarily found in organic storerooms.

a. $BrCH_2CH_2CH(OC_2H_5)_2$

b.

CH_3O —[indole ring]— N–H

c. $C_6H_5CH_2CHCO_2H$
$\quad\quad\quad\quad |$
$\quad\quad\quad NH_2$

d.

[pyrrolidine ring] N–H, CO_2H

e. $H_2NCH_2CH_2CH_2CHCO_2H$
$\quad\quad\quad\quad\quad\quad |$
$\quad\quad\quad\quad\quad NH_2$

f. $H_2NCH_2CONHCH_2CO_2H$

g. $CH_3CHCONHCH_2CO_2H$
$\quad\quad |$
$\quad\quad NH_2$

h.
$\quad\quad\quad\quad\quad\quad\quad\quad\quad CO_2H$
$\quad\quad\quad\quad\quad\quad\quad\quad\quad |$
$C_6H_5CH_2CHCONHCHCH_2CH_2CO_2H$
$\quad\quad\quad\quad |$
$\quad\quad\quad\quad NH_2$

i.

[pyrrolidine ring] N, $COCH_2CH_3$, CH_3

j.

[quinoline ring with CH_3]

k.

[ring with CO_2H, CO_2H, CO_2H, CO_2H]

l.

[indole ring] $CH_2CH_2CH_2CO_2H$, N–H

4. A peptide was completely hydrolyzed, and the component amino acids were determined and identified as follows:

       1 glycine unit (Gly)
       2 alanine units (Ala)
       1 serine unit (Ser)
       1 aspartic acid unit (Asp)
       1 proline unit (Pro)

A large number of partial hydrolyses were carried out, and the following dipeptides were identified: Ala $\longrightarrow$ Asp; Ala $\longrightarrow$ Pro; Asp $\longrightarrow$ Ser (no $-C(NH_2)CO_2H$ linkage present, as shown by lack of reaction with HIO_4); Pro $\longrightarrow$ Gly; Ser $\longrightarrow$ Ala; Gly $\longrightarrow$ Ala. What is the peptide?

5. Assume that $BaC^{14}O_3$ and $KC^{14}N$ are available and that $HO_2CCH_2CHNH_2C^{14}O_2H$ and $HOCH_2CHNH_2C^{14}O_2H$ have to be prepared. Write out syntheses.

6. Assume that $C^{14}H_3SCH_2CH_2CHNH_2CO_2H$ and $C_6H_5CH_2CHNH_2C^{14}O_2H$ were fed to the plant which produces ephedrine. Ephedrine was then isolated from the plant and was found to have a high level of radioactivity. Suggest degradative procedures which indicate the location of radiocarbon in the molecule.

7. An alkaloid of unknown structure possessed a molecular formula $C_8H_{17}NO$. The substance when acetylated formed a monoacetate, and in a terminal-methyl determination gave 0.7 mole of acetic acid. The alkaloid also gave an iodoform test. When oxidized under controlled conditions, the alkaloid produced $C_6H_{11}NO$, a neutral substance which gave no acetic acid in a terminal-methyl determination. Hydrolysis in acid of $C_6H_{11}NO$ gave an amino acid, $C_6H_{13}NO_2$, which gave no nitrogen in a Van Slyke determination. With correct structures, trace the above interconversions.

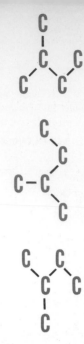

24

Lipids, Terpenes, and Steroids

A large group of compounds found in nature are water-insoluble, but very soluble in hydrocarbons and ether. *Lipids, terpenes,* and *steroids* possess this property, and as a consequence they can easily be separated from the natural products discussed in Chaps. 22 and 23. These substances either are hydrocarbons or contain oxygen functions much diluted (in an intramolecular sense) by large hydrocarbon groups, which determine their solubility properties.

A more fundamental reason for treating these classes of compounds in the same chapter is their close biogenetic relationship to one another.

Lipids

Lipids are esters of long-chain carboxylic acids, which are usually unbranched. *Fats,* the most important members of this class, are found widely distributed throughout the animal and vegetable worlds. Fats are one of the three main classes of foods and provide one quarter to one half of the average human caloric intake. These values do not accurately reflect the relative amounts of foodstuffs consumed on a weight basis. Fats provide about 9.5 kcal/g on total combustion, which is over twice the average value of 4.0 for proteins and carbohydrates.

Fats are esters of glycerol (glycerine). When ingested, they are emulsified in the intestines by salts of the bile acids (page 564), and brought into contact with enzyme systems, by which they are hydrolyzed. The *fatty acids* thus liberated are absorbed into the intestinal mucosa, where resynthesis to fat occurs. The fat then passes into the portal system of the body, traveling as minute particles complexed with serum protein. Metabolism occurs mainly in the liver.

Structures and Properties. Fats usually consist of glycerides that contain more than one kind of fatty acid residue. Hydrolysis of these esters is readily accomplished with sodium hydroxide to form glycerol and soap (saponification). Fatty acids fall roughly into three groups: saturated, unsaturated, and those which contain branches or rings.

$$3NaOH + \begin{array}{c} CH_2O_2CR \\ | \\ CHO_2CR \\ | \\ CH_2O_2CR \end{array} \longrightarrow \begin{array}{c} CH_2OH \\ | \\ CHOH \\ | \\ CH_2OH \end{array} + 3NaO_2CR$$

Glyceride   Glycerol   Soap (metal salt of a long-chain acid)

The saturated fatty acids belong to the homologous series $CH_3(CH_2)_n CO_2H$, where n is usually an even number ranging from 2 to 12. As the molecular weight of compounds in which n is even increases, the melting points also increase in a regular fashion, as indicated in Table 24.1. A fat is usually an ester of *two or three* different fatty acids, and when hydrolyzed it gives a mixture of fatty acids. Isolation of individual fatty acids from such mixtures is rather difficult. Techniques commonly employed are fractional distillation or chromatography of their methyl esters, fractional crystallization of their metal salts, and fractional complex formation of the acids with urea.

Palmitic and stearic acid are the most commonly encountered saturated fatty acids. The glyceride of the former is the major constituent of palm oil, and the glyceride of the latter is the main component of animal fats. The lower saturated fatty acids, such as butyric acid, occur as glycerides in the milk fat of mammals. The characteristic and repulsive odor of rancid butter is partially due to the liberation of butyric acid by enzymatic hydrolysis of the glyceride.

TABLE 24.1   *Saturated Fatty Acids*

Name	Formula	Mp, °C
Butyric acid	$CH_3(CH_2)_2CO_2H$	−4.7
Caproic acid	$CH_3(CH_2)_4CO_2H$	−1.5
Caprylic acid	$CH_3(CH_2)_6CO_2H$	16.5
Capric acid	$CH_3(CH_2)_8CO_2H$	31.3
Lauric acid	$CH_3(CH_2)_{10}CO_2H$	43.6
Myristic acid	$CH_3(CH_2)_{12}CO_2H$	58.0
Palmitic acid	$CH_3(CH_2)_{14}CO_2H$	62.9
Stearic acid	$CH_3(CH_2)_{16}CO_2H$	69.9
Arachidic acid	$CH_3(CH_2)_{18}CO_2H$	75.2
Behenic acid	$CH_3(CH_2)_{20}CO_2H$	80.2
Lignoceric acid	$CH_3(CH_2)_{22}CO_2H$	84.2
Cerotic acid	$CH_3(CH_2)_{24}CO_2H$	87.7

TABLE 24.2   *Unsaturated Fatty Acids*

Name	Formula
Palmitoleic acid	$CH_3(CH_2)_5CH=CH(CH_2)_7CO_2H$ (cis)
Oleic acid	$CH_3(CH_2)_7CH=CH(CH_2)_7CO_2H$ (cis)
Ricinoleic acid	$CH_3(CH_2)_5CH(OH)CH_2CH=CH(CH_2)_7CO_2H$ (cis)
Linoleic acid	$CH_3(CH_2)_3(CH_2CH=CH)_2(CH_2)_7CO_2H$
Linolenic acid	$CH_3(CH_2CH=CH)_3(CH_2)_7CO_2H$
Eleostearic acid	$CH_3(CH_2)_3(CH=CH)_3(CH_2)_7CO_2H$ (cis, trans, trans)

Unlike the glycerides of saturated fatty acids, which are usually low-melting solids, the glycerides of unsaturated fatty acids are frequently oils. Peanut, corn, cottonseed, soybean, linseed, castor, and tung oils are all rich in glycerides of unsaturated acids. The unsaturated acids usually contain 16 or more carbon atoms in their chain, and only rarely fewer. Table 24.2 lists the common unsaturated fatty acids.

The methylene groups bound to the double bonds in these oils are subject to chemical attack by oxygen (page 419). A complex series of reactions results, which involve air oxidation, hydroperoxide formation, polymerization, and cross-linking of polymer chains. The oxygen-initiated polymerization is responsible for use of multiply unsaturated fats as drying oils. Thus linseed oil is used as a binder and carrier of pigment in paints. Rancidity associated with vegetable oils is due to oxidative cleavage of the double bonds to give lower, odoriferous aldehydes and acids. This chemical lability is overcome through commercial hydrogenation of vegetable oils over a nickel catalyst (page 352) to produce fats which are stable solids and are utilized as shortening and oleomargarine.

Fats that possess branched or cyclic fatty acid chains are relatively rare. Chaulmoogra oil, which is found in the seed of an East Indian plant, contains glycerides of three cyclic fatty acids. The oil, which has been used for centuries in the treatment of leprosy in China and India, consists of glycerides of the following acids:

$-(CH_2)_{10}CO_2H$ Hydnocarpic acid

$-(CH_2)_{12}CO_2H$ Chaulmoogric acid

$-(CH_2)_6CH=CH(CH_2)_4CO_2H$ Gorlic acid

Lipids that occur in the cells of active tissues (brain, liver, kidney, etc.) of animals are more complex. They differ from fats in that they contain a phosphate ester of a nitrogenous base in place of one of the fatty acid components. A number of examples of these *phosphatides* are listed. *Lecithin*, a powerful emulsifying agent, is extracted from either egg yolk or soybean oil. *Cephalin* has been isolated from brain tissue.

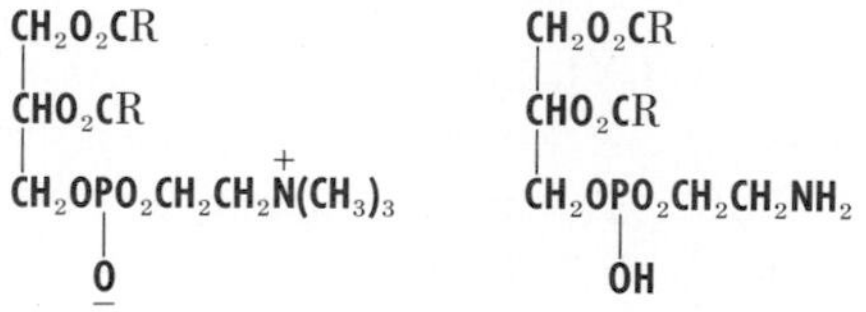

$$CH_2O_2CR$$
$$CHO_2CR$$
$$CH_2OPO_2CH_2CH_2\overset{+}{N}(CH_3)_3$$
$$\underset{O}{|}$$

α-Lecithin

$$CH_2O_2CR$$
$$CHO_2CR$$
$$CH_2OPO_2CH_2CH_2NH_2$$
$$\underset{OH}{|}$$

α-Cephalin

Synthesis of Linoleic Acid. Preparation of this naturally occurring fatty acid illustrates the use of acetylene synthesis as applied to the construction of long-chain compounds. Figure 24.1 indicates the reactions used, a number of which require comment.

Conventional substitution reactions (page 216) applied to hexamethylene glycol lead to a mixture of 1-chloro-6-iodohexane and 1,6-diiodohexane, which are separated by fractional distillation. When treated with sodium acetylide, the former compound gives 8-chloro-1-octyne. This reaction illustrates the greater reactivity as a leaving group (page 242) of iodine as compared to chlorine. The product is coupled by a substitution reaction with 2-octyn-1-yl methanesulfonate, which is also prepared by a conventional acetylene synthesis. The product contains a 16-carbon chain with a terminal chlorine and two acetylenic

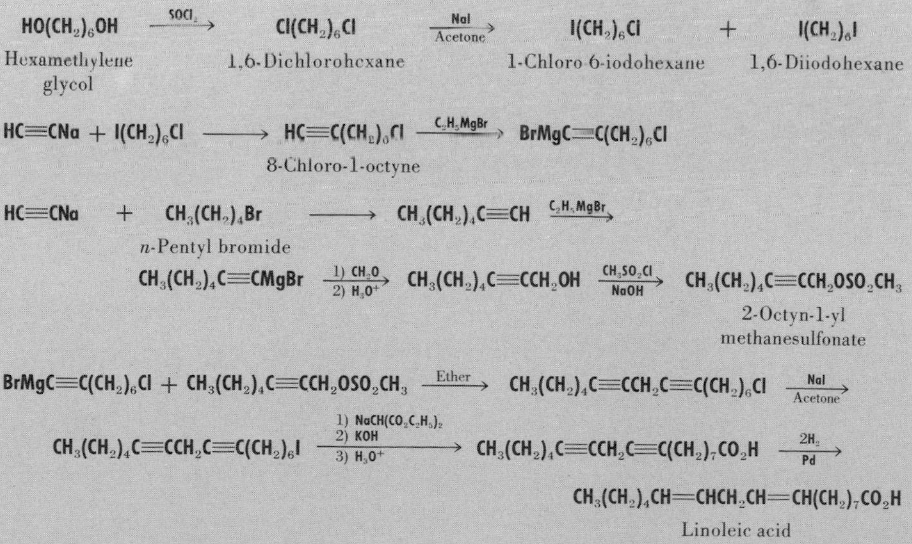

$$HO(CH_2)_6OH \xrightarrow{SOCl_2} Cl(CH_2)_6Cl \xrightarrow[\text{Acetone}]{NaI} I(CH_2)_6Cl \quad + \quad I(CH_2)_6I$$

Hexamethylene glycol   1,6-Dichlorohexane   1-Chloro-6-iodohexane   1,6-Diiodohexane

$$HC{\equiv}CNa + I(CH_2)_6Cl \longrightarrow HC{\equiv}C(CH_2)_6Cl \xrightarrow{C_2H_5MgBr} BrMgC{\equiv}C(CH_2)_6Cl$$

8-Chloro-1-octyne

$$HC{\equiv}CNa \quad + \quad CH_3(CH_2)_4Br \longrightarrow CH_3(CH_2)_4C{\equiv}CH \xrightarrow{C_2H_5MgBr}$$

n-Pentyl bromide

$$CH_3(CH_2)_4C{\equiv}CMgBr \xrightarrow[\text{2) H}_2\text{O}^+]{\text{1) CH}_2\text{O}} CH_3(CH_2)_4C{\equiv}CCH_2OH \xrightarrow[\text{NaOH}]{\text{CH}_3\text{SO}_2\text{Cl}} CH_3(CH_2)_4C{\equiv}CCH_2OSO_2CH_3$$

2-Octyn-1-yl methanesulfonate

$$BrMgC{\equiv}C(CH_2)_6Cl + CH_3(CH_2)_4C{\equiv}CCH_2OSO_2CH_3 \xrightarrow{\text{Ether}} CH_3(CH_2)_4C{\equiv}CCH_2C{\equiv}C(CH_2)_6Cl \xrightarrow[\text{Acetone}]{\text{NaI}}$$

$$CH_3(CH_2)_4C{\equiv}CCH_2C{\equiv}C(CH_2)_6I \xrightarrow[\text{3) H}_2\text{O}^+]{\substack{\text{1) NaCH(CO}_2\text{C}_2\text{H}_5)_2 \\ \text{2) KOH}}} CH_3(CH_2)_4C{\equiv}CCH_2C{\equiv}C(CH_2)_7CO_2H \xrightarrow[\text{Pd}]{2H_2}$$

$$CH_3(CH_2)_4CH{=}CHCH_2CH{=}CH(CH_2)_7CO_2H$$

Linoleic acid

FIG. 24.1 Synthesis of linoleic acid.

linkages. An additional two carbon atoms are added to the chain by a malonic ester synthesis (page 260). Linoleic acid is produced by partial hydrogenation of the acetylenic linkages (page 443).

Waxes

Waxes are found in such diverse places as the head of the sperm whale and the bee's honeycomb. The compounds are usually monoesters of long-chain unbranched fatty acids and alcohols. The acid components vary in carbon content from C_{24} to C_{36}, and the alcohols fall in the range from C_{16} to C_{36}. Certain of the waxes contain steroids (page 560) as their alcoholic component. These esters are frequently found as mixtures with nonesterified alcohols and high-molecular-weight unbranched hydrocarbons.

Carnauba wax, which occurs as a protective coating on the leaves of a Brazilian palm, is widely used in automobile and floor waxes. *Lanolin*, obtained from wool wax, is widely used as a base for skin and hair preparations. Table 24.3 lists some of the alcohol components of esters isolated from naturally occurring waxes.

Fatty Acids from Microorganisms

A number of novel fatty acids that possess acetylenic and, occasionally, allenic linkages have been isolated from microorganisms. One of the most interesting of these is *mycomycin*, which is produced by the fungus *Norcardia acidophilus*. The compound, which is extremely unstable, is the first naturally occurring substance found that owes its optical activity to an allenic group (page 128). A somewhat similar compound isolated from a fungus is *nemotinic acid*, which is also optically active and possesses antibiotic properties.

Mycomycin   Nemotinic acid

TABLE 24.3   *Alcoholic Components of Waxes*

Name	Structure	Source
Cetyl alcohol	$CH_3(CH_2)_{14}CH_2OH$	Sperm whale
n-Octacosanol	$CH_3(CH_2)_{26}CH_2OH$	Wheat
Oleyl alcohol	$CH_3(CH_2)_7CH=CH(CH_2)_7CH_2OH$	Sperm whale
Cocceryl alcohol	$CH_3(CH_2)_{18}CO(CH_2)_{13}CH_2OH$	Cochineal (a scale insect)

A number of other fatty acids carrying acetylenic linkages are found in the plant world. *Tariric, ximenynic,* and *erythrogenic* acids all contain at least one carbon-carbon triple bond.

$CH_3(CH_2)_{10}C≡C(CH_2)_4CO_2H$ $CH_3(CH_2)_5CH=CHC≡C(CH_2)_7CO_2H$ $CH_2=CH(CH_2)_4C≡CC≡C(CH_2)_7CO_2H$

      Tariric acid   Ximenynic acid   Erythrogenic acid

A group of branched-chain fatty acids that contain an odd number of carbon atoms have been isolated from strains of a tubercle bacillus. Examples are *tuberculostearic* and *mycolipenic acid,* both of which are optically active.

$$\overset{*}{CH_3(CH_2)_7}\underset{\underset{CH_3}{|}}{CH}(CH_2)_8CO_2H$$

$$CH_3(CH_2)_{17}\underset{\underset{CH_3}{|}}{CH}CH_2\underset{\underset{CH_3}{|}}{CH}CH=\underset{\underset{CH_3}{|}}{C}CO_2H$$

   Tuberculostearic acid   Mycolipenic acid

Isoprenoids

Isoprenoids are a family of natural products whose structures are composed of *isoprene* units. Although isoprene itself (see below) has not been encountered in nature, the biogenetic path of synthesis of the terpenes involves the incorporation of this C_5 repeating unit into a large variety of open and ring structures. The *terpenes* contain two of these units, *sesquiterpenes* three units, *diterpenes* four units, *triterpenes* six units, and *tetraterpenes* eight units. Natural rubber (Chap. 25) is a *polyterpene* of high molecular weight. Usually in the isoprenoids, the head of one isoprene unit is attached to the tail of the next, although a number of examples of head-to-head and tail-to-tail linkages are encountered.

$$Head \longrightarrow CH_2=\underset{\underset{CH_3}{|}}{C}CH=CH_2 \longleftarrow Tail$$

            Isoprene

Terpenes (C_{10} Compounds). Table 24.4 records the structures, names, and sources of representative terpenes found in nature. These volatile substances provide plants and flowers with much of their fragrance, and certain of them are used commercially in perfumes and flavors. Some of the terpenes were known in antiquity and were employed as medicines. Camphor (from the camphor tree) and α-pinene are among the commercially important terpenes. The former is used as a plasticizer in the manufacture of celluloid and photographic film base, and the latter is the chief component of turpentine (paint thinner).

TABLE 24.4   Representative Terpenes Found in Nature

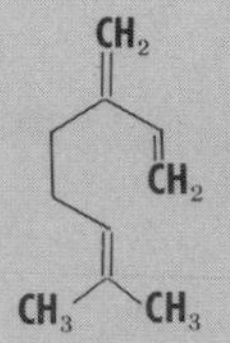

Myrcene
(bayberry)

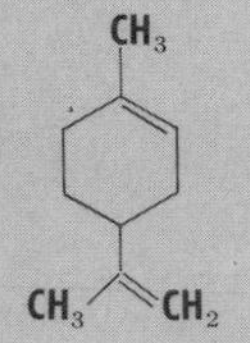

d-Limonene
(lemon, orange)

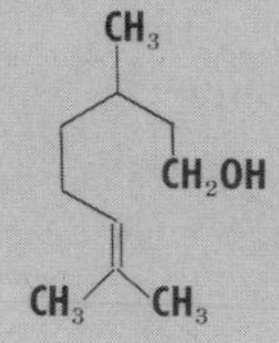

Citronellol
(rose oil)

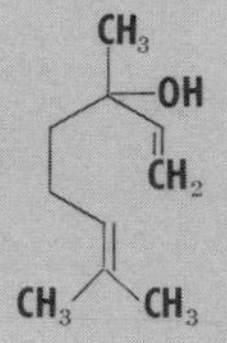

Linalool
(flowers of
ylang-ylang)

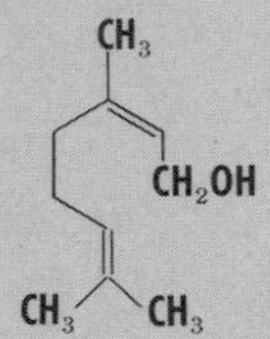

Geraniol
(gingergrass)

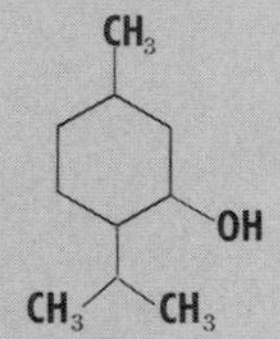

Menthol
(Japanese
peppermint oil)

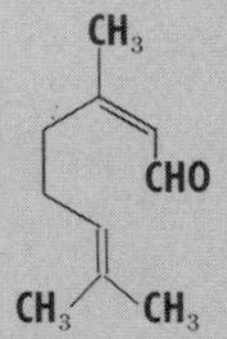

Citral
(oil of lemon grass)

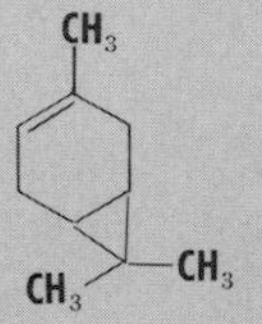

Δ^3-Carene
(oleoresin of
Pinus longifolia)

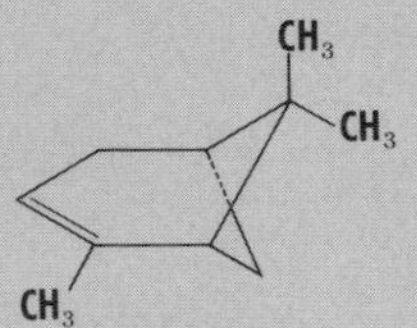

α-Pinene
(turpentine oil)

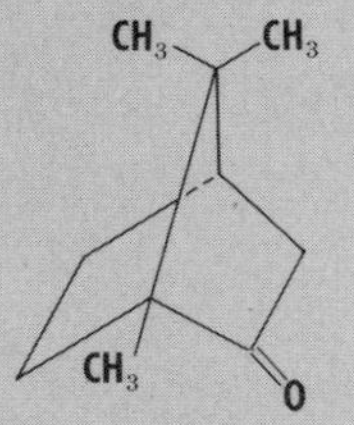

Camphor
(camphor tree)

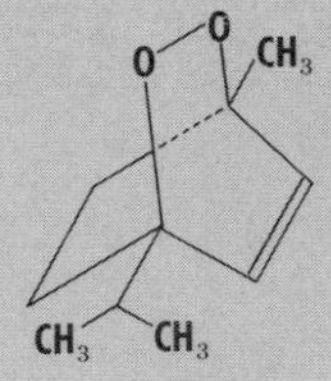

Ascaridole
(chenopodium
oil)

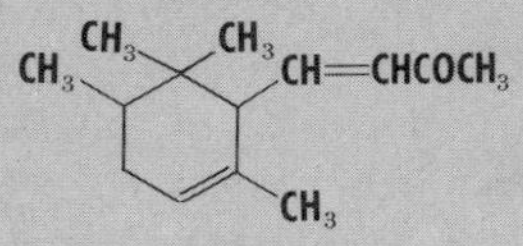

α-Irone, not a
true terpene
(violet)

The total synthesis of camphor is recorded in Fig. 24.2.   Many of the steps employed in this synthesis are condensation reactions.

A number of open-chain terpenes when heated with acid undergo ring closure to give other terpenes, as in the following example.

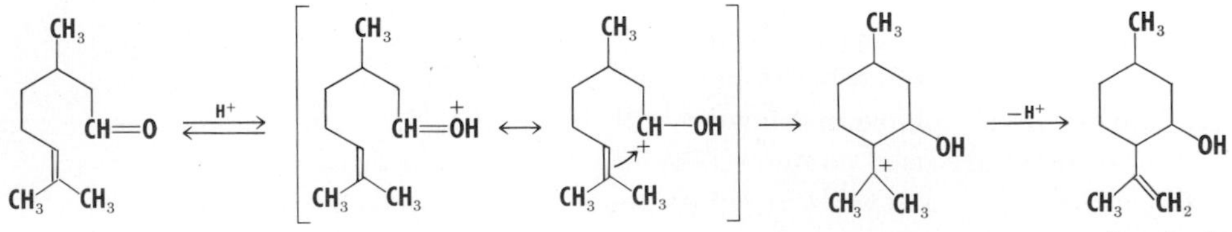

Citronellal

Isopulegol

Aromatization of the more plentiful terpenes provides such compounds as *p*-cymene, which can be oxidized to useful phenols (page 429).

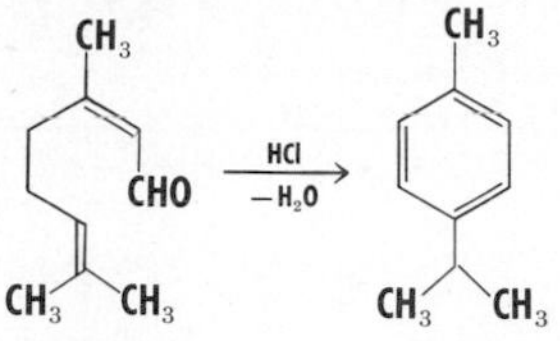
HCl
$-H_2O$

Citral   *p*-Cymene

Sesquiterpenes (C_{15} Compounds). Compounds of this group are composed of three isoprene units, which are arranged in enough different ways to provide open-chain monocyclic, dicyclic, and even tricyclic structures. The great variety of ring systems found in sesquiterpenes is illustrated in Table 24.5. Elucidation of the structures of these substances has led not only to the discovery of new organic reactions, but even to new aromatic systems (e.g., azulene). Some of the compounds (e.g., cedrol) have been synthesized.

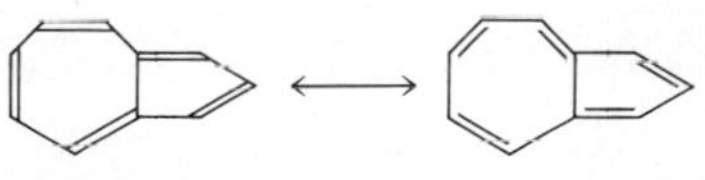

Azulene

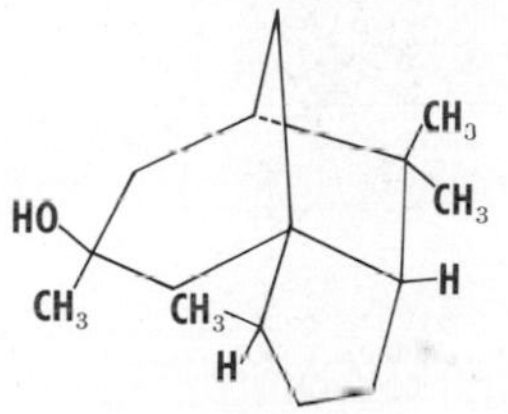

Cedrol

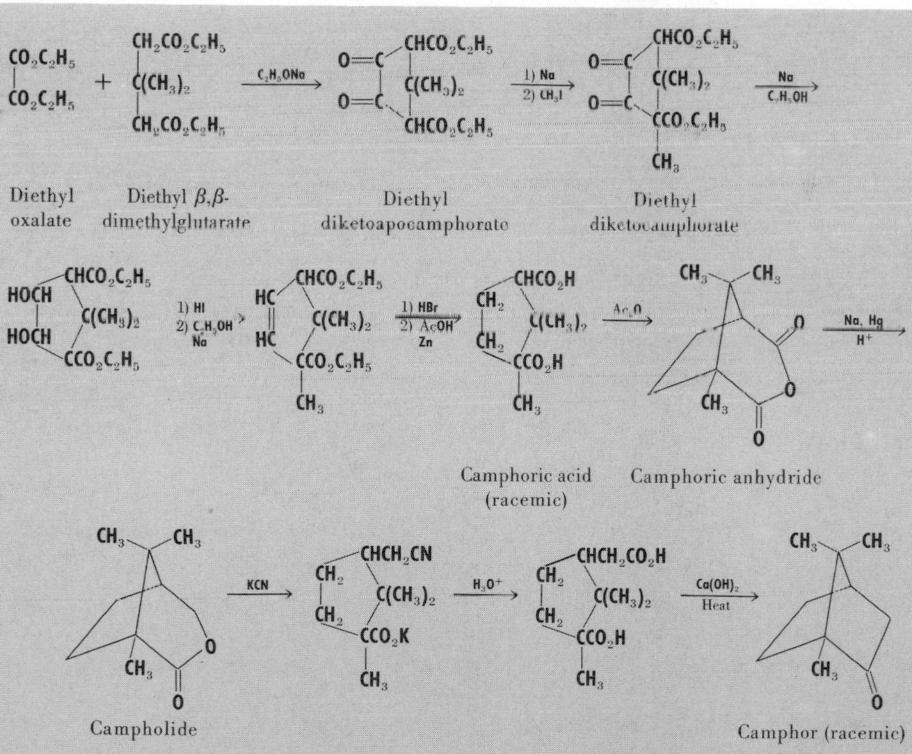
Diethyl oxalate
Diethyl β,β-dimethylglutarate
C_2H_5ONa
Diethyl diketoapocamphorate
1) Na
2) CH_3I
Diethyl diketocamphorate
Na
C_2H_5OH
1) HI
2) C_2H_5OH
Na
1) HBr
2) AcOH
Zn
Ac_2O
Camphoric acid (racemic)
Camphoric anhydride
Na, Hg
H^+
Campholide
KCN
H_3O^+
$Ca(OH)_2$
Heat
Camphor (racemic)

FIG. 24.2 Total synthesis of camphor.

TABLE 24.5   *Representative Naturally Occurring Sesquiterpenes*

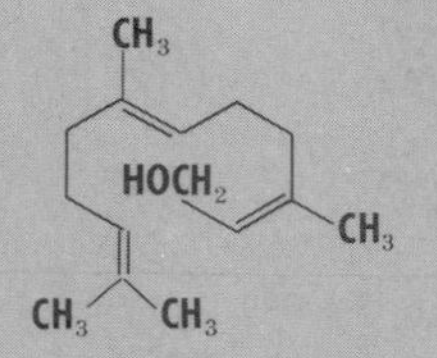

Farnesol
(ambrette-seed oil,
lily of the valley scent)

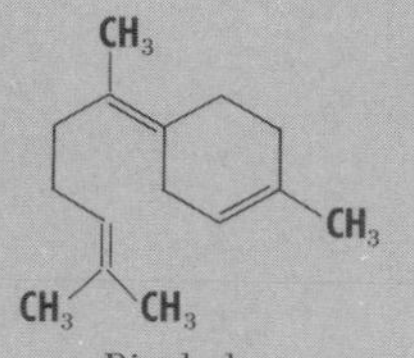

Bisabolene
(widely distributed
in many plants)

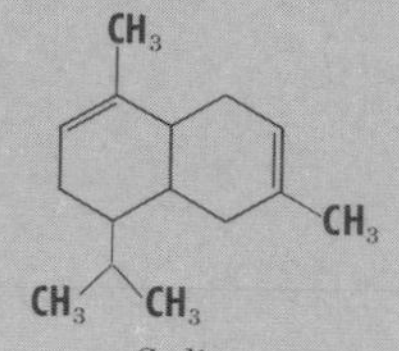

Cadinene
(oil of cade and
of cubebs)

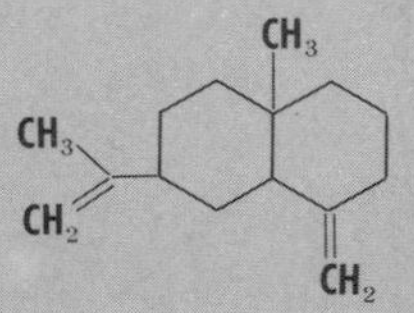

β-Selinene
(oil of celery)

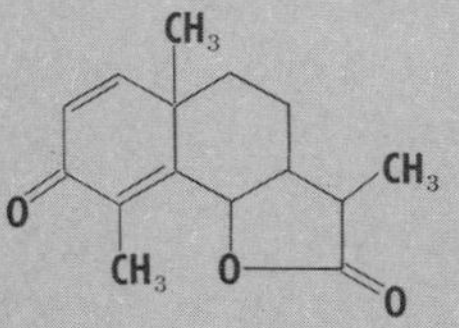

Santonin
(an anthelmintic from
species of *Artemisia*)

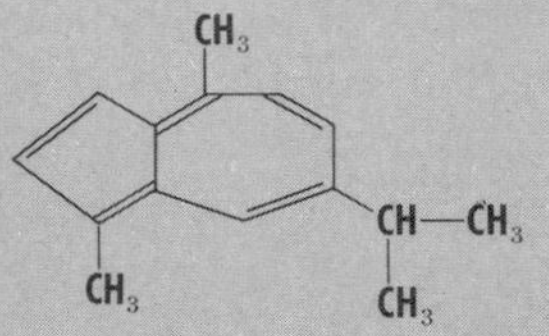

Guaiazulene
(geranium oil,
blue-violet color)

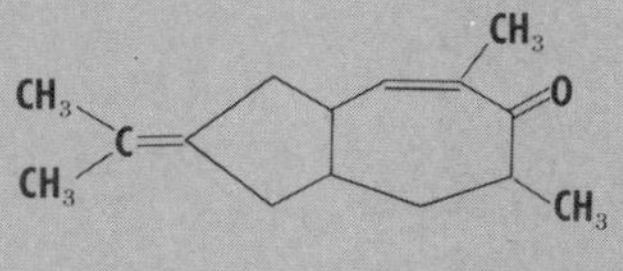

β-Vetivone
(vetiver oil)

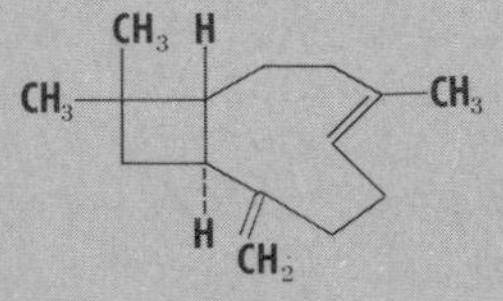

Caryophyllene
(oil of cloves)

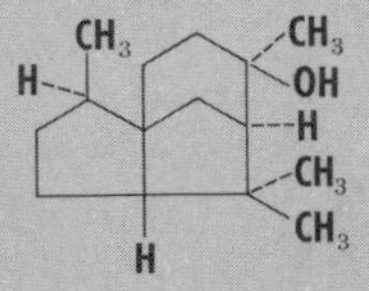

Cedrol
(cedar-wood oil)

Diterpenes (C$_{20}$ Compounds).   The diterpenes (four isoprene units) can have either cyclic or acyclic structures.   *Phytol* occurs as an ester of the porphyrin portion of the chlorophyll molecule (Fig. 21.2).   *Vitamin A,* which contains one ring and an isoprenoid side chain, is a fat-soluble substance found in fish oils, particularly in shark-liver oil.   The substance is required for normal eyesight and for the growth of mammals. The light-sensitive pigments which function in photoreception in the retina are synthesized in the body from the vitamin.   *Agathic acid* is one of the *resin acids.*   A second important resin acid is *abietic acid,* the most abundant component of rosin obtained from various species of pine.   Rosin is used in the manufacture of varnish; it is the component which imparts hardness and gloss to the dried film.

$$(CH_3)_2CHCH_2CH_2(CH_2CHCH_2CH_2)_2CH_2C\!=\!CHCH_2OH$$
$$\overset{|}{CH_3} \qquad\quad \overset{|}{CH_3}$$

Phytol

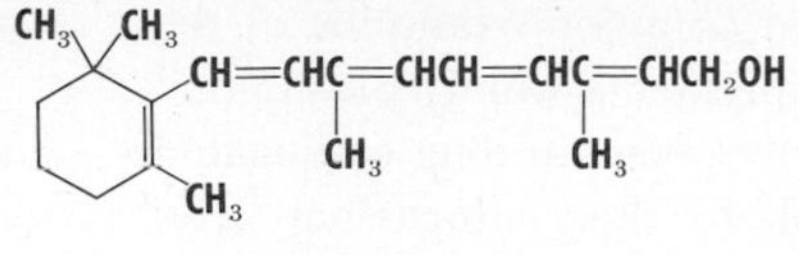

Vitamin A

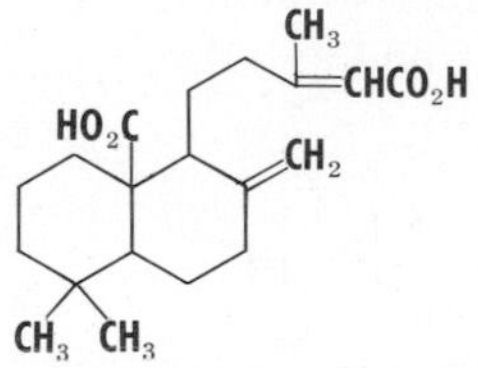

Agathic acid

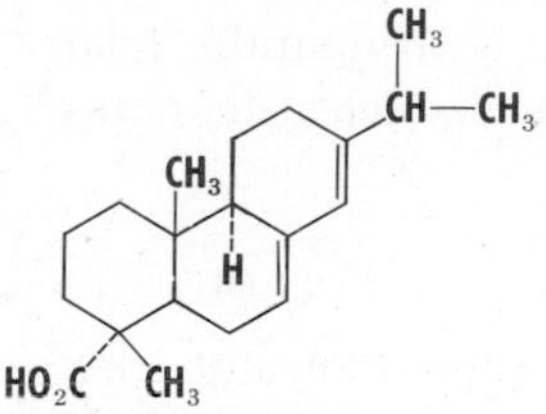

Abietic acid

Vitamin A was first synthesized in 1947 and is currently produced for use in vitamin preparations, both by synthesis and by extraction from shark liver. The synthesis was given in detail earlier (page 288) as an illustration of the repeated application of condensation reactions in a complex commercial process.

Triterpenes (C_{30} Compounds). Both open-chain and condensed-ring systems are found in triterpenes, which are composed of six isoprene units. *Squalene*, which has been isolated from the unsaponifiable fraction of shark-liver oils, possesses a structure that contains the skeleton of two farnesol (page 558) molecules fused head to head. *Ambrein* is one of the components of ambergris (substance excreted by the sperm whale) and is used in making perfumes. The compound possesses three six-membered rings out of the five possible that can be constructed from six isoprene units. *β-Amyrin*, from *Manila elemi*, contains the maximum number of rings, whereas *lupeol* has four six-membered and one five-membered ring. Most of the other triterpenes possess structures based on one or the other of these two ring systems.

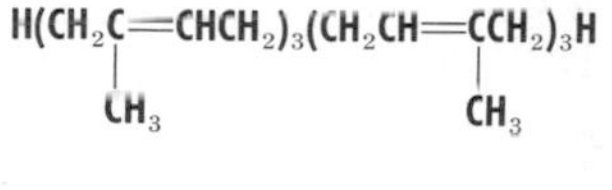

Squalene

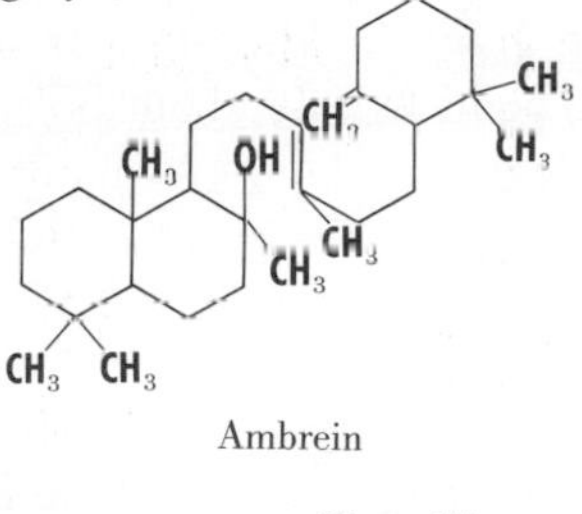

Ambrein

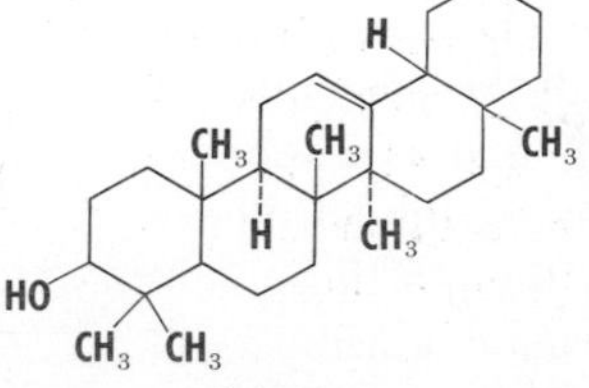

β-Amyrin

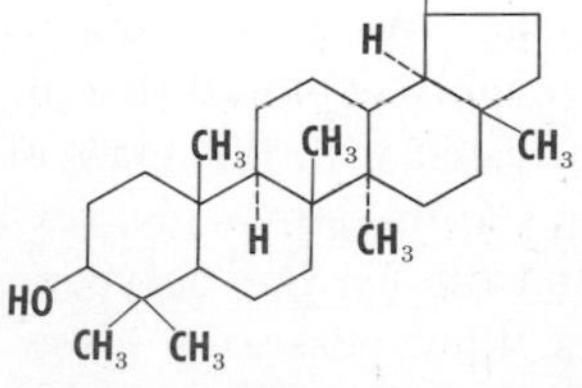

Lupeol

Tetraterpenes (C_{40} Compounds). The most common examples of the tetraterpenes are the carotenoids, which are pigments widely distributed in vegetables and animal fats. These substances contain long conjugated systems of double bonds, which are responsible for their color (Chap. 27). *Lycopene*, which contains no rings, is the red coloring matter of tomatoes and other fruit. This substance is structurally related to the carotenes, which provide the carrot with its characteristic orange color and are also found in green leaves.

$$CH_3 \quad CH_3 \quad\quad CH_3 \quad\quad CH_3 \quad\quad\quad CH_3 \quad\quad CH_3 \quad\quad CH_3 \quad CH_3$$
$$CH{=}CHC{=}CHCH{=}CHC{=}CHCH{=}CHCH{=}CCH{=}CHCH{=}CCH{=}CH$$
$$CH_3 \quad\quad\quad\quad\quad\quad\quad\quad\quad\quad\quad\quad\quad\quad\quad\quad\quad\quad\quad\quad\quad\quad\quad CH_3$$

Lycopene (red)

$$CH_3 \quad CH_3 \quad\quad CH_3 \quad\quad CH_3 \quad\quad\quad CH_3 \quad\quad CH_3 \quad\quad CH_3 \quad CH_3$$
$$CH{=}CHC{=}CHCH{=}CHC{=}CHCH{=}CHCH{=}CCH{=}CHCH{=}CCH{=}CH$$
$$CH_3 \quad\quad\quad\quad\quad\quad\quad\quad\quad\quad\quad\quad\quad\quad\quad\quad\quad\quad\quad\quad\quad\quad\quad CH_3$$

γ-Carotene (yellow)

$$CH_3 \quad CH_3 \quad\quad CH_3 \quad\quad CH_3 \quad\quad\quad CH_3 \quad\quad CH_3 \quad\quad CH_3 \quad CH_3$$
$$CH{=}CHC{=}CHCH{=}CHC{=}CHCH{=}CHCH{=}CCH{=}CHCH{=}CCH{=}CH$$
$$CH_3 \quad\quad\quad\quad\quad\quad\quad\quad\quad\quad\quad\quad\quad\quad\quad\quad\quad\quad\quad\quad\quad\quad\quad CH_3$$

β-Carotene (yellow)

Carotenoids are composed of two vitamin A units joined at the end of the molecule that carries the hydroxyl group. The relationship is more than formal, since the liver is able to convert the carotenoids into vitamin A, although the yield is only about 55% of theoretical in the case of β-carotene.

Steroids

Steroids are a family of compounds which contain the perhydro-1,2-cyclopentanophenanthrene ring system. The compounds of this group are widely distributed in plants and animals, and are among the most important natural products. As a consequence, the chemistry of the steroids has been so thoroughly explored that almost all the principles of the science could be illustrated with this class of compound as a vehicle. To this family belong the sterols, bile acids, sex hormones, the hormones of the adrenal cortex, and the cardiac aglycones. Although these substances are not terpenes, they possess a close biogenetic kinship with certain triterpenes, particularly squalene and *lanosterol*.

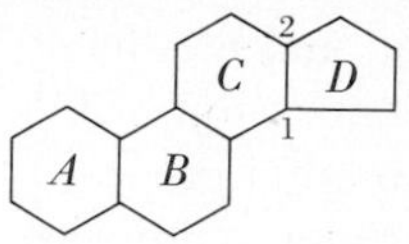

Perhydro-1,2-cyclopentanophenanthrene
ring system

Biogenesis of Cholesterol. Cholesterol is found in all tissues of animals, particularly in the brain, spinal cord, and in gallstones. The ring system is numbered as indicated in the following formula.

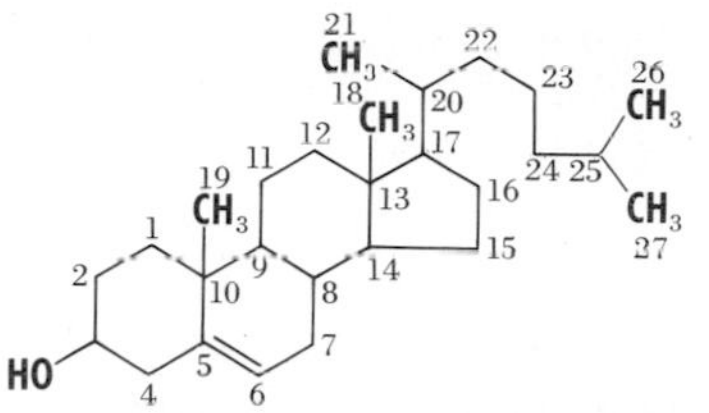

Cholesterol

The biogenesis of cholesterol has been extensively studied, and the results are summarized below. When $CH_3C^{14}O_2H$ and $C^{14}H_3CO_2H$ are fed to experimental animals, the cholesterol produced in the tissues of the animals is labeled with C^{14}. The origin (in terms of CH_3 and CO_2H of acetic acid) of most carbon atoms of cholesterol has been determined.

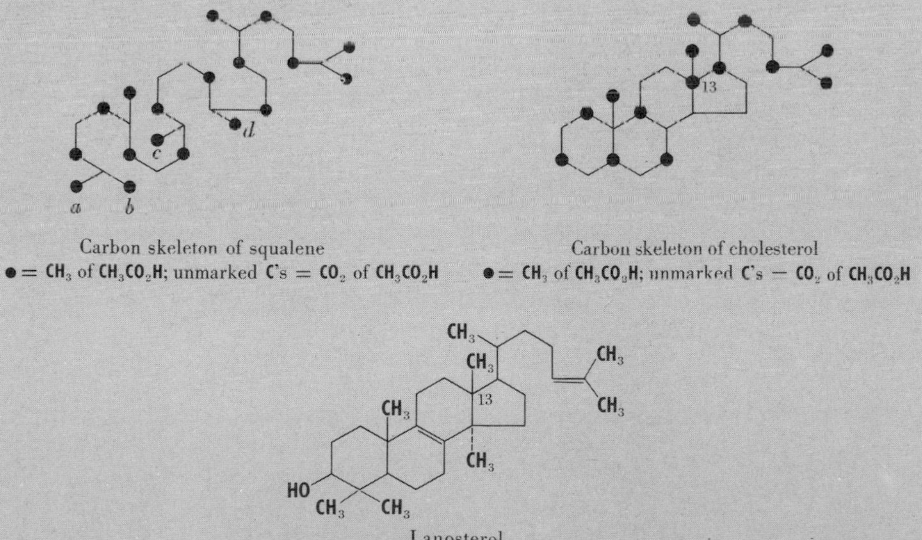

Carbon skeleton of squalene
● = CH_3 of CH_3CO_2H; unmarked C's = CO_2 of CH_3CO_2H

Carbon skeleton of cholesterol
● = CH_3 of CH_3CO_2H; unmarked C's = CO_2 of CH_3CO_2H

Lanosterol

FIG. 24.3 *Biogenesis of cholesterol.*

Squalene has also been derived from labeled acetic acid, and was found to be a cholesterol precursor through the biogenetic conversion of C^{14}-labeled squalene into cholesterol. In this conversion, methyl groups *a*, *b*, and *d* were probably lost from squalene, and methyl group *c* probably migrated to C-13 of cholesterol to provide the angular methyl group of the steroid. *Lanosterol* (found in wool fat) is also derived from squalene. Again, migration of one methyl group (group *c*) of squalene to the angular position at C-13 of lanosterol is required to provide a skeletal similarity between the two substances. Lanosterol has also been demonstrated to be a precursor of cholesterol. Thus the biogenetic sequence acetic acid ⟶ squalene ⟶ lanosterol ⟶ cholesterol has been established. Figure 24.3 indicates these relationships.

Sterols. Sterols possess a hydroxyl group at C-3, a double bond at C-5 (usually), and a side chain at C-17 of the perhydrocyclopentanophenanthrene nucleus. *Cholestanol* occurs in very small amounts in animal tissue, mixed with larger amounts of cholesterol. *Coprostanol*, which is the epimer (at C-5) of cholestanol, is found in the feces. Cholestanol and coprostanol are saturated steroids, and their configurations can be designated either with conventional plane projections or with conformational structures, as is indicated in Fig. 24.4.

The most common stereochemical variables in sterols are configurations of the C-3 hydroxyl and the mode of fusion of rings *A* and *B*. The hydroxyl at C-3 of sterols found in nature is cis to the angular methyl groups; this configuration is said to be *β*, and the opposite configuration is designated as *α*. The configuration of the side chain of naturally occurring steroids is usually *β*, and rings *B/C* and *C/D* are usually fused trans.

Although cholesterol is not found in the plant world, a number of closely related sterols, known as phytosterols, are encountered. Perhaps the most important of these is ergosterol, irradiation of which with ultraviolet light produces calciferol, or vitamin D_2. This substance is necessary for the normal growth of bones and teeth in mammals. Lack of the vitamin in the diet of children produces rickets, which is caused by faulty deposition of calcium phosphate in the growth of bones. Close relatives of vitamin D_2, with side chains similar to that of cholesterol, have been isolated from fish oils and from the skin of hogs.

Stigmasterol
(soybean oil)

β-Sitosterol
(wheat-germ oil)

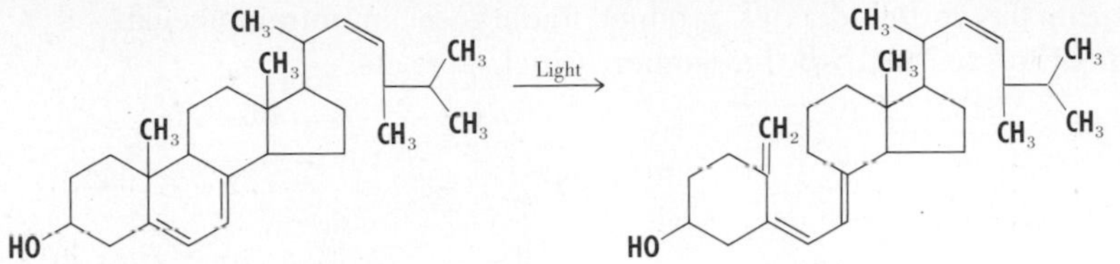

Ergosterol
(yeast)

Calciferol
(vitamin D$_2$)

The steric course of addition of bromine to the double bond of cholesterol serves to illustrate a number of stereoelectronic principles developed earlier. A positively charged bromonium ion (page 338) is formed by donation of a positive bromine atom to the double bond from the least sterically hindered side of the cholesterol molecule (rate-determining stage). In a second stage, the three-membered ring is opened by approach of a bromide ion to C-6 from the β-side. Only this reaction path provides a completely trans (diaxial) ring opening. The initial product is thermodynamically unstable compared to the equatorial-equatorial isomer, because the bulky bromines occupy the relatively hindered axial positions in the 5-α,6-β-isomer. When allowed to stand

Cholestanol
A/B ring fusion trans

Coprostanol
A/B ring fusion cis

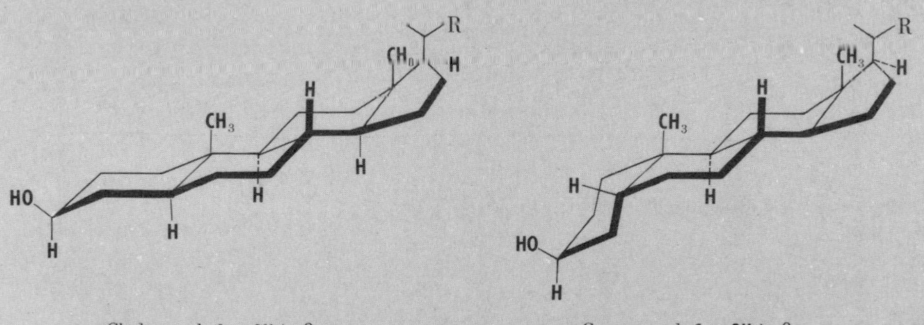

Cholestanol, C$_3$—OH is β or up

Coprostanol, C$_3$—OH is β or up

FIG. 24.4   *Configurations of cholestanol and coprostanol.*

in chloroform, the initial diaxial product undergoes an intramolecular rearrangement to give the 5-β,6-α-isomer, which persists.

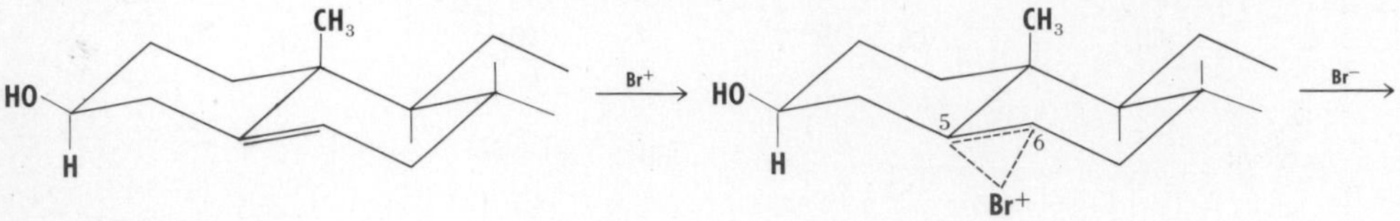

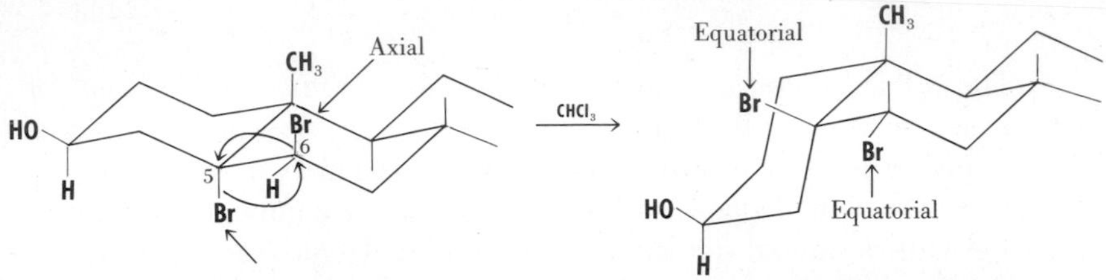

5-α,6-β-Cholesterol dibromide, initial and relatively unstable product

5-β,6-α-Cholesterol dibromide, final and relatively stable product

The fully trans arrangement of bromine atoms in 5-α,6-β-cholesterol dibromide facilitates the iodide-ion-catalyzed elimination of bromine from the molecule (page 401). The 5-β,6-α-isomer undergoes the reaction more slowly.

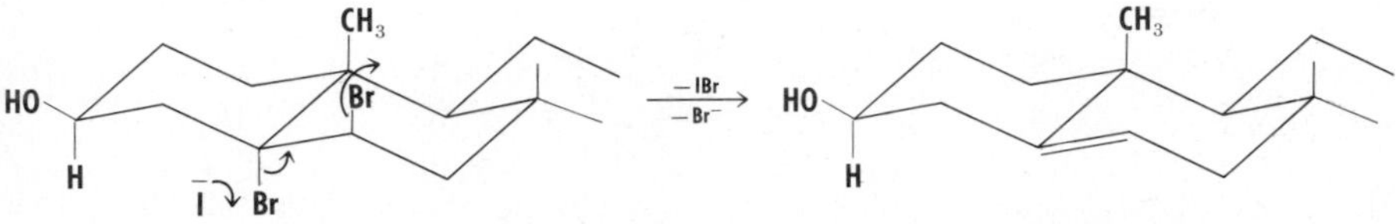

5-α,6-β-Cholesterol dibromide

Cholesterol

Bile Acids. Bile is an emulsifying agent generated by mammals, which aids the absorption of fats and other lipids into the body fluids. The substance is a mixture of amides derived from bile acids and the amino acids glycine ($H_2NCH_2CO_2H$) and taurine ($H_2NCH_2CH_2SO_3H$). Hydrolysis of these amides produces the bile acids, which contain a carboxyl group in the side chain of the steroid nucleus and varying numbers of hydroxyl groups in the 3-, 7-, and 12-positions of the ring system. These hydroxyl groups are invariably oriented α (below the plane of the page), and the *A/B* rings are fused cis. Cholic and desoxycholic are the most abundant bile acids.

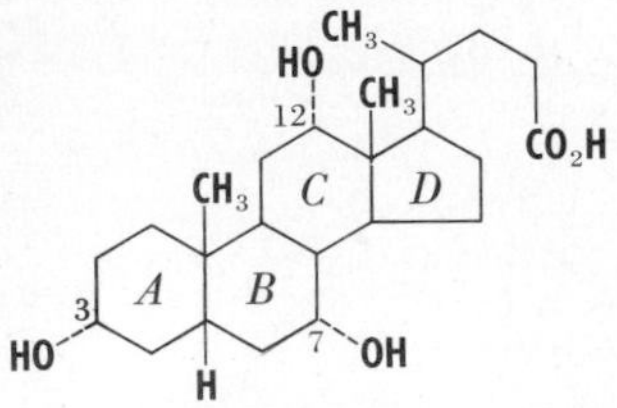

Cholic acid

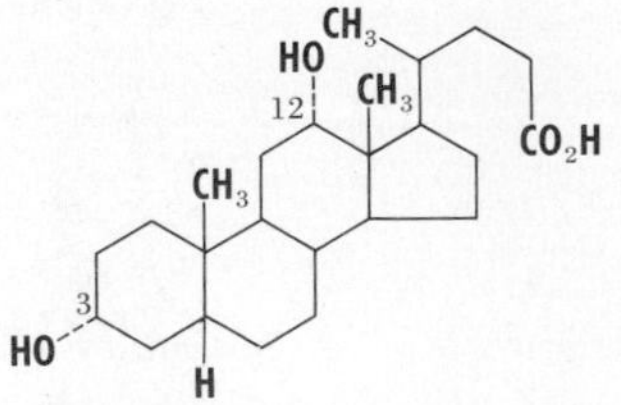

Desoxycholic acid

Conformational analysis (page 122) explains why acetylation occurs more easily with hydroxyl groups at **C**-3 of cholic acid than with those at **C**-7 and **C**-12. Equatorially oriented hydroxyl groups are less hindered than those in axial positions, and are therefore more easily attacked by acylating agents (page 310). Only the hydroxyl on **C**-3 of cholic acid occupies an equatorial position. Furthermore, the hydroxyl at **C**-7 is very much sterically hindered, because the cis fusion of rings *A* and *B* places one of the methylene groups of ring *A* axial and cis to this function.

Cholic acid

Sex Hormones. Sex hormones are steroids generated by the gonads (ovaries or testes) when stimulated by the peptide hormones, which are liberated to the blood stream by the anterior lobe of the pituitary gland. These steroids are responsible for development of sex characteristics and for sexual responses of male and female mammals. Female hormones are called *estrogens*, and male hormones, *androgens*. Both estrogens and androgens are produced by the adrenal glands of each species.

Of the estrogens, *estradiol* is the primary hormone, and *estrone* and *estratriol* are derived substances which also possess activity. The isolation of estradiol represents one of the feats of organic chemistry. Less than 12 mg of the compound was isolated from about 10,000 pounds of hog ovaries.

Estrone   Estradiol   Estratriol

A second type of hormone, called *progesterone*, is secreted by the *corpus luteum*, a tissue of the ovary. This hormone is involved in the preparation for and maintenance of pregnancy. Unlike the physiological activity of progesterone, which is limited to a few steroid molecules, estrogenic activity is found in many other types of compounds, among which are substituted stilbenes such as stilbestrol.

Progesterone   Stilbestrol

Male sex hormones (androgens) bear a structural resemblance to progesterone with respect to the character of the *A* and *B* rings, and to the estrogens with regard to substituents at C-17. *Testosterone* and *androsterone* are the prominent members of the group. Testosterone is excreted by the testes and is the primary hormone. Androsterone is produced from the primary hormone and is excreted in the urine. About 10 mg of testosterone was isolated from 100 kg of testes tissue of bulls.

Testosterone   Androsterone

Total Synthesis of Estrone. Since the isolation and determination of the structure of the steroids, one of the goals of the organic chemist has been the total synthesis of these compounds. This objective was achieved in a number of laboratories in the period from 1940 to 1955. One of the syntheses of estrone is recorded in Fig. 24.5 as an example of the application of many reactions treated earlier to the construction of a complex molecule. Only key steps are discussed.

Compound III, prepared by a Friedel-Crafts acylation reaction (page 375), was subjected to a Stobbe condensation (page 291) to give lactone IV. This substance underwent β-elimination (page 399) when treated first with base and then with acid. The resulting double bond was reduced, and the three carboxyl groups were esterified to give triester V. This compound was subjected to a Dieckmann condensation (page 324), and the β-ketoester produced was methylated directly (page 224) to give VI. When subjected to the Reformatsky reaction (page 295), VI gave VII, which underwent β-elimination when treated with formic acid. Dilute base selectively hydrolyzed the least hindered of the three ester functions (page 306), and the liberated carboxyl group was

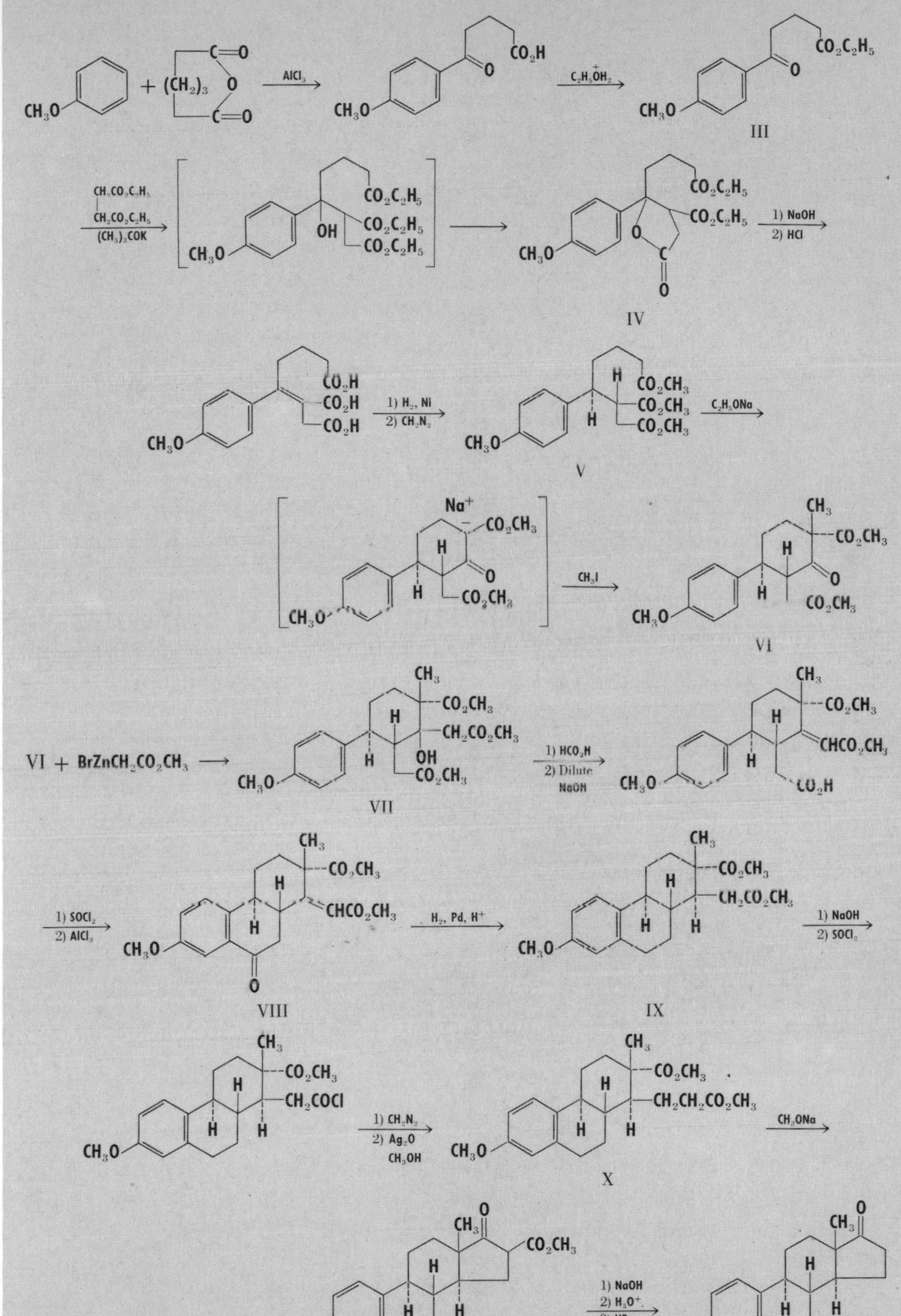

FIG. 24.5 *Total synthesis of estrone.*

converted to its acid chloride, which was cyclized (page 377) to give VIII.

The ketonic function of VIII was hydrogenolyzed to a methylene group (page 444), and the double bond was reduced to give IX, in which the four asymmetric carbon atoms possess the desired relative configurations. The less hindered ester function of IX was selectively hydrolyzed, and the product was subjected to an Arndt-Eistert reaction to give X. This diester was cyclized with a Dieckmann reaction to produce β-ketoester XI. Hydrolysis and decarboxylation (page 259) gave racemic methyl ether of estrone. This compound was demethylated (page 244) to produce racemic estrone, which was resolved through its *l*-menthoxyacetate to give optically active estrone, identical with the naturally occurring material.

Corticosteroids. Twenty-eight different steroids have been isolated from extracts of the adrenal cortex of various animals, and the structures of these substances have all been elucidated. Seven of the compounds are active in prolonging the life of adrenalectomized animals. These substances control the electrolyte balance and the metabolic formation of carbohydrate from protein in the body. *Desoxycorticosterone* is used in the treatment of Addison's disease, whereas *cortisone* and 17-*hydroxy-corticosterone* reduce inflammation in skin diseases and rheumatoid arthritis. The synthesis of cortisone and 17-hydroxycorticosterone from other, more available steroids not containing oxygen at C-11 was attended by great difficulty during the early research in this field. The biochemical oxidation of readily available progesterone by a species of mold (*Rhizopus*) was found to occur in yields of about 90%. This reaction is now utilized as a key step in the industrial production of many of these corticosteroids.

Desoxycorticosterone   Cortisone   17-Hydroxycorticosterone

Cardiac Glycosides. The cardiac glycosides possess the property of causing the muscles of the heart to contract, and in small amounts are used for treatment of certain heart ailments. The compounds occur naturally as glycosides in the seeds or leaves of the purple foxglove and constitute the active principles in the African arrow poisons from *Strophanthus* seeds. *Digitoxigenin* and *digoxigenin* are representative examples of the aglycone portion of these sugar derivatives.

Digitoxigenin   Digoxigenin

Problems

1. Draw the structures of the following compounds, and indicate in an appropriate way the isoprene units they contain.

a. Menthol
b. α-Pinene
c. Camphor
d. Farnesol

e. Santonin
f. Guaiazulene
g. Caryophyllene
h. Abietic acid

i. Vitamin A
j. β-Amyrin
k. β-Carotene

2. With compounds of up to six carbon atoms as starting materials, write syntheses of the following compounds:

a. Palmitic acid
b. Oleic acid

c. Duodecanedioic acid
d. Stilbestrol

3. Write conformational structures of cholestanol and coprostanol, and label each hydrogen, methyl, or hydroxyl group attached to every position of the six-membered rings as α or β and as *a* (axial) or *e* (equatorial).

4. Write conformational structures for the following compounds:

a. Stigmasterol
b. 7-β-Hydroxycoprostanol

c. Testosterone
d. Digitoxigenin

e. 11-α-Chlorocholestanol

5. Write a synthesis of the following substance, which might be used as an intermediate in steroid syntheses.

6. Indicate the steric structure of the product you would expect to obtain from the following reactions:

a. Epoxidation of a compound that possesses the structure of cholestanol except for a double bond in the 9,11-position.

b. Hydrolysis in strong acid of the above epoxide.

c. Bromination of a compound that contains the structure of coprostanol except for a double bond in the 9,11-position (give structure of the kinetically controlled product).

d. Treatment of digoxigenin with one mole of acetic anhydride in pyridine; with two moles of acetic anhydride in pyridine.

e. The Diels-Alder adduct of ergosterol with maleic anhydride.

7. Why do you suppose that most fatty acids contain an even number of carbon atoms?

8. Classify each reaction recorded in Figs. 24.1, 24.2, and 24.5 according to the schemes developed in Chaps. 10 to 20.

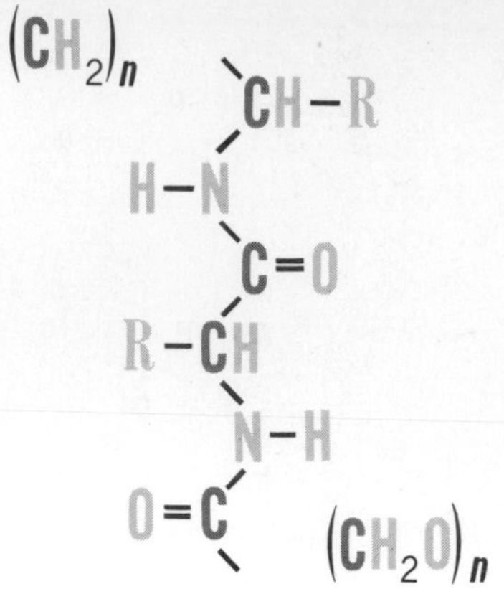

$$(CH_2)_n$$

$$CH-R$$

$$H-N$$

$$C=O$$

$$R-CH$$

$$N-H$$

$$O=C \quad (CH_2O)_n$$

25

Natural and Synthetic Polymers

The term *polymer*, in its purest sense, refers to a large molecule made by the addition of many molecular units to each other.

$$nA \longrightarrow A(-A-)_{n-2}A$$

Monomer   Polymer

Minor modifications of the meaning of the word have been made to include large molecules derived from some small monomer unit by condensation reactions in which some small molecule is eliminated. The following is a generalized example of condensation polymerization in which water is eliminated.

$$nB\text{-}(\text{-}OH)_2 \longrightarrow HO-B(-O-B-)_{n-2}BOH + (n-1)H_2O$$

Monomer   Polymer

In many polymers, the fundamental units are not all the same, but are two or more similar molecules. Such substances are called *copolymers* to distinguish them from *homopolymers*, which contain only one kind of fundamental unit.

$$nA + mC \longrightarrow (-A-C-A-C-C-A-)_{n+m}$$

Comonomers   Copolymer

The products of addition or condensation of small numbers of monomer units are designated by the use of Greek prefixes.

Monomer   A
Dimer   A—A
Trimer   A—A—A
Tetramer A—A—A—A
Pentamer A—A—A—A—A
          etc.

The importance of polymers in our life is almost breath-taking. Proteins and carbohydrates, which constitute two of the three principal classes of human foodstuffs, are natural polymers of high molecular weight. Natural rubber, synthetic elastomers (synthetic rubbers), plastics, synthetic fibers, and resins are all polymers whose uses reach into virtually every facet of our lives. The tonnage of polymers marketed by the American chemical industry exceeds by a wide margin the volume of all other synthetic organic chemicals.

Vinyl Polymers

A wide variety of vinyl monomers undergo *addition polymerization* to produce a wide variety of high polymers. Familiar products of vinyl polymerization include a variety of synthetic elastomers, Plexiglas, polystyrene, Orlon, and most of the ion-exchange resins. Natural rubber is a prototype of the class.

Natural Rubber. Natural rubber is a mixture of hydrocarbons having the empirical composition C_5H_8. Rubber is highly unsaturated, and careful study of the ozonolysis of rubber leaves little doubt that it is a linear polymer of isoprene $[CH_2{=}C(CH_3)CH{=}CH_2]$ in which the residual double bonds are located exclusively between C-2 and C-3 of the isoprene units. Although isoprene is not the biological precursor of rubber, the latter may be thought of as the product of the 1,4-addition polymerization of isoprene. Production of a synthetic material identical with natural rubber was first accomplished in 1955.

$$n CH_2{=}\overset{\overset{\displaystyle CH_3}{|}}{C}{-}CH{=}CH_2 \xrightarrow[\text{TiCl}_4]{[(CH_3)_2CHCH_2]_3Al} {-}({-}CH_2{-}\overset{\overset{\displaystyle CH_3}{|}}{C}{=}CHCH_2{-}){-}_n$$

The average molecular weight of rubber is estimated to be in the range of 60,000 to 350,000, which corresponds to a degree of polymerization (number of monomer units per molecule) of 1,000 to 5,000. The steric configuration of the polymer molecules has a critical effect upon their physical properties. All, or nearly all, olefinic linkages in rubber have the cis configuration.

$$\underset{\substack{\text{RCH}_2}}{\overset{\substack{\text{CH}_3}}{}}{\diagdown}C{=}C{\diagup}\underset{\substack{\text{CH}_2{-}\text{R}}}{\overset{\substack{\text{H}}}{}}$$

cis-Polyisoprene

Gutta-percha, a trans isomer of rubber, is horny rather than elastic. Hydrogenation of both polymers gives the same product. The difference in physical properties must, therefore, be associated with differences in the configurations about the double bonds in the natural polymers. Analysis of stretched rubber by X-ray diffraction shows that the polymer

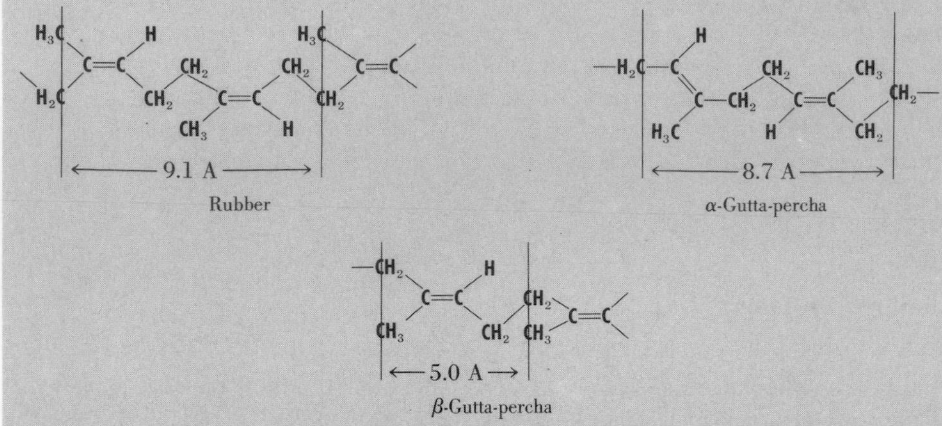

FIG. 25.1   Stereoisomers of polyisoprene.

has a repeat period of 8.2 A, whereas the two forms of gutta-percha have periods of 8.7 and 4.8 A. The short period of β-gutta-percha almost uniquely identifies that material as an all-trans polyisoprene. Figure 25.1 represents the molecules in extended configurations. The bond angles may appear unnaturally acute because some of the methylene groups are projected from above or below the principal plane.

Rubber latex, a colloidal suspension of rubber in water, occurs in the interstitial tubules of many plants, including the dandelion, golden-rod, and rubber tree. The tree is native to Brazil, but has been intro-duced into the former British colonies of the Far East. During World War II, interruption of the flow of rubber from the plantations of Ceylon, Indonesia, and the countries of the Malay Peninsula created a crisis for the Allied Nations that stimulated fervid effort to develop substitutes for rubber. While the early "synthetic rubbers" were inferior in many respects to natural rubber, synthetic elastomers have now been developed which are superior to natural rubber for many applications.

Coagulation of rubber latex by addition of acetic acid and salts gives *crepe* or *gum* rubber. The product must be fortified against air oxidation by addition of antioxidants (page 611).

Gum rubber does not have high tensile strength and becomes very brittle at low temperatures. The widespread use of rubber as an elastic structural material was made possible by development of the *vulcaniza-tion* process in 1839 by Charles Goodyear, who accidentally discovered that addition of sulfur to hot rubber causes changes which improve the physical properties in a spectacular manner. Vulcanization establishes *cross-links* between linear polymer chains. Cross-linking probably occurs both through saturation of double bonds and by way of coupling and addition reactions of **C—H** groups α to the double bonds.

$$-[-CH_2C(CH_3)=CHCH_2-]-_n$$

$$+ \ S \ \longrightarrow$$

$$-[-CH_2C(CH_3)=CHCH_2-]-_m$$

$$-[-CH_2C(CH_3)=CHCH-]-_n$$
$$|$$
$$-[-CH_2C(CH_3)-CHCH_2-]-_m$$
$$|$$
$$S$$
$$|$$

Soft rubber contains about 1 to 2% sulfur, and *hard rubber*, which has lost most of its plasticity, contains up to 35% sulfur, enough to effect complete saturation of the rubber if all cross-linking occurred by addition.

Initiation of Polymerization. Polymerization of vinyl monomers occurs in the presence of small amounts of a wide variety of reagents known as *initiators.* Since initiators are often destroyed, it is not proper to refer to the substances as catalysts, although the latter term is sometimes used. Initiators are believed to form some reactive species, such as an ion or a free radical, which can add to carbon-carbon double bonds to form a new ion or radical which can, in turn, add to another unit. Various polymerization processes are most easily described in terms of the chemical nature of the *growing polymer chains.*

Free-radical Polymerization. The most widely used initiators are those which produce reactive free radicals at a controllable rate. There are three principal classes of free-radical initiators:

1. Compounds, such as peroxides and certain azo compounds, which undergo thermal decomposition at temperatures not far above room temperature.

$$(CH_3)_3COOC(CH_3)_3 \ \xrightarrow{100-130°} \ 2(CH_3)_3CO\cdot$$

Di-*tert*-butyl   *tert*-Butoxy
peroxide   radical

$$\overset{CN}{\underset{|}{}} \quad \overset{CN}{\underset{|}{}}$$
$$(CH_3)_2CN=NC(CH_3)_2 \ \xrightarrow{60-100°} \ 2(CH_3)_2\overset{\cdot}{C}CN + N_2$$

Azo-*bis*-isobutyronitrile   2-Cyano-2-propyl radical

2. *Photosensitizers* which, on the absorption of light, decompose or react with other molecules to give radicals.

$$(CH_3)_2C=O \ \xrightarrow[light]{Ultraviolet} \ (CH_3)_2C=O^*$$
(Excited state of acetone)

$$(CH_3)_2C=O^* + R-H \ \longrightarrow \ (CH_3)_2\overset{\cdot}{C}OH + R\cdot$$
Hydrogen
atom
donor

3. *Redox systems* in which a one-electron transfer reaction, often involving a metal ion, produces reactive radicals.

$$Fe^{++} + H_2O_2 \ \longrightarrow \ Fe^{3+} + OH^- + \cdot OH$$

Chain initiation:

$ROOR \xrightarrow{100°} 2RO\cdot$

$RO\cdot + CH_2{=}CHO_2CCH_3 \longrightarrow ROCH_2\overset{\cdot}{C}HO_2CCH_3$

     Vinyl acetate

Chain propagation:

$RO{-}(-CH_2\overset{\cdot}{C}H{-})_n CH_2\overset{\cdot}{C}HO_2CCH_3 + CH_2{=}CHO_2CCH_3 \longrightarrow RO{-}(-CH_2CH{-})_{n+1}CH_2\overset{\cdot}{C}HO_2CCH_3$

    O_2CCH_3 O_2CCH_3

                           $(R\cdot)$

Chain termination:

$2R\cdot \longrightarrow R{-}R$

FIG. 25.2 *Peroxide-initiated polymerization of vinyl acetate.*

Figure 25.2 shows an example of peroxide-initiated polymerization.

Although free radicals are highly reactive and short-lived, they show a high degree of selectivity in some reactions. For example, a high degree of order is found in the structure of all vinyl polymers, which indicates that addition virtually always occurs in the sense:

$R\cdot + CH_2{=}CHX \longrightarrow RCH_2\overset{\cdot}{C}HX$

rather than in the opposite sense:

$R\cdot + CH_2{=}CHX \longrightarrow RCHX\overset{\cdot}{C}H_2\cdot$

This is, of course, the same observation as was made concerning the addition of reagents such as **HBr** to olefins by the free-radical mechanism (page 347).

Various other reactions of free radicals can compete with the addition reaction. Such side reactions may involve the monomer, the polymer, or foreign additives and impurities. "Side reactions" may have a spectacular influence on the course of a polymerization and are often used to control polymer properties and monomer stability.

Inhibitors are substances which degrade growing radicals to inactive products. Each time such a reaction occurs a growing chain is terminated. Common inhibitors are oxygen, iodine, quinones, and polycyclic aromatic hydrocarbons. Typical inhibitor action is that of benzoquinone.

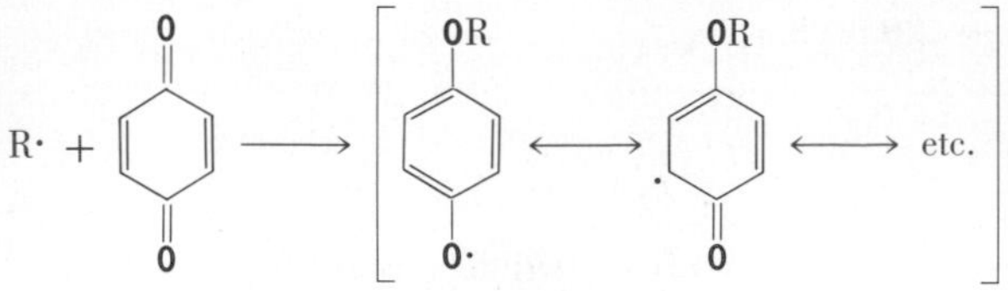

Benzoquinone   Resonance-stabilized radical
             incapable of adding to
               monomer

$$2 \quad \underset{\text{O·}}{\overset{\text{OR}}{\bigcirc}} \quad \longrightarrow \quad \text{inert products}$$

Most vinyl monomers are stored with small amounts of added inhibitors to protect them against premature polymerization. Slow oxidation of monomers, which produces peroxides (cf. hydrocarbon oxidation, page 611), is a source of initiators that cause polymerization during storage. As a consequence, antioxidants, which are not effective polymerization inhibitors in the absence of oxygen, are often used to stabilize monomers. Polymerization of a monomer containing an inhibitor is characterized by an *induction period* during which little or no polymerization occurs. After all the inhibitor has been destroyed, polymerization assumes its normal course. Stabilizers are usually removed before polymerization is initiated.

Chain-transfer agents are molecules that can react with growing chains to interrupt the growth of a particular chain. The products, however, are radicals capable of adding to a monomer to start the growth process again. The over-all effect is to reduce the average molecular weight of the polymer without reducing the polymerization rate. The chain-transfer agents commonly used to regulate the molecular weight of commercial polymers include carbon tetrachloride, mercaptans, and toluene.

$$R· + CCl_4 \longrightarrow RCl + Cl_3C· \xrightarrow{\text{CH}_2=\text{CHX}} Cl_3CCH_2\dot{C}HX$$

$$R· + R'SH \longrightarrow RH + R'S· \xrightarrow{\text{CH}_2=\text{CHX}} R'SCH_2\dot{C}HX$$

$$R· + C_6H_5CH_3 \longrightarrow RH + C_6H_5CH_2· \xrightarrow{\text{CH}_2=\text{CHX}} C_6H_5CH_2CH_2\dot{C}HX$$

Copolymerization occurs when a mixture of two or more monomers polymerizes, so that units from each monomer enter the same polymer chain. Such a copolymer has properties quite different from those of mixtures of the individual *homopolymers* (polymer from a single monomer). The high selectivity of free radicals is reflected in the preferences shown by growing radicals in a copolymerization. For example, maleic anhydride, which will not form a homopolymer, gives high-molecular-weight copolymers with styrene, butadiene, and vinyl acetate. In the copolymers, there is a nearly perfect alternation of monomer units.

$$\left(\begin{array}{c} -\text{CH}-\text{CH}_2-\text{CH}-\text{CH}- \\ | \qquad \qquad | \qquad | \\ \text{C}_6\text{H}_5 \quad \text{O}=\text{C} \quad \text{C}=\text{O} \\ \diagdown \ \diagup \\ \text{O} \end{array} \right)_x$$

Styrene-maleic anhydride copolymer

Growing radicals with maleic anhydride "ends" add preferentially to styrene, and styryl-terminated radicals add more rapidly to the anhydride than to styrene.

$$\text{RCH—}\overset{\cdot}{\text{CH}} + \text{C}_6\text{H}_5\text{CH}=\text{CH}_2 \longrightarrow \text{RCH—CH—CH}_2\overset{\cdot}{\text{CHC}}_6\text{H}_5$$

$$\text{RCH}_2\overset{\cdot}{\text{CHC}}_6\text{H}_5 + \text{CH}=\text{CH} \longrightarrow \text{RCH}_2\text{CH—CH—CH}\cdot$$

Cationic Polymerization. Strong acids cause polymerization of a number of vinyl monomers. The growing chains are carbonium ions, and the growing ends are probably closely associated with anions. Initiators that are most commonly used are Lewis acids, such as boron trifluoride, stannic chloride, or aluminum chloride, assisted by a small amount of promoter, such as water (see the discussion of Lewis acid cocatalysts on page 602). Polymerization of isobutene to give the product known as *butyl rubber* is a typical example.

$$\text{BF}_3 + \text{H}_2\text{O} \rightleftharpoons \text{HO}\overset{-}{\text{BF}}_3 \ \overset{+}{\text{H}}$$

$$\text{HO}\overset{-}{\text{BF}}_3 \ \overset{+}{\text{H}} + (\text{CH}_3)_2\text{C}=\text{CH}_2 \longrightarrow (\text{CH}_3)_3\overset{+}{\text{C}} \ \text{F}_3\overset{-}{\text{B}}\text{OH} \ \xrightarrow{n(\text{CH}_3)_2\text{C}=\text{CH}_2}$$

$$(\text{CH}_3)_3\text{C}\left(-\text{CH}_2\underset{\underset{\text{CH}_3}{|}}{\overset{\overset{\text{CH}_3}{|}}{\text{C}}}-\right)_{n+1}\text{CH}_2\overset{+}{\text{C}}-\text{CH}_3 \ \text{F}_3\overset{-}{\text{B}}\text{OH} \longrightarrow (\text{CH}_3)_3\left(-\text{CH}_2\underset{\underset{\text{CH}_3}{|}}{\overset{\overset{\text{CH}_3}{|}}{\text{C}}}-\right)_{n+1}\text{CH}_2\text{C}=\text{CH}_2 + \text{BF}_3 + \text{H}_2\text{O}$$

Isobutene, styrene, butadiene, and vinyl ethers are converted to high polymers by acid catalysis, but the process is not nearly as general as radical polymerization. The close relationship of cationic polymerization to acid-catalyzed additions and rearrangements (Chaps. 15 and 20) is worthy of note.

Anionic Polymerization. Strong bases initiate polymerization of vinyl compounds that bear electron-withdrawing substituents. The reaction is closely akin to nucleophilic addition reactions of the same monomers (Chap. 13). In the absence of proton-donor solvents, chain growth can occur.

$$\overset{-}{\text{B}}\text{:} + \text{CH}_2=\text{CHX} \longrightarrow \text{BCH}_2\overset{-}{\text{CHX}} \xrightarrow{\text{CH}_2=\text{CHX}} \text{BCH}_2\text{CHCH}_2\overset{-}{\text{CHX}} \longrightarrow$$
$$\overset{|}{\text{X}}$$

$$\text{B}(\text{CH}_2\text{CH})_n\text{CH}_2\overset{-}{\text{CHX}} \xrightarrow[\text{termination steps}]{\text{Chain}} \text{polymer}$$
$$\underset{\text{X}}{|}$$

Details of anionic polymerization have received little attention because there are few examples of useful applications. Molecular weights of products are low, although careful study could, perhaps, lead to significant improvements. Acrylonitrile, α,β-unsaturated esters and ketones, and conjugated nitroolefins all undergo the reaction in the presence of bases. Polymerization of vinylidene cyanide [CH_2=$C(CN)_2$] is initiated by traces of water, which demonstrates the remarkable "acidity" of the olefin.

The term π acid has been applied to alkenes and aromatic compounds heavily substituted by electron-withdrawing groups. The compounds react readily with nucleophilic reagents and form molecular complexes with "π bases." The latter are unsaturated compounds substituted with electron-donating substituents. 1,3,5-Trinitrobenzene is a strong π acid, and tetracyanoethylene is said to be the strongest π acid known.

Organometallic Polymerization. Recently a new group of polymerization initiators have been developed which are mixtures of organometallic compounds. The first were mixtures of alkali metal alkyls with various salts and alkoxides. Developed by Morton, the initiators are known as *alfin catalysts.* More important are the initiators first announced by Ziegler. These new "catalysts" are prepared by mixing aluminum alkyls (R_3Al) with various metal halides. In nearly all published work, the cocatalyst mentioned is titanium tetrachloride. Ziegler initiators accomplish some very dramatic new polymerizations, including low-temperature polymerization of ethylene and polymerization of propylene. In addition, the new initiators produce crystalline (page 591) polymers from monomers such as styrene and propylene.

Little is yet known of the mechanism of organometallic polymerization. It is possible that the addition step should be regarded as a Lewis acid–Lewis base attack on alkene groups. In the following equation, the M's refer to metal compounds.

$$M_1 \text{—} R \quad C\text{=}C \quad M_2 \longrightarrow \overset{+}{M_1} \; R\text{—}C\text{—}C\text{—}\overset{-}{M_2}$$

Lewis base   Lewis
(R^- donor)   acid

As most Ziegler systems contain suspended solids, addition may well occur through the agency of two metal atoms located on solid surfaces. Almost any terminal alkene (C=CH_2) can be polymerized by Ziegler initiators. Functional groups interfere with the action of the catalysts which are most effective in alkene polymerization. Monomers that bear functional groups polymerize in the presence of other organometallic initiators, many of which have not yet been thoroughly described in the literature. It was through the agency of a Ziegler system that the first synthetic all-cis polyisoprene was prepared. More recently, the natural rubber structure has also been reproduced by polymerization of isoprene by metallic lithium.

Condensation Polymers

Polyesters, polyamides, and *polyethers,* and products of the condensation of formaldehyde with amines and reactive aromatic substrates are the common condensation polymers. Not all the products are actually made by condensation reactions.

$$(n + 2)\text{HO(CH}_2)_5\text{CO}_2\text{H} \xrightarrow{\text{H}^+, \Delta} \text{HO(CH}_2)_5\overset{\text{O}}{\underset{}{\text{C}}}\left[-\text{O(CH}_2)_5\overset{\text{O}}{\underset{}{\text{C}}}-\right]_n -\text{O(CH}_2)_5\text{CO}_2\text{H} + n\text{H}_2\text{O}$$

$$(n + 1)\text{HOCH}_2\text{CH}_2\text{OH} + (n + 1)\text{HO}_2\text{C(CH}_2)_4\text{CO}_2\text{H} \xrightarrow{\text{H}^+, \Delta}$$

Ethylene Adipic
glycol acid

$$\text{HOCH}_2\text{CH}_2-\left[-\overset{\text{O}}{\text{OC(CH}_2)_4}\overset{\text{O}}{\text{COCH}_2\text{CH}_2}-\right]_n-\overset{\text{O}}{\text{OC(CH}_2)_4}\text{CO}_2\text{H} + n\text{H}_2\text{O}$$

The best known of the polyesters is an ethylene glycol-terephthalic acid polyester, which is spun into a fiber called Dacron. The polymer is made by transesterification of diethyl terephthalate with ethylene glycol. Direct esterification is unsuitable, because of the insolubility of terephthalic acid.

$$\text{HOCH}_2\text{CH}_2\text{OH} + \text{C}_2\text{H}_5\overset{\text{O}}{\text{OC}}-\bigcirc-\overset{\text{O}}{\text{COC}_2\text{H}_5} \xrightarrow{\text{H}^+}$$

Diethyl terephthalate

$$\text{HOCH}_2\text{CH}_2\text{O}-\left[-\overset{\text{O}}{\text{C}}-\bigcirc-\overset{\text{O}}{\text{COCH}_2\text{CH}_2\text{O}}-\right]_n-\overset{\text{O}}{\text{C}}-\bigcirc-\text{CO}_2\text{C}_2\text{H}_5 + n\text{C}_2\text{H}_5\text{OH}$$

Dacron

Polyamides, which include nylon, the granddaddy of all synthetic fibers, are made by techniques similar to those used in the synthesis of polyesters.

$$(n + 1)\text{HN}_2(\text{CH}_2)_6\text{NH}_2 + (n + 1)\text{HO}_2\text{C(CH}_2)_4\text{CO}_2\text{H} \longrightarrow (n + 1) \text{ Salt} \xrightarrow{\Delta}$$

$$\text{H}_2\text{N(CH}_2)_6\text{NH}-\left[-\overset{\text{O}}{\text{C(CH}_2)_4}\overset{\text{O}}{\text{CNH(CH}_2)_6\text{NH}}-\right]_n-\overset{\text{O}}{\text{C(CH}_2)_4}\text{CO}_2\text{H} + n\text{H}_2\text{O}$$

Nylon

Polyamides can also be made from ω-amino acids or by a ring-opening reaction of lactams.

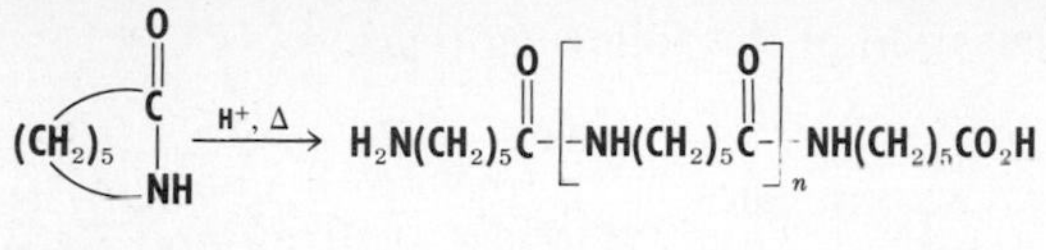

$$\underset{\varepsilon\text{-Caprolactam}}{(CH_2)_5 \overset{O}{\underset{NH}{\overset{\|}{\underset{|}{C}}}}} \xrightarrow{H^+, \Delta} H_2N(CH_2)_5 \overset{O}{\overset{\|}{C}} \left[-NH(CH_2)_5 \overset{O}{\overset{\|}{C}} - \right]_n NH(CH_2)_5CO_2H$$

Polyethers are, in principle, derived from glycols, but they are usually made by polymerization of cyclic ethers. Ethylene oxide is a particularly important monomer, which undergoes polymerization in the presence of either acids or bases.

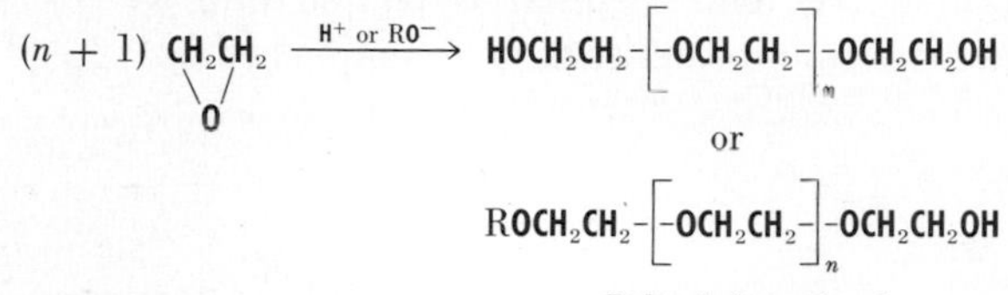

$$(n + 1) \underset{O}{CH_2CH_2} \xrightarrow{H^+ \text{ or } RO^-} HOCH_2CH_2 \left[-OCH_2CH_2 - \right]_m -OCH_2CH_2OH$$

or

$$ROCH_2CH_2 \left[-OCH_2CH_2 - \right]_n -OCH_2CH_2OH$$

Polyethylene glycol

Urea and polyfunctional amides condense with formaldehyde to form an important class of resins that are thermosetting materials. The reactants condense to form linear polymers, which form infinite networks on heating. Such plastics are called *thermosetting*, since the fluid material is heated in a mold to form an infusible product.

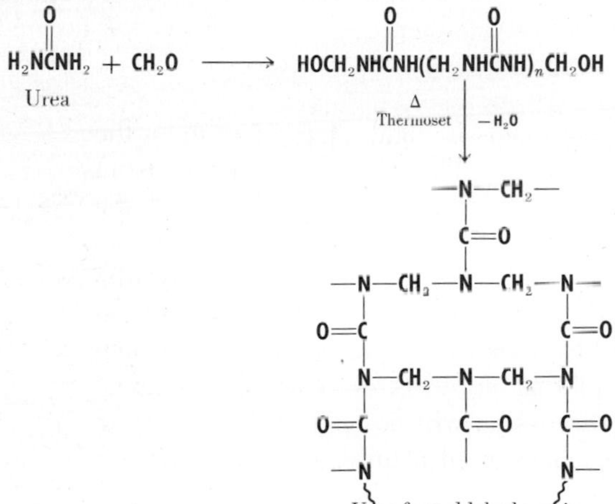

$$\underset{Urea}{H_2N\overset{O}{\overset{\|}{C}}NH_2} + CH_2O \longrightarrow HOCH_2NH\overset{O}{\overset{\|}{C}}NH(CH_2NH\overset{O}{\overset{\|}{C}}NH)_nCH_2OH$$

$$\Delta \bigg\downarrow -H_2O$$
Thermoset

Urea-formaldehyde resin

Phenol and its derivatives also copolymerize with aldehydes to form useful resins. The best known is Bakelite, produced from phenol itself and formaldehyde. The course of reaction is fairly well understood. Condensation first occurs to give hydroxymethyl phenols.

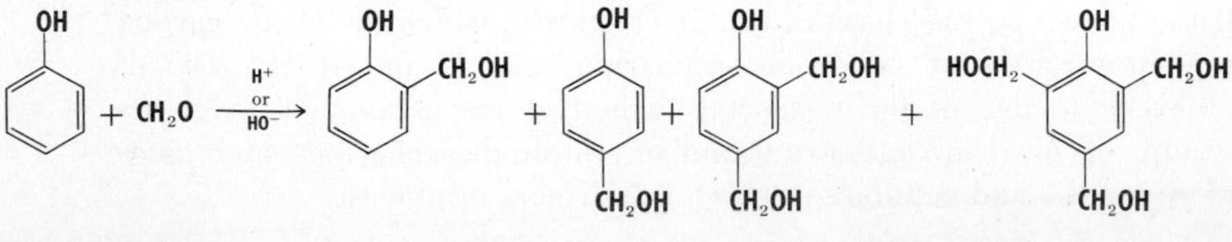

Acid catalysts cause further condensation of the following type:

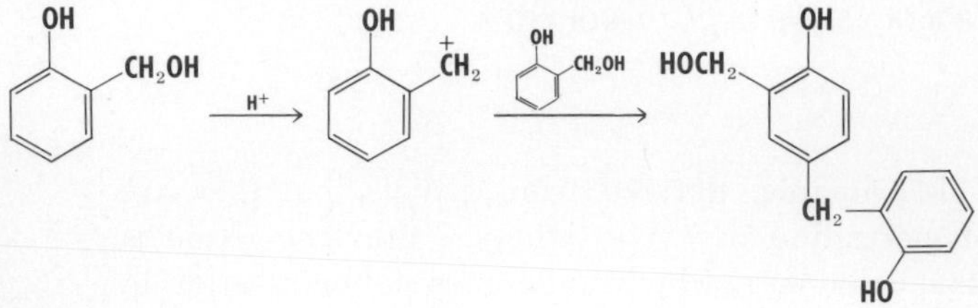

At a low degree of polymerization the fluid material is poured into a mold. The final cure to produce an infinite network is accomplished by heating.

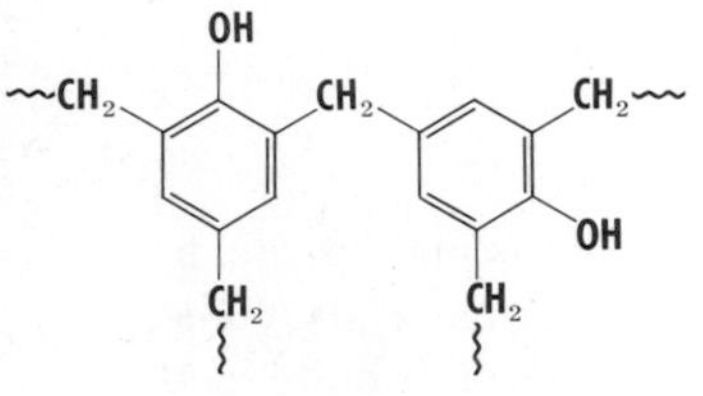

Phenol-formaldehyde resin

Natural Polymers

The physical form of living organisms is highly dependent upon the physical properties of natural polymers. The plant world depends in large part upon polymeric carbohydrates for rigid structures, and the muscle tissue of animals is based largely upon the basic protein structure, which is polymeric in nature. Furthermore, many critical life-substances, such as nucleic acids and viruses, are high-molecular materials. No attempt will be made to present a comprehensive description of such materials or to discuss the fascinating subjects of their physiological function and biogenetic origin. Discussion will be restricted to the most obvious features of the chemical structures of natural polymers.

Polysaccharides

Polymeric carbohydrates are familiar natural products which include cellulose, starch, and glycogen (the carbohydrate stored in animal livers). All the known polysaccharides are glycosides in which the acetal carbon atom (page 504) of one monosaccharide unit is linked by way of an oxygen to one of the nonacetal carbon atoms of another monosaccharide. Typical linkages are found in simple disaccharides such as α- and β-maltose and cellobiose, which are dimers of glucose.

α-Glucose   β-Glucose

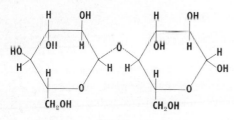

α-Maltose
(4-[α-D-Glucosyl]-α-D-glucopyranose)

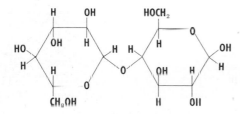

β-Maltose
(4-[α-D-Glucosyl]-β-D-glucopyranose)

Cellobiose
(4-[β-Glucosyl]-β-D-glucopyranose)

The glycosidic carbon atom (C-1) is linked by either α- or β-linkage to either C-4 or C-6 of the next monosaccharide unit. The most common polymers contain only glucose units.

Starch stored in the roots, seeds, and fruits of plants (e.g., corn, potatoes, wheat, tapioca, and rice) provides the principal commercial source. All starches give only glucose on complete hydrolysis, but both 1,4- and 1,6-linkages occur in most starches. Hot water separates starch into an insoluble fraction, amylopectin, and a soluble fraction, amylose.

Amylose is hydrolyzed completely to maltose by the enzyme *maltase*. If amylose is methylated and then hydrolyzed, the major product is 2,3,6-trimethylglucose, and small amounts of 2,3,4,6-tetramethylglucose are also found.

Methylated amylose

HCl, H_2O

2,3,4,6-Tetramethylglucose　　　　$+ (n + 1)$　　　　2,3,6-Trimethylglucose

The structure of the major product indicates that the polymer is held together by 1,4-linkages, and the amount of the tetramethylglucose produced gives a measure of the number of nonacetal end groups and, therefore, of the average molecular weight of the amylose. The extra methyl group at the acetal ends of the polymer chains is lost easily, since it is bound by a glycoside linkage.

Amylopectin gives only about a 50% yield of maltose when digested by maltase. Since the enzyme is specific for hydrolysis of 1,4-linkages, there must be some other links in amylopectin. Exhaustive methylation of amylopectin followed by hydrolysis gives a higher yield of 2,3,4,6-tetramethylglucose than is obtained from amylose. However, physical measurements (page 590) show that amylopectin has a much higher molecular weight than amylose. Therefore, there must be a number of nonacetal "ends" on an amylopectin molecule; hence the substance must be a branched rather than a linear polymer. The conclusion is borne out by estimation of the number of acetal end groups, which is larger for amylose than for amylopectin. The structure of the two starches can be shown schematically, as in Fig. 25.3.

Assignment of the branch points as 1,6-linkages is indicated by isolation of 2,3-dimethylglucose after methylation and hydrolysis, and by isolation of isomaltose after hydrolysis of amylopectin with *amylases* other than maltase. Assignment of the α-configuration to the glycoside linkage is made on the basis of enzyme specificities established by study of the enzymolysis of small polysaccharide units.

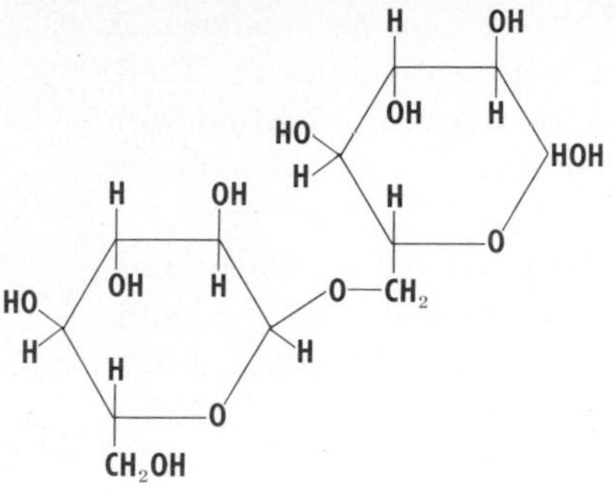

Isomaltose

Glycogen, the reserve carbohydrate of animals, is stored in the liver and muscles. On complete hydrolysis, the polymer gives glucose units. Methylation studies and degradation by enzymatic hydrolysis show that the substance is linked by 1,4-β-glycoside linkages with some 1,6-linkages, a branched structure being the result.

Cellulose is a glucose polymer of high molecular weight found in all plants. About 50% of wood and 90% of cotton fiber are cellulose. To the best of our knowledge, cellulose is completely linear, and the glucose units are joined by β-1,4-linkages.

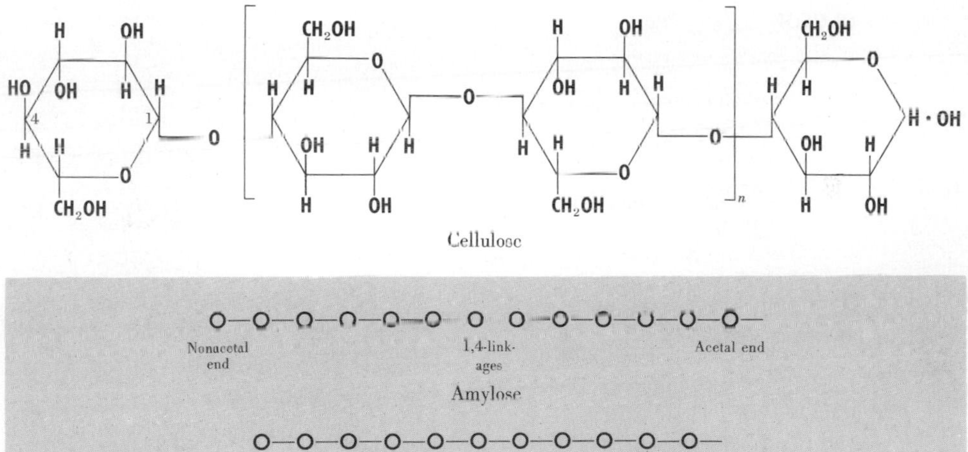

Cellulose

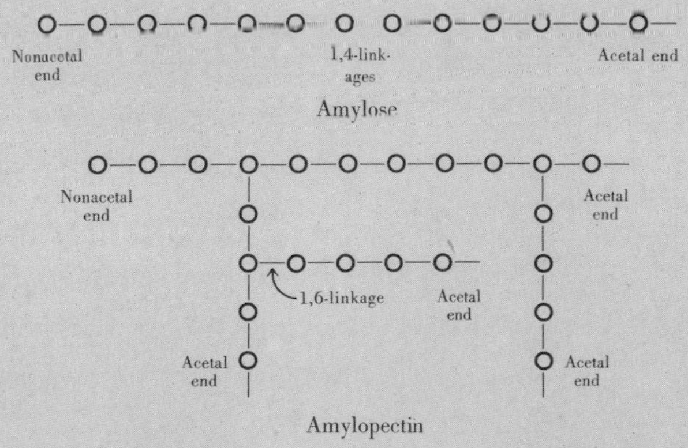

FIG. 25.3 Starch structures.

Lignin. Wood contains another, noncarbohydrate, polymer known as *lignin.* The structure of lignin has not been entirely elucidated. There is no doubt that soluble "lignins" obtained by digestion of wood with aqueous alkalis and alkaline bisulfites (as is done in the manufacture of paper) are polymers containing a variety of groups. Since there is no unequivocal evidence that native lignin can be dissolved in totally inert solvents, a strong case can be constructed for the view that native lignin may have a simple repetitive structure which is chemically modified during solubilizing processes. Various degradations, such as oxidative cleavage, zinc-dust distillation, and dry distillation of lignin, give guaiacol and its derivatives.

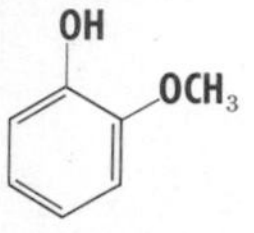

Guaiacol	Protocatechuic acid	Isohemipinic acid

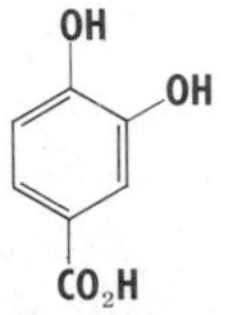

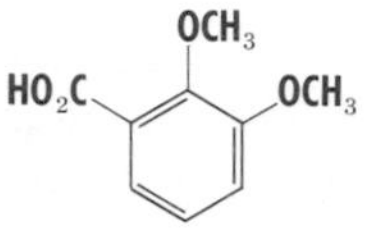

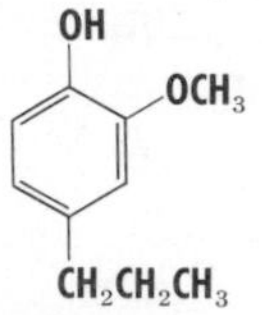

4-*n*-Propyl guaiacol	Vanillin	Eugenol

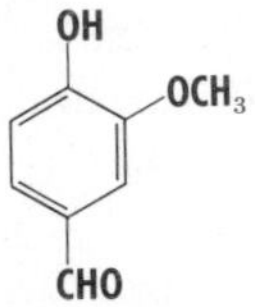

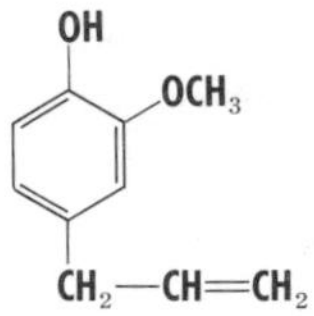

Typical lignin degradation products

Such degradation studies lead to the view that the basic unit in lignin is the following:

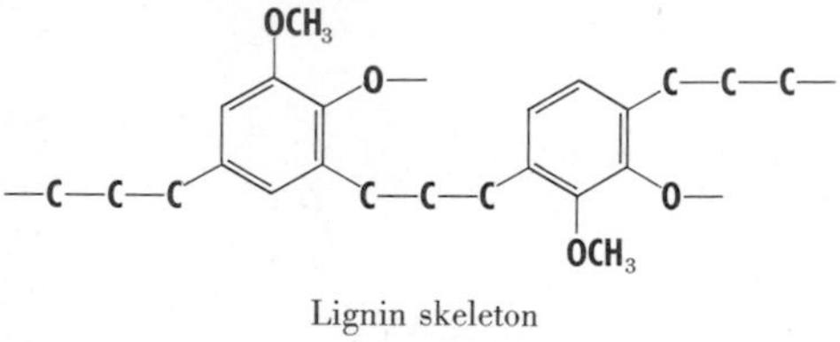

Lignin skeleton

Consideration of the oxygen content of lignin has led Freudenberg to the hypothesis that the connecting three-carbon unit must be in the same state of oxidation as glycerol. There are many possible ways of formulating monomeric structures having such a composition.

$ArCHOHCCHOHCH_2OH$ $ArCHOHCOCH_3$ $ArCHOHCH_2CHO$ $ArCH_2COCH_2OH$

$ArCH_2CHOHCHO$ $ArCOCH_2CH_2OH$ $ArCOCHOHCH_2OH$ $ArCOCHOHCH_3$

$Ar = HO$—

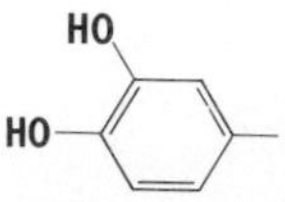

Acid-catalyzed condensation of any of the above molecules, followed by cyclic-ether formation, could give polymers having ligninlike structures. Since many modern biogenetic schemes for the interrelation of natural products involve acid-catalyzed reactions, the Freudenberg hypothesis seems very reasonable. The changes visualized may be illustrated with 1-guaiacylglycerol.

Lignin is at present a waste product in the processing of wood during manufacture of paper and other cellulose products. The future will probably see development of significant uses for this source of interesting chemicals.

There are two principal processes for conversion of wood into paper. Both are primarily designed to remove lignin as water-soluble derivatives. In the *sulfite process*, an alkaline bisulfite solution sulfonates some of the aromatic nuclei. The reaction, which probably involves the displacement of phenolic hydroxyl groups by bisulfite, is related to the bisulfite catalysis of the displacement of —**OH** by —**NH₂** in the Bucherer reaction (page 311).

In the *alkali process*, lignin is degraded and solubilized by virtue of the acidity of phenolic hydroxyl groups.

Proteins

Proteins are omnipresent in living matter. *Fibrous proteins* constitute the structural matter of animals, in the form of skin, muscle, silk fibers, connective tissue, and so forth. *Soluble*, or *globular*, *proteins* play critical roles in all life processes as enzymes, metabolic intermediates, character-determining genetic factors, etc. The soluble proteins are subdivided according to their solubility properties. Six groups commonly defined are (1) albumins, soluble in pure water; (2) globulins, soluble in dilute salt solutions but insoluble in water; (3) glutelins, soluble in dilute acid or alkali; (4) prolamines, soluble in 80% alcohol but not in water; (5) histones, soluble in dilute acid by virtue of being strongly basic but insoluble in neutral solutions; (6) protamines, soluble in water and strongly basic.

Many proteins occur in association with other groups, called *prosthetic* groups. Prosthetic groups are easily separated from their conjugated proteins, but the nature of the attraction between the partners is not known. Binding may involve only van der Waals forces in some instances and labile chemical bonds in others.

Hydrolysis of proteins, from which prosthetic groups have been removed with acids, bases, or enzymes, produces mixtures of amino acids as the principal products. All evidence shows that simple proteins are linear copolymers of α-amino acids in which the units are linked by *peptide* (amide) linkages.

Segment of a protein chain

Short sequences of amino acids are known as *peptides* or *polypeptides*. The dividing line between proteins and polypeptides is not clearly defined. Complete determination of the sequence of amino acid residues in proteins and more complex polypeptides was originally considered beyond the reach of classic degradative methods.

A brilliant investigation of the structure of insulin, which is variously referred to as a small protein or a large natural polypeptide, led Sanger and his coworkers to announce a complete determination of the sequence of amino acid residues in the molecule. The material tends to form aggregates. Estimates of the effective molecular weight run as high as 50,000. However, a unit having a molecular weight of 6,000 has been separated. The amino end groups were tagged by treatment with 2,4-dinitrofluorobenzene, and the protein was then subjected to both partial and total hydrolysis. The dinitrophenyl (DNP) groups are not removed by acid hydrolysis.

DNP-amino acid

Tagging with DNP groups, followed by complete hydrolysis, showed that the fragment with a molecular weight of 6,000 has one glycine and one phenylalanine end group per molecule. Since cystine is one of the hydrolytic fragments, Sanger inferred that the molecule consisted of two peptide chains held together by a disulfide linkage.

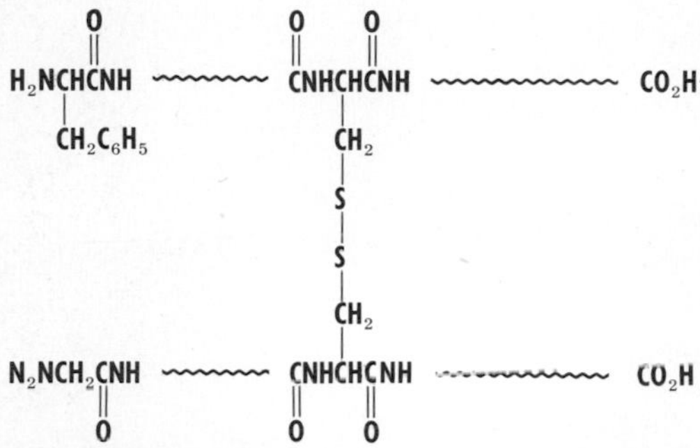

$$
\begin{array}{c}
\overset{O}{\overset{\|}{\text{H}_2\text{NCHCNH}}} \sim\!\sim\!\sim \overset{O\quad\;\;O}{\overset{\|\quad\;\;\|}{\text{CNHCHCNH}}} \sim\!\sim\!\sim \text{CO}_2\text{H} \\
\underset{\text{CH}_2\text{C}_6\text{H}_5}{|} \qquad\qquad \underset{\text{CH}_2}{|} \\
\underset{\text{S}}{|} \\
\underset{\text{S}}{|} \\
\underset{\text{CH}_2}{|} \\
\underset{\underset{O}{\|}}{\text{N}_2\text{NCH}_2\text{CNH}} \sim\!\sim\!\sim \underset{O\quad\;\;O}{\underset{\|\quad\;\;\|}{\text{CNHCHCNH}}} \sim\!\sim\!\sim \text{CO}_2\text{H}
\end{array}
$$

Oxidation with performic acid broke the disulfide linkages, giving peptides containing cysteic acid residues.

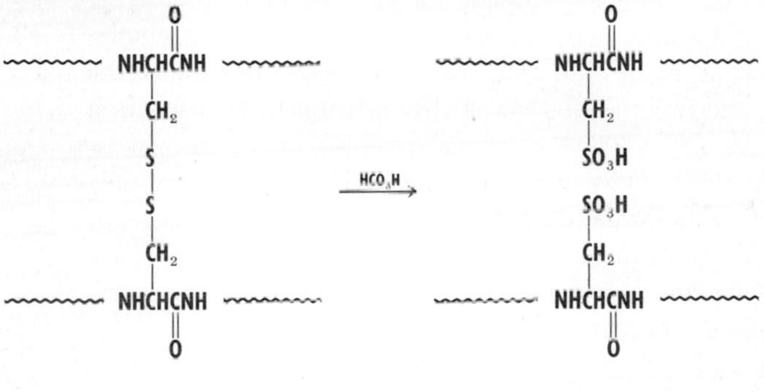

$$
\begin{array}{ccc}
\sim\!\sim \overset{O}{\overset{\|}{\text{NHCHCNH}}} \sim\!\sim & & \sim\!\sim \overset{O}{\overset{\|}{\text{NHCHCNH}}} \sim\!\sim \\
\underset{\text{CH}_2}{|} & & \underset{\text{CH}_2}{|} \\
\underset{\text{S}}{|} & \xrightarrow{\text{HCO}_3\text{H}} & \underset{\text{SO}_3\text{H}}{|} \\
\underset{\text{S}}{|} & & \underset{\text{SO}_3\text{H}}{|} \\
\underset{\text{CH}_2}{|} & & \underset{\text{CH}_2}{|} \\
\sim\!\sim \underset{\underset{O}{\|}}{\text{NHCHCNH}} \sim\!\sim & & \sim\!\sim \underset{\underset{O}{\|}}{\text{NHCHCNH}} \sim\!\sim
\end{array}
$$

The two derived peptides were separated, and each was converted to a DNP derivative and subjected to partial hydrolysis. The hydrolysate was examined by paper chromatography, and a number of small, DNP-tagged, peptides were identified. From one of the peptides fragments such as the following were found:

DNP   phenylalanine
DNP   phenylalanyl-valine
DNP   phenylalanyl-valyl-aspartic acid
DNP   phenylalanyl-valyl-aspartyl-glutamic acid

The results imply a partial sequence near the end of one peptide chain, and similar results were obtained with other peptides. Then the peptides were subjected to partial hydrolysis with enzymes that show a high preference for cleavage of particular peptide linkages, and the DNP degradations were pursued with fragments isolated from the enzymolysis. The final structures assigned to the chains were†

Phenylalanyl-valyl-aspartyl-glutaminyl-
histidyl-leucyl-cysteyl-glycyl-seryl-
histidyl-leucyl-valyl-glutamyl-alanyl-
leucyl-tyrosyl-valyl-valyl-cysteyl-glycyl-
glutamyl-arginyl-glycyl-phenylalanyl-
phenylalanyl-tyrosyl-threonyl-
prolyl-lysyl-alanine

and

Glycyl-isoleucyl-valyl-glutamyl-
glutamyl-cysteyl-cysteyl-alanyl-seryl-
valyl-cysteyl-seryl-leucyl-tyrosyl-
glutamyl-leucyl-glutamyl-asparaginyl-
tyrosyl-cysteyl-asparagine

The pairs of cystein units which are involved in the disulfide linkage between the chains in insulin have not been identified.

Considerable progress has been made in the synthesis of polypeptides from amino acids. Direct polymerization of amino acids or their esters by nonenzymatic methods is almost valueless, as the chance of producing material having the right amino acids in the correct sequence is remote. Peptide linkages must be made one at a time, and careful attention is accorded to blocking the functional groups that are not to be used in a particular condensation.

If amino acids or their esters are heated to high temperatures, they form *diketopiperazines*. The procedure has limited value for synthesis of mixed dipeptides. Mixtures are formed during attempts to prepare mixed diketopiperazines, and unsymmetrical diketopiperazines are ordinarily hydrolyzed to give mixtures of the two possible dipeptides.

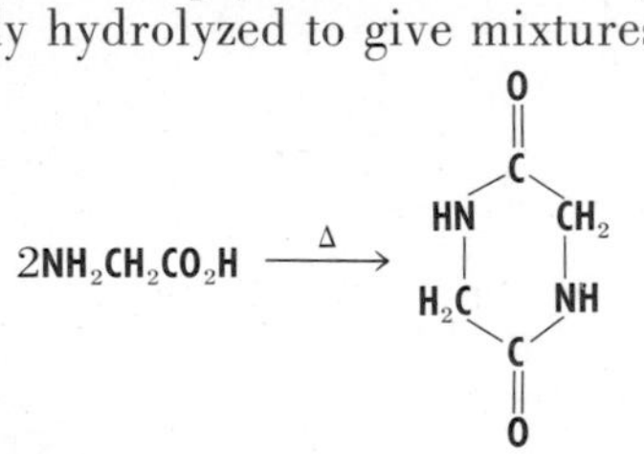

$$2NH_2CH_2CO_2H \xrightarrow{\Delta}$$

2,5-Diketopiperazine

Careful hydrolysis of diketopiperazines gives *dipeptides*.

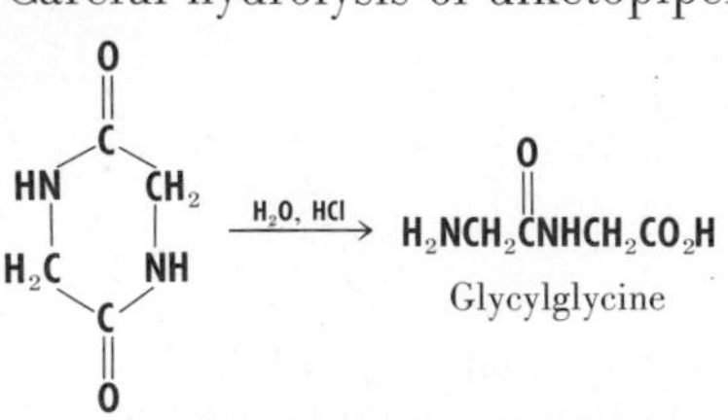

$$\xrightarrow{H_2O, \ HCl} H_2NCH_2CNHCH_2CO_2H$$

Glycylglycine

† See page 528 for the structures of the various amino acid residues.

Fischer developed the first really successful peptide synthesis by using a chloroacid chloride, rather than an α-amino compound, as an acylating agent. The method was applied to the synthesis of a number of polypeptides.

$$CICH_2COCl \; + \; NH_2CH_2CO_2C_2H_5 \longrightarrow CICH_2CONHCH_2CO_2C_2H_5 \xrightarrow{NH_3} NH_2CH_2CONHCH_2CO_2C_2H_5 \xrightarrow{CICH_2COCl}$$

Chloroacetyl   Ethyl glycinate   Ethyl chloroacetylglycinate
chloride

$$CICH_2CONHCH_2CONHCH_2CO_2C_2H_5 \xrightarrow{NaOH} CICH_2CONHCH_2CONHCH_2CO_2H \xrightarrow{NH_3} NH_2CH_2CONHCH_2CONHCH_2CO_2H$$

Glycylglycylglycine

More than a quarter of a century after Fischer's work, Bergman (1932) developed the first significant new method of peptide synthesis. His innovation consisted of protecting the amine group of one amino acid

with a *carbobenzoxy group* $C_6H_5CH_2\overset{O}{\overset{\|}{O}}C-$. Carbobenzoxy groups have the important property of being removable by *catalytic hydrogenolysis.* Many other acylating agents had been tried earlier in attempts to camouflage basic amino groups. However, all such groups had required removal by hydrolysis, which always resulted in extensive disruption of the peptide linkages. In recent years the most significant new aids in the synthesis of peptide linkages have been a series of "condensing agents" such as carbodiimides ($>C=N=C<$) and tetraethyl phosphite. These reagents condense with one reactant (i.e., amino or carboxyl group) to form intermediates (phosphonamides or mixed anhydrides) which are reactive substrates in nucleophilic substitution reactions. The peptide linkage is then established by such a substitution reaction. The following example illustrates a typical procedure using both carbobenzoxylation and condensation with tetraethyl phosphite.

$$C_6H_5CH_2OH \; + \; CICCl \longrightarrow C_6H_5CH_2OCOCl + HCl$$

Benzyl   Phosgene   Carbobenzoxy
alcohol   chloride

$$C_6H_5CH_2CHCO_2H \xrightarrow{C_6H_5CH_2OCCl} C_6H_5CH_2CHCO_2H \xrightarrow{SOCl_2} C_6H_5CH_2CHCOCl \xrightarrow{H_2NCH_2CO_2C_2H_5}$$
$$\quad | \qquad\qquad\qquad\qquad\qquad\qquad\qquad | \qquad\qquad\qquad\qquad\qquad |$$
$$\quad NH_2 \qquad\qquad\qquad\qquad\qquad NHCOCH_2C_6H_5 \qquad\qquad NHCOCH_2C_6H_5$$
$$\qquad\qquad\qquad\qquad\qquad\qquad\qquad\qquad\qquad\qquad\qquad\qquad\qquad\qquad\quad \overset{\|}{O}$$

Phenylalanine   Carbobenzoxy-
                                       phenylalanyl chloride

$$C_6H_5CH_2CHCONHCO_2C_2H_5 \xrightarrow{H_2, Pd} C_6H_5CH_2CHCONHCH_2CO_2C_2H_5$$
$$\quad | \qquad\qquad\qquad\qquad\qquad\qquad\qquad\qquad | $$
$$\quad NHCOCH_2C_6H_5 \qquad\qquad\qquad\qquad NH_2$$
$$\qquad \overset{\|}{O} \qquad\qquad\qquad\qquad\qquad\qquad\text{Ethyl phenylalanylglycinate}$$

$$C_6H_5CH_2OCONHCH_2CO_2H \xrightarrow{(C_2H_5O)_2POP(OC_2H_5)_2} \left[C_6H_5CH_2OCONHCH_2\overset{\overset{\displaystyle O}{\|}}{C}OP(OC_2H_5)_2 \right] \xrightarrow[-(C_2H_5O)_2POH]{\overset{\displaystyle NH_2}{C_6H_5CH_2CHCONHCH_2CO_2C_2H_5}}$$

Carbobenzoxyglycine

$$C_6H_5CH_2OCONHCH_2CONHCHCONHCH_2CO_2C_2H_5 \xrightarrow[-C_6H_5CH_2Br]{HBr, C_2H_5OH} H_2NCH_2CONHCHCONHCH_2CO_2C_2H_5$$
$$\overset{\displaystyle |}{CH_2C_6H_5} \qquad\qquad\qquad\qquad\qquad \overset{\displaystyle CH_2C_6H_5}{|}$$

Ethyl glycylphenylalanylglycinate
35% over-all

Physical Properties of Polymers

Polymeric materials range in their physical properties enough to be used as elastomers, fibers, adhesives, and rigid plastics. Study of the correlation of physical properties with chemical structure is in its infancy, but some reasonable conclusions have already been reached.

Molecular Weight. Conventional methods of molecular-weight measurement, which depend upon colligative properties such as freezing-point depression or boiling-point elevation, are of little value in the high-polymer field. The failure of such methods, in which the number of moles of a solute in a dilute solution are counted, arises from the relatively small number of molecules in a typical sample of a polymer. For example, 1 g of a polymer of molecular weight 100,000 would depress the freezing point of 100 g of benzene by only $5.12 \times 10^{-4°}$. Such a minute change is essentially impossible to measure with any sort of accuracy. The one colligative property which has been useful is *osmotic pressure.* If a solution of polymer is separated from pure solvent by a membrane which is permeable only to the solvent molecules, the solvent molecules pass both ways through the membrane. However, the rate of diffusion from pure solvent is faster than from the solution (which has a slightly lower vapor pressure). As a consequence, a hydrostatic head is created on the solution side of the membrane which, at equilibrium, compensates for the difference in vapor pressure of the solvent on the two sides of the membrane. Precise determination of the height of the osmotic head gives a delicate method for determination of the small change in vapor pressure due to dilution of the solvent with a relatively small number of solute molecules. Precision osmometry has been much used as a standard for the calibration of other methods of determining molecular weights.

Empirical observations lead to the generalization that the *viscosity* of polymer solutions increases with increasing molecular weight of the solute. No exact theory has been developed to correlate the effect with molecular weight. Furthermore, the magnitude of the effect is sensitive to the shape as well as to the size of polymer molecules. Since viscosity measurements are very easy to carry out, viscosimetry is often used to obtain approximate relative values of molecular weights. If viscosity effects for a particular type of polymer are calibrated by comparison with another method, the viscosity method can be used for routine determinations.

The rate at which molecules undergo sedimentation in an ultra-centrifuge is a function of their weight; hence both *sedimentation* rate and equilibrium are used to measure the molecular weight of polymers. The methods give an estimate of the average weight of solute molecules, as contrasted with osmotic measurements, which give the *average number* of molecules per sample unit. Weight-average and number-average molecular weights for typical samples are usually different, since the former are strongly affected by a relatively small number of very massive particles, and the latter may be dominated by a small number of molecules of low molecular weight.

Light scattering has also been used to determine molecular size. The measurement depends upon the fact that light is scattered by particles which are large in comparison with the wavelength of the light.

The molecular weights of polymers cover a very wide range. Some useful synthetic polymers, such as certain ethylene oxide polymers, have molecular weights of only a few thousand, but the synthetic fibers usually fall in the range of hundreds of thousands. The amylose fraction of starch is in the 10,000 to 50,000 range, but amylopectin and cellulose are probably as high as 500,000. Proteins show great ranges of molecular weight. Insulin, for example, has a value of 45,000, whereas the tobacco mosaic virus, with molecules that look like boulders to the electron microscope, has a molecular weight of more than 15,000,000. If synthetic polymers are *cross-linked* by bonding between polymer chains, their molecular weights approach infinity; an entire sample may be essentially one molecule (Fig. 25.4).

If the molecular weights of polymers become very high, either by cross-linking or by linear extension, their solubility in all solvents drops essentially to zero. The effect is shown by three-dimensional polymers such as phenol-formaldehyde resins, cross-linked ion-exchange resins, and, possibly, by native lignin before chemical degradation to destroy cross-links.

Crystallinity. Since polymers never consist of a single molecular species, a sample cannot be a crystal in exactly the same way as a pure compound in which the molecules pack in a perfectly ordered way.

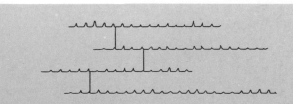

FIG. 25.4   *Schematic representation of a cross-linked polymer.*

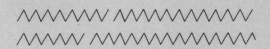

FIG. 25.5   *Schematic representation of a crystalline polymer.*

However some polymers have many of the physical characteristics of crystals and are said to be crystalline. In a crystalline polymer, long segments of linear polymer chains are oriented in a regular manner with respect to one another. The occurrence of an occasional discontinuity at chain ends has only a negligible effect (Fig. 25.5).

The best evidence for crystallinity is the X-ray diffraction pattern of a polymer. The patterns obtained are of the same type as those given by microcrystalline solids. A crystalline polymer may be oriented by a mechanical stress, such as stretching, and the resulting material will be optically anisotropic; i.e., the refractive index will be different along the direction of the stress than in the perpendicular direction. Such an oriented polymer also has different absorption spectra along different axes.

"Crystalline" polymers tend to be relatively strong and nonelastic. The best examples are synthetic fibers such as nylon and dacron. The polymers are noncrystalline (*amorphous*) when spun into thread, but crystallization is induced by slow stretching.

Polymers which have polar functional groups show a considerable tendency to be crystalline. Orientation of the chains is aided by alignment of the dipole moments of the groups on different chains. However, polar groups are not a necessary prerequisite to crystallization, as has been demonstrated by production of crystalline polyethylene, polypropylene, and polystyrene by polymerization with organometallic initiators. Polypropylene and polystyrene are especially interesting, since preliminary evidence suggests that the molecules owe their crystalline character to the systematic repetition of one configuration of asymmetric centers along a polymer chain. The term *isotactic* is applied to such a configuration (Fig. 25.6).

In each chain, all asymmetric centers have the same configuration, which may be either *d* or *l*. Of course, there are equal numbers of *d* and *l* chains in any polymer sample. The polymer is, therefore, a racemate.

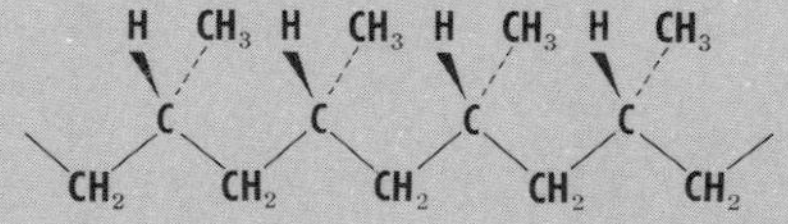

$$\text{H} \quad \text{CH}_3 \quad \text{H} \quad \text{CH}_3 \quad \text{H} \quad \text{CH}_3 \quad \text{H} \quad \text{CH}_3$$

FIG. 25.6   *Segment of an isotactic polymer chain.*

Any irregularity, such as introduction of bulky groups or inclusion of comonomer units, will tend to prevent crystallinity. The amorphous character of polyethylene prepared by high-temperature free-radical polymerization is attributed to end groups developed occasionally by rearrangements of growing radicals.

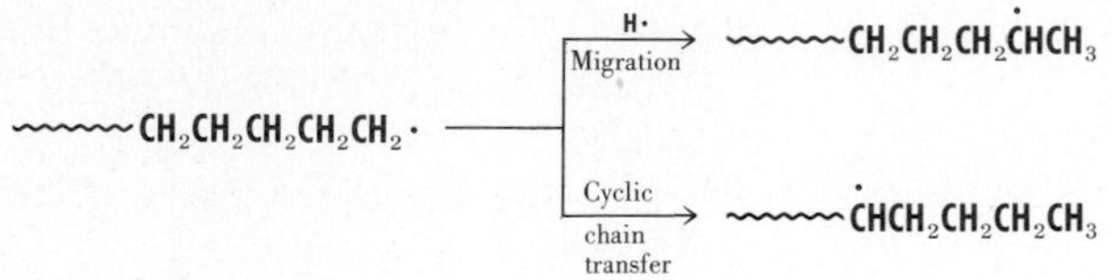

$$\sim\sim\sim CH_2CH_2CH_2CH_2CH_2\cdot \quad
\begin{array}{l}
\xrightarrow[\text{Migration}]{\text{H}\cdot} \sim\sim\sim CH_2CH_2CH_2\overset{\cdot}{C}HCH_3 \\[2em]
\xrightarrow[\substack{\text{chain}\\\text{transfer}}]{\text{Cyclic}} \sim\sim\sim \overset{\cdot}{C}HCH_2CH_2CH_2CH_3
\end{array}$$

A fine example of disordering effects is found in the polymerization of methylmethacrylate ($CH_2\!=\!C(CH_3)CO_2CH_3$). Pure polymethacrylate is tough and somewhat brittle. The desirable nonshattering qualities of Plexiglas are obtained by copolymerization of a few per cent of ethyl acrylate ($CH_2\!=\!CHCO_2C_2H_5$) with the methacrylate. The same effect can be obtained by adding a *plasticizer* such as diethyl sebacate ($C_2H_5O_2C(CH_2)_8$-$CO_2C_2H_5$) to polymethyl methacrylate. The long plasticizer molecules intrude between polymer chains and form a solid solution which is disordered. In order to be effective, a plasticizer must be compatible with (soluble in) the polymer.

Crystalline polymers have rather sharply defined melting points. Even amorphous polymers show *second-order transition points* at which the material changes from a brittle to a more elastic form. Plasticizers are frequently added to plastics to lower their second-order transition temperatures, in order to prevent their becoming brittle at low temperatures.

Elastomers are highly disordered systems that undergo plastic deformation very easily and recover relatively slowly after stretching. The deformation of such "rubbery" materials is accomplished by the uncoiling of randomly piled polymer chains (Fig. 25.7).

Most natural polymers are highly ordered. The molecules fairly bristle with functional groups, and hydrogen bonds are particularly important in creating both internal and external order in polymer chains. It is now believed that polysaccharides and proteins often have a helical configuration of the chains, so that many hydrogen bonds are established between nonadjacent units in the same chain. The coiled chains may then pack in an orderly manner, giving a crystalline macrostructure.

As a matter of supplementary interest, a number of commercial polymers are identified in Table 25.1.

Stretching

FIG. 25.7   *Elastic deformation.*

TABLE 25.1   Commercial Polymers

Monomer units	Trade names
CONDENSATION POLYMERS	
1. Phenol–formaldehyde	Bakelite Phenolic, Durez, Insurok, Durite, Makalot, Heresite, Neillite, Resinox, Textolite
2. *p*-Substituted phenol–formaldehyde	Bakelite Phenolic, Durez, Amberol, Super Beckacite
3. Furfural–phenol	Durite
4. Resorcinol–formaldehyde	Penacolite
5. Urea–formaldehyde	Beetle, Plascon, Uformite
6. Urea–butanol–formaldehyde	Beetle, Uformite, Beckamine
7. Melamine–formaldehyde	Melmac, Catalin Melamine, Plascon Melamine, Melantine, Resimine
8. Melamine–butanol–formaldehyde	Melmac, Uformite
9. Aniline–formaldehyde	Cibanite, Dilectene
10. Phenolsulfonic acid–formaldehyde	Amberlite, Dowex (ion exchange)
11. Urea–ethylenediamine–formaldehyde	Amberlite (anion exchange)
12. Adipic acid–hexamethylenediamine	Nylon
13. Phthalic anhydride–glycerol–linoleic acid	Glyptal, Rezyl, Duraplex
14. Sebacic acid–ricinoleic acid–glycerol	Paraplex
15. Ethylene oxide	Carbowax, Epon Resins
16. Dimethyldihydroxysilane	Silastic, Silicone Rubber
17. Methylchlorosilane–dimethylchlorosilane	Silicon Resin
18. Furfuryl alcohol	Resin X, Duralon, Furetone
VINYL POLYMERS	
1. Ethylene	Polythene
2. Tetrafluoroethylene	Teflon
3. Styrene	Bakelite Polystyrene, Chemaco Polystyrene, Loalin, Lustron, Styron, Styramic

Problems

1. Write equations which illustrate each of the following:

a. Condensation polymerization
b. Addition polymerization
c. Chain transfer
d. Initiation of polymerization by an organometallic compound
e. Photochemical initiation of polymerization
f. Formation of a cross-linked polymer
g. Use of carbobenzoxylation in peptide synthesis
h. Enzymolysis of a polysaccharide
i. Copolymerization
j. End-group marking with DNP

TABLE 25.1   *Commercial Polymers* (*Continued*)

Monomer units	Trade names

VINYL POLYMERS (Continued)

4. 2,5-Dichlorostyrene	Mathison Plastic
5. β-Pinene	Piccolyte
6. Indene–coumarone	Coumar, Piccoumaron, Nevindene
7. Isobutylene	Vistanex
8. Methyl acrylate	Acryloid
9. Methyl methacrylate	Plexiglas, Lucite
10. Vinyl acetate	Gelva, Vinylite
11. Polyvinyl alcohol–formaldehyde	Formvar
12. Polyvinyl alcohol–butyraldehyde	Butvar, Butacite, Vinylite, Saflex
13. Vinyl chloride	Flamenol, PVC, Geon, Koroseal, Vinylite
14. Vinylidene chloride	Saran

Copolymers

1. Vinyl chloride–vinyl acetate	Vinylite, Tygon
2. Vinyl chloride–vinyl acetate–maleic anhydride	Vinylite VMCH
3. Vinylidene chloride–vinyl chloride	Saran, Velon, Geon
4. Vinylidene chloride–acrylonitrile	Saran
5. Vinyl carbazole	Polectron

SYNTHETIC ELASTOMERS

1. Styrene–butadiene	Buna S, Chemigum, Hycar OS, Butaprene S, GR–S
2. Acrylonitrile–butadiene	Perbunan, Hycar OR, Chemigum, Butaprene N
3. Isoprene–isobutylene	Butyl Rubber, GR–1
4. Chloroprene	Neoprene, GR–1
5. Chloroprene–isoprene	Neoprene FR

2. Each of the following compounds has one or more specialized uses in some branch of polymer chemistry. Speculate as to the use of each.

a. $n\text{-}C_8H_{15}SH$

b. $(C_6H_5)_3CCH(C_6H_5)_2$

c. $(HOCH_2)_4C$[Pentaerythritol]

d. Di-*n*-butyl phthalate

e. A mercury-vapor lamp

f.

$$CH{=}CH_2$$
(benzene ring)
$$CH{=}CH_2$$

3. Explain the following facts:

a. Acrylic anhydride $[(CH_2{=}CHCO)_2O]$ polymerizes to give a soluble (not cross-linked) polymer which contains no residual unsaturation.

b. Vinylbenzoquinone does not polymerize.

c. Nitroglycerine $[O_2NOCH_2CH(ONO_2)CH_2ONO_2]$ is an excellent plasticizer for nitro-cellulose (formed by the action of nitric acid on cellulose).

   d. When the compound formulated below is treated with a trace of water, it evolves a gas and forms a polymer.

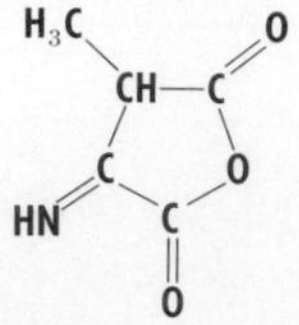

   e. Small amounts of cyclopentadiene, C_5H_6, inhibit the polymerization of butadiene.

   4. Devise syntheses of the following materials from lignin or its degradation products.

a.

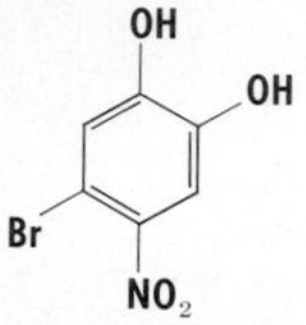

b.

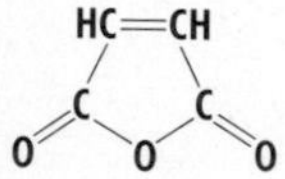

c.

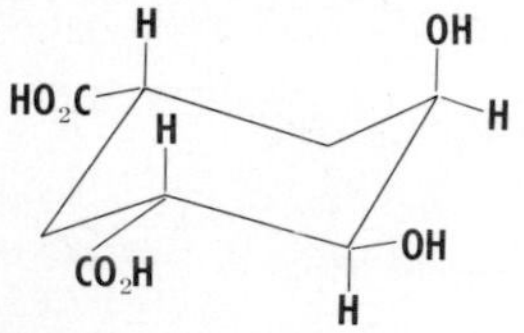

(Need not be a stereospecific synthesis)

d.

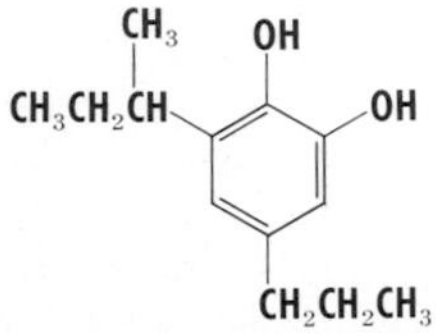

e. A cross-linked condensation polymer

f.

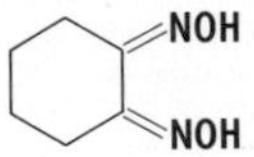

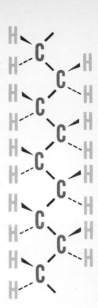

26

Petroleum Chemistry

The economic and chemical significance of petroleum has attained a level that almost defies description. Huge lakes of native petroleum lie beneath the surface of the earth in many parts of the world—notably in the United States, in the northern countries of South America, in the Middle East, especially in Iraq and Saudi Arabia, and in the Russian Ukraine. The beginning of a period of extensive exploitation of these natural sources coincided rather closely with the development of internal-combustion engines in the early years of the twentieth century. Since that time, use of petroleum products as gasoline, fuel oil, and lubricants has attained such proportions that the economy of any modern country would collapse if its sources of petroleum were abruptly terminated. In addition, a large proportion of the less expensive materials for organic syntheses are by-products of the industry.

The realization has grown in recent years that the world's supply of petroleum is not inexhaustible and that the day will arrive when we shall have used up this product of ages of geologic synthesis. There is no accurate way of predicting the time when depletion will become serious. Exploration continues to reveal new oil fields. New methods of effecting more efficient removal of oil from pools have been developed, and further spectacular improvement is in prospect, for it is known that a substantial fraction of the content of some fields is still left adsorbed on subsoil clays. Organic chemists have made a substantial contribution to the extension of natural resources by developing a wide variety of methods for conversion of the less useful petroleum fractions into premium motor fuels.

TABLE 26.1   *Typical Petroleum Fractionation*

Fraction	Boiling range, $^\circ C$
Petroleum ether	20–60
Solvent naphtha	60–120
Gasoline	40–200
Kerosene	175–325
Gas oil	300–500
Vacuum distillate†	>400
Residual petroleum coke or asphalt	

† Actual distillation temperature is lower at reduced pressure.

Composition of Petroleum

The composition of petroleum varies widely among the various oil fields throughout the world. The major constituents are always saturated hydrocarbons of a wide range of molecular weights, ranging from methane up to small amounts of very heavy oils in the C_{50} range. Cyclopentane and cyclohexane derivatives, known as *naphthenes*, are found in varying amounts. Some deposits, such as those in California and Borneo, contain substantial amounts of aromatics. Sulfur, nitrogen, and oxygen compounds are present in minor amounts. The sulfur content of an oil is particularly important, since that element must be removed in order to prevent development of corrosive acids by oxidation during use. Petroleum also contains minute traces of other elements, such as metals, which are currently considered unimportant. However, if efficient means could be found to remove some of the latter, such as vanadium, from the huge volume of petroleum processed, the concentrated impurity could become quite valuable.

Volatile hydrocarbons such as methane, ethane, propane, and the butanes are drawn off separately as "natural gas" and are consumed in large part as heating fuel. Fractional distillation of natural gas at low temperatures separates the constituents for sale as pure chemicals. The liquid residue is subjected to fractionation, the products of which are listed in Table 26.1.

Gasoline. The chemistry of combustion of gasoline in the cylinder of an internal-combustion engine is a process both complicated and delicate. Under ideal conditions, the fuel is completely oxidized to carbon dioxide and water. Under favorable operating conditions, complete combustion is approached fairly closely, although some carbon monoxide and other incompletely oxidized compounds are found in most exhaust fumes.

$$C_nH_{2n+2} + \frac{3n+1}{2}O_2 \longrightarrow nCO_2 + (n+1)H_2O$$

A mixture of gasoline and air is sucked into the cylinder as the piston descends. The valve closes and the returning piston compresses the fuel. The ratio of the volume of vapor before and after compression is called the compression ratio. As the piston reaches the top of the compression stroke, an electric spark across the gap between the points of the spark plug ignites the mixture in which the gasoline is present partly as vapor and partly as liquid droplets. The burning mixture produces a relatively large volume of gases, which expand, delivering power to the piston, which is once again in descent.

Efficient engine operation requires two particularly important characteristics in a gasoline. First, the fuel must have the right volatility in order to give prompt ignition with a minimum amount of the gasoline in the gaseous state at the top of the compression cycle. If all the gasoline were vaporized, the power of the thrust, which depends largely upon an increase in the volume of vapor, would be seriously impaired. The second requirement is that the burning of the fuel mixture occur at the right rate to deliver a smooth thrust to the descending piston. If reaction is too rapid, combustion becomes detonation, and a shock wave results which causes the engine to "knock" and to dissipate much of the power to the engine block. Straight-run gasoline fractions from crude petroleum have a boiling range of from 40 to 200°, with a large portion of the mixture composed of C_6 to C_9 hydrocarbons boiling near 100°. Such a mixture has the proper volatility characteristics, but does not necessarily give good antiknock performance. Highly branched hydrocarbons are much less prone to knock than are their normal isomers.

2,2,4-Trimethylpentane, which has been given the unfortunate name of "isooctane" by petroleum technologists, has been adopted as a standard for good antiknock behavior, whereas n-heptane is the standard poor fuel.

        CH₃ CH₃
        | |
CH₃CCH₂CHCH₃
    |
    CH₃

2,2,4 Trimethylpentane
    (Isooctane)

The antiknock rating of a gasoline is the percentage of 2,2,4-trimethylpentane which must be blended with n-heptane to match the performance of the test fuel. Some hydrocarbons are now known to be even better than "isooctane." The use of secondary standards allows the extension of the scale of "octane numbers" to above 100. Typical values are shown in Table 26.2.

Octane numbers of a straight-run gasoline may range from 20 to 70. The octane numbers may be improved in two ways:

1. Additives have been found which inhibit the explosive burning of the end gas. The best of these is *tetraethyl lead*. *Ethyl gasoline* is a fuel whose octane number has been increased to 80 by addition of tetraethyl lead in amounts ranging from 0.75 to 3.00 ml/gal.

TABLE 26.2   *Octane Ratings of Pure Hydrocarbons*

Hydrocarbon	Octane number
Methane	110
Ethane	104
n-Pentane	61
n-Hexane	25
2-Methylpentane	75
2,2-Dimethylbutane	96
n-Heptane	0
2,3,3-Trimethylbutane	101
n-Octane	−17
Cyclohexane	77
Benzene	108
Toluene	104

2. A straight-run gasoline fraction may be improved by isomerization to give a higher percentage of branched compounds. The process, known as *reforming*, consists in passing a gasoline over a catalyst, such as an aluminum halide, at room temperature or slightly above. Normally both *cracking* (page 603) and isomerization occur, although the former process is minimized at low temperatures, as is illustrated by the following examples.

$$CH_3(CH_2)_3CH_3 \xrightarrow[\text{Room temperature}]{\text{AlBr}_3} \text{butanes} + (CH_3)_2CHCH_2CH_3 + \text{higher-boiling products}$$
$$\phantom{CH_3(CH_2)_3CH_3 \xrightarrow[\text{Room temperature}]{}} 5\% \qquad\quad 55.9\% \qquad\qquad\quad 3.9\%$$

$$CH_3(CH_2)_5CH_3 \xrightarrow[96°]{\text{AlCl}_3}$$

lower alkanes + methylpentanes + dimethylbutanes + 2,2,3-trimethylbutane + high-boiling products
64.6%   5.4%   1.9%   0.5%   24.4%

Cracking and *alkylation* processes, which are used to increase the over-all yield of gasoline from petroleum, and the mechanism of isomerization will be discussed subsequently.

Kerosene. Kerosene, the petroleum fraction boiling immediately above gasoline, is used in domestic and other small heating units. In order to obtain a clean (soot-free) flame, some of the rather high aromatic content of kerosenes must be removed. The unsaturated compounds are removed by extraction with sulfuric acid, hydrogen fluoride, or sulfur dioxide. Kerosene may also be cracked over a wide variety of catalysts to form gasoline and gaseous alkanes and alkenes. Straight-run kerosene from most oils has a high *naphthene* content.

Gas Oil. Gas oil, also known as *fuel oil* or *diesel oil*, boils in the range from 250 to 400°. Some is consumed in oil-burning furnaces, and a large proportion is cracked as a step in gasoline manufacture. Increasing amounts are used in diesel engines, which operate on a very different principle from that of ignition-system engines. In a diesel engine, air alone is first drawn into the cylinder and then compressed to a higher pressure (compression ratio of 12:1 to 20:1) than is used in ignition systems. The rapid compression raises the temperature to about 300°. The fuel is then injected as fine spray, and spontaneous ignition occurs. Structural features which lead to good antiknock performance in automobile engines tend to give undesirably slow ignition in diesel engines; therefore diesel fuels are rated by *cetane numbers* rather than by octane numbers. The scale is defined by assigning cetane (*n*-hexadecane, a compound with a very low octane number) a rating of 100 and giving α-methylnaphthalene, which ignites very slowly, the value of zero. Gas oil, like kerosene, is converted in part to gasoline by catalytic cracking, followed by reforming and recombination of the fragments.

Lubricating Oil. High-molecular-weight fluid residues from distillation are used widely as lubricants. As with the fractions used for fuels, it is necessary to rectify greases in order to remove those constituents which do not have the proper physical properties. Extraction with solvents such as β-chloroethyl ether (Chlorex), liquid sulfur dioxide, and phenol removes aromatic and other unsaturated compounds. Normal paraffins are often removed by dissolution of the oil in a mixture of methyl ethyl ketone and toluene. The solution is cooled to cause crystallization of *paraffin waxes*. Additives are then put in the refined oil to stabilize it against oxidation and to improve its physical properties. Small amounts of synthetic resins have a remarkable effect on the extension of the fluid range of oils. Such compounds are known as *pour-point depressants*, since they lower the temperature at which the oil becomes too viscous to pour.

Other Products. Various mixtures of distillable fractions are used widely as solvents. Solvent *naphthas* include *petroleum ether*, a 30 to 60° fraction chiefly containing pentanes and hexanes, and fractions known in laboratories as *ligroin*. *Mineral oil* is a high-boiling fraction that has been decolorized by treatment with adsorbents. *Petrolatum* is a semisolid fraction which has been extracted to remove much of the dark colored material. If any destructive distillation of petroleum is carried on exhaustively without addition of hydrogen, a highly carbonaceous residue known as *petroleum coke* is obtained. Such a residue is inevitably obtained in any process designed to increase the yield of volatile hydrocarbons, since the over-all process demands redistribution of hydrogen atoms to the ends of the short chains created by cracking.

The Reactions of Petroleum Technology

The transformations of petroleum constituents are chemically complex in detail, but involve relatively few fundamental reaction patterns. High-temperature cracking without catalysts must involve free-radical reactions, but most of the reactions are carried out in the presence of acidic catalysts, including sulfuric acid, aluminum halides, and a wide variety of metal oxides. Such catalytic reactions can usually be correlated by the hypothesis that carbonium ions are involved as intermediates. Representations based upon this assumption are certainly oversimplified, but lead to a basic understanding of much of petroleum chemistry.

Isomerization

Reforming of a gasoline fraction to increase branching is the simplest of the common reactions of petroleum chemistry. Model studies have been carried out with butane, pentane, and simple alicyclics that yield relatively uncomplicated product mixtures. For example, the butanes may be equilibrated fairly rapidly in contact with aluminum halides at temperatures of $100°$ or higher.

$$CH_3CH_2CH_2CH_3 \underset{150°}{\overset{AlBr_3 \text{ or } AlCl_3}{\rightleftarrows}} (CH_3)_3CH$$
$$\sim 20\% \qquad\qquad\qquad \sim 80\%$$

It is found that pure dry aluminum bromide is not an effective catalyst unless the system contains some trace of alkyl halide, alcohol, or a combination of an alkene and water. Such *promoters* produce carbonium ions which initiate chain reactions leading to rearrangement. The key step is an exchange reaction involving *hydrogen transfer* from a hydrocarbon to a carbonium ion. Rearrangement of the new carbonium ion leads to isomerization.

Initiation:

$$R—Cl + AlCl_3 \rightleftarrows \overset{+}{R} \ \overset{-}{AlCl_4}$$
(Promoter)

H transfer:

$$\overset{+}{R} + CH_3CH_2CH_2CH_3 \longrightarrow RH + CH_3\overset{+}{CH}CH_2CH_3$$

$$CH_3\overset{+}{CH}CH_2CH_3 \rightleftarrows \overset{+}{CH_2}CH_2CH_2CH_3$$

Rearrangement:

$$CH_3\overset{+}{CH}CH_2CH_3 \longrightarrow (CH_3)_2\overset{+}{CH}CH_2 \xrightarrow{CH_3CH_2CH_2CH_3} (CH_3)_2CHCH_3 + CH_3\overset{+}{CH}CH_2CH_3$$

Chain termination:

$$\overset{+}{R} + \overset{-}{AlCl_4} \longrightarrow R—Cl + AlCl_3$$

Conversion of *n*-butane into isobutane is of importance industrially, and is interesting as a prototype for catalytic reforming of low-octane gasolines. Considerable amounts of *n*-butane are produced in cracking reactions and converted to isobutane, which is needed for synthesis of aviation gasoline by alkylation of olefins.

Another much studied isomerization is interconversion of cyclohexane and methylcyclopentane. Equilibrium is established very rapidly in the presence of acid catalysts. The equilibrium constant is very temperature-sensitive; cyclohexane is relatively more stable at low temperatures.

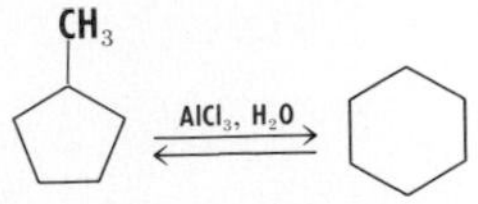

12.5% (25°)　　87.5% (25°)
25.6% (77°)　　74.4% (77°)

The chain-propagating steps of the reaction are as follows:

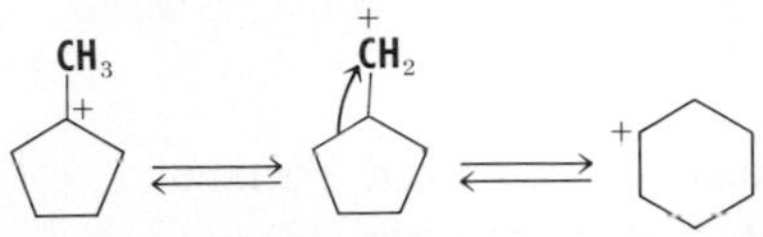

Both of the above reaction sequences involve steps, such as the rearrangement of tertiary carbonium ions to primary isomers, which are not observed in carbonium-ion rearrangements such as those discussed in Chap. 20. The apparent anomaly is readily understood by consideration of differences in reaction conditions. Carbonium ions involved in reactions such as nucleophilic substitution are formed once and have only very short lifetimes. Carbonium ions produced in catalytic isomerization live a relatively long time, since nucleophiles are present in the reaction mixtures in low concentration. Furthermore, the cations may be formed repeatedly. *Consequently, interconversions involving relatively unstable ions can be achieved in reforming operations.*

Noncatalytic reforming is frequently applied to low-octane, straight-run, and cracked gasoline stocks. The process is commercially desirable because of its low cost. No very illuminating model studies have been carried out, but indications are strong that the success of the process depends upon the destruction of *normal* paraffins by selective cracking and that little true isomerization is involved. If this is correct, noncatalytic reforming involves free-radical intermediates, as discussed below in connection with thermal cracking.

Cracking

High-boiling petroleum fractions can be cracked to form useful amounts of gasoline and gaseous hydrocarbons. Both thermal and catalytic cracking are used. Table 26.3 shows typical results of standardized thermal-cracking experiments with various stocks.

The ease of cracking of stocks varies with their chemical nature. Paraffins are cracked more rapidly than naphthenes by the thermal process, but the reverse is true of *catalytic cracking*, which is carried out over acidic oxide catalysts. Until recently catalytic cracking was

TABLE 26.3   *Yields of Products from Cracking of Various Stocks at 425° for 1 Hour*

Stock	Boiling range, °C	Yield of gasoline	Total yield of all new fractions
Naphtha	180–220		17
Kerosene	220–270	15	25
Gas oil	270–300	16	33
Gas oil	300–325	18	46
Total residue	>300	18	
Heavy distillate	250–286 at 6 mm	22	85

regarded as commercially impractical, because of the high costs of catalysts which agglomerate and rapidly deteriorate as they become covered with tars. Recently a new technique utilizing *fluidized catalysts* has largely solved the problem. A fluidized catalyst bed consists of particles of finely divided solid kept suspended in a gas stream. The bed is handled as a fluid. Oil to be cracked is preheated and mixed with a stream of fluidized catalyst suspended in hydrocarbon gases. The mixture is passed through the reaction chamber, and the catalyst is separated subsequently in a Cyclone separator. The catalyst is passed through a *regenerator*, where carbonaceous deposits are burned off at about 600°. Silica-alumina cracking catalysts are regenerated thousands of times without noticeable deterioration.

Free-radical Mechanism. The weakest bonds in an alkane are carbon-carbon bonds, and at temperatures above 450° these bonds begin to break at an appreciable rate to produce free radicals. Fragmentation and subsequent chain reactions initiated by radicals account for the thermal cracking of heavy hydrocarbon oils. The changes may be illustrated with the well-studied pyrolysis of *n*-butane, which is outlined in Fig. 26.1. Methyl and ethyl radicals, produced by fragmentation, carry on reaction chains by abstracting hydrogen atoms from *n*-butane. Small amounts of hydrogen are also produced as a result of the formation of hydrogen atoms by fragmentation. Chains are terminated by radical union and disproportionation.

Isopropyl radicals can give an olefin only if the fragmentation to hydrogen atoms occurs. Consequently, compounds containing isopropyl groups give considerable amounts of hydrogen. The cracking of isopentane illustrates the reactions.

$$\begin{array}{c} CH_3 \\ \diagdown \\ \diagup \\ CH_3 \end{array} CHCH_2CH_3 + R\cdot \longrightarrow RH + \begin{array}{c} CH_3 \\ \diagdown \\ \diagup \\ CH_3 \end{array} CHCH_2CH_2\cdot$$

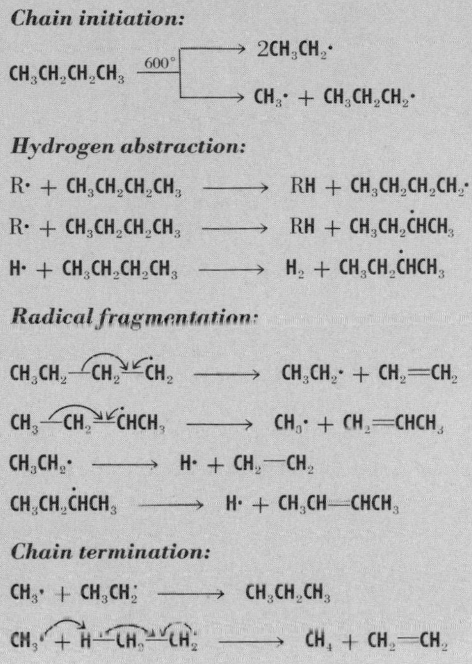

Chain initiation:

$$CH_3CH_2CH_2CH_3 \xrightarrow{600^\circ} \begin{cases} 2CH_3CH_2\cdot \\ CH_3\cdot + CH_3CH_2CH_2\cdot \end{cases}$$

Hydrogen abstraction:

$$R\cdot + CH_3CH_2CH_2CH_3 \longrightarrow RH + CH_3CH_2CH_2CH_2\cdot$$

$$R\cdot + CH_3CH_2CH_2CH_3 \longrightarrow RH + CH_3CH_2\dot{C}HCH_3$$

$$H\cdot + CH_3CH_2CH_2CH_3 \longrightarrow H_2 + CH_3CH_2\dot{C}HCH_3$$

Radical fragmentation:

$$CH_3CH_2-CH_2\overset{\curvearrowright}{-}CH_2 \longrightarrow CH_3CH_2\cdot + CH_2{=}CH_2$$

$$CH_3-CH_2\overset{\curvearrowright}{-}CHCH_3 \longrightarrow CH_3\cdot + CH_2{=}CHCH_3$$

$$CH_3CH_2\cdot \longrightarrow H\cdot + CH_2-CH_2$$

$$CH_3CH_2\dot{C}HCH_3 \longrightarrow H\cdot + CH_3CH{=}CHCH_3$$

Chain termination:

$$CH_3\cdot + CH_3CH_2\cdot \longrightarrow CH_3CH_2CH_3$$

$$CH_3\cdot + H-CH_2\overset{\curvearrowright}{-}CH_2\cdot \longrightarrow CH_4 + CH_2{=}CH_2$$

FIG. 26.1 *Thermal cracking of n-butane.*

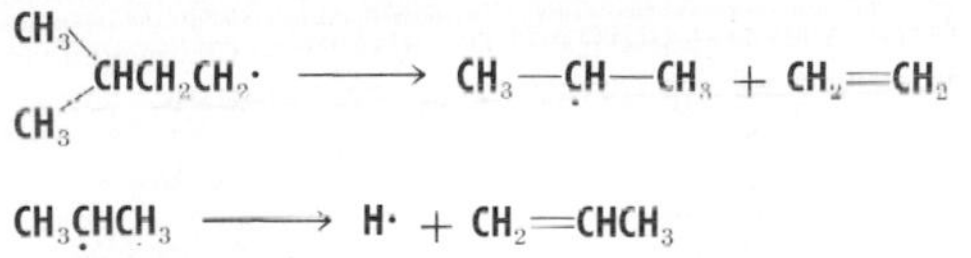

$$\begin{matrix} CH_3 \\ \diagdown \\ \diagup \\ CH_3 \end{matrix} CHCH_2CH_2\cdot \longrightarrow CH_3-\dot{C}H-CH_3 + CH_2{=}CH_2$$

$$CH_3\dot{C}HCH_3 \longrightarrow H\cdot + CH_2{=}CHCH_3$$

Table 26.4 shows the composition of the product mixture formed in the cracking of isopentane.

TABLE 26.4. *Products of Pyrolysis of Isopentane*

Product	Yield, %
Hydrogen	7.5
Methane	31.0
Ethane	5.5
Ethylene	11.0
Propylene	14.5
Butene-2	10.5
Isobutene	15.0

Rearrangement of larger alkyl radicals may occur by cyclic hydrogen abstraction.

Some rearrangements may involve 1,2-shifts, although such reactions are not nearly as important in the free-radical field as they are in carbonium-ion chemistry.

$$CH_3CH_2\overset{\cdot}{C}H_2 \cdot \longrightarrow CH_3\overset{\cdot}{C}HCH_3$$

Cracking of petroleum stocks is carried out under fairly high pressure, and both gaseous and liquid phases are usually present in the reactor. The reactions are too complex to describe by a complete set of equations. However, results are consistent with the view that reactions of the types illustrated by simple hydrocarbons are responsible for the changes which occur in petroleum cracking. In the highly concentrated reaction mixtures encountered in petroleum cracking, yields of gaseous products are relatively low, and some products with increased molecular weight are formed. Yields of gases are low because of the tendency of radicals to abstract hydrogen from hydrocarbon molecules before the radicals are completely broken down by fragmentation. High-molecular-weight products probably arise from addition of radicals to alkenes formed by cracking. The addition reaction is the same as the chain-growth reaction in free-radical polymerization of vinyl compounds (Chap. 25). The following is an arbitrarily chosen example in which a typical naphthenic structure is used.

Products of transfer, fragmentation, and
⟶ further polymerization
reactions

Catalytic Cracking. Oxide catalysts probably cause cracking by way of carbonium ions formed on catalyst surfaces. The process can be carried out at lower temperatures than those required for thermal cracking. In practice, fairly high temperatures and short contact times, achieved by high space velocities of the stock and fluid catalyst, are used. Table 26.5 shows some typical results of cracking experiments.

Critical reactions in catalytic cracking may be formulated in the same way as the isomerization reactions of carbonium ions shown on page 239. The actual cracking involves the additional step of carbonium-ion fragmentation which has been observed with model compounds.

The octane number of catalytically cracked gasoline is usually higher than that of a thermal-cracking product. The difference probably reflects the fact that 1,2-rearrangements are faster with carbonium ions than with free radicals. Such rearrangements tend to produce many branches in the molecules and also facilitate aromatization by converting cyclopentanes to cyclohexanes. Octane numbers of cracked gasolines are often low, and can be improved somewhat by a brief reforming treatment with an oxide or aluminum halide catalyst at low temperature (to avoid further cracking to gaseous products).

One superior feature of catalytic cracking is the low yield of methane. Chemically the result can be attributed to the reluctance of any chemical system to form the methyl cation. From a practical point of view, the result is desirable because methane is essentially useless for further rebuilding into gasoline.

Difficult:

TABLE 26.5 *Catalytic Cracking of an East Texas Gas Oil with Boiling Range of 250 to 540°*

Temperature, °C	413	477	474	513
Contact time, sec	30	30	15	15
Yields, %				
C_1–C_3 gas†	3.1	13.0	6.8	17.8
Butanes	7.9	15.9	12.7	14.1
Gasoline (C_4-free)	36.2	41.5	41.5	39.8
Gas oil	56.9	32.3	?	29.8

† Measured as volume per cent; may contain some of the butane fraction. Other yields are expressed as weight per cent.

Alkylation and Polymerization

High-octane gasoline is obtained by catalytic recombination of C_2 to C_4 alkenes and alkanes from cracking processes. Paraffin alkylation with olefins is the most important procedure. Alkylation is carried out at low temperature, where equilibrium relationships favor $C-C$ bond formation rather than cracking, in the presence of strongly acidic catalysts such as sulfuric acid or liquid hydrogen fluoride.

$$(CH_3)_3CH + (CH_3)_2C{=}CH_2 \xrightarrow[0-15°]{H_2SO_4} (CH_3)_3CCH_2CH(CH_3)_2$$
Isooctane

The reaction may be regarded as an acid-catalyzed dimerization of isobutene followed by a hydrogen transfer with isobutane. The latter reaction is favored in competition with the formation of higher isobutene polymers by use of excess alkane in the feed stock.

$$(CH_3)_2C{=}CH_2 + H_2SO_4 \rightleftharpoons (CH_3)_3\overset{+}{C} + HS\overset{-}{O_4}$$

$$(CH_3)_3\overset{+}{C} + (CH_3)_2C{=}CH_2 \rightleftharpoons (CH_3)_3CCH_2\overset{+}{C}(CH_3)_2$$

$$(CH_3)_3CCH_2\overset{+}{C}(CH_3)_2 + (CH_3)_3CH \longrightarrow (CH_3)_3CCH_2CH(CH_3)_2 + (CH_3)_3\overset{+}{C}$$

Many alkylation reactions are carried out with gaseous alkenes and alkanes. The production of diisopropyl from isobutane and ethylene is particularly interesting, since a rearrangement occurs.

$$(CH_3)_3CH + CH_2{=}CH_2 \xrightarrow[550°]{AlCl_3} (CH_3)_2CHCH(CH_3)_2$$
Diisopropyl
(2,3-Dimethylbutane)

$$(CH_3)_3\overset{+}{C} + CH_2{=}CH_2 \longrightarrow (CH_3)_3CCH_2\overset{+}{CH_2} \xrightarrow{Rearrangements}$$

$$(CH_3)_2\overset{+}{C}CH(CH_3)_2 \xrightarrow{(CH_3)_3CH} (CH_3)_2CHCH(CH_3)_2 + (CH_3)_3\overset{+}{C}$$

Dimerization of C_3 and C_4 alkenes may be controlled to give high yields of diolefins. Catalytic hydrogenation of the latter yields high-octane fuels.

$$2(CH_3)_2C{=}CH_2 \xrightarrow{H_2SO_4} (CH_3)_3CCH{=}C(CH_3)_2 + (CH_3)_3CCH_2\underset{\underset{CH_3}{|}}{C}{=}CH_2 \xrightarrow{H_2,\ Ni} (CH_3)_3CCH_2CH(CH_3)_2$$
Diisobutene   Isooctane

$$(CH_3)_2C{=}CH_2 + CH_3CH{=}CH_2 \xrightarrow{H_2SO_4} (CH_3)_2CHCH{=}C(CH_3)_2 \xrightarrow{H_2,\ Ni} (CH_3)_2CHCH_2CH(CH_3)_2$$

Isobutene, propylene, and ethylene are all produced in cracking processes, but in insufficient amounts to satisfy industrial needs for gasoline synthesis and other chemical processes. The supplies are therefore augmented by dehydrogenation of the corresponding alkanes over a hydrogenation catalyst such as an oxide mixture containing chromium. Hydrogen produced in this way can be utilized directly at the refinery site.

$$(CH_3)_3CH \xrightarrow[400°]{Catalyst} (CH_3)_2C=CH_2 + H_2$$

Hydrogenation in Petroleum Refining

The ratio of carbon to hydrogen in petroleum is greater than that in desirable fuels. Therefore various procedures have been developed to make possible more complete utilization of petroleum stock. In principle, cracking with the addition of hydrogen could produce only materials of low molecular weight, with the complete elimination of heavy oils and coke. In practice, this cannot be done and is probably commercially unfeasible because of the high cost of hydrogen produced outside of the refinery. Cracked stocks are often hydrogenated to destroy nonaromatic unsaturation, and the hydrogen-rich products can be blended with gas oil as a means of introducing more available hydrogen during cracking. The hydrogen makes itself available by means of the previously described hydrogen-transfer reactions of free radicals and carbonium ions. A typical sequence of operations is as follows:

1. Crack 350–540° gas oil.
2. Separate by distillation into naphtha, gas oil, and heavy oil (> 540°).
3. Partially hydrogenate the naphtha to produce a hydrogen-donor stock.
4. Mix the hydrogen-rich naphtha with the 540° oil.
5. Heat the mixture to 400° to effect some hydrogen transfer to the heavy-oil constituents. (Such mild treatment produces relatively little change in the molecular-weight distribution.)
6. Distill the naphtha which has increased unsaturation.
7. Crack the hydrogen-rich heavy oil in a catalytic process.

Hydroforming is a modified cracking process carried out over a hydrogenation catalyst such as molybdenum-aluminum oxide. Hydrogen is introduced into the system to maintain the activity of the catalyst, but the process actually is one of *dehydrogenation*. Cyclization and aromatization of paraffins and the aromatization of naphthenes occur.

Hydrofining is mild catalytic hydrogenation of unsaturated and sulfur-containing gasolines. Saturation of alkenes makes the gasoline much less sensitive to air oxidation, and removal of sulfur as hydrogen sulfide improves the response of fuels to lead tetraethyl and prevents formation of corrosive acids during combustion.

Hydrocarbon Oxidation

At low temperatures, hydrocarbons are oxidized by a free-radical chain mechanism. The first oxidation product in the simplest cases is a hydroperoxide.

$$\text{Chain propagation} \begin{cases} R\cdot + O_2 \longrightarrow RO_2\cdot \\ RO_2\cdot + RH \longrightarrow RO_2H + R\cdot \end{cases}$$

At temperatures of $100°$ or higher, breakdown of hydroperoxides is rapid. Since the products are radicals capable of initiating oxidation chains, the oxidation process is autocatalytic at high temperatures. Branching-chain reactions are probably responsible for the rapid combustion of fuels at high temperature.

$$RO_2H \longrightarrow RO\cdot + HO\cdot$$

Relative reactivities of hydrocarbons in oxidation are predictable on the basis of the relative ease of hydrogen abstraction from various **C—H** bonds. Olefins and alkylaromatics, which are converted to resonance-stabilized radicals, are readily oxidized at low temperatures.

Cumene   Cumyl hydroperoxide

Tertiary hydrogens are most easily removed from paraffins, and *tert*-hydroperoxides can be produced in reasonable yields.

$$(CH_3)_3CH + O_2 \longrightarrow (CH_3)_3COOH$$
$$\text{\textit{tert}-Butyl hydroperoxide}$$

Decalin   9-Decalyl hydroperoxide

Partial oxidation of natural gas is used on a limited commercial scale to produce mixtures of carboxylic acids, aldehydes, ketones, and alcohols. Incomplete combustion of methane is utilized to produce carbon black, which has many uses as an adsorbent. Low-temperature oxidation of fuel stocks during storage and of lubricating oils under operating conditions are major problems to petroleum producers. Instability of alkene-containing gasolines is due to oxidation which results in formation of resinous condensation products derived from primary oxidation products. Such products are called *gums* and are undesirable, since they lead to fouling of fuel lines and carburetion systems. As was previously indicated (page 609), the stability of cracked gasoline is improved by hydrogenation. Further protection against oxidation is provided by addition of *antioxidants,* which inhibit oxidation by destroying peroxy radicals ($RO_2\cdot$). The best antioxidants are *phenols.* and *aromatic amines.* The reactivity of inhibitors is increased by introduction of alkyl or other electron-donor groups as substituents on the aromatic nuclei.

$$OH$$
$$(CH_3)_3C \qquad C(CH_3)_3$$
$$CH_3$$

$$NHC_6H_5$$

2,6-Di-*tert*-butyl-4-methylphenol   *N*-Phenyl-β-naphthylamine

Typical antioxidants

Interestingly enough, compounds which are effective as chain-stoppers in oxidation are ineffective as inhibitors of vinyl polymerization (page 574) and vice versa. The fact demonstrates that the radicals trapped by the antioxidants are $RO_2\cdot$ rather than $R\cdot$, since the latter should behave chemically like growing polymer radicals. Empirically, one generalizes that aromatics which have a high electron density are highly reactive toward peroxy radicals. The generalization is consistent with a mechanism of inhibitor action which includes intermediate formation of a molecular complex between the radical and the inhibitor. Partial transfer of an electron from the inhibitor to the radical would stabilize the complex.

$$RO_2\cdot + \quad \text{[radical complex]} \quad \xrightarrow{RO_2\cdot}$$

Radical complex

$$(CH_3)_3C \qquad C(CH_3)_3 \qquad + RO_2H$$
$$H_3C \quad O_2R$$

Other Sources of Motor Fuels

The destructive hydrogenation of coal has been used in wartime by petroleum-poor countries to produce high-grade motor fuels. The process is successful and of interest, because of the large amount of coal in the earth's crust. At present it is too expensive to compete with petroleum as a source of fuel.

The Fischer-Tropsch synthesis of normal hydrocarbons from carbon monoxide and hydrogen can be controlled to give sizable yields of products in the gasoline boiling range.

$$nCO + (2n + 1)H_2 \xrightarrow[20-30°]{\text{Co or Ni catalyst}} C_nH_{2n+2} + H_2O$$

The products can be reformed to produce high-octane gasoline. By modification of the reaction conditions, the Fischer-Tropsch synthesis can be controlled to yield considerable amounts of normal alcohols. If a fluidized catalyst is used, the hydrogenation of carbon monoxide is known as the *Hydrocol* process.

Another source of petroleumlike material is *shale oil*. The oil is present in clays known as shales. No effective way has yet been developed to extract the oil, which is strongly adsorbed, although exploratory work is in progress that may eventually make available another vast source of oil.

Problems

1. Define each of the following terms:

a. Kerosene	*f.* Reforming	*k.* Cetane number
b. Gas oil	*g.* Shale oil	*l.* Antioxidant
c. Cracking	*h.* Fluidized catalysts	*m.* Naphthene
d. Hydroforming	*i.* Alkylation	*n.* Hydrogen transfer
e. Hydrofining	*j.* Octane number	

2. Formulate reasonable mechanisms for the following reactions:

a. $(CH_3)_3CH + CH_3CH=CH_2 \xrightarrow{AlCl_3, HCl}$ Major $\begin{cases} \text{2,3-dimethylpentane} \\ \text{2,4-dimethylpentane} \end{cases}$ + $\begin{cases} \text{trimethylpentanes} \\ \text{propane} \\ \text{isopentane} \\ \text{2,3-dimethylbutane} \end{cases}$

b. $(CH_3)_2CHCH_2CH_3 + (CH_3)_3CCl \xrightarrow{AlCl_3, \, 0.001 \text{ sec}} (CH_3)_2CClCH_2CH_3 + (CH_3)_3CH$

c. $CH_3CH=CH_2 + 2(CH_3)_3CH \xrightarrow{AlCl_3, HCl} CH_3CH_2CH_3 + C_8H_{18}$

d. $CH_3(CH_2)_6CH_3 \xrightarrow{Cr_2O_3-Al_2O_3}$ +

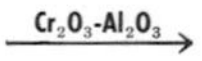

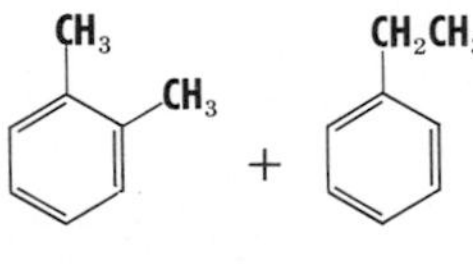

e. 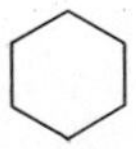 $\longrightarrow CH_2=CHCH=CH_2 + CH_2=CH_2 + H_2$

3. Devise syntheses of the following compounds, using petroleum chemicals as starting materials.

a. Toluene	*d.* Maleic anhydride	*f.* $(CH_3)_3CCO_2H$
b. $BrCH_2CH_2CH_2CH_2Br$	*e.* $CH_3CH_2COCH_3$	*g.* $CH_2(CO_2C_2H_5)_2$
c. $CH_2=CHCH=CH_2$		

4. Outline a research program designed to discover and test new cracking catalysts.

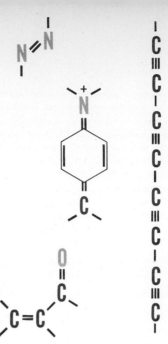

27

Spectra and Dyes

Absorption of light by organic compounds attracts the interest of chemists for a variety of reasons. Semiempirical interpretation of spectral data is of great value in characterization and identification of unknown materials and in quantitative analyses. Theoretical interpretation of spectra has proved to be the best testing ground for mathematical methods of theoretical chemistry and has provided a valuable tool in working out exact energy relationships among organic compounds. Finally, the many organic dyestuffs have made a major contribution to the aesthetic side of our lives and at one time provided the major stimulus for development of industrial organic chemistry.

Absorption Spectra

Visible light has wavelengths between 4,000 and 8,000 A. The peculiar quality of such light is entirely dependent upon the mechanisms of message relay along the optic nerve; the chemist makes no real distinction between visible and invisible light. Light with wavelengths shorter than 4,000 A is called ultraviolet, and that having wavelengths longer than 8,000 A is known as infrared.

> The term *wavelength* has been introduced without comment. The physical fact that light has wave character is readily revealed if one recollects that a beam of light does not travel in a straight line but tends to "bend around corners" to some extent. In particular, one can observe that shadows do not have sharp edges. The light of longer wavelength (red) strays faster than short waves (blue) from the beam boundary defined by the shadowing edge. One of the ways of measuring the wavelength of light is by study of the interference, or diffraction, of light beams passed through two fine parallel slits. All light, irrespective of wavelength, has the same velocity, 3.00×10^{10} cm/sec.

Certain experiments show that light has a particle as well as a wave nature. Study of electrons emitted from a metallic surface shows that the energy of the electrons is a function of the wavelength of the light. For a given wavelength, the *number* of electrons emitted is determined by the light intensity. In other words, it seems that the energy is transferred from light with the conservation of momentum. The conclusion that light is made up of a stream of particles which all have the same velocity but have different energies is quite contrary to the laws of classical mechanics. At the present time, we regard a light beam as a stream of particles, known as *photons*. However, the motion of photons is described by wave equations rather than by the equations of classical mechanics. It has previously been noted, in the discussion of electrons (Chap. 5), that classical mechanics suffers collapse when applied to small particles. When photons are absorbed by a compound, they are converted either into electronic energy or into kinetic energy.

Unless photons are of appropriate wavelength, corresponding to the separation in energy between the discrete energy levels of the molecules, absorption cannot occur. If a series of light beams of varying wavelengths is passed through a thin layer of a compound, some wavelengths will be absorbed and others will be transmitted. A record of the amount of light absorbed by a sample as a function of the wavelength of the light is called an *absorption spectrum*. In principle, all absorption spectra should consist of lines, but in practice one observes absorption *bands*. A spectrum has a series of maxima and minima connected by smooth curves. Typical absorption spectra are shown in Fig. 27.1.

Symbols. The fundamental equations of spectroscopy relate wavelength and frequency of light to energy.

(1) $\quad \lambda\nu = c$

·Wavelength $\times$ frequency = velocity

(2) $\quad E = h\nu$

Energy = Planck's constant $\times$ frequency

(3) $\quad E = \dfrac{hc}{\lambda}$

(4) $\quad \dfrac{1}{\lambda} = \bar{\nu} =$ wave numbers; $\qquad \nu = c\bar{\nu}$

To place the measurement of light energy on a familiar basis, a quantity, known as the *einstein,* is defined as the energy of Avogadro's number (6.02×10^{23}) of photons. For example, the energy of an einstein of 4,000-A light is given by the following equations:

(5) $\quad E = \dfrac{6.62 \times 10^{-27} \text{ erg sec} \times 3.00 \times 10^{10} \text{ cm/sec}}{4,000 \times 10^{-8} \text{ cm}}$

$\qquad = 4.97 \times 10^{-12}$ erg/photon

(6) $\quad E_{(E)} = 4.97 \times 10^{-12} \times 6.02 \times 10^{23} = 2.99 \times 10^{12}$ erg/einstein

$\qquad = 71.4$ kcal/einstein

The energies required to break a single bond in organic molecules range from 38 (**O—O**) to 103 (**C—H**) kcal/mole. Absorption of visible or ultraviolet light is potentially capable of breaking chemical bonds, causing photochemical reactions.

Light absorption in the *visible and ultraviolet* regions causes the excitation of *electrons*. Near infrared excites molecules to higher vibrational states (higher frequencies of the motions of molecules that bend and stretch bonds). Microwaves, which have very low energy per photon, raise molecules as a whole to higher rotational levels. Electronic and vibrational spectra are widely used in the characterization of organic compounds. Figure 27.2 summarizes the relationships between light absorption in various spectroscopic "regions" and the types of molecular excitation associated with absorption.

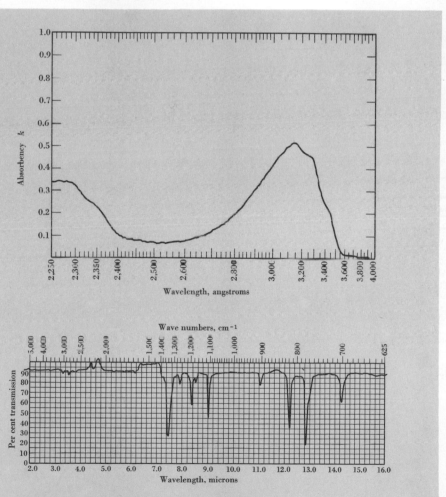

FIG. 27.1 *Typical absorption spectra.*

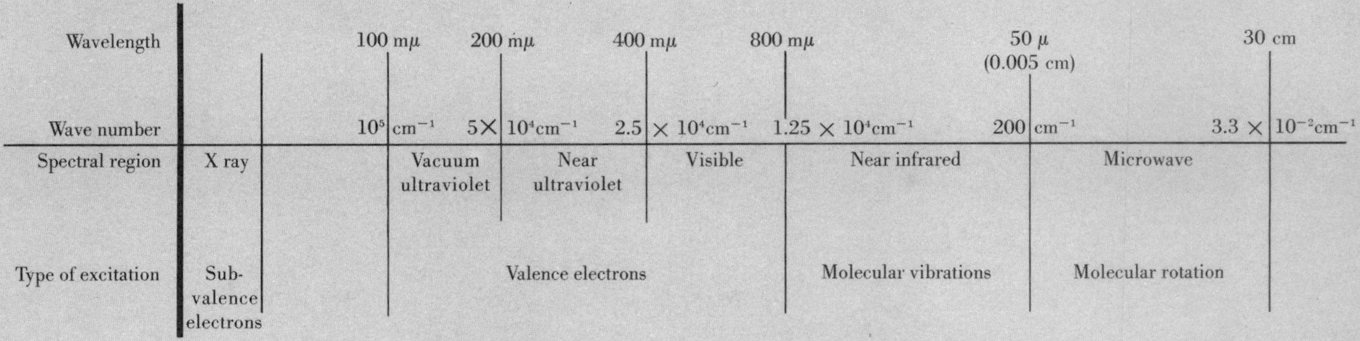

Wavelength	100 mμ	200 mμ	400 mμ	800 mμ	50 μ (0.005 cm)	30 cm
Wave number	10^6 cm^{-1}	5×10^4 cm^{-1}	2.5×10^4 cm^{-1}	1.25×10^4 cm^{-1}	200 cm^{-1}	3.3×10^{-2} cm^{-1}
Spectral region	X ray	Vacuum ultraviolet	Near ultraviolet	Visible	Near infrared	Microwave
Type of excitation	Sub-valence electrons	Valence electrons			Molecular vibrations	Molecular rotation

FIG. 27.2   Correlation between spectroscopic regions and types of molecular excitation.

Quantitative spectrophotometric measurements are usually reported in terms of the Beer-Lambert absorption law [Eq. (7)].

(7) $\dfrac{I}{I_0} = e^{-kcl}$

    I = intensity of transmitted light
    I_0 = intensity of incident light
    k = molar absorption coefficient
    c = concentration of the absorbing species in moles per liter
    l = sample thickness

Equation (8) is another useful form of Eq. (7).

(8) $2.303 \log \dfrac{I_0}{I} = kcl$

Visible and Ultraviolet Spectra

The near-ultraviolet spectrum extends from the visible spectrum (4,000 A) to about 2,100 A. The lower limit is determined by practical considerations. Oxygen absorbs strongly at wavelengths below 2,100 A; hence a light beam to be used for spectrophotometry in the far ultraviolet cannot pass through air. Vacuum spectrophotometers have been built for study of the far ultraviolet, but high cost and other considerations have prevented routine use of such instruments.

Alkanes show no absorption above 1,600 A, since all the electrons in C—H and C—C bonds are very firmly bound. In saturated compounds containing hetero atoms, longer-wavelength absorption arises from excitation of nonbonding electrons. Those atoms, such as iodine, bromine, and sulfur, which lose electrons most easily absorb at the longest wavelengths (Table 27.1).

Electrons in unsaturated groups are easily excited to higher π orbitals. With a few exceptions, found in highly symmetrical compounds, $\pi \longrightarrow \pi$ transitions are very intense (have large absorption coefficients). Furthermore, there is a remarkable similarity among the

TABLE 27.1   *Absorption Due to Hetero Atoms*

Compound	Absorption characteristics
CH_3CH_2F	Below 1,600 A
CH_3CH_2Cl	Strong absorption at 2,000 A
CH_3CH_2Br	Maximum at 2,040 A
CH_3CH_2I	Maximum at 2,500 A
$CH_3CH_2OCH_2CH_3$	Intense maximum at 1,820–1,890 A
$CH_3CH_2SCH_2CH_2$	Intense maximum at 3,100 A

TABLE 27.2   *Vacuum-ultraviolet Maxima of Unconjugated Chromophoric Groups†*

Compound	λ_{max} A
$CH_2\!=\!CH_2$	1,625
$CH\!\equiv\!CH$	1,775
$HC\!\equiv\!N$	1,750
$(CH_3)_2C\!=\!O$	1,870

† Compounds containing these chromophores may also have *weak* absorption maxima at long wavelengths. Such bands are not due to $\pi \longrightarrow \pi$ transitions.

$\pi \longrightarrow \pi$ transitions of all unsaturated groups, *irrespective* of the atoms they contain. The association between unsaturation and light absorption was first recognized by Graebe and Liebermann in 1868. A few years later Witt coined the term *chromophore* to describe the role of groups such as $C\!=\!C$, $C\!=\!O$, $N\!=\!N$, and NO_2.

Unconjugated double bonds have absorption maxima in the vaccum ultraviolet and show sharply rising absorption just above 2,000 A, at the end of the far ultraviolet. Positions of absorption maxima for $\pi \longrightarrow \pi$ transitions of simple unsaturated compounds are summarized in Table 27.2.

Conjugation shifts $\pi \longrightarrow \pi$ bands to longer wavelengths and increases their number and intensity. As is illustrated by the examples in Table 27.3, compounds containing two conjugated double bonds have intense maxima near 2,000 A, which can often be observed with ordinary spectrophotometers.

Further extension of a conjugated system produces regular shifts to longer wavelengths. To a remarkably close approximation, the wavelength of the first strong absorption bond in a conjugated system is proportional to the distance between the terminal atoms of the conjugated system. All-trans polyenes always absorb at longer wavelengths than their stereoisomers, which are less extended because of the presence of cis linkages. Examples of absorption characteristics of extensively conjugated systems are shown in Table 27.4.

TABLE 27.3   *Positions of First $\pi \longrightarrow \pi$ Maxima in Compounds Containing Two Conjugated Double Bonds*

Compound	λ_{max}	k
$CH_2\!=\!CHCH\!=\!CH_2$	2,170	21,000
$CH_3CH\!=\!CHCHO$	2,170	16,000
$CH_2\!=\!CHC\!\equiv\!CH$	2,190	6,500
$CH_2\!=\!CHC\!\equiv\!N$	2,100	10,000
$CH_3CH\!=\!CHNO_2$	2,290	9,500

TABLE 27.4   First $\pi \longrightarrow \pi$ Absorption Maxima of Conjugated Molecules

Compound	λ_{max}	k
$CH_2{=}CHCH{=}CHCH{=}CH_2$	2,580	35,000
$CH_3CH{=}CHCH{=}CHCH{=}CHCH_2OH$	2,650	53,000
$CH_2{=}CHCH{=}CHCHO$	2,630	27,000
$CH_3(CH{=}CH)_4CH_3$	2,960	52,000

$$H_3C \quad CH_3 \qquad CH_3 \qquad\qquad CH_3$$
$$CH{=}CHC{=}CHCH{=}CHC{=}CHCH_2OH$$
$$CH_3$$

Vitamin A

	3,600	70,000
	3,280	51,000

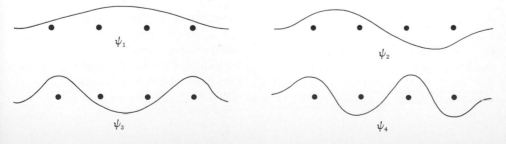

Lycopene

| | 4,700 | 185,000 |

The concept of the wave nature of electrons in unsaturated systems leads to a qualitative understanding of absorption spectra. The π electrons of ethylene may be regarded as having an associated wavelength about twice as long as the carbon-carbon double bond.

ψ_1

The approximation is crude, since it treats the positive potential of the carbon nuclei as though it were entirely concentrated halfway between nuclei. Chopping off the wave, which should really be extended to infinity, is another approximation. The second π orbital, which is unused in the ground state of ethylene (page 105), has a node midway between the nuclei, and the wavelength is half that of the occupied orbital.

ψ_2

In a $\pi \longrightarrow \pi$ transition, an electron is promoted from the lower to the higher orbital. The four π orbitals of butadiene may be represented by four standing waves which have zero, one, two, and three nodes.

ψ_1

ψ_2

ψ_3

ψ_4

TABLE 27.5   *Absorption Spectra of Aromatic Hydrocarbons*

	λ_{max}	k_{max}	λ_{max}	k_{max}	λ_{max}	k_{max}
	2,550	220	2,020	6,900	1,840	83,000
Naphthalene	3,120	250	2,750	5,600	2,200	110,000
Anthracene	†		3,750	7,900	2,520	200,000
Phenanthrene	3,300	250	2,950	13,000	2,520	50,000
Naphthacene	†		4,730	11,000	2,780	130,000
Pyrene	3,520	630	3,340	50,000	2,400	89,000
Chrysene	3,600	630	3,200	13,000	2,680	141,000
Azulene	6,070	263	3,410	4,360	2,730	55,000

† Low-intensity bonds may be merged with intense absorption at lower wavelengths.

The lowest orbitals, ψ_1 and ψ_2, are occupied by four electrons in the ground state of butadiene. In the first $\pi \longrightarrow \pi$ transition, an electron is excited from ψ_2 to ψ_3. Transition from ψ_1 to ψ_2 in ethylene shortens the wavelength of an electron a great deal, and therefore requires much energy. Since the $\psi_3 \longrightarrow \psi_4$ transition in butadiene does not decrease the length of the electron wave as much, butadiene absorbs at longer wavelengths (less excitation energy) than ethylene. The concept is essentially that of the *free-electron* model for conjugated systems. The method, with appropriate refinements, yields good results in quantitative calculations of the spectra of conjugated systems.

Aromatic Compounds. Aromatic hydrocarbons absorb at wavelengths close to those characteristic of open-chain polyene systems having similar dimensions. Because of the symmetry of aromatic systems, some transitions are "forbidden" and occur only with low intensity. Table 27.5 includes data for representative aromatic hydrocarbons. Azulene, which has a beautiful blue color, has a maximum at 6,070 A, showing that the rough correlation between the length of a conjugated system and its absorption characteristics sometimes breaks down very badly.

A $\pi \longrightarrow \pi$ transition of a conjugated hydrocarbon tends to separate electrons from the nuclei to which they are bound. The excited state is said to be more "polar" than the ground state. Polarity is described in the resonance method by the statement that structures such as I and III contribute relatively more to the excited state than to the ground state.

$$\overset{+}{C}H_2 - \overset{-}{C}H_2 \longleftrightarrow CH_2 = CH_2 \longleftrightarrow \overset{-}{C}H_2 - \overset{+}{C}H_2$$
$$\text{I} \qquad\qquad\qquad \text{II} \qquad\qquad\qquad \text{III}$$

Substituent Effects. Substituent effects on $\pi \longrightarrow \pi$ transitions have been studied intensively. Electron-donor substituents, such as alkyl, hydroxyl, alkoxyl, and amino, shift absorption to longer wavelengths (*bathochromic shift*). Such groups are known as *auxochromes*, since their effects are auxiliary to those of chromophores. Effects of such groups are as would be expected. The excitation process vacates a low-energy π orbital, allowing the unsaturated system to interact more strongly with the substituents in the excited state than in the ground state (Fig. 27.3). Electron-accepting substituents have an opposite effect, making excitation harder and shifting absorption maxima to shorter wavelengths.

Substituent effects have been studied most extensively with derivatives of benzene. Examples are shown in Table 27.6.

Steric Inhibition of Resonance. Since resonance interactions in conju-

TABLE 27.6 *Substituent Effects on the Absorption Spectra of Benzenoid Compounds*

Compound	λ_{max}	k_{max}
Benzene	2,540	204
Toluene	2,610	225
Chlorobenzene	2,635	190
Phenol	2,700	1,450
Aniline	2,800	1,430
Phenolate ion ($C_6H_5O^-$)	2,870	2,600
Anilinium ion ($C_6H_5NH_3^+$)	2,540	160

$$R_2\overset{..}{N}-CH=CH_2 \quad \longleftrightarrow \quad R_2\overset{+}{N}=CH-\overset{-}{CH_2}$$

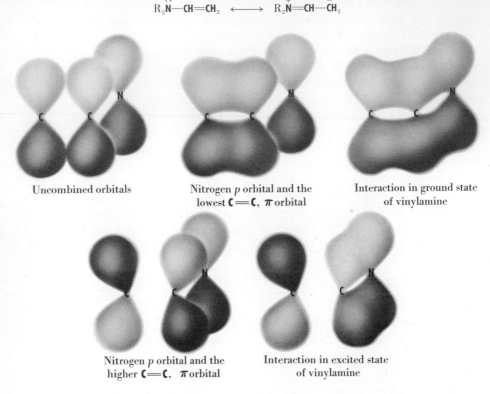

Uncombined orbitals   Nitrogen p orbital and the   Interaction in ground state
                               lowest $C=C$, π orbital   of vinylamine

Nitrogen p orbital and the   Interaction in excited state
higher $C=C$, π orbital   of vinylamine

FIG. 27.3   *Schematic representation of interactions in ground and excited states of a vinylamine.*

gated systems are increased by $\pi \longrightarrow \pi$ transitions, steric hindrance to coplanarity of conjugated systems makes the transitions more difficult. If steric hindrance is small, the intensity of absorption will fall with little change in the position of absorption maxima.   The effect is due to the fact that some of the normal vibrations of a slightly distorted molecule will occasionally bring the system into the coplanar configuration required for low-energy transitions.   If, on the other hand, steric hindrance is severe, so that coplanarity is not attained in any of the normal vibrational motions of the molecule, the excitation energy is increased, and λ_{max} will be observed at relatively short wavelengths.   Comparison of absorption by cis-trans isomers is reported in Table 27.7.   The cis isomers are sterically more hindered in each case.   Figure 27.4 illustrates steric hindrance in *cis*-stilbene.

Forbidden Transitions of Unsaturated Compounds.   In addition to $\pi \longrightarrow \pi$ transitions, compounds which contain double bonds to hetero atoms often have weak absorption bands at relatively long wavelengths. The transitions are known as $n \longrightarrow \pi$, since they involve excitation of

TABLE 27.7   *Absorption Spectra of Cis-Trans Isomers*

	Trans		Cis	
	λ_{max}	k_{max}	λ_{max}	k_{max}
$C_6H_5CH{=}CHC_6H_5$	2,950	27,000	2,800	10,500
$C_6H_5CH{=}CHCH{=}CH_2$	2,800	28,000	2,650	14,000
$C_6H_5CH{=}CHCO_2H$	2,730	21,000	2,640	9,500
$C_6H_5N{=}NC_6H_5$	3,170	20,000	3,240	15,000

nonbonding electrons from a hetero atom to a high-energy π orbital of the unsaturated system. Figure 27.5 contains a schematic comparison of $n \longrightarrow \pi$ and $\pi \longrightarrow \pi$ transitions.

The $n \longrightarrow \pi$ transitions of aliphatic aldehydes and ketones occur at about 2,850 A. Despite their low intensity ($k \cong 100\text{--}200$) the bands arc quite useful for characterization purposes. Conjugation with unsaturated systems shifts $n \longrightarrow \pi$ bands to longer wavelengths. The bands are found in the vicinity of 3,500 A in spectra of diaryl ketones. The characteristic yellow color of quinones and α-diketones is due to $n \longrightarrow \pi$ bands, as are the red and orange colors of azo compounds.

Charge-resonance and Electron-resonance Spectra. Conjugated ions and free radicals contain π electrons which are spread over a number of carbon atoms. Roughly, one can think of such electrons as rattling about in large boxes. Excitation of the loosely bound electrons is relatively easy, and ions and radicals, such as those derived from triphenylmethyl, have long-wavelength absorption bands. Absorption by anions and cations is usually intense, and the bands are called *charge-resonance spectra*. The first transitions of free radicals do not, as a first approximation, change the distribution of charge in the system, and the bands are known as *electron-resonance spectra*. The latter type of transition is characterized by low intensity.

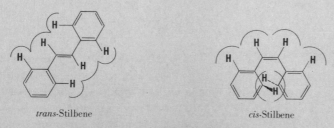

trans-Stilbene   *cis*-Stilbene

FIG. 27.4   *Configurations of cis- and trans-stilbene.   Hemicircles represent interference radii of hydrogen atoms.*

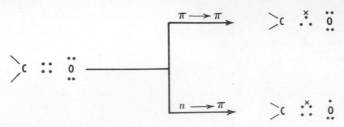

(✕ is the excited electron)

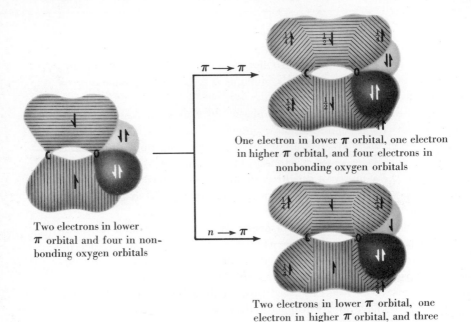

FIG. 27.5   *Comparison of n ⟶ π and π ⟶ π transitions of a carbonyl compound.*

Infrared Spectra

Near-infrared light excites molecules to higher vibrational-energy levels.   A nonlinear molecule containing n atoms has $3n - 6$ modes of vibrational motion.   Not all these modes are associated with observable infrared absorption bands for two reasons: First, in symmetrical molecules, some of the fundamental modes will be identical, or degenerate. Second, in order to be infrared-active, a vibration must change the dipole moment of the molecule in the course of excitation to a higher level.   An example of the latter *selection rule* is found with the carbon-carbon double-bond stretching frequency. The frequency falls between 1,600 and 1,680 cm^{-1} in most olefinic compounds but is absent in symmetrical *trans*-alkenes. Such compounds have no dipole moments, and none is introduced by stretching the C=C bond.

| *trans*-Olefin, | *cis*-Olefin, |
| infrared inactive | infrared active |

Infrared spectra of most organic molecules are so complex that a complete assignment of all absorption bands to particular vibrational modes is seldom made. There are, however, two principal ways in which the spectra are used in characterization studies. First, if comparison of the spectra of two samples shows them to be identical, one normally assumes that the samples are also identical. Second, *qualitative characterization* of the functional groups in molecules is the most useful general function of infrared spectra. Most groups have associated with them certain vibrational modes which vary very little from molecule to molecule. The infrared absorption bands arising from these vibrations are known as *group frequencies*.

Group Frequencies. The region in which group frequencies are usually sought lies between 3,500 and 1,500 cm^{-1}. The frequencies for stretching bonds to hydrogen are found at the high-frequency end of the region. The first are the O—H frequencies which lie between 3,500 and 3,700 cm^{-1}. However, hydrogen bonding makes O—H bonds easier to stretch and shifts the absorption to lower frequencies.

| Acetic acid monomer | Acetic acid dimer |
| $\tilde{\nu} = 3,521$ cm^{-1} | $\tilde{\nu} = 3,073$ cm^{-1} |

Table 27.8 lists some of the most useful of the infrared group frequencies.

The distribution of group frequencies within the broad spectral regions indicated in Table 27.8 can also be correlated with small variations in structure. Detailed characterization of a group frequency has been carried out exhaustively with the carbonyl group. The reasons for concentration on this particular function are several. First, the carbonyl is found in a number of important functional groups. Second, many natural

TABLE 27.8   Infrared Group Frequencies

Group	Frequencies, cm⁻¹
—O—H	3,500–3,700
>N—H	3,300–3,500
>C—H	2,880–3,030
—C≡C—	2,200–2,260
—C≡N	2,250
>C=O	1,660–1,870
>C=C<	1,600–1,680
—NO₂	1,500–1,650

products contain carbonyl groups.   And, third, *only* the carbonyl group contributes important absorption in the 1,660 to 1,870 cm⁻¹ region. Table 27.9 shows a partial classification of carbonyl absorption frequencies.

Other group frequencies, such as those due to C—C and C—O single-bond stretching, occur in the region below 1,600 cm⁻¹. However, assignments are difficult to make in the low-frequency region, because of interference from *skeletal* vibrations. The latter are complex motions in which many atoms within a molecule move in coordinated fashion. Some of the less complicated skeletal frequencies have been useful in characterization work, but the majority are not regularly reproduced in a large number of molecules and are useful primarily as characteristic "fingerprints" of individual compounds.

Raman Spectra

Raman spectra are closely related to infrared spectra. Both arise from the excitation of vibrational motions. Since different methods of excitation are used, the selection rules are different. Raman spectrometers rivaling infrared instruments in convenience of operation have not yet been developed, but the newer models show great promise. Since Raman data complement those from infrared, further development of Raman spectroscopy is anticipated.

When a beam of light is passed through a transparent material, some of the light is scattered at wide angles to the direction of incidence. In the spectrum of the scattered light, there are new lines, superimposed on the original spectrum. The *shifts* in the frequency correspond to molecular vibrational frequencies in the scattering material and constitute the Raman spectrum of the transmitting medium. Raman intensity depends upon the change in *polarizability* accompanying the excitation.

As a consequence, symmetrical vibrations, which are "forbidden" in the infrared, give rise to the strongest Raman lines.

Nuclear Magnetic Resonance Absorption

Many atomic nuclei possess magnetic moments associated with the spins of fundamental nuclear particles. Under normal circumstances, the individual nuclear moments within any material are oriented randomly, so that the system has no net magnetic moment. However, if the substance is placed between the poles of a powerful magnet, the moments tend to become aligned with the external magnetic field. Small amounts of energy are required to turn molecules so that the nuclear moments are out of alignment with the field. Two or more discrete energy states are set up, since the magnetic energy of nuclei is quantized. Normal thermal energy is sufficient to give an almost random distribution of nuclear moments in the most powerful magnetic fields available. However, in such a field, there will be a small net orientation with the field, and one can measure the energy required to promote nuclei to higher-energy states, out of alignment with the applied field. Measurement of this excitation energy is the basis of *nuclear magnetic resonance* (nmr) *absorption spectroscopy.*

TABLE 27.9   Carbonyl Absorption Frequencies

Group	Frequencies, cm^{-1}
Anhydride	1,800–1,850, 1,740–1,790
Acid chloride	1,770–1,815
Ester	
Aliphatic, saturated	1,739–1,750
Aliphatic, α,β-unsat. and aromatic	1,717–1,730
Carboxylic acid	
Aliphatic, saturated	1,705–1,725
Aliphatic, α,β-unsat.	1,700–1,710
Aromatic	1,680–1,700
Amide	1,630–1,700
Aldehyde	1,695–1,740
Ketone	
Aliphatic, saturated	1,706–1,725
Aliphatic, α,β-unsat.	1,665–1,685
Aliphatic, $\alpha,\beta,\alpha',\beta'$-diunsat.	1,660–1,670
Aryl-alkyl	1,680–1,700
Diaryl	1,660–1,670
Cyclopentanone	1,745–1,749
Cyclohexanone	1,706–1,720

The technique of measurement is simple in principle but difficult in practice. The sample is placed between the poles of a magnet and is surrounded by a spiral coil connected to a radio-frequency generator. The frequency of the impulse from the generator is varied, and when the frequency corresponds to the separation between the nuclear states, energy is absorbed by the system. Since variation of the rf signal cannot be accomplished easily, a more usual way of finding the resonance frequency is to vary the strength of the magnetic field slowly while maintaining the rf signal constant. Absorption of energy may be detected as a change in the electrical impedance of the coil or, in a double-coil apparatus, is detected by a small electric current induced in a second coil around the sample. In either case, absorption is translated into electrical current, which is amplified and translated into a trace either on an oscilloscope or on an automatic recorder.

Nuclei which contain odd numbers of particles have magnetic moments. The most important of these in organic chemistry is hydrogen. Protons absorb at higher frequencies than any other nuclei with the exception of the tritium (H^3) nucleus.

Chemical Shifts. The most important feature of nmr absorption is that the frequency of absorption is affected by the chemical environment of nuclei. The effect is due to shielding of nuclei by nearby electrons. Because of the chemical shifts, it is possible to resolve absorption spectra into bands due to each kind of hydrogen atom in a molecule. Figure 27.6

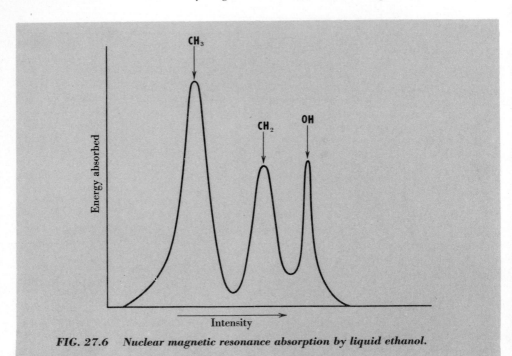

FIG. 27.6   *Nuclear magnetic resonance absorption by liquid ethanol.*

shows an nmr spectrum of ethanol in which three peaks, due to CH_3, CH_2, and **OH** protons, are resolved.   Since the absorption frequency is a function of the magnitude of the external field, the spectrum is given in arbitrary frequency units.   Proton absorption lies in the vicinity of 21 mega-cycles/sec in a field of 5000 gauss.   The area under the three peaks in Fig. 27.6 is accurately proportional to the numbers of protons of each type in the ethanol molecule.   Measurement of areas included by various absorption bands provides an accurate measure of the relative numbers of protons of various types within molecules.

Spin-Spin Coupling.   Bands, such as those shown in Fig. 27.6, can be resolved into components.   Fine structure is due to the splitting of magnetic-energy levels, because of interactions of a particular nuclear moment with those of nearby magnetic nuclei.   At the present time, the theory of spin-spin splitting is not well developed, but, potentially, the observation of details of fine structure offers a delicate means for deter-mination of the distribution pattern of protons (and other magnetic nuclei) within molecules.   In a sense, nmr spectroscopy offers an entirely new approach to the study of organic structures.   Other methods deal mainly with carbon skeletons.   Proton magnetic resonance spectrophotom-etry offers the intriguing possibility of making proton patterns, rather than carbon skeletons, a fundamental scheme of structural characterization

Dyes

Man's use of natural coloring materials to relieve the drabness of his own physical make-up is evident in the very earliest civilizations. Both organic and inorganic pigments were extracted from plant, animal, and mineral sources and used by men to dye their clothes, paint their skins, and create works of art for aesthetic pleasure and religious worship.

Destruction of the ancient superstition that the synthesis of organic compounds was a unique function of living systems was followed closely by serious attempts to prepare organic dyes in the chemical laboratory. Woulfe, in 1771, prepared picric acid by treating natural indigo with nitric acid, and Runge made aurin from coal tar in 1834.   However, the real birth of the dyestuff industry took place in 1856 when Perkin obtained the purple dye mauve by oxidation of aniline with chromic acid.   The reaction became the first commercial dye synthesis.   Dyes then became the backbone of the fine organic chemistry industry and retained that position until World War I.   In 1913 Germany was manufacturing 75% of the world's dyestuffs and consequently dominated the field of organic chemistry, including the rising pharmaceutical industry.   The war neces-sitated development of domestic chemical industries in other countries, especially in Great Britain and the United States.

Dyeing

There are two systems of classification of dyes. In addition to the obvious system based upon chemical structure, the methods of application to textile fibers are used widely as a basis for classification. Such a scheme is logical, because of the importance of technological aspects in determining the usefulness of a dye. To be successful, a dye must be capable of attaching itself firmly to the fiber, so that washing will not remove the color. It should also be chemically stable to a reasonable degree, especially toward the action of sunlight.

Direct Dyes. *Direct dyes* are absorbed directly on the fiber from aqueous solution. *Acid dyes* are salts of sulfonic or carboxylic acids which are precipitated on the fiber by acidification of the bath. *Basic dyes* are ammonium salts or zinc chloride complexes of amines. Direct dyes are used most commonly with wool and to some extent with synthetic polyamides. Some high-molecular-weight basic dyes are firmly enough absorbed on cotton and rayon to be of limited use with these fibers.

Ingrain Dyes. Azo dyes formed in the fiber by the coupling of a diazonium ion with an amine or phenol are known as ingrain dyes. The technique is especially useful with cotton.

Mordant Dyes. A *mordant* is an additive which is adsorbed on a fiber and which can, in turn, bind a dye. For example, tannic acid, a naturally occurring phenolic polymer, is often used as a mordant for basic dyes. However, the term *mordant dye* is reserved for dyes fixed by use of metal oxides as mordants. Aluminum and chromium oxides, which form highly insoluble precipitates with bifunctional dyes, are commonly used mordants.

Vat Dyes. Vat dyes are insoluble substances that can be reduced to alkali-soluble materials. The dye is applied by allowing it to reoxidize in the presence of the fiber.

Chemical Classes of Dyes

Azo Dyes. This class is the largest single group of dyes. The first member of the series was discovered in 1862 by Griess. The dyes are produced by coupling of diazonium salts with aromatic amines and phenols. Their use in ingrain dyeing was described above, and acid and acidic azo dyes may be prepared by the inclusion of sulfonic acid groups or excess basic functions. Nomenclature of the compounds, as of all dyes, is exceedingly unsystematic. The lack of order arises both from the complexity of molecular structure and from a natural desire of manufacturers to conceal the chemical identity of new products. Compounds containing two, three, and four azo linkages are known respectively as *disazo*, *trisazo*, and *tetrakisazo* compounds.

Alizarin Yellow R
(a mordant dye)

Orange II
(an acid dye)

Fast Scarlet G
(an ingrain dye)

Bismarck Brown R
(a basic diazo dye)

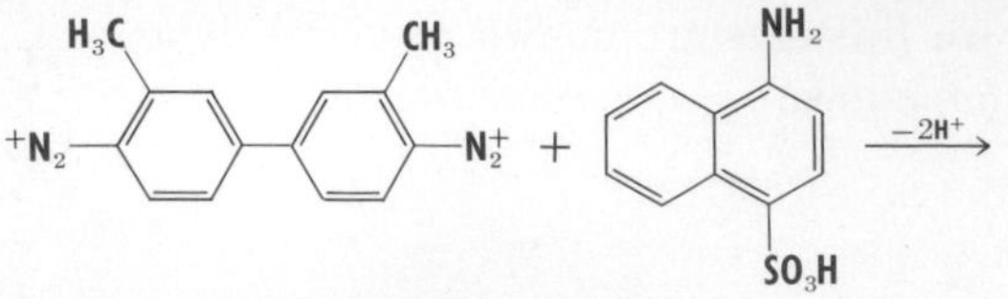

Diazotized 3,3'-dimethylbenzidine

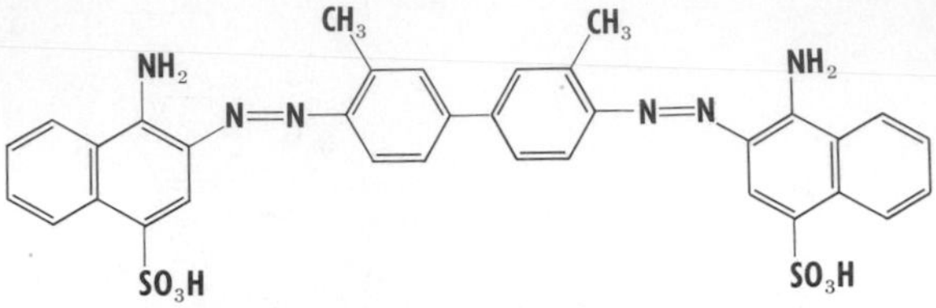

Benzopurpurin 4B
(the first direct dye
for cotton)

Triphenylmethane Dyes. Triphenylmethane dyes are the salts of triarylmethyl cations. The dyes always contain amino or hydroxyl groups as substituents to stabilize the positive charge. The dyes are little used now because, despite their brilliance, they are not satisfactorily "fast" to light. Triphenylmethane dyes are usually made by some combination of oxidation and acid-catalyzed condensation of carbonyl compounds or alcohols with aromatic amines.

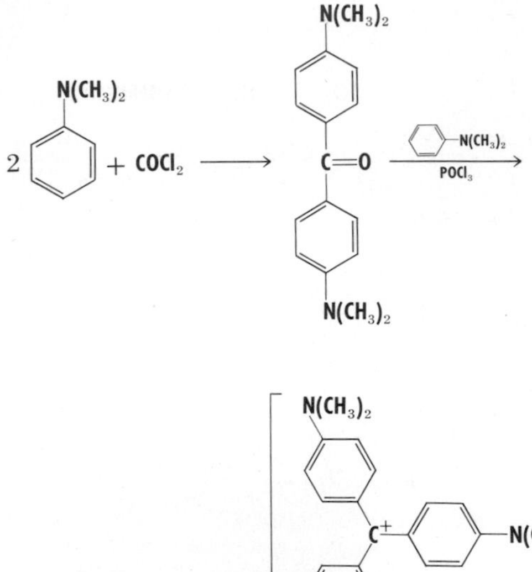

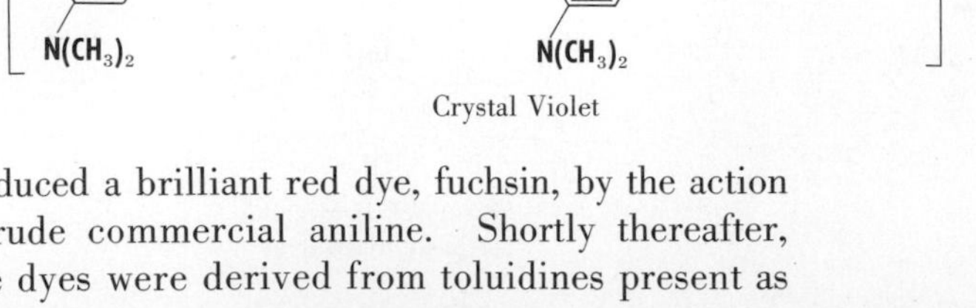

Crystal Violet

In 1859 Verquin produced a brilliant red dye, fuchsin, by the action of stannic chloride on crude commercial aniline. Shortly thereafter, Hofmann showed that the dyes were derived from toluidines present as impurities in the aniline.

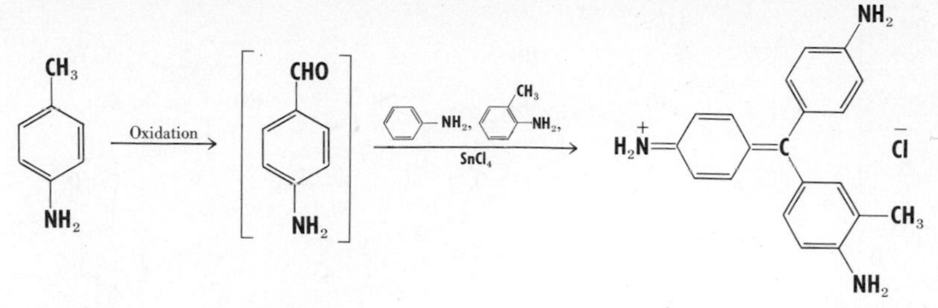

Possible
intermediate

Fuchsin
(Rosaniline)

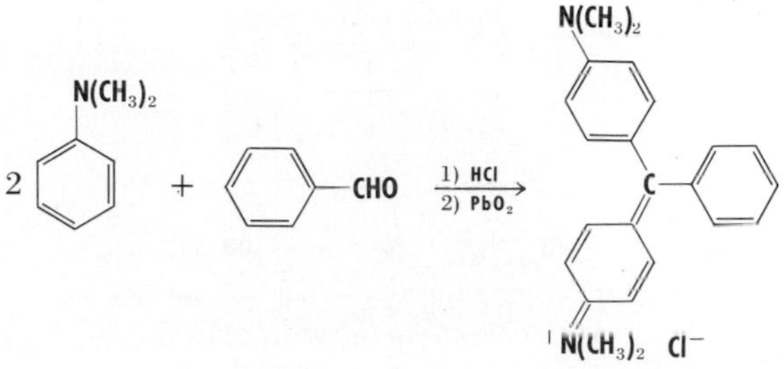

Malachite Green
75%

Phthaleins. Phthalein dyes are beautiful substances formed by the condensation of aromatic amines and phenols with phthalic anhydride. The group includes phenolphthalein, a familiar indicator.

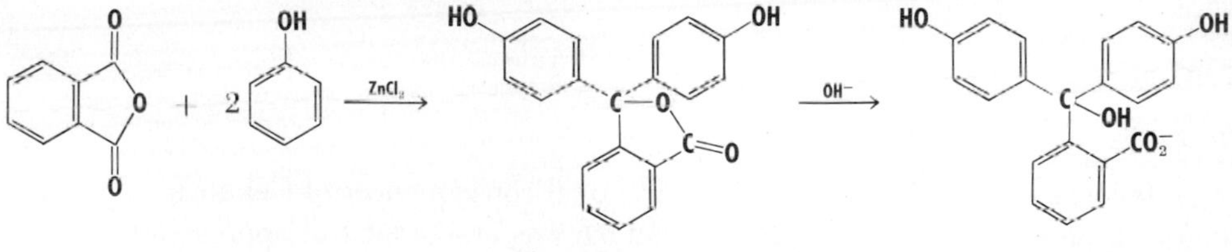

Phenolphthalein
(colorless)

Monoanion (colorless)

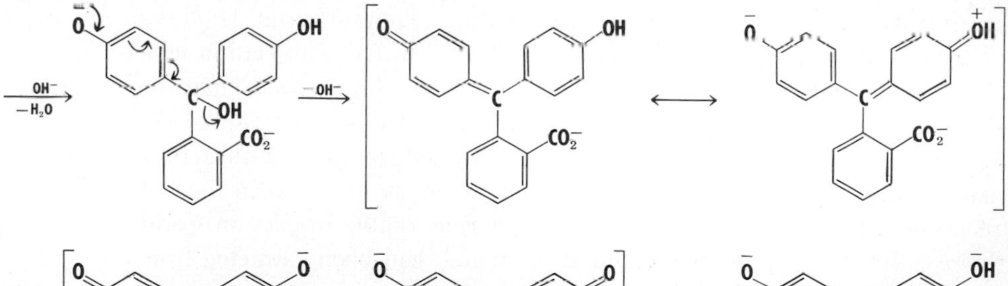

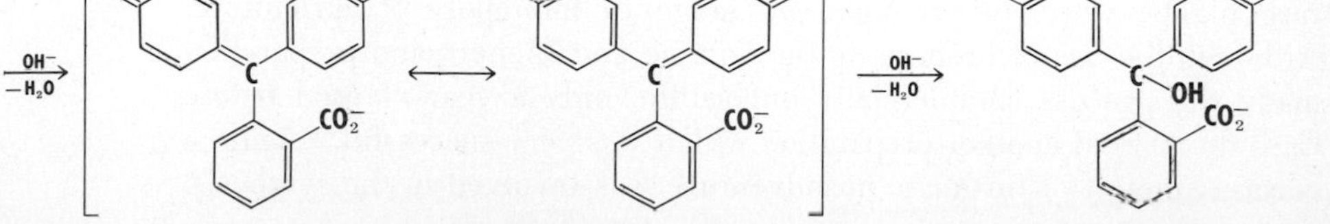

Dianion (red)

Trianion
(colorless)

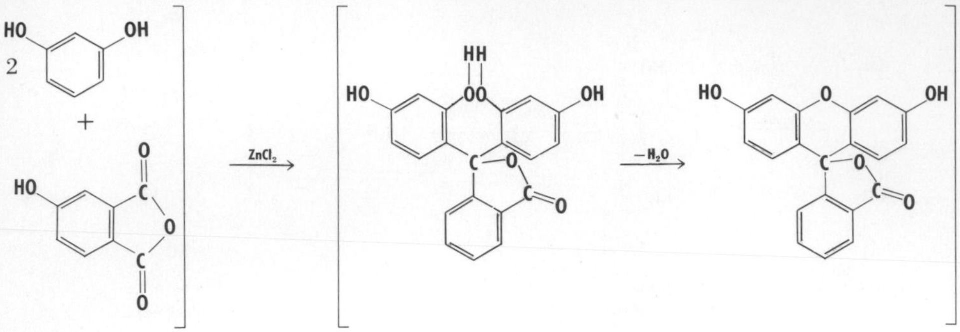

Probable intermediates

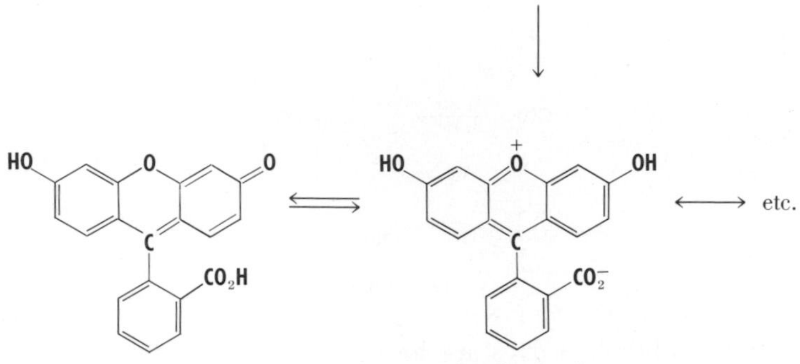

(Dipolar form)

Fluorescein
(yellow with intense green fluorescence)

Quinone Dyes.   One of the earliest practical consequences of Kekulé's enunciation of a theory of aromatic structure was assignment of approximately correct structures to a large number of natural dyes.   Graebe and Liebermann (1868) came to the conclusion that *alizarin,* an important natural dye, contained a quinone ring system.   They inferred, from the acidity of alizarin, the analytical data, and an intuitive correlation with the properties of Graebe's newly characterized anthraquinone, that the dye was a dihydroxyanthraquinone.   Consequently they attempted the synthesis of such a compound.   That the procedure yielded alizarin is astonishing in retrospect, since a rearrangement is involved in the last reaction.   Nonetheless, the synthesis had a remarkable impact on world finance, since it implied that exotic dyes, which had been extracted from rare plants, were, in principle, no longer a monopoly of agriculture. Although the use of bromine in the Graebe and Liebermann preparation made the process commercially unfeasible, only a year elapsed before Caro discovered another preparation which was very successful.   Again a certain amount of fortunate misadventure was involved in the synthesis.

Graebe and Liebermann synthesis:

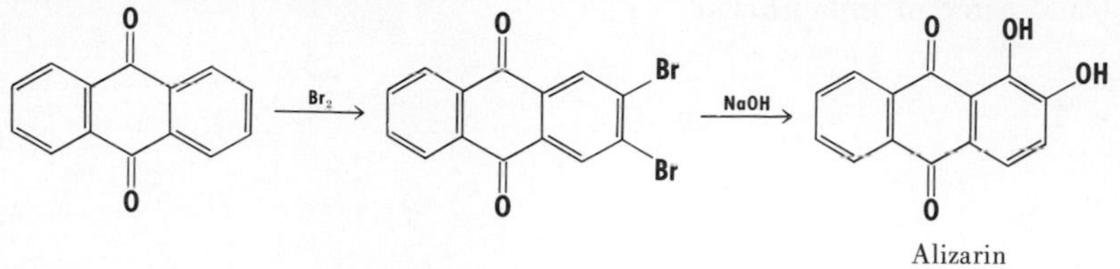

Alizarin
(a mordant dye)

Caro synthesis:

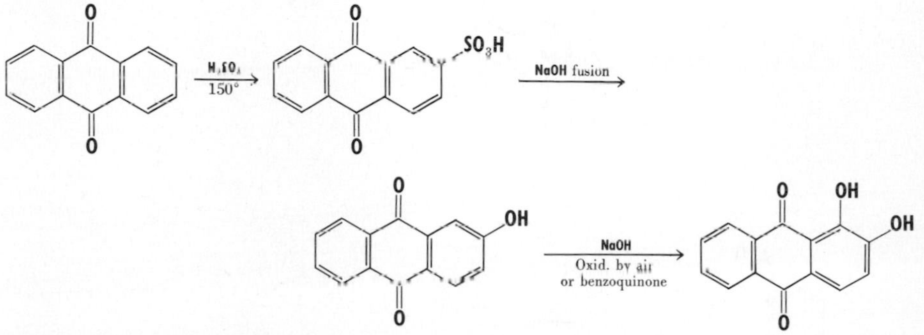

Quinones of sufficiently high molecular weight may be used as vat dyes. The dye is applied in the form of the colorless, alkali-soluble hydroquinone and is oxidized to the insoluble quinone in the dyeing vat. The name Indanthrene is applied to the fastest dyes made by I. G. Farben.†

The name Indanthrone was coined because the substance was made in an unsuccessful attempt by Bohn (1901) to prepare an analogue of *indigo* from anthracene.

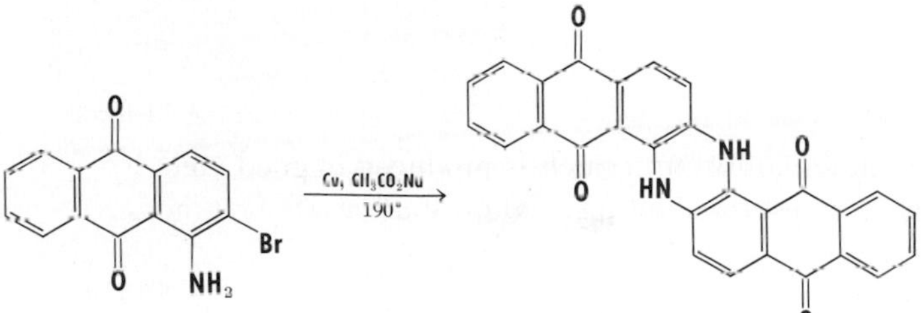

Indanthrone (blue)

† Most of the German dye manufacturers formed a combine known as the *Interessen Gemeinschaft für Farbenindustrie.* The move, which came in 1924, was designed to help Germany regain ascendancy in world trade. Shortly thereafter, the British counterpart, Imperial Chemical Industries (I.C.I.) was organized. Although the two combines have been exceedingly prosperous in peacetime, neither they nor the nonmonopolistic American chemical industry have ever gained lasting advantage in world chemistry. In fact, in the field of fine chemicals, all three of the economic giants have been challenged very successfully by the vigorous industry in smaller countries such as Switzerland, the Netherlands, and the Scandinavian nations.

The following examples show other quinoid dyes which are sold under the trade name of Indanthrene.

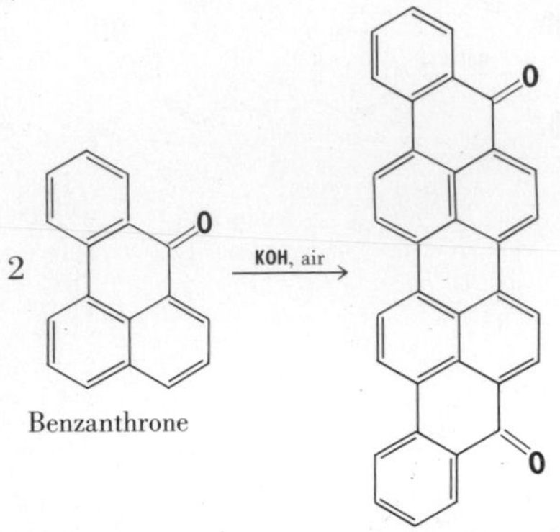

Benzanthrone

Dibenzanthrone
(Violanthrone)

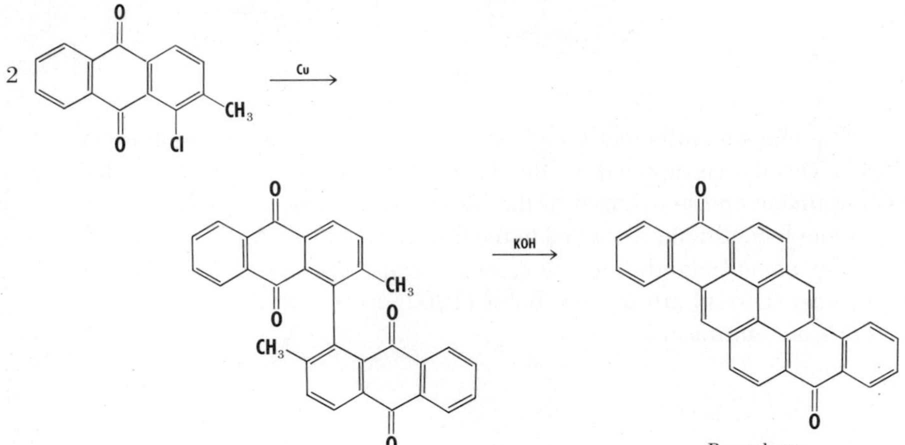

Pyranthrone

The structure of dibenzanthrone, which is produced in good yield by the above reaction, was established by Scholl's alternate synthesis.

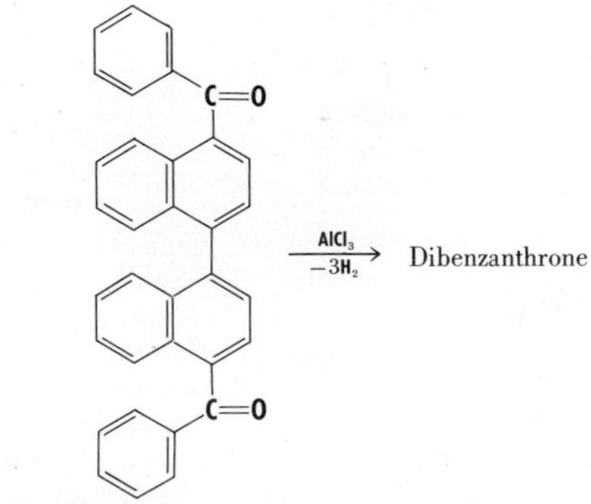

4,4′-Dibenzoyl-1,1′-binaphthyl

Indigo Dyes. The story of indigo has as much romance as any tale in the archives of chemistry. The blue dye was known by ancient man as an extract from several species of *Indigofera*. It was produced principally in the Orient, to a limited extent in West Africa, and in small amounts from the European woad plant. By the middle of the nineteenth century, indigo had become a principal item in trade between Europe and the Orient. After the synthesis of alizarin, much effort was directed toward elucidation of the indigo structure, so that attempts to synthesize the molecule could be placed on a rational basis. After 18 years of study Baeyer announced the structure of indigo in 1883. In 1880 he accomplished a total synthesis (one not involving materials derived from indigo), but it was not until 1887 that he was able to develop a practical, commercial synthesis. The following is a *brief* résumé of the work that led Baeyer to his structure assignment.

1. Work before Baeyer's studies—degradation of indigo

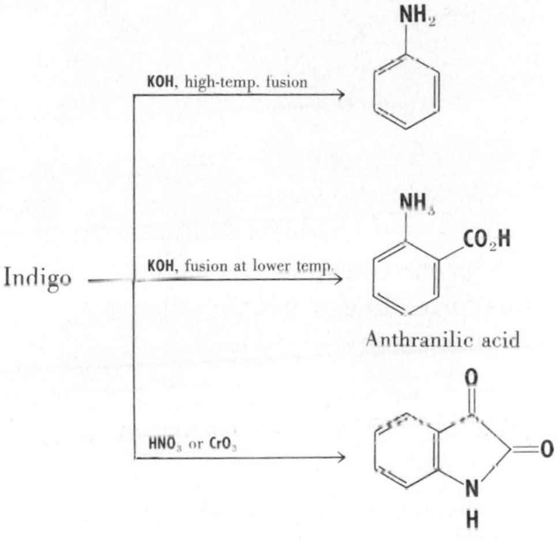

Anthranilic acid

Isatin

2. Baeyer's studies

a. Attempts to reduce isatin to indigo gave many products which did not include the dye. The products did include indole and indoxyl.

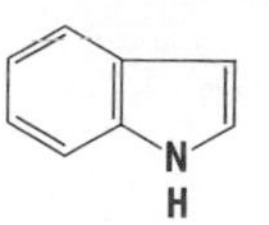

Indole 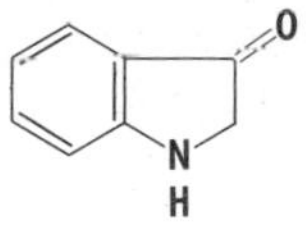   Indoxyl

b. The condensation to indigo was finally accomplished by a curious combination of reagents.

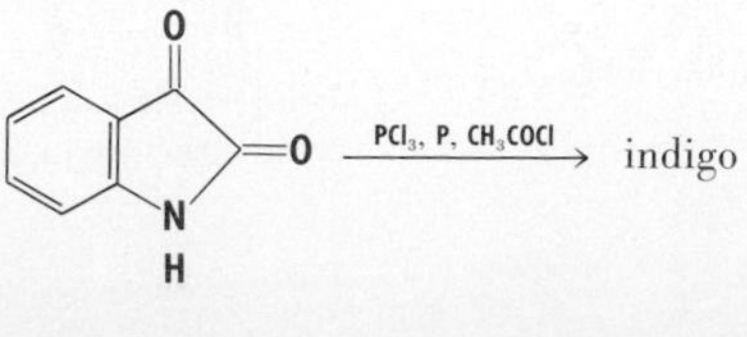

$$\xrightarrow{\text{PCl}_3,\ \text{P},\ \text{CH}_2\text{COCl}} \text{indigo}$$

The synthesis of indigo indicated that the molecule probably contains two isatin systems coupled together. However, the points of attachment were not made at all clear by the first preparation.

   c. Baeyer carried out a very tedious and uneconomical synthesis of isatin in order to establish a *total synthesis* of indigo.

CH₂CO₂H   HNO₃   CH₂CO₂H / NO₂   Zn-HCl   CH₂CO₂H / NH₂

Phenylacetic acid   (Separate from by-products)   (Not isolable)

C=O   Oxindole   HNO₂   NOH / 3-Oximino-oxindole   Sn-Hg   NH₂ / 3-Aminooxindole   FeCl₃   O / Isatin

   3. Baeyer and his coworkers then developed (1882) a synthesis in which the four-carbon chain between the benzene rings was formed before the heterocyclic rings were closed—thus providing a nearly definitive synthesis.

CH=CHCO₂H / NO₂   Br₂   CHBrCHBrCO₂H / NO₂   KOH, alcohol   C≡CCO₂H / NO₂   Heat

o-Nitrocinnamic acid   (*o*-Nitrophenyl)-propiolic acid

C≡CH / NO₂   CuCl   C≡C Cu / NO₂   K₃Fe(CN)₆   C≡C—C≡C / NO₂ O₂N   H₂SO₄

(*o*-Nitrophenyl)-acetylene   Cuprous acetylide

Diisatogen (structure not rigorously known)   (NH₄)₂S   Baeyer formula for indigo   Indigo (established by X-ray crystal structure in 1928)

As would be expected with a material of as much commercial interest as indigo, establishment of the correct structure was followed shortly by a number of commercially practical syntheses, and synthetic indigo appeared on the market in 1896. All industrially successful processes involve air oxidation of indoxyl as a final step.

N-Phenylglycine   Indoxyl

Anthranilic   N-Phenylglycine-
acid   o-carboxylic acid

Indigo is a vat dye which is reduced to the alkali-soluble *leuco indigo* (indigo white).

Leuco indigo

Indigo is still used in large quantity and in the United States is best known as the coloring of "blue jeans."

Of the other indigoid dyes, Tyrian Purple is probably the best known. The dye is "the purple" to which those of noble lineage are said to be born. The dye was obtained in minuscule amounts from mollusks of the family *Murex*. Degradative studies have shown that the dye is 5,5′,7,7′-tetrabromoindigo. Although the material can now be made synthetically, it is too expensive to be of any commercial interest.

Cyanine Dyes. Cyanines are salts containing as the cation a large organic unit in which the positive charge is spread over two heterocyclic nuclei. The compounds have limited value as dyestuffs, since they are quite costly and highly photosensitive. Many members of the class have been made for testing as sensitizers in photographic processes, and recently some have been used as dyes for synthetic fibers.

Cyanines are made by condensation reactions of 2- and 4-methyl-quinolines.

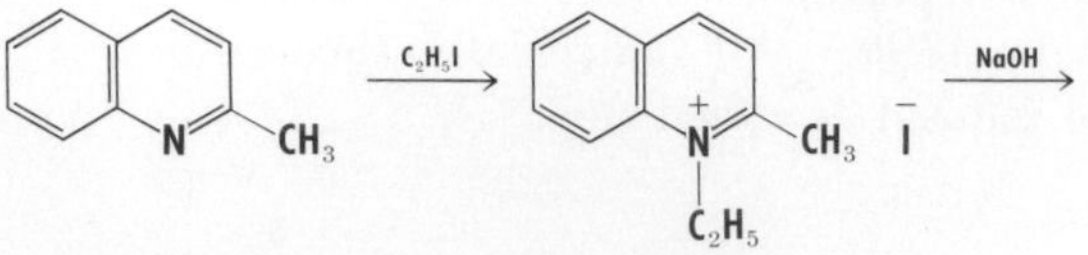

Quinaldine

N-Ethylquinaldinium iodide
(Quinaldine ethiodide)

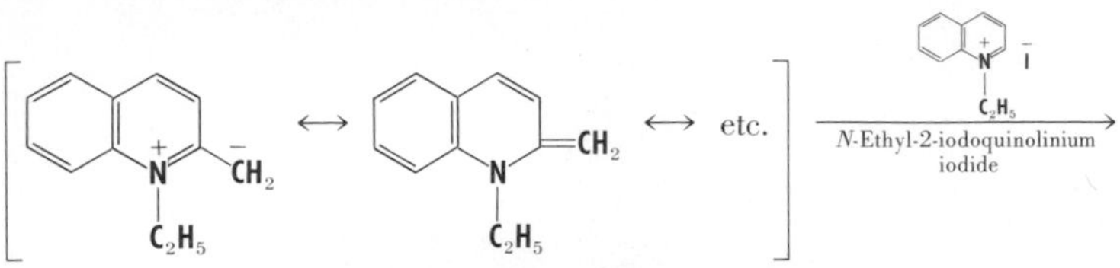

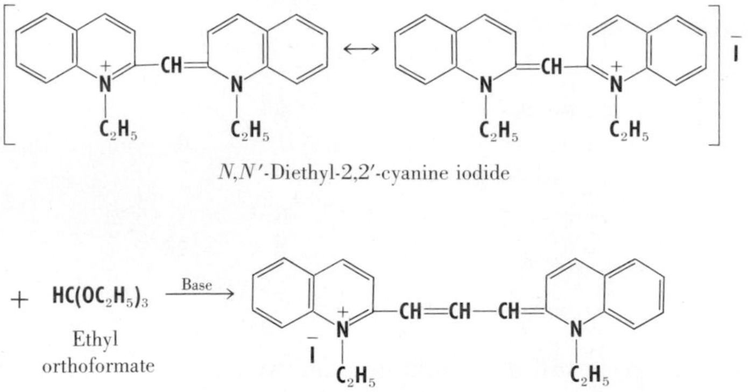

N-Ethyl-2-iodoquinolinium
iodide

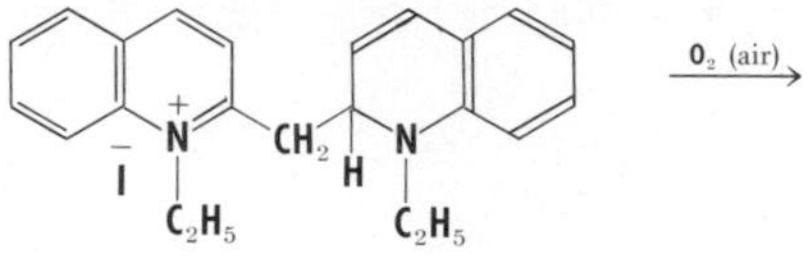

N,N'-Diethyl-2,2'-cyanine iodide

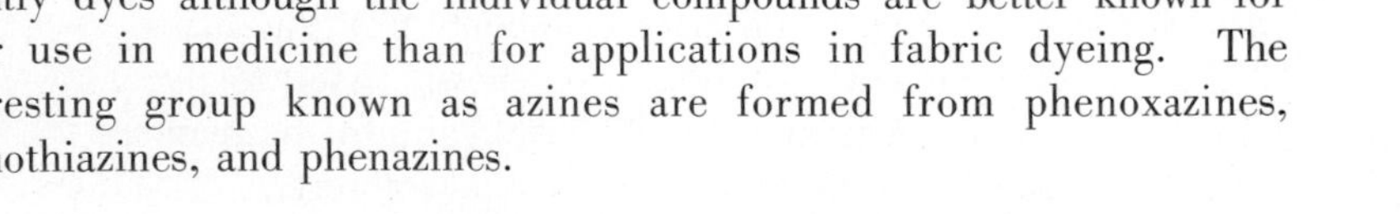

Ethyl
orthoformate

Azine Dyes. Cations derived from aromatic heterocycles are frequently dyes although the individual compounds are better known for their use in medicine than for applications in fabric dyeing. The interesting group known as azines are formed from phenoxazines, phenothiazines, and phenazines.

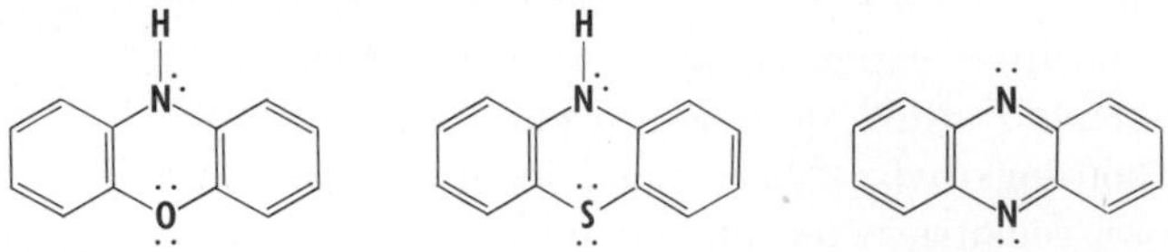

Phenoxazine

Phenothiazine

Phenazine

The dyes are notable because reduction to leuco forms is fast enough to give reversible behavior at electrodes so that oxidation potentials of azine dyes can be measured. Methylene Blue is probably the best known example of the class.

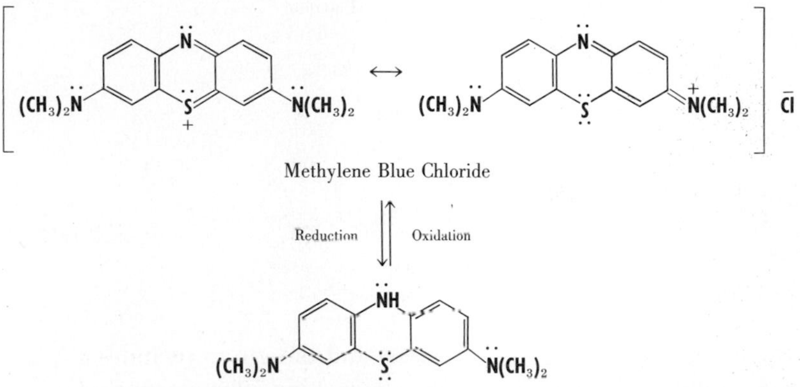

Methylene Blue Chloride

Reduction | Oxidation

Leuco Methylene Blue

Phthalocyanine Dyes. Rather recently (1934), phthalocyanine was discovered during investigation of a blue material formed as a by-product in the commercial preparation of phthalimide. The substance was found to contain iron (from the reaction vessels) held in the center of a heterocyclic macroring. Other metals may replace iron. The most direct synthesis, and the one that led to a correct structural assignment, consists of heating phthalonitrile with a metal. Commercially, the dyes are made by heating phthalic anhydride with urea and a metal oxide catalyst.

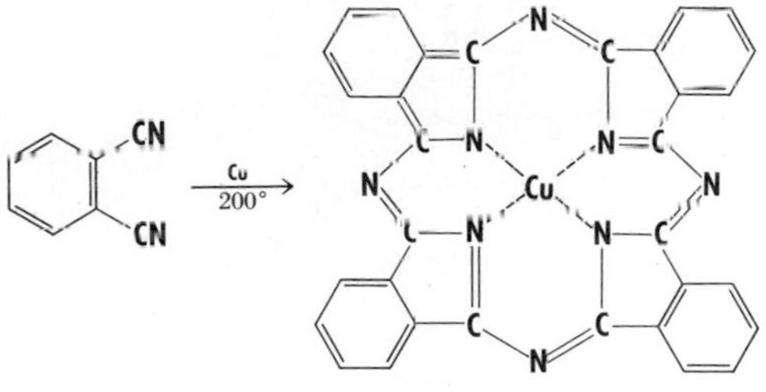

Copper phthalocyanine
(blue)

Flavones. The derivatives of the oxygen heterocycle *chromone* are widely known as brilliant plant pigments. In the plants they occur as glycosides (page 513), but the dyes are readily obtained by hydrolysis. As one would expect from their *o*-ketophenol structures, flavones form metal complexes and are therefore mordant dyes.

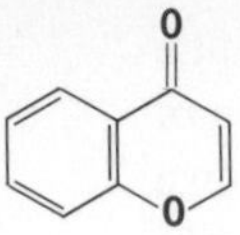

Chromone
(colorless)

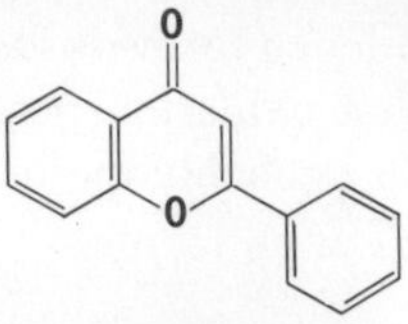

Flavone
(colorless)

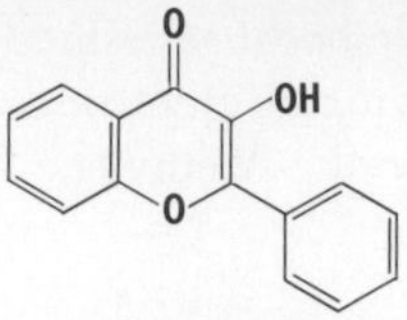

Flavonol
(yellow)

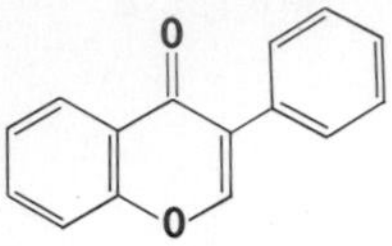

Isoflavonol

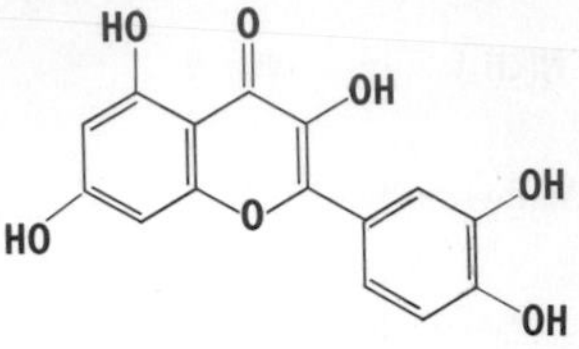

Quercetin
(orange—gives yellow mordants)

Pyrilium salts are salts of oxygen bases, and the group includes a number of brilliantly colored dyes. The interesting phenomenon of strongly basic oxygen is illustrated by the colorless pyrone systems.

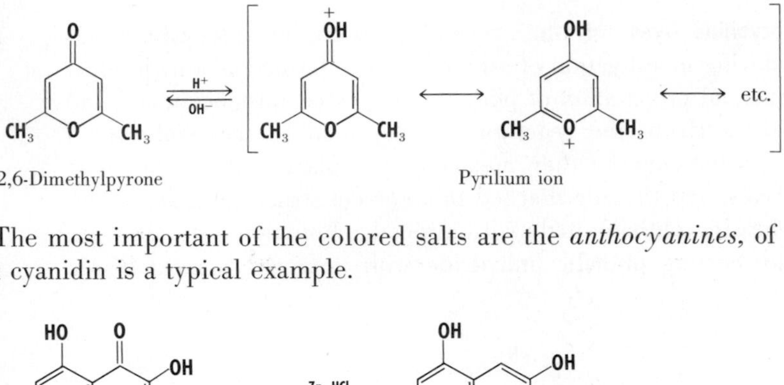

2,6-Dimethylpyrone

Pyrilium ion

The most important of the colored salts are the *anthocyanines,* of which cyanidin is a typical example.

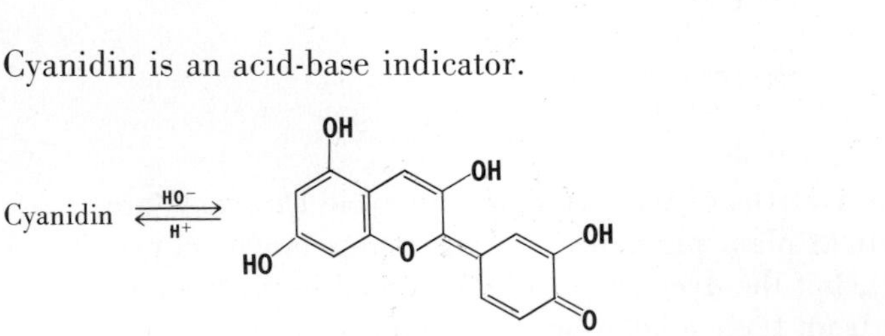

Quercetin

Cyanidin chloride
(red)

Cyanidin is an acid-base indicator.

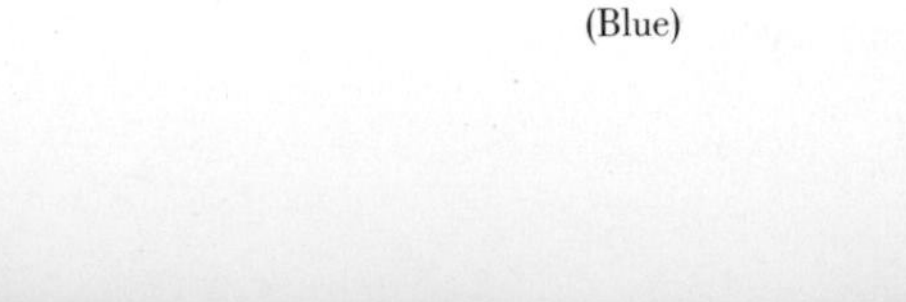

Cyanidin

(Blue)

Problems

1. List the types of information usually sought from infrared, Raman, ultraviolet, and nmr spectra.

2. Compound *A* has a strong carbonyl bond in the infrared at 1,710 cm^{-1} and only one, very weak, absorption maximum at 2,850 A in the ultraviolet. The compound is treated with dilute base and is converted to an isomeric compound *B*, which has a strong absorption bond at 2,250 A and has a carbonyl bond at 1,670 cm^{-1} in the infrared. What chemical change occurred?

3. Suggest ways in which one might differentiate the following pairs of compounds by spectroscopic methods.

a. $C_6H_5COCH_2CH_3$ and $C_6H_5CH_2COCH_3$

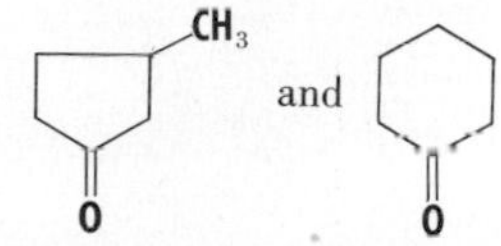

d. $(C_6H_5)_2CHCH_3$ and $C_6H_5CH_2CH_2C_6H_5$

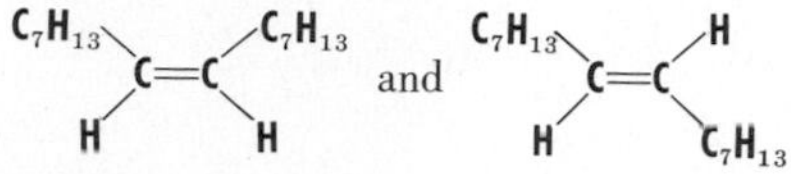

b.
and

e. $CH_3CH{=}CHCH_2CH_2CH{=}CHCH_3$ and
$CH_3CH{=}CHCH{=}CHC_3H_7$

c.
and

4. Which of the following would you expect to function as vat dyes, direct dyes, ingrain dyes, and mordants? Remember that a single compound may sometimes be applied in two or more ways and that some dyes cannot be attached to fabrics.

a. 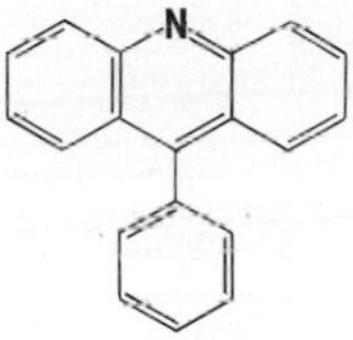
Chrysaniline

d. 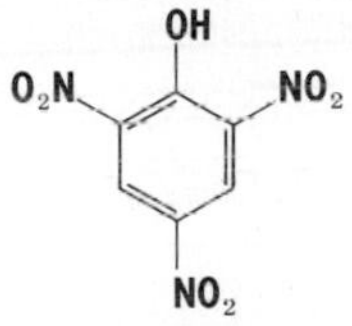
Picric acid

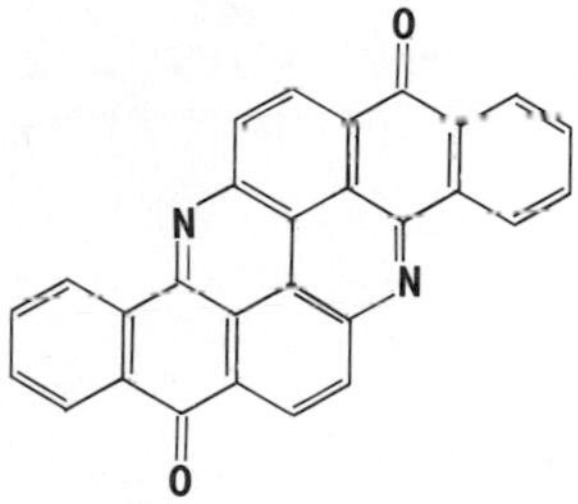

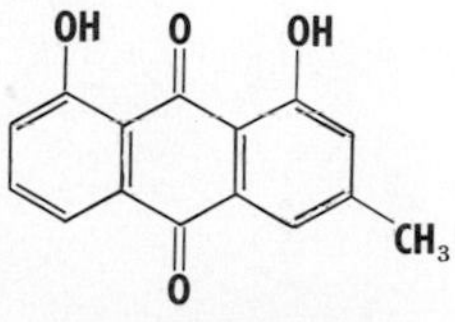

b.

e. 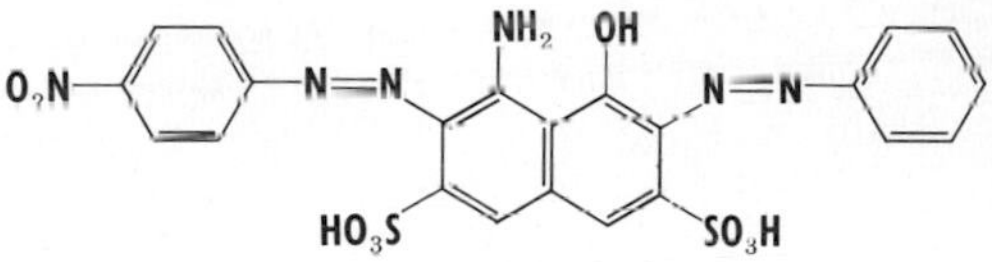
Naphthol Blue Black

c.
Chrysophanic acid

5. Polyacrylonitrile can be spun into satisfactory fibers (Orlon, Acrilan). However, it is difficult to dye the product:

$$--- (CH_2CH)_n ---$$
$$| $$
$$CN$$

Can you suggest any way of modifying the structure [for example by copolymerization (page 575)] so as to improve the dyeing characteristics?

6. How would you synthesize each of the following from benzene, naphthalene, and their simple derivatives?

a.

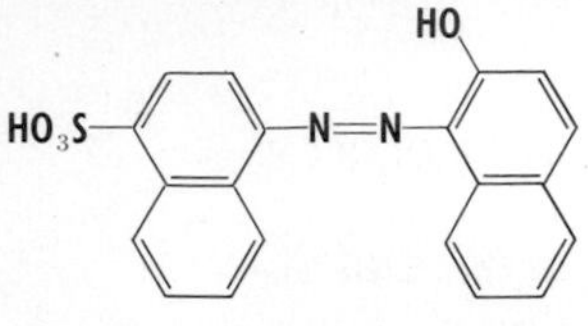

Fast Red A

b.

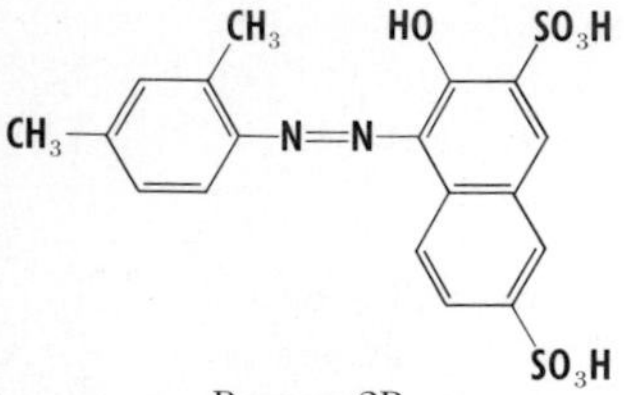

Ponceau 2R

c.

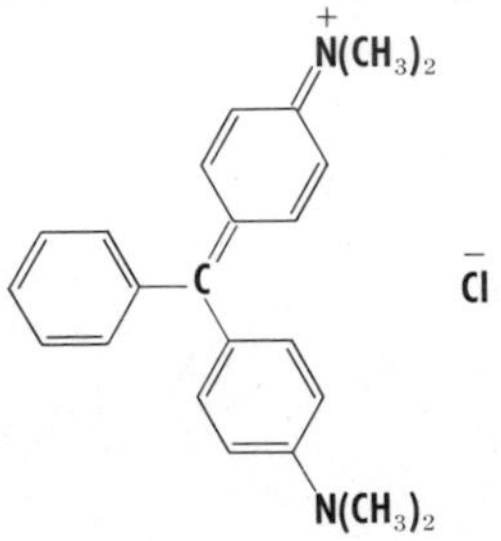

Malachite Green

28

Nomenclature

Much of the nomenclature found in this chapter has been encountered previously, particularly in Chaps. 2, 3, and 4. However, a more complete and integrated treatment of the subject is developed here. This material supplements previous discussion of nomenclature and serves as a reference for the many names given to compounds throughout the book.

Common Names

For various reasons many of the important organic compounds have common or trivial names of obscure origin, which of themselves give no faithful indication of structure. Such names have to be catalogued in one's memory in the same way as names of individuals. This kind of nomenclature develops historically, since compounds are frequently named before their structures are known. The resulting common names are not fully displaced by more systematic names, since, for complex molecules, the latter are sometimes long and cumbersome. For example, *cortisone* has the little-used systematic name 1,2-[3-hydroxy-3-hydroxyacetylcyclopentano]-4,7-dioxo-2,13-dimethyl- $\triangle$ ^{8,14}-perhydrophenanthrene.

Cortisone

Hydrocarbons. Names of hydrocarbons are of vital importance, since many of them have roots which are used repeatedly in names of other classes of compounds. Table 28.1 includes the most important of these names.

TABLE 28.1   *Names of Hydrocarbons*

Formula	*Name*	*Formula*	*Name*

Alkanes

Formula	*Name*	*Formula*	*Name*
CH_4	Methane	$CH_3(CH_2)_{10}CH_3$	Dodecane
CH_3CH_3	Ethane	$CH_3(CH_2)_{11}CH_3$	Tridecane
$CH_3CH_2CH_3$	Propane	$CH_3(CH_2)_{12}CH_3$	Tetradecane
$CH_3(CH_2)_2CH_3$	*n*-Butane	$CH_3(CH_2)_{13}CH_3$	Pentadecane
$(CH_3)_3CH$	Isobutane	$CH_3(CH_2)_{14}CH_3$	Hexadecane
$CH_3(CH_2)_3CH_3$	*n*-Pentane	$CH_3(CH_2)_{15}CH_3$	Heptadecane
$(CH_3)_2CHCH_2CH_3$	Isopentane	$CH_3(CH_2)_{16}CH_3$	Octadecane
$(CH_3)_4C$	Neopentane	$CH_3(CH_2)_{17}CH_3$	Nonadecane
$CH_3(CH_2)_4CH_3$	Hexane	$CH_3(CH_2)_{18}CH_3$	Eicosane
$CH_3(CH_2)_5CH_3$	Heptane	$CH_3(CH_2)_{19}CH_3$	Heneicosane
$CH_3(CH_2)_6CH_3$	Octane	$CH_3(CH_2)_{20}CH_3$	Docosane
$CH_3(CH_2)_7CH_3$	Nonane	$CH_3(CH_2)_{28}CH_3$	Triacontane
$CH_3(CH_2)_8CH_3$	Decane	$CH_3(CH_2)_{33}CH_3$	Pentatriacontane
$CH_3(CH_2)_9CH_3$	Undecane	$CH_3(CH_2)_{38}CH_3$	Tetracontane

Alkenes

Formula	*Name*	*Formula*	*Name*
$CH_2{=}CH_2$	Ethylene	$CH_3CH_2CH_2CH{=}CH_2$	α-Amylene
$CH_3CH{=}CH_2$	Propylene	$CH_3CH_2CH{=}CHCH_3$	β-Amylene
$CH_3CH_2CH{=}CH_2$	*unsym*-Butene	$(CH_3)_2CHCH{=}CH_2$	Isopentylene
$CH_3CH{=}CHCH_3$	*sym*-Butene	$(CH_3)_2C{=}CHCH_3$	Trimethylethylene
$(CH_3)_2C{=}CH_2$	Isobutene	$(CH_3)_2C{=}C(CH_3)_2$	Tetramethylethylene
$CH_2{=}CH{-}CH{=}CH_2$	Butadiene	$CH_2{=}\underset{\underset{CH_3}{\mid}}{C}{-}CH{=}CH_2$	Isoprene
$CH_2{=}C{=}CH_2$	Allene		

Cycloalkanes and cycloalkenes

	Cyclopropane		Cyclopentadiene
	Cyclopropene		Cyclohexane
	Cyclobutane		Cyclohexene
	Cyclobutene		*unconj*-Cyclohexadiene
	Cyclopentane		*conj*-Cyclohexadiene
	Cyclopentene		Decalin

TABLE 28.1   **Names of Hydrocarbons** (Continued)

Formula	Name	Formula	Name
		Aromatic hydrocarbons	

Formula	Name	Formula	Name
	Benzene		Naphthalene
	Toluene		Tetralin
	o-Xylene		Anthracene
	m-Xylene		Phenanthrene
	p-Xylene		Pyrene
	Mesitylene		Coronene
	Durene		
	p-Cymene	$C_6H_5CH{=}CH_2$	Styrene
		$C_6H_5CH{=}CHC_6H_5$	Stilbene

Names of hydrocarbons contain three parts: (1) roots, which indicate the carbon skeleton; (2) endings, which designate the degree of unsaturation; (3) prefixes, which distinguish isomeric structures. Names of saturated hydrocarbons (alkanes and cycloalkanes) all end in *-ane*, and provide roots for names of more complex compounds. Alkenes are named similarly, except that they possess the ending *-ene*. The prefix *n-* (normal) designates an unbranched chain, whereas the prefix *iso-* (*i-*) indicates the presence of a $(CH_3)_2CH$ group at the end of the major chain of alkane or alkene. The prefix *neo-* indicates a $(CH_3)_3C$—C group at the end of a major chain. The prefix *cyclo-* is used to designate both cyclic alkanes and alkenes. The prefixes *sym-* (symmetrical) and *unsym-* (unsymmetrical) are used to designate structural isomers of compounds such as certain alkenes or trisubstituted aromatic compounds. The prefixes *o-* (ortho), *m-* (meta), and *p-* (para) indicate the relative positions of two substituents attached to a benzene ring (e.g., as in the names of the xylenes in Table 28.1).

Hydrocarbon Groups. Hydrocarbon groups (sometimes called radicals), formed by removing single hydrogen atoms from hydrocarbon structures, are usually named by replacing the suffix *-ane* by *-yl* and *-enyl*. The two groups that can be derived from propane are distinguished by the prefixes *n-* and *iso-*.

$CH_3CH_2CH_2$— $(CH_3)_2CH$—

n-Propyl   Isopropyl

Four groups are derived from butane and isobutane. The discriminants *sec-* and *tert-* stand for "secondary" and "tertiary." A secondary group always has the part structure $(C)_2CH$—, and a tertiary group has the part structure $(C)_3C$—. The terms "secondary" and "tertiary" lead to unique structural designations only with the simpler groups, and are useful in specific nomenclature only when used without ambiguity.

$$CH_3CH_2CH_2CH_2— \qquad CH_3CH_2\overset{\displaystyle CH_3}{\underset{|}{CH}}— \qquad CH_3\overset{\displaystyle CH_3}{\underset{|}{CH}}CH_2— \qquad (CH_3)_3C—$$

n-Butyl   *sec*-Butyl   Isobutyl   *tert*-Butyl

Only four of the eight hydrocarbon groups that contain five carbon atoms can be named uniquely, and the prefix *sec-* as applied to this system is useless.

$$CH_3(CH_2)_3CH_2— \qquad (CH_3)_2CHCH_2CH_2— \qquad CH_3CH_2\overset{\displaystyle CH_3}{\underset{\underset{\displaystyle CH_3}{|}}{\overset{|}{C}}}— \qquad (CH_3)_3CCH_2—$$

n-Pentyl   Isopentyl   *tert*-Pentyl   Neopentyl

Simple unsaturated hydrocarbon groups have very important names of more or less obscure origin. The more important of these are listed below.

CH_2=CH—	CH_2=$CHCH_2$—	CH_3CH=$CHCH_2$—	HC≡CCH_2—
Vinyl	Allyl	Crotyl	Propargyl

p-$CH_3C_6H_4$—	$C_6H_5CH_2$—	C_6H_5CH=	C_6H_5C≡
p-Tolyl	Benzyl	Benzal	Benzo

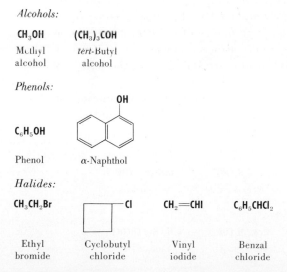

C_6H_5—	—C_6H_4—		
Phenyl	Phenylene	α-Naphthyl	β-Naphthyl

Saturated hydrocarbon groups are referred to as alkyl groups and are designated by the general symbol R. Unsaturated hydrocarbon groups are called alkenyl groups, while the aromatic hydrocarbon groups are called aryl groups and are represented by the general symbol Ar.

Use of Group Names. Names of alkyl and aryl groups are directly applied to the nomenclature of alcohols, halides, esters, amines, ketones, and analogues of these compounds in which sulfur and phosphorus replace oxygen and nitrogen. In names of compounds, the prefixes *di-* and *tri-* are used to show the identity of groups attached to the functional group. In some cases (e.g., with phenols), the two words are shortened into one by leaving out letters. When two different hydrocarbon groups are involved, they are arranged in alphabetical order, and discriminants are disregarded in determining this order. Parts of names are combined into one word with amines, but are separated in names of many other classes.

Alcohols:

CH_3OH	$(CH_3)_3COH$
Methyl alcohol	*tert*-Butyl alcohol

Phenols:

OH

C_6H_5OH	
Phenol	α-Naphthol

Halides:

CH_3CH_2Br	Cl	CH_2=CHI	$C_6H_5CHCl_2$
Ethyl bromide	Cyclobutyl chloride	Vinyl iodide	Benzal chloride

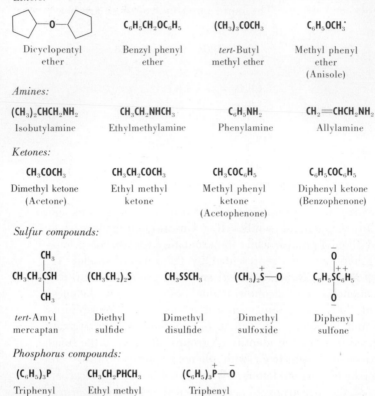

Ethers:

Dicyclopentyl ether

$C_6H_5CH_2OC_6H_5$
Benzyl phenyl ether

$(CH_3)_3COCH_3$
tert-Butyl methyl ether

$C_6H_5OCH_3$
Methyl phenyl ether (Anisole)

Amines:

$(CH_3)_2CHCH_2NH_2$
Isobutylamine

$CH_3CH_2NHCH_3$
Ethylmethylamine

$C_6H_5NH_2$
Phenylamine

$CH_2\!=\!CHCH_2NH_2$
Allylamine

Ketones:

CH_3COCH_3
Dimethyl ketone (Acetone)

$CH_3CH_2COCH_3$
Ethyl methyl ketone

$CH_3COC_6H_5$
Methyl phenyl ketone (Acetophenone)

$C_6H_5COC_6H_5$
Diphenyl ketone (Benzophenone)

Sulfur compounds:

$CH_3CH_2\underset{\underset{CH_3}{|}}{\overset{\overset{CH_3}{|}}{C}}SH$
tert-Amyl mercaptan

$(CH_3CH_2)_2S$
Diethyl sulfide

CH_3SSCH_3
Dimethyl disulfide

$(CH_3)_2\overset{+}{S}\!-\!\overset{-}{O}$
Dimethyl sulfoxide

$C_6H_5\overset{\overset{O}{|}}{\underset{\underset{O}{|}}{\overset{++}{S}}}C_6H_5$
Diphenyl sulfone

Phosphorus compounds:

$(C_6H_5)_3P$
Triphenyl phosphine

$CH_3CH_2PHCH_3$
Ethyl methyl phosphine

$(C_6H_5)_3\overset{+}{P}\!-\!\overset{-}{O}$
Triphenyl phosphine oxide

Carboxylic Acids and Related Compounds. A second important set of enumerative roots is found in names of carboxylic acids. The acids, for purposes of nomenclature, are considered the parents of all compounds containing *acyl* (R**CO**—) or *aroyl* (Ar**CO**—) groups. Names of the acyl and aroyl groups are derived from names of the parent acids, as is indicated in Table 28.2. The roots, which indicate the number of carbon atoms in an acyl or aroyl group, are italicized in the names of acids in this table.

Names of acyl and aroyl groups are used with various endings in the nomenclature of aldehydes, acid halides, anhydrides, amides, and nitriles, as illustrated by the following examples.

Aldehydes:

CH_3CHO
Acetaldehyde

$(CH_3)_3CCHO$
Pivalaldehyde

C_6H_5CHO
Benzaldehyde

$OHC(CH_2)_4CHO$
Adipaldehyde

Acid halides:

CH_3CH_2COCl
Propionyl chloride

$CH_2\!=\!CHCOBr$
Acrylyl bromide

$\alpha\text{-}C_{10}H_7COF$
α-Naphthoyl fluoride

$C_6H_5CH\!=\!CHCOCl$
Cinnamoyl chloride

TABLE 28.2 Names of Common Carboxylic Acids

Acids		Related acyl or aroyl groups	
Structure	Name	Structure	Name
HCO_2H	*Formic* acid	$HCO-$	Formyl
CH_3CO_2H	*Acetic* acid	CH_3CO-	Acetyl
$CH_3CH_2CO_2H$	*Propionic* acid	CH_3CH_2CO-	Propionyl
$CH_3(CH_2)_2CO_2H$	*n-Butyric* acid	$CH_3CH_2CH_2CO-$	n-Butyryl
$(CH_3)_2CHCO_2H$	*Isobutyric* acid	$(CH_3)_2CHCO-$	Isobutyryl
$CH_3(CH_2)_3CO_2H$	*Valeric* acid	$CH_3(CH_2)_3CO-$	n-Valeryl
$(CH_3)_2CHCH_2CO_2H$	*Isovaleric* acid	$(CH_3)_2CHCH_2CO-$	Isovaleryl
$(CH_3)_3CCO_2H$	*Pivalic* acid	$(CH_3)_3CCO-$	Pivalyl
$CH_2{=}CHCO_2H$	*Acrylic* acid	$CH_2{=}CHCO-$	Acrylyl
$CH_3CH{=}CHCO_2H$	*Crotonic* acid	$CH_3CH{=}CHCO-$	Crotonyl
$C_6H_5CO_2H$	*Benzoic* acid	C_6H_5CO-	Benzoyl
$C_6H_5CH{=}CHCO_2H$	*Cinnamic* acid	$C_6H_5CH{=}CHCO-$	Cinnamoyl
$C_6H_5CH_2CO_2H$	*Phenylacetic* acid	$C_6H_5CH_2CO-$	Phenylacetyl
	α-Naphthoic acid	$\alpha\text{-}C_{10}H_7CO-$	α-Naphthoyl
	β-Naphthoic acid	$\beta\text{-}C_{10}H_7CO-$	β-Naphthoyl

Diacids			
Structure	Name	Structure	Name
HO_2CCO_2H	Oxalic acid		Maleic acid
$HO_2CCH_2CO_2H$	Malonic acid		
$HO_2C(CH_2)_2CO_2H$	Succinic acid		
$HO_2C(CH_2)_3CO_2H$	Glutaric acid		Fumaric acid
$HO_2C(CH_2)_4CO_2H$	Adipic acid		
$HO_2C(CH_2)_5CO_2H$	Pimelic acid		
$HO_2C(CH_2)_6CO_2H$	Suberic acid		Phthalic acid
$HO_2C(CH_2)_7CO_2H$	Azelaic acid		
$HO_2C(CH_2)_8CO_2H$	Sebacic acid		Isophthalic acid
			Terephthalic acid

Anhydrides:

$(CH_3CO)_2O$ $CH_3CO_2COC_6H_5$ $(CH_2)_3$

Acetic anhydride	Acetic benzoic anhydride	Glutaric anhydride	Phthalic anhydride

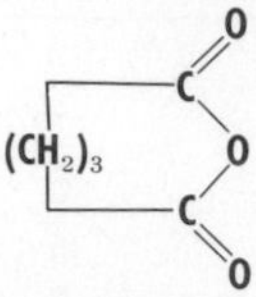

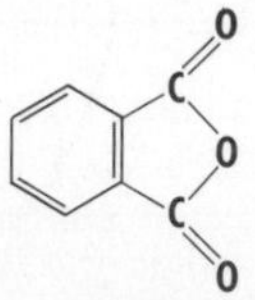

Amides:

$C_6H_5CH_2CONH_2$ $CH_3(CH_2)_2CONH_2$ $C_6H_5CONH_2$ $H_2NCOCH_2CH_2CONH_2$

Phenylacetamide   Butyramide   Benzamide   Succinamide

Nitriles:

$(CH_3)_2CHCH_2CN$ $CH_2{=}CHCN$ $CH_3CH{=}CHCN$ $\beta\text{-}C_{10}H_7CN$

Isovaleronitrile   Acrylonitrile   Crotononitrile β-Naphthonitrile

Other Acids. Sulfonic and phosphonic acids are designated by simply writing in sequence the name of the parent hydrocarbon and the class name. The same system is occasionally applied to carboxylic acids.

CH_3SO_3H $p\text{-}CH_3C_6H_4SO_3H$ $C_6H_5PO_3H_2$

Methanesulfonic acid p-Toluenesulfonic acid   Benzenephosphonic acid

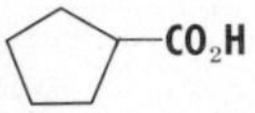

Cyclopentanecarboxylic acid 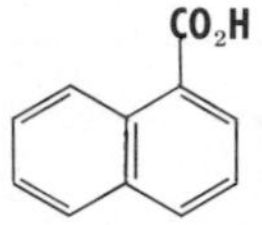 α-Naphthalenecarboxylic acid

Esters. Esters of both organic and inorganic acids are named as alkyl or aryl derivatives of the corresponding acids. The portion of the name dealing with the acid-derived part of the molecule is taken from the name of the anion of the acid, as is indicated in the following examples.

CH_3O_2CH $CH_3O_2CCH_2CO_2CH_3$ $CH_3CH_2O_2CC_6H_5$ $CH_3O_2CCH{=}CH_2$

Methyl formate   Dimethyl malonate   Ethyl benzoate   Methyl acrylate

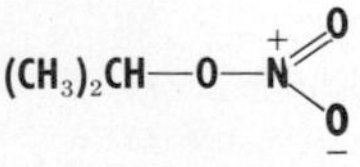

Isopropyl nitrate n-Butyl nitrite   Ethylsulfuric acid 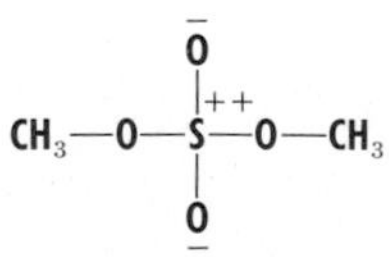   Dimethyl sulfate

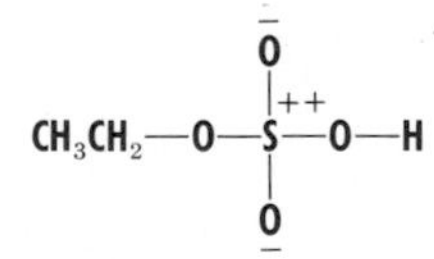

Trimethyl phosphate   Isopropyl benzenesulfonate 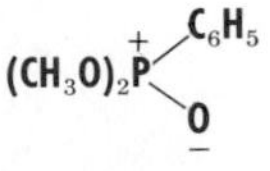   Dimethyl benzenephosphonate

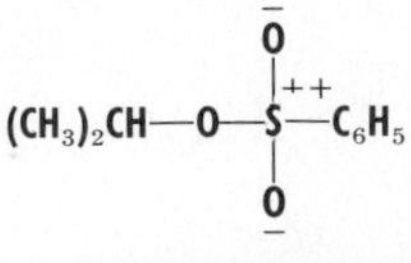

Derived Names

Many compounds are named as derivatives of simpler parent molecules in which substituents have replaced hydrogen attached to carbon. The system is very useful, especially in chemical discussion, as a means of assigning graphic names which convey a clear visual image of a structural formula to a reader or listener. In general, the best names are obtained by choosing the parent structure in such a way as to make a number of substituents similar or identical in character. All compounds of moderate complexity inevitably have a host of names which vary in their pictorial qualities.

Hydrocarbons. Frequently hydrocarbons are named as derivatives of methane, ethane, ethylene, acetylene, cycloalkanes, cycloalkenes, benzene, or other aromatic ring systems. In many cases, positions of attachment of substituents to the parent substance need to be designated with numbers. Carbon atoms of the parent molecule are numbered in such a way as to keep the numbers given substituents as small as possible. Substituents are mentioned in the name in order of increasing values of the numbers given them. The system is best learned through its application, as in the following examples.

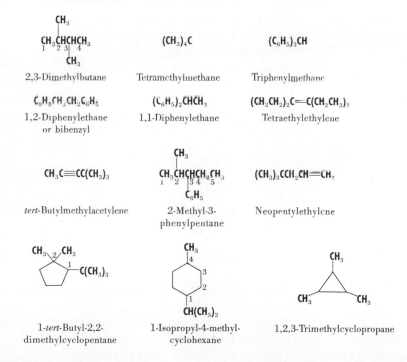

The terms *ortho, meta,* and *para* are used as prefixes to designate relative positions of substituents on disubstituted benzenes. The words are also used as adjectives and are sometimes employed to indicate substituent relationships independent of a particular name. An alternative method again makes use of numbers, as in the following examples.

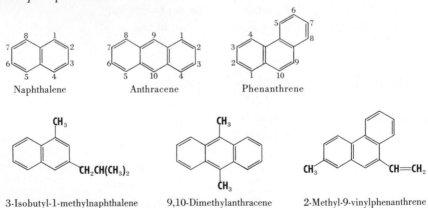

o-Dimethylbenzene   *m*-Dimethylbenzene   *p*-Dimethylbenzene
or 1,2-dimethylbenzene   or 1,3-dimethylbenzene   or 1,4-dimethylbenzene
(*o*-Xylene)   (*m*-Xylene)   (*p*-Xylene)

1,2-Dimethyl-4-*n*-propylbenzene   1-Isopropyl-3-methyltetralin   *p*-Dibenzylbenzene or 1,4-dibenzylbenzene

Polycyclic aromatic rings are numbered according to rigidly fixed rules, as illustrated with naphthalene, phenanthrene, and anthracene. Within the limitations of these fixed assignments, the numbers used in names are chosen in such a way as to have the lowest possible values. The 1- and 2-positions of naphthalene are also designated as α and β, respectively, and the 1- and 8-positions in the same molecule are referred to as the *peri* positions.

Naphthalene   Anthracene   Phenanthrene

3-Isobutyl-1-methylnaphthalene   9,10-Dimethylanthracene   2-Methyl-9-vinylphenanthrene

If alkenes other than ethylene are regarded as parent compounds, the double bond must be located in the carbon skeleton by number. The longest hydrocarbon chain that contains the double bond is numbered from the end closest to the double bond. Numbers are assigned in such a way as to place the double bond between two *consecutively* numbered carbon atoms, and the parent name contains the lower number to locate the position of the double bond. The following examples illustrate these conventions.

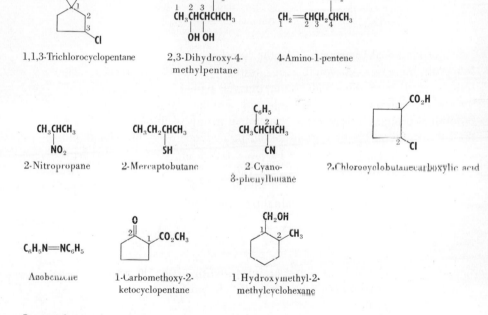

CH₃CHCH₂CH=CHCH₃
6 5 4 3 2 1

5-Methyl-2-hexene

CH₃C=CHCH=CH₂
5 4 3 2 1

4-Phenyl-1,3-pentadiene

3-Allyl-1-cyclobutene

Compounds Containing Functional Groups. Compounds that contain functional groups can frequently be named as derivatives of hydrocarbons, and the function can be located on the parent carbon skeleton by number. Such a system works particularly well with functional groups which themselves are not part of the major carbon chain.

1,1,3-Trichlorocyclopentane

2,3-Dihydroxy-4-methylpentane

4-Amino-1-pentene

2-Nitropropane

2-Mercaptobutane

2-Cyano-3-phenylbutane

2-Chlorocyclobutanecarboxylic acid

Azobenzene

1-Carbomethoxy-2-ketocyclopentane

1-Hydroxymethyl-2-methylcyclohexane

In an alternative system, a parent structure containing a functional group is chosen and numbered in such a way as to give the functional group the lowest possible number. This system works best when a functional group itself is part of a major carbon chain, as with many aldehydes, acids, and ketones.

HOCH₂CH₂CO₂H

3-Hydroxypropionic acid

CH₃CCHO

2,2-Dimethylpropionaldehyde

BrCH₂CH₂OCH₂CH₃

2-Bromodiethyl ether

(CH₃)₃CCC(CH₃)₃

Hexamethyl acetone

Alcohols are sometimes named as derivatives of methyl alcohol, except that the term *carbinol* is used in place of the words "methyl alcohol."

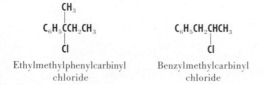

$(CH_3)_2CHOH$ $C_6H_5\overset{\underset{\textstyle CH_3}{|}}{C}HOH$ $(CH_3)_3C\overset{\underset{\textstyle CH(CH_3)_2}{|}}{C}HOH$

Dimethylcarbinol   Methylphenylcarbinol   *tert*-Butylisopropylcarbinol

Essentially the same system of nomenclature is applied to alkyl halides. The functional unit C—X is called *carbinyl halide,* and compounds are named accordingly.

$C_6H_5\overset{\underset{\textstyle Cl}{|}}{\overset{\overset{\textstyle CH_3}{|}}{C}}CH_2CH_3$ $C_6H_5CH_2\overset{\underset{\textstyle Cl}{|}}{C}HCH_3$

Ethylmethylphenylcarbinyl   Benzylmethylcarbinyl
chloride   chloride

Polyfunctional Compounds. As the number of functional groups in a molecule increases, the number of possible names also increases. The following rules help in standardizing derived names.

1. A parent structure is selected which contains the principal functional group. The principal functional group is chosen according to the following list, the first group taking precedence over the second, etc.

a. Functional groups which by their nature must terminate a chain, such as CO_2H, SO_3H, $CONH_2$, CN, CHO.

b. Functional groups other than OH or SH in which oxygen and sulfur occur in a nonterminal position, such as

$$C\overset{\underset{\textstyle O}{\|}}{-}C \quad C-O-C \quad C-S-C \quad C\overset{\underset{\textstyle O}{\underset{-}{|}}}{-}\overset{+}{S}-C \quad C-S-S-C \quad C\overset{\underset{\textstyle O}{\|}}{-}O-C$$

c. Hydroxyl, mercapto, and amino functions (OH, SH, NH_2).

d. Carbon-carbon multiple bonds (C=C and C≡C).

e. Other groups.

2. Functional and hydrocarbon groups not included in the parent structure are treated as substituents, whose names are prefixed to the name of the parent structure. These groups are arranged in alphabetical order, and their positions on the chain are designated by number.

3. The *carbon chain* of the parent structural unit is numbered in such a way as to give the principal function the lowest number. When there is further choice, the chain is numbered to give the lowest values to carbon atoms attached to substituents.

4. Carbon side chains carrying functional groups are treated like other substituents, except that they are enclosed in brackets. The position of the functional group on this side chain is indicated by a

number put inside the bracket. The carbon side chain is numbered from the end nearest its point of attachment to the parent structure.

Acquaintance with the above conventions is best acquired through practice in naming compounds. The following examples illustrate the principles involved.

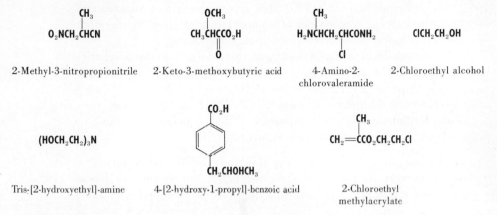

2-Methyl-3-nitropropionitrile   2-Keto-3-methoxybutyric acid   4-Amino-2-chlorovaleramide   2-Chloroethyl alcohol

Tris-[2-hydroxyethyl]-amine   4-[2-hydroxy-1-propyl]-benzoic acid   2-Chloroethyl methylacrylate

Use of Greek Letters. Greek letters are often used in place of numbers in forming derived names. When the parent structure contains a principal functional group not containing carbon (e.g., hydroxyl, amino, nitro, etc.), the carbon carrying that group is α, the next carbon is β, etc. However, when the principal functional group contains carbon (e.g., aldehyde, ketone, carboxylic acid, ester, nitrile, amide), the adjacent carbon is α, etc. When two chains need to be labeled, as with ketones or ethers, Greek letters bearing primes are used.

$$\underset{\delta}{C}-\underset{\gamma}{C}-\underset{\beta}{C}-\underset{\alpha}{C}-OH \qquad \underset{\delta}{C}-\underset{\gamma}{C}-\underset{\beta}{C}\ \underset{\alpha}{C}-CO_2H$$

Compare with

$$\underset{5}{C}-\underset{4}{C}-\underset{3}{C}-\underset{2}{C}-\underset{1}{CO_2H}$$

$$\underset{\gamma}{C}H_3\underset{\beta}{C}H_2\underset{\alpha}{C}HC_6H_5 \qquad \underset{\gamma}{C}H_3\underset{\beta}{C}H_2\underset{\alpha}{C}HCO_2H \qquad \underset{\beta}{H}O\underset{\alpha}{C}H_2\underset{\alpha}{C}H_2\underset{\alpha'}{C}\underset{\beta'}{C}H_2CH_2OH$$
$$\quad\ \ \ OH \qquad\qquad\qquad NH_2 \qquad\qquad\qquad\qquad O$$

α-Phenylpropyl   α-Aminobutyric   β,β'-Dihydroxydiethyl
alcohol   acid   ketone

IUC System

As the number and complexity of known organic compounds grew during the second half of the nineteenth century, the need for a systematic and standard nomenclature became painfully clear. This need was particularly evident in indexes to the periodical literature, which had become confused by the variety of casually selected names. Consequently, representatives from the principal European countries met in 1892 at the Geneva Conference to establish a rigorous scheme for naming all organic compounds. The resulting *Geneva System* has since been modified at conferences of the International Union of Chemistry (IUC) at Liége in 1932 and at Amsterdam in 1949. This section contains a summary of enough of the rules of this system of nomenclature to allow the majority of compounds in this book to be given systematic names.

The system divides compounds into three large classes; aliphatics (compounds containing no rings), alicyclics (nonaromatic cyclic compounds), and aromatics. These classes overlap, because cyclic compounds often carry attached aliphatic chains.

Rules for Naming Aliphatic Compounds. The following rules must be followed closely in naming aliphatic compounds.

1. Choose, as the parent carbon skeleton, the longest sequence of carbon atoms that contains the principal functional groups. Carbon-carbon unsaturation and a second function may be included simultaneously in root names. Two identical functional groups may also be included in the root name, but other combinations cannot be made.

2. Name the parent structure, using as a base the root of the name of the alkane that contains the same number of carbon atoms as the chosen structure. Add suffixes to the root name to show the degree of unsaturation of the parent structure and the nature of the principal functional group.

3. Number the carbon atoms of the parent skeleton by applying the following criteria *in order*. If criterion *a* applies, disregard *b* and *c* if they give contradictory results.

   a. Assign the carbon atom of the principal functional group the number 1 if it is terminal, as is CO_2H or **CHO**.
   b. Assign numbers so that the location of the principal functional group has the lowest possible number if that group is nonterminal.
   c. Assign numbers so that substituents are located by means of the lowest possible numbers. If there are two kinds of substituents, give preference to the first-mentioned substituents (alphabetical preference) in minimizing values of numbers.

4. If an *attached carbon skeleton* is branched or bears substituents, it too must be numbered. Choose numbers so as to minimize the number of the carbon atom at the point of attachment of the side chain to the parent carbon skeleton. Names of substituents on the side chain and numbers locating them are enclosed in brackets with the name of the substituent group. Primed numbers are not utilized in the IUC system.

Naming of Aliphatic Hydrocarbons. The following suffixes are included in hydrocarbon names to indicate the degree of unsaturation: saturated, *-ane;* double bond, *-ene;* triple bond, *-yne.* Class names are alkane, alkene, and alkyne.

$$CH_3CH_2CH_2CH_3$$

Butane

$$\underset{\underset{CH_3}{|}}{CH_3CHCH_3}$$

2-Methylpropane

$$CH_3CH_2\underset{\underset{CH_2CH_3}{|}}{\overset{\overset{CH_3}{|}}{CHCHCH_2}}CH(CH_3)_2$$

4-Ethyl-2,5-dimethylheptane

$$CH_3CH_2CH_2\underset{\underset{CH_3}{|}}{\overset{\overset{CH(CH_3)_2}{|}}{CHCHCH_2}}CH_3$$

4-[2-Propyl]-3-methylheptane

$$CH_3CH{=}CHCH_3$$

2-Butene

$$CH_3CH{=}\overset{\overset{CH_3}{|}}{C}CH_2CH_3$$

3-Methyl-2-pentene

$$\underset{\underset{CH_3}{|}}{CH_3CHCH}\overset{\overset{CH_2CH_2CH_3}{|}}{CHCH}{=}CH_2$$

3-[1-Propyl]-4,5-dimethyl-1-hexene

$$CH_3CH{=}CHCH_2CH{=}CH_2$$

1,4-Hexadiene

$$CH_3CH_2\overset{\overset{CH_3}{|}}{C}HC{\equiv}CH$$

3-Methyl-1-pentyne

Naming of Aliphatic Compounds That Contain Functional Groups.

Table 28.3 lists characteristic suffixes used to indicate the presence of principal functions in parent structures. In some names, such as those of carboxylic acids, the generic name takes the form of an adjective, and the class name follows as a separate word.

In the name of a compound belonging to one of the classes listed in Table 28.3, the class-designating suffix follows the suffix which shows the degree of unsaturation. The endings -*ane*, -*ene*, and -*yne* are shortened to -*an*, -*en*, and -*yn* when they occur in the *penultimate position*. These principles are illustrated with the names of the following compounds.

$$CH_3\underset{\underset{CH_3}{|}}{CH}CHCH_2OH$$

2,3-Dimethyl-1-butanol

$$CH_3CH{=}CH\underset{\underset{O}{||}}{C}CH_3$$

3-Penten-2-one

$$CH_3\underset{\underset{OH}{|}}{\overset{\overset{CH_3}{|}}{C}}CH_2CH_2CH_2CO_2H$$

5-Hydroxy-5-methylhexanoic acid

TABLE 28.3   *Characteristic Suffixes in Names of Principal Functional Groups*

Functional group	Suffix	Name of saturated class
Hydroxyl (—**OH**)	-ol	Alkanol
Aldehyde carbonyl (—**CHO**)	-al	Alkanal
Ketone carbonyl (—**CO**—)	-one	Alkanone
Carboxylic acid (—**CO₂H**)	-oic acid	Alkanoic acid
Amide (—**CONH₂**)	-oic amide	Alkanoic amide
Nitrile (—**C≡N**)	-onitrile	Alkanonitrile
Acid halide (—**COX**)	-oyl halide	Alkanoyl halide

$$\underset{\substack{\text{Cl} \\ | \\ \text{NH}_2}}{\text{CH}_3\text{CHCHCN}}$$

3-Amino-2-chlorobutanonitrile

$$\text{CH}_3\text{OCH}_2\text{CH}_2\text{CHO}$$

3-Methoxypropanal

$$\text{HO}_2\text{C(CH}_2)_6\text{CO}_2\text{H}$$

Octanedioic acid

$$\underset{\substack{\text{CH}_2\text{CH}_2\text{OH} \\ | \\ \\ \text{OH}}}{\text{CH}_3\text{CHCH}_2\text{CH}_2\text{CONH}_2}$$

4-Hydroxy-3-[2-hydroxyethyl]-
pentanoic amide

$$\underset{\substack{\text{Br} \\ |}}{\text{CH}_3\text{CH}_2\text{CHCOCl}}$$

2-Bromobutanoyl
chloride

$$\text{HC}{\equiv}\text{CC}{\equiv}\text{CCH}_2\text{CO}_2\text{H}$$

Hexa-3,5-diynoic
acid

All functional groups other than those listed in Table 28.3 are assigned secondary roles in the IUC system of nomenclature, and compounds that contain them are named as hydrocarbon derivatives. The characteristic common to these secondary functional groups is their lack of carbon atoms. Names of most of these functional groups are prefixed to the name of the parent hydrocarbon, as in the following examples.

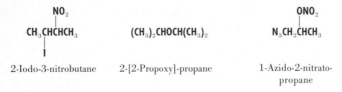

$$\underset{\substack{\text{NO}_2 \\ | \\ \\ \text{I}}}{\text{CH}_3\text{CHCHCH}_3}$$

2-Iodo-3-nitrobutane

$$(\text{CH}_3)_2\text{CHOCH(CH}_3)_2$$

2-[2-Propoxy]-propane

$$\underset{\substack{\text{ONO}_2 \\ |}}{\text{N}_3\text{CH}_2\text{CHCH}_3}$$

1-Azido-2-nitrato-
propane

Names of acidic functional groups, such as sulfonic and phosphonic acids, are placed after the name of the hydrocarbon skeleton. The technique seems awkward when applied to acids, but it greatly simplifies nomenclature of derived esters.

$$\underset{\substack{| \\ \text{SO}_3\text{H}}}{\text{CH}_3\text{CHCH}_2\text{CH}_3}$$

Butane-2-sulfonic
acid

$$\underset{\substack{| \\ \text{PO}_3\text{H}}}{\text{CH}_3\text{CHCH}_3}$$

Propane-2-
phosphonic acid

$$\underset{\substack{| \\ \text{SO}_3\text{CH(CH}_3)_2}}{\text{CH}_3\text{CH}_2\text{CHCH}_2\text{CH}_3}$$

2-Propyl pentane-
3-sulfonate

Esters of carboxylic acids are named as derivatives of the parent acid. The suffix of the parent acid (*-oic acid*) is changed to *-oate,* as in the following examples.

$$\text{CH}_3\text{CH}_2\text{CH}_2\text{CO}_2\text{CH}_2\text{CH}_3$$

Ethyl butanoate

$$(\text{CH}_3)_2\text{CHO}_2\text{CCH}{=}\text{CHCH}_2\text{CH}_3$$

2-Propyl 2-pentenoate

Hetero atoms such as nitrogen, oxygen, sulfur, and silicon are sometimes treated as if they were part of the carbon skeleton in names of some compounds. The skeleton is named just as though the hetero atom were carbon, and an appropriate word and locating number are prefixed to the name. Characteristic prefixes are *oxa-* (oxygen); *aza-*

(nitrogen); *thia-* (sulfur); *sila-* (silicon). This device is useful in naming complex structures which otherwise would require naming and numbering of two or more complex groups.

CH$_3$CH$_2$CH$_2$OCH$_2$CHCH$_3$ with CH$_3$ branch
2-Methyl-4-oxaheptane

HO$_2$C(CH$_2$)$_3$O(CH$_2$)$_3$CO$_2$H
5-Oxanonanedioic acid

CH$_3$CH$_2$Si(CH$_3$)$_3$
2,2-Dimethyl-
2-silabutane

(CH$_3$)$_2$C—N═N—C(CH$_3$)$_2$ with CN groups
2,2,4,4-Tetramethyl-3,4-
diaza-3-hexenodinitrile

CH$_3$CH$_2$CH$_2$SCH$_2$CHCH$_2$CHO with CH$_3$ branch
3-Methyl-5-thiaoctanal

The prefixes *oxa-* and *aza-* must be carefully distinguished from *-oxo* and *azo*. The suffix *-oxo* denotes a keto group, whereas the term *azo* names the functional group —N═N—.

Alicyclic Compounds. Although certain systematic differences exist, the nomenclature of alicyclic compounds is similar to that of aliphatics. In principle, each ring system is assigned its own name, and if unsymmetrical, a unique numbering system. Carbocyclic rings bear names which are merely those of the corresponding open-chain hydrocarbons with the prefix *cyclo-* attached.

Cyclopropane   Cyclopentene   1,4-Cyclohexadiene   Cyclooctane

Heterocyclic rings containing only a single hetero atom can be named by use of the prefixes *oxa-*, *aza-*, etc., but are more commonly designated by individual names of trivial origin. The rings are usually numbered from the hetero atom.

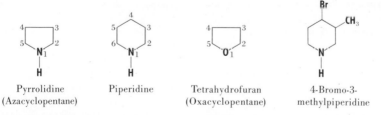

Pyrrolidine   Piperidine   Tetrahydrofuran   4-Bromo-3-
(Azacyclopentane)   (Oxacyclopentane)   methylpiperidine

Alicyclic compounds which contain functional groups outside of the ring system are usually named as derivatives of the cycle regardless of functional preferences.

Cyclohexane with CO$_2$H group
Cyclohexanecarboxylic acid

Cyclopentane with CHO group
Cyclopentanealdehyde

Aromatic Compounds.   Aside from the fact that aromatic rings have individual names and unique numbering systems, aromatic is more consistent than aliphatic nomenclature.   Most ring systems have only one name, and the substituents are located by number in the IUC system. Aliphatic side chains are designated and numbered when necessary according to the rules developed for aliphatic compounds.

1-[2-Methyl-1-propyl]-   1-Bromo-5-   6,7-Dimethoxy-
4-[2-propyl]-benzene   nitronaphthalene   isoquinoline

Other Systematic Nomenclature

Systematic nomenclature other than that prescribed by the IUC is widely used, although in most cases such notations are really modifications or simplifications of IUC nomenclature.   Usually these modifications apply to side chains and ways of ordering substituents.   The following examples illustrate the types of changes that are sometimes made.

3-Isopropylhexanoic acid   1-*sec*-Butyl-3-*tert*-butylbenzene

Miscellaneous Nomenclature

Nomenclature that does not fit well into the other categories of this chapter is treated here.   Nomenclature associated with stereochemistry is not considered in this chapter, since a thorough discussion is found in Chap. 6 on pages 121, 138, and 142.

Salts of Organic Compounds.   Names of salts formed by neutralization of organic acids with strong bases are patterned directly after inorganic nomenclature.   The suffix *-ate* always substitutes for *-ic* in the name of the acid when a salt is named.

$CH_3\overset{-}{CO_2}\overset{+}{Na}$ $CH_3\overset{-}{SO_3}\overset{+}{Li}$ $C_6H_5\overset{=}{PO_3}\overset{++}{Ba}$

Sodium   Lithium   Barium
acetate   methanesulfonate   benzenephosphonate

Metal salts of phenols and alcohols are named by use of the suffix *-oxide*, which substitutes for *-ol* in the name of the parent compound.

$$CH_3CH_2\overset{-}{O}\overset{+}{K} \qquad (CH_3)_2CH\overset{-}{O}\overset{+}{Na} \qquad C_6H_5\overset{-}{O}\overset{+}{Na}$$

| Potassium ethoxide | Sodium isopropoxide | Sodium phenoxide |

Organic Cations. Many compounds containing nitrogen, phosphorus, sulfur, and sometimes oxygen can be converted to cations. In each case, the unshared pair of electrons on these atoms is used to bond an extra atom or group. A similar thing happens when protons add to ammonia or water to form the ammonium (NH_4^+) and oxonium (H_3O^+) ions. The entire group of organic cations is known as *onium* ions, and individual compounds are named accordingly.

$$CH_3\overset{+}{\underset{\underset{H}{|}}{O}}CH_3 \quad \overset{-}{Cl} \qquad CH_3CH_2CH_2\overset{+}{N}(CH_3)_3 \quad \overset{-}{Br} \qquad (CH_3)_3\overset{+}{P}H \quad \overset{-}{Cl}O_4 \qquad (CH_3)_2CH\overset{+}{S}(CH_3)_2 \quad \overset{-}{Cl}$$

| Dimethyloxonium chloride | Propyltrimethyl-ammonium bromide | Trimethylphos-phonium perchlorate | Dimethyliso-propylsulfonium chloride |

Reaction Intermediates. A few compounds containing trivalent carbon are sufficiently stable to be detected, usually as short-lived reaction intermediates. Since these species are frequently discussed in the chemical literature and in conversation, they possess names despite the fact that they are not usually isolated. Neutral species produced (formally) by removing one hydrogen atom from a hydrocarbon are known as free radicals and are designated by names of the corresponding groups.

$$CH_3\cdot \qquad C_6H_5CH_2\cdot \qquad (C_6H_5)_3C\cdot \qquad CH_3\overset{\cdot}{C}HOCH_2CH_3$$

| Methyl free radical | Benzyl free radical | Triphenylmethyl free radical | α-Ethoxyethyl free radical |

Anions, derived in a formal sense by removal of H^+ from a hydrocarbon, are called *carbanions*. Cations, derived by removal of H^- from a hydrocarbon, are termed *carbonium ions*. It is logical to use these class terms as the names of the methyl anion and cation in assigning derived names, in the same way that carbinol is employed as a word substituting for methanol in the carbinol system of alcohol nomenclature.

$$\overset{-}{C}H_3 \qquad (CH_3)_2\overset{-}{C}H \qquad (C_6H_5)_3\overset{-}{C} \qquad (NO_3)_3\overset{-}{C}$$

| *The* carbanion (Methyl anion) | Dimethylcarbanion (Isopropyl anion) | Triphenylcarbanion (Triphenylmethyl anion) | Trinitrocarbanion (Trinitromethyl anion) |

$$\overset{+}{C}H_3 \qquad (CH_3)_3\overset{+}{C} \qquad CH_3\overset{+}{C}HOCH_2CH_3 \qquad CH_3\overset{+}{C}{=}O$$

| *The* carbonium ion (Methyl cation) | Trimethyl-carbonium ion (*tert*-Butyl cation) | Ethoxymethyl-carbonium ion | Methyl-oxocarbonium ion |

As indicated by the names in parentheses, ions may be designated by naming the trivalent groups and adding the words "anion" or "cation." Many authors have used the words "carbanion" and "carbonium ion" in this way. For instance, the *tert*-butyl cation is sometimes termed the *tert*-butyl carbonium ion. The latter name is redundant and ambiguous.

Organometallic Compounds. Organometallic compounds contain bonds between carbon and metals, and are named as alkyl or aryl derivatives of metals.

$$CH_3Na \qquad (C_6H_5)_2Cd \qquad C_6H_5HgCl$$

Methylsodium   Diphenylcadmium   Phenylmercuric chloride

Derivatives of Aldehydes and Ketones. A large number of compounds exist which can be made experimentally from aldehydes and ketones. These substances are often named by reference to the parent carbonyl compound. The following examples illustrate the nomenclature of the principal structural types treated in this manner.

$$(CH_3)_2C{=}NOH \qquad CH_3CH{=}NNHC_6H_5 \qquad CH_2{=}NNHCONH_2$$

Acetone oxime or   Acetaldehyde   Formaldehyde
acetoxime   phenylhydrazone   semicarbazone

Replicate Structures. Occasionally complex compounds can be given descriptive names through reference to particular structural units which occur more than once in a molecule and thereby give the molecule high symmetry. If a compound can be visualized as consisting of two identical groups fused together, the prefix *bi-* is used with the group name to designate the compound. The device is rarely used with aliphatic compounds, since simpler and better names are available. A number of examples in which this system is applied are listed.

$$C_6H_5{-}C_6H_5 \qquad C_6H_5CH_2CH_2C_6H_5 \qquad\qquad CH_3CCCH_3$$

Biphenyl   Bibenzyl   *o,o'*-Bitolyl   Biacetyl

If two or more identical units are attached to a central function, the prefixes *bis-* (two), *tris-* (three), and *tetrakis-* (four) may be used to indicate the structural replication.

$$(CH_3)_2C{-}N{=}N{-}C(CH_3)_2 \qquad\qquad (HOCH_2CH_2)_3N$$

α,α'-Azo-bis-isobutyronitrile   tris-[2-Hydroxyethyl]-amine

N-Substitution. Special notation has been developed to locate substituents attached to nitrogen without use of numbers. Capital *N* before names of substituents indicates that the substituent is attached to a nitrogen in the parent structure.

$CH_3CONHCH_2CH_3$	C_6H_5NHBr	$(CH_3CH_2)_2NNO_2$
N-Ethylacetamide	*N*-Bromoaniline	*N*-Nitrodiethylamine

Bicyclic Compounds. A general system of nomenclature has been developed to supplement the many common and derived names given to bicyclic compounds. In this general system, the number of carbons in each of the three bridges is noted and enclosed in brackets, the numbers are arranged in decreasing order and separated by periods. The term *bicyclo-* appears immediately before the bracket, and prefixed to this term are the substituents, the usual orders being applied. The total number of carbons *in the ring system* is named in the usual way, and the name appears immediately after the bracket, note being taken of any carbon-carbon double bonds appearing in the ring system itself. The ring system is numbered from the most highly substituted bridgehead position, and proceeds around the largest ring in such a way as to give substituents the lowest possible numbers. Carbons of the smallest bridge are then numbered. The examples illustrate the application of these rules.

Bicyclo[2.2.1]heptane

1-Isopropyl-4-methylbicyclo-[3.1.0]hex-2-ene

1,7,7-Trimethylbicyclo-[2.2.1]heptan-2-one

Problems

1. Assign an IUC name and at least one other name to the following compounds:

a. $(CH_3)_2CHCOCH_3$

b. $CH_3CH_2CHC{\equiv}CCH_3$
   | CH_3

c. $CH_3\overset{\displaystyle OH}{\underset{}{C}}HCHCH_2CH(CH_3)_2$
   | C_6H_5

d. $CH_3CHCONHCH(CH_3)_2$
   | CH_3

e. $C_6H_5CH_2OC_2H_5$

f. $(CH_3)_2C{=}CHCHO$

g. $CH_3CHCH_2CH_2OCHCH_2CH_3$
   | CH_3 | CH_3
   | Br

h. $CH_2{=}CHCHCH{=}CHC{=}CHCH_3$
      | CH_3 | $CH_2CH_2CH_3$

i. $BrCH_2CH_2SO_2CH_3$

j. $OHC(CH_2)_3CO_2H$

k. $CH_3CH_2CHCO_2H$
$\qquad\ \ \underset{|}{NH_2}$

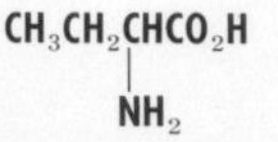

l. $C_6H_5SSC_6H_5$

m. $(CH_3)_3CCH_2CH_2NHCH_3$

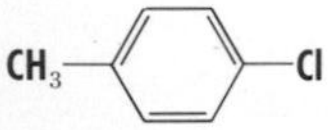

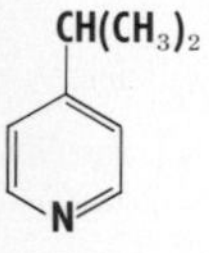

n. $-CH_2Cl$

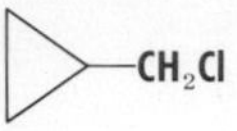

o. $CH_3-$$-Cl$

p. $\underset{\displaystyle}{CH(CH_3)_2}$

q. $CH=CH_2$ Cl

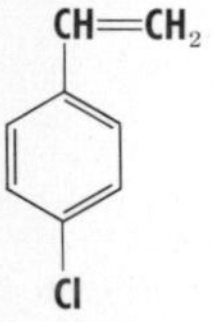

r.

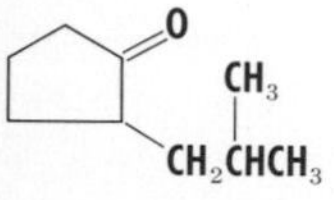

s.

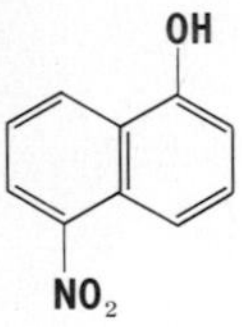

t.

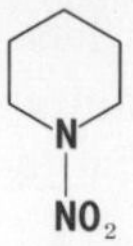

u.

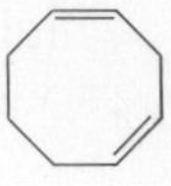

v.

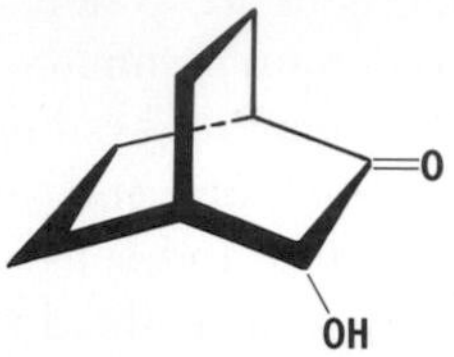

w.

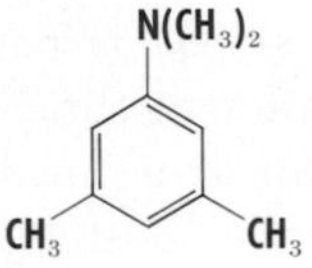

x.

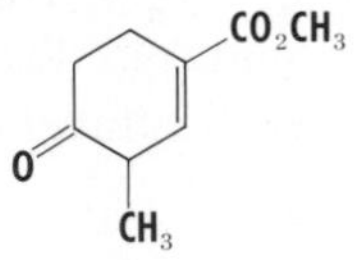

y.

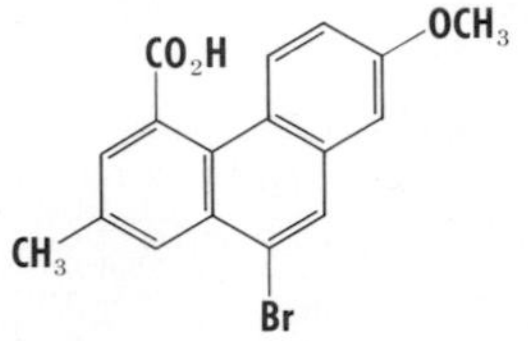

z.

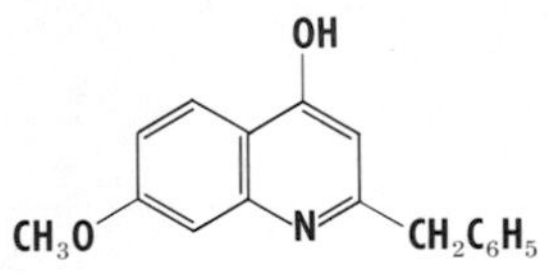

2. Write structural formulas for the following compounds. Give an IUC name to each compound not already designated by that system.

a. Pivalic acid
b. *tert*-Amyl bromide
c. α,β'-Dibromodiethyl sulfoxide
d. 2,4-Dinitro-5-methylbenzoic acid
e. α-Naphthyl β-naphthoate
f. 2,2'-Bipyridyl
g. Trieicosyl carbonium ion
h. Acetylacetone
i. 4-Methyl-2-cyclohexenone
j. Tetrabutylammonium bromide

k. Allyl benzyl ether
l. 2-Methyl-4-methoxy-2-hexene
m. *N*-Methyl-*N*-acetylaniline
n. 3-Hexene-1-carboxylic acid
o. β-Phenylbutyramide
p. *m*-[2-Butyl]-benzoic acid
q. Divinylcarbinol
r. Ethylmethylphenylcarbanion
s. 2-Carbomethoxycyclobutanone
t. α-Phenylethanol

u. 9,10-Dihydroxy-1-methyl-4-nitroanthracene

v. Isobutyl isobutyrate

w. [2.2.1]Bicycloheptane

x. 4-Oxanonane

y. 4,8-Dithiaundecane

z. 2,4-Dinitrophenylhydrazone of acetophenone

3. Criticize the following names, and where possible write the correct name and structure for the compound.

a. [2.2.2]Bicycloheptane

b. 5-Methyl-α-chlorobutanoic acid

c. 3-Carboxy-1-butanol

d. 4-Propylhexanal

e. 2-Methyl-4-chlorobutanoic amide

f. 1-Cyclohexanone

g. 4-Isopropyl-5-octanone

h. 4-Methyl-8-nitronaphthalene

i. Methyl propyl cation

j. Triphenylmethyl carbonium ion [for $(C_6H_5)_3C^+$]

k. Bibutyl

l. Tetraphenylcarbinol

m. *sec*-Valeric acid

n. *trans*-Maleic acid

o. Dibenzoylmethane

p. Methyl 3-nitrophthalate

q. 3-Naphthoic acid

r. α-Methylglutaric acid

s. 3-Methyl-3-ketohexanoic acid

t. 2-Vinylhexanoic acid

J
Am
Chem
Soc
Helv
Chim
Acta
Ber

29

Literature of Organic Chemistry

The development of organic chemistry has created a vast and sprawling literature which reaches into physics on the one side and biology on the other. In spite of the many languages, different systems of nomenclature, and the hundreds of thousands of organic compounds known, a good library readily supplies the organic chemist with the sources of information he needs if they are available at all. Types of source material include the following.

1. Advanced general textbooks provide a general picture of the state of development of the field as a whole.

2. Reference books provide specific information regarding special topics, synthetic procedures, and properties of organic compounds.

3. Reviews of research literature summarize advances made in particular fields of investigation.

4. Handbooks and dictionaries provide physical constants for particular organic compounds, and in some cases references to the original literature.

5. Encyclopedias are exhaustive collections of information regarding organic compounds. They frequently include physical data and references to the original literature.

6. Abstracts of research literature summarize the content of individual articles printed in all significant journals.

7. Research journals themselves are the primary source of all scientific information. They are made up of articles setting forth research results.

This chapter, which is designed as an introduction to the chemical literature, very briefly covers these seven categories. For the first three particularly, only representative works have been selected from the large number available. Where choice is possible, the books written in English are stressed.

Advanced Textbooks

Advanced General Texts. Four works that belong in this category are listed below. The first of these (E. E. Royals) is organized according to reactions associated with alkanes, unsaturated carbon-carbon linkages, and carbonyl groups. This book presents theory, many examples of specific reactions, and some discussion of commercial processes. The book by G. W. Wheland is written in a critical and theoretical vein with very detailed treatment of certain subjects such as stereochemistry, molecular rearrangements, and free-radical reactions. The book by R. C. Fuson emphasizes synthetic methods and gives many specific reactions with yield data. The last book (by P. Karrer) is the largest and is the only one that treats natural products in any detail.

"Advanced Organic Chemistry," E. E. Royals, Prentice-Hall, Inc., Englewood Cliffs, N.J., 1954.

"Advanced Organic Chemistry," 2d ed., G. W. Wheland, John Wiley & Sons, Inc., New York, 1949.

"Advanced Organic Chemistry," R. C. Fuson, John Wiley & Sons, Inc., New York, 1950.

"Organic Chemistry" (English trans.), 4th ed., P. Karrer, Elsevier Publishing Company, Amsterdam, 1950.

Physical and Theoretical Organic Texts. The rapid development of physical-organic and theoretical-organic chemistry has led to the writing of a large number of texts, some of which are listed. These books are concerned with such topics as resonance, reaction mechanisms, stereochemical principles, steric effects, and correlations between structure and reactivity and between structure and physical properties.

"Physical Organic Chemistry," L. P. Hammett, McGraw-Hill Book Company, Inc., New York, 1940.

"Resonance in Organic Chemistry," G. W. Wheland, John Wiley & Sons, Inc., New York, 1955.

"Steric Effects in Organic Chemistry," edited by M. S. Newman, John Wiley & Sons, Inc., New York, 1956.

"Structure and Mechanism in Organic Chemistry," C. K. Ingold, Cornell University Press, Ithaca, N.Y., 1953.

"Physical Organic Chemistry," J. Hine, McGraw-Hill Book Company, Inc., New York, 1956.

"The Reactive Intermediates of Organic Chemistry," J. E. Leffler, Interscience Publishers, Inc., New York, 1956.

"Progress in Stereochemistry," vols. I and II, edited by W. Klyne and P. de la Mare, Butterworths Scientific Publications, London, 1954.

Reference Books

General Organic Chemistry.   One of the most exhaustive general reference books written in English is that edited by Rodd.   This work presents the whole field of organic chemistry in an integrated and systematic way. The first four volumes of a projected five were published by 1956.

"Chemistry of Carbon Compounds," vols. I–IV, edited by E. H. Rodd, Elsevier Publishing Company, Amsterdam, 1952–1959.

Synthetic Organic Chemistry.   The works listed below are among the most useful available to research chemists who carry out chemical syntheses.   They range in size from Wagner and Zook, which consists of one volume, to Theilheimer, which in 1959 occupied twelve volumes. These books contain large numbers of references to the research literature and in many cases describe sample procedures for carrying out reactions. Three of these works are discussed in greater detail.

"Synthetic Organic Chemistry," R. B. Wagner and H. D. Zook, John Wiley & Sons, Inc., New York, 1953.
"Organic Reactions," vols. I–IX, edited by R. Adams, John Wiley & Sons, Inc., New York, 1942–1958.
"Organic Preparations" (English trans.), C. Weygand, Interscience Publishers, Inc., New York, 1945.
"Organic Syntheses," collective vols. I–III, edited by H. Gilman, A. H. Blatt, and E. C. Horning, and single vols. XXX–XXXVIII, edited by A. C. Cope, R. S. Schreiber, R. T. Arnold, C. C. Price, W. S. Johnson, T. L. Cairns, J. Cason, J. C. Sheehan, and N. J. Leonard, John Wiley & Sons, Inc., New York, 1948–1958.
"Newer Methods of Preparative Organic Chemistry" (English trans.), edited originally by W. Foerst, Interscience Publishers, Inc., New York, 1948.
"Methods of Organic Chemistry" (in German, referred to as Houben-Weil), 11 vols. published, edited by Eugen Müller, Georg Thieme Verlag, Stuttgart, 1952–1958.
"Synthetic Methods of Organic Chemistry," vols. I–IV in German, vols. V–XII in English, W. Theilheimer, S. Karger, Basel, and Interscience Publishers, Inc., New York, 1946–1958.

A new volume of "Organic Reactions" appears almost every year. It summarizes the facts concerning seven to twelve different general organic reactions, such as the Friedel-Crafts alkylation reaction or the Mannich synthesis.   Each chapter is written by a different author familiar with the field, and contains discussions of scope and limitations of reactions, sample procedures, tables of examples, and numerous references.

In "Organic Syntheses," detailed and verified procedures for interconversions of organic compounds are set forth.   A new volume, edited by a different author, is published almost every year, and every ten years collective volumes appear.   Great emphasis is placed on reproducibility of experimental results in these volumes, and a representative group of reactions is selected.

In the multivolume "Synthetic Methods of Organic Chemistry" (frequently referred to as Theilheimer), a classification of organic transformations is systematically developed into which organic reactions taken from the literature each year are fitted.   An elaborate general index aids in locating procedures for the preparation of particular classes of compounds, irrespective of starting material.   This compendium contains the most comprehensive and up-to-date listing of organic synthetic methods.

Collections of Special Topics.   Two works have been selected as representative of this group.   Gilman's "Treatise" consists of a series of chapters, each written by a different author on subjects which range from alkaloids to infrared spectra.   Cook's three volumes also comprise chapters written by different authors on a wide range of different topics, each of which records "recent advances" in a particular field that has undergone rapid development.

"Organic Chemistry: an Advanced Treatise," vols. I–IV, 2d ed., edited by
    H. Gilman, John Wiley & Sons, Inc., New York, 1943–1953.
"Progress in Organic Chemistry," vols. I–III, edited by J. W. Cook, Butter-
    worths Scientific Publications, London, 1952–1955.

Special Topics.   Only a small fraction of the large number of books devoted to special topics are mentioned here.   Those works which supplement the latter chapters of this textbook have been selected.

"Grignard Reactions of Nonmetallic Substances," M. S. Kharasch and O.
    Reinmuth, Prentice-Hall Inc., Englewood Cliffs, N.J., 1954.
"Reduction with Complex Metal Hydrides," N. G. Gaylord, Interscience
    Publishers, Inc., New York, 1956.
"The Chemistry of Acetylenic Compounds," vols. I and II, A. W. Johnson,
    Edward Arnold & Co., London, 1946–1950.
"Free Radicals in Solution," C. Walling, John Wiley & Sons, Inc., New York,
    1957.
"The Organic Chemistry of Nitrogen," N. V. Sidgwick, revised by T. W. J.
    Taylor and W. Baker, Oxford University Press, New York, 1937.
"Heterocyclic Compounds," vols. I–VI, edited by R. C. Elderfield, John Wiley
    & Sons, Inc., New York, 1950–1957.
"The Chemistry of Heterocyclic Compounds," 11 vols., edited by A. Weissber-
    ger, Interscience Publishers, Inc., New York, 1950–1958.
"Advances in Carbohydrate Chemistry," vols. I–XIII, edited by W. W. Pigman,
    M. L. Wolfrom, C. S. Hudson, and S. M. Cantor, Academic Press, Inc.,
    New York, 1945–1958.
"Amino Acids and Proteins," D. M. Greenberg, Charles C Thomas, Publisher,
    Springfield, Ill., 1951.
"The Alkaloids," vols. I–V, edited by R. H. F. Manske and H. L. Holmes,
    Academic Press, Inc., New York, 1950–1958.
"Progress in the Chemistry of Fats and Other Lipids," vols. I–V, R. T. Holman,
    W. O. Lundberg, and T. Malkin, Academic Press, Inc., New York, 1953,
    and Pergamon Press, London, 1957.

"The Terpenes," vols. I–V, 2d ed., J. Simonsen, L. M. Owen, D. H. R. Barton, and W. C. J. Ross, Cambridge University Press, New York, 1947–1957.

"Natural Products Related to Phenanthrene," 3d ed., L. F. Fieser and M. P. Fieser, Reinhold Publishing Corporation, New York, 1949.

"Sterine, Gallensäuren und verwandte Naturstoffe," H. Lettre, H. H. Inhoffen, and R. Tschesche, Ferd. Enke Verlag, Stuttgart, 1954.

"Natural and Synthetic High Polymers," 2d ed., K. H. Meyer, Interscience Publishers, Inc., New York, 1950.

"The Chemistry of Petroleum Hydrocarbons," vols. I–III, edited by B. T. Brooks, C. E. Boord, S. S. Kurtz, and L. Schmerling, Reinhold Publishing Corporation, New York, 1954–1955.

Analytical and Other Techniques.   A large number of books on techniques of organic chemistry have been published which range all the way from simple laboratory methods to the use of spectrophotometers. Only a few representative works are listed.

"Semimicro Qualitative Organic Analysis," N. D. Cheronis and J. B. Entrikin, Thomas Y. Crowell Company, New York, 1947.

"The Systematic Identification of Organic Compounds," 4th ed., R. L. Shriner, R. C. Fuson, and D. Y. Curtin, John Wiley & Sons, Inc., New York, 1956.

"Quantitative Analysis Via Functional Groups," S. Siggia, John Wiley & Sons, Inc., New York, 1954.

"Quantitative Organic Analysis," J. S. Fritz and G. S. Hammond, John Wiley & Sons, Inc., New York, 1957.

"Technique of Organic Chemistry," vols. I–IX (I, II, III, and VII in 2d ed.), edited by A. Weissberger, Interscience Publishers, Inc., New York, 1946–1956.

"Chromatography," E. Lederer and M. Lederer, Elsevier Publishing Company, Amsterdam, 1953.

"The Infrared Spectra of Complex Molecules," L. J. Bellamy, John Wiley & Sons, Inc., New York, 1954.

"Determination of Organic Structures by Physical Methods," E. A. Braude and F. C. Nachod, Academic Press, Inc., New York, 1955.

Reviews of Research Literature

A number of journals and books are published each year by chemical societies of various countries whose purpose is to review the research literature.   *Chemical Reviews* is a journal published every two months in which review articles appear covering topics which range over the whole field of chemistry, and which are not restricted to recent work. *Annual Reports* is a series of books (45 in number through 1958) published once a year which reviews the chemical research literature of the prior year.   *Quarterly Reviews,* which is published four times a year, resembles *Chemical Reviews.*   "Progress in the Chemistry of Organic Natural Products" is a collection of 12 volumes, with a new volume appearing almost every year.   The chapters in these volumes review the recent literature in the field of natural products. Although some of the chapters are in German and French, over half are in English.

Chemical Reviews, published for the American Chemical Society.
Annual Reports, published for the Chemical Society (London).
Quarterly Reviews, published by the Chemical Society (London).
"Progress in the Chemistry of Organic Natural Products," vols. I–XII, edited by L. Zechmeister, Springer-Verlag, Berlin and Vienna, 1938–1955.

Handbooks and Dictionaries of Organic Compounds

Handbooks and dictionaries containing lists of organic compounds are useful for looking up the physical constants of common substances. Of those listed, only the "Dictionary of Organic Compounds" carries references to the literature. "Lange's Handbook of Chemistry" and the "Handbook of Chemistry and Physics" contain not only extensive lists of organic compounds and their physical properties, but also much other useful data. Among these are tables of specific heats, heats of combustion, laboratory arts and recipes, physical constants, conversion factors, mathematical equations, logarithm tables, etc. Most organic chemists own either one or both of these last two works.

"Dictionary of Organic Compounds," vols. I–IV, revised ed., edited by I. Heilbron and H. M. Bunbury, Eyre and Spottiswoode, London, 1953.
"The Merck Index of Chemicals and Drugs," 6th ed., Merck and Co., Inc., Rahway, N.J., 1952.
"Lange's Handbook of Chemistry," 9th ed., N. A. Lange, Handbook Publishers, Inc., Sandusky, Ohio, 1956.
"Handbook of Chemistry and Physics," 40th ed., edited by C. D. Hodgman, Chemical Rubber Publishing Co., Cleveland, Ohio, 1958.

Encyclopedias of Organic Compounds

Two great multivolume works can be classed as encyclopedias of organic compounds. The "Handbuch der organischen Chemie," written in German, is commonly referred to as "Beilstein," after its first editor. In the approximately one hundred volumes and supplements are listed *all the organic compounds known through 1929.* "The Encyclopaedia of Organic Chemistry," Elsevier Publishing Company, Amsterdam, which is written in English, is commonly referred to as "Elsevier." Although "Elsevier" has objectives similar to those of "Beilstein," the first volumes, which appeared in 1946, deal only with relatively complicated organic compounds. Unfortunately publication has been discontinued. The importance of "Beilstein" is great enough to justify a brief description of how it is used.

Beilstein. A book has been written ("A Brief Introduction to the Use of Beilstein's Handbuch der organischen Chemie," E. H. Huntress,

John Wiley & Sons, Inc., New York, 1938) which describes the organization of this compendium and facilitates its use. For ordinary purposes, the following short description will serve.

The fourth edition of "Beilstein" consists of three sets of volumes. The *main series* covers the literature through 1909, the *first supplementary series* from 1909 through 1919, and the *second supplementary series* from 1919 through 1929. A third series, covering the next ten-year period, is currently being prepared. Each supplementary series contains the same number of volumes as the main series, and the arrangement of material in each supplementary series *parallels* that of the main series. For example, page 341 of volume III of the *main series* lists 3,3-dimethyl-2-hydroxybutanoic acid. Volume III of the *first supplementary* series lists this same compound on a page which has two numbers. The conventional page number appears at the top right (page 125). In the top middle appears the number 341. As soon as a compound is located in any series, it can quickly be found in any other series.

Three procedures are available for locating a particular compound in "Beilstein." The simplest method involves use of the cumulative formula indexes. Here compounds are listed in order of increasing complexity of their molecular formulas. Structural isomers are differentiated on the basis of names of the compounds. The task of looking up these isomers is considerably facilitated by an acquaintance with German nomenclature.

A second cumulative index exists in which names of compounds are arranged in alphabetical order. The requisites for using this index are a knowledge of German nomenclature and some knowledge of the organization of "Beilstein." Use of this method for finding a particular compound is perhaps the least satisfactory.

The third method of finding a compound in "Beilstein" requires familiarity with the organization of the dictionary. A brief description of this organization is given here. The four major divisions are as follows:

Acyclic compounds	Volumes I–IX
Isocyclic compounds	Volumes X–XVI
Heterocyclic compounds	Volumes XVII–XXVII
Carbohydrates, carotenoids, and hydrocarbon polymers	Volumes XXX, XXXI

The indexes occupy volumes XXVIII and XXIX. Compounds are listed within each of the first two major divisions in the following order of *basic classes of compounds:*

1. Hydrocarbons	7. Selenium compounds
2. Hydroxy (oxy) compounds	8. Amines
3. Carbonyl (oxo) compounds	9. Hydroxylamines
4. Carboxylic acids	10. Hydrazines
5. Sulfinic acids	11. Azo compounds
6. Sulfonic acids	12. Other relatively rare groups

Polyfunctional molecules are found *under that class which appears last in the above list.*   For example, hydroxycarboxylic acids appear under carboxylic acids, and aminocarboxylic acids under amines.   Within each class, *compounds are listed in order of decreasing saturation,* and after this, *in order of increasing molecular weight.*   Compounds that contain functional groups not found among the basic classes of compounds are considered *derivatives of these basic classes.*   These derivatives are listed immediately after the parent compounds.   For instance, after propionic acid are listed its amide, ester, etc.   These derivatives are arranged in the following order:

1. *Functional derivatives,* or compounds which can be hydrolyzed to the parent compound.

2. *Substitution derivatives,* or compounds that contain halogen, nitroso, nitro, or azido (—N_3) groups.

3. *Sulfur compounds,* which are listed as derived from the corresponding oxygen compounds.

When a functional derivative can be hydrolyzed into two or more organic molecules, the substance is listed as a derivative of the hydrolytic product appearing last in the list of basic classes of compounds.   For example, esters are listed as derivatives of carboxylic acids.   With *polysubstituted derivatives,* the principle of *last in order of listing* also applies.   The same is true for derivatives of derivatives (second-order derivatives).

Heterocyclic compounds are defined as any compounds with one or more atoms other than carbon in the ring (even cyclic anhydrides and lactones).   Ring compounds are first listed according to their *hetero number,* and then according to the system developed above.   The hetero number for each parent ring system can be determined by consulting the "Beilstein" guide or through use of the indexes.

Although the above system seems complicated, compounds can be located in "Beilstein" rather quickly.   No adequate substitute for this work has yet appeared.

Abstracts

Chemical Abstracts.   The American Chemical Society publishes an abstract journal known as *Chemical Abstracts,* which summarizes all original articles on chemistry that appear in journals in all countries of the world.   This journal is published twice a month, and each year exhaustive author, subject, and formula indexes appear.   Every ten years a decennial index is published, and in 1951 a cumulative formula index appeared which covers the period from 1920 to 1946.

Chemisches Zentralblatt.   This journal is the German counterpart of *Chemical Abstracts* and serves as a second source of abstracts of research articles.   The formula index of *Chemisches Zentralblatt* is very useful.   Collective indexes (formula, subject, and author) have appeared every five years up to 1939. Before 1939, the coverage of this journal was more complete than that of *Chemical Abstracts*.

Basic Literature

Research journals are fundamental to the science. Almost every country in which research in chemistry is conducted publishes a research journal. The following list includes the major journals of the world. The boldface portions of the names indicate how the names of these journals are abbreviated in *Chemical Abstracts*. The languages used and fields of chemistry covered by the journals are also indicated.

*Journal of the **American Chem**ical **Soc**iety,* in English, all branches of chemistry.
*Journal of **Org**anic **Chem**istry,* in English (USA), organic chemistry.
*Journal of **Biol**ogical **Chem**istry,* in English (USA), biological chemistry.
*Journal of the **Chem**ical **Soc**iety,* in English (British), all branches of chemistry.
***Biochem**ical **Journal**,* in English (British), biological and natural-product chemistry.
***Can**adian **Journal** of **Chem**istry,* in English, all branches of chemistry.
***Chem**ische ***Ber**ichte,* in German, all branches of chemistry.
***Ann**alen der ***Chem**ie,* in German, organic chemistry.
***Z**eitschrift für ***physiol**ogische ***Chem**ie,* in German, organic and biological chemistry.
***Helv**etica ***Chim**ica ***Acta**,* in German, French, Italian, and English (Swiss), all branches of chemistry.
***Monatsh**efte für ***Chem**ie,* in German (Austrian), all branches of chemistry.
***Bull**etin de la ***soc**iété ***chim**ique de ***France**,* in French, all branches of chemistry.
Bull**etin des ***soc**iétés ***chim**iques ***Belges (Belgian), in French, English, and Dutch, all branches of chemistry.
***Rec**ueil des ***trav**aux ***chim**iques des ***Pays-Bas**,* in English, French, German, and Dutch (Dutch), all branches of chemistry.
***Acta Chem**ica ***Scand**inavica,* in German, English, and French, all branches of chemistry.
***Arkiv** för ***Kemi**,* in English, German, and French (Swedish), all branches of chemistry.
***Gazz**etta ***chim**ica ***ital**iana,* in Italian, all branches of chemistry.
***Coll**ection of ***Czech**oslovak ***Chem**ical ***Commun**ications,* in English, Russian, and German, all branches of chemistry.
***Bull**etin of the ***Chem**ical ***Soc**iety of ***Japan**,* in Japanese, English, German, and French, all branches of chemistry.
*Journal of **Gen**eral **Chem**istry (**U. S. S. R.**), or **Zhur**nal **Obshche**ǐ **Khim**ii,* in Russian, all branches of chemistry.
***Tetrahedron**,* various languages, international journal of organic chemistry.

Besides these research journals, a number of other journals frequently contain information of interest to the organic chemist. The *Journal of Chemical Education* (USA) carries articles of interest to teachers and students.   Journals such as **Science** (USA), **Nature** (British), **Chemistry & Industry (London)** (British, fondly referred to as "Blue bits"), **Experientia** (Swiss), and **Angewandte Chemie** (German) contain preliminary announcements of research results, review articles, letters to the editor, and news of general interest to the profession.

Literature Search for a Particular Organic Compound

The most rapid way of finding all original references to a given organic compound is the following:

1. Calculate the molecular formula for the compound, and name the substance in two or three ways.

2. Consult the cumulative formula index of "Beilstein," and differentiate among possible structural isomers by the name of the compound. References to the compound are listed in the text of the main series and the first and second supplements, and cover the literature exhaustively through 1929.

3. Consult the collective formula index of *Chemical Abstracts,* which covers the years 1920 through 1946.

4. The years 1946 to the present are covered by the yearly formula indexes of *Chemical Abstracts.*

5. Consult the formula indexes of *Chemisches Zentralblatt* from the year 1929 to the present.   The five-year collective indexes of 1934 and 1939 aid in this search.

The systematic organization of "Beilstein" and the subject indexes are also useful, although subject indexes are difficult to use because names change from language to language and from one period to another.

Problems

1. Give the structure for the parent compound of the following substances according to the "Beilstein" classification system.

a. $(CH_3)_2CHCH_2Br$

b. $CH_3CHCH_2CH_2CO_2CH_3$
          |
          OH

c.

d. $H_2NCH_2CH_2CH_2NH_2$

e.

2. Find the following compounds in "Beilstein," and record the page numbers in the main or supplementary series where the compounds are found.   List the latest reference to a research journal found in "Beilstein" for the compounds.

a. $CH_3(CH_2)_2CO_2(CH_2)_3CH_3$

b. $C_6H_5OC_6H_5$

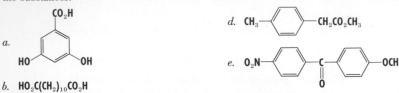

c.

d. CH₃CH=CHCHO

e.

f. $CH_3OCH_2CH_2NH_2$

3. Look up the following compounds in *Chemical Abstracts*. List all references to the substances.

a.

HO   OH

d. CH_3—⟨ ⟩—$CH_2CO_2CH_3$

b. $HO_2C(CH_2)_{10}CO_2H$

c. $(CH_3)_3CC≡CC(CH_3)_3$

e. O_2N—⟨ ⟩—C—⟨ ⟩—OCH_3
                     ‖
                     O

4. Do a complete literature search for the following compounds. List all references to the original literature you can find.

a. CH₃—CH—CH—CO₂H
          | |
          CH₃ CH₃

b. CH₃—⟨ ⟩—CH₂CH₂—⟨ ⟩—OCH₃

c. CH₃CCH₂CCH₂CH₂CO₂H
        ‖ |
        O   CH₃

d. $(CH_2)_8$ ⌐C=O
               └C=O

e. C₆H₅CH—CHC₆H₅
          | |
          OH   NH₂

5. Using "Theilheimer," "Organic Synthesis," "Organic Reactions," or the original literature, write out syntheses of the following compounds. Over the arrows write the conditions and hoped-for yields. Reason by analogy from known cases. Start with compounds at least three steps back from your final product.
a. Synthesis of both diastereomeric racemates of

OH
|
CH₃CHCHCH₃

        OH

b. (CH₂)₁₁ C⟨OH
                  CH₃

c.

d.

e.

f. $(CH_3)_2CHCH_2CH_2CCH_2CH_2CO_2CH_3$
                        ‖
                        O

g. $(CH_3)_3CNH_2$

h. $[(CH_3)_3C]_3COH$

Index

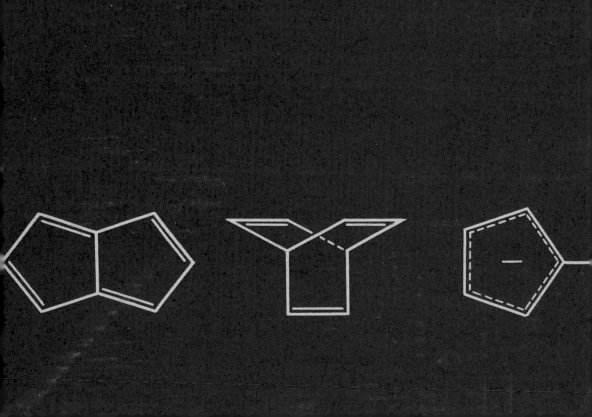